STUDY GUIDE AND SOLUTIONS MANUAL
TO ACCOMPANY

Organic Chemistry

SECOND EDITION

STUDY GUIDE AND SOLUTIONS MANUAL TO ACCOMPANY

Organic Chemistry

SECOND EDITION

G. Marc Loudon   Joseph G. Stowell

Purdue University

The Benjamin/Cummings Publishing Company, Inc.
Menlo Park, California • Reading, Massachusetts
Don Mills, Ontario • Wokingham, UK • Amsterdam • Sydney
Singapore • Tokyo • Madrid • Santiago • Bogota • San Juan

Sponsoring Editor: *Diane Bowen*
Production Supervisor: *Karen Gulliver*
Production Coordinator: *Pat Waldo/Partners in Publishing*
Copy Editors: *Mimi Hills and Rene Lynch*

ISBN 0-8053-6644-X

910 -BA- 95 94 93 92

The Benjamin/Cummings Publishing Company
2727 Sand Hill Road
Menlo Park, California 94025

How to Study Organic Chemistry

"You must be brilliant!" This is sometimes the response one gets on revealing to an acquaintance that one is studying chemistry and, specifically, organic chemistry. It may come as a surprise that many highly successful students of organic chemistry are not brilliant but of average intelligence. Why do they succeed? The answer is that they know how to organize, study, and learn organic chemistry efficiently, and they are interested enough in the subject to expend the effort required.

Our teaching experience has shown us that although many students want to learn organic chemistry, they do not know how to study the subject properly. Studying and learning a technical subject such as organic chemistry is very different from studying, say, world history. In this preface, we present some suggestions — some *detailed* suggestions — for developing productive study skills in organic chemistry. One benefit of learning and applying these skills is that they can be used, with slight modification, with virtually *any* technical subject. We believe that these skills should have lasting value for dealing with an increasingly technological world.

Here are the general guidelines for proper study; we'll discuss each one below:

1. Read and use the text *properly*.
2. Work problems.
3. Keep up with the assigned material.
4. Seek assistance when necessary.

Reading the Textbook It seems obvious that one should read the text for a course. We have found in our teaching, however, that many students do not know how to read and use a science textbook *properly*. Reading an organic chemistry text is very different from reading a novel or a history book. In reading a novel, one can frequently skim words and paragraphs and get a good sense of the whole. If one cannot define a word, further reading makes the meaning clear in context. In contrast, a science text must be read *in detail*. One term must be clearly understood before the reader moves on to the next term. Another difference is that reading literature is in some respects a *passive* process. That is, the book speaks to the reader, who lies back and "listens;" the reader is entertained and enlightened. Reading a scientific or technical text, in contrast, must be an *active* process. One must interact with the text during the reading process in order to remain attentive and incorporate the material effectively into one's own knowledge base. Is a computer manual best read by taking it to bed and reading it like a novel? No. The best way is to turn on the computer and try each command as it is encountered. One doesn't go to page 2 until one masters page 1. Organic chemistry should be approached in the same way.

Let's go through one section of the text to illustrate the active-learning approach. Open your text to Section 5.1 on page 135. This section deals with a chemical reaction. Since *most* sections of the text deal with reactions, this section is fairly typical. It is not important that you understand the chemical terms at this point. Instead, focus on the study techniques. (We suggest that you re-read this discussion again when you get to Chapter 5.)

First, let's see how the section is organized. One or two examples (in this case, two examples) of the reaction to be studied are presented first (Eqs. 5.1 and 5.2). Then there a few practical facts about the reaction in the first full paragraph on page 136, beginning "Bromine and chlorine. . ." There follows in Eqs. 5.3–5.6 a *mechanism* of the reaction — a stepwise description of how the reaction proceeds. Section 5.1B gives some further applications of the reaction that follow directly from the mechanism. Finally, there are some in-text problems on page 138. Let's summarize the organization:

1. The reaction to be studied
2. Practical facts about the reaction
3. The mechanism of the reaction
4. Further applications
5. Problems

Now let's read the section. The first sentence contains no fewer than three chemical terms: *halogens*, *electrophilic addition*, and *alkenes*. You *must* understand these terms before reading on. We hope that the meaning of the word *halogens* is clear from your freshman chemistry course. If not, you must get a freshman chemistry text and review it. The term *electrophilic addition* is introduced in the previous chapter. When you read this section, you will probably remember seeing the term, but if not, you *must* go to the index, look it up, and review it. Finally, the term *alkenes* will probably present little difficulty, since you will find that this is the subject of the entire previous chapter. The point is that *you must understand each term before proceeding to the next.*

Notice the importance of continued review! Many students and professors alike suffer from their apparent adherence to a fallacious idea about learning, which one of our colleagues calls the "immunization theory of learning." Students would state the theory as follows: "If I've seen it once, I should never have to see it again...*ever*." Professors would modify the theory to read, "If I've taught it once, I should never have to teach it again, and students should remember everything I taught." This theory negates a fundamental caveat about learning: *Continued reinforcement is one of the best ways to learn.* When you learn, you should expect to forget something after the first exposure, and you should expect to have to re-learn it, probably more than once. Each relearning, however, takes less time and generally brings with it deeper understanding.

Whew! We've covered one sentence. Let's go on to the reaction. Look at the relationship of the reactants and products. From which parts of the reactants do the different atoms in the product originate? In this case the answer is fairly obvious from the simplicity of the reaction and the use of color in the text. In some cases the answer will be less obvious. In those cases you should *formulate a hypothesis* about the origin of the atoms in the product. (The *mechanism* will tell you whether your hypothesis is correct.) Developing your hypothesis forces you to *think* about the reaction.

Now take a sheet of paper and fold it lengthwise in half. Write this reaction on the paper with the reactants on the left and the products on the right. Write the reaction using the R-group notation in as general a form as possible. (You will learn about the R-group notation in Section 3.8 beginning on text page 81.) The reaction arrow should be duplicated on the left and right sides of the fold. Thus, your folded sheet should look as follows:

$$\underset{\substack{\\ \\ \text{X = halogen}}}{\overset{R}{\underset{R'}{\diagdown}}C=C\overset{R}{\underset{R}{\diagup}}} + X_2 \xrightarrow{CCl_4} \quad \overset{fold}{\Big|} \quad \xrightarrow{CCl_4} \quad R-\overset{\overset{R}{|}}{\underset{\underset{X}{|}}{C}}-\overset{\overset{R}{|}}{\underset{\underset{X}{|}}{C}}-R \qquad X = \text{halogen}$$

This sheet will become your *reaction review sheet.* After you have completed your first assignment you may have three or four such reactions on your sheet. Review them by folding the sheet over so that only the reactants are visible, and write the products. Then fold the sheet over so that only the products are visible and *write the reactants.* The ability to give the starting materials required to form a product will be particularly valuable when you learn about *organic synthesis* — how to prepare one organic compound from another. This is one aspect of learning reactions that some students either neglect or don't think about. Finally, write one or more examples of the reaction other than the ones shown in the text using particular R groups of your own choosing. Using these techniques, review the reactions from your first assignment during two subsequent study sessions; notice the reinforcement involved in this review. Then drop them from your review. In other words, you will be constantly reviewing reactions from three consecutive assignments. Before a quiz or examination, go back and review all reactions to be covered. You'll be amazed that you'll remember most of them, and the ones you don't remember will come back very quickly!

Back to the text! In the first sentence on page 136 is a new term, *vicinal dihalides*, shown in boldface. Write this term on a sheet of paper, and opposite the term write the page number. For three consecutive periods, *write* on scratch paper the meaning of this as well as other terms you collect. (Writing the definition rather than speaking it forces you to use more precise language.) Write an example, if appropriate.

The practical facts about the reaction are next. These tell you, for example, what the CCl4 is doing over the reaction arrow: It is an inert solvent.

Our next stop in the reading is the reaction mechanism embodied in Eqs. 5.3–5.6 and the accompanying discussion. You should follow each step in detail and try to relate each step of the mechanism to a simple reaction you have seen before. As you study the mechanism, write the mechanism of one of the example reactions in the text — for example, the reaction in Eq. 5.1. When you feel that you understand the mechanism, write the mechanism of the reaction in Eq. 5.2.

There are three purposes to studying mechanisms. First, mechanisms show why a reaction is reasonable by demonstrating that an overall reaction is a sequence of simple fundamental processes that are already familiar. Second, mechanisms show the relationship between reactions. By seeing the mechanistic similarities among seemingly different reactions, the reactions become easier to learn. Finally, mechanistic thinking allows one to *predict* the products of new reactions.

Mechanisms are not to be memorized! They are to be studied and *understood.*

The reading continues in a similar vein up to Problems 1 and 2 on text page 138. Work these problems when you come to them. (We'll have more to say about problem solving below.)

Notice how you are almost always writing something as you read. You are forcing yourself to *think* about the material. You are constantly turning back in the text to review material that you have seen before but have forgotten. Notice that we have *not* suggested highlighting the text or outlining the chapter. *These can easily become passive activities* because they don't force you to think about the material. Keep your learning *active.*

Once you finish reading a chapter, you will find the Study Guide sections of this manual to be useful. Each of these sections contains a glossary of terms with appropriate text references. Since these lists are alphabetized, they allow you to look at the terms out of the order in which they occur in the text and thus test whether you really do understand what they mean. As with your own sheet of terms, *write* a definition of each term and an example, if appropriate. The Study Guide also contains a *conceptual* outline of each chapter and a *reaction* outline. These make useful "quick reviews" of the material that can be used instead of a detailed re-reading of the chapter. They will not, however, substitute for proper reading of the text. If something is unfamiliar in these outlines, go back to the text and re-read it.

You should also correlate your lecture notes with material in the text. What part of the reading has the professor emphasized? Has the professor presented the material in a different manner from the text? Are there any inconsistencies? If so, do not hesitate to ask the professor or an assistant to help you resolve them.

Working Problems   What is it that you are asked to do on an examination? Work problems! Thus, it stands to reason that working problems is one of the best ways to prepare for an examination. It is also one of the best ways to learn organic chemistry. You should work as many problems as you can. However, *how* you work them is much more important than *how many* you work.

Work the in-text problems as you come to them in your reading. Work though an entire set, if possible, without looking at the answer book. Then open this Solutions Guide and check your answers. There are three reasons why your answer might differ from that in the Solutions Guide. First, your answer may be wrong. Be sure you understand why your answer is wrong by reading the solution carefully. The second reason that your answer may differ from the one in the Solutions Guide is that there are more than one correct answer. Many problems, particularly problems in organic synthesis, have more than one acceptable answer. A third and less likely reason that your answer may differ is that there is an error in the Solutions Guide. Although we have endeavored to produce an accurate Solutions Guide, it is possible that it contains an occasional error. If you feel that you understand a problem, do not hesitate to ask for assistance if you feel your answer is correct.

Many students leave the Solutions Guide open in front of them when they "work" problems. If the answer does not come to them immediately, they read the Solutions Guide and say, "Oh, I knew that." This is not the proper approach to problem solving. Consult the Solutions Guide only after you have gone as far as you can with reasonable effort.

Many problems have several parts. Work one or two parts. If you have no difficulty, move on to the next problem.

After completing a chapter, work as many problems at the end of the chapter as possible. These problems are arranged in order of increasing sophistication. Many of these problems require material from earlier chapters. Do not hesitate to review this material when necessary. The continued reinforcement will pay handsome dividends. See how far into the assigned problem set you can work. Finally, do not be distressed if you do not have time to attempt every assigned problem. Decide how much time you can devote to problems, and (to quote a famous sportscaster) make that time Q.T. *(quality time)*.

Old examinations make excellent sources of problems and also provide a sense of the style and level of difficulty that will be used by your professor in asking questions. Do not hesitate to use them if they are available. Work these examinations after you feel that you have done all you can to master the material. Let these be a final practice for the real thing — an intellectual "final scrimmage."

Keeping Up   Organic chemistry is cumulative, like mathematics. Each concept and each reaction builds on the last. Individual assignments in organic chemistry are not generally difficult to cover, but it is very difficult to catch up once you are behind. Decide how much time you can afford to spend on organic chemistry and spend it *regularly and productively*. An analogy we like to use with our students is that studying organic chemistry is akin to playing a sport or practicing a musical instrument. Do you practice for the big game only once for fifteen hours? Or do you practice each day for a much shorter time? The mind reacts toward intellectual activity much like the body does toward physical activity. Many short, intense, productive sessions are preferable to one long, exhausting session (known in student parlance as a "cram").

Another useful technique that has an analogy in the worlds of sports and performance is to put the material away for a few days before an examination. Use your study time to keep up with new material. This technique serves two purposes: First, it keeps you from getting behind. But, even better, something mysterious happens when your mind is allowed to reflect unconsciously on the old material. When you return to this material for a final review, you will have a deeper understanding of it and a sense of perspective about it of which you were not previously aware!

Seeking Assistance   Do not hesitate to seek assistance if you have continuing difficulty with some aspect of organic chemistry. Although many students feel intimidated by their professors, the fact is that most professors enjoy assisting students who have made a serious effort to master the material. Do not be afraid to seem ignorant in front of your professor. His or her job is to take you from ignorance to understanding.

Furthermore, good questions from confused students can help a professor become a better teacher!

Remember, you do not have to be brilliant to succeed in organic chemistry. You do have to be, or learn to be, disciplined, industrious, and organized. We hope you will use the text and this manual to best advantage, and that you find organic chemistry to be interesting and intellectually stimulating.

West Lafayette, Indiana
May 1988

G.M.L.
J.G.S.

Table of Contents

Chapter 1 / *Introduction to Structure and Bonding* 1

Terms / 1
Concepts / 2
Solutions to In-Text Problems / 5
Solutions to Additional Problems / 7

Chapter 2 / *Electronic Structures of Atoms and Molecules* 15

Terms / 15
Concepts / 15
Rules / 17
Solutions to In-Text Problems / 18
Solutions to Additional Problems / 19

Chapter 3 / *Alkanes and the Functional Groups* 23

Terms / 23
Concepts / 23
Solutions to In-Text Problems / 29
Solutions to Additional Problems / 33

Chapter 4 / *Introduction to Alkenes. Equilibria and Reaction Rates* 39

Terms / 39
Concepts / 39
Rules / 45
Solutions to In-Text Problems / 46
Solutions to Additional Problems / 50

Chapter 5 / *Addition Reactions of Alkenes* 57

Terms / 57
Concepts / 57
Reactions / 59
Solutions to In-Text Problems / 63
Solutions to Additional Problems / 69

Chapter 6 / *Introduction to Stereochemistry* 81

Terms / 81
Concepts / 81
Solutions to In-Text Problems / 87
Solutions to Additional Problems / 90

Chapter 7 / *Cyclic Compounds. Stereochemistry and Chemical Reactions* 99

Terms / 99
Concepts / 99
Rules / 109
Solutions to In-Text Problems / 110
Solutions to Additional Problems / 116

Chapter 8 / *Introduction to Alkyl Halides, Alcohols, Ethers, Thiols, and Sulfides* 129

Terms / 129
Concepts / 130
Reactions / 138
Solutions to In-Text Problems / 140
Solutions to Additional Problems / 145

Chapter 9 / *Substitution and Elimination Reactions of Alkyl Halides* 153

Terms / 153
Concepts / 153
Reactions / 159
Solutions to In-Text Problems / 160
Solutions to Additional Problems / 165

Chapter 10 / *Chemistry of Alcohols, Glycols, and Thiols* 177

Terms / 177
Concepts / 177
Reactions / 180
Solutions to In-Text Problems / 185
Solutions to Additional Problems / 194

Chapter 11 / *Chemistry of Ethers, Epoxides, and Sulfides* . . **205**

Terms / 205
Concepts / 205
Solutions to In-Text Problems / 211
Solutions to Additional Problems / 218

Chapter 12 / *Infrared Spectroscopy and Mass Spectrometry* . . **231**

Terms / 231
Concepts / 231
Solutions to In-Text Problems / 236
Solutions to Additional Problems / 239

Chapter 13 / *Nuclear Magnetic Resonance Spectroscopy* **245**

Terms / 245
Concepts / 245
Solutions to In-Text Problems / 251
Solutions to Additional Problems / 257

Chapter 14 / *Chemistry of Alkynes* . . . **265**

Terms / 265
Concepts / 265
Reactions / 268
Solutions to In-Text Problems / 271
Solutions to Additional Problems / 275

Chapter 15 / *Dienes, Resonance, and Aromaticity* **285**

Terms / 285
Concepts / 285
Reactions / 293
Solutions to In-Text Problems / 296
Solutions to Additional Problems / 305

Chapter 16 / *Chemistry of Benzene and Its Derivatives* **319**

Terms / 319
Concepts / 319
Reactions / 325
Electrophilic Aromatic Subctitution
    Summary / 328
Solutions to In-Text Problems / 329
Solutions to Additional Problems / 337

Chapter 17 / *Allylic and Benzylic Reactivity* **351**

Terms / 351
Concepts / 351
Reactions / 354
Rules / 355
Solutions to In-Text Problems / 356
Solutions to Additional Problems / 360

Chapter 18 / *Chemistry of Aryl Halides, Vinylic Halides, and Phenols* **373**

Terms / 373
Concepts / 373
Reactions / 377
Organohalide Summary / 379
Solutions to In-Text Problems / 380
Solutions to Additional Problems / 385

Chapter 19 / *Chemistry of Aldehydes and Ketones. Carbonyl-Addition Reactions* **405**

Terms / 405
Concepts / 406
Reactions / 412
Solutions to In-Text Problems / 420
Solutions to Additional Problems / 427

Chapter 20 / *Chemistry of the Carboxylic Acids* **443**

Terms / 443
Concepts / 443
Reactions / 448
Solutions to In-Text Problems / 452
Solutions to Additional Problems / 456

Chapter 21 / *Chemistry of Carboxylic Acid Derivatives* **471**

Terms / 471
Concepts / 471
Reactions / 478
Solutions to In-Text Problems / 485
Solutions to Additional Problems / 492

Chapter 22 / *Chemistry of Enols, Enolate Ions, and α,β-Unsaturated Carbonyl Compounds . . .* **511**

Terms / 511
Concepts / 511
Reactions / 517
Solutions to In-Text Problems / 526
Solutions to Additional Problems / 542

Chapter 23 / *Chemistry of Amines . . . .* **565**

Terms / 565
Concepts / 565
Reactions / 570
Solutions to In-Text Problems / 578
Solutions to Additional Problems / 587

Chapter 24 / *Naphthalene and the Aromatic Heterocycles . . .* **607**

Terms / 607
Concepts / 607
Reactions / 611
Solutions to In-Text Problems / 620
Solutions to Additional Problems / 626

Chapter 25 / *Pericyclic Reactions . . . .* **649**

Terms / 649
Concepts / 649
Reactions / 653
Solutions to In-Text Problems / 657
Solutions to Additional Problems / 665

Chapter 26 / *Amino Acids, Peptides, and Proteins . . . .* **678**

Terms / 678
Concepts / 678
Reactions / 683
Solutions to In-Text Problems / 689
Solutions to Additional Problems / 695

Chapter 27 / *Carbohydrates and Nucleic Acids . . . .* **711**

Terms / 711
Concepts / 711
Reactions / 721
Solutions to In-Text Problems / 724
Solutions to Additional Problems / 731

Acknowledgements

The authors and publishers wish to acknowledge the following people:

Mr. Craig Shelly of SoftShell Company, P. O. Box 632, Henrietta NY 14467, whose CHEMINTOSH Desk Accesory was used to produce most of the structures used in this book.

Pat Waldo of *Partners in Publishing*, Brisbane, California, who supervised the copy-editing and production of this book.

Kelly Martin, who facilitated the production of this text with able secretarial assistance.

G.M.L. acknowledges the love and understanding of his family, who thought that the writing was over when the text was finished.

Chapter 1 / Introduction to Structure and Bonding

CHAPTER 1 TERMS

arrow formalism 1.3,1.5
atomic number 1.2A
bond angle 1.6B
bond dipole 1.2C
bond length 1.6B
Brønsted acid 1.4
Brønsted base 1.4
Brønsted–Lowry acid–base concept 1.4
chemical bond 1.2
conformation 1.6B
conjugate acid 1.4
conjugate acid–base pair 1.4
conjugate base 1.4
covalent bond 1.2B
curved–arrow formalism 1.3,1.5
debye 1.2C
dielectric constant 1.2A
dihedral angle 1.6B
dipole 1.2C
dipole moment 1.2C
dissociate 1.2A
double bond 1.2B
electrolysis 1.2
electron diffraction 1.6A
electron shell 1.2A
electronegativity 1.2C
electrophile 1.3
electrostatic law 1.2A
formal charge 1.2B

halogen 1.2A
ion 1.2A
ionic bond 1.2A
ionic compound 1.2A
isoelectronic 1.2A
Lewis acid 1.3
Lewis base 1.3
Lewis (dot) structure 1.2B
molecular model 1.6B
noble gas 1.2A
nonbonding electron pair 1.2B
nucleophile 1.3
octet rule 1.2A
organic chemistry 1.1B
polar bond 1.2C
polar molecule 1.2C
polarized 1.2C
pyramidal geometry 1.6B
regular tetrahedron 1.6B
resonance hybrid 1.7
resonance structures 1.7
serendipity 1.1B
single bond 1.2B
tetrahedron 1.6B
trigonal geometry 1.6B
triple bond 1.2B
unshared electron pair 1.2B
valence electron 1.2A
valence shell 1.2A

The glossary in this and subsequent chapters is a list of the key terms and concepts contained in the chapter. These terms and concepts will be used throughout the text. It probably will not help you to memorize the exact definition given in the text; rather, define each of these terms and concepts in your own words and give an example if appropriate.

CHAPTER 1 CONCEPTS

I. Chemical Bonds:

A. Ionic Bonds:
1. **Ionic bonds** are formed between ions of different charges.
2. They can be dissociated by solvent into free ions.

$$\overset{+}{N}\overset{-}{a}\overset{-}{Cl} \xrightarrow{\text{H}_2\text{O}} \text{Na}^+ + \text{Cl}^-$$

B. Covalent Bonds:
1. **Covalent bonds** are formed between atoms by sharing electrons.
2. All organic compounds contain covalent bonds.
3. Covalent bonds are **polarized** when the atoms have different electronegativities.
   a) Electrons are attracted to the more **electronegative** atom.
   b) The more electronegative atom has a partial negative charge.
   c) The less electronegative (more electropositive) atom has a partial positive charge.
4. Polarized bonds have **dipole moments** called **bond dipoles**.
5. Bond dipoles add vectorially to give the permanent dipole moment.

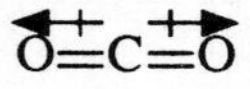

$$\mu = 0 \text{ D} \qquad\qquad\qquad \mu = 1.97 \text{ D}$$

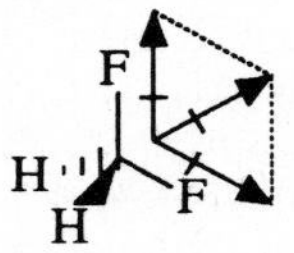

C. Octet Rule:
1. Atoms gain or lose valence electrons to form ions that are **isoelectronic** with the noble gases (Group VIIIA elements).
2. If we count all bonding electrons and all **unshared electron pairs**, the octet rule is usually obeyed by atoms involved in covalent bonding.

D. Lewis Structures:
1. In **Lewis Structures**:
   a) A single bond is represented by a pair of dots (:) or a single line (—).
   b) A double bond is represented by two pairs of dots (::) or a double line (=).
   c) A triple bond is represented by three pairs of dots (:::) or a triple line (≡).
   d) A pair of unshared electrons is represented by two dots (:).
2. **Formal charges** can be assigned to individual atoms in a molecule or ion by:
   a) Counting the number of unshared electrons on the atom of interest.
   b) Adding half of the electrons shared by the atom.
   c) Subtracting the result from the group number of the atom.

$$:\overset{-}{C} \equiv \overset{+}{O}:$$

II. Acids and Bases:

A. Brønsted–Lowry Acids and Bases:
1. A **Brønsted–Lowry acid** is a molecule or ion that can donate a proton (H$^+$).
2. A **Brønsted–Lowry base** is a molecule or ion that can accept a proton (H$^+$).
3. Members of a **conjugate acid–base pair** differ by only *one* proton (H$^+$).

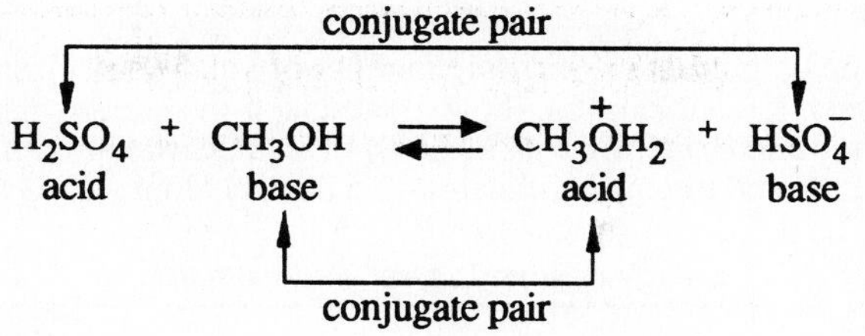

$$\text{conjugate pair}$$

$$H_2SO_4 \; + \; CH_3OH \;\rightleftharpoons\; CH_3\overset{+}{O}H_2 \; + \; HSO_4^-$$

acid   base   acid   base

$$\text{conjugate pair}$$

B. Lewis Acids and Bases:

1. A **Lewis acid** is a molecule or ion that is at least two electrons short of a full octet.
2. Lewis acids are also called:
    a) **Electrophiles.**
    b) Electron-deficient species.
3. A **Lewis base** is a molecule or ion that has at least one pair of unshared electrons.
4. Lewis bases are also called:
    a) **Nucleophiles.**
    b) Electron-rich species.

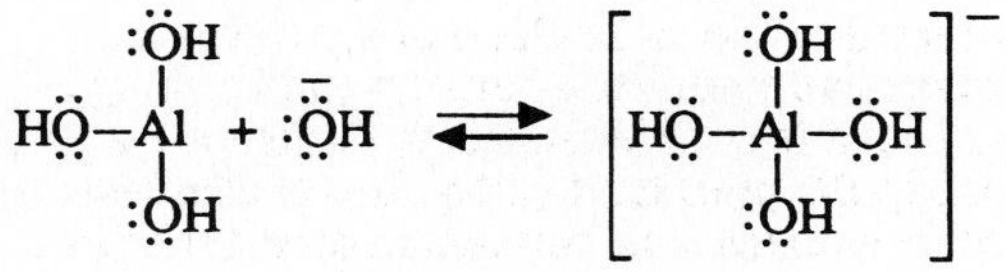

$$HÖ{-}Al \; + \; :ÖH \;\rightleftharpoons\; \left[HÖ{-}Al{-}ÖH \right]^-$$

III. Molecular Structure:

A. Bond Lengths:

1. **Bond lengths** between atoms of a given type *decrease* with the amount of multiple bonding.
2. Bond length *increases* with the size of the bonded atom.
3. Bond length between a given atom and atoms of a single row *decrease* with increasing electronegativity.

B. Bond Angles:

1. Groups bonded to a central atom are arranged so that they are as far apart as possible.
2. A central atom with four groups attached is tetrahedral, having angles of 109.5°.
3. A central atom with three groups attached is trigonal planar, having angles of 120°.
4. A central atom with two groups attached is linear, having angles of 180°.
5. A pair of unshared electrons is considered as a group.

C. Conformations:

1. **Conformations** of a molecule are obtained by rotation of a group about a bond.
2. Each unique conformation dictates a unique molecular geometry.

IV. The Periodic Table:

A. Rows:

1. The number of electrons in the **valence shell** of a neutral Group A atom is equal to the group number.
2. Atoms gain or lose valence electrons to form stable ions that are isoelectronic with the noble gases (Group VIIIA elements).
3. The valence electrons in all atoms of a given row come from the same valence shell.
    a) The energy required to remove an electron from a neutral atom *increases* to the right.
    b) The energy required to gain an electron to a neutral atom *decreases* to the right.

B. Columns:
    1. All atoms in a given column have the same number of valence electrons.
    2. The distance between the nucleus and the valence electrons *increases* down a column.
        a) The energy required to remove an electron from a neutral atom *decreases* down a column.
        b) The energy required to gain an electron to a neutral atom *increases* up a column.

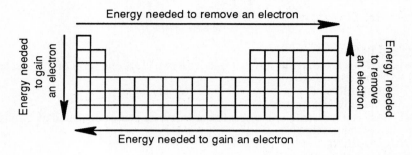

V. Representations:

A. Curved-arrow Formalism:
    1. The movement of electrons is portrayed using curved arrows is called **curved-arrow formalism**.
        a) The arrow always originates from the source of electrons.
        b) The arrow always points to the electron destination.
    2. The products are drawn by breaking and forming appropriate bonds.
    3. Charges are assigned when necessary.

$$CH_3\ddot{O}{:}^{-} + \;:\!\ddot{Br}\!-\!\overset{\displaystyle H}{\underset{\displaystyle H}{C}}\!-\!H \longrightarrow CH_3\ddot{O}\!-\!\overset{\displaystyle H}{\underset{\displaystyle H}{C}}\!-\!H + \;:\!\ddot{Br}\!:^{-}$$

B. Resonance Structures:
    1. **Resonance structures** are used to represent molecules and ions when a single Lewis structure is inadequate.
    2. Resonance structures represent the movement of electrons *only*!
    3. The conversion from one structure to another is represented by a single double-headed arrow.
    4. A **resonance hybrid** is a weighted average of the different resonance structures.
    5. Sometimes a resonance hybrid is depicted as a single structure in which:
        a) The resonating bonds are depicted by dashed lines.
        b) Partial charges are indicated by a lower-case Greek delta and the appropriate charge ($\delta+$ or $\delta-$)

CHAPTER 1 SOLUTIONS

Solutions to In-Text Problems

1. (a) $:\ddot{\text{F}}{:}^{-}$ (b) Ca^{2+} (c) $H{:}^{-}$ (d) $:\ddot{\text{N}}e{\cdot}^{+}$

2. (a) 1 (b) 8 (c) 2 (d) 4 (e) 1

3. 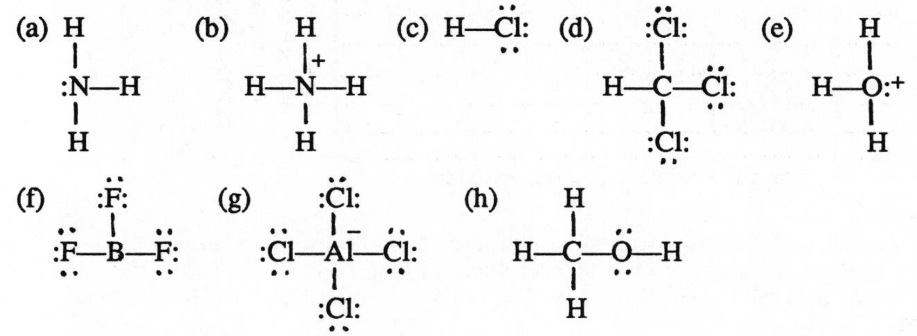 (a)
```
      H
      |
  :N—H
      |
      H
```
(b)
```
      H
      |+
  H—N—H
      |
      H
```
(c) H—$\ddot{\text{C}}$l:

(d)
```
      :Cl:
       |
  H—C—Cl:
       |
      :Cl:
```
(e)
```
      H
      |
  H—O:+
      |
      H
```

(f)
```
  :F:
   |
  :F—B—F:
```
(g)
```
       :Cl:
        |  ⁻
  :Cl—Al—Cl:
        |
       :Cl:
```
(h)
```
      H
      |
  H—C—O—H
      |
      H
```

4. 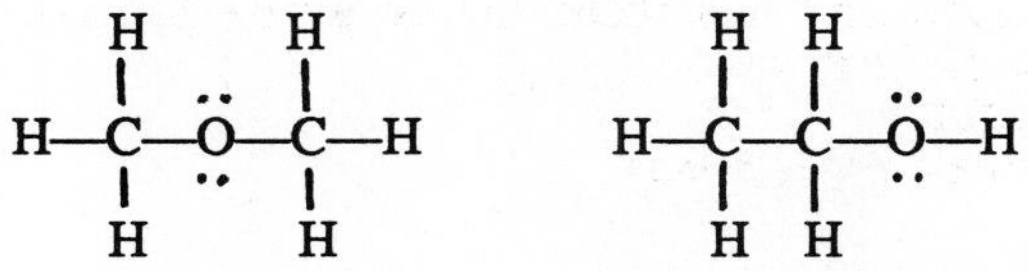
```
  H     H
  |     |
H—C—O—C—H
  |     |
  H     H
```
dimethyl ether

```
  H  H
  |  |
H—C—C—O—H
  |  |
  H  H
```
ethanol

➤ We shall find that in many cases there are several structures (or, for larger molecules, hundreds!) that correspond to the same atomic composition. Compounds that have the same atomic composition, but different atomic connectivities, are called **structural isomers**. Thus, diethyl ether and ethanol are structural isomers. We shall learn more about isomers in Chapter 3.

5. (a) 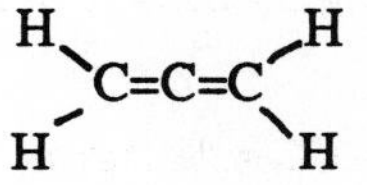
```
  H           H
    \        /
     C=C=C
    /        \
  H           H
```
allene

(b) 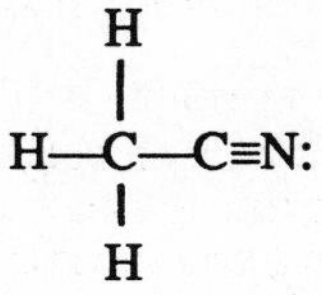
```
      H
      |
  H—C—C≡N:
      |
      H
```
acetonitrile

6. 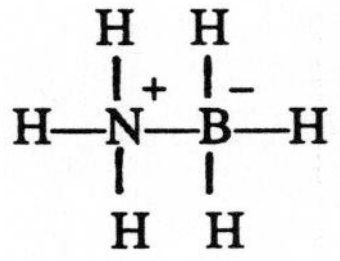
```
  H  H
  |+ |-
H—N—B—H
  |  |
  H  H
```
The net charge on the entire complex is zero.

7. The C—Cl bond dipoles are positive on carbon and negative on Cl. The C=O bond dipole is positive on carbon and negative on oxygen. The C—C and C—H bonds are, to a first approximation, nonpolar. (We shall see why this is an approximation in Chapter 10.) The carbon with the most partial positive character is the one bound to the most electronegative atoms — that is, the carbon in the C=O bond:

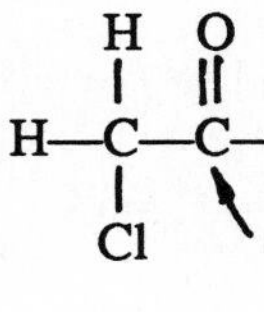

```
    H  O
    |  ||
H—C—C—Cl
    |
    Cl   connected to two electronegative atoms
```

8. From the table of electronegativities, the N—H bond dipoles are positive on H and negative on N. Yet N has the formal positive charge.

9. The curved-arrow formalism and structures of the products are as follows: (Arrows in the reactants refer to the forward reaction, and arrows in the products refer to the reverse reaction.)

(1)

$$:\overset{\cdot\cdot}{\underset{\cdot\cdot}{Cl}}:^- \quad \overset{\overset{:\overset{\cdot\cdot}{Cl}:}{|}}{\underset{\underset{:\overset{\cdot\cdot}{Cl}:}{|}}{Al}}{-}\overset{\cdot\cdot}{\underset{\cdot\cdot}{Cl}}: \longrightarrow :\overset{\cdot\cdot}{\underset{\cdot\cdot}{Cl}}{-}\overset{\overset{:\overset{\cdot\cdot}{Cl}:}{|}}{\underset{\underset{:\overset{\cdot\cdot}{Cl}:}{|}}{Al}}^{-}{-}\overset{\cdot\cdot}{\underset{\cdot\cdot}{Cl}}:$$

(2)

$$H{-}\overset{\overset{H}{|}}{\underset{\underset{H}{|}}{N}}: \quad \overset{\overset{:\overset{\cdot\cdot}{F}:}{|}}{\underset{\underset{:\overset{\cdot\cdot}{F}:}{|}}{B}}{-}\overset{\cdot\cdot}{\underset{\cdot\cdot}{F}}: \longrightarrow H{-}\overset{\overset{H}{|}}{\underset{\underset{H}{|}}{N}}^+{-}\overset{\overset{:\overset{\cdot\cdot}{F}:}{|}}{\underset{\underset{:\overset{\cdot\cdot}{F}:}{|}}{B}}^-{-}\overset{\cdot\cdot}{\underset{\cdot\cdot}{F}}:$$

10. In the first reaction, NH_3 on the left is the conjugate acid of the base $^-NH_2$ on the right, and ^-OH on the left is the conjugate base of the acid H_2O on the right. In the second reaction, one NH_3 on the left is the conjugate acid of the base $^-NH_2$ on the right, and the other NH_3 on the left is the conjugate base of the acid $^+NH_4$ on the right.

$$H_2\overset{\cdot\cdot}{N}{-}H \quad ^-:\overset{\cdot\cdot}{O}H \longrightarrow \qquad H_2\overset{\cdot\cdot}{N}{-}H \quad :NH_3 \longrightarrow$$

11. $H_3C{-}\overset{\cdot\cdot}{\underset{\cdot\cdot}{O}}{-}H \; + \; ^-:\overset{\cdot\cdot}{O}H \; \rightleftarrows H_3C{-}\overset{\cdot\cdot}{\underset{\cdot\cdot}{O}}:^- \; + \; H{-}\overset{\cdot\cdot}{O}H$$

Of course, the reverse reaction could also have been written, since the same conjugate acids and bases are involved either way!

12.

$$H\overset{\cdot\cdot}{\underset{\cdot\cdot}{O}}:^- \quad H{-}\overset{\overset{H}{|}}{\underset{\underset{H}{|}}{C}}{-}\overset{\cdot\cdot}{Cl}: \longrightarrow H\overset{\cdot\cdot}{\underset{\cdot\cdot}{O}}{-}\overset{\overset{H}{|}}{\underset{\underset{H}{|}}{C}}{-}H \; + \; :\overset{\cdot\cdot}{\underset{\cdot\cdot}{Cl}}:^-$$

13. (a) $H\overset{\cdot\cdot}{\underset{\cdot\cdot}{O}}{-}\overset{\overset{}{\underset{\underset{CH_3}{|}}{}}}{CH_2} \; + \; :\overset{\cdot\cdot}{\underset{\cdot\cdot}{Cl}}:^-$

(b)

$$\overset{H_2C}{\underset{H_2C}{\diagup\diagdown}}\overset{\overset{\cdot\cdot}{O}:}{\underset{\overset{\cdot\cdot}{\underset{\cdot\cdot}{O}}:}{\diagup}}:\overset{\cdot\cdot}{O}:$$

(c) $H_3Al \; + \; H{-}CH_3 \; + \; :\overset{\cdot\cdot}{\underset{\cdot\cdot}{Br}}:^-$

(d)

$$\overset{CH_2{-}H}{\underset{CH_3 \quad CH_3}{\overset{|}{\underset{\diagup\diagdown}{C^+}}}} \qquad :\overset{\cdot\cdot}{\underset{\cdot\cdot}{Br}}:^-$$

14. $H_3\overset{\cdot\cdot}{N}: \quad CH_3{-}\overset{\cdot\cdot}{\underset{\cdot\cdot}{Br}}: \longrightarrow H_3N^+{-}CH_3 \; + \; :\overset{\cdot\cdot}{\underset{\cdot\cdot}{Br}}:^-$

15. (a) H_2O is bent, with an H—O—H angle somewhat less than 109°.

(b) The $^-BF_4$ anion is tetrahedral.

(c) The carbon of formaldehyde is trigonal-planar. The H—C—H and H—C—O bond angles are 120°.

(d) The acetonitrile molecule is linear; that is, the C—C—N angle is 180°. The H—C—H angles are tetrahedral.

16. When the hydrogens are as far apart as possible, the dihedral angle is 60°. When the hydrogens are as close together as possible, the dihedral angle is 0°.

(a)   (b)

       dihedral angle = 60°   dihedral angle = 0°

17. Resonance structures of benzene indicate that each carbon-carbon bond has partial double-bond character (1.5 bonds between each carbon):

Solutions to Additional Problems

18. (c) CsF; cesium and fluorine atoms are most widely separated on the periodic table.

19. (a) Incomplete octet on carbon; formal charge on carbon = +1.
    (b) Complete octet on nitrogen; formal charge on nitrogen = 0.
    (c) Complete octet on carbon; formal charge on carbon = –1.
    (d) Incomplete octet on boron; formal charge on boron = 0.
    (e) Incomplete octet on iodine; formal charge on iodine = +1.

20. (a)   (b)   (c)

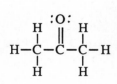

     acetone   chloroethylene   pyridine

(d)   (e)

     ketene   methylacetylene

➤ There are a number of possible correct structures for (a), (c), and (e).

21.   (a), (c), (d), and (e) are Lewis acids because they contain atoms with incomplete octets.

22.   (a) Perchlorate: +3 on chlorine; –1 on each oxygen; –1 net charge.
      (b) Methylene: 0 on all atoms; 0 net charge,
      (c) 0 on all atoms; 0 net charge
      (d) Trimethylamine oxide: +1 on nitrogen; –1 on oxygen; 0 on all other atoms; 0 net charge.
      (e) Ozone: 0 on left oxygen; +1 on central oxygen; –1 on right oxygen; 0 net charge.
      (f) Sulfate: –1 on all oxygens; +2 on sulfur; –2 net charge.
      (g) Hypochlorite: 0 on chlorine; –1 on oxygen; –1 net charge
      (h) Ethyl radical: 0 on all atoms; 0 net charge.

23.   (a) Not reasonable, because in the product the octet rule is violated on oxygen.
      (b) Reasonable.
      (c) Reasonable. Note that water has attacked the central carbon which, in the right-hand resonance structure, has electron-deficient (Lewis-acid) character.
      (d) Reasonable. Note that CH_3NH_2 has attacked the carbon, which, in the central resonance structure, is electron-deficient.
      (e) Not reasonable, because the octet rule is violated on oxygen.

➤ Notice (parts c and d) that any one of several resonance structures can be invoked to understand or predict chemical reactivity.

24.   (a)

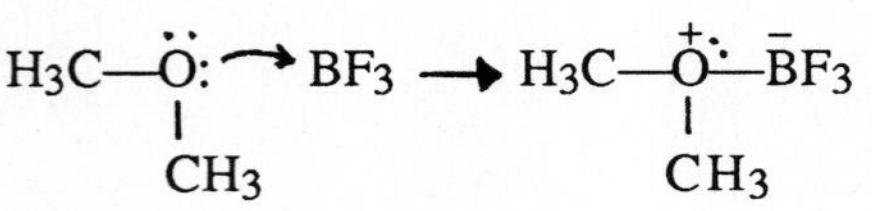

      (b)

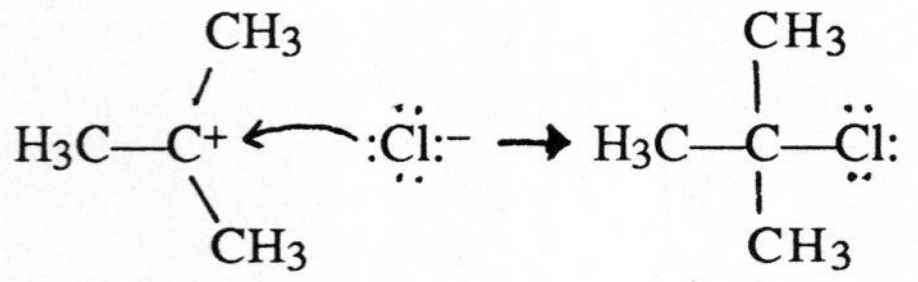

      (c)

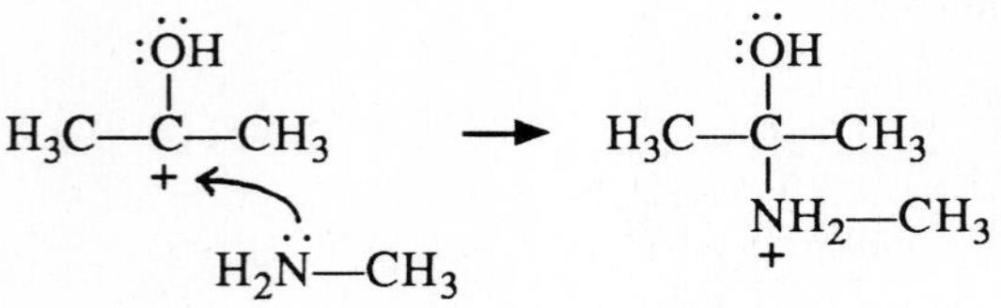

      (d)

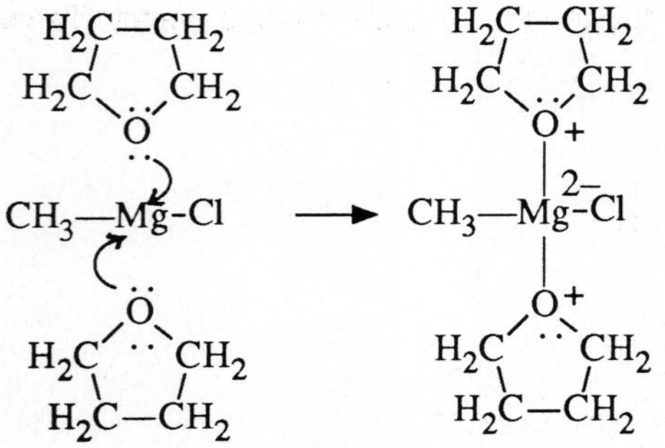

(e)

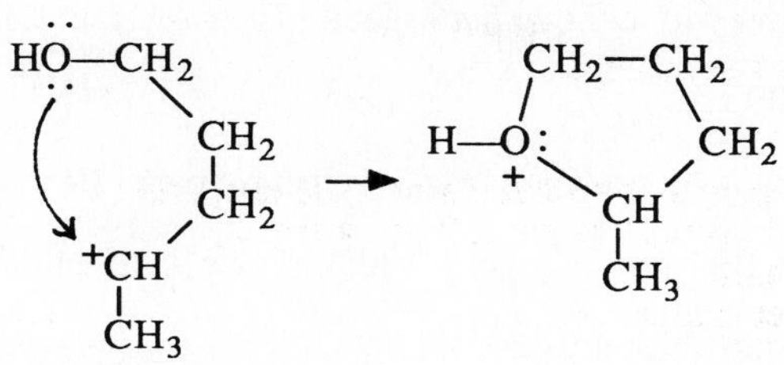

$$HO-CH_2$$ ... → $$H-O:$$

(f)

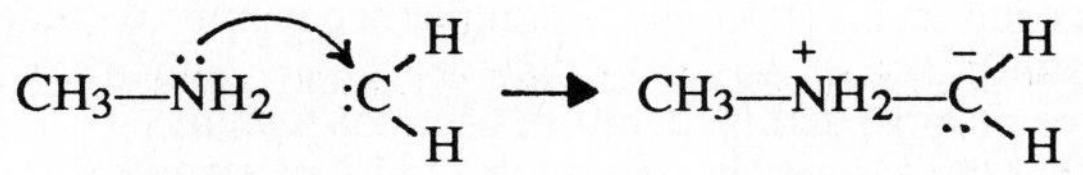

$$CH_3-NH_2 \quad :C\overset{H}{\underset{H}{}} \longrightarrow CH_3-\overset{+}{N}H_2-\overset{-}{C}\overset{H}{\underset{H}{}}$$

(g) $(H_3C)_3B \quad ^-:C\equiv O:^+ \longrightarrow (H_3C)_3B^- \!\!-\!\! C\equiv O:^+$

25.

$$H-\overset{\overset{H}{|}}{\underset{\underset{H}{|}}{B}}\!\!-\!\!H \quad H-\ddot{O}H \rightarrow H-\overset{\overset{H}{|}}{\underset{\underset{H}{|}}{B}} + H-H + ^-\!\!:\!\ddot{O}H$$

$$H-\overset{\overset{H}{|}}{\underset{\underset{H}{|}}{B}} \quad ^-\!:\!\ddot{O}H \rightarrow H-\overset{\overset{H}{|}}{\underset{\underset{H}{|}}{B}}\!\!-\!\!\ddot{O}H$$

$$H-\overset{\overset{H}{|}}{\underset{\underset{H}{|}}{B}}\!\!-\!\!\ddot{O}H \quad H-\ddot{O}H \rightarrow H-\overset{\overset{H}{|}}{\underset{\underset{}{}}}{B}\!\!-\!\!\ddot{O}H + H-H + ^-\!:\!\ddot{O}H$$

$$H-\overset{\overset{H}{|}}{\underset{\underset{}{}}{B}}\!\!-\!\!\ddot{O}H \quad ^-\!:\!\ddot{O}H \rightarrow H-\overset{\overset{H}{|}}{\underset{\underset{OH}{|}}{B}}\!\!-\!\!\ddot{O}H$$

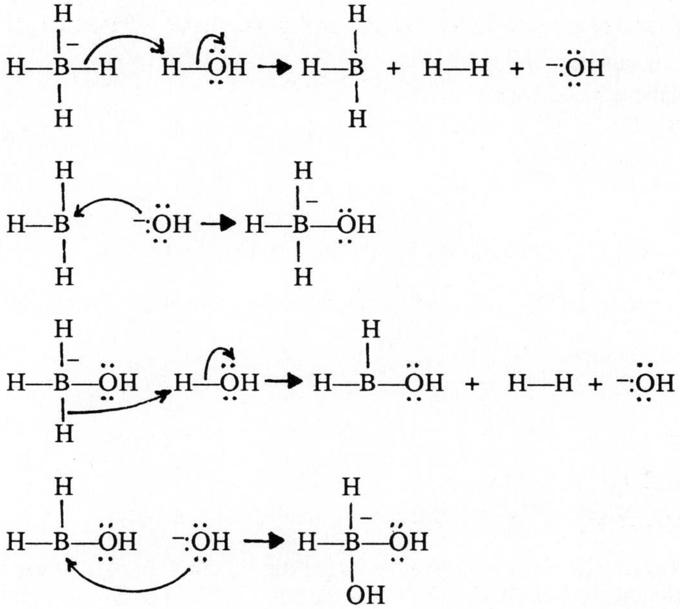

The reactions continue in the same fashion, with the formation of hydrogen and ⁻OH by the attack of the electrons in the B—H bond on H_2O, then by the attack of ⁻OH thus formed on trivalent boron. The last two steps in the sequence are:

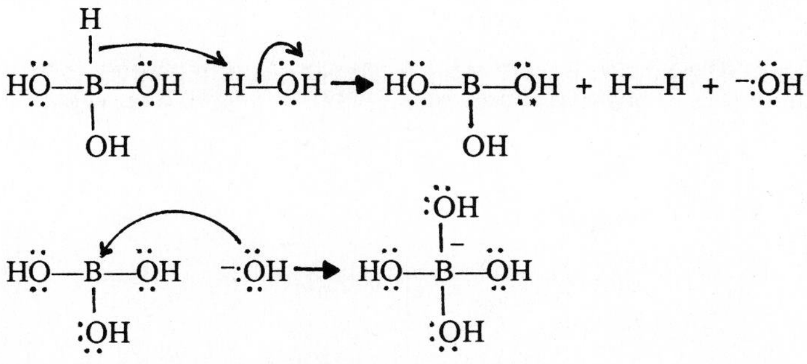

$$H\ddot{O}-\overset{\overset{H}{|}}{\underset{\underset{OH}{|}}{B}}\!\!-\!\!\ddot{O}H \quad H-\ddot{O}H \rightarrow H\ddot{O}-\overset{\overset{}{}}{\underset{\underset{OH}{|}}{B}}\!\!-\!\!\ddot{O}H + H-H + ^-\!:\!\ddot{O}H$$

$$H\ddot{O}-\overset{}{\underset{\underset{:\ddot{O}H}{|}}{B}}\!\!-\!\!\ddot{O}H \quad ^-\!:\!\ddot{O}H \rightarrow H\ddot{O}-\overset{\overset{:\ddot{O}H}{|}}{\underset{\underset{:\ddot{O}H}{|}}{B}}\!\!-\!\!\ddot{O}H$$

You should fill in the intervening steps.

26. (a) BeH_2 is linear (bond angle = 180°)
     (b) $:CH_2$ has three groups around carbon — an electron pair and two hydrogens. The carbon in this species is approximately trigonal (H—C—H angle $\cong$ 120°).
     (c) The Cl—Si—C angle is essentially tetrahedral (109.5°).
     (d) $^+CH_3$ is trigonal-planar (H—C—H angle $\cong$ 120°).
     (e) The central oxygen in ozone bears three groups: two other oxygens and an electron pair. Hence, ozone is bent with an O—O—O angle of about 120°.
     (f) The carbons of the CH_2 groups are trigonal-planar (H—C—H angle $\cong$ 120°). The central carbon has two attached groups; hence, the C=C=C angle is 180°.
     (g) The carbon is tetrahedral. Because the nitrogen bears three attached groups, it is trigonal-planar (O—N=O angle $\cong$ 120°).
     (h) The carbons and the nitrogen are tetrahedral.
     (i) The oxygen bears four groups — three hydrogens and an electron pair — and hence is approximately tetrahedral (or pyramidal, if we consider only the atoms).
     (j) The central carbon of the carbonate ion bears three groups, and is therefore trigonal-planar.
     (k) The six water molecules arrange themselves so that the Mn—O bonds are mutually perpendicular. This is called *octahedral* geometry.

octahedral
manganese hexahydrate

27. (a) The longest bond is the C—C bond. It is longer than the C—O bonds because O is more electronegative than C.
     (b) The shortest bonds are the H—C bonds, because H is in a "row" of the periodic table above carbon and oxygen.
     (c) The two C—O bonds are equivalent by resonance:

     (d) The most polar bonds are the C—O bonds, because C and O differ most in electronegativity.

28. If electronegativity were the only factor involved, CH_3F would have the larger dipole moment. However, from the definition in Eq. 1.5, dipole moment is the product of charge *and bond length*. The longer C—Cl bond compensates for the smaller electronegativity of chlorine.

29. From the definition of dipole moment (Eq. 1.5), we have, with $\mathbf{r}$ = 0.92 Å and μ = 1.75 D,

$$\mu = q \cdot \mathbf{r} \quad \text{or} \quad 1.75 = 0.92q$$

Solving for q, we find that q = (1.75/0.92) = 1.90 esu. Since there are 4.8 esu per electron charge, then q = (1.90/4.8) = 0.40 electron charge. Thus, there is 0.40 positive charge on H and 0.40 negative charge on F in H—F.

30. (a)

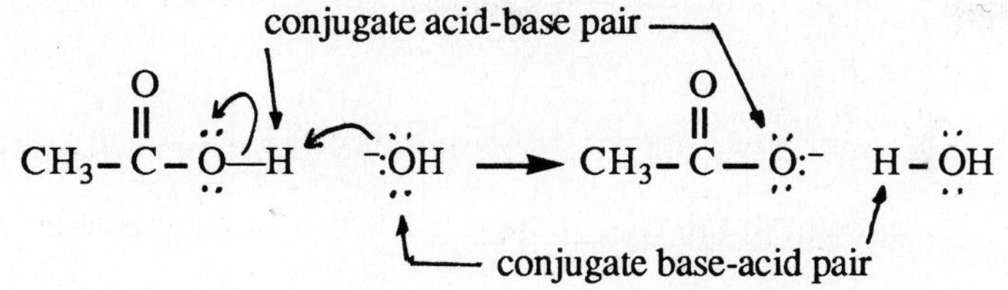

conjugate acid-base pair

$CH_3 - C - O - H$ $:OH$ → $CH_3 - C - O:^-$ $H - OH$

conjugate base-acid pair

(b)

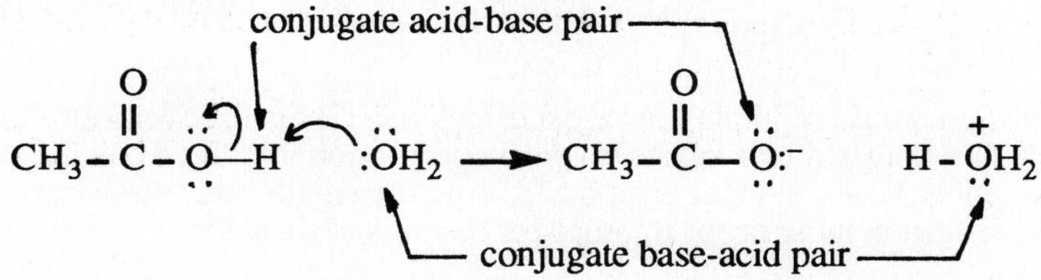

conjugate acid-base pair

$CH_3 - C - O - H$ $:OH_2$ → $CH_3 - C - O:^-$ $H - OH_2^+$

conjugate base-acid pair

(c)   conjugate acid-base pair

$(CH_3)_3N - H$ $:OCH_3$ → $(CH_3)_3N:$ $H - OCH_3$

conjugate base-acid
pair

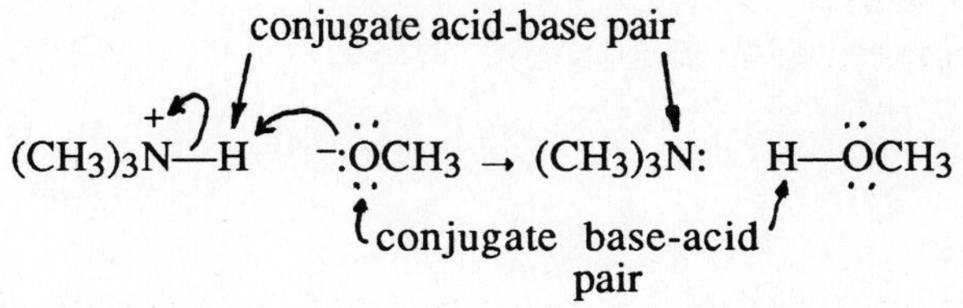

(d)

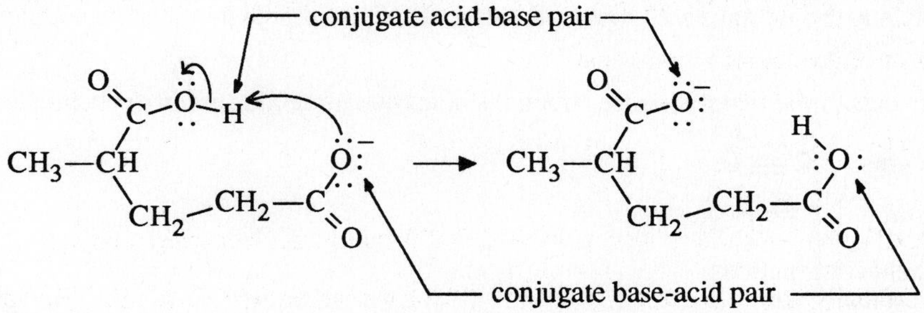

conjugate acid-base pair

$O = C - O - H$ $O = C - O:^-$

$CH_3 - CH$ $CH_3 - CH$ H
                                                                    $O:$
$CH_2 - CH_2 - C = O$ → $CH_2 - CH_2 - C = O$

conjugate base-acid pair

➤ Notice that an acid-base reaction may occur within the same molecule.

(e)   conjugate acid-base pair

H_3C $H - OH_2^+$ H_3C $:OH_2$

    $C = CH_2$ → $C^+ - CH_3$

H_3C H_3C

conjugate base-acid pair

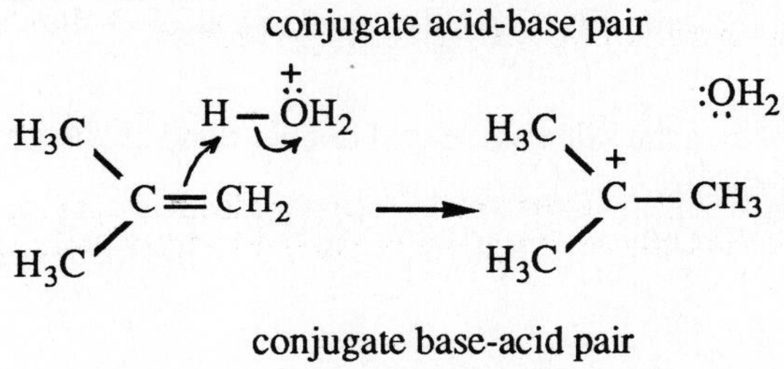

(f)

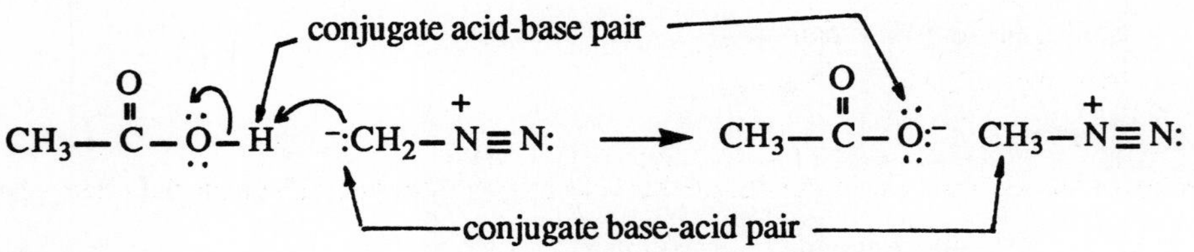

conjugate acid-base pair

$$CH_3-\overset{\overset{O}{\|}}{C}-\overset{..}{\underset{..}{O}}-H \quad ^-:CH_2-\overset{+}{N}\equiv N: \quad \longrightarrow \quad CH_3-\overset{\overset{O}{\|}}{C}-\overset{..}{\underset{..}{O}}:^- \quad CH_3-\overset{+}{N}\equiv N:$$

conjugate base-acid pair

31. A linear water molecule would have zero dipole moment, because the O—H bond dipoles would be oriented in opposite directions and would cancel. Hence, the nonzero dipole moment for water shows that it is a bent molecule. Banish Professor Szents to the South Pole!

32. A solvent with a high dielectric constant would separate ions most effectively. This follows from Eq. 1.2, which states that the energy of attraction between two ions is inversely proportional to the dielectric constant ε. The larger the ε, the smaller the attraction of two ions for each other. And the smaller this attraction, the more easily the ions are separated. This separation must occur in order for the ions to dissolve.

33. No matter how the CH_2 groups are turned, the resultant bond dipole lies along the bisector of the H—C—H angle:

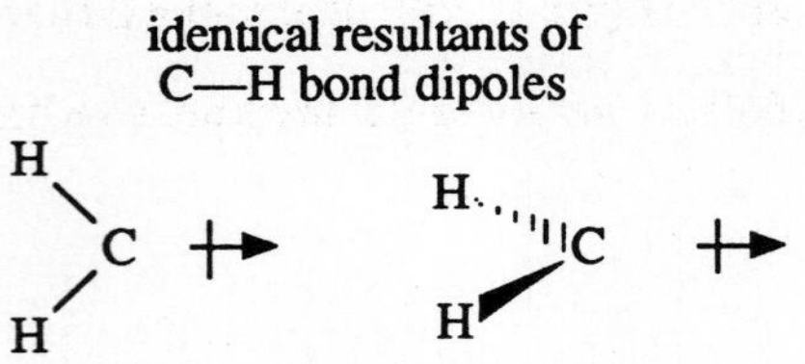

identical resultants of
C—H bond dipoles

Hence, both forms of ethylene should have zero dipole moment. Thus, the dipole moment cannot permit a choice between these two forms.

34. The predicted dipole moments of the two resonance structures of carbon monoxide are in opposite directions:

dipole moment contributions
of each resonance form

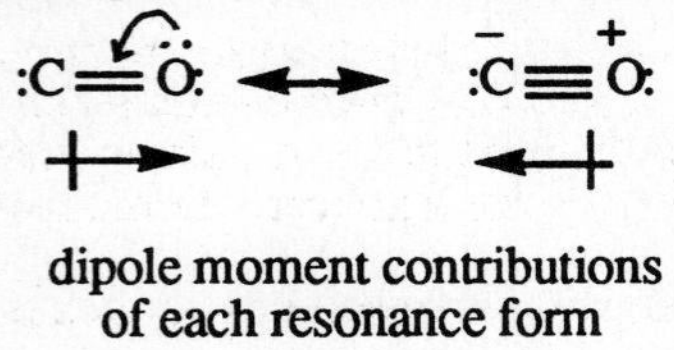

Since a given structure is the weighted average of its resonance structures, it follows that the electron distribution in a given molecule is the average of the electron distributions of its resonance forms. Because the dipole moments of the two resonance forms are in opposite directions, they tend to cancel — thus, a near-zero dipole moment for CO.

35. (a) Resonance structures show that each oxygen shares the same amount of double-bond character and negative charge. Hence, all C—O bonds are equivalent:

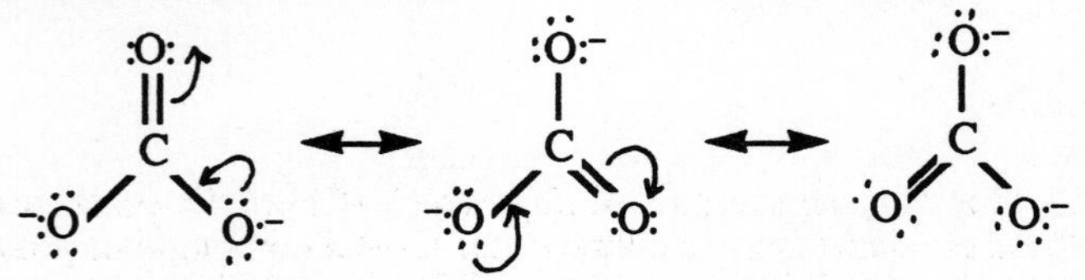

(b) The resonance structures of ozone indicate delocalization of negative charge to the two outer oxygens

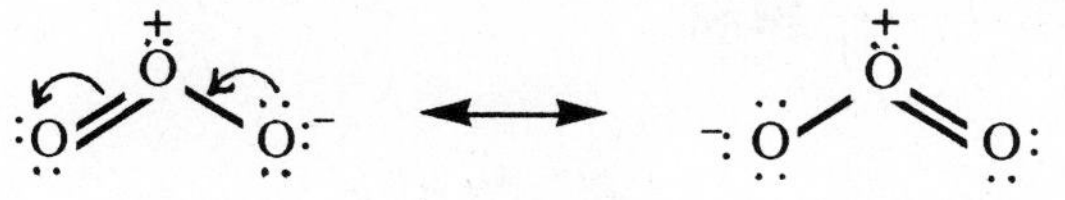

(c) Delocalization of an electron pair from the double bond to oxygen leaves an electron-deficient, positively charged carbon:

$$H_2C=\overset{+}{\underset{..}{O}}-H \leftrightarrow H_2\overset{+}{C}-\overset{..}{\underset{..}{O}}-H$$

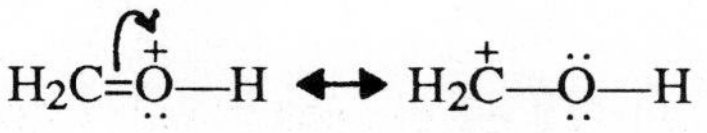

(d) Delocalization of an electron pair from the triple bond onto nitrogen leaves an electron-deficient, positively charged carbon; compounds with electron-deficient atoms behave as Lewis acids.

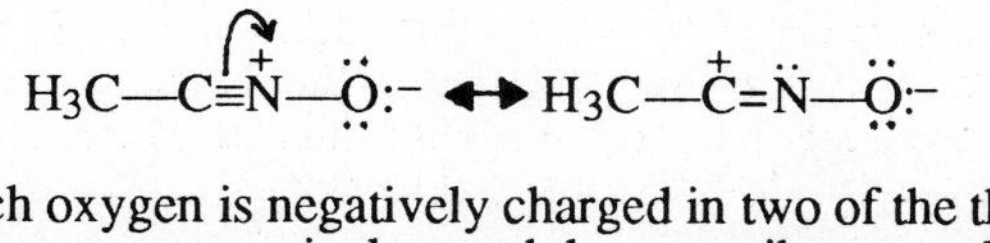

$$H_3C-C\equiv\overset{+}{N}-\overset{..}{\underset{..}{O}}:^- \leftrightarrow H_3C-\overset{+}{C}=\overset{..}{N}-\overset{..}{\underset{..}{O}}:^-$$

36. Each oxygen is negatively charged in two of the three resonance structures. Furthermore, the resonance structures are equivalent and thus contribute equally to the structure of the carbonate ion. Hence, there is 2/3 negative charge on each oxygen.

37. (a) The resonance structures show (1) that each carbon-carbon bond has 50% double-bond character, and (2) that there is 0.5 positive charge on each of the terminal carbons.
(b) The structure on the right is not reasonable because it violates the octet rule; there are five bonds to nitrogen.

38. (a)

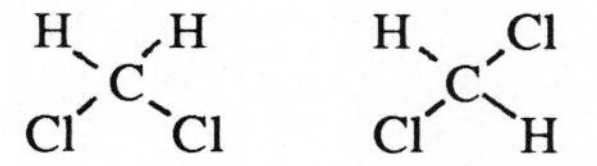

```
   H   H          H   Cl
    \ /             \ /
     C               C
    / \             / \
  Cl   Cl         Cl   H

"adjacent"       "opposite"
```

(b) The "adjacent" form should have nonzero dipole moment; the "opposite" form should have zero dipole moment.
(c) The failure to observe more than one form is consistent with a tetrahedral structure, because there is only one tetrahedral structure possible for CH_2Cl_2. However, the *failure* to observe a phenomenon does not prove that the phenomenon doesn't exist. Hence, it would be conceivable, were there no other evidence to support the tetrahedral structure, that CH_2Cl_2 is the "adjacent" form (CH_2Cl_2 has a nonzero dipole moment).

39. Let us perform the vector constructions suggested. First, we start with the resultants of each pair of C—Cl bond dipoles:

```
        Cl
       /
      /
    [ ]
   [    C
   [   /
    Cl            C···Cl
                   \  \
                    Cl
```

Next, we add the two resultants together:

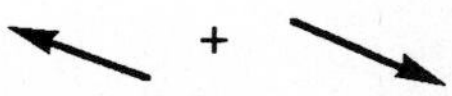

$$\nwarrow \ + \ \searrow \ = 0 \text{ dipole moment}$$

By analogy to the result in Problem 33 for C—H bonds, the resultant of any two C—Cl bond dipoles lies along the bisector of the Cl—C—Cl angle. Since these two bisectors are colinear, the C—Cl bond dipoles point in exactly opposite directions and therefore cancel. This result is not peculiar to CCl_4; it holds for any tetrahedral species XY_4.

Chapter 2 / Electronic Structures of Atoms and Molecules

CHAPTER 2 TERMS

antibonding molecular orbital 2.4
atomic orbital 2.2
azimuthal quantum number 2.2
bond dissociation energy 2.4
bonding molecular orbital 2.4
cylindrical symmetry 2.4
d orbital.. 2.2
electron density, ψ^2 .... 2.2
electronic configuration 2.3
f orbital 2.2
Heisenberg uncertainty principle 2.1
Hund's rule 2.3
hybrid orbital 2.6A
l (quantum number).................................... 2.2
m (quantum number)................................... 2.2
magnetic quantum number 2.2
molecular orbital 2.4
n (quantum number) 2.2

node 2.2
orbital 2.2
p orbital 2.2
Pauli exclusion principle 2.3
principle quantum number 2.2
probability 2.1
quantized 2.2
quantum mechanics 2.1
quantum number 2.2
relative probability 2.2
s orbital 2.2
s (quantum number)...................................2.2
sigma bond (σ bond) 2.4
spin quantum number 2.2
wave, ψ 2.2
wave-particle duality 2.1
wavefunction 2.2
zero probability 2.2

CHAPTER 2 CONCEPTS

I. The Wave Nature of the Electron:

A. Electrons Have Wavelike Properties:
1. The motion of electrons can be described by mathematically derived **wavefunctions** (ψ).
    a) The wavefunctions dictate the three–dimensional regions of space in which the electron has the highest probability of existing.
    b) The **electron density** is equal to ψ^2.
2. The exact position of an electron cannot be specified; only the probability that it occupies a certain region of space can be specified.

B. The Four Quantum Numbers:
1. The **principal quantum number** (n):
    a) Has positive, non–zero integral values.
    b) Relates to the energy of an electron occupying the **orbital**.
2. The **azimuthal quantum number** (l):
    a) Has positive integral values from zero to n.
    b) Relates to the shape, energy, and number of atomic orbitals.
3. The **magnetic quantum number** (m):
    a) Has both positive and negative integral values from $-l$ to $+l$.
    b) Relates to the relative orientation of the orbitals.

4. The **spin quantum number** (s):
   a) Has values of $+\frac{1}{2}$ or $-\frac{1}{2}$.
   b) Relates to the spin of the electron.
5. No two electrons of an atom can have the same combination of all four quantum numbers.

C. The Periodic Table and the Quantum Numbers:
   1. The rows correspond to the principal quantum numbers.
   2. Sets of columns correspond to the azimuthal quantum numbers.
      a) The IA and IIA Group elements (light metals).
         (1) $l = 0$.
         (2) one orbital orientation ($m = 0$).
         (3) one or two electrons in the one orbital.
      b) The IIIA → VIIIA Group elements (nonmetals, postransition metals, noble gases).
         (1) $l = 1$.
         (2) three orbital orientations ($m = -1, 0, +1$).
         (3) one or two electrons in each of the three orbitals.
      c) The IB → VIIIB Group elements (transition metals).
         (1) $l = 2$.
         (2) five orbital orientations ($m = -2, -1, 0, +1, +2$).
         (3) one or two electrons in each of the five orbitals.
      d) The Lanthanide and Actinide Group elements (rare earths).
         (1) $l = 3$.
         (2) seven orbital orientations ($m = -3, -2, -1, 0, +1, +2, +3$).
         (3) one or two electrons in each of the seven orbitals.

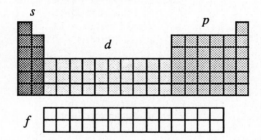

D. Energies:
   1. Electrons have only specific energies.
      a) The greater the principal quantum number, the greater the energy.
      b) Electrons are distributed evenly among orbitals of equal energy.
   2. Some orbitals contain wave peaks and troughs separated by **nodes**.
      a) The higher the principal quantum number (energy), the greater the number of nodes.

II. Orbitals:

A. Atomic Orbitals:
   1. **Atomic orbitals** are defined by the four quantum numbers.
   2. s **Orbitals** are spherical and have only one orientation.
   3. p **Orbitals** have two lobes (one positive and one negative) and have three different orientations.

B. Hybrid Orbitals:
   1. **Hybrid orbitals** are obtained by combining atomic orbitals.
      a) The number of hybrid orbitals equals the number of atomic orbitals that are mixed to obtain them.
      b) The hybrid orbitals obtained have the same energy.
   2. Hybrid orbitals are always oriented so that they are as far apart as possible.

C. Molecular Orbitals:
   1. **Molecular orbitals** are derived from the combination (overlap) of atomic orbitals.
      a) Addition of atomic orbitals affords **bonding molecular orbitals**.
      b) Subtraction of atomic orbitals affords **antibonding molecular orbitals**.
      c) An equal number of bonding and antibonding molecular orbitals are always obtained.

2. Each molecular orbital is populated with a maximum of two electrons.
    a) Electrons are evenly distributed between molecular orbitals of equal energy.
    b) Electrons are placed in molecular orbitals starting with the molecular orbitals of lowest energy.
3. When bonding and antibonding molecular orbitals are equally populated with electrons, there is *no* net bonding.

CHAPTER 2 RULES

<u>Heisenberg Uncertainty Principle</u>: The position of very small particles (such as electrons and other atomic and subatomic particles) cannot be described with unlimited precision at any given time.

<u>Hund's Rule</u>: Electrons of equal energy (that is, with the same principal and azimuthal quantum numbers) are evenly distributed among orbitals of equal energy.

<u>Pauli Exclusion Principle</u>: No two electrons of an atom can have the same four quantum numbers. This is why only two electrons with spin $-\frac{1}{2}$ or $+\frac{1}{2}$ can occupy a given orbital.

CHAPTER 2 SOLUTIONS

Solutions to In-Text Problems

1.

n	l	m	s
4	0 (4s)	0	±1/2
	1 (4p)	−1	±1/2
		0	±1/2
		+1	±1/2
	2 (4d)	−2	±1/2
		−1	±1/2
		0	±1/2
		+1	±1/2
		+2	±1/2
	3 (4f)	−3	±1/2
		−2	±1/2
		−1	±1/2
		0	±1/2
		+1	±1/2
		+2	±1/2
		+3	±1/2

2.   A $3s$ orbital is three concentric "balls" of electron density, each separated by a node, as shown in the following "cutaway" diagram:

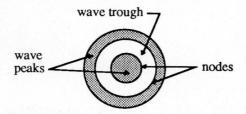

3.   (a) Lithium atom: $1s^22s^1$
     (b) Nitrogen atom: $1s^22s^22p^3$
     (c) Sodium atom: $1s^22s^22p^63s^1$
     (d) Fluoride ion: $1s^22s^22p^6$
     (e) Potassium ion: $1s^22s^22p^63s^23p^6$

4.   (a)

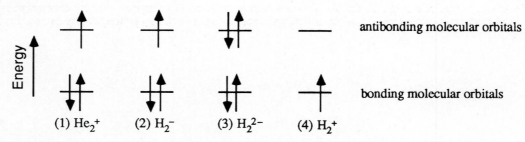

Of these, (1), (2), and (4) would exist as diatomic species, because they have more electrons in bonding molecular orbitals than in antibonding ones. Species (3), however, would dissociate into two H:$^-$ ions. (b) H_2 has two electrons in a bonding molecular orbital. Species (1), (2), and (4) have a net one electron in a bonding molecular orbital (that is, an excess of one bonding over antibonding electrons). Hence, we estimate that the bond dissociation energies of these species would be about half that of the hydrogen molecule — that is, about 52 kcal/mol. This remarkably close to the actual value, which is about 60 kcal/mol.

5.   If we take the oxygen of water to be sp^3 hybridized, then two of the sp^3 hybrid orbitals contain unshared electron pairs. The other two sp^3 hybrid orbitals contain one electron each; each of these overlaps with the $1s$ orbital of a hydrogen atom to give two sp^3–$1s$ sigma bonds — the O—H bonds of water.

Solutions to Additional Problems

6.   (a) Chlorine atom: $1s^2 2s^2 2p^6 3s^2 3p^5$
       (b) Chloride ion: $1s^2 2s^2 2p^6 3s^2 3p^6$
       (c) Argon atom: $1s^2 2s^2 2p^6 3s^2 3p^6$
       (d) Magnesium atom: $1s^2 2s^2 2p^6 3s^2$

7.   Answer (d): The $2d$ orbital would require that the l quantum number (3) exceed the n quantum number, a situation that is not allowed in quantum theory.

8.   (a) A $2s$ orbital ($n = 2, l = 0$) has only one spherical node (Fig. 2.2). A $2p$ orbital ($n = 2, l = 1$) has one non-spherical node -- the nodal plane that separates the two lobes of the orbital (Fig. 2.4). A $3p$ orbital ($n = 3, l = 1$) should have two nodes, one of which is nonspherical (that is, a planar node) and the other spherical, and indeed this is precisely what is shown in Fig. 2.5.
       (b) There are 3 nodes in a $4s$ orbital, and 0 nonspherical nodes; hence, there are 3 spherical nodes. There are 2 nodes in a $3d$ orbital, and 2 nonspherical nodes; hence, there are 0 spherical nodes.

9.

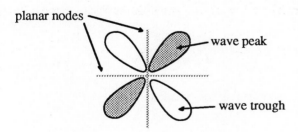

planar nodes — wave peak — wave trough

(The absolute positions of peaks and troughs can be reversed, as long as peaks and troughs alternate across each node. Thus, peaks could be troughs, and troughs peaks.)

10.   (a) As we can see from the table in the answer to Problem 1, there are seven equivalent f orbitals.
       (b) Since $l = 3$ for an f orbital, and since the maximum value of the l quantum number is $n - 1$, then f orbitals first appear in principal quantum level 4.
       (c) We expect to see four nodes for a $5f$ orbital.
       (d) Three of these are nonspherical; hence, there is one spherical node in a $5f$ orbital.

11.   In order to determine how large an electron is, we would have to measure its size. Such a measurement would require that we pinpoint the location of the electron in space. The uncertainty principle tells us that this is not possible.

12. From the previous problems, we determine that the 4*p* orbital has three nodes, one of which is nonspherical (that is, a plane). Thus, there are two spherical nodes. We can extrapolate from our picture of the 3*p* orbital in Fig. 2.5:

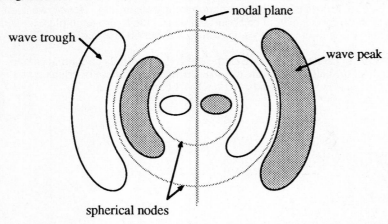

13. Quantum theory says that the energy *E* of light absorbed must be precisely equal to the energy difference between the orbitals which, from the statement of the problem, is 1.635×10^{-11} erg. This energy is then

$$E = hc/\lambda = (6.625 \times 10^{-27}\ \text{erg-sec})(3 \times 10^{10}\ \text{cm/sec})/(1.635 \times 10^{-11}\ \text{erg})$$
$$= (1.22 \times 10^{-5}\ \text{cm})(10^{-8}\ \text{Å/cm}) = 1220\ \text{Å}$$

This light is in the far ultraviolet region of the electromagnetic spectrum.

14. (a)

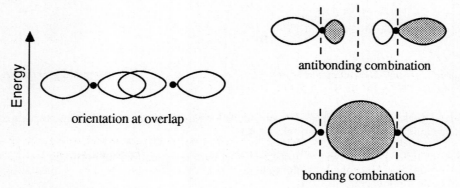

(b) The vertical dashed lines represent the nodes.
(c) Two electrons in the bonding molecular orbital would be a sigma bond, because the molecular orbital has cylindrical symmetry.

15. (a) and (b) In this case, the orientation of the orbitals at overlap is side-to-side:

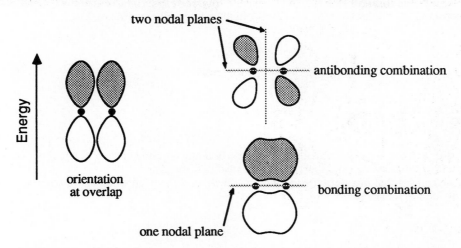

Notice that the molecular orbital of higher energy has more nodes than the one of lower energy.

(c) When two electrons occupy the bonding molecular orbital, the resulting bond is *not* a sigma bond, because the resulting molecular orbital is not cylindrically symmetric. [This type of bond is called a *pi bond* (π-bond)].

16. When a hydrogen molecule absorbs light, an electron jumps from a bonding molecular orbital into an antibonding molecular orbital:

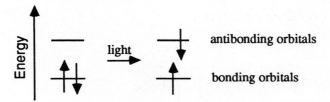

After light absorption, the hydrogen molecule has no net bonding electrons, and there is no energetic advantage to bonding. Hence, the molecule falls apart into hydrogen atoms.

17. (a) The configuration of the atom with atomic number = 8: $1s^3 2s^3 2p^2$

(b) The second noble gas has a filled $2p$ orbital; but there are only two $2p$ orbitals ($m = 0, +1$); so the $2p$ level holds six electrons (three in each of the $2p$ orbitals). With filled $1s$, $2s$, and $2p$ levels, the second noble gas has $(3 + 3 + 6) = 12$ electrons; hence, its atomic number is 12.

(c) Since there are three values of spin, each orbital can hold three electrons. [We had to know this to get the right answer to parts (a) and (b)].

(d) The corresponding rule might be called a "nontet rule."

18. In Lewis terms, the product of reaction (2) violates the octet rule on nitrogen. In molecular orbital terms, there are four N—H bonding molecular orbitals (the four σ bonds) and four corresponding antibonding molecular orbitals. The extra electron in the product of reaction (2) would have to go into an antibonding

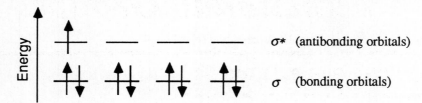

Although the population of one antibonding orbital results in less bonding — and hence, less stability — it still gives a situation with net overall bonding, and therefore is not strictly forbidden.

➤ From this example we can see that quantum theory enriches Lewis theory by accounting for some observations that are difficult to understand with Lewis theory.

Chapter 3 / Alkanes and the Functional Groups

CHAPTER 3 TERMS

acetylene .... Introduction
aliphatic hydrocarbon .... Introduction
alkane .... Introduction
alkene .... Introduction
alkyl group 3.2A, 3.8
alkyne .... Introduction
anti conformation 3.5B
aromatic hydrocarbon .... Introduction
aryl group 3.8
boiling point 3.4A
combustion 3.6
condensed structural formula 3.1
conformation 3.5A
conformational isomer 3.5B
conformational strain 3.5B
connectivity 3.1
cracking 3.7
cyclo- 3.3
cycloalkane 3.3
dihedral angle 3.5A
dispersion force 3.4A
eclipsed form 3.5B
elemental analysis 3.6
empirical formula 3.6
fractional distillation 3.7
functional group 3.8
gauche conformation 3.5B
homologous series 3.1
hydrocarbon .... Introduction
internal rotation 3.5A
iso- 3.2
isomer 3.2
IUPAC 3.2

melting point 3.4B
methylene group 3.1
molecular formula 3.6
n- 3.1
n-alkane 3.1
neo- 3.1
Newman projection 3.5A
normal alkane 3.1
octane number 3.7
olefin .... Introduction
paraffin .... Introduction
petroleum 3.7
phenyl group 3.8
primary 3.2B
principal chain 3.2A
quaternary 3.2B
rotational isomer 3.5B
sec- 3.2A
secondary 3.2B
skeletal structure 3.3
staggered form 3.5B
steric effect 3.5B
structural formula 3.1
structural isomer 3.2
substituent group 3.2A
systematic nomenclature 3.2
tert- 3.2A
tertiary 3.2B
torsional isomer 3.5B
torsional strain 3.5B
van der Waals force 3.4A
van der Waals radius 3.5B
van der Waals repulsion 3.5B

CHAPTER 3 CONCEPTS

I. Hydrocarbons:

    A. <u>Aliphatic Hydrocarbons</u>:
        1. Alkanes:
            a) **Alkanes** are also known as **paraffins**.
            b) Alkanes are **hydrocarbons** that contain only single bonds.

c) *n*-Alkanes:
    (1) The family of **n-alkanes** is an example of a **homologous series.**
    (2) Successive members of the *n*-alkanes series differ by one **methylene group**, —CH$_2$—.

$$CH_3CH_2CH_3 \qquad \text{propane}$$
$$CH_3CH_2CH_2CH_3 \qquad \text{butane}$$

d) Cycloalkanes:
    (1) **Cycloalkane**s contain carbon chains in closed loops or rings.
    (2) The cycloalkane family is an example of a homologous series.

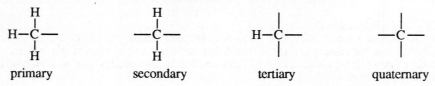

cyclopentane

e) Classification of carbon substitution:
    (1) **Primary** — a carbon bonded to only one other carbon.
    (2) **Secondary** — a carbon bonded to two other carbons.
    (3) **Tertiary** — a carbon bonded to three other carbons.
    (4) **Quaternary** — a carbon bonded to four other carbons.

primary   secondary   tertiary   quaternary

2. Alkenes:
    a) **Alkenes** are hydrocarbons that contain carbon–carbon double bonds.
    b) Alkenes are also known as **olefins.**

$$CH_3\text{–}CH{=}CH_2 \qquad \text{propene}$$

3. Alkynes:
    a) **Alkynes** are hydrocarbons that contain carbon–carbon triple bonds.
    b) Alkynes are also known as **acetylenes.**

$$H\text{—}C{\equiv}C\text{—}H \qquad \text{acetylene}$$

B. Aromatic Hydrocarbons:
    1. **Aromatic hydrocarbons** consist of benzene and its substituted derivatives.
    2. Aromatic hydrocarbons are also called arenes.

benzene   toluene

II. Representations of Organic Molecules:

A. Molecular Formula:
   1. The **molecular formula** indicates the atomic composition of a compound.
   2. All noncyclic alkanes (alkanes without rings) have the general formula C_nH_{2n+2}, in which n is the number of carbons in the alkane.

   decane $C_{10}H_{22}$ ($n = 10$; H = $2n + 2 = 22$)

   3. The general formula for an alkane containing a *single* ring is C_nH_{2n}, in which n is the number of carbons in the alkane.

   cyclopentane C_5H_{10}

B. Structural Formula:
   1. A **structural formula** is a Lewis structure.
   2. The structural formula shows the **connectivity** of the atoms.
   3. For any one molecule there is only one connectivity pattern but there are many different orientations.

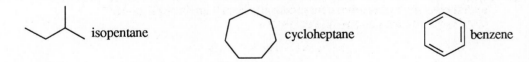

propane

C. Condensed Structural Formula:
   1. The **condensed structural formula** shows the connectivity of the carbon atoms.
   2. The hydrogens are understood to be connected to carbon atoms with single bonds.
   3. A chain of methylene groups can be condensed further to —$(CH_2)_n$—, in which n is the number of methylene groups.

   $CH_3CH(CH_3)_2$ isobutane

D. Skeletal Structures:
   1. **Skeletal structures** for alkanes show only the carbon–carbon bonds.
   2. Carbons are located at each vertex and at the ends of the structure.

   isopentane   cycloheptane   benzene

E. Functional Groups:
   1. A **functional group** is a group of atoms and their associated chemical bonds that has about the same type of chemical reactivity whenever it occurs in different compounds.
   2. An **alkyl group** is abbreviated **R-**.
   3. The **phenyl group** is abbreviated **Ph-**.
   4. An **aryl group** is abbreviated **Ar-**.

III. Systematic (IUPAC) Nomenclature of Alkanes:

A. Unbranched Alkanes:
   1. The unbranched alkanes are named according to the number of carbons present. (See Table 3.1 on page 57 of the text.)

B. Branched–chain Alkanes:
   1. The older names for the branched–chain alkane isomers of 4, 5, and 6 carbons are still recognized.

2. Other branched alkanes are named according to the **principal chain** (the longest continuous carbon chain) no matter how the molecule is drawn.
    a) The carbons are numbered consecutively from one end to the other in the direction that gives the **substituent groups** the lowest numbers.
        (1) When branching occurs on different carbons of the principal chain, the carbons are numbered to give the lowest number at the *first* point of difference.
        (2) The names of the substituent groups (alkyl groups) are derived from the alkane of the same number of carbons by dropping the final *ane* and adding *yl*.
    b) In the case of multiple substituents, each substituent receives its own number; the prefixes *di, tri, tetra*, etc., are used to indicate the number of identical groups.

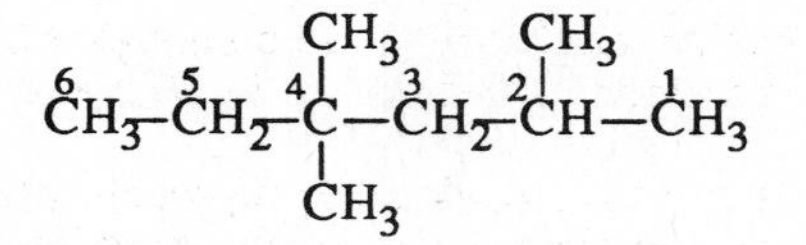

$$\underset{\text{CH}_3}{\overset{\text{CH}_3 \qquad \text{CH}_3}{\overset{6}{\text{CH}_3}-\overset{5}{\text{CH}_2}-\overset{4}{\text{C}}-\overset{3}{\text{CH}_2}-\overset{2}{\text{CH}}-\overset{1}{\text{CH}_3}}}$$
2,4,4-trimethylhexane

3. The name is constructed by writing the carbon number on which the branch occurs, a hyphen, the name of the substituent group at the branch, and the name of the parent alkane.
    a) Substituent groups are cited in alphabetical order regardless of their location in the principal chain.
        (1) The numerical prefixes *di, tri*, etc., are *ignored* in alphabetizing.
        (2) The prefixes *tert-* and *sec-* are *ignored* in alphabetizing.
        (3) The prefixes iso, neo, and cyclo are *considered* in alphabetizing.
    b) When numbering of different groups is not resolved by the other rules, the first–cited group receives the lowest number.

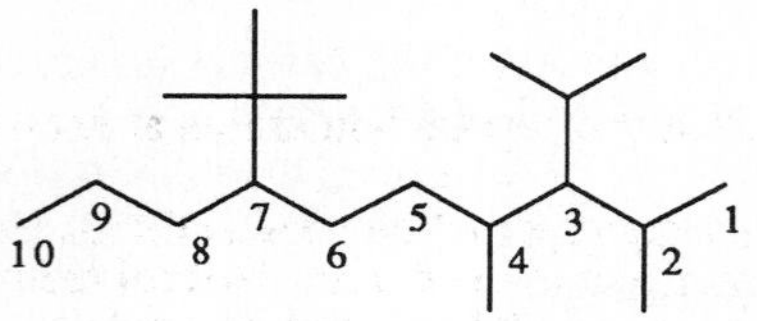

7-*t*-butyl-3-isopropyl-2,4-dimethyldecane

C. Cycloalkanes:
    1. The prefix *cyclo* is attached to the alkane name corresponding to the number of carbons in the ring.
    2. The numerical prefix 1- is not necessary for cycloalkanes with only one substituent.
    3. For cycloalkanes having two or more substituents, the carbons are numbered consecutively in the direction that gives the substituent groups the lowest numbers.

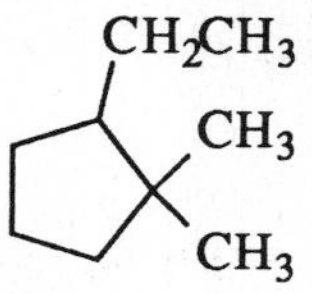

2-ethyl-1,1-dimethylcyclopentane

IV. Physical Properties:

A. van der Waals Force:
    1. The **van der Waals force (dispersion force)** is the cohesive force that must be overcome in order to vaporize a liquid hydrocarbon.
        a) When two molecules approach each other closely, as in a liquid, the electron clouds of one molecule repel the electron clouds of the other.
        b) The deficiency of electrons (positive charge) in part of one molecule is attracted by the excess of electrons (negative charge) in part of the other.

B. Steric Effect:
    1. The **van der Waals radius** is one measure of the size of an atom or a group of atoms.
    2. When two nonbonded groups are separated by the sum of their van der Waals radii, their mutual attractive interaction is greatest.

3. **van der Waals repulsion** occurs when the distance separating two groups of atoms is less than the sum of their van der Waals radii.
    a) An energetically unfavorable effect on any chemical or physical process that results from van der Waals repulsion is termed a *steric effect*.
    b) A molecule destabilized by the operation of a steric effect is said to be *strained*.
    c) When strain is introduced into a molecule by an **internal rotation**, the strain is termed *torsional strain*.

C. Boiling Point:
    1. The **boiling point** is the temperature at which a substance undergoes a transition from the liquid to the gaseous state.
    2. Boiling points increase with increasing molecular weight within a homologous series — typically 20–30 °C per carbon atom. This increase is due to the greater van der Waals attraction among larger molecules.
    3. Boiling points tend to be lower for highly branched molecules that approach spherical proportions because they have less molecular surface available for van der Waals attraction.

D. Melting Point:
    1. The **melting point** of a substance is the temperature at which it undergoes the transition from the solid to the liquid state.
    2. Melting points trend to increase with increasing molecular weight within a homologous series.
    3. Many highly symmetrical molecules have unusually high melting points.
    4. A sawtooth pattern of melting point behavior is observed within a number of homologous series.

V. Conformations of Alkanes:

A. Newman Projection:
    1. In a **Newman projection**, a circle is used to represent the two carbon atoms at each end of the bond of interest.
    2. The bonds drawn to the center of the circle are attached to the carbon nearest the observer.
    3. The bonds drawn to the periphery of the circle are attached to the carbon farthest from the observer.
    4. The angle θ between the bonds on different carbons is called the **dihedral angle**.
    5. Molecules that differ only by an internal rotation are called **rotational isomers, conformational isomers**, or **torsional isomers**.

B. Conformations of Ethane:
    1. The **eclipsed form** of ethane occurs when $\theta = 0°$ (the C—H bonds on the respective carbons are superimposed).
    2. The **staggered form** of ethane occurs when $\theta = 60°$ (a C—H bond of one carbon bisects the angle between two C—H bonds of the other).
      a) One staggered form of ethane can convert into another by an internal rotation about the carbon–carbon bond.
      b) An ethane molecule must briefly pass through the eclipsed form when an internal rotation occurs.
    3. The eclipsed and staggered forms of ethane have different energies.
      a) The staggered form of ethane is a stable conformation.
      b) The eclipsed form of ethane is an unstable conformation.

C. Conformations of Butane:
  1. The *anti* **conformation** of butane occurs when $\theta = 180°$ between the two C—CH_3 bonds.
  2. The *gauche* **conformation** of butane occurs when $\theta = 60°$ between the two C—CH_3 bonds.
  3. The *anti* and *gauche* conformations of butane have different energies.
      a) The *anti* conformation of butane is the *most* stable conformation (lowest energy).
      b) The *gauche* conformations of butane are not as stable as the *anti* conformation.
      c) The eclipsed conformations of butane are unstable conformations (high energy).

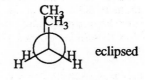

VI. Combustion of Alkanes:

A. Combustion:
  1. In complete **combustion**, an alkane combines with oxygen to produce carbon dioxide and water.
  2. Under conditions of oxygen deficiency, incomplete combustion may occur with the formation of such by-products as carbon monoxide, CO.

B. Elemental Analysis:
  1. The use of combustion in the quantitative determination of elemental compositions is called **elemental analysis**.
  2. In elemental analysis, a small, preweighed sample is completely burned and the CO_2 and H_2O produced in the combustion are collected and weighed.
      a) The weight of the carbon in the sample can be determined by the weight of the carbon dioxide produced.
      b) The weight of the hydrogen in the sample can be determined by the weight of the water produced.
      c) The weight of the oxygen, if present, is determined by difference.
  3. Elemental analysis is used to determine the **empirical formula** of a compound.
      a) The percentages of the elements are determined from the combustion products.
      b) The mole ratios of the elements are determined from the percentages of the elements.
      c) The empirical formula is determined from the mole ratios of the elements by:
          (1) dividing each mole ratio by the lowest mole ratio;
          (2) multiplying the resulting formula by successive integers (2, 3, 4, . . .) until a whole number for all of the elements is obtained.
      d) The molecular formula may be equal to the empirical formula or to an integral multiple of the empirical formula.
      e) In some cases, the empirical formula must be combined with a molecular weight to obtain the molecular formula.

CHAPTER 3 SOLUTIONS

Solutions to In-Text Problems

1. (a) If the number of carbons is n, then the number of hydrogen atoms is $2n + 2$. Hence, the number of hydrogens is $2(18) + 2$, or 38.
    (b) Since $2n + 2 = 30$, then n, the number of carbons, $= 14$.
    (c) There cannot be an n-alkane with any odd number of hydrogen atoms, because $2n + 2$ must be an even number.

2. Extrapolating from the boiling points of undecane and dodecane in Table 3.1, we estimate that the boiling point of tridecane differs from that of dodecane by about 20°. Hence, the boiling point of tridecane should be about 236°.

3   (a) The longest chain contains eight carbons; hence, the compound is named as an octane: 4-ethyl-5-methyloctane
    (b) The name is 4-ethyl-5,5,6-trimethylnonane.

4. This type of problem requires a systematic approach. The simplest structure is that of heptane itself:

$CH_3CH_2CH_2CH_2CH_2CH_2CH_3$

Next, we consider the compounds with a principal chain of six carbons and one methyl branch:

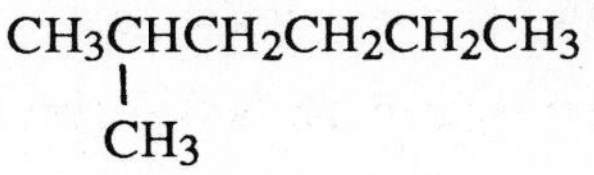

$CH_3CHCH_2CH_2CH_2CH_3$ $CH_3CH_2CHCH_2CH_2CH_3$
      | |
      CH_3 CH_3

        2-methylhexane 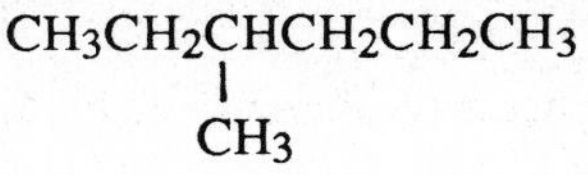   3-methylhexane

Notice that moving the methyl branch to the right one more carbon gives 3-methylhexane, which we have already considered.

Next, we consider the compounds with a principal chain of five carbons and two methyl branches:

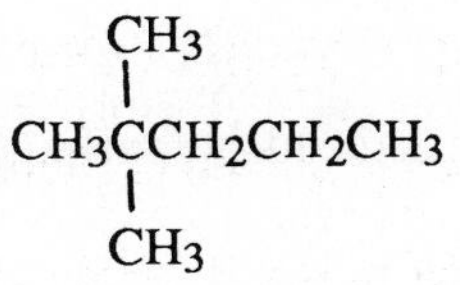

    CH_3 CH_3
    | |
$CH_3CCH_2CH_2CH_3$ $CH_3CH_2CCH_2CH_3$ $CH_3CH-CHCH_2CH_3$
    | | | |
    CH_3 CH_3 CH_3 CH_3

  2,2-dimethylpentane 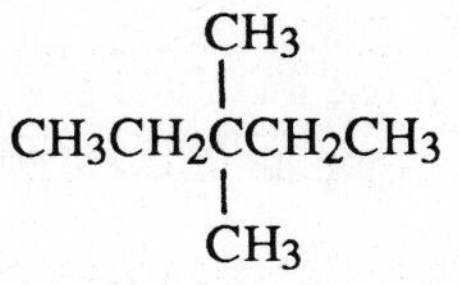   3,3-dimethylpentane 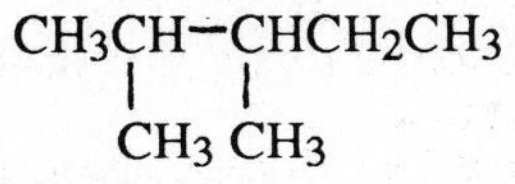   2,3-dimethylpentane

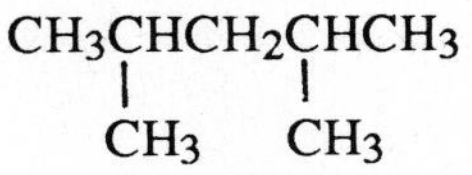

$CH_3CHCH_2CHCH_3$
    | |
    CH_3 CH_3

2,4-dimethylpentane

Then there is the compound with a five-carbon principal chain and one ethyl branch:

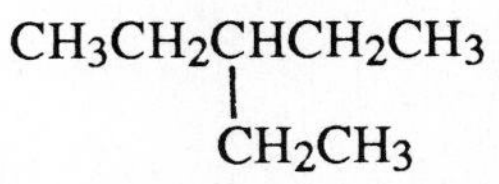

$CH_3CH_2CHCH_2CH_3$
        |
        CH_2CH_3

  3-ethylpentane

Next, we move to the compound with a four-carbon principal chain:

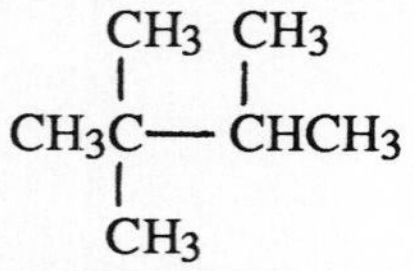

$$CH_3CH_3$$

CH₃C— CHCH₃

CH₃

2,2,3-trimethylbutane

Notice that if we put a methyl and an ethyl group on the same carbon, or on adjacent carbons, we end up with compounds we have already listed (which ones?).

5.   (a)

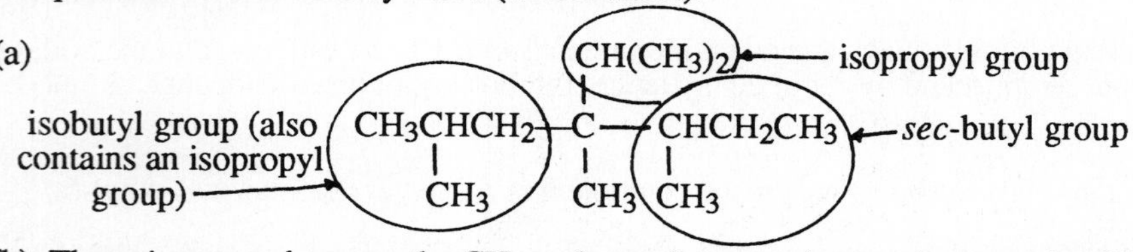

isobutyl group (also contains an isopropyl group) CH₃CHCH₂ C CHCH₂CH₃ — *sec*-butyl group

CH(CH₃)₂ — isopropyl group

(b) The *primary carbons* are the CH₃ carbons; the *secondary carbons* are the CH₂ carbons; and the *quaternary carbon* is the one carbon bearing the CH(CH₃)₂ and CH₃ groups.

(c) A methyl group is any one of the seven CH₃ groups; an ethyl group is the CH₂CH₃ group at the end of the principal chain; the isopropyl, isobutyl, and *sec*-butyl groups are circled in the structure above.

6.   (a)   (b)   (c)   (d)

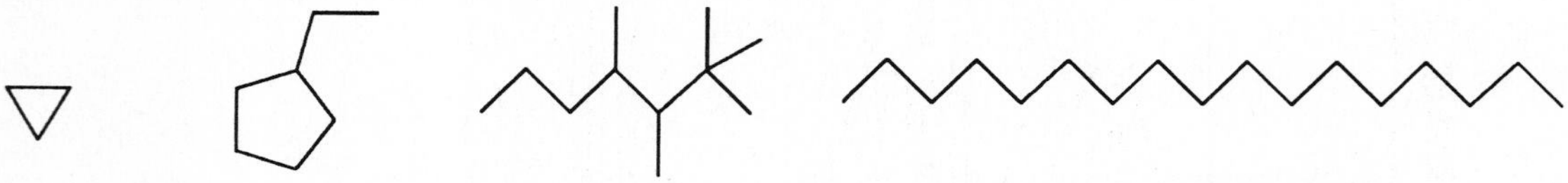

7.   The correct name is 1-ethyl-2,4-dimethylcyclopentane. Notice that the 1,2,4-numbering gives the lowest number at first point of difference. There are two possible names corresponding to the 1,2,4-numbering; of these, the one above is chosen because ethyl is cited before methyl in the name, and thus receives the lowest number.

8.   The highly symmetrical molecule 2,2,3,3-tetramethylbutane is more nearly spherical and therefore has a smaller surface area than octane. Hence, 2,2,3,3-tetramethylbutane has the lower boiling point. Since highly symmetrical compounds have higher melting points, then 2,2,3,3-tetramethylbutane has the higher melting point. In summary:

	boiling pt.	melting pt.
2,2,3,3-tetramethylbutane	106.5°	100.7°
octane	125.7°	–118.3°

9.   Because gasoline is less dense than water, it floats to the top of water where it has access to air. Thus, combustion of gasoline can be supported even in the presence of water.

10. (a) Rotational isomers of isopentane are forms A, C, and E; eclipsed forms are forms B, D, and F:

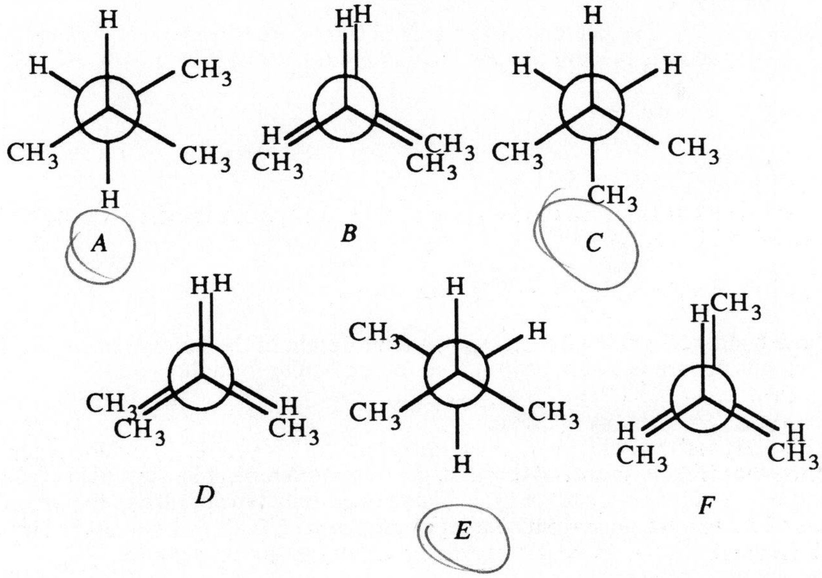

(b)

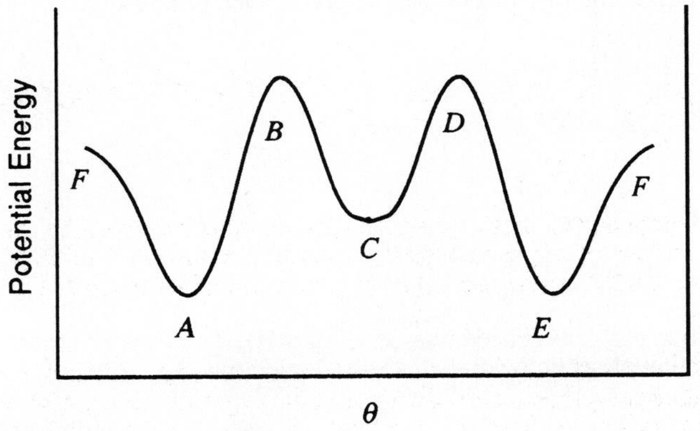

(c) Forms A and E have the lowest energy because they each have one fewer *gauche* interaction than form C; hence, these forms are present in greatest amount at equilibrium. Forms B and D are eclipsed and each have a CH_3–CH_3 eclipsing interaction that is not present in form F; hence, these forms have the highest energy.

11. The two *gauche* forms of butane are not superimposable; in fact, they are *nonsuperimposable mirror images*.

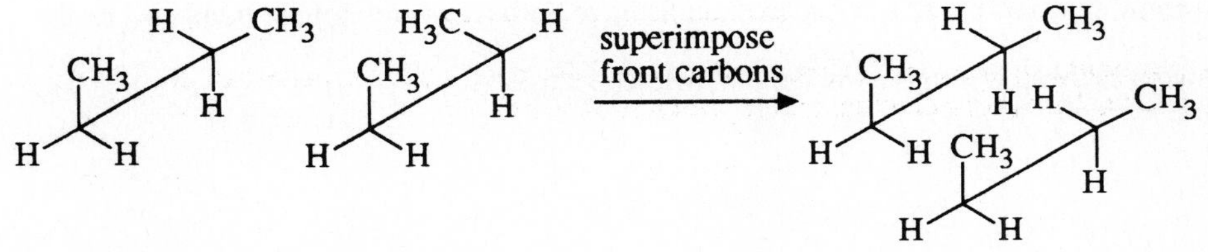

(We shall learn about compounds related in this way in Chapter 6.)

12. This would not be an acceptable candidate, because a compound of sixteen carbons can have no more than $2(16) + 2$, or 34, hydrogens.

13. The molecular weight of C_3H_6O is 58.08. The percent carbon is $3(12.01)/58.08 = 62.04$; the percent hydrogen is $6(1.008)/58.08 = 10.41$; and the percent oxygen is $16.00/58.08 = 27.55$.

14. Using the methods discussed in Sec. 3.6, we have:

$$\text{Amount of carbon} = \left(\frac{12.01}{44.01}\right)(20.92) = 5.71 \text{ mg}$$

$$\text{Amount of hydrogen} = \left(\frac{1.008}{18.106}\right)(7.04) = 0.79 \text{ mg}$$

Since the amounts of carbon and hydrogen add up to 6.50 mg (the total weight of the sample), there can be no other elements in X. These amounts of carbon and hydrogen give the molecular formula

$$C_{(5.71/12.01)}H_{(0.79/1.008)} = C_{0.48}H_{0.78} = C_1H_{1.63} = C_8H_{13}.$$

Because no hydrocarbon can have an odd number of hydrogens, the minimum molecular formula is $C_{16}H_{26}$. Because X is an alkane, it must be a *cycloalkane*, since a cycloalkane is the only type of alkane for which the number of hydrogens is less than $2n + 2$, where $n =$ the number of carbons.

15. (a) $CH_3CH_2CH_2CH_2NH_2$ or any of its isomers.
(b) An alcohol of this formula must have either one ring or one double bond. One possibility for each of these options is

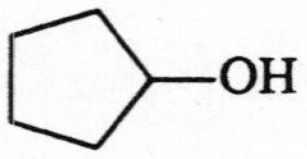

(c) The elemental analysis translates into a formula of

$$C_{3.331}H_{6.657}O_{3.331} \text{ or } CH_2O.$$

Since a carboxylic acid must have at least two oxygens (inside rear cover of text), the minimum molecular formula is $C_2H_4O_2$. A structure that fits is that of acetic acid:

16. (a) An amide must have a nitrogen; the compound cannot be an amide.
(b) The compound could be an ether or (e) an alcohol.
(c) The compound could be neither a carboxylic acid nor (f) an ester, since these must have at least one double bond. A compound with the formula $C_5H_{12}O_2$ cannot have any double bonds. Why? If a fully unsaturated compound of n carbons has $2n + 2$ hydrogens, then compounds with fewer than $2n + 2$ hydrogens must have rings or double bonds.
(d) The compound could not be a phenol, because phenols have both rings and double bonds. [See the explanation for (c)].
(e) and (f) The answers to these were given in (b) and (c), respectively.

Solutions to Additional Problems

17. To estimate the appropriate boiling points, add about 25° per additional carbon. (Addition of 20-30° per additional carbon would provide an equally valid estimate.)

    (a) 152° (same number of carbons)
    (b) 127° (one fewer carbon)
    (c) 55° (one more carbon)
    (d) 205° (two additional carbons)

18. To answer this problem, we use the same systematic approach that we used in Problem 4. To save time, it helps to draw only the carbon skeleton. Thus, our first alkane,

    $CH_3CH_2CH_2CH_2CH_2CH_2CH_2CH_3$ octane,

    can be represented as   C—C—C—C—C—C—C—C

    Continuing in this manner we have:

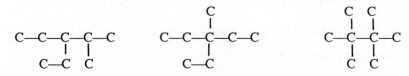

2-methylheptane   3-methylheptane   4-methylheptane

2,3-dimethylhexane   2,4-dimethylhexane   2,5-dimethylhexane

2,2-dimethylhexane   3,3-dimethylhexane   3,4-dimethylhexane   3-ethylhexane

2,3,4-trimethylpentane   2,2,3-trimethylpentane   2,2,4-trimethylpentane   2,3,3-trimethylpentane

3-ethyl-2-methylpentane   3-ethyl-3-methylpentane   2,2,3,3-tetramethylbutane

You may have drawn other structures, such as "2-ethyl-2-methylpentane:"

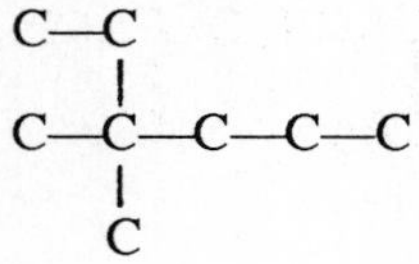

However, this structure is one we have already drawn; its correct name is 3,3-dimethylhexane. When we draw a structure, we always have to double-check the longest carbon chain.

19.   In the given structure, reproduced below, carbons 2, 3, 4, 6, 7, 8, and 9 are secondary; carbon 5 is tertiary; carbon 1 is quaternary; and carbon 10 is primary.

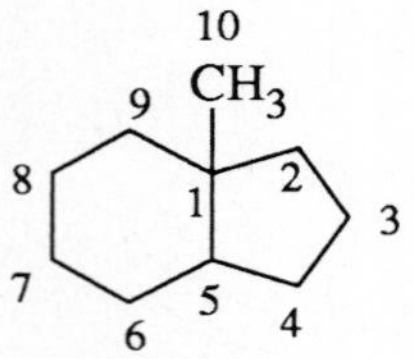

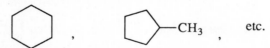

20.   (a) Neopentane has one quaternary carbon and four primary carbons:

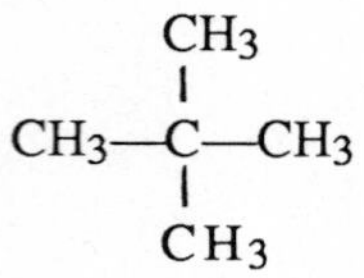

$$CH_3-\underset{\underset{\displaystyle CH_3}{|}}{\overset{\overset{\displaystyle CH_3}{|}}{C}}-CH_3$$

(b) Cyclopentane

(c) Any C_6H_{12} isomer, which could be

⬡ ,   ⬠—CH$_3$,   etc.

cyclohexane   methylcyclopentane

(d) This one is tricky:

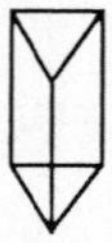

The trivial name of this compound is *prismane*.

21.   (a) 4-ethyl-5-methyloctane. Notice that the longest continuous carbon chain is not written horizontally.
(b) 5-ethyl-4,4-dimethyloctane. Why not 4-ethyl-5,5-dimethyloctane? Because 4,4,5 has a lower number *at first point of difference* than 4,5,5.
(c) 2,3-dimethylhexane
(d) 4-isopropylheptane
(e) 2,5-diethyl-1,1-dimethylcyclopentane

22. (a)   CH₃
         |
      CH₃CCH₂CH₂CH₃
         |
         CH₃

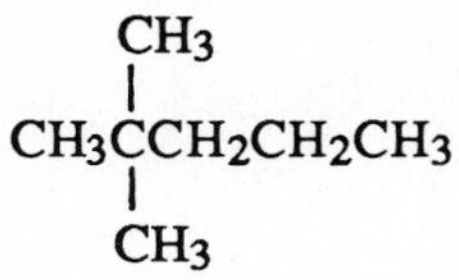

(b)   CH₃   CH₂CH₂CH₃
      | |
   CH₃CH—CH—CH—CHCH₂CH₃
             | |
             CH₃   CH₃

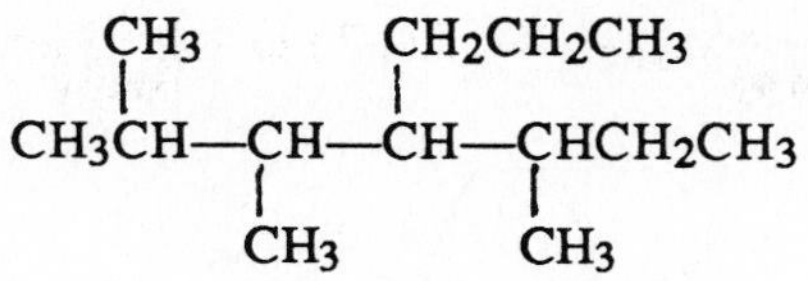

(c)   CH₂CH(CH₃)₂
                     |
              CH₃CHCH₂CHCHCH₂CH₃
                 | |
                 CH₃   CH₃

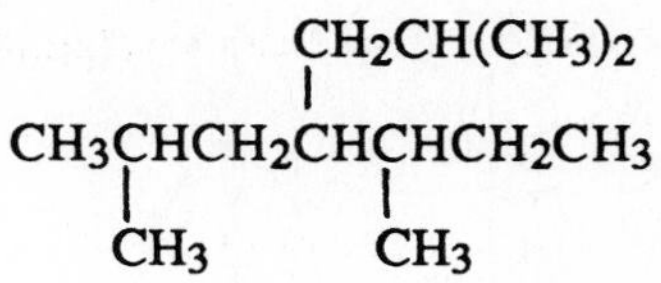

23. Let's first write the indicated structures; then we'll rename them.

(a)   C₂H₅
           |
      CH₃CH₂CHCHCH₃   3-ethyl-2-methylpentane; Ima numbered from the wrong
                | end of the chain
                CH₃

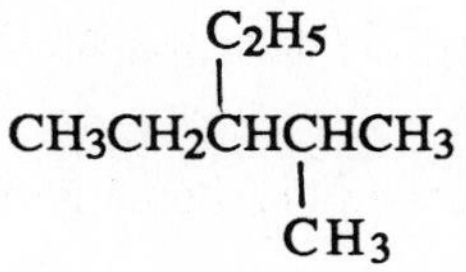

(b) CH₃(CH₂)₃CH(CH₂)₄CH₃   No problem with this one; Ima got it right!
              |
              CH₂C(CH₃)₃

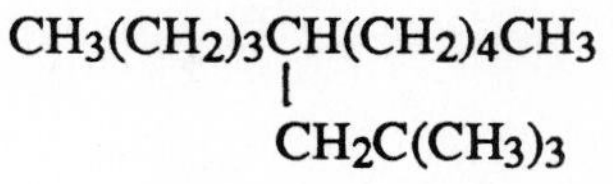

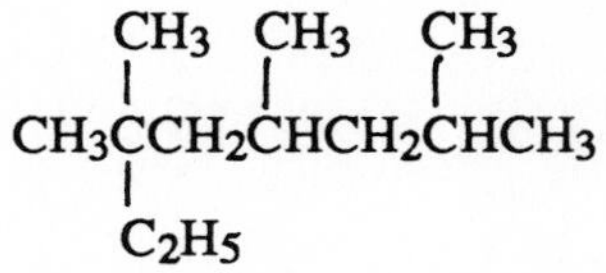

(c)   CH₃ CH₃   CH₃
       | | |
    CH₃CCH₂CHCH₂CHCH₃   2,4,6,6-tetramethyloctane
       |
       C₂H₅

(d)

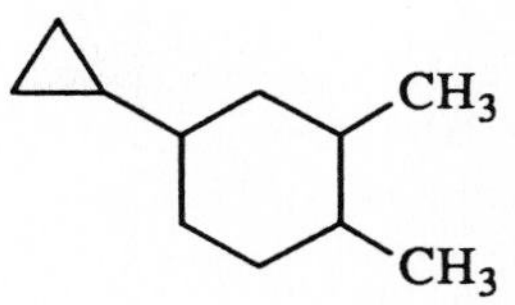

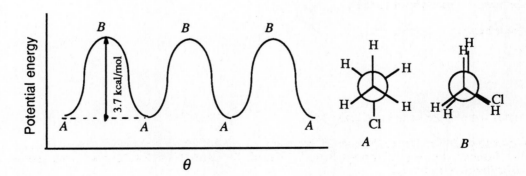

        4-cyclopropyl-1,2-dimethylcyclohexane

Ima forgot about the "first point of difference" rule.

(e)   CH₃
        |
   CH₃C—CHCH₂CH₂CH₃   4-t-butyloctane
        | |
       H₃C CH₂CH₂CH₂CH₃

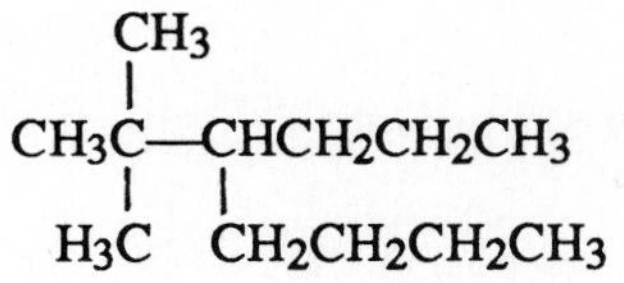

24.

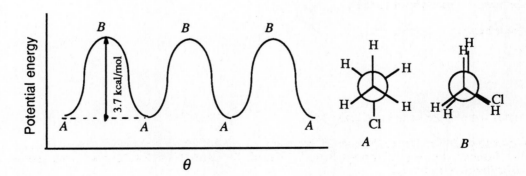

25. The curve would look the same — that is, three potential-energy barriers of equal height. However, these barriers would be higher than those in ethane, because they correspond to a situation in which there are three CH₃-CH₃ eclipsing interactions:

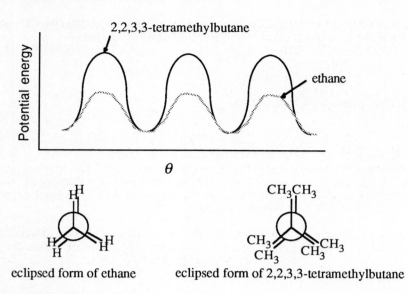

eclipsed form of ethane   eclipsed form of 2,2,3,3-tetramethylbutane

26. (a) The graph is as follows:

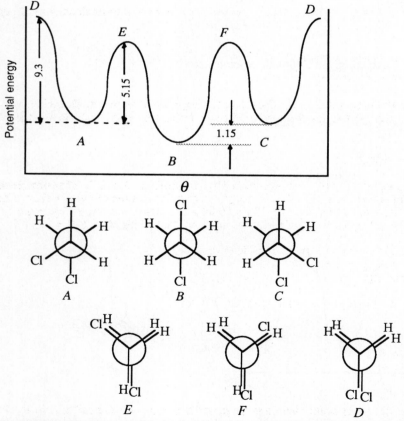

(b) The *anti* form *B* is present in greatest amount because it has the lowest energy.

27. Not only are there steric effects (which, as the problem suggests, are about the same as those in butane) when the C—Cl dipoles are aligned, but there are also repulsions between like charges in the dipoles.

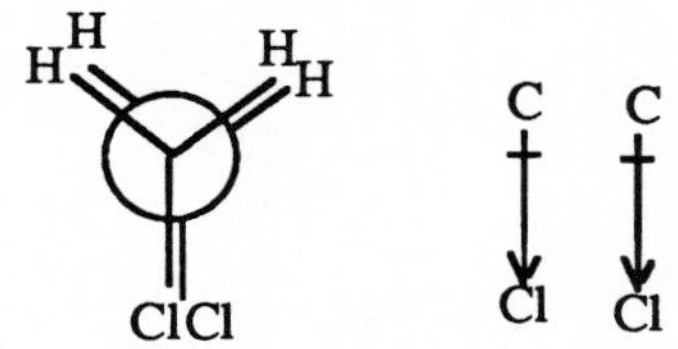

positive and negative ends of
C—Cl bond dipoles are adjacent

28. There are great steric repulsions between the *t*-butyl groups in the compound on the left. The only way for the molecule to relieve these repulsions is to stretch the appropriate bonds and flatten itself by widening the C—C—C angles. This also costs energy, but presumably not as much as retaining the shorter bond lengths and narrower angles.

29. The barrier to internal rotation is caused by repulsions between eclipsed CH_3 groups on adjacent atoms. These repulsions are reduced when the methyls are farther apart. Since the Si—Si bond is much longer than the C—C bond, it follows that the repulsions between methyls are reduced in the compound on the right. Hence, the energy barrier is larger for the compound on the left.

30. (a) The expected dipole moment for the *anti* form is zero, because the polar C—Br bonds point in opposite directions; hence their bond dipoles cancel. Likewise, for every C—H bond, there is another C—H bond pointing in the opposite direction.
(b) It follows from (a) that the observed dipole moment is due solely to the relatively small amount of *gauche* form present. Hence,

$$\mu = \mu_{anti}N_{anti} + \mu_{gauche}N_{gauche}$$

or $\qquad 1.0 = (0)(N_{anti}) + \mu_{gauche}(0.18)$

Solving for μ_{gauche}, we find that this equals 5.56 D. This is a very large dipole moment. But this is what we would expect for a compound in which two C—Br bond dipoles (as well as the smaller C—H bond dipoles) are pointing in the same direction.

31. $C_nH_{2n} + (3n/2)O_2 \rightarrow nCO_2 + nH_2O$

32. You must first be able to interpret the skeletal structure; if you have trouble, see Sec. 3.3. The formula of decalin is $C_{10}H_{18}$. The molecular weight is 138.24. The percent carbon is the mass of carbon divided by the mass of the compound times 100, or $(120.1/138.24) \times 100 = 86.88\%$; similarly, the percent hydrogen is 100 times the mass of hydrogen divided by the mass of the compound, or $(18.14/138.24) \times 100 = 13.12\%$.

33. (a) Using the procedure in Sec. 3.6, we find that the empirical formula is

$C_{(87.42/12.01)}H_{(12.58/1.008)}$ or $C_{7.28}H_{12.48}$ or $CH_{1.71}$ or C_7H_{12}.

(b) The following structures meet the requirements of the problem:

➤ Structures such as the ones above, in which two rings are joined at one carbon, are called *spirocyclic compounds*. We shall learn about such compounds in Chapter 7.

34. (a) The part of the CO_2 that is oxygen is the fraction oxygen in CO_2 times the weight of the sample:

Fraction oxygen in $CO_2 = (2)(16.00)/44.01 = 0.7271$; amount of oxygen $= (0.7271)(21.96) = 15.97$ mg.

Likewise, the part of the water that is oxygen is $(16.00/18.016) \times 8.99 = 7.98$ mg.

The total oxygen consumed is therefore $15.97 + 7.98 = 23.95$ mg.

There are 32 mg of oxygen per millimole; hence 23.95 mg corresponds to $(23.95/32.00) = 0.748$ mmol consumed. At 0 °C, this would correspond to $(0.748$ mmol$)(22.4$ mL/mmol$) = 16.755$ mL. Applying a gas-law correction to this number, the volume at 25 °C is $(16.755)(298$ K$)/(273$ K$) = 18.29$ mL.

(b) To calculate the molecular formula, we apply the techniques described in Sec. 3.6. The weight of carbon in the sample is derived from the amount of carbon dioxide, and the weight of hydrogen is derived from the amount of water:

Weight of carbon $= (21.96$ mg$)(12.01)/(44.01) = 5.99$ mg
Weight of hydrogen $= (8.99)(2)(1.008)/(18.016) = 1.006$ mg

The empirical formula is $C_{(5.99/12.01)}H_{(1.006/1.008)} = C_{0.5}H_1 = CH_2$. Since the group weight of CH_2 is 14 mass units, the molecular formula of the hydrocarbon is $(CH_2)_{10}$, or $C_{10}H_{20}$.

➤ Notice in part (a) of this problem that you had to apply something that you probably learned in high-school or freshman chemistry — namely, application of the properties of an ideal gas. We shall use a number of concepts from earlier courses in our study of organic chemistry. Do not hesitate to use these concepts — and to review them — when necessary.

35. First, we must calculate the molecular formula by the now-familiar process. In doing so, we assume (since we are told that the unknown compound is an amide) that the percentage unaccounted for is oxygen, which is therefore 18.37%. (Amides contain oxygen; see tables inside rear cover of text.) The molecular formula is

$C_{(55.14/12.01)}H_{(10.41/1.008)}N_{(16.08/14.01)}O_{(18.37/16.00)}$, or $C_{4.59}H_{10.33}N_{1.15}O_{1.15}$, or C_4H_9NO.

Since the compound contains an isopropyl group $(CH_3)_2CH—$, two possible structures are

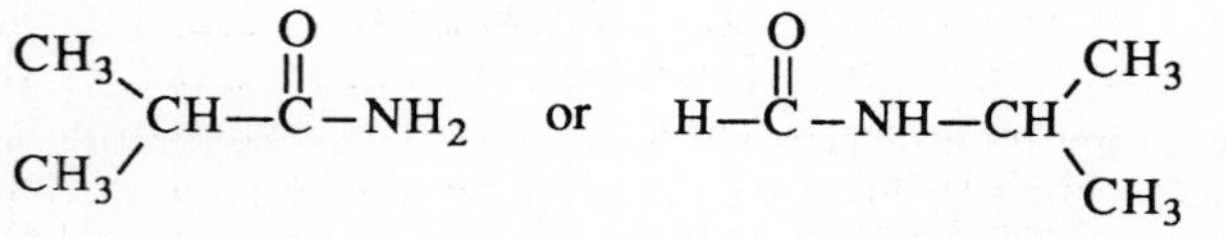

36. The functional groups in acebutolol:

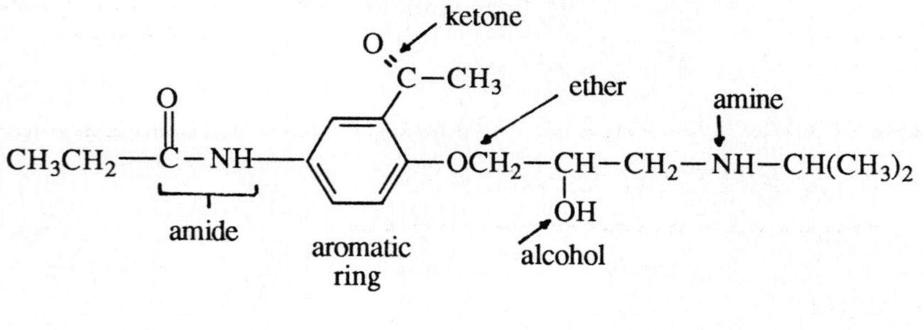

Chapter 4 / Introduction to Alkenes. Equilibria and Reaction Rates

CHAPTER 4 TERMS

addition reaction 4.5
alkene .... Introduction
Cahn–Ingold–Prelog (*E–Z*) system 4.2B
calorimeter 4.4B
carbocation 4.5A
carbocation rearrangement 4.6
catalysis 4.8
catalyst 4.8
chemical equilibrium 4.4A
cis-alkene 4.1B
cis–trans isomerism 4.1B
E conformation 4.2B
electrophile 4.5A
electrophilic addition reaction 4.5C
endothermic reaction 4.4B
energy barrier 4.7A
entgegen 4.2B
enthalpy 4.4B
enthalpy of combustion 4.4B
e n z y m e 4.8
equilibrium constant 4.4A
exothermic reaction 4.4B
fermentation 4.8
free energy 4.4A
ΔG° 4.4A
$\Delta G^{\circ\ddagger}$ 4.7A
ΔH° 4.4B
Hammond's postulate 4.7C
heat of formation 4.4B
Hess's law 4.4B

hydration 4.8
hydride shift 4.6
hyperconjugation 4.5B
Markovnikov's rule 4.5
multistep reaction 4.7B
nucleophile 4.5A
olefin .... Introduction
π-bond 4.1A
rate-determining step 4.7B
rate-limiting step 4.7B
reaction free-energy diagram 4.7A
reaction mechanism 4.5C
reaction rate 4.7A
reactive intermediate 4.5A
regioselective 4.5
saturated hydrocarbon .... Introduction
sp^2 hybridization 4.1A
sp^2 orbital 4.1A
standard enthalpy of combustion 4.4B
standard free energy 4.4A
standard free energy of activation 4.7A
standard heat of combustion 4.4B
standard heat of formation 4.4B
stereoisomer 4.1B
trans-alkene 4.1B
transition state 4.7A
transition-state theory 4.7A
unsaturated hydrocarbon .... Introduction
Z conformation 4.2B

CHAPTER 4 CONCEPTS

I. Structure and Bonding in Alkenes:

   A. Carbon Hybridization:
      1. The carbons of ethylene are *sp²*-hybridized.
         a) The axes of the three *sp²* orbitals on each carbon lie in a plane at mutual 120° angles.
         b) The *p* orbital is perpendicular to the three *sp²* orbitals.
         c) The electron density of *sp²* orbitals is closer to the nucleus than that in *sp³* orbitals.

larger amt. of S character in sp2 orbitals

d) sp^2 orbitals have 33% s character.

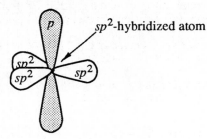

B. Molecular Bonds:
  1. σ-bond:
      a) The end–to–end overlap of an sp^2 orbital with another orbital results in a σ-bond.
          (1) The additive combination of such atomic orbitals results in **bonding (σ) molecular orbitals.**
          (2) The subtractive combination of such atomic orbitals results in **antibonding (σ*) molecular orbitals.**
      b) The electron density of σ-bonds is concentrated between the two bonding atoms.

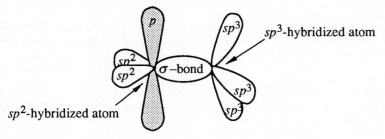

  2. π-bond:
      a) The side–to–side overlap of two p orbitals results in a π-bond.
          (1) The additive combination of p atomic orbitals results in **bonding (π) molecular orbitals.**
          (2) The subtractive combination of p atomic orbitals results in **antibonding (π*) molecular orbitals.**
      b) π-bonds contain a **nodal plane.**
          (1) Bonding π-orbitals of ethylene have a nodal plane that coincides with the plane of the sp^2–sp^2 orbitals on each carbon.
          (2) Antibonding π-orbitals of ethylene have a nodal plane that coincides with the plane of the sp^2–sp^2 orbitals on each carbon, as well as a nodal plane between each p orbital.
      c) The electron density of π-orbitals is concentrated *above and below* the plane containing the sp^2 orbitals.

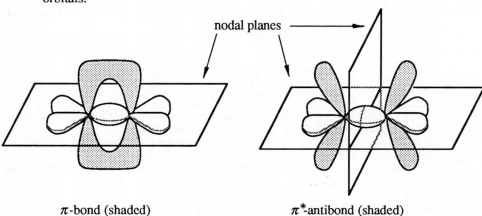

π-bond (shaded) π*-antibond (shaded)

3. Electron distribution:
    a) Bonding molecular orbitals have lower energy than the antibonding molecular orbitals.
    b) Electrons are distributed using the Pauli principle.
4. Bond length:
    a) sp^2 atomic orbitals have more s character than sp^3 atomic orbitals.
    b) The electron density in sp^2 orbitals is closer to the nucleus than the electron density in sp^3 orbitals.
    c) A bond derived from overlap with an sp^2 molecular orbital is shorter in length than one derived from overlap with an sp^3 molecular orbital.

C. Stereoisomers:
    1. **Stereoisomers** are compounds that have the same atomic connectivity but differ in the spatial arrangement of constituent atoms.
    2. *Cis* and *trans* isomers (or *E* and *Z* isomers) differ from each other by the interconversion of the two groups on *one* sp^2 carbon of a double bond.

D. *Cis–Trans* Isomerism:
    1. Interconversion of *cis* and *trans* isomers requires a 180° rotation about the double bond.
    2. The π-bond must be broken for an internal rotation of 180° about the double bond to occur; hence, this rotation *does not* occur readily.

E. Dipole Moment:
    1. The electron density lies closer to the nucleus in sp^2 orbitals than it does in sp^3 orbitals.
    2. In bonds between alkyl groups and trigonal carbons, the electrons are drawn away from the alkyl groups towards the trigonal carbons.
    3. Some alkenes have greater dipole moments than alkanes.

II. Nomenclature of Alkenes:

A. Systematic Nomenclature:
    1. Unbranched alkenes:
        a) An unbranched alkene is named by replacing the *ane* suffix in the name of the corresponding alkane with the ending *ene*.
        b) The chain is numbered from one end to the other so that the double bond receives the lowest number.

$$\overset{5}{C}H_3\overset{4}{C}H_2\overset{3}{C}H=\overset{2}{C}H\overset{1}{C}H_3 \qquad \text{2-pentene}$$

    2. Branched alkenes:
        a) The names of alkenes with branched chains are derived from their principal chains.
        b) The principal chain contains the greatest number of double bonds.
            (1) When two or more candidates have the same number of double bonds, the principal chain is longest chain.
            (2) The principal chain is numbered to give the lowest numbers to the double bonds at the *first* point of difference.

c) The names of branched alkenes are written in the following order:
  (1) the positions of substitution;
  (2) the substituents;
  (3) the positions of double bonds;
  (4) the principal chain; and
  (5) the number of double bonds.
 d) Substituents are numbered from their point of attachment.

$$
\overset{4\quad\ \ 3\quad\ \ 2\quad\ \ 1}{CH_2-CH=CH-CH_3}
$$

$$
CH_3-CH_2-CH-\underset{|}{CH}-\overset{\ \ }{CH}=\overset{6\quad\ 7\quad\ 8\quad\ 9}{CH-CH_2-CH_3}
$$
$$
\underset{5}{|}\qquad\ \ CH=CH_2
$$

5-(1-ethyl-2-propenyl)-2,6-nonadiene

3. *Cis* and *trans* isomers contain only one hydrogen bonded to each sp^2 carbon of the double bond.
  a) A *cis* **isomer** has the two hydrogens on the same side of the double bond.
  b) A *trans* **isomer** has the two hydrogens on opposite sides of the double bond.

$$
\begin{array}{ccc}
H & & H \\
\diagdown & & \diagup \\
& C=C & \\
\diagup & & \diagdown \\
CH_3CH_2 & & CH(CH_3)_2
\end{array}
$$

cis-2-methyl-3-hexene

4. *E* and *Z* isomers contain two different groups on each sp^2 carbon of the double bond.
  a) A priority is assigned to each group on an alkene carbon by applying the rules *in order*:
  (1) Atoms of higher atomic number have higher priority.
  (2) An isotope of higher atomic mass receives higher priority.
  (3) The higher priority is assigned to the group with the atom of higher atomic mass at the *first* point of difference.
  (4) If the difference between two groups is due to the number of otherwise identical atoms, the higher priority is assigned to the group with the greater number of identical atoms.
  (5) Multiple bonds are replicated.

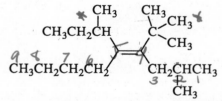

$$
\begin{array}{ccc}
CD_3 & & H \\
\diagdown & & \diagup \\
& C=C & \\
\diagup & & \diagdown \\
CH_3 & & CH_3
\end{array}
$$

(*E*)-1,1,1-trideutero-2-methyl-2-butene   (*Z*)-5-*sec*-butyl-4-*tert*-butyl-2-methyl-4-nonene

III. Relative Stabilities:

A. Free Energy and Chemical Equilibrium:
  1. A more stable compound has a lower **standard free energy** $G°$.
  2. The $\Delta G°$ of a reaction equals the $G°$ of the products minus the $G°$ of the reactants, and is related to the **equilibrium constant** K_{eq}.

$$
\Delta G° = -RT\ln K_{eq} = -2.303RT\log K_{eq}
$$

  a) A positive $\Delta G°$ indicates that the reactants are more stable than the products; thus the reactants will be present in a greater amount.
  b) A negative $\Delta G°$ indicates that the products are more stable than the reactants; thus the products will be present in a greater amount.
  3. Chemical equilibria favor the more stable compounds (the compounds of lower **free energy**).

B. Heats of Formation:
   1. The $\Delta H°$ of a reaction equals $H°$ of the products minus $H°$ of the reactants.
      a) A reaction in which $\Delta H°$ is negative (heat is liberated) is called **exothermic**; all combustion reactions are exothermic.
      b) A reaction in which $\Delta H°$ is positive (heat is absorbed) is called **endothermic**.
   2. The **standard heat of formation** ($\Delta H_f°$) of a reaction can be derived from heats of combustion by applying **Hess's law**.
      a) Chemical reactions and their associated energies may be added like algebraic equations.
      b) Heats of formation can be used to derive relative energies of isomers.

$4 (C + O_2 \rightarrow CO_2)$	$\Delta H° = 4\ (-94.08\ \text{kcal/mol})$
$4 (H_2 + \frac{1}{2} O_2 \rightarrow H_2O)$	$= 4\ (-57.80\ \text{kcal/mol})$
$(CO_2 + 4 H_2O \rightarrow CH_3–CH=CH–CH_3 + 6 O_2)$	$= +604.73\ \text{kcal/mol}$
$4 C + 4 H_2 \rightarrow CH_3–CH=CH–CH_3$	$\Delta H_f° = -2.67\ \text{kcal/mol}$

   3. The **enthalpy** of a reaction is related to the energy differences associated with different arrangements of chemical bonds; the free energy of a reaction is related to the position of **chemical equilibrium**.

C. Alkene Isomers:
   1. In general, *trans*-alkenes are more stable than their *cis*-isomers because of steric effects.
   2. An alkene is stablized by substitution of alkyl groups on the double bond.
   3. The alkene with the greatest number of alkyl groups on the double bond is usually most stable.

IV. Reactions of Alkenes:

A. Addition Reactions:
   1. The most characteristic reaction of the carbon–carbon double bond is an **addition reaction**.
   2. With 1-alkenes, only one of the two possible addition products is formed.
      a) Addition of a dipolar molecule H—X to an alkene proceeds so that the hydrogen goes to the less substituted carbon of the double bond (**Markovnikov's rule**).
      b) When there are equal amounts of branching at the two alkene carbons, both possible products are observed.
   3. With unsymmetrical alkenes, two addition products are possible in principle.

B. Carbocations:
   1. A **carbocation** (**carbonium ion**) has an electron-deficient carbon atom—it has a carbon that is short of an octet by one electron pair.
      a) Carbocations are Lewis acids (**electrophiles**).
      b) Carbocations can be attacked by Lewis bases (**nucleophiles**).
      c) Carbocations can result from the protonation of a π bond.
   2. The electron-deficient carbon of a carbocation is a trigonal carbon.
      a) The trigonal carbon of a carbocation is sp^2-hybridized.
      b) The $2p$ orbital on the trigonal carbon of a carbocation contains no electrons.
      c) Carbocations are stabilized by alkyl substituents.
      d) The electrons in adjacent C—H bonds overlap with the empty p orbital of a carbocation; this is called **hyperconjugation**.
      e) The greater the substitution at a trigonal carbon, the greater the stabilization by hyperconjugation.
   3. Carbocations are classified by the degree of alkyl substitution at the electron-deficient carbon atom.
      a) Primary—one alkyl group attached.
      b) Secondary—two alkyl groups attached.
      c) Tertiary—three alkyl groups attached.
   4. The relative stability of isomeric carbocations is in the following order:

tertiary > secondary > primary

C. Addition of Hydrogen Halides:
   1. The addition of hydrogen halides to alkenes follows the Markovnikov rule.
      a) The hydrogen of the acid molecule adds to the less substituted alkene carbon atom.
      b) The halide adds to the more substituted alkene carbon atom.
   2. Mechanism:
      a) The alkene is first protonated to give a carbocation.
      b) Attack of the nucleophile (Lewis base) halide on the carbocation completes the reaction.
      c) The addition of hydrogen halides to some alkenes is accompanied by rearrangement.

D. Hydration of Alkenes:
   1. **Hydration** of alkenes follows the Markovnikov rule.
      a) Hydrogen adds to the less substituted alkene carbon atom.
      b) An —OH group adds to the more substituted carbon atom.
   2. Mechanism:
      a) The alkene is first protonated to give a carbocation.
      b) Attack of the nucleophile (Lewis base) water on the carbocation and loss of a proton from the resulting adduct completes the reaction.
      c) The hydration of some alkenes is accompanied by rearrangement.
   3. Hydration of alkenes is an acid-catalyzed reaction.
      a) **Catalysts** increase the reaction rate but are not consumed in the reaction.
      b) Catalysts lower the standard free energy of activation for a reaction.
      c) Stronger acids are more effective catalysts because a stronger acid is more effective in protonating a given base (the alkene) than a weaker acid.
      d) **Enzymes** are biologically occurring catalysts.

E. Mechanisms:
   1. A **reaction mechanism** is the *complete* description of a reaction pathway, including any **reactive intermediates**.
   2. The carbocation is an example of a reactive intermediate (a species that is present in very low concentration because it reacts as quickly as it is formed).

F. Rearrangement of Carbocations:
   1. Rearrangement is favored by increased stability of the rearranged ion.
      a) Rearrangement involving an alkyl group is termed an alkyl migration.

$$CH_3\!-\!\overset{\displaystyle CH_3}{\underset{\displaystyle CH_3}{C}}\!-\!\overset{+}{C}H\!-\!CH_3 \longrightarrow CH_3\!-\!\overset{+}{C}\!-\!\overset{\displaystyle CH_3}{\underset{\displaystyle CH_3}{C}}H\!-\!CH_3$$

      b) Rearrangement involving a hydrogen is termed a **hydride shift**.
      c) The reaction pathway involving the more stable carbocation is the one that is observed.

$$CH_3\!-\!\overset{\displaystyle H}{\underset{\displaystyle CH_3}{C}}\!-\!\overset{+}{C}H\text{-}CH_3 \longrightarrow CH_3\!-\!\overset{+}{C}\!-\!\overset{\displaystyle H}{\underset{\displaystyle CH_3}{C}}H\text{-}CH_3$$

      secondary carbocation   tertiary carbocation

   2. A **carbocation rearrangement** can be expected when it will lead to an ion of greater stability.

V. Reaction Rates:

A. Transition State Theory:
   1. As reactants change into products, they pass through an unstable state of maximum free energy called the **transition state**.
      a) The transition state has a higher energy than either the reactants or products.
      b) The transition state represents an **energy barrier** to the interconversion of the reactants and products.

2. The energy barrier, $\Delta G^{\circ \ddagger}$, is called the **standard free energy of activation**.
    a) The higher the energy barrier, the slower the rate.
    b) Reactions are faster at higher temperatures.

B. <u>Multistep Reactions</u>:
    1. A free-energy <u>minimum</u> between reactants and products represents an intermediate.
    2. A free-energy <u>maximum</u> between reactants and products represents a transition state.

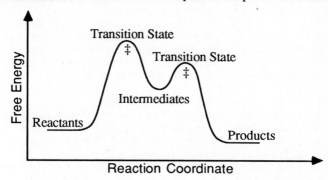

3. The rate of the overall reaction equals the rate of the rate-determining step.
    a) The **rate-determining** step is the step with the transition state of highest free energy.
    b) An increase in the rate of the rate-determining step will increase the overall reaction rate.

C. <u>Hammond's Postulate</u>:
    1. The structure of a transition state approximates the structure of the unstable intermediate immediately preceding or following it on the reaction coordinate. Thus, the structure of the transition state for alkene protonation approximates the structure of the carbocation intermediate formed in the reaction.
    2. The factors that contribute to the relatively high energy of a carbocation also contribute to the instability of the corresponding transition state.
    3. It is *not* the stabilities of the carbocation intermediates themselves that determine which of two reaction paths is faster.
    4. The relative stabilities of the transition states for carbocation formation determine the relative rates of the two processes.

CHAPTER 4 RULES

<u>Hammond's Postulate</u>: The structure of a transition state for a reaction approximates the structure of the unstable intermediate preceding or following it on the reaction coordinate.

<u>Hess's Law</u>: Chemical reactions and their associated energies may be added like algebraic equations.

<u>Markovnikov's Rule</u>: In the addition of a dipolar molecule to an alkene, the positive atom of the dipole becomes attached at the less substituted carbon, and the negative atom at the more substituted carbon, of the alkene double bond.

CHAPTER 4 SOLUTIONS

Solutions to In-Text Problems

1. Compounds (b), (c), and (d) can exist as *cis-trans* isomers; compound (a) cannot. In principle, compound (e) could also exist as a *trans* isomer, but in reality such an isomer is far too strained to exist, as examination of a model will show. Compound (d) can be *cis* or *trans* at either double bond, and there are thus three isomers possible: *cis-cis*, *cis-trans* (or *trans-cis*), and *trans-trans*. A general test for the existence of *cis-trans* isomers is that the two groups on each carbon of the double bond must be different.

2.

   (a)   (b) 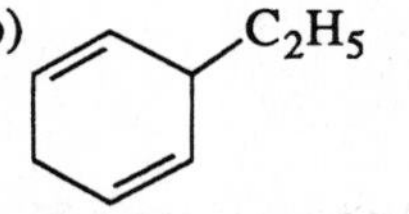 C_2H_5 (c)
   $$CH_2{=}CH{-}CH{=}CH{-}CH{-}CH{=}CH{-}CH{=}CH{-}CH_3$$
   $$CH_2{-}CH_2{-}CH{=}CH{-}CH_3$$

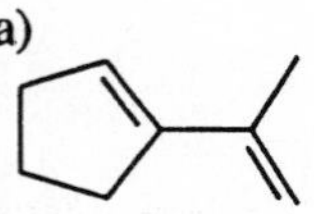

3. (a) 3-heptene (b) 1,3-dimethyl-1-cyclopentene
   (c) 5-allyl-2,6-nonadiene (Remember, the 2-propenyl group is called the *allyl* group.)

4. (a) (Z)-3-isopropyl-2-hexene (b) (4Z)-4-isobutyl-1,4-hexadiene

5.

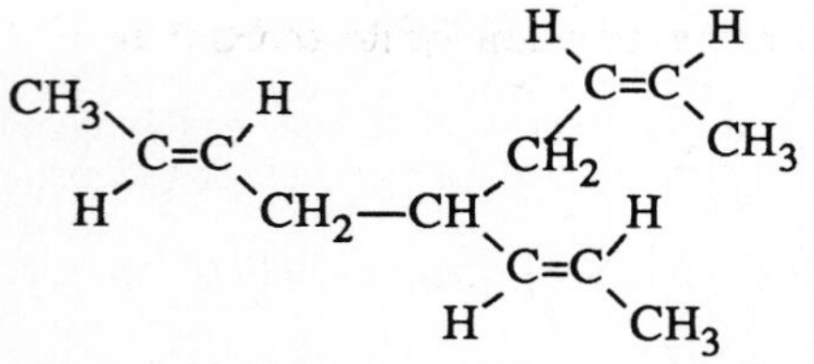

6. (a) The upper group receives higher priority. If you chose the lower group, it was probably because of the two chlorines, which are the atoms of highest mass. However, if we follow the rules properly, we never get to the chlorines — they never enter into the decision. We first look at the atoms attached to the double bond; there is no decision at this point. We then go to the *atom of highest priority* — that is, the oxygen. Here we decide in favor of the upper group, because the attached atom is carbon, whereas in the lower group it is H.

   (b) The upper group (cyclobutyl) has higher priority. When we "replicate" the vinyl group, it looks as shown below. Eventually, we arrive at the starred (*) atoms; at this point, there is nothing attached to the vinyl group, while there is a CH_2 attached to the cyclobutyl group.

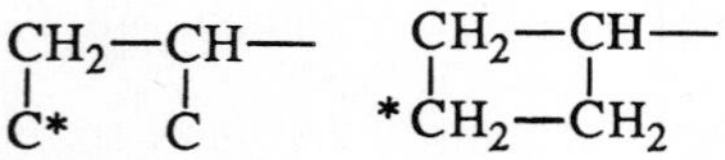

   $$
   \begin{array}{ll}
   CH_2{-}CH{-} & CH_2{-}CH{-}\\
   \ \ \ |\quad\ | & \ \ \ |\qquad |\\
   \ C*\quad C & *CH_2{-}CH_2\\
   \text{vinyl} & \text{cyclobutyl}
   \end{array}
   $$

   (c) The lower group has higher priority, because O has higher mass than C.

   (d) In (d), the lower group HC≡C— has higher priority for the same reason that vinyl has higher priority than isopropyl (see text page 99). For replication of this group, see text page 99.

7. (a) Since *trans*-2-butene has like bond dipoles pointing in exactly opposite directions, its dipole moment should be zero. As the text indicates, the dipole moment of *cis*-2-butene, although small, is not zero. Hence, *cis*-2-butene has the larger dipole moment.

(b) The molecules orient themselves so that oppositely charged ends of their dipole-moment vectors are adjacent:

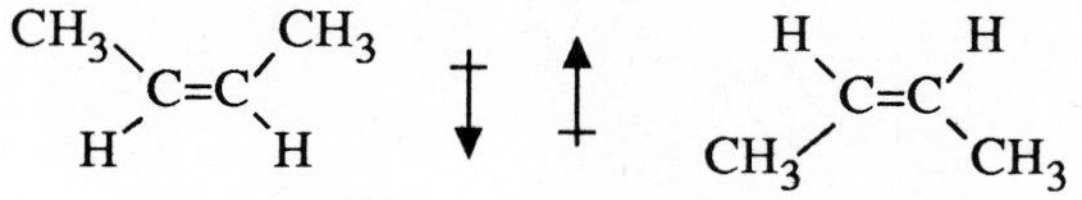

oppositely charged ends
of dipoles are adjacent

Attraction between oppositely charged ends of the dipole-moment vectors provides a cohesive force that raises the boiling point.

8. Taking antilogs of Eq. 4.6, we have $K_{eq} = 10^{-\Delta G°/2.303RT}$ from which we calculate

$$K_{eq} = 10^{(3.5/1.364)} = 3.68 \times 10^2$$

➤ Your calculator should be very handy for making this type of calculation. After calculating and entering the ratio (3.5/1.364), press the "10^x" button to get the correct answer.

9. To calculate the concentrations at equilibrium, we first need to know the equilibrium constant. This follows directly from Eq. 4.6, in the form used in the solution to Problem 8. We find that

$$K_{eq} = 10^{(0.7/1.364)} = 10^{0.5132} = 3.26.$$

If we let x be the concentration of C at equilibrium, then the equilibrium expression for the reaction is

$$K_{eq} = [C]/[B][A] = x/(0.2 - x)(0.1 - x) = 3.26$$

from which we obtain the quadratic equation

$$x^2 - 0.6068x + 0.02 = 0$$

Applying the quadratic formula, we obtain as solutions for x

$$x = \frac{0.6068}{2} \pm \frac{\sqrt{0.3682 - 0.0800}}{2} = 0.3034 \pm 0.2684$$

Choosing the physically meaningful value of x, we have

$$x = [C] = 0.0350M \quad [B] = 0.2 - x = 0.1650M \quad [A] = 0.1 - x = 0.0650M$$

10. (a) The solution requires a Hess's law calculation:

	$\Delta H°$ (kcal/mol)
$4H_2 + 2O_2 \rightarrow 4H_2O$	−231.20
$4C + 4O_2 \rightarrow 4CO_2$	−376.20
$4CO_2 + 4H_2O \rightarrow 6O_2 + (CH_3)_2C=CH_2$	+603.36

Sum:

$4C + 4H_2 \rightarrow (CH_3)_2C=CH_2 \qquad \Delta H_f° = -4.04$ kcal/mol

(b) Using some data in Eqs. 4.10a and b, we have the following ΔH_f° values:

$$C_4H_8 \;+\; 4O_2 \;\rightarrow\; 4CO_2 \;+\; 4H_2O$$

$$-0.03 \qquad\quad 0 \qquad -376.20 \quad -231.20$$

Hence, $\Delta H^\circ \;=\; +(-376.20 - 231.20) - (-0.03) = -607.19$ kcal/mol

11. (a)

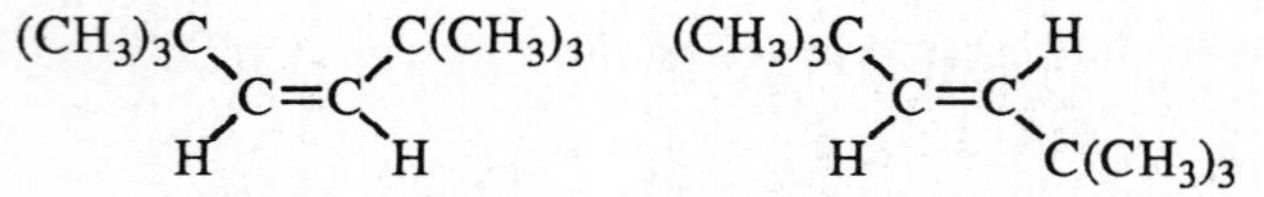

isomers of 2,2,5,5-tetramethyl-3-hexene

The *cis* isomer should have much more strain because of repulsions between the very large *t*-butyl groups; therefore the *cis* isomer has the higher enthalpy.
(b) The formation of *trans*- from *cis*-2,2,5,5-tetramethyl-3-hexene should have the greater equilibrium constant. Because the *cis* isomer of this alkene is more strained than the *cis* isomer of 2-butene, more energy should be liberated in the *cis*-to-*trans* conversion.

12. The small difference is the result of two compensating effects: destabilizing *cis* interactions vs. the stabilizing effect of alkyl substituents on the double bonds.

3-methyl-2-pentene: 2,3-dimethyl-2-butene:

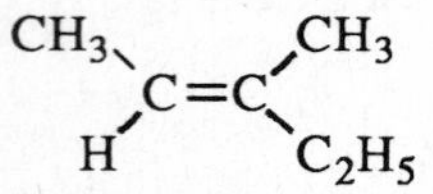

fewer cis-interactions,   more cis-interactions,
but fewer alkyl groups   but more alkyl groups
on the double bond   on the double bond

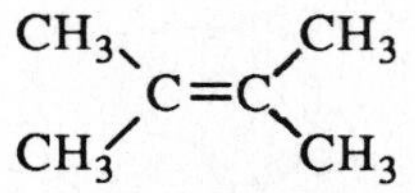

13. HBr adds so that the bromine is bound at the carbon bearing the methyl group:

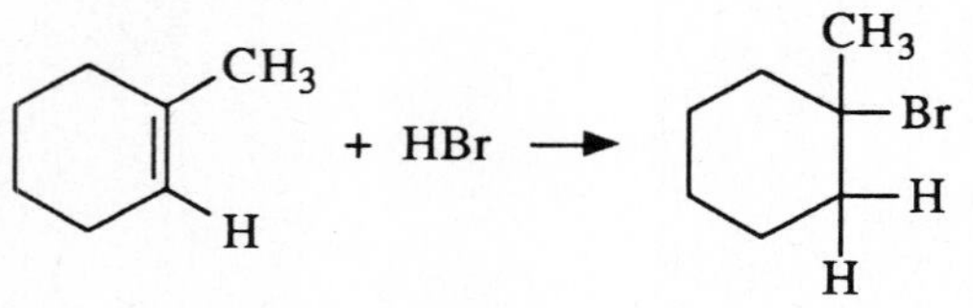

14. The hint tells us to consult a table of electronegativities. From this table, we see that Cl is more electronegative than iodine. Hence, chlorine should be bound to the more substituted carbon of the double bond:

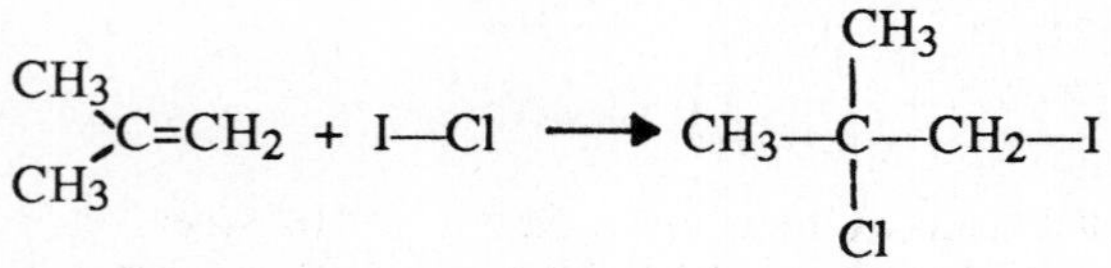

15. The first product is that of ordinary Markovnikov addition:

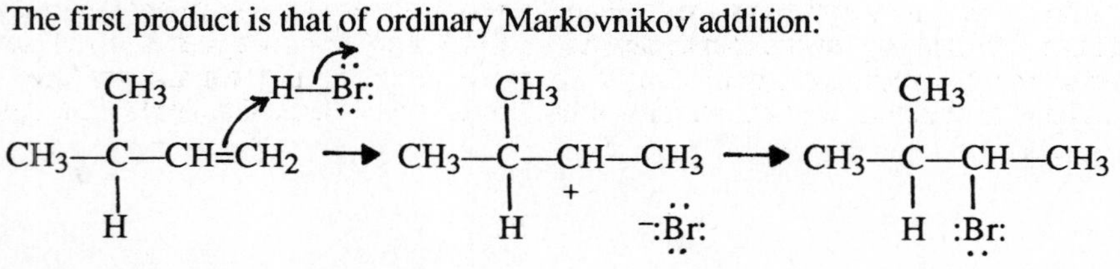

The second arises from rerrangement of a hydrogen -- a *hydride shift*. We begin with the same carbocation intermediate as above:

$$CH_3-\underset{\underset{\displaystyle :\ddot{B}r:^-}{\overset{\displaystyle |}{H}}}{\overset{\displaystyle CH_3}{\overset{\displaystyle |}{C}}}\!\!-CH-CH_3 \longrightarrow CH_3-\underset{\underset{\displaystyle :\ddot{B}r:^-}{\overset{\displaystyle +}{}}}{\overset{\displaystyle CH_3}{\overset{\displaystyle |}{C}}}\!\!-CH_2-CH_3 \longrightarrow CH_3-\underset{\underset{\displaystyle :\ddot{B}r:}{\overset{\displaystyle |}{}}}{\overset{\displaystyle CH_3}{\overset{\displaystyle |}{C}}}\!\!-CH_2-CH_3$$

16. Only (a) could be prepared this way. The alkene starting material would be 1-pentene:

$$CH_2=CH-CH_2-CH_2-CH_3$$

The only alkene from which (b) could be derived by addition would be 1-pentene; but, as we have just observed, this alkene would give (a) instead. Some of compound (c) would be obtained from the alkene

$$CH_2=CH-\underset{\displaystyle C_2H_5}{\overset{\displaystyle CH_3}{\overset{\displaystyle |}{\underset{\displaystyle |}{C}}}}\!\!-CH_3$$

However, the major product would be a rearrangement product, by analogy to Eq. 4.22.

17.

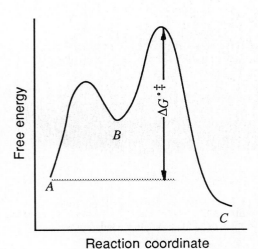

18. Addition of HBr to isobutylene gives a tertiary carbocation intermediate, while addition to *trans*-2-butene gives a secondary carbocation intermediate. On the assumption that the transition states have structures and energies resembling the respective carbocations, the transition state derived from isobutylene should be considerably more stable. It is not the absolute free energy of the transition state, but the *difference* between its free energy and that of the starting material, that determines the rate. Only if we can assume that the two alkenes have nearly the same free energies can we conclude that the reaction with the transition state of lower free energy — addition to isobutylene — is faster.

19. This reaction involves a carbocation rearrangement analogous to that discussed in Problem 15.

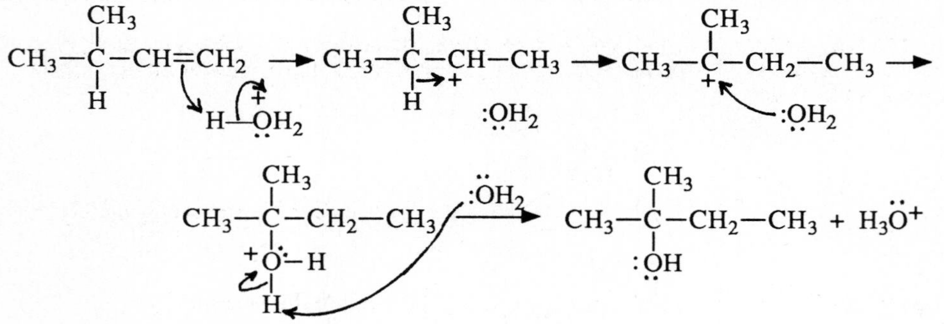

20. (a)   (b)   (c)

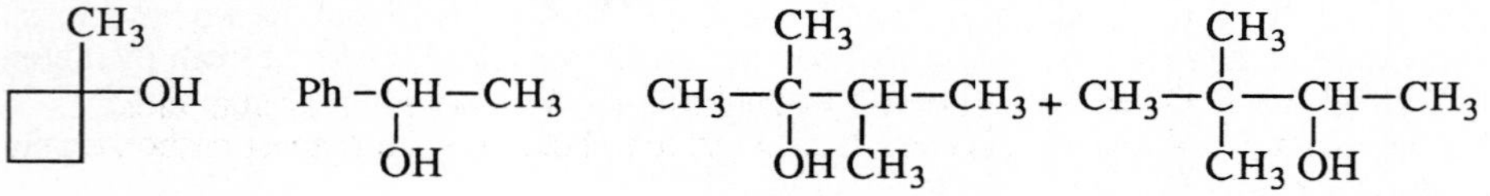

(mostly)   (some)

Notice that the alkene in (c) is the same one that gave extensive rearrangement in HCl addition (Eq. 4.22). Since the same type of intermediate is involved — a carbocation — we should expect the same type of rearrangement. The two products are the same as in HCl addition, except that the nucleophile is H_2O instead of Cl^-.

Solutions to Additional Problems

21. Using the same shorthand that we used in Problem 18, Chapter 3, we shall draw only the carbon skeletons of each alkene. In addition to considering chain branching, we must consider double-bond position and stereochemistry.

(1) C=C—C—C—C—C   (2) C—C=C—C—C—C   (3) C—C—C=C—C—C

     1-hexene   (E)- and (Z)-2-hexene   (E)- and (Z)-3-hexene

(4) 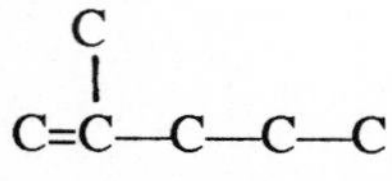   2-methyl-1-pentene   (5) 3-methyl-1-pentene   (6) 4-methyl-1-pentene   (7) 2-methyl-2-pentene

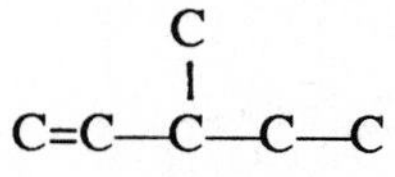

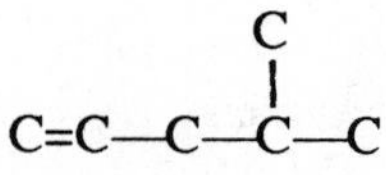

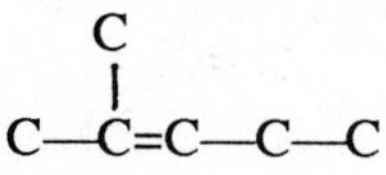

(8) 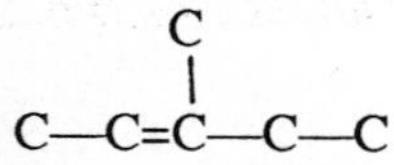   (E)- and (Z)-3-methyl-2-pentene   (9) (E)- and (Z)-4-methyl-2-pentene   (10) 2,3-dimethyl-1-butene

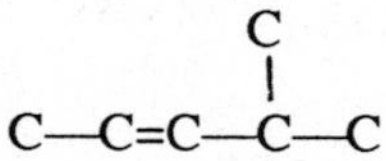

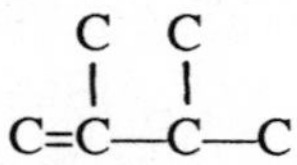

(11) 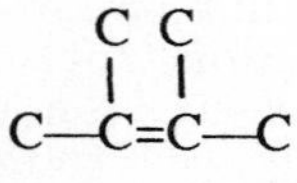 2,3-dimethyl-2-butene   (12) 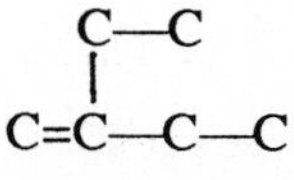 2-ethyl-1-butene   (13) 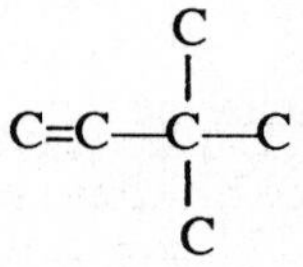 3,3-dimethyl-1-butene

22. The following compounds will give a single isomer when treated with HBr: (1), (3), (4), (6), (7), (8), (10), (11), and (12). The others will give mixtures; compounds (5) and (13) will give rearrangement products.

23. Compound (1) has the largest heat of formation, because it has the fewest alkyl substituents on the double bond. Compound (11) has the smallest heat of formation, because it has the largest number of alkyl substituents on the double bond.

24.

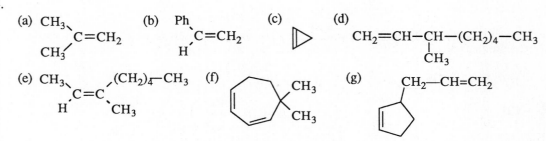

25. (a) 1-pentene   (b) 6-methyl-1-heptene   (c) 1-ethyl-1-cyclopentene   (d) 3-ethyl-1-cyclopentene
    (e) (3E)-2-butyl-1,3-pentadiene. (Notice in this case that the principal chain is the longest carbon chain containing the *most* double bonds.)
    (f) 2-isopropyl-1-methyl-1,3-cyclohexadiene   (g) 1-(1-cyclopentenyl)-1-cyclopentene
    (h) 5-[(Z)-1-propenyl]-(6E)-1,6-nonadiene

26. First we draw the structures, then we write the correct names.
    (a) CH_3—CH_2—$CH=CH_2$ correct name: 1-butene
    (b) 2-hexene is a correct name.

(c)

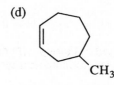

(d)

correct name: (E)-4,4-dimethyl-2-pentene   correct name: 4-methyl-1-cycloheptene

(e) 2-methyl-1,3-butadiene is a correct name.

(f)

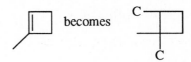

correct name: (Z)-3-methyl-2-pentene

27. (a) E Notice that the compound is E even though identical groups are on the same side of the double bond.
    (b) Z (c) E (d) E The 1-cyclobutenyl group has higher priority than the 1-methyl-1-cyclobutyl group because, when the double bond is "replicated," there are in effect two carbon substituents on the ring:

28. (a) Hydration of propene (CH_3—$CH=CH_2$) gives isopropyl alcohol.
    (b) n-Propyl alcohol cannot be made by alkene hydration, because the only alkene to which water could be added to get n-propyl alcohol would be propene — and such an addition would violate the Markovnikov rule. As we have just seen in (a), Markovnikov addition of water to propene gives isopropyl alcohol, not n-propyl alcohol.

29. (a) The two alkenes are

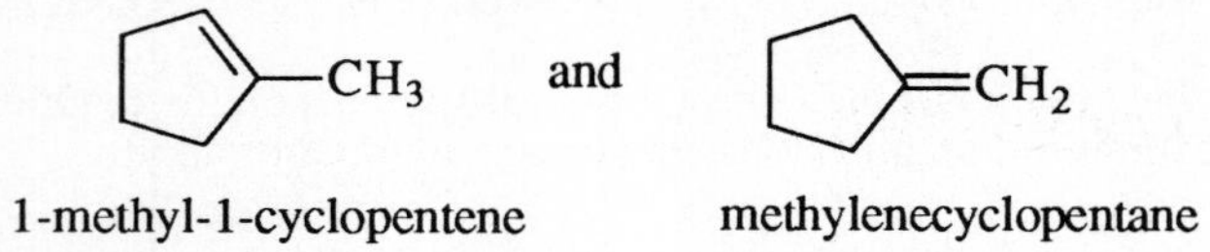

1-methyl-1-cyclopentene   methylenecyclopentane

(We have not studied the nomenclature of the latter compound.)

(b) The products would be different if DBr were used, because the D of DBr ends up at different carbons. However, the products aren't *very* different — they differ only in the position of the isotope:

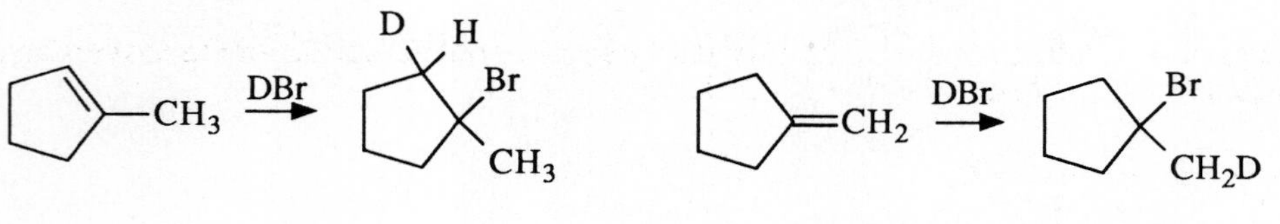

30.

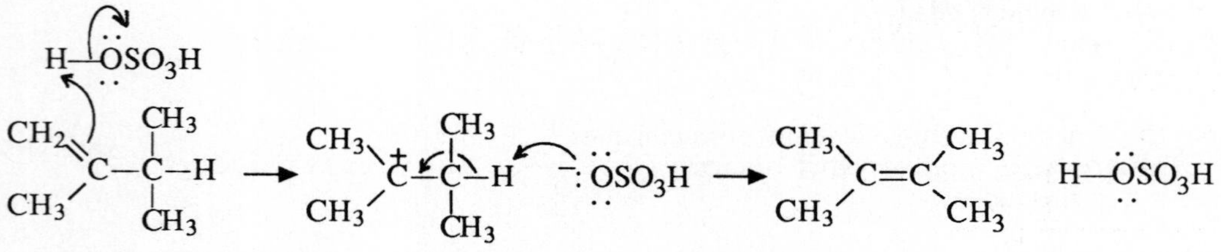

➤ Notice that in each case the curved arrows go *from* the source of the electrons *to* their destination.

31. Since the boron bears three groups (three fluorines and no electron pairs), it is trigonal; the F—B—F angles are 120°, and the molecule is planar. Trigonal-planar geometry suggests sp^2 hybridization for boron. An orbital diagram for boron is as follows:

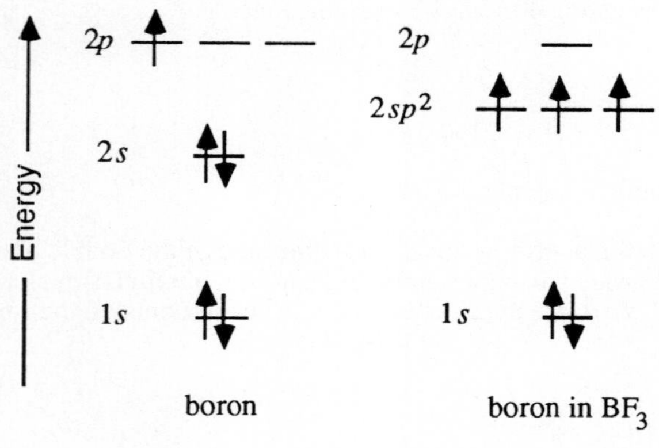

32. From your model, you should see that it is impossible to bridge the distance between the two *trans* carbons with only two other carbons — unless, of course, either (a) you break your models, or (b) your models are constructed of bubble gum. (See diagram at the top of the next page.)

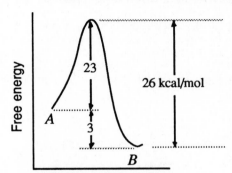

this distance too great to be bridged by only two carbons

33. First, we convert the equilibrium constant into a standard free energy. From the usual formula,

$$\Delta G° = -2.303RT \ln K_{eq} = -1.364(\log 150) = -2.97 \text{ kcal/mol. (Assume 298 K or 25 °C.)}$$

(We'll call this 3 kcal/mol in round numbers.) The standard free energy of activation for the conversion of B to A, as we can see from the curve below, is $23 + 3 = 26$ kcal/mol.

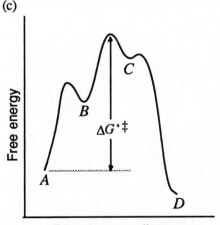

34. (a) When the reaction comes to equilibrium, the compound present in greatest amount will be the compound with the smallest standard free energy — namely, compound D.
(b) The rate-determining step of the reaction is the step with the transition state of largest standard free energy — namely, the step $B \rightarrow C$.
(c)

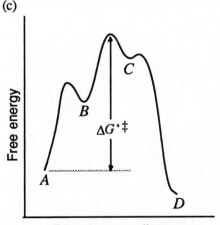

(d) $C \rightarrow D$ is faster, because it has the smaller free energy of activation (smaller energy barrier).

35. (a) Methyl is more electron-donating, because the compound on the left could not have a larger dipole moment than the one on the right if the C—CH$_3$ bonds did not provide a greater dipole-moment contribution in the direction of the C—Cl bonds than the C—H bonds.

(b) The *E* isomer (the compound on the left) has the greater dipole moment. In the compound on the left, the C—CH_3 bond dipole reinforces the C—Cl bond dipole; in the compound on the right, the C—CH_3 bond dipole opposes the C—Cl bond dipole.

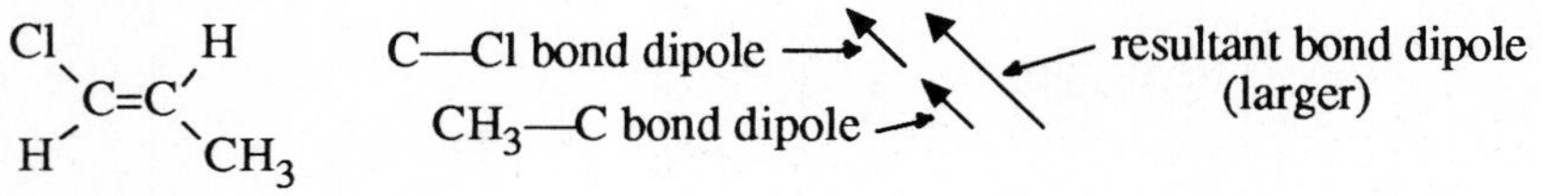

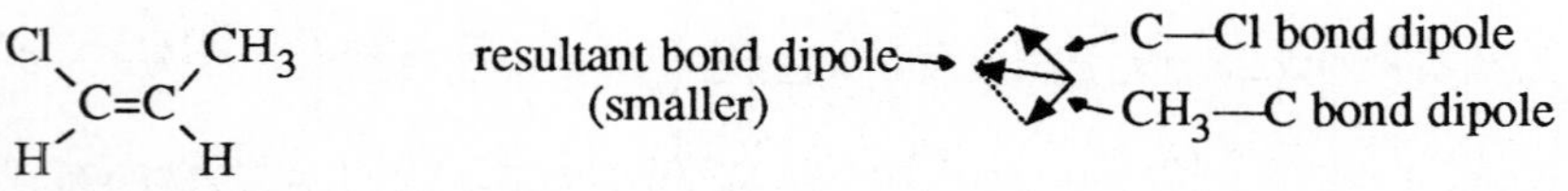

Of course, the C—H bond dipole also contributes, but its effect, as we deduced in the last problem, is smaller.

➤ We must realize that the data in this problem do not prove that methyl groups are electron-donating toward alkene carbons — only that they are *more electron-donating than hydrogens*. It is formally possible that the methyl groups are electron-withdrawing, and that the hydrogens are more so; were this true, we would arrive at exactly the same answers. (To say that methyl is less electron-withdrawing is the same as saying that it is more electron-donating!) However, a large body of evidence indicates that CH_3—C= bonds are indeed polarized away from the CH_3 group.

36.   (a) The compounds in the problem are:

$$CH_3-CH=CH-CH=CH-(CH_2)_2-CH_3 \qquad CH_3-CH=CH-CH_2-CH=CH-CH_2CH_3$$

   2,4-octadiene   2,5-octadiene

(Whether the dienes are *E* or *Z* makes no difference for purposes of this problem.)   Clearly, the 2,4-octadiene is more stable, because it has the smaller heat of formation.
(b) In the 2,4-isomer, there can be overlap of *p* orbitals not only across the formal double bond, but also *across the single bond between the two alkene units*:

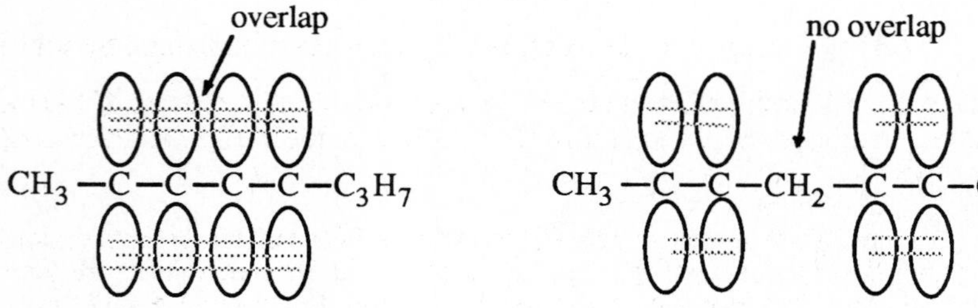

This additional overlap provides more bonding and therefore greater stability. (Remember, bonding releases energy.) In the 2,5-isomer, the *p* orbitals of the alkene units are too far apart to interact appreciably.

37.   (a) This addition follows the Markovnikov rule, because the positive end of the CH_3O—H dipole (H) goes to the less substituted carbon, and the negative end (CH_3O) to the more substituted carbon of the double bond.
(b) Using the box below the problem, we see that the —OCH_3 group must come from the methanol; according to (a), methanol has added across the carbon-carbon double bond. This occurs with acid catalysis. This reaction is very much like hydration, except that CH_3O—H, rather than HO—H, has added to the alkene. In the first step, the double bond is protonated by the acid to give a carbocation. Protonation occurs on the least substituted carbon of the double bond because a tertiary carbocation is formed:

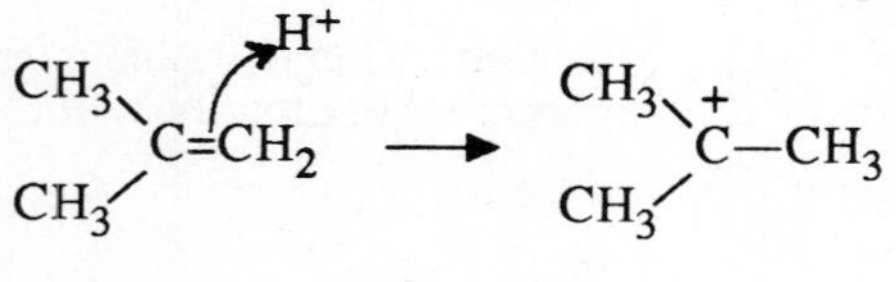

Then methanol attacks the carbocation. Loss of a proton gives the ether product.

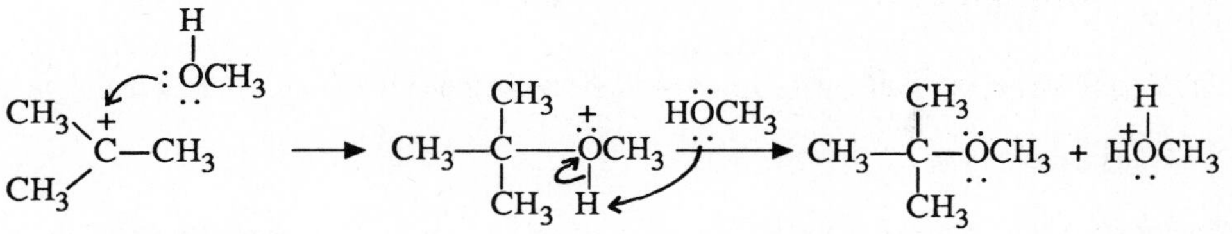

38. (a) Branching stabilizes the alkane by 2 kcal/mol, but stabilizes the alkene by about 4 kcal/mol. Hence, alkenes are more stabilized by branching.
(b) Carbocations are stabilized much more by branching than alkenes are.
(c) Since the product of (2) is the most highly branched carbocation, this reaction has the most favorable (negative) $\Delta H°$. Because alkene branching is less important, we can ignore it to a first approximation.
(d) Taking the enthalpy of the proton arbitrarily as zero, the $\Delta H°$ of the first reaction is

$$\Delta H°(1) = \Delta H°(CH_3\overset{+}{C}HCH_2CH_3) - \Delta H°(CH_2{=}CHCH_2CH_3)$$

From the information given in the problem, we can also write

$$\Delta H°(CH_3\overset{+}{C}HCH_2CH_3) = \Delta H°[(CH_3)_2CH\overset{+}{C}H_2] - 23$$

Substituting this in the previous equation, we have

$$\Delta H°(1) = \Delta H°[(CH_3)_2CH\overset{+}{C}H_2] - 23 + 0.03 = \Delta H°[(CH_3)_2CH\overset{+}{C}H_2] - 22.97$$

For reaction (2),

$$\Delta H°(2) = \Delta H°[(CH_3)_2CH\overset{+}{C}H_2] - 131 + 4.04 = \Delta H°[(CH_3)_2CH\overset{+}{C}H_2] - 126.96$$

For reaction (3),

$$\Delta H°(3) = \Delta H°[(CH_3)_2CH\overset{+}{C}H_2] + 4.04$$

The problem asks us for the relative $\Delta H°$ values of the three reactions. When we compare these by subtraction, the term $\Delta H°[(CH_3)_2CH\overset{+}{C}H_2]$ cancels. When we subtract the $\Delta H°$ values, we find that reaction (2) is more exothermic than (1) by 104 kcal/mol, and more exothermic than (3) by 131 kcal/mol. That is, reaction (2) is most favorable, as we deduced in part (c).

➤ The numbers in this problem provide a graphic quantitative demonstration of the effect of carbocation stability on the outcome of a reaction. The formation of more stable carbocations is favored by *more than a hundred kilocalories per mole*! As the problem indicates, these results are from the gas phase, and the numbers in solution aren't so large; but the effect is nevertheless a major one.

39. (a) The $\Delta G°$ for the reaction is the difference of the two free energies:

$\Delta G° = 18.13 - 18.89 = -0.76$ kcal/mol.

Converting this into an equilibrium constant by the formula in the answer to Problem 8, we find that

$\Delta G° = 10^{-(-0.76/1.364)} = 3.61$ at 298 K or 25 °C

(b) The equilibrium constant tells us *nothing* about the rate at which this conversion takes place. Just because we know the relative energies of two compounds doesn't mean that we know the height of the energy barrier separating them. There is an analogy here to two towns that lie at different altitudes. The relative altitudes of the towns doesn't tell us whether we have to cross a plain or a mountain pass to travel between them.

40. (a) 2-Methylpropene is more stable, because it is the more highly branched alkene.
    (b) The hydration of 2-methylpropene is faster because it has the smaller $\Delta G°‡$.
    (c) Letting B = the $\Delta G°‡$ for hydration of 1-butene, and P = the $\Delta G°‡$ for hydration of 2-methylpropene, the reaction-free energy diagram can be written as follows:

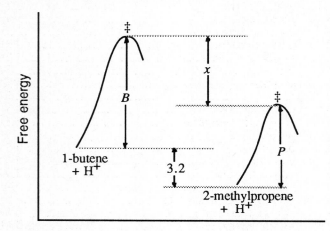

(d) This problem asks for the quantity x in the figure above. We are given

$B = P + 5.46$

Graphically, $P + x = 3.2 + B$, or $P + x = 3.2 + P + 5.46$. Solving for x, we find

$x = 8.66$ kcal/mol.

Thus, the transition state for hydration of 2-methylpropene is 8.66 kcal/mol more stable than that for hydration of 1-butene. This is reasonable by Hammond's postulate, since the transition state for hydration of 2-methylpropene resembles a tertiary carbocation, while the transition state for hydration of 1-butene resembles a secondary carbocation.

41. The experimental result supports the first mechanism and rules out the second. Were the second mechanism occurring, the proton labeled as deuterium would be lost into the pool of HBr in the solution. When the alkene is reprotonated, it could be reprotonated by either HBr or DBr. Hence, the final product would contain less than one equivalent of deuterium. In the first mechanism, the deuterium never escapes from the molecule and is therefore completely retained.

Chapter 5 / Addition Reactions of Alkenes

CHAPTER 5 TERMS

addition polymer	5.9A
atom abstraction	5.8B
bond dissociation energy	5.8D
bromohydrin	5.1A
bromonium ion	5.1A
catalytic hydrogenation	5.7A
chlorohydrin	5.1B
concerted reaction	5.3A
cracking	5.9B
cycloaddition	5.4
degree of unsaturation	5.10
diborane	5.3A
diol	5.4
energy barrier	5.8D
free radical	5.8
free–radical chain reaction	5.8B
free–radical inhibitor	5.8B
free–radical initiator	5.8B
free–radical polymerization	5.9A
glycol	5.4
halohydrin	5.1B
heat of hydrogenation	5.7B
heterogeneous catalysis	5.7A
heterolysis	5.8A
heterolytic cleavage	5.8A
homogeneous catalysis	5.7A
homolysis	5.8A
homolytic cleavage	5.8A
hydroboration	5.3A
hydroboration–oxidation	5.3A
hydrogen peroxide	5.5
hydrogenation	5.7

hypobromous acid	5.1B
hypochlorous acid	5.1B
initiation step	5.8B
iodohydrin	5.1B
mercurinium ion	5.3B
molozonide	5.5
monomer	5.9A
organoborane	5.3A
osmate ester	5.4
osmium tetroxide	5.4
oxymercuration	5.3B
oxymercuration–reduction	5.3B
ozone	5.5
ozonide	5.5
ozonolysis	5.5
percentage yield	5.2
pericyclic reaction	5.3A
peroxide	5.8
polyethylene	5.9A
polymer	5.9A
polymerization	5.9A
polypropylene	5.9A
potassium permanganate	5.4
propagation step	5.8B
recombination	5.8B
β-scission	5.9B
sodium borohydride	5.3B
termination step	5.8B
unsaturation number	5.10
vicinal dihalide	5.1A
vicinal glycol	5.4

CHAPTER 5 CONCEPTS

I. Free Radicals:

A. Heterolysis vs. Homolysis—Free Radicals:
    1. **Heterolytic cleavage (heterolysis):**
        a) Heterolysis occurs when bond breakage results in the *uneven* distribution of the shared electrons.
        b) Heterolysis is designated by a curved arrow.

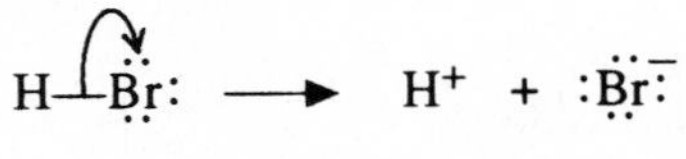

$$H{-}\ddot{Br}: \longrightarrow H^+ + :\ddot{Br}:^-$$

2. **Homolytic cleavage (homolysis):**
   a) Homolysis occurs when bond breakage results in the *even* distribution of the shared electrons.
   b) Homolysis is designated by single-barbed "fishhook" arrows.

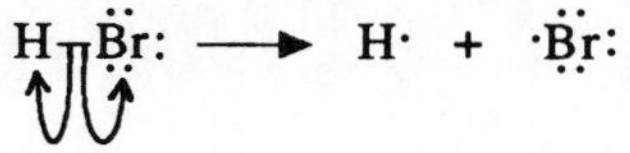

$$H \overset{\cdot \cdot}{\underset{\cdot \cdot}{Br}}: \longrightarrow H\cdot \ + \ \cdot \overset{\cdot \cdot}{\underset{\cdot \cdot}{Br}}:$$

3. **Free radicals** contain at least one unpaired electron.

B. Structure and Stability of Free Radicals:
   1. Free radicals are classified as:
      a) Primary—two hydrogens attached.
      b) Secondary—one hydrogen attached.
      c) Tertiary—no hydrogens attached.
   2. Stability of free radicals:

   tertiary > secondary > primary

   3. Free radicals are stabilized by alkyl substituents.

II. Bond Dissociation Energies:

A. Enthalpy:
   1. **Bond dissociation energy** is defined as the $\Delta H°$ of a homolytic cleavage.
   2. A bond dissociation energy measures the intrinsic strength of a chemical bond.
   3. Hess's law can in principle be used to calculate the $\Delta H°$ of any reaction from bond dissociation energies.

III. Elemental Analysis of Alkenes:

A. Unsaturation Number:
   1. The **unsaturation number** of a molecule is equal to the total number of its rings and multiple bonds.
      a) Every ring or double bond reduces the maximum number of hydrogens by 2.
      b) Every triple bond reduces the maximum number of hydrogens by 4.
   2. The unsaturation number is equal to half the difference between the maximum number and the actual number of hydrogens.
   3. Each Group VIIA element (halogen) is equivalent to 1 hydrogen.
   4. Each Group VIA element (O, S, Se, Te) has no effect on the unsaturation number.
   5. Each Group VA element (N, P, As, Sb) is equivalent to –1 hydrogen.
   6. Formula (Eq. 5.77):

$$U = \frac{2C + 2 + N - (H + X)}{2}$$

IV. Writing Organic Reactions:

A. Percentage Yield:
   1. The **theoretical yield** is the ideal amount of product formed.
   2. The **actual yield** is the amount of product isolated.
   3. The **percentage yield** is the actual yield divided by the theroretical yield times 100%.

CHAPTER 5 REACTIONS

I. Halogenation of Alkenes:

A. Addition of Chlorine and Bromine to Alkenes:
   1. An electrophilic addition.
   2. Gives **vicinal dihalides**.
   3. Mechanism involves a cyclic **halonium-ion intermediate**.

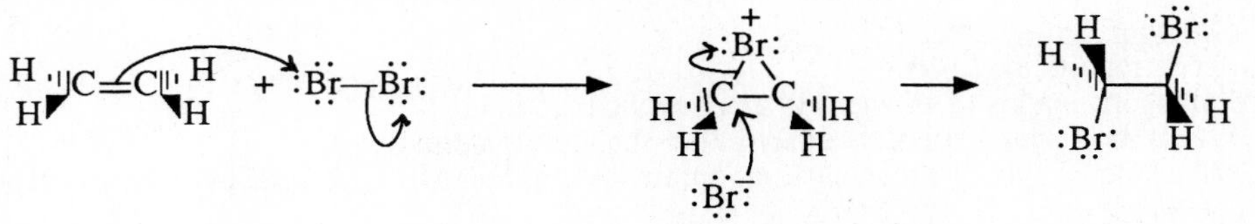

B. Halohydrin Formation:
   1. An electrophilic addition.
   2. Halides in the presence of water add to alkenes to give **halohydrins**.
   3. Follows the Markovnikov rule.
   4. The —OH group adds to the more substituted alkene carbon atom.

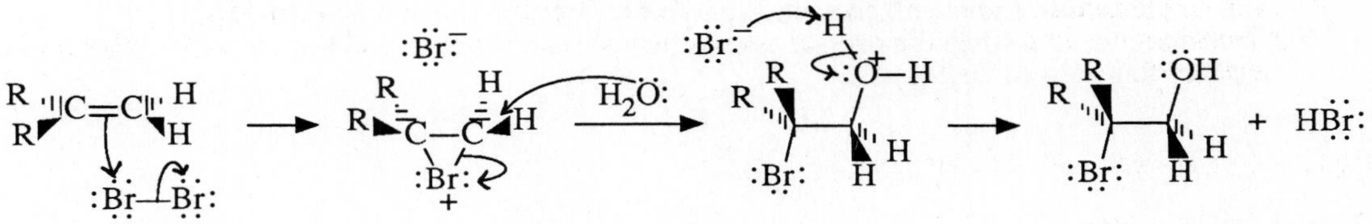

II. Hydroboration–Oxidation:

A. Hydroboration:
   1. An electrophilic addition.
   2. **Diborane** reacts with alkenes to give trialkylboranes.
   3. Borane adds to alkenes via a concerted, **pericyclic reaction**.
   4. Follows the Markovnikov rule.

B. Oxidation:
   1. **Organoboranes** are oxidized by alkaline H_2O_2 to alcohols.
   2. The boron is replaced by an —OH group at each carbon atom.
   3. The —OH group ends up at the less highly substituted carbon of the alkene.
   4. Carbocations are not involved; rearrangements do not occur.

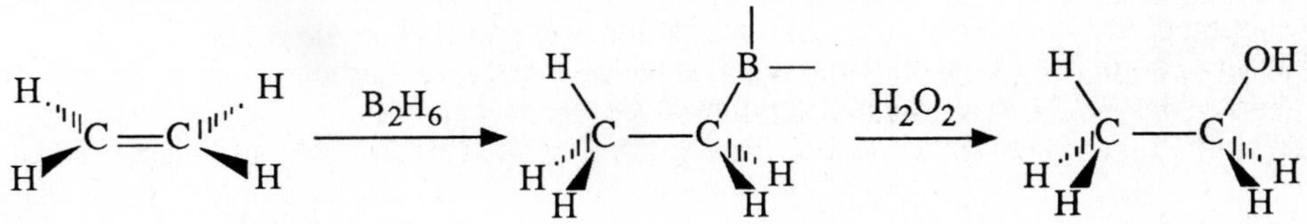

III. Oxymercuration–Reduction of Alkenes:

A. Oxymercuration of Alkenes:
   1. An electrophilic addition.
   2. Mercury (II) salts add to alkenes to form cyclic **mercurinium ions**.

B. Reduction:

1. Sodium borohydride in aqueous base effects replacement of the mercury with a hydrogen atom.
2. Carbocations are not involved; rearrangements do not occur.

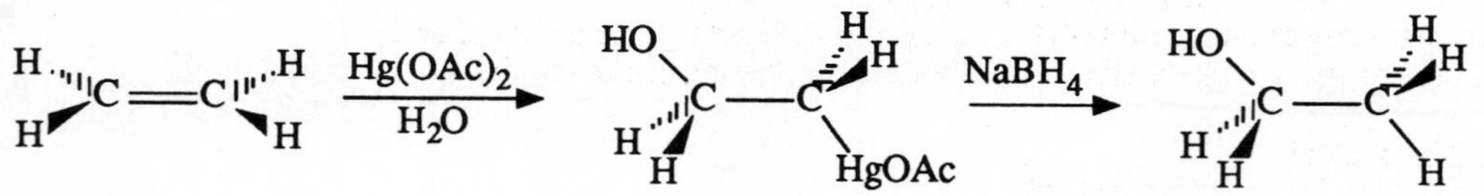

IV. Conversion of Alkenes to Glycols:

A. With Potassium Permanganate:

1. An electrophilic addition.
2. Permanganate adds to alkenes via a pericyclic reaction.
3. **Glycols** are formed spontaneously under the reaction conditions.
4. Used as the Baeyer test for unsaturation; the by-product MnO_2 formed as a brown precipitate is a positive test.

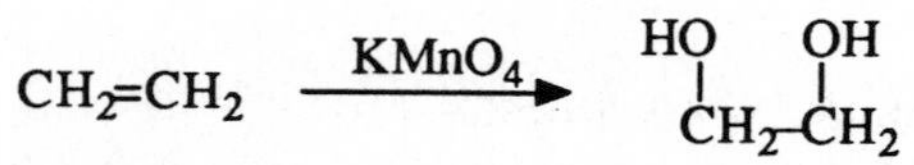

$$CH_2=CH_2 \quad \xrightarrow{KMnO_4} \quad \overset{HO}{\underset{CH_2}{|}} \overset{OH}{\underset{CH_2}{|}}$$

B. With Osmium Tetroxide:

1. An electrophilic addition.
2. Osmium tetroxide adds to alkenes via a pericyclic reaction to form **osmate esters**.
3. Glycols are formed when the osmate ester is treated with water and sodium bisulfite is used to reduce the osmium salts to Os(0).

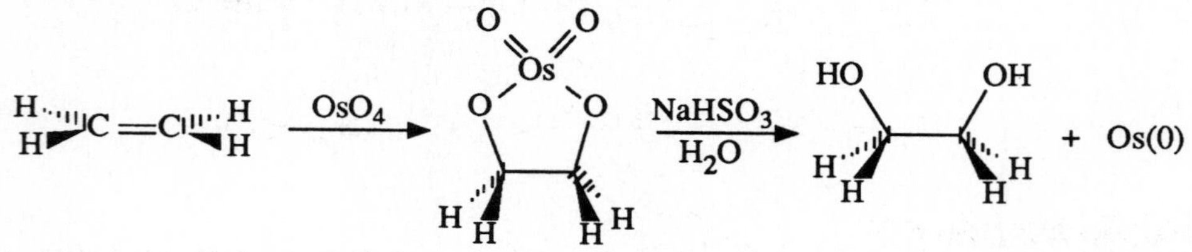

V. Ozonolysis of Alkenes:

A. Addition of Ozone:

1. **Ozone** adds to alkenes via a pericyclic reaction to form a **molozonide**.
2. The molozonide is rapidly transformed into an **ozonide**.

B. Reduction of Ozonides:

1. Reaction of dimethyl sulfide with ozonides produces ketones and/or aldehydes.
2. The C=C bond is cleaved and an oxygen is added to each sp^2 carbon.

C. Oxidation of Ozonides:

1. Reaction of H_2O_2 with ozonides produces ketones and/or carboxylic acids.
2. The C=C bond is cleaved and an oxygen is added to each sp^2 carbon.
3. Each H attached to an sp^2 carbon is replaced by an —OH group.

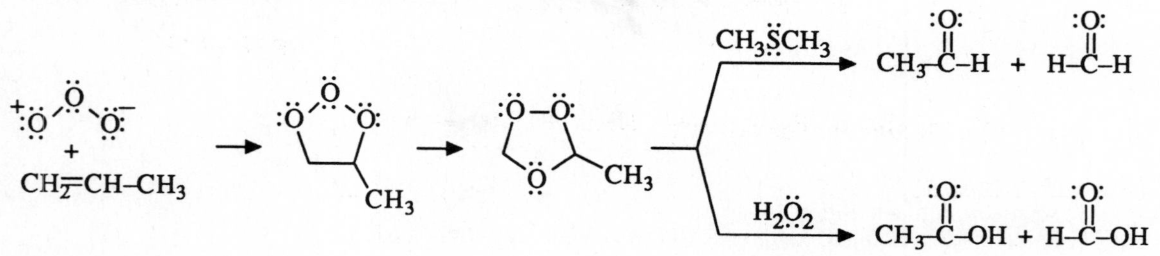

VI. Hydrogenation of Alkenes into Alkanes:

A. Catalysts:

1. Catalysts are used in small amounts.
2. **Heterogeneous catalysts** are insoluble in the reaction medium.
3. **Homogeneous catalysts** are soluble in the reaction medium.

B. Hydrogenation:

1. A catalyst must be present.
2. The reaction takes place on the catalyst surface.

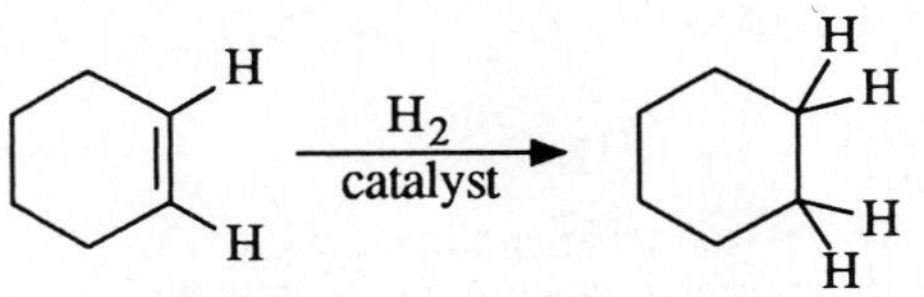

3. Benzene rings are hydrogenated only under vigorous conditions.

VII. Addition of Hydrogen Bromide to Alkenes:

A. The Peroxide Effect:

1. **Peroxides** react with heat or light to produce free radicals.
2. The addition of HBr in the presence of peroxides occurs with anti-Markovnikov regioselectivity.

$$CH_3{-}CH{=}CH_2 \xrightarrow[\text{peroxides}]{HBr} CH_3{-}\dot{C}H{-}CH_2Br + :\ddot{\underset{..}{Br}}\cdot$$

$$CH_3{-}\dot{C}H{-}CH_2Br \xrightarrow{HBr} CH_3{-}CH_2{-}CH_2Br + :\ddot{\underset{..}{Br}}\cdot$$

B. Free-Radical Chain Reactions:

1. **Initiation step**—radicals are formed by homolytic cleavage of a free-radical initiator.
2. **Propagation step**—a radical reacts with a nonradical to produce a new radical. Typical propagation steps are:
   a) **Atom abstraction.**
   b) Addition to a double bond.
3. **Termination step**—one or more radicals react to form nonradicals.
   a) **Recombination** is a typical termination step.
   b) Free-radical inhibitors act by serving as efficient radical-chain terminators.

$$RO{-}OR \xrightarrow[\text{or heat}]{\text{light}} RO\cdot + \cdot OR \qquad \text{initiation}$$

$$RO\cdot + H{-}Br \rightarrow RO{-}H + Br\cdot$$

propagation

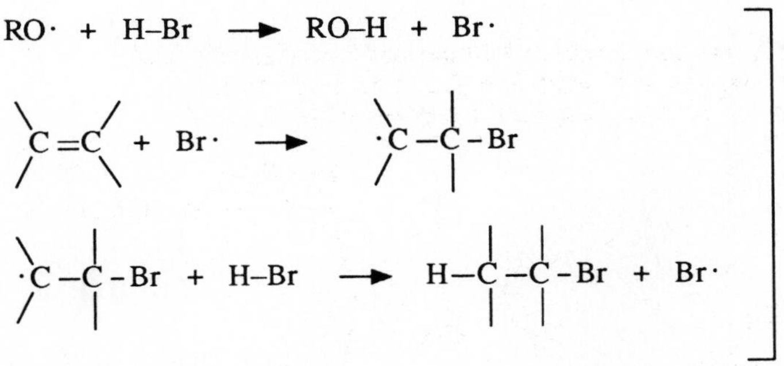

VIII. Industrial Use and Preparation of Alkenes:

A. Free-Radical Polymerization of Alkenes:
   1. Alkenes in the presence of free-radical initiators form **polymers**.
   2. **Polymerization** occurs via a free-radical mechanism.

$$RO-OR \xrightarrow[\text{or heat}]{\text{light}} RO\cdot + \cdot OR$$

$$CH_2=CH_2 + RO\cdot \longrightarrow RO-CH_2-\dot{C}H_2$$

$$RO-CH_2-\dot{C}H_2 + CH_2=CH_2 \longrightarrow RO-CH_2-CH_2-CH_2-\dot{C}H_2$$

$$RO-CH_2-CH_2-CH_2-\dot{C}H_2 \xrightarrow{CH_2=CH_2} -(-CH_2-CH_2-)_n$$

B. Thermal Cracking of Alkanes:
   1. **Thermal cracking** breaks larger saturated hydrocarbons into a mixture of smaller hydrocarbons.
   2. β-**Scission** is one process of thermal cracking that produces ethylene.

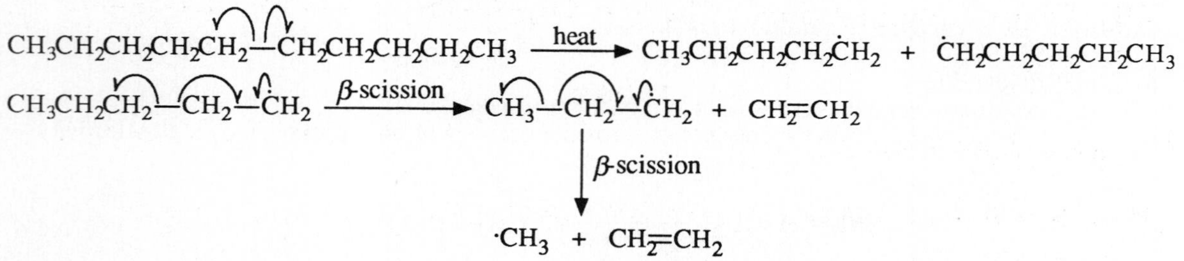

$$CH_3CH_2CH_2CH_2CH_2-CH_2CH_2CH_2CH_2CH_3 \xrightarrow{\text{heat}} CH_3CH_2CH_2CH_2\dot{C}H_2 + \dot{C}H_2CH_2CH_2CH_2CH_3$$

$$CH_3CH_2\dot{C}H_2-CH_2-CH_2 \xrightarrow{\beta\text{-scission}} CH_3-CH_2-\dot{C}H_2 + CH_2=CH_2$$

$$\Big\downarrow \beta\text{-scission}$$

$$\cdot CH_3 + CH_2=CH_2$$

CHAPTER 5 SOLUTIONS

Solutions to In-Text Problems

1. The alkene is methylenecyclohexane:

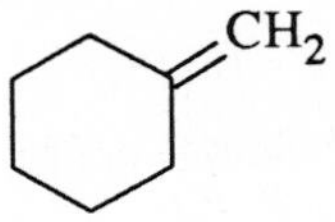

methylenecyclohexane

2. The mechanism resembles that for halogenation. First, an iodonium ion is formed. Then azide attacks the iodonium ion at the more substituted carbon atom.

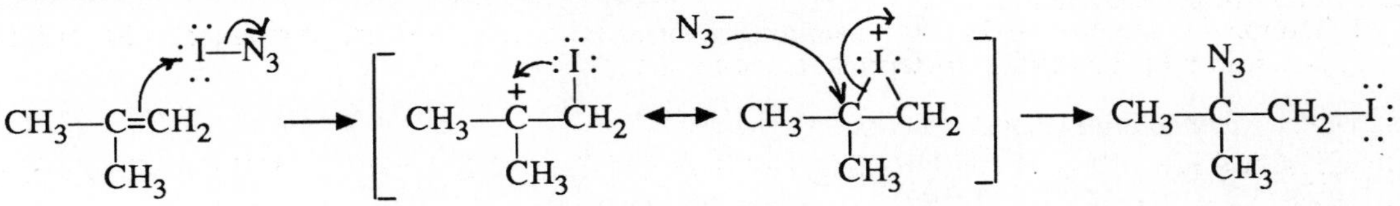

iodonium ion

3. (a) Ethanol, CH_3—CH_2—OH

(b) CH_3—$\underset{\underset{CH_3}{|}}{CH}$—$\underset{\underset{OH}{|}}{CH}$—$CH_2CH_3$

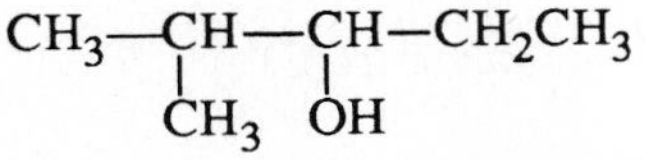

(c)

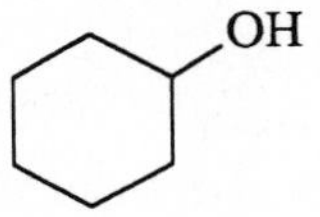

(d) Since both ends of the double bond are substituted with one alkyl group, we would get a mixture:

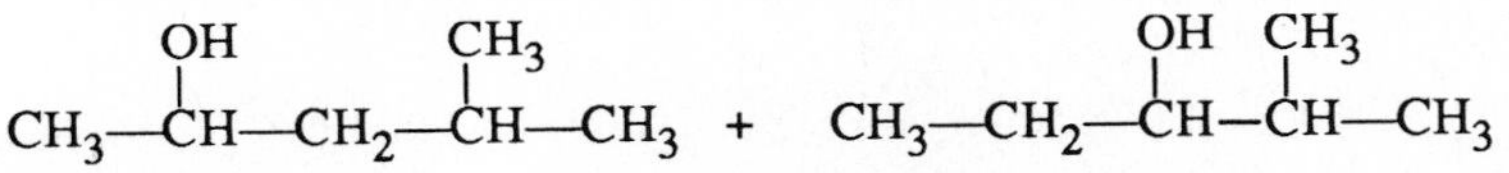

CH_3—$\underset{\underset{OH}{|}}{CH}$—$CH_2$—$\underset{\underset{CH_3}{|}}{CH}$—$CH_3$ + CH_3—CH_2—$\underset{\underset{OH}{|}}{CH}$—$\underset{\underset{CH_3}{|}}{CH}$—$CH_3$

(We might expect somewhat more of the first compound and less of the second because of the steric effect of the methyl branch.)

4. The alkenes are derived by mentally removing OH and H from adjacent carbons of these products:

(a) C_2H_5—$\underset{\underset{CH_3}{|}}{C}$=$CH_2$

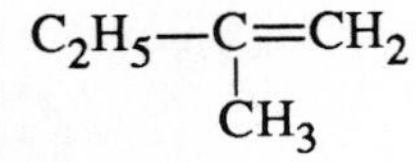

(b)

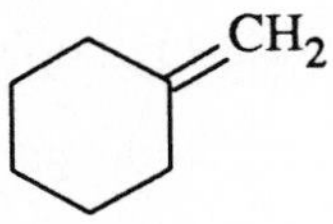

➤ Whenever we study a reaction used in synthesis, we should think about it in *both the forward and reverse directions*. This problem illustrates "reverse thinking." Can you think of an alcohol that could *not* be prepared by hydroboration-oxidation?

5. (a) CH_3—CH_2—OH   The same product would be obtained from hydroboration-oxidation.

(b) CH_3—$\underset{\underset{OH}{|}}{CH}$—$(CH_2)_7$—$CH_3$ HO—CH_2—$(CH_2)_8$—CH_3

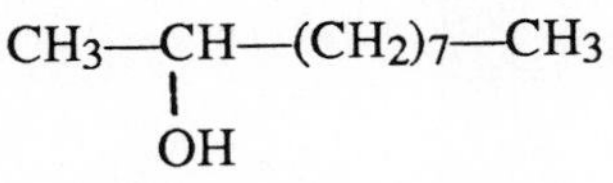

from oxymercuration-reduction

from hydroboration-oxidation

(c)

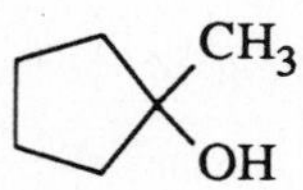

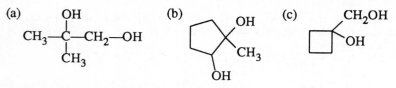

CH₃ — from oxymercuration-reduction

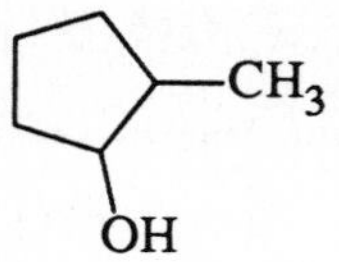

-CH₃ — from hydroboration-oxidation

(d)

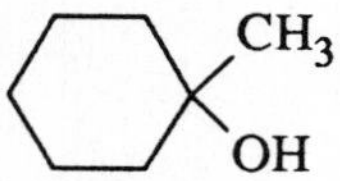

CH₃ — from oxymercuration-reduction

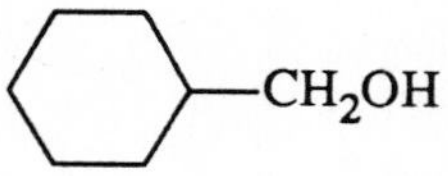

-CH₂OH — from hydroboration-oxidation

6. The products are the glycols derived from addition of the elements of HO—OH across the double bond:

(a)
$$CH_3-\underset{\underset{CH_3}{|}}{\overset{\overset{OH}{|}}{C}}-CH_2-OH$$

(b)

OH / CH₃ / OH (cyclopentane ring)

(c)

CH₂OH / OH (cyclobutane ring)

7. Again we are asked to think about a reaction in reverse.

(a) CH₃—CH=CH—CH₃ (*cis* or *trans*)

(b) There are *four* alkenes that could give this alcohol!

$$CH_2=CH-CH=CH_2 \qquad HO-CH_2-\underset{\underset{OH}{|}}{CH}-CH=CH_2 \qquad HO-CH_2-CH=CH-CH_2OH$$

(*cis* or *trans*)

8. The formation of the cyclic intermediate with permanganate is analogous to the reaction shown in Eq. 5.35a:

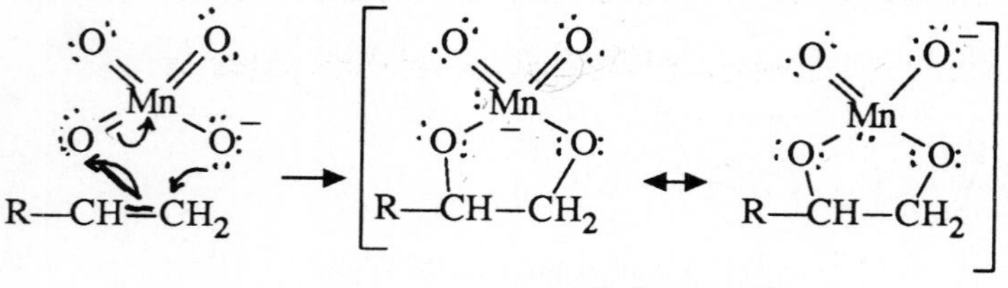

$$\left[\ldots \right]$$

cyclic intermediate

9. (a)

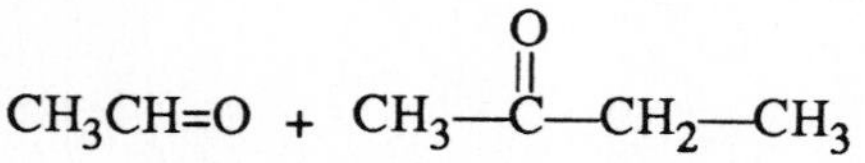

$$CH_3CH=O + CH_3-\overset{\overset{O}{\|}}{C}-CH_2-CH_3 \qquad CH_3-\overset{\overset{O}{\|}}{C}-OH + CH_3-\overset{\overset{O}{\|}}{C}-CH_2-CH_3$$

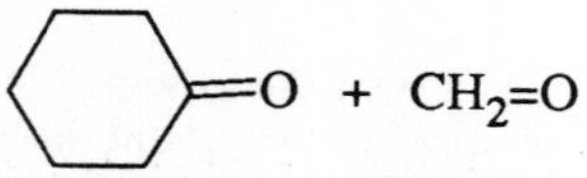

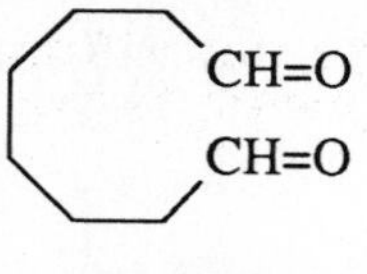

with dimethyl sulfide 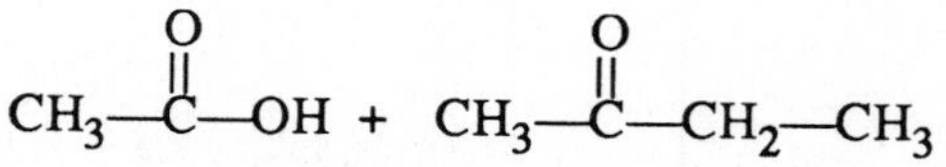   with hydrogen peroxide

(b)

=O + CH₂=O

with dimethyl sulfide

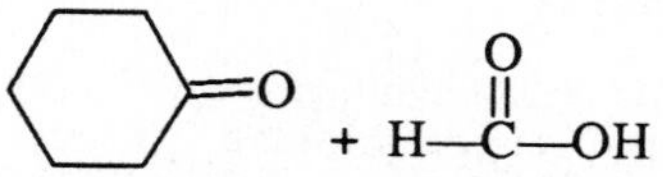

$$=O + H-\overset{\overset{O}{\|}}{C}-OH$$

with hydrogen peroxide

(c)

CH=O / CH=O

with dimethyl sulfide

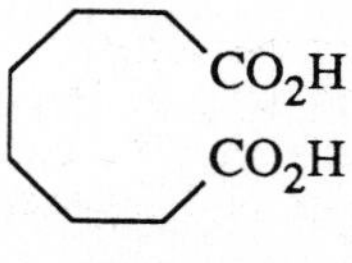

CO₂H / CO₂H

with hydrogen peroxide

(d) No reaction; the compound is an alkane and has no double bond.

10. (a)   (b)   (c)

$CH_3CH_2CH_2CH=CHCH_2CH_2CH_3$

Cis and *trans* (or *E* and *Z*) alkene isomers give the same ozonolysis products; hence, we can't determine whether an alkene is *cis* or *trans* (or *E* or *Z*) from its ozonolysis products. Of the alkenes in this problem, only the one in (a) has this ambiguity.

11. In order to get hexane, the alkenes have to have unbranched carbon chains containing six carbon atoms. The possibilities are 1-hexene, *cis*- and *trans*-2-hexene, and *cis*- and *trans*-3-hexene.

$CH_2=CHCH_2CH_2CH_2CH_3$, $CH_3CH=CHCH_2CH_2CH_3$, and $CH_3CH_2CH=CHCH_2CH_3$

                              (*cis* and *trans*)   (*cis* and *trans*)

12. The hydrogenation reaction is as follows (heats of formation are below each compound):

$$CH_3-\underset{\underset{-4.04}{\underset{|}{CH_3}}}{C}=CH_2 + H_2 \longrightarrow CH_3-\underset{\underset{x}{\underset{|}{CH_3}}}{CH}-CH_3$$

We are given that the $\Delta H°$ of this reaction is -28.1 kcal/mol. Hence,

$\Delta H° = -28.1 = x - (-4.04)$ or $x = -32.14$ kcal/mol. This is the heat of formation of 2-methylpropane.

13. (a) The two hydrogenation reactions and the relevant heats of formation for each compound are:

cis-$CH_3CH=CHCH_3$ + H_2 $CH_3CH_2CH_2CH_3$ $\Delta H_1°$

   $\Delta H_{cis}°$ 0 $\Delta H_{butane}°$

$trans$-$CH_3CH=CHCH_3$ + H_2 $CH_3CH_2CH_2CH_3$ $\Delta H_2°$

   $\Delta H_{trans}°$ 0 $\Delta H_{butane}°$

Subtracting these heats of hydrogenation, we have

$\Delta H_2° - \Delta H_1° = [\Delta H_{butane}° - \Delta H_{trans}°] - [\Delta H_{butane}° - \Delta H_{cis}°]$
$= \Delta H_{trans}° - \Delta H_{cis}°$

This shows that subtraction of the two heats of hydrogenation is the same as subtraction of the two heats of formation, as required.

(b) The difference in the heats of hydrogenation is not the same as the difference in the heats of formation because hydrogenation of each alkene gives a different alkane. We can show this rigorously by going through the same procedure as in (a). When we do so, letting $\Delta H_1°$ = the heat of hydrogenation of 2-methylpropene, and $\Delta H_2°$ = the heat of hydrogenation of 1-butene, we find

$$\Delta H_2^\circ - \Delta H_1^\circ = \Delta H_f^\circ(\text{2-methylpropene}) - \Delta H_f^\circ(\text{1-butene}) + R$$

where $R = \Delta H_f^\circ(\text{butane}) - \Delta H_f^\circ(\text{2-methylpropane})$

That is, the difference in heats of hydrogenation equals the difference in heats of formation of the alkenes plus a remainder R, which is the difference in heats of formation of the product alkanes. In other words, in the Hess's-law calculation, the heats of formation of the products do not cancel because the products are different in the two hydrogenation equations.

14. (a) $(CH_3)_2\dot{C}$—CH_2—Br: (b) $\cdot CH_2$—$CH{=}CH$—$CH{=}CH_2$ (c) $R\cdot + CH_2{=}CH_2$

15. (a) is homolytic: $H\!-\!H \longrightarrow 2H\cdot$

 (b) is heterolytic: $H\!-\!\ddot{O}H \longrightarrow H^+ + {^-}{:}\ddot{O}H$

 (c) is homolytic: $H\!-\!\ddot{O}H \longrightarrow H\cdot + \cdot\ddot{O}H$

 (d) is heterolytic: $CH_2{=}CH_2 \; H\!-\!\ddot{B}r: \longrightarrow {^+}CH_2$—$CH_3 + :\ddot{B}r:^-$

 (e) is homolytic: $CH_2{=}CH_2 \; H\!-\!\ddot{B}r: \longrightarrow \cdot CH_2$—$CH_3 + \cdot\ddot{B}r:$

Reaction (a) is simple dissociation of a diatomic molecule into atoms; reaction (b) is ionization of H_2O; and reaction (d) is the first step in addition of HBr to an alkene, a reaction that we studied in Chapter 4.

16. The two radicals $:\ddot{B}r\cdot$ and R—$\dot{C}H$—CHBr—R (Eq. 5.58b) recombine to give this product.

17. (a)   (b)   (c)

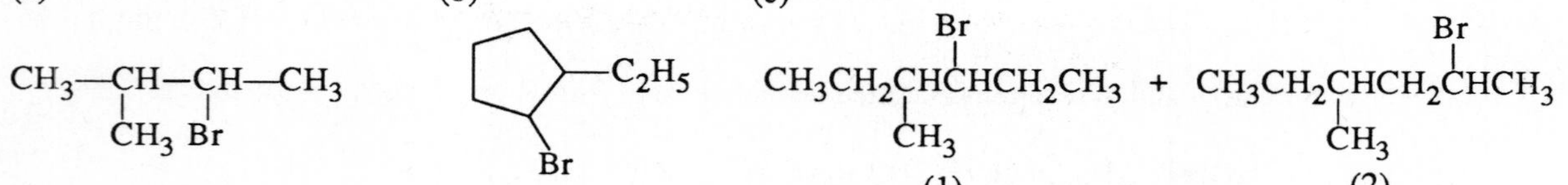

CH_3—CH—CH—CH_3
        | |
        CH_3 Br

Although a mixture of (1) and (2) would probably form in (c), we might expect more of (2) than of (1) because of the steric effect of the methyl branch.

The mechanism for the reaction of 1-ethyl-1-cyclopentene:

Initiation: RO—OR $\longrightarrow$ 2RO$\cdot$

$RO\cdot + H\!-\!\ddot{B}r: \longrightarrow RO\!-\!H + :\ddot{B}r\cdot$

Propagation:

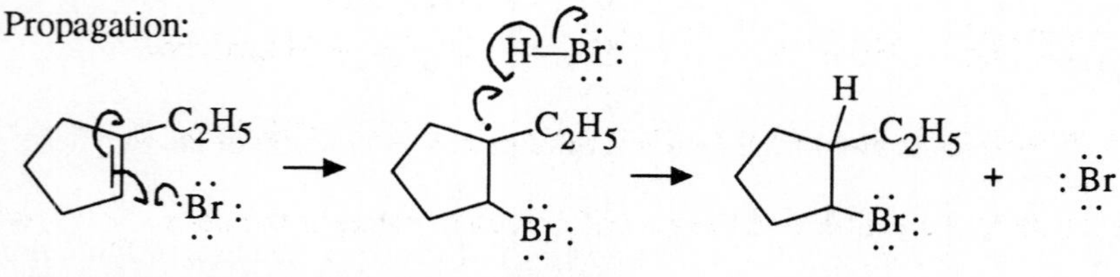

Termination (one of several possibilities):

$2:\ddot{B}r\cdot \longrightarrow Br_2$

18. The heat of formation of a species is the enthalpy for formation of one mole of the species from the elements in their natural states. The equation for formation of the hydrogen atom from "the elements" (hydrogen) is

$$H_2 \longrightarrow 2H\cdot$$

The $\Delta H°$ for this reaction is the bond dissociation energy of hydrogen, 104 kcal/mol (Table 5.2). The heat of formation per mole of hydrogen atoms is half of this, or 52 kcal/mol. By similar reasoning, the $\Delta H_f°$ for the bromine atom is half of the bond dissociation energy for Br_2, or 23 kcal/mol.

19. The equation and the relevant heats of formation are:

$$C_2H_6 \longrightarrow \cdot CH_2CH_3 + \cdot H \qquad \Delta H° = 100 \text{ kcal/mol (Table 5.2)}$$

$$\begin{array}{ccc} x & 28.0 & 52.0 \\ & \text{(Table 5.1)} & \end{array}$$

Hence, $100 = 52.0 + 28.0 - x$ or $x = -20$ kcal/mol $= \Delta H_f°$ of ethane.

20. Consider the products of each dissociation reaction. Dissociation of the tertiary C—H bond of 2-methyl-propane (isobutane) gives a tertiary radical, while dissociation of a primary (methyl) hydrogen gives a primary free radical:

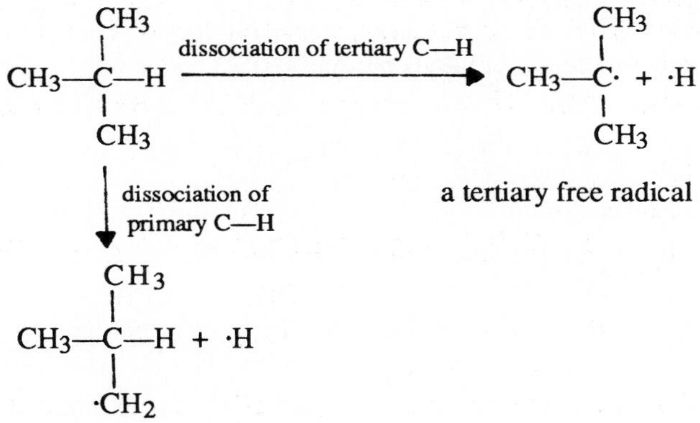

Since a tertiary free radical is more stable, less energy is required to form it; hence, the bond dissociation energy of the tertiary C—H bond is smaller.

21. $CH_2=CH_2 \longrightarrow \cdot CH_2-CH_2\cdot$ $\Delta H° = +63$ kcal/mol

   $Cl-Cl \longrightarrow 2\cdot Cl$ $\Delta H° = +58$ kcal/mol

   $Cl\cdot + \cdot CH_2-CH_2\cdot + \cdot Cl \longrightarrow Cl-CH_2-CH_2-Cl$ $\Delta H° = -82 \times 2 = -164$ kcal/mol

(We *approximate* this $\Delta H°$ as twice the enthalpy of the reaction $CH_3CH_2\cdot + Cl\cdot \rightarrow CH_3CH_2Cl$.)

The sum of these reactions is the desired reaction, and the sum of their $\Delta H°$ values is the desired $\Delta H°$, which is –43 kcal/mol.

An analogous procedure for the other two reactions gives –29 kcal/mol for the bromination and –9 kcal/mol for the iodination. Clearly, reaction (c) — the iodination — is least favorable. In view of the approximations used, these numbers could be off by several kcal/mol, but their relative values are probably not far off.

(Explanation continued next page)

Furthermore, these numbers are enthalpies, whereas it takes free energies to calculate equilibrium constants. Nevertheless, these numbers indicate in a semi-quantitative way that iodination is least likely to be favorable; and indeed, in Sec. 5.1A, we learned that addition of I_2 to alkenes at room temperature favors the alkene, and vicinal di-iodides tend to lose I_2 to give alkenes.

22.   The structure of polyvinyl chloride:

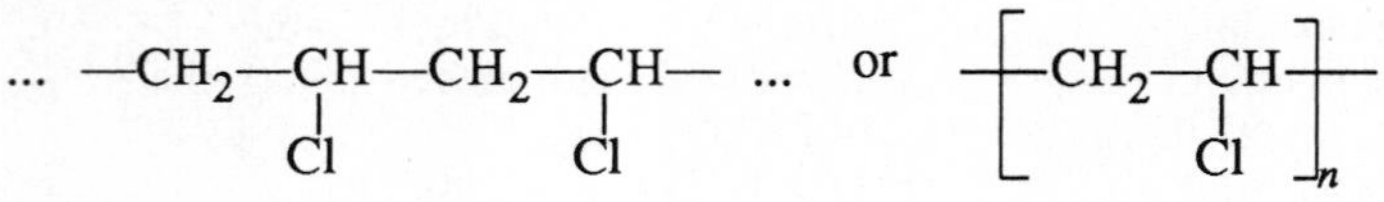

And the structure of polypropylene:

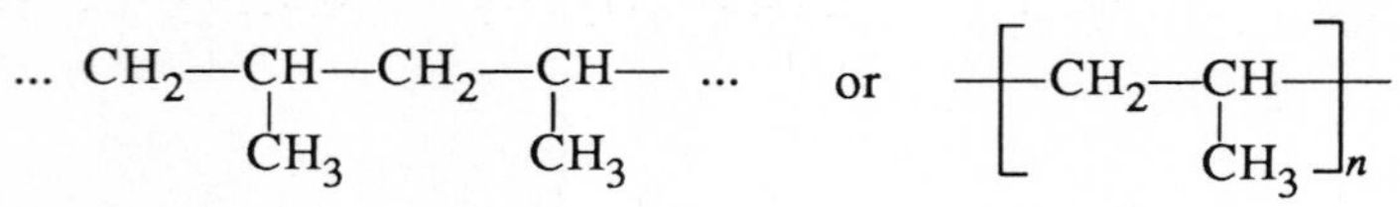

The free-radical mechanism for polymerization of vinyl chloride to PVC:

First, the radical formed by decomposition of the initiator AIBN (see Eq. 5.61) adds to vinyl chloride: (We'll call this radical R· for simplicity.)

The resulting radical adds to another molecule of vinyl chloride:

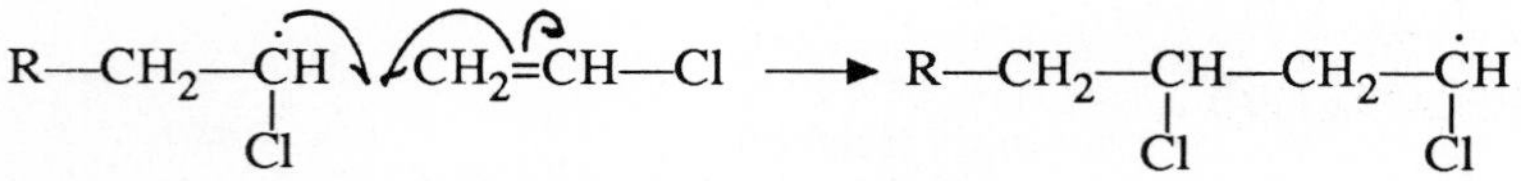

And this process continues indefinitely until radical chains are terminated:

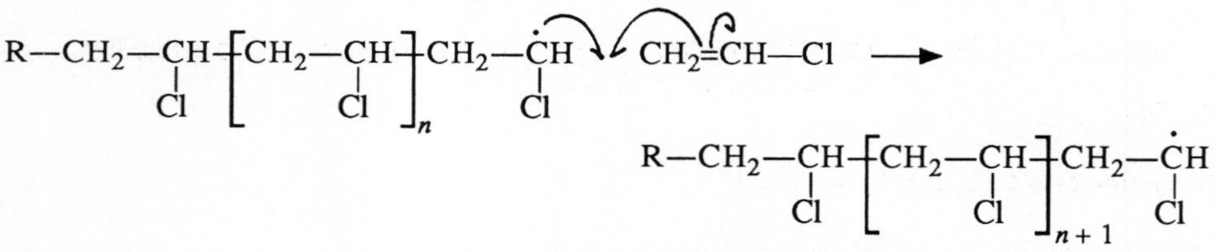

23.   (a) $U = \dfrac{2C + 2 - (X + H)}{2} = \dfrac{6 + 2 - (8)}{2} = 0$

       (b) $U = \dfrac{2(5) + 2 + 2 - 8}{2} = 3$

24.   The empirical formula of a compound with the given analysis is CH_2. No matter how many carbons such a compound has, it can only have one ring or one double bond.

25.   A carbon-carbon triple bond introduces two degrees of unsaturation ($U = 2$).

Solutions to Additional Problems

26. (a)

Br—CH$_2$CHCH$_2$CH$_3$
      |
      Br

(b)

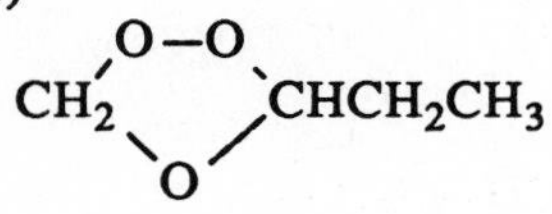

CH$_2$ ⟨O—O⟩ CHCH$_2$CH$_3$
    O

(c)

CH$_2$=O + O=CHCH$_2$CH$_3$

(d)

    O   O
    ‖   ‖
H—C—OH + HO—C—CH$_2$CH$_3$

(e)

CO$_2$ + H$_2$O

(f)

    Br
    |
CH$_3$CHCH$_2$CH$_3$

(g)

        OH
        |
HOCH$_2$CHCH$_2$CH$_3$

(h)

   OH
   |
ICH$_2$CHCH$_2$CH$_3$

Notice that iodine and water add to alkenes as I—OH, even though iodine itself does not.

(i)

CH$_3$CH$_2$CH$_2$CH$_3$

(j)

BrCH$_2$CH$_2$CH$_2$CH$_3$

(k)

(CH$_3$CH$_2$CH$_2$CH$_2$)$_3$B

(l)

CH$_3$CH$_2$CH$_2$CH$_2$OH

(m)

           OH
           |
AcOHg—CH$_2$CHCH$_2$CH$_3$

(n)

     OH
     |
CH$_3$CHCH$_2$CH$_3$

Because sodium borohydride often follows oxymercuration, it is easy to forget to include it; don't forget that it is necessary in order to remove the acetoxymercuri group.

(o)   I

CH$_3$CHCH$_2$CH$_3$

(p)   Same as (o); don't forget that there is no peroxide effect for addition of HI to alkenes.

27. For simplicity let us abbreviate the ethyl group as Et.

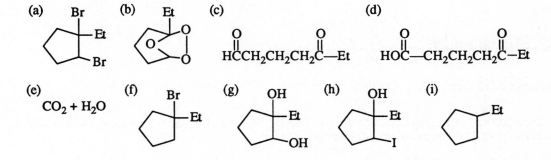

(a) Br / Et / Br

(b) Et / O / O

(c)

    O   O
    ‖   ‖
HCCH$_2$CH$_2$CH$_2$C—Et

(d)

     O   O
     ‖   ‖
HOC—CH$_2$CH$_2$CH$_2$C—Et

(e)   CO$_2$ + H$_2$O

(f) Br / Et

(g) OH / Et / OH

(h) OH / Et / I

(i) Et

(j)

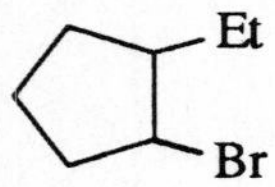

(k)

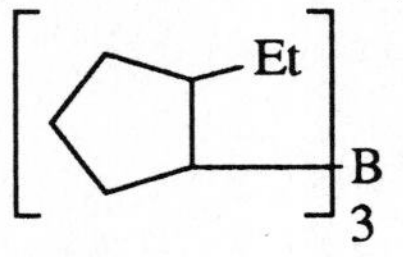

(l)

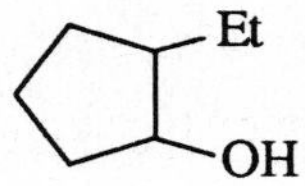

(m) OH

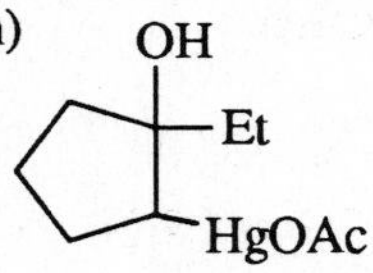

(n) OH

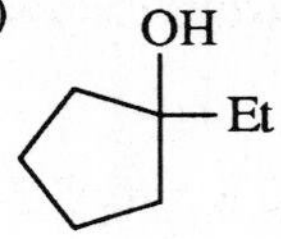

(o)

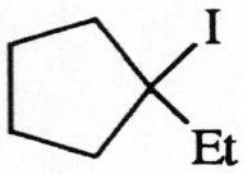

(p) Same as (o)

28. In some cases, the answers given are not the only correct possibilities.

(a)

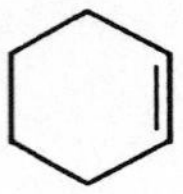

or either of the 3-hexenes

(b)

(c)

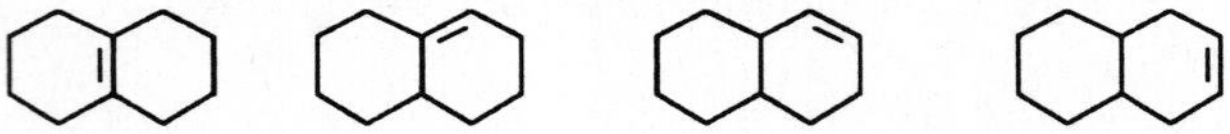

(d)

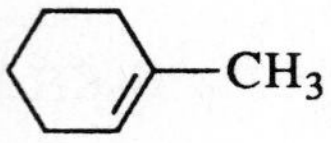

—CH₃   and

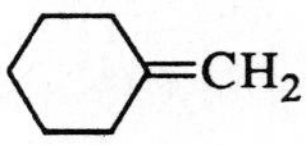

=CH₂

(e)

(f)

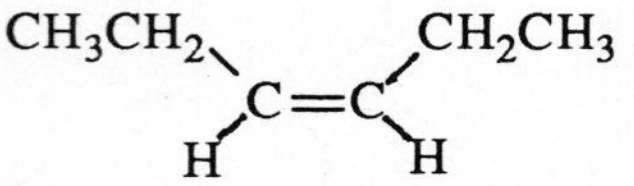

CH₃CH₂   CH₂CH₃
       C=C

H   H

and

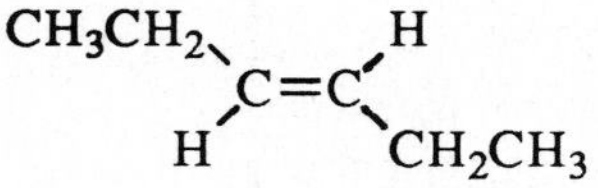

CH₃CH₂   H
       C=C

H   CH₂CH₃

(g)

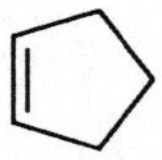

29. One approach is to see whether the unsaturation number is a simple integral number (Eq. 5.77, p. 171). Another approach is to recognize simply that a compound with an odd number of nitrogens must have an odd number of hydrogens, and a compound with an even number of nitrogens must have an even number of hydrogens.

(a) Yes   (b) No   (c) Yes

30. (a)

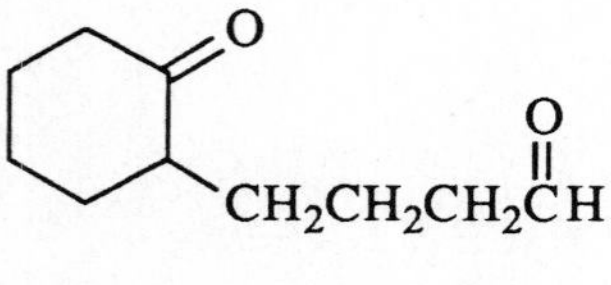

(b)

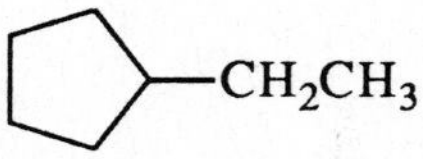

$\overset{O}{\overset{\|}{CH_2CH_2CH_2CH}}$

(c)

—CH₂CH₃

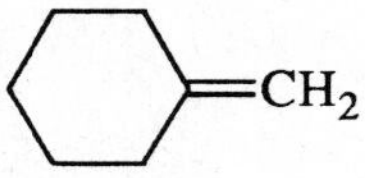

=CH₂

(d)

CH₃

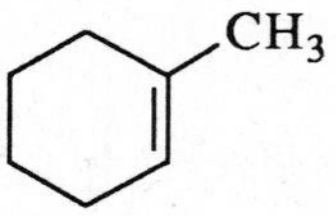

31. (a) Oxymercuration–reduction of 1-pentene would work, but hydroboration–oxidation would not. Why? See Eq. 5.32, text p. 146.

$$CH_2=CHCH_2CH_2CH_3 \xrightarrow[H_2O]{Hg(OAc)_2} \xrightarrow{NaBH_4} \overset{OH}{\underset{|}{CH_3CHCH_2CH_2CH_3}}$$

(b) NOW we can use hydroboration:

$$CH_2=CHCH_2CH_2CH_3 \xrightarrow[]{B_2H_6} \xrightarrow[^-OH]{H_2O_2} HOCH_2CH_2CH_2CH_2CH_3$$

(c) $Br_2 + CH_2=CH_2 \longrightarrow Br-CH_2-CH_2-Br$

(d)

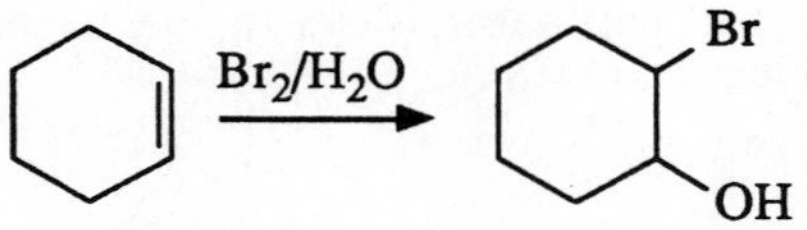

(e)

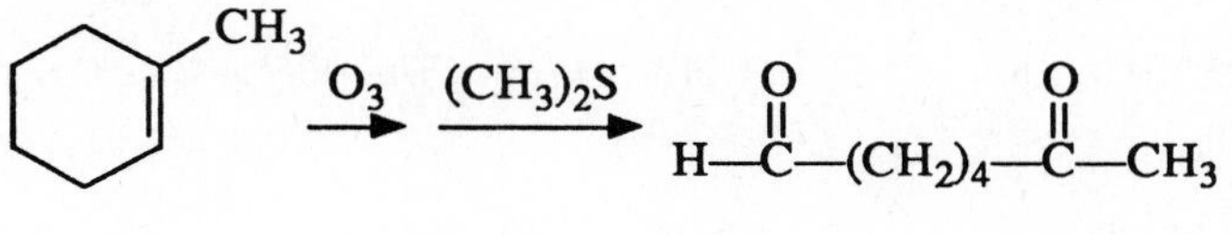

(f)

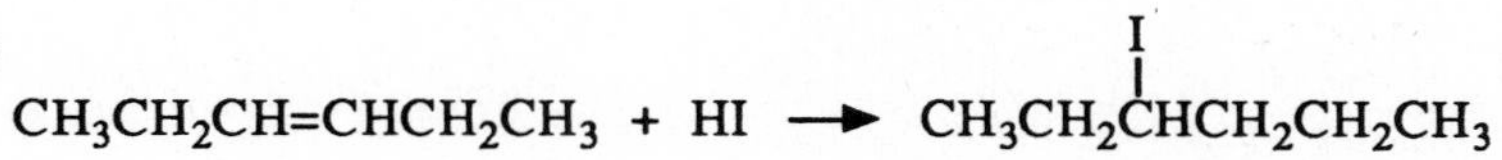

$$CH_3CH_2CH=CHCH_2CH_3 + HI \longrightarrow CH_3CH_2\overset{\overset{\displaystyle I}{|}}{C}HCH_2CH_2CH_3$$

(g)

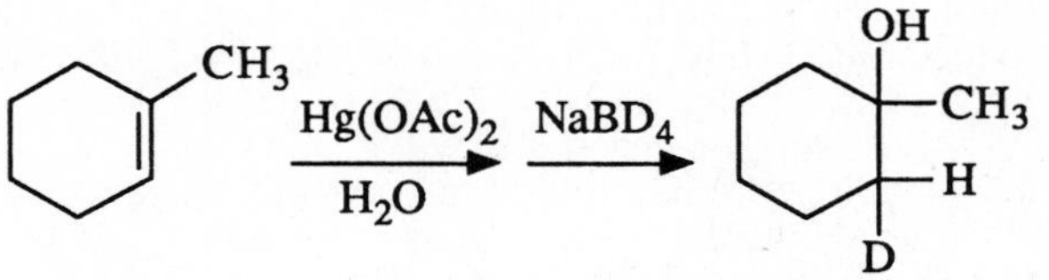

(h)

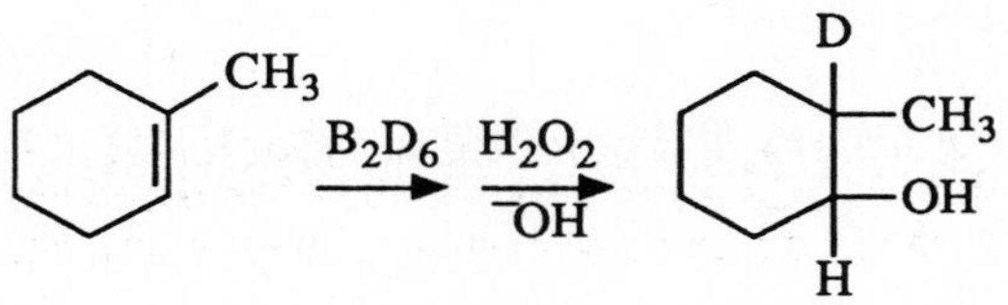

(i)

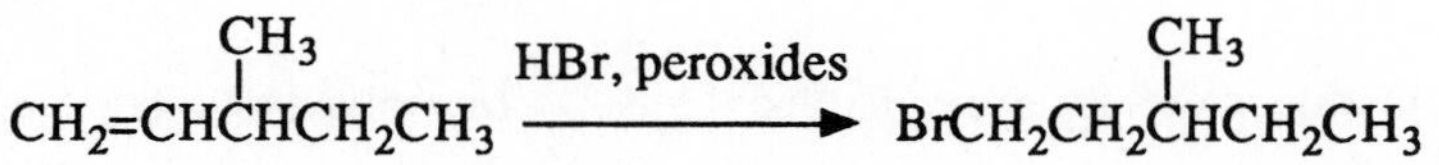

(j)

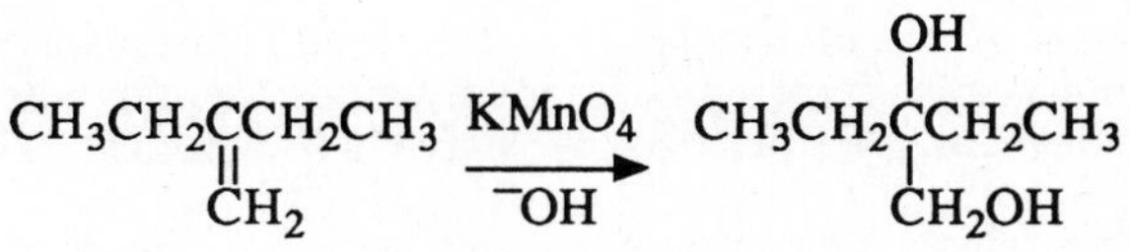

Osmium tetroxide (OsO_4) would also work for (j).

32. This problem demonstrates how mechanisms can be used to predict the outcome of chemical reactions. The answer in each case depends on the nucleophile that is available to react with the bromonium ion.
(a) The only nucleophile available is Br^- from the bromine. Hence, the product is the dibromide:

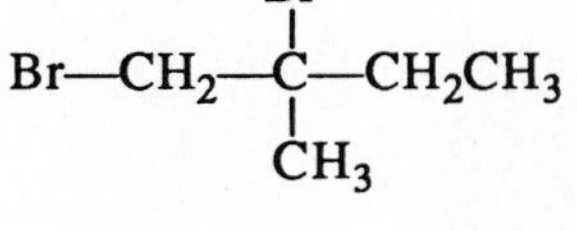

(b) When H_2O is present, it is the nucleophile that reacts with the bromonium ion, and the product is the bromohydrin.

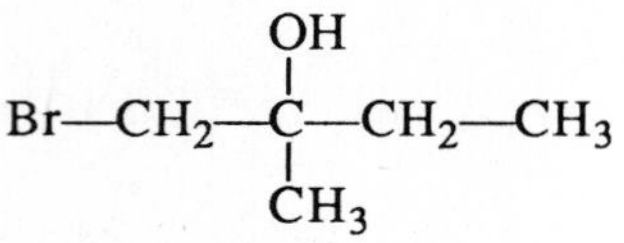

$$Br—CH_2—\underset{\underset{CH_3}{|}}{\overset{\overset{OH}{|}}{C}}—CH_2—CH_3$$

(c) When CH_3OH is present, it reacts with the bromonium ion. The mechanism is exactly like the one for bromohydrin formation, except that methanol is the nucleophile instead of water:

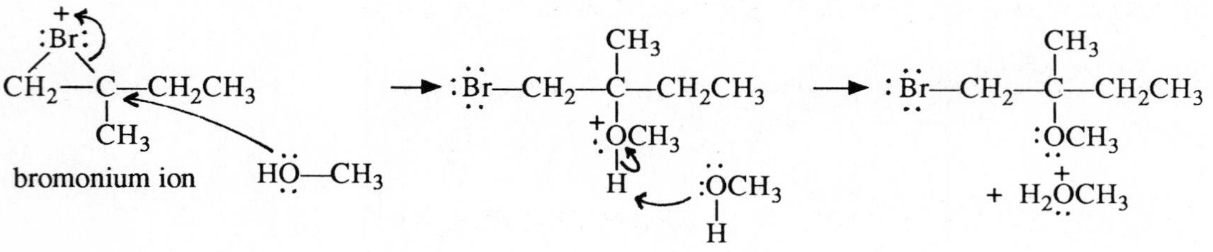

(d) When Br^- is present in excess, it competes with CH_3OH as a nucleophile for the bromonium ion. We predict a mixture of the products in (a) and (c), depending on how much excess Br^- is added. The more Br^- is present, the more dibromide will be obtained.

33. In this problem we use the same sort of reasoning as in Problem 32. In this case, we are concerned with the nucleophile that attacks the mercurinium ion. When water attacks this ion, we get the products of oxymercuration, as in Eq. 5.28b, p. 145. When the solvents in the problem are used instead of water, they act as nucleophiles in their respective reactions to give the following products:

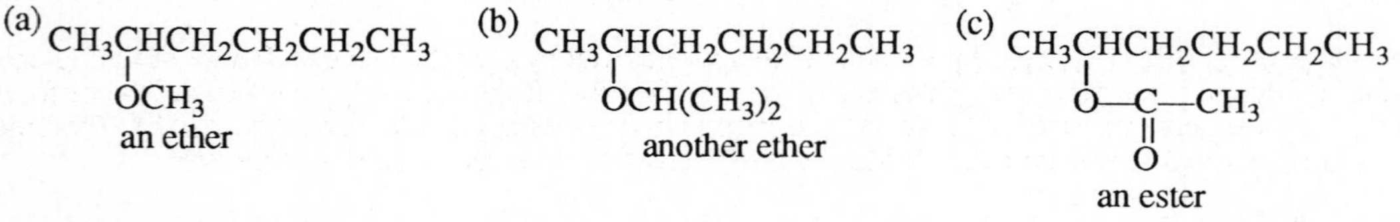

(a) $CH_3\underset{\underset{OCH_3}{|}}{C}HCH_2CH_2CH_2CH_3$ (b) $CH_3\underset{\underset{OCH(CH_3)_2}{|}}{C}HCH_2CH_2CH_2CH_3$ (c) $CH_3\underset{\underset{\underset{O}{\|}}{O—C—CH_3}}{|}HCH_2CH_2CH_2CH_3$

an ether   another ether   an ester

Each of these variations works in practice. (See, for example, Sec. 11.1B.) Any solvent R—OH can be used, whether R = H, alkyl, or CH_3CO.

34. (a) The first product results from a carbocation rearrangement (see Sec. 4.6); the second is from an ordinary Markovnikov addition. That is, the first two products arise from a process involving carbocation intermediates. In the presence of peroxides, free-radical addition of HBr takes place to give only the last product. This is the peroxide effect.
(b) The mechanism that gives rise to the first two products is exactly like the mechanism summarized in Eq. 4.25 and preceding equations, with HBr instead of HCl. The mechanism that gives rise to the last product is the usual free-radical mechanism:

$$RO—OR \longrightarrow 2\,R—O\cdot \quad \text{(initiation)}$$

$$R—O\cdot + H—Br \longrightarrow R—O—H + Br\cdot \quad \text{(initiation)}$$

$(CH_3)_3C\!-\!CH\!=\!CH_2\quad \cdot Br \longrightarrow (CH_3)_3C\!-\!\dot{C}H\!-\!CH_2\!-\!Br$

(propagation steps)

$H\!-\!Br$

$(CH_3)_3C\!-\!\dot{C}H\!-\!CH_2\!-\!Br \longrightarrow (CH_3)_3C\!-\!CH_2\!-\!CH_2\!-\!Br + Br\cdot$

(c) The free-radical conditions give the faster reaction, because otherwise this reaction would not be observed. The carbocation processes leading to the first two products continue to operate even in the presence of peroxides. These processes are in competition with the free-radical process. If the free-radical process weren't faster, the products of this process would not be observed.

35. (a) Activation by light suggests a free-radical mechanism for this reaction.

$CF_3\!-\!I \xrightarrow{\ \text{light}\ } \cdot CF_3 + I\cdot$ (initiation)

$CH_3CH_2CH_2CH\!=\!CH_2\quad CF_3 \longrightarrow CH_3CH_2CH_2\dot{C}HCH_2\!-\!CF_3$

$I\!-\!CF_3$

$CH_3CH_2CH_2\dot{C}HCH_2\!-\!CF_3 \longrightarrow CH_3CH_2CH_2\overset{\displaystyle I}{\underset{\displaystyle |}{C}}HCH_2CF_3 + \cdot CF_3$

We know that $\cdot CF_3$ adds first because, in any free-radical mechanism, the last species to add ends up at the more substituted carbon of what was the double bond.

(b) CF₃I would add more rapidly to 2-methyl-1-pentene. Addition of $\cdot CF_3$ to this alkene gives a *tertiary* free radical, whereas addition to 3-methyl-1-pentene gives a *secondary* free radical. (Be sure to write out these processes if this statement is not clear!) By Hammond's postulate, the more stable radical is formed more rapidly.

36. Since we know (page 160) that hydroquinone is a free-radical inhibitor, and since the change in the bottle of styrene did not occur in the presence of this inhibitor and did occur in its absence, we infer that the process involved is a free-radical reaction. Alkenes polymerize by a free-radical mechanism (Sec. 5.9A). Evidently, the styrene polymerized to polystyrene (Table 5.3, Problem 40a) by a free-radical mechanism.

37. (a) Breaking the central carbon-carbon bond is favored because this gives two stable tertiary free radicals:

$(CH_3)_3C\!-\!C(CH_3)_3 \longrightarrow 2\ (CH_3)_3C\cdot$

Breaking other carbon-carbon bonds gives a methyl radical.

(b) The faster a reaction, the lower the temperature at which it goes at a given rate. The cracking of 2,2,3,3-tetramethylbutane is the faster reaction, and therefore takes place at a given rate at lower temperature than the cracking of ethane. Cracking of 2,2,3,3-tetramethylbutane is faster than cracking of ethane because stable tertiary free radicals are formed. Cracking of ethane, however, gives relatively unstable methyl radicals.

(c) The $\Delta H°$ for the reaction in (a) is given by the difference in heats of formation of products and starting materials:

$$\Delta H°(\text{reaction}) \ =\ 2\Delta H_f°(\text{t-butyl radical}) - \Delta H_f°(\text{2,2,3,3-tetramethylbutane})$$
$$=\ 2(9.4) - (-53.99) = 72.8\ \text{kcal/mol}$$

The equation for the cracking of ethane is

$CH_3\!-\!CH_3 \longrightarrow 2\ \cdot CH_3$

and the corresponding $\Delta H°$ is

$$\Delta H°\text{(reaction)} \quad = \quad 2\Delta H_f°\text{(methyl radical)} - 2\Delta H_f°\text{(ethane)}$$
$$= \quad 68.8 - (-20.24) = 89.04 \text{ kcal/mol}$$

These calculations show that cracking of ethane is almost 18 kcal/mol more unfavorable than cracking of 2,2,3,3-tetramethylbutane. This gives quantitative support to the conclusions reached in (a). The underlying assumption is that free energies of activation and enthalpies for cracking are approximately the same.

38. (a) Ozonolysis breaks at the double bonds of successive units in the polymer:

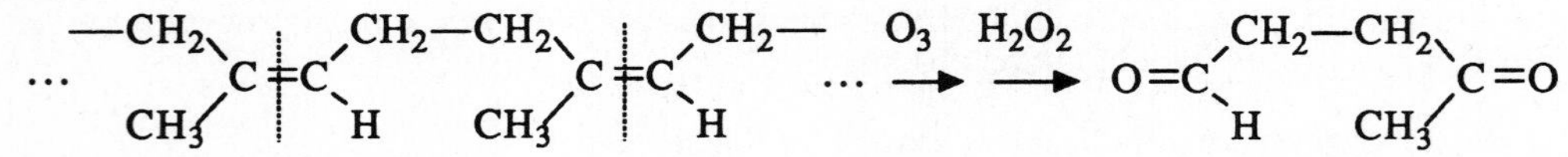

(b) Gutta-percha is the *E* isomer of natural rubber (recall that ozonolysis reactions of *cis–trans* isomers give the same products):

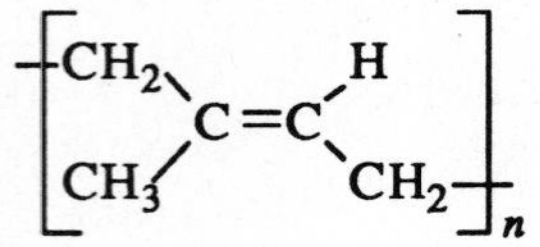

gutta-percha

39. The answer to this problem lies in the bond-energy approach that was used to explain why H—I and H—Cl do not show the peroxide effect. (See Eqs. 5.68b and 5.69b.) The first propagation step for addition of H—CN is addition of ·CN to an alkene:

$$CH_2\text{=}CH_2 + ·CN \rightarrow ·CH_2\text{—}CH_2\text{—}CN \quad \Delta H° = +63 - 105 = -42 \text{ kcal/mol}$$

The second propagation step is abstraction of H from H—CN by the carbon radical formed:

$$·CH_2\text{—}CH_2\text{—}CN + H\text{—}CN \rightarrow CH_3\text{—}CH_2\text{—}CN + ·CN \quad \Delta H° = +122 - 100 = +22 \text{ kcal/mol}$$

Like the second propagation step of HCl addition, the second propagation step of H—CN addition is unfavorable (only more so). Free-radical HCN addition to alkenes therefore does not occur for the same reason that free-radical HCl addition does not occur.

There is another reason why free-radical HCN addition does not occur. An initiation step is abstraction of a hydrogen atom from HCN by an alkoxy radical:

$$H\text{—}CN + ·\ddot{O}R \rightarrow ·CN + H\text{—}\ddot{O}R$$

The $\Delta H°$ for this step is somewhat unfavorable (122 – 119 = +3 kcal/mol), so the intiation phase of the reaction never really gets off the ground!

40. (a) The structure of polystyrene:

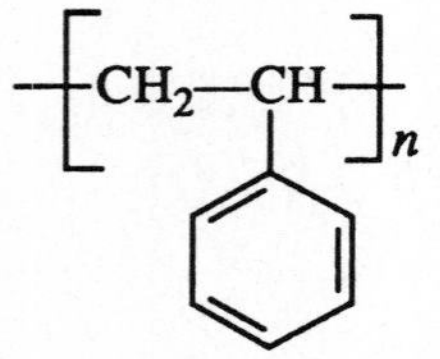

(b) Styrene, the monomer from which polystyrene is formed, has only one vinyl group, and therefore forms a linear polymer. Both ends of the divinylbenzene, however, can polymerize. When divinylbenzene gets incorporated into polystyrene, it forms a crosslink between chains.

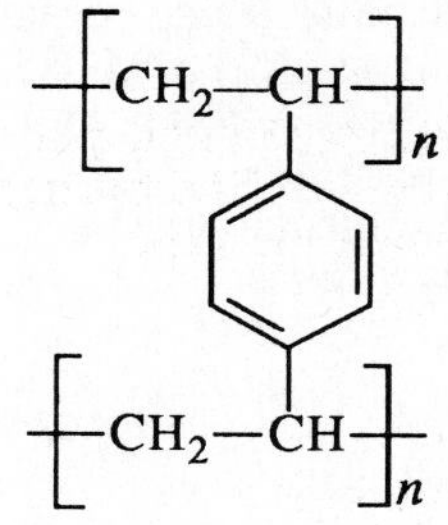

$$\left[CH_2-CH\right]_n$$

(Such crosslinking makes the polymer more rigid.)

41. In each case we would expect addition to the triple bond. However, since there are *two* π bonds in an alkyne, addition can occur twice: once to the starting alkyne, and again to the alkene addition product:

(a) Ph—C=CHBr   Br
    | |
    Br   Ph—C—CHBr$_2$
                        |
product of one   Br
addition
                   product of two
                   additions

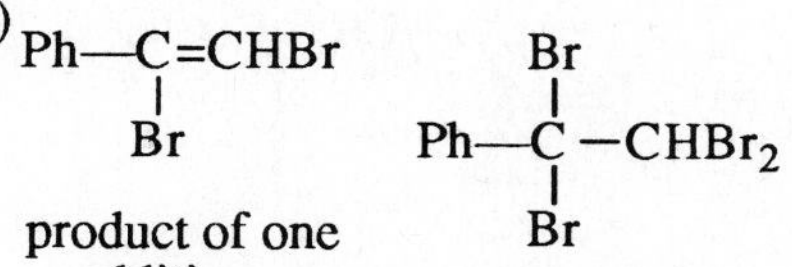

(b) Ph—CH=CH$_2$ Ph—CH$_2$—CH$_3$

product of one   product of two
addition   additions

42. Let us follow the suggestions in the box on page 177. The analysis leads to the structural formula

$$C_{7.34}H_{11.75} \text{ or } C_5H_8$$

Since the product of hydrogenation has ten carbons, let us adopt $C_{10}H_{16}$ as our provisional molecular formula.

The ozonolysis product has nine carbons. This means that one of the carbons was "chopped off" by the ozonolysis reaction. The only way this could happen is if compound *A* contains part-structure $C=CH_2$.

Because of the structure of the hydrogenation product, there must be a six-membered ring in *A*. After ozonolysis, this will give two $C=O$ groups separated by four carbons. Thus, we arrive at the following analysis:

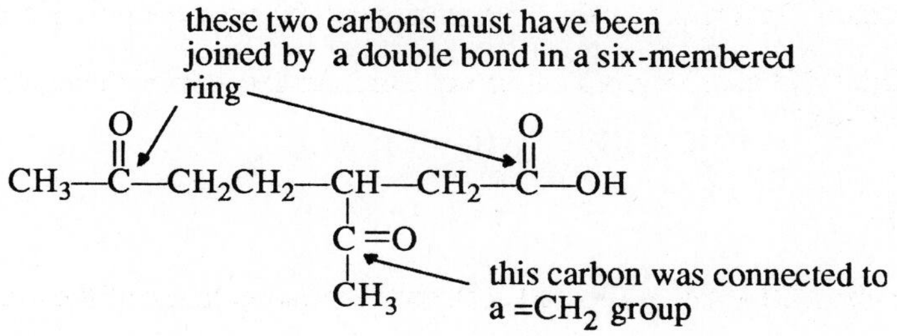

these two carbons must have been
joined by a double bond in a six-membered
ring

            O   O
            || ||
CH$_3$—C—CH$_2$CH$_2$—CH—CH$_2$—C—OH
                       |
                     C=O
                       |
                     CH$_3$ this carbon was connected to
                               a $=CH_2$ group

This leaves the following compound as the only possibility for *A*:

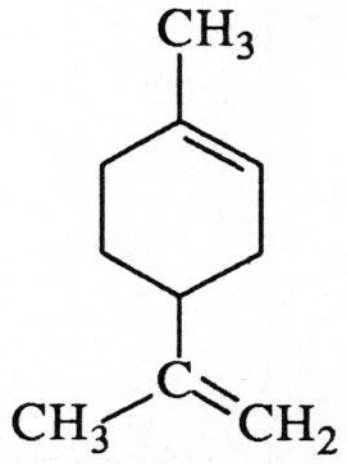

CH$_3$

CH$_3$ C   CH$_2$

43. The elemental analysis of *A* corresponds to an empirical formula of CH_2. Hence, the compound has one double bond no matter how many carbons it has. (We know it has a double bond rather than a ring because it undergoes typical alkene reactions.) 200 mL of H_2 corresponds to (200 mL/22,400 mL-mol^{-1}) = 0.00893 mol of hydrogen at 0 °C. The molecular weight of *A* is then (1.0 g/0.00893 mol) = 112 g/mol. A compound with an empirical formula of CH_2 and a molecular weight of 112 must have the molecular formula C_8H_{16}. Since compound *A* gives a single type of four-carbon ozonolysis fragment, both ends of the molecule must be identical. This can only be so if compound *A* is either *cis*- or *trans*-4-octene. Ozonolysis cannot distinguish between these two isomers.

$$CH_3CH_2CH_2CH{=}CHCH_2CH_2CH_3 \quad \text{4-octene}$$

44. All we have to do is fill in the curved arrows, making sure that we follow the rules:

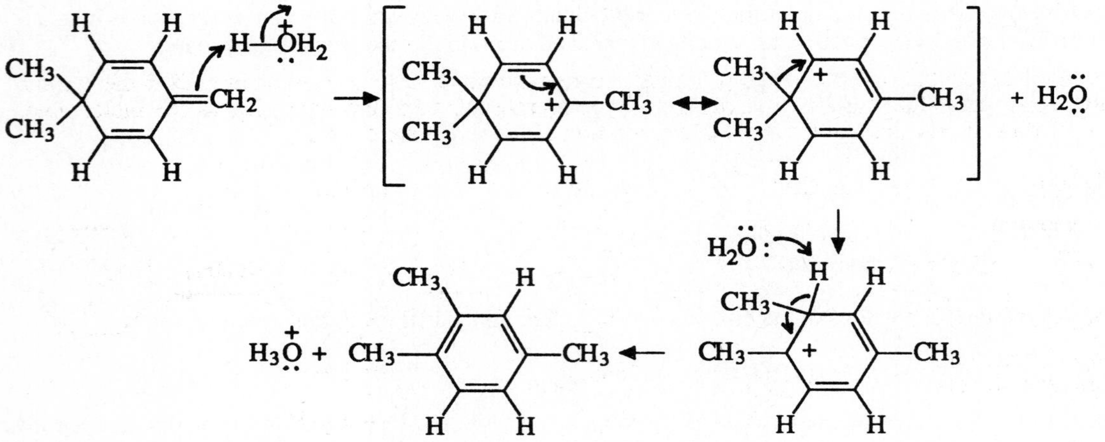

45. Now we have to make the appropriate connections *as well as* provide the arrow formalism.
    (a) The carbon-carbon double bond on the left is protonated (why this double bond and not the other one?). An OH oxygen from within the molecule attacks the resulting carbocation. Loss of a proton gives the product.

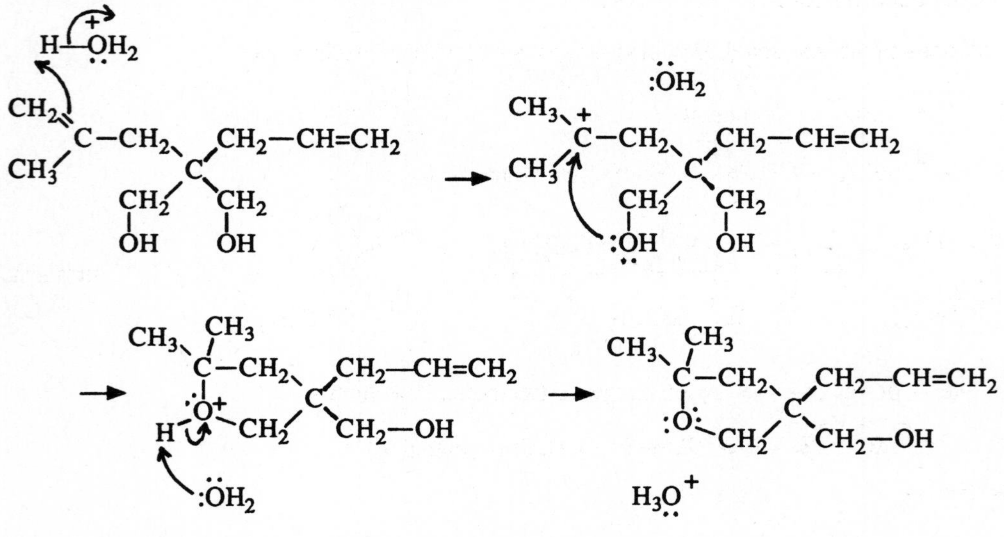

Be sure you see that the product as drawn above is the same as the one in the problem!

➤ We might ask why water doesn't attack the carbocation formed in the initial protonation. As we shall learn in Chapter 11, intramolecular reactions (reactions within the same molecule) that give five- or six-membered rings are particularly rapid. The —OH group within the molecule is already there, ready to pounce on the carbocation; water, on the other hand, would have to find the carbocation by diffusion. We shall see the same principle in operation in subsequent parts of this problem.

(b) The nucleophile that attacks the bromonium ion is within the same molecule — the nitrogen across the ring. Let's start the mechanism with the bromonium ion, which forms just as in the bromination of an ordinary alkene (Eq. 5.4).

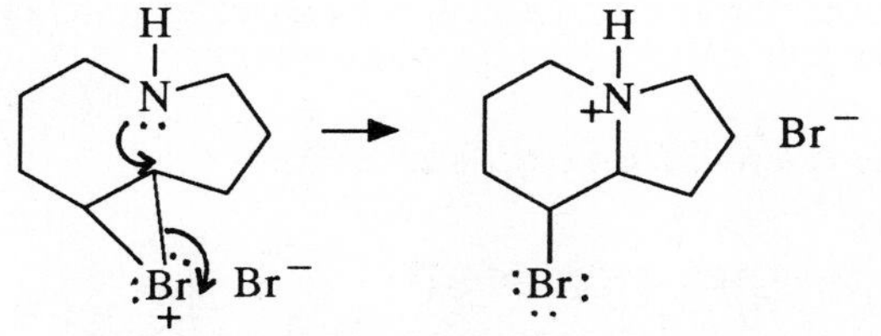

(c) One of the double bonds undergoes ordinary oxymercuration. During oxymercuration of the second double bond, the —OH introduced in the first oxymercuration, rather than water, acts as the nucleophile. We begin with the product resulting from oxymercuration of the first double bond.

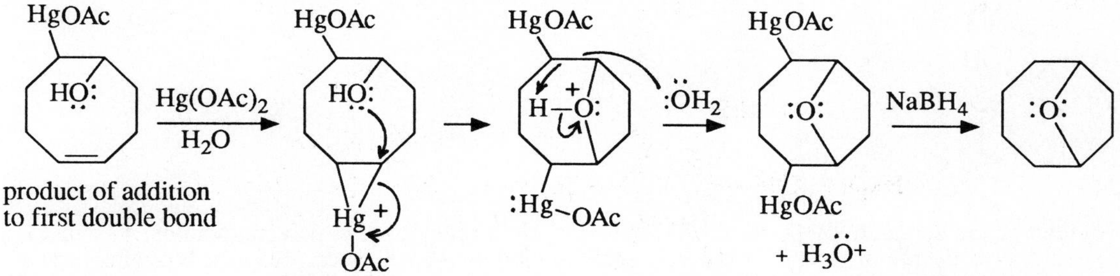

product of addition
to first double bond

This mechanism shows formation of the major (56%) product. The other product is formed by an exactly analogous process; the —OH group simply attacks the other carbon of the mercurinium ion. Since both carbons are equally substituted, there is little reason to prefer one over the other, and, indeed, the products are formed in nearly equal amounts.

(d) The conditions of the reaction (peroxides) suggest a free-radical mechanism.

$$RO{-}OR \longrightarrow 2\,RO\cdot \quad \text{(initiation)}$$

$$RO\cdot + H{-}SC_2H_5 \longrightarrow RO{-}H + \cdot SC_2H_5 \quad \text{(initiation)}$$

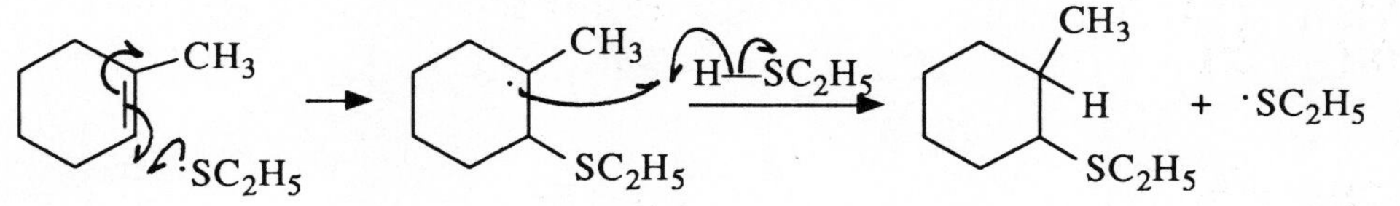

(e) The conditions of this reaction as well suggest a free-radical mechanism.

$$RO\cdot \qquad Br{-}CBr_3 \longrightarrow RO{-}Br + \cdot CBr_3 \quad \text{(initiation)}$$

(See Problem 45d.)

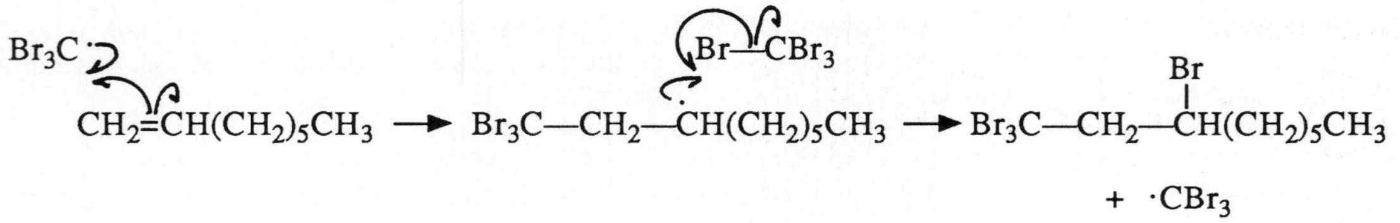

(f) Protonation of the double bond is followed by a carbocation rearrangement, then by attack of water on the rearranged carbocation. We'll follow the suggestion in the text and draw out the ring carbons.

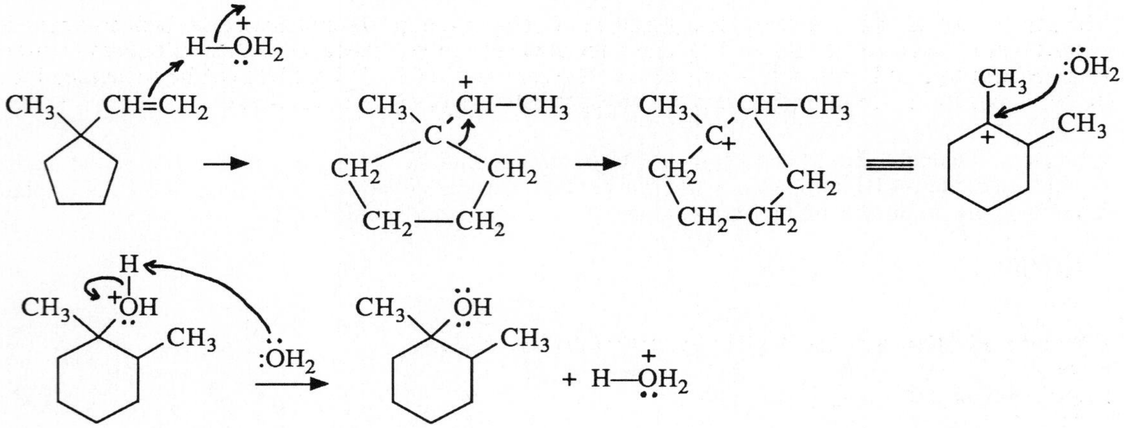

46. (a) In the scheme below, hydroboration of 1-ethyl-1-cyclohexene can give two compounds, *A1* and *A2*. Compound *A1* is the major product, but a very small amount of *A2* is formed. Because hydroboration is reversible, all alkenes and boron hydrides are in equilibrium. Hence, *A2* can reverse not only to give the starting alkene, but also alkene *B*. Alkene *B* can hydroborate to give two boranes, *A2* and *C*. Borane *C* can lose boron hydride to give either of two alkenes, *B* or *D*. Finally, *D* can hydroborate to give back *C* or yet another borane *E*, which is the compound in the problem. In oAll alkenes and organoborane adducts are in equilibrium. Since in compound *E* the large, highly branched boron group is located away from the branch point in the carbon chain, this is the least hindered and therefore more stable component of the equilibrium. Notice that this does not happen in all hydroborations, but only when the hydroboration mixture is subjected to high temperature. The temperature causes enough of an increase in the rates of all reactions so that everything comes to equilibrium.

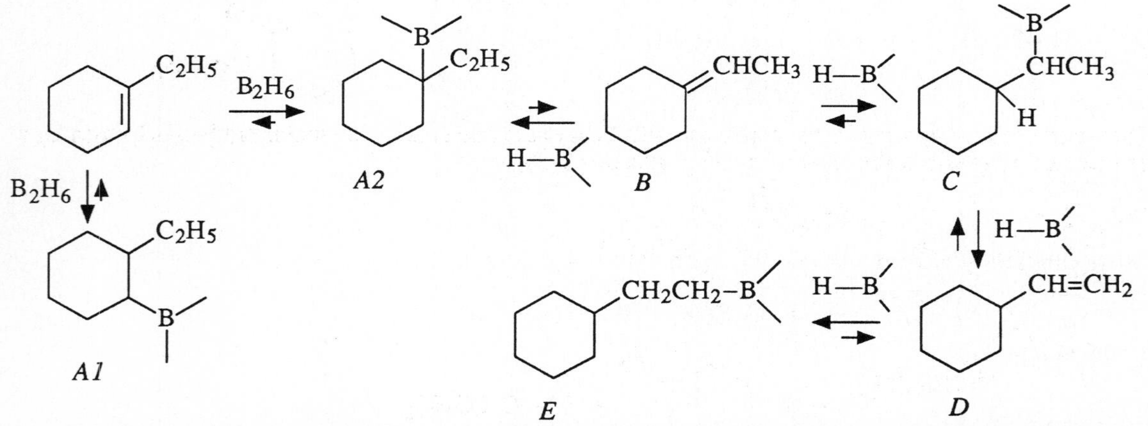

(b) There is a small amount of cyclopentene present even after hydroboration is "complete," because of the reversibility of hydroboration. When the cyclopentene is removed by distillation, the equilibrium is pulled toward cyclopentene and diborane. The 1-decene traps the liberated diborane to form (eventually) tridecylborane. On working up the reaction mixture with alkaline H_2O_2, 1-decanol is formed from this borane.

To summarize:

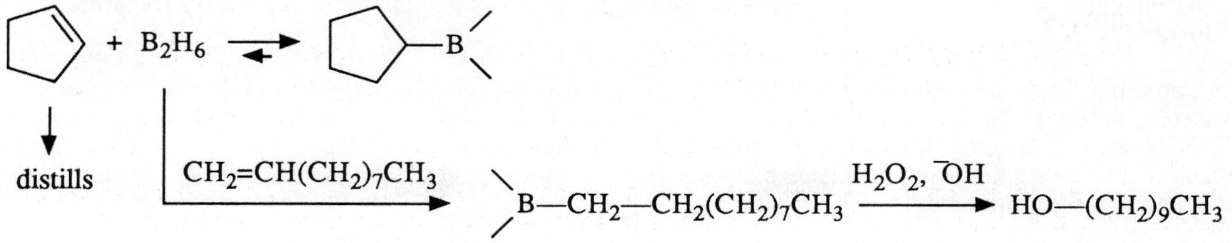

47. The analytical data lead to an empirical formula of C_7H_{12}. From the bromination data, both compounds have a double bond. Since all carbons are accounted for in the ozonolysis product of *A*, this compound must contain a ring. However, a carbon is missing in the ozonolysis product of *B*. This carbon can be accounted for by the presence of a $=CH_2$ group in *B*. Thus, we have the following structures for *A* and *B*:

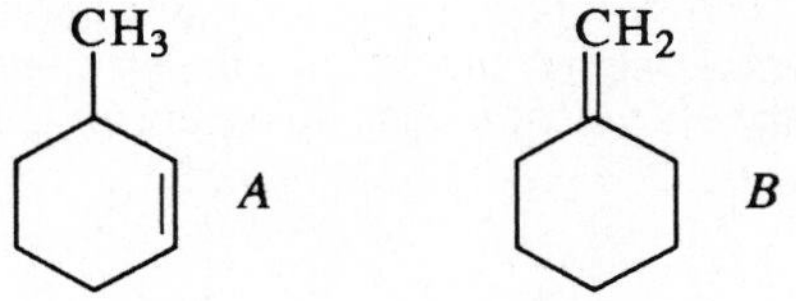

48. (a) In the initiation step, the O—Cl bond splits into free radicals:

The propagation steps are as follows:

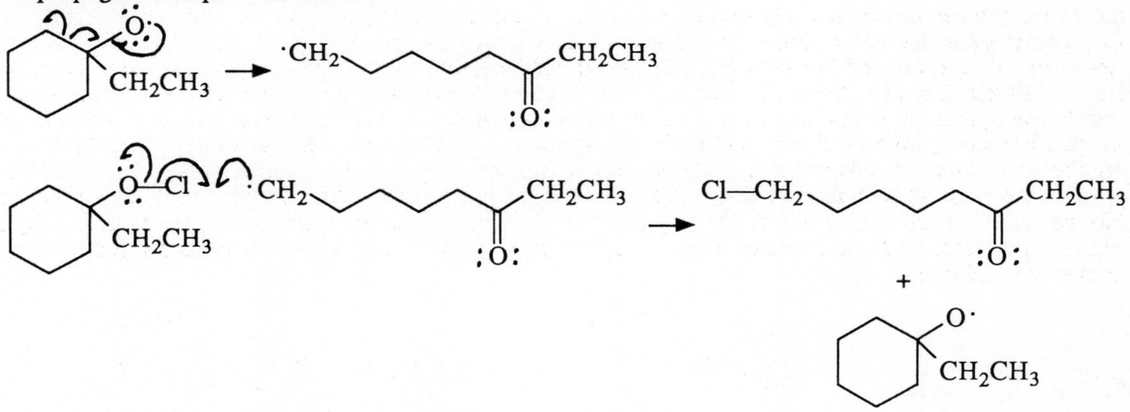

(b) The minor product is formed by a mechanism identical to the one in (a). The major product is formed by a similar mechanism in which the bond to the alkyl group is broken:

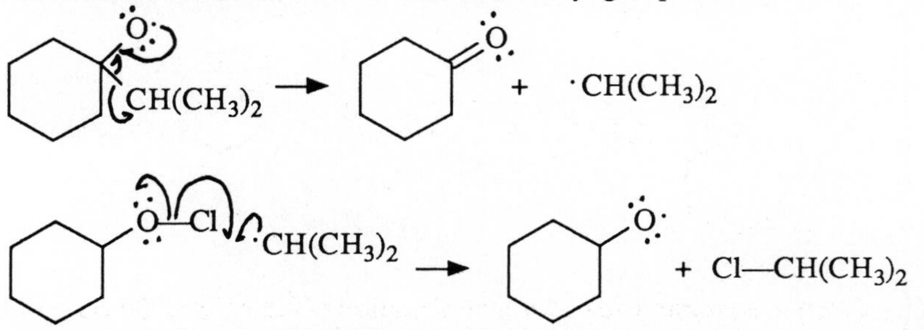

In this case, the bond to the alkyl group is broken because it gives a secondary free radical. Breaking the bond to the ring as in (a) gives a primary free radical. Because secondary free radicals are more stable than primary free radicals, they are formed more rapidly. Hence, the pathway leading to the secondary free radical is observed.

49. Compound B has the empirical formula CH_2. The hydrogenation data suggests a molecular weight corresponding to C_6H_{12}. A six-carbon alkene that gives only acetone as an ozonolysis product can only be 2,3-dimethyl-2-butene; this is B. Formation of B from the starting alkene therefore requires a rearrangement somewhere along the way. A reasonable place for this rearrangement is in the addition of HBr to the starting alkene to give compound A:

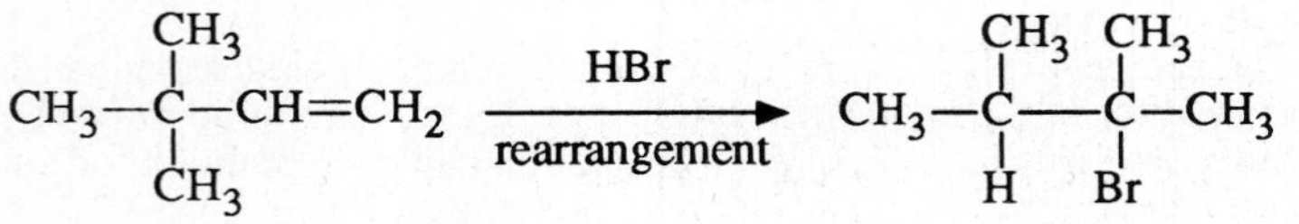

(See Eq. 4.25 for the mechanism of this reaction with HCl in place of HBr.) Now that we know what A and B are, we have to decide how B forms from A. In order to form B from A, we have to remove the elements of H—Br from adjacent carbons. From the structure of the products, the H evidently ends up on the oxygen of the base. A mechanism using the arrow formalism is the following:

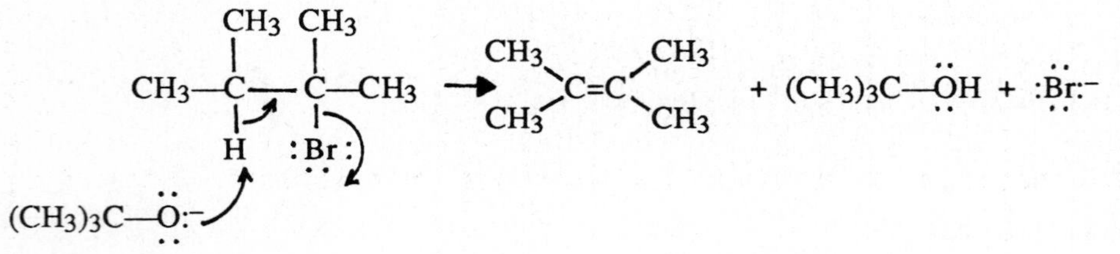

Chapter 6 / Introduction to Stereochemistry

CHAPTER 6 TERMS

absolute stereochemical configuration 6.2
absolute stereochemistry 6.2
achiral 6.1
amine 6.8B
amine inversion 6.8B
anomalous dispersion 6.5
asymmetric carbon 6.1
Biot's law 6.10
center of symmetry 6.1
chiral 6.1
chirality 6.1
conformational diastereomer 6.8A
conformational enantiomer 6.8A
cyclic permutation 6.9
D,L–system 6.2
dextro 6.3B
dextrorotatory 6.3B
diastereoisomer 6.6
diastereomer 6.6
diastereomeric relationship 6.6
enantiomer 6.6
enantiomeric relationship 6.1
Fischer projection 6.9
internal mirror plane 6.1
isomer 6.6
levo 6.3B
levorotatory 6.3B

meso compound 6.7
observed optical rotation, α 6.3B
optical activity 6.3B
optical rotation 6.3B
optically active 6.3B
optically inactive 6.4
optically pure 6.3C
plane of symmetry 6.1
plane-polarized light 6.3A
polarimeter 6.3B
polarized light 6.3A
R,S system 6.2
R configuration 6.2
racemate 6.4
racemic mixture 6.4
racemic modification 6.4
racemization 6.4
rectus 6.2
S configuration 6.2
sinister 6.2
specific rotation, $[\alpha]$ 6.3B
stereochemical configuration 6.2
stereochemistry .... Introduction
stereoisomer 6.6
structural isomer 6.6
symmetry element 6.1

CHAPTER 6 CONCEPTS

I. Symmetry:

    A. Chirality:
        1. **Stereoisomers** are compounds that have the same atomic connectivity but a different arrangement of their atoms in space.
        2. A carbon with four different groups attached is called an **asymmetric carbon**.
          a) A molecule with *one* asymmetric carbon is chiral—its mirror image is nonsuperimposable.
          b) A molecule with more than one asymmetric carbon *may* be chiral.
        3. A chiral molecule has no elements of symmetry.
        4. Molecules that are not chiral are **achiral**.

B. Symmetry Elements:
   1. A **plane of symmetry** (**internal mirror plane**) is a plane that divides a molecule into two halves
      that are mirror images of each other.

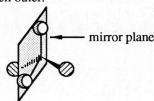

— mirror plane

   2. A point of symmetry (**center of symmetry**) is a unique point at the center of the molecule such that
      all straight lines drawn through it touch equivalent parts of the molecule at equal distances.

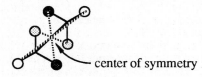

— center of symmetry

II. Stereoisomers:

A. Enantiomers and Chirality:
   1. **Enantiomers** are mirror images that are not superimposable.
   2. Molecules that can exist as enantiomers are said to be **chiral**.
   3. A pair of enantiomers have many identical physical properties: boiling point, melting point, density,
      index of refraction, heat of formation, standard free energy, and more.
   4. A pair of enantiomers can be distinguished by their behavior towards **polarized light**.
   5. Individual enantiomers of chiral substances are optically active.

mirror plane

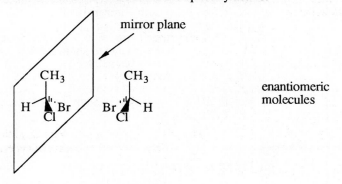

enantiomeric
molecules

B. Diastereomers:
   1. In order for a pair of molecules with more than one asymmetric carbon to be enantiomers, they must
      have different configurations at *every* asymmetric carbon.
   2. **Diastereomers** are stereoisomers that are not mirror images.
   3. Diastereomers have different values of their physical properties: melting points, boiling points, indices
      of refraction, heats of formation, standard free energies, and if a pair of diastereomers happen to be
      chiral, different **optical rotations**.
   4. Diastereomers can in principle be separated by conventional means: fractional distillation,
      crystallization, etc.

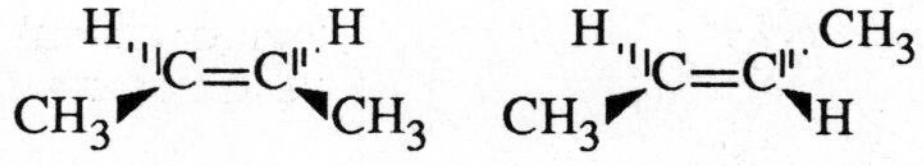

diastereomers

C. *Meso* Compounds:
    1. A *meso* **compound** is an achiral compound with asymmetric atoms.
    2. A *meso* compound has a mirror image that is superimposable.
    3. A *meso* compound is a single compound; it is *not* the same as a racemic mixture.
    4. A *meso* compound has an element of symmetry such as a plane or center of symmetry.

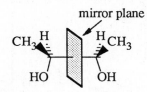

D. Racemates:
    1. A mixture containing equal amounts of each enantiomer of a pair is called a **racemate**, a **racemic mixture**, or a **racemic modification**.
    2. Racemates are denoted by (±)- before the name of the compound.
    3. The physical properties of racemates differ from those of the pure enantiomers.
    4. Racemates have no optical rotation; they are **optically inactive**.
    5. The process of forming a racemate from a pure enantiomer is called **racemization**.

III. Conformational Stereoisomers:

A. Chiral Molecules without Asymmetric Atoms:
    1. If a molecule is composed of enantiomeric pairs that are rapidly interconverting under ordinary conditions, the molecule is considered achiral.
    2. Conformational stereoisomers are molecular conformations that are stereoisomers of each other. (All molecular conformations are either mutually identical, or mutually stereoisomeric.)
      a) **Conformational enantiomers** are a pair of conformers that are mirror images and are not superimposable.

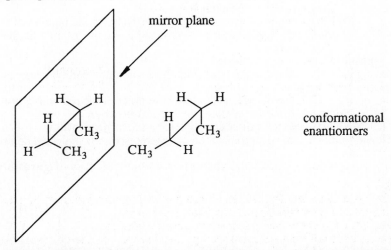

      b) **Conformational diastereomers** are nonidentical conformers that are not mirror images and are not superimposable.

B. <u>Asymmetric Nitrogen—Amine Inversion:</u>
   1. **Amines** are derivatives of ammonia in which one or more of the hydrogen atoms have been replaced by an organic group.
   2. Enantiomers of amines cannot be separated because they rapidly interconvert by **amine inversion**.
   3. During an amine inversion, the nitrogen atom converts from an sp^3 to an sp^2 and back to an sp^3 hybridized atom.

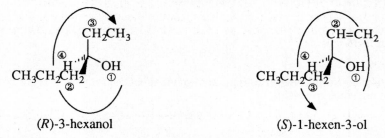

IV. Nomenclature and Optical Activity:

A. <u>Nomenclature of Chiral Molecules:</u>
   1. An enantiomer is classified in the **R,S system** by:
      a) Identifying an asymmetric carbon and the four different groups bound to it.
      b) Assigning priorities to the four different groups by applying the following rules in order:
         (1) Atoms of higher atomic number have higher priority.
         (2) An isotope of higher atomic mass receives higher priority.
         (3) If the relative priority of two groups cannot be decided at the atoms attached to the asymmetric carbon, consider the next atoms along the paths of highest priority until a difference is found.
            (*a*) The higher priority is assigned to the group with the atom of higher atomic mass at the *first* point of difference.
            (*b*) If the difference between two groups is due to the number of otherwise identical atoms, the higher priority is assigned the to the group with the greater number of identical atoms.
         (4) Multiple bonds are replicated.
      c) Viewing the molecule along the bond with the asymmetric carbon nearer and the group of lowest priority farther away.
      d) Considering the clockwise or counterclockwise order of the remaining group priorities.
         (1) A clockwise direction dictates an **R configuration**.
         (2) A counterclockwise direction dictates an **S configuration**.
   2. The configuration of each asymmetric carbon of a stereoisomer is indicated before the systematic name of the compound.
   3. The *R* or *S* designation specifies the **absolute stereochemical configuration** of the molecule.

(*R*)-3-hexanol   (*S*)-1-hexen-3-ol

B. <u>Determination of Absolute Configuration:</u>
   1. The **absolute configuration** of a compound *cannot* be assigned from the sign of its optical rotation.
   2. X-ray crystallography can be used to assign absolute configurations.
   3. Chemical reactions that *do not* break any of the bonds to the asymmetric carbon can sometimes be used to convert a compound of known absolute configuration to the compound of interest.

C. Optical Activities:
   1. A pair of enantiomers rotate the plane of polarized light by equal amounts but in opposite directions.
   2. There is no simple relationship between the sign of optical rotation and absolute configuration.
   3. **Optical activity** changes with the wavelength (color) of the light.
      a) A sample that rotates light in a clockwise direction is **dextrorotatory** and is denoted by (+)- or (*d*)- at the begining of the name.

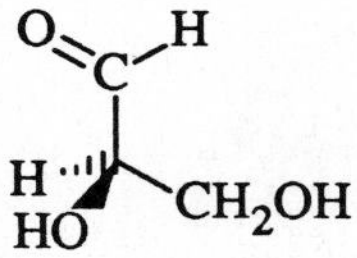

(+)-glyceraldehyde
(*d*)-glyceraldehyde
(*R*)-(+)-glyceraldehyde

      b) A sample that rotates light in a counterclockwise direction is **levorotatory** and is denoted by a (–)- or (*l*)- at the begining of the name.

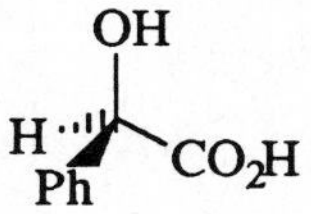

(–)-mandelic acid
(*l*)-mandelic acid
(*R*)-(–)-mandelic acid

   4. **Observed optical rotation** α is proportional to the number of optically active molecules present in the light beam.
   5. **Specific rotation** $[\alpha]$ is a constant of proportionality relating observed rotation to concentration and path length at a given temperature and wavelength (**Biot's law**).

$$\alpha = [\alpha]cl$$

where $[\alpha]$ has the units of mL-g^{-1}-dm^{-1}

D. Fischer Projections:
   1. A **Fischer projection** is a planar representation of a molecule.
   2. Each asymmetric carbon is drawn so that two bonds are vertical and two bonds are horizontal.
      a) The horizontal bonds come out of the plane of the paper.
      b) The vertical bonds go into the plane of the paper.
      c) The asymmetric carbon is indicated by the intersection of the vertical and horizontal lines.

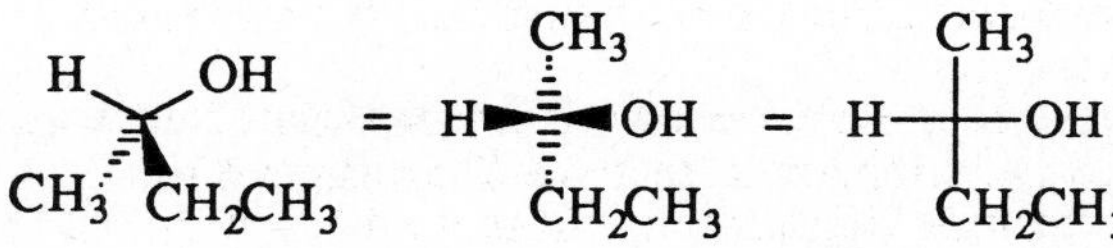

   3. Several different Fischer projections can be written for the same molecule.
      a) A Fischer projection may be turned 180° in the plane of the paper.
      b) A Fischer projection may *not* be turned 90° in the plane of the paper.
      c) A Fischer projection may *not* be lifted from the plane of the paper and turned over.
      d) The three groups at either end of a Fischer projection may be interchanged in a **cyclic permutation**.

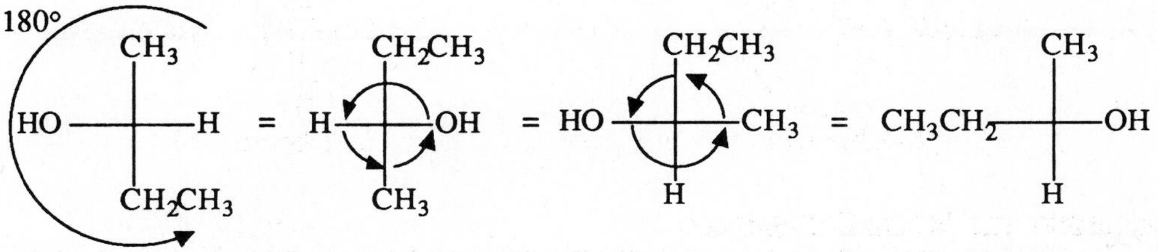

4. The *R,S* system can be applied to a Fischer projection.
  a) Assign priorities to the four groups of the asymmetric carbon.
  b) Position the group of lowest priority in either of the two vertical positions (remember, these positions are away from the observer).
  c) A clockwise orientation of the three groups of higher priority indicates an *R* configuration.

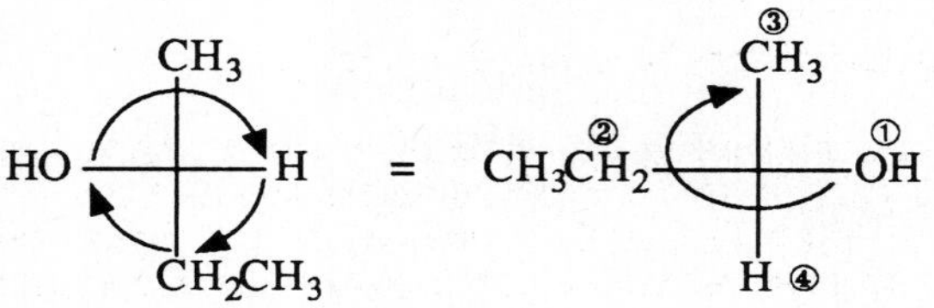

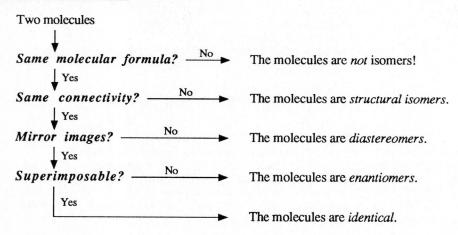

(*R*)-2-butanol

d) A counterclockwise orientation of the three groups of higher priority indicate an *S* configuration.

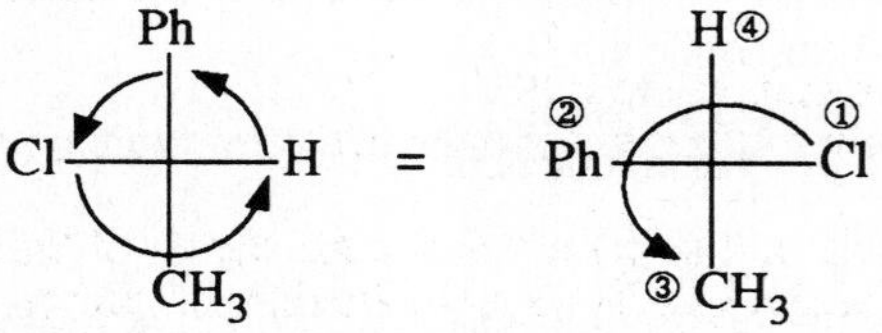

(*S*)-1-chloro-1-phenylethane

CHAPTER 6 RULES

Biot's Law: Optical activity depends on the concentration of the chiral substance.

Relationships Between Two Molecules:

Two molecules

↓

Same molecular formula? —No→ The molecules are *not* isomers!

↓ Yes

Same connectivity? —No→ The molecules are *structural isomers.*

↓ Yes

Mirror images? —No→ The molecules are *diastereomers.*

↓ Yes

Superimposable? —No→ The molecules are *enantiomers.*

↓ Yes

The molecules are *identical.*

CHAPTER 6 SOLUTIONS

Solutions to In-Text Problems

1. Compounds (a) and (d) are chiral; compound (d) has an asymmetric nitrogen.

2. (a) Chiral (b) Achiral, unless you include the writing. (c) Achiral, assuming that it is sharpened with a perfectly symmetrical point, and assuming that it has no writing on the side. (d) Chiral (if you consider the internal organs); otherwise achiral. (e) Achiral (f) Chiral. There are left- and right-handed scissors. Actually, the author, a right-hander, didn't know this until a wrong answer to this question prompted a reviewer to comment how badly the scissor-making industry discriminates against left-handers!

3. (a) A plane of symmetry is any plane bisecting any H—C—H angle and containing the other two H's (see illustration below).
   (b) A plane of symmetry is any plane containing the center of the ball.
   (c) A plane of symmetry is any plane containing the tip of the cone and the center of the base (see illustration below).
   (d) A plane of symmetry is any plane containing the tip and passing through the center of the base.
   (e) A plane of symmetry is the plane that bisects the angle H—C—H and contains the carbon and chlorine atoms (see illustration below); another plane of symmetry is the plane that bisects the angle Cl—C—Cl and contains the carbon and the two hydrogen atoms.

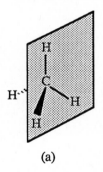

(a)

(c)

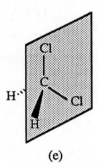

(e)

4. (a)   (b) 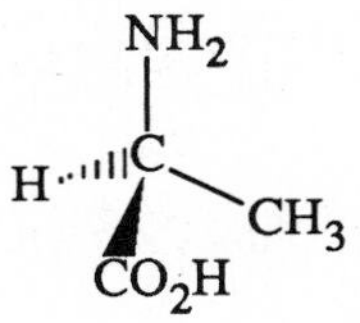   (c)

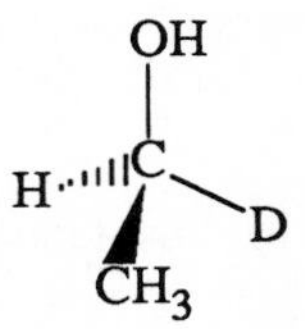

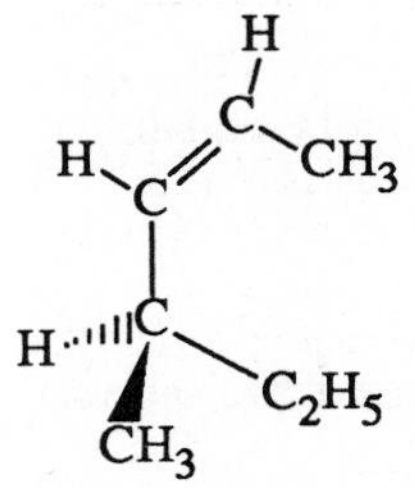

5. (a), (b), and (c) all have the *S* configuration.

6. (a) $0.1M$ means $(0.1 \text{ mol/L})(150 \text{ g/mol})(0.001 \text{ L/mL}) = 0.015 \text{ g/mL}$. Using this number for c in Eq. 6.1, we have

$$[\alpha] = \frac{\alpha}{c \cdot l} = \frac{0.20°}{0.015} = +13.3° = \text{specific rotation of } D.$$

(b) Since we have an equal amount of the compound and its enantiomer, we have a racemate. The observed rotation is 0°.

(c) The observed rotation is half what it is in (a) — that is, +0.1°.

(d) Specific rotation is a physical constant independent of concentration; therefore, it is the same as in (b), namely, +13.3°.

(e) Since enantiomers have equal but opposite rotations, the specific rotation of the enantiomer is –13.3°.

(f) In this solution the 0.005 mole of *L* cancels the rotation of 0.005 mole of *D*. The rotation will be the same as a solution that contains 0.005 mole of *D*. The concentration of *D* is

(0.005 mol/100 mL)(150 g/mol) = 0.0075 g/mL

Since the concentration is half what it is in (a), the observed rotation is also half, and is therefore 0.10°.

7. Double the concentration; if the specific rotation is positive, the observed rotation will increase; if the specific rotation is negative, the observed rotation will decrease. More rigorously, to determine the specific rotation, we would plot observed rotation vs. concentration. The slope of the line is the specific rotation; this slope will thus have the same sign as the specific rotation.

8. The racemic 2-butanol makes no contribution to the optical activity. Hence, the only effect of its addition on the observed rotation is to dilute the *R* enantiomer by a factor of two; its concentration after the dilution is therefore 0.05 *M*. The molecular weight of 2-butanol is 74.12. Hence, the concentration of (*R*)-2-butanol after the dilution, in g/mL, is

$$(0.05 \text{ mol/L})(74.12 \text{ g/mol})(10^{-3} \text{ L/mL}) = 3.70 \times 10^{-3} \text{ g/mL}$$

The observed rotation, from Eq. 6.1, is

$$\alpha = (13.9 \text{ deg-mL-g}^{-1}\text{dm}^{-1})(0.0037 \text{ g/mL})(0.5 \text{ dm}) = 0.026°$$

9. We can deduce the configuration of the product from that of the starting material:

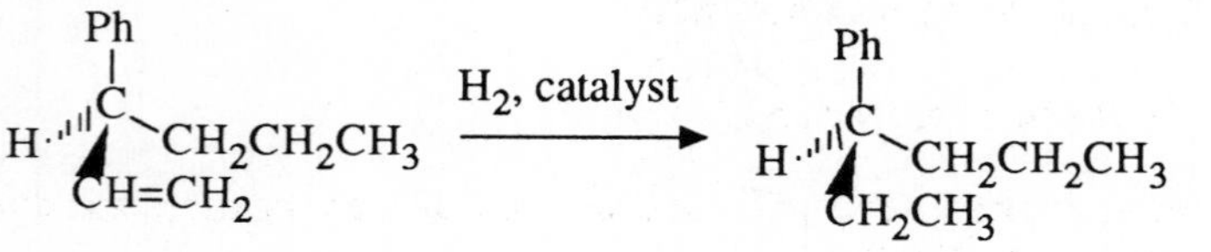

Since no bonds to the asymmetric carbon are broken, the product has the same relative configuration as the starting material. If the configuration is the same, why is the designation different? The reason is that the relative priorities of the groups changed as a result of the reaction.

➤ To say that two compounds have the same relative configuration does *not* necessarily mean that their *R,S* designations are the same, as this example shows.

10. (a) Diastereomers   (b) Enantiomers   (c) Diastereomers

11. The internal plane of symmetry in the *meso* isomers of this compound goes through the central carbon. Hence, this carbon can have either of two configurations. The only requirement for *meso* compounds of this structure is that the carbons at opposite ends of the molecule must have opposite configurations.

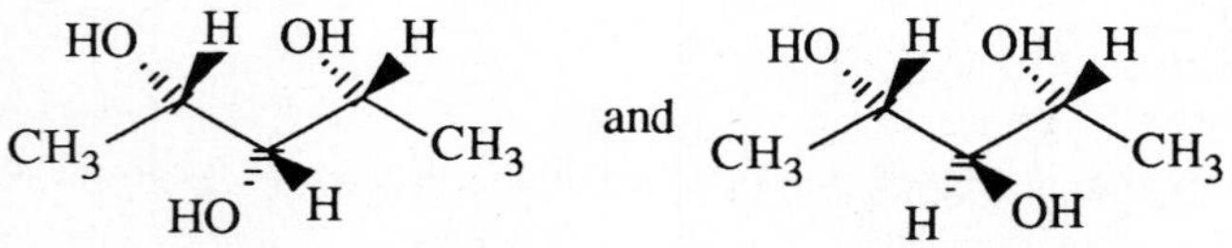

two *meso* diastereomers

12. Let us draw these three rotational isomers:

A B C

Isomer C has a center of symmetry (dot), and is therefore itself achiral. Isomers A and B are chiral and are enantiomers. (To see this may require manipulating models.) Because these enantiomers are interconverting rapidly, 2,3-butanediol behaves as if it is achiral. In principle, however, we could isolate either A or B separately; these individual rotational isomers would show optical activity.

13. The S configuration of the asymmetric carbon is unaffected by amine inversion, whereas the nitrogen interconverts between R and S configurations. Thus, the amine inversion interconverts S,R and S,S stereoisomers, which are *diastereomers*.

14. (a)   (b)

(related by a cyclic permutation   (related by a 180° rotation in the
of the top three groups)   plane of the page)

Many other valid Fischer projections are possible for both compounds.

15. (a) Identical. (Rotate 180° in the plane of the page to see identity.)
    (b) Diastereomers.
    (c) Enantiomers. (Carry out two cyclic permutations on the right structure: one counterclockwise on the upper carbon, and the other counterclockwise on the lower carbon.)

    ➤ The secret of working this type of problem is to place as many corresponding groups as possible in identical positions before deciding on the relationship. In (c), for example, the carboxy (—CO_2H) groups are in the same positions in both structures; since the remaining groups are *not* in corresponding positions, it follows immediately that the two structures differ in configurations at *both* carbons and are therefore enantiomers. The manipulation described in (c) will verify that this is so.

16. (a) This is clearly a *meso* compound, and therefore has opposite configurations at the two asymmetric carbons. As the structure is drawn, the top carbon has the R configuration and the bottom carbon the S configuration.
    (b) S configuration.
    (c) All three carbons have the R configuration.

17. Pasteur has isolated the $2R,3R$ and the $2S,3S$ enantiomers.

enantiomers   *meso* form (yet to be isolated)

The stereoisomer that remained to be isolated, shown above, was the *meso* form (the 2*S*,3*R* stereoisomer). That is, *meso*-tartaric acid was unknown to Pasteur.

18. As we showed in Problem 39 of Chapter 1, tetrahedral CCl_4 must have a dipole moment of zero. Pyramidal CCl_4, however, should have a nonzero dipole moment. Since the four C—Cl bonds are oriented in the same general direction, the dipole moment should be substantial. (In fact, CCl_4 has zero dipole moment, an observation consistent with the tetrahedral structure.)

Solutions to Additional Problems

19. Once again, we adopt the practice of showing only the carbon skeletons.

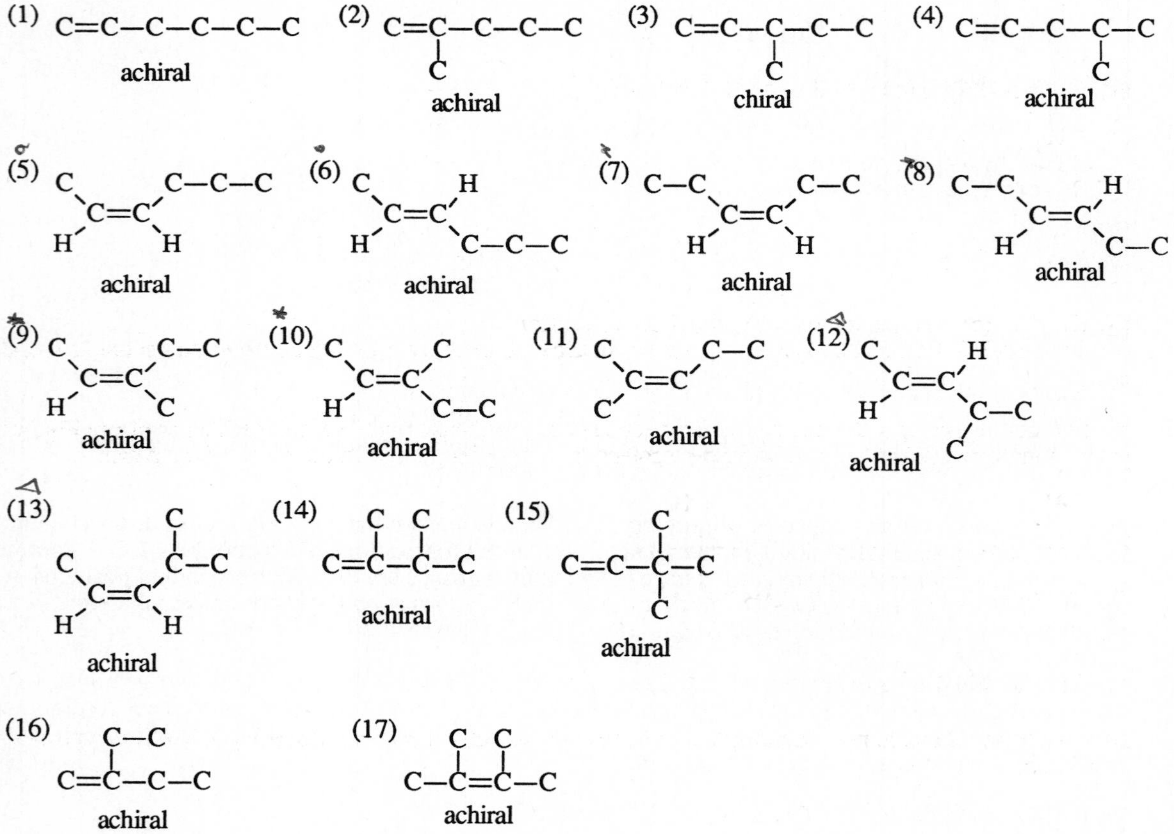

(1) C=C—C—C—C—C
achiral

(2) C=C—C—C—C
      |
      C
achiral

(3) C=C—C—C—C
      |
      C
chiral

(4) C=C—C—C—C
         |
         C
achiral

(5)
```
C          C—C—C
 \        /
  C=C
 /        \
H          H
```
achiral

(6)
```
C          H
 \        /
  C=C
 /        \
H          C—C—C
```
achiral

(7)
```
C—C        C—C
   \      /
    C=C
   /      \
  H        H
```
achiral

(8)
```
C—C        H
   \      /
    C=C
   /      \
  H        C—C
```
achiral

(9)
```
C          C—C
 \        /
  C=C
 /        \
H          C
```
achiral

(10)
```
C          C
 \        /
  C=C
 /        \
H          C—C
```
achiral

(11)
```
C          C—C
 \        /
  C=C
 /        \
C          C
```
achiral

(12)
```
C          H
 \        /
  C=C
 /        \
H          C—C
              |
              C
```
achiral

(13)
```
          C
          |
C         C—C
 \       /
  C=C
 /       \
H         H
```
achiral

(14)
```
    C C
    | |
C=C—C—C
```
achiral

(15)
```
      C
      |
C=C—C—C
      |
      C
```
achiral

(16)
```
  C—C
  |
C=C—C—C
```
achiral

(17)
```
  C C
  | |
C—C=C—C
```
achiral

Compounds (5) and (6), (7) and (8), (9) and (10), (12) and (13) are diastereomeric pairs. Compound (3) exists as a pair of enantiomers. All other pairs are structural isomers.

20. The asymmetric carbons are indicated by arrows.

(a)

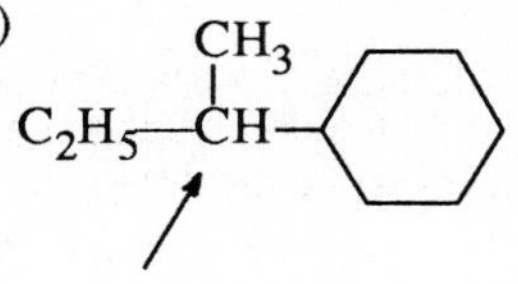

$$C_2H_5 \!\!-\!\! \underset{\underset{\uparrow}{}}{\overset{CH_3}{CH}} \!\!-\!\! \bigcirc$$

(b)

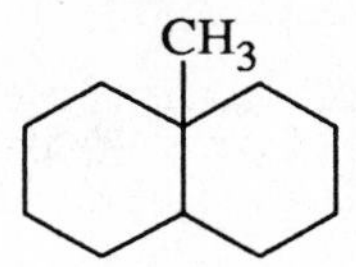

no asymmetric carbons

(c)

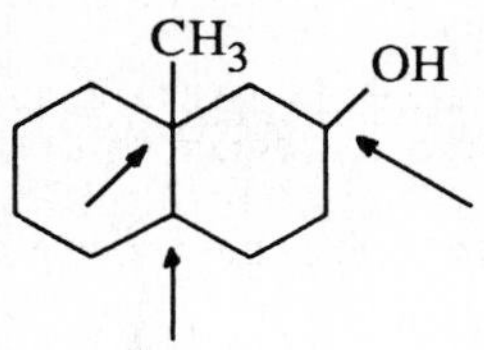

(d)

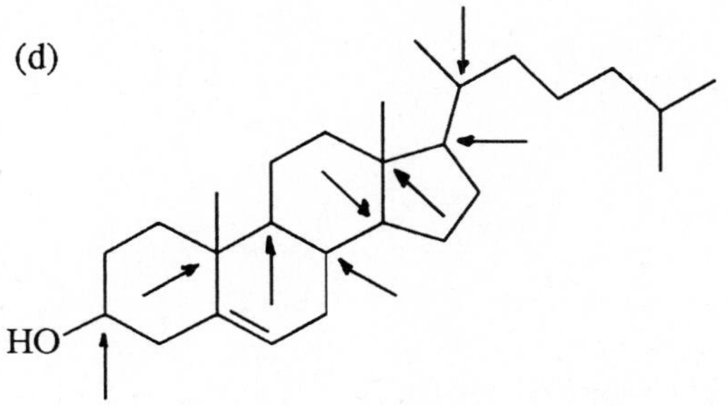

(e)

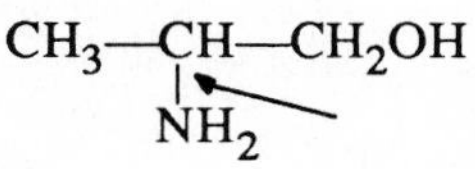

$$CH_3 \!\!-\!\! \underset{\underset{\downarrow}{NH_2}}{CH} \!\!-\!\! CH_2OH$$

21. (a) The top carbon is *S*, and the bottom one is *R*.

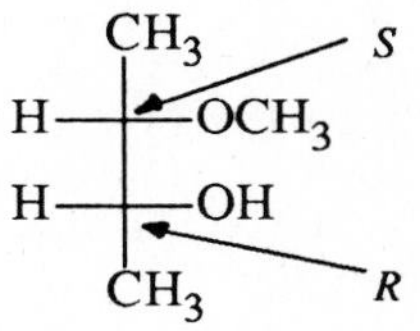

(b) *R*.   (c) The phosphorus has the *R* configuration.
(d) In *meso*-3,4-dimethylhexane, the two asymmetric carbons have opposite configurations; one is *R* and one is *S*.

22. This is another one of those exercises that must be done systematically. We first pick an arbitrary Fischer projection; then we form a second Fischer projection by rotating it 180° in the plane of the paper.

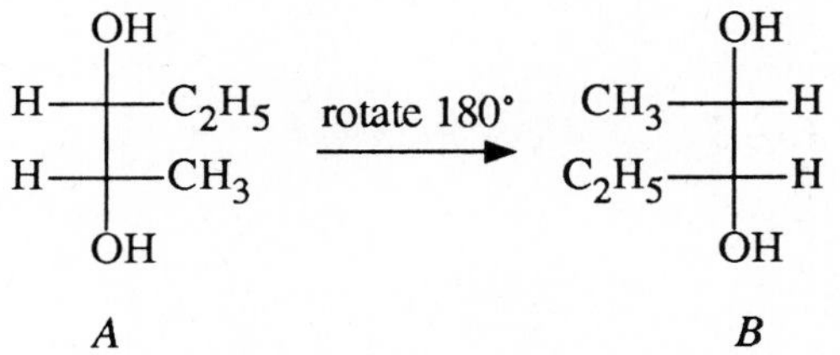

Now we form all cyclic permutations of *A* by rotating the bottom carbon. Counting *A* itself, this gives three projections:

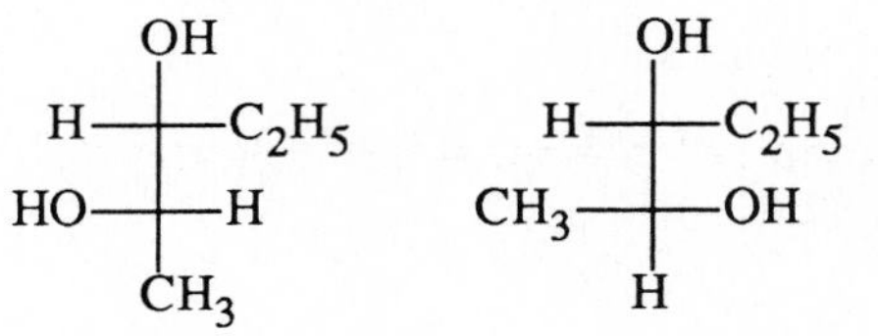

Next, we take a cyclic permutation of *A* on the top carbon to get *A'*, and then get two more projections by rotating the bottom carbon:

$$
\begin{array}{c}
\text{H} \\
\text{C}_2\text{H}_5\!-\!\!\!\!\overset{|}{\underset{|}{}}\!\!\!\!-\!\text{OH} \\
\text{H}\!-\!\!\!\!\overset{|}{\underset{|}{}}\!\!\!\!-\!\text{CH}_3 \\
\text{OH}
\end{array}
\qquad
\begin{array}{c}
\text{H} \\
\text{C}_2\text{H}_5\!-\!\!\!\!\overset{|}{\underset{|}{}}\!\!\!\!-\!\text{OH} \\
\text{HO}\!-\!\!\!\!\overset{|}{\underset{|}{}}\!\!\!\!-\!\text{H} \\
\text{CH}_3
\end{array}
\qquad
\begin{array}{c}
\text{H} \\
\text{C}_2\text{H}_5\!-\!\!\!\!\overset{|}{\underset{|}{}}\!\!\!\!-\!\text{OH} \\
\text{CH}_3\!-\!\!\!\!\overset{|}{\underset{|}{}}\!\!\!\!-\!\text{OH} \\
\text{H}
\end{array}
$$

A'

Then we take the last cyclic permutation of *A* to get *A''*, and then write the cyclic permutations of this on the bottom carbon:

$$
\begin{array}{c}
\text{C}_2\text{H}_5 \\
\text{HO}\!-\!\!\!\!\overset{|}{\underset{|}{}}\!\!\!\!-\!\text{H} \\
\text{H}\!-\!\!\!\!\overset{|}{\underset{|}{}}\!\!\!\!-\!\text{CH}_3 \\
\text{OH}
\end{array}
\qquad
\begin{array}{c}
\text{C}_2\text{H}_5 \\
\text{HO}\!-\!\!\!\!\overset{|}{\underset{|}{}}\!\!\!\!-\!\text{H} \\
\text{HO}\!-\!\!\!\!\overset{|}{\underset{|}{}}\!\!\!\!-\!\text{H} \\
\text{CH}_3
\end{array}
\qquad
\begin{array}{c}
\text{C}_2\text{H}_5 \\
\text{HO}\!-\!\!\!\!\overset{|}{\underset{|}{}}\!\!\!\!-\!\text{H} \\
\text{CH}_3\!-\!\!\!\!\overset{|}{\underset{|}{}}\!\!\!\!-\!\text{OH} \\
\text{H}
\end{array}
$$

A''

Now we repeat the same routine on structure *B*, which we redraw below:

$$
\begin{array}{c}
\text{OH} \\
\text{CH}_3\!-\!\!\!\!\overset{|}{\underset{|}{}}\!\!\!\!-\!\text{H} \\
\text{C}_2\text{H}_5\!-\!\!\!\!\overset{|}{\underset{|}{}}\!\!\!\!-\!\text{H} \\
\text{OH}
\end{array}
\qquad
\begin{array}{c}
\text{OH} \\
\text{CH}_3\!-\!\!\!\!\overset{|}{\underset{|}{}}\!\!\!\!-\!\text{H} \\
\text{HO}\!-\!\!\!\!\overset{|}{\underset{|}{}}\!\!\!\!-\!\text{C}_2\text{H}_5 \\
\text{H}
\end{array}
\qquad
\begin{array}{c}
\text{OH} \\
\text{CH}_3\!-\!\!\!\!\overset{|}{\underset{|}{}}\!\!\!\!-\!\text{H} \\
\text{H}\!-\!\!\!\!\overset{|}{\underset{|}{}}\!\!\!\!-\!\text{OH} \\
\text{C}_2\text{H}_5
\end{array}
$$

B

$$
\begin{array}{c}
\text{CH}_3 \\
\text{H}\!-\!\!\!\!\overset{|}{\underset{|}{}}\!\!\!\!-\!\text{OH} \\
\text{C}_2\text{H}_5\!-\!\!\!\!\overset{|}{\underset{|}{}}\!\!\!\!-\!\text{H} \\
\text{OH}
\end{array}
\qquad
\begin{array}{c}
\text{CH}_3 \\
\text{H}\!-\!\!\!\!\overset{|}{\underset{|}{}}\!\!\!\!-\!\text{OH} \\
\text{HO}\!-\!\!\!\!\overset{|}{\underset{|}{}}\!\!\!\!-\!\text{C}_2\text{H}_5 \\
\text{H}
\end{array}
\qquad
\begin{array}{c}
\text{CH}_3 \\
\text{H}\!-\!\!\!\!\overset{|}{\underset{|}{}}\!\!\!\!-\!\text{OH} \\
\text{H}\!-\!\!\!\!\overset{|}{\underset{|}{}}\!\!\!\!-\!\text{OH} \\
\text{C}_2\text{H}_5
\end{array}
$$

B'

$$
\begin{array}{c}
\text{H} \\
\text{HO}\!-\!\!\!\!\overset{|}{\underset{|}{}}\!\!\!\!-\!\text{CH}_3 \\
\text{C}_2\text{H}_5\!-\!\!\!\!\overset{|}{\underset{|}{}}\!\!\!\!-\!\text{H} \\
\text{OH}
\end{array}
\qquad
\begin{array}{c}
\text{H} \\
\text{HO}\!-\!\!\!\!\overset{|}{\underset{|}{}}\!\!\!\!-\!\text{CH}_3 \\
\text{HO}\!-\!\!\!\!\overset{|}{\underset{|}{}}\!\!\!\!-\!\text{C}_2\text{H}_5 \\
\text{H}
\end{array}
\qquad
\begin{array}{c}
\text{H} \\
\text{HO}\!-\!\!\!\!\overset{|}{\underset{|}{}}\!\!\!\!-\!\text{CH}_3 \\
\text{H}\!-\!\!\!\!\overset{|}{\underset{|}{}}\!\!\!\!-\!\text{OH} \\
\text{C}_2\text{H}_5
\end{array}
$$

B''

We end up with a total of eighteen, count 'em, eighteen Fischer projections.

23.   Forms *A* and *B* are enantiomers; form *C* is a *meso* compound and is a diastereomer of *A* and *B*.

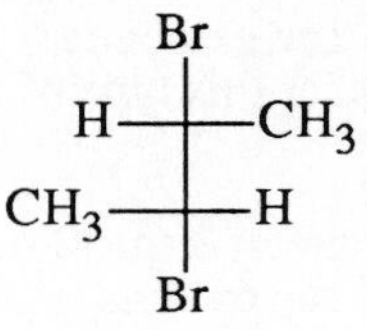

| *A* | *B* | *C* |

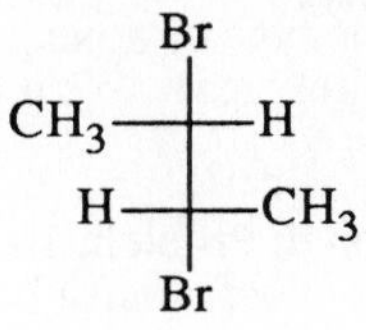

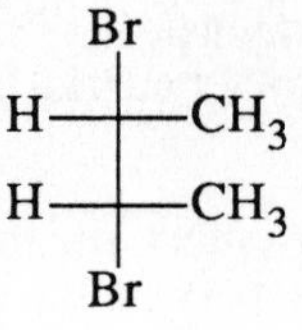

As the previous problem should have taught us, these are not the only Fischer projections of these stereoisomers that one might draw.

24.   (a) True.
      (b) True, by definition.
      (c) False; mirror images can be identical. Mirror-images are enantiomers only if they are nonsuperimposable.
      (d) False; in particular, many compounds with a single asymmetric carbon, such as bromochlorofluoromethane, are chiral but have no diastereomers.
      (e) True, by definition.
      (f) False; many *cis-trans* isomers are achiral diastereomers.
      (g) False; *meso* compounds are achiral compounds with more than one asymmetric carbon.
      (h) False; all chiral compounds are optically active, at least *in principle*. It is possible, however, that the optical activity of a chiral compound may be so small that it is difficult to detect.
      (i) False; by definition, diastereomers are stereoisomers that do *not* have an enantiomeric relationship.
      (j) False; there is no connection between the *R* or *S* designation and the sign of optical rotation.
      (k) False; although this *may* be true, it is not always true. There are other symmetry elements that are characteristic of achiral compounds, such as a center of symmetry and other, more obscure, symmetry elements.

25.   There are eight different types of hydrogens that can be substituted, labeled *a-h* below:

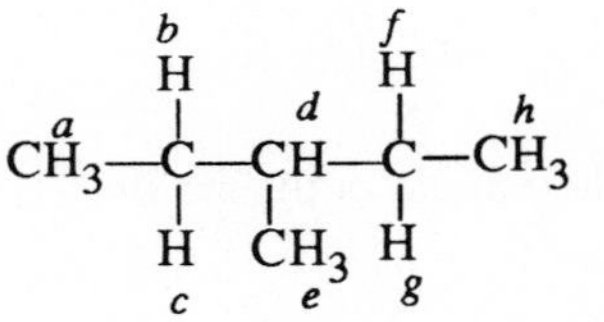

Substitution of each of these in turn gives the following isomers:

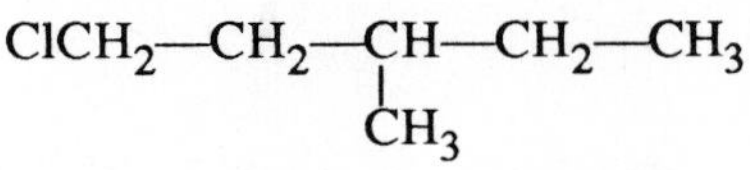

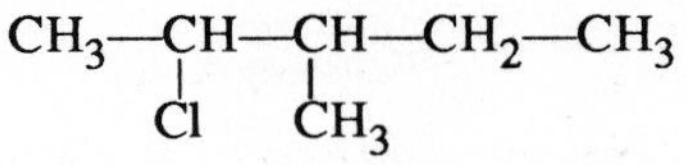

When either hydrogen *a* or hydrogen *h* is substituted, the carbon at position *d* becomes asymmetric. Hence, compounds *A* and *H* are enantiomers. When the hydrogens at positions *b* and *c* are substituted, *two* carbons become symmetric: the carbon at position *d* and the one at positions *b/c*. Hence, for a given configuration of carbon *h*, compounds *B* and *C* are *diastereomers*. For the same reason, compounds *F* and *G* are, respectively, enantiomers of *B* and *C*, and are diastereomers of each other. The rest of the compounds are structural isomers.

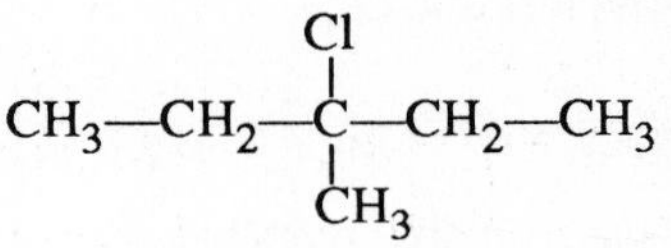

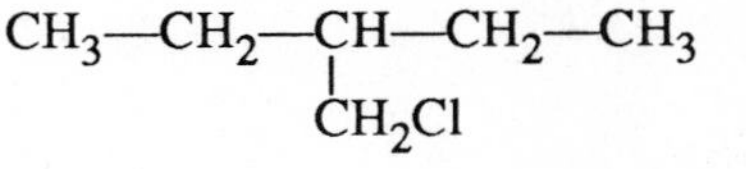

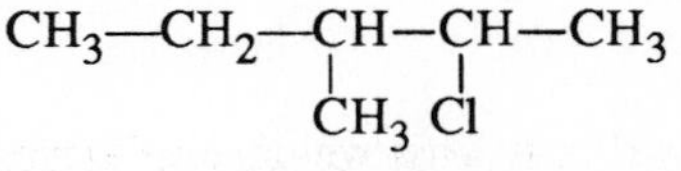

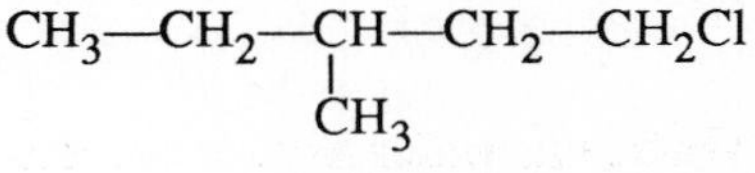

➤ Notice that hydrogens a and h look as if they might be completely equivalent. However, the fact that we get enantiomers when we substitute each in turn shows that these hydrogens *aren't* equivalent! We can make a similar statement for hydrogens b and c, and hydrogens f and g. The type of nonequivalence exhibited by H^a and H^h, by H^b and H^c, and by H^f and H^g is rather subtle, but definitely real. We'll consider this type of nonequivalence in Section 10.8.

26. (a) We have already drawn these rotational isomers: see the solution to Problem 10 in Chapter 3 (p. 30 of this book). Isomers A and E are rotational enantiomers (in the same sense that *gauche* butane can exist as rotational enantiomers). These rotational isomers are then chiral. Isomer C contains a plane of symmetry, and is therefore achiral.
(b) 2-Methylbutane is not a chiral compound because the two chiral rotational isomers are in such rapid equilibrium that they cannot be isolated separately.
(c) Since enantiomers have identical heats of formation, then isomers A and C have the same heats of formation. The heat of formation of isomer E, however, is different. In fact, we would expect its heat of formation to be higher because of the greater number of *gauche* interactions in E.

27. Compound B undergoes rapid racemization by amine inversion (Sec. 6.8B). Since compound A lacks the unshared electron pair, it cannot undergo inversion, and it can exist in isolable enantiomeric forms.

28. We first convert the molar concentration into g/mL, and then apply Eq. 6.1.

$$0.5M = (0.5 \text{ mol/L})(146.2 \text{ g/mol})(10^{-3} \text{ L/mL}) = 0.0731 \text{ g/mL}$$

$$\alpha = [\alpha]cl = (76 \text{ deg-mL/g-dm})(0.0731 \text{ g/mL})(0.5 \text{ dm}) = 2.78°$$

29. (a) Since the rotation of a racemate is zero, its percent optical purity is also zero.
(b) Using the formula, the percent optical purity is $(5/53) \times 100 = 9.43\%$.
(c) Each enantiomer contributes to the observed rotation in proportion to its mole fraction. Let the concentrations of the two enantiomers be n^* and n, respectively, and the mole fractions of the two be X^* and X, respectively. Then

$$X^* = \frac{n^*}{n^* + n} \quad \text{and} \quad X = \frac{n}{n^* + n}$$

Let α^* = the specific rotation of the major enantiomer, and let α_m = the specific rotation of the minor enantiomer. Then

$$\text{observed rotation} = \alpha = \alpha^* X^* + \alpha_m X = \frac{\alpha^* n^*}{n^* + n} + \frac{\alpha_m n}{n^* + n}$$

Now it is true that

$$\alpha^* = -\alpha_m$$

because enantiomers have equal and opposite rotations. Substituting this in the previous equation, we have

$$\alpha = \frac{\alpha^*(n^* - n)}{(n^* + n)} \quad \text{or} \quad \frac{\alpha}{\alpha^*} = \frac{(n^* - n)}{(n^* + n)}$$

which, after multiplying both sides by 100, is what we desired to show.

(d) $0.0943 = X^* - X = X^* - (1 - X^*)$

Hence, $X^* = 1.094/2 = 0.55$, and $X = 1 - 0.55$, or 0.45. Hence, the mixture contains 55% of the major enantiomer and 45% of the minor one.

➤ The difference between the mole percents of the major and minor enantiomers is sometimes referred to as the *enantiomeric excess* (EE). In this example, the EE is 9.4%; this difference is always equal to the percent optical purity.

30. (a) The repeating units of the two forms of polypropylene:

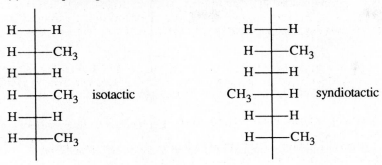

(b) If we regard the two ends — the initiating and terminating ends — of the polymer chain to be different, both forms are chiral! However, the ends make such a small contribution to the properties of the molecule that they can be ignored. Regarding the two ends as identical, we can find a carbon *near* the middle of both chains that separates both molecules *almost* into mirror-image halves. Hence, both forms are almost *meso* and therefore *virtually* achiral. Rigorously, however, such a carbon could not be in the *exact* center of the molecule; hence, the molecules are chiral, but their chirality is so slight that it could not be detected in a practical sense.

➤ If you were frustrated by not knowing what assumption to make about the ends, then you were obviously on the right track, and you can consider yourself as having worked the problem correctly. If every problem in the world had a simple answer, life would be pretty dull!

(c)

$$
\begin{array}{ccc}
H & \!\!\!-\!\!\!| & H \\
CH_3 & \!\!\!-\!\!\!| & CO_2CH_3 \\
H & \!\!\!-\!\!\!| & H \\
CH_3 & \!\!\!-\!\!\!| & CO_2CH_3 \\
H & \!\!\!-\!\!\!| & H \\
CH_3O_2C & \!\!\!-\!\!\!| & CH_3
\end{array}
\qquad \text{atactic poly(methyl methacrylate)}
$$

31. (a) To be sure we cover every possibility, let us draw all 2^3 structures:

$$
\begin{array}{cccc}
\overset{\displaystyle CH_3}{\underset{\displaystyle CH_3}{
\begin{array}{l}
H\!-\!\!|\!-\!Cl \;\; S \\
H\!-\!\!|\!-\!Cl \\
H\!-\!\!|\!-\!Cl \;\; R
\end{array}}}
&
\overset{\displaystyle CH_3}{\underset{\displaystyle CH_3}{
\begin{array}{l}
Cl\!-\!\!|\!-\!H \;\; R \\
Cl\!-\!\!|\!-\!H \\
Cl\!-\!\!|\!-\!H \;\; S
\end{array}}}
&
\overset{\displaystyle CH_3}{\underset{\displaystyle CH_3}{
\begin{array}{l}
H\!-\!\!|\!-\!Cl \;\; S \\
Cl\!-\!\!|\!-\!H \\
Cl\!-\!\!|\!-\!H \;\; S
\end{array}}}
&
\overset{\displaystyle CH_3}{\underset{\displaystyle CH_3}{
\begin{array}{l}
Cl\!-\!\!|\!-\!H \;\; R \\
H\!-\!\!|\!-\!Cl \\
H\!-\!\!|\!-\!Cl \;\; R
\end{array}}}
\\
A & B & C & D
\end{array}
$$

Structures E, F, G, H are Fischer projections:

E
```
        CH3
   H ──┼── Cl   S
  Cl ──┼── H
   H ──┼── Cl   R
        CH3
```

F
```
        CH3
  Cl ──┼── H    R
   H ──┼── Cl
  Cl ──┼── H    S
        CH3
```

G
```
        CH3
   H ──┼── Cl   S
   H ──┼── Cl
  Cl ──┼── H    S
        CH3
```

H
```
        CH3
  Cl ──┼── H    R
  Cl ──┼── H
   H ──┼── Cl   R
        CH3
```

Not all structures are different. Thus, $A = B$, $E = F$, $C = G$, and $D = H$. Let us refer to these stereoisomers as A, E, C, and D, respectively.

(b) Compounds C and D are chiral and are enantiomers; compounds A and E are diastereomeric *meso* compounds and are therefore achiral.

(c) In the *achiral* stereoisomers A and E, carbon-3 is asymmetric, because the two groups at each end are different (if only by their stereochemistry). In the *chiral* stereoisomers C and D, carbon-3 is not asymmetric. Another way to look at this is the following. Interchange of any two groups at an asymmetric carbon must give a stereoisomer. Interchange of the H and Cl at carbon-3 of A and E indeed interchange these two stereoisomers; therefore carbon-3 must be asymmetric. But interchange of the H and Cl at carbon-3 of either C or D gives back an identical compound! (The Fischer projection is different, but turning it 180° in the plane of the page shows that it is the same as the starting structure in each case.) Hence, carbon-3 in both compounds is asymmetric.

32. Because hydrogenation makes two groups that were different *before* the reaction the same *after* the reaction, the carbon that was asymmetric before the reaction is not asymmetric after the reaction.

$$CH_2=CH-\underset{\underset{CH_3}{|}}{CH}-CH_2CH_3 \xrightarrow{H_2/\text{catalyst}} CH_3CH_2-\underset{\underset{CH_3}{|}}{CH}-CH_2CH_3$$

  chiral   achiral

An achiral compound *cannot* show optical activity.

33. In the reaction an alkene carbon becomes an asymmetric carbon. It has the same groups around it as the $4S$ carbon of the starting material. The product in which the newly asymmetric carbon has the R configuration is *meso* and therefore optically inactive. The product in which the newly asymmetric carbon has the S configuration is chiral and optically active.

```
        CH3
   H ──┼── OCH3
  CH3 ─┼── H
        CH=CH2
```
$\xrightarrow[\text{CH}_3\text{OH}]{\text{Hg(OAc)}_2 \ \text{NaBH}_4}$
```
           CH3
      H ──┼── OCH3   S
     CH3 ─┼── H
      H ──┼── OCH3   R
           CH3
```
achiral;
optically inactive

$+$
```
           CH3
      H ──┼── OCH3   S
     CH3 ─┼── H
    CH3O ─┼── H      S
           CH3
```
chiral;
optically active

34.
(a)-(b) Diastereomers	(a)-(c) Identical	(a)-(d) Diastereomers
(a)-(e) Diastereomers	(b)-(c) Diastereomers	(b)-(d) Enantiomers
(b)-(e) Diastereomers	(c)-(d) Diastereomers	(c)-(e) Diastereomers
(d)-(e) Diastereomers		

35. Just as there can be only one tetrahedral CH_2Cl_2, there can only be one tetrahedral derivative of *any* molecule of the general form XY_2Z_2. Hence, with X = Pt, Y = NH_3, and Z = Cl, there is only one tetrahedral form of this complex if it is tetrahedral. Since there are two isomers known, the tetrahedral structure is ruled out. In contrast, there can be two square-planar structures — one with like ligands adjacent, and the other with like ligands on opposite sides:

36. (a) For tetrahedral geometry, there are two enantiomers:

(b) For square-planar geometry, there are three diastereomers. These are found by making all possible pairwise switches between adjacent groups and ruling out identities. (Switches of nonadjacent groups give identical molecules, because these molecules are *truly* planar, and can be lifted out of the plane of the paper for superposition.)

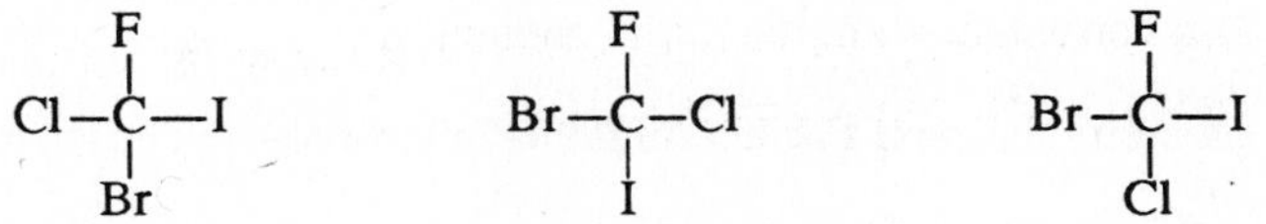

(c) For pyramidal geometry, there are three diastereomeric sets of enantiomers:

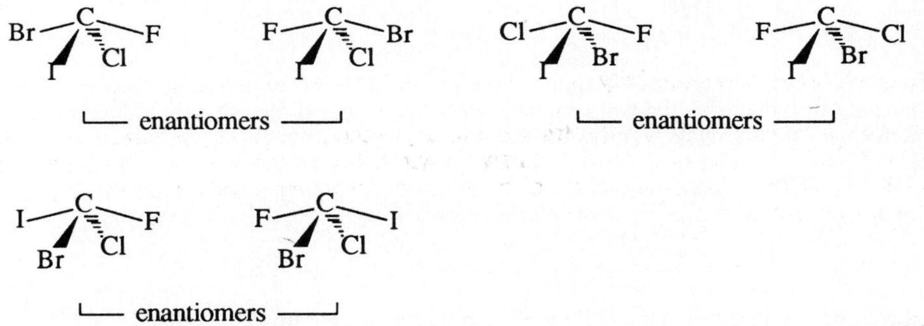

37. Fischer obtained enantiomers as a result of this transformation, since the melting points are the same and the optical rotations are equal and opposite. Let us see what the two possible geometries predict for an interchange of two groups. Since the interchange of any two groups at the asymmetric carbon gives enantiomers for compounds of tetrahedral configuration, the result is clearly consistent with this geometry:

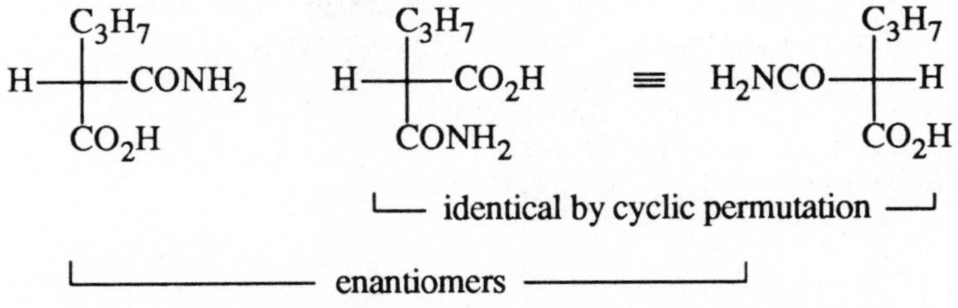

If the compound were pyramidal, and Fischer *happened* to be dealing with the isomer in which the CO_2H and the $CONH_2$ groups are opposite, he would also get enantiomers:

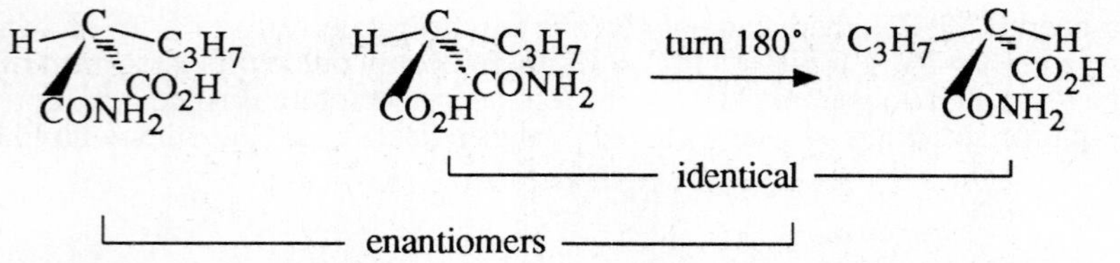

$$H-C(C_3H_7)(CO_2H)(CONH_2) \qquad H-C(C_3H_7)(CO_2H)(CONH_2) \xrightarrow{\text{turn } 180°} C_3H_7-C(H)(CO_2H)(CONH_2)$$

|———— identical ————|

|———————— enantiomers ————————|

But if Fischer *happened* to be dealing with the stereoisomer in which these groups were in *adjacent* positions, he would obtain diastereomers, which presumably would have rotations of unequal absolute magnitude and different melting points:

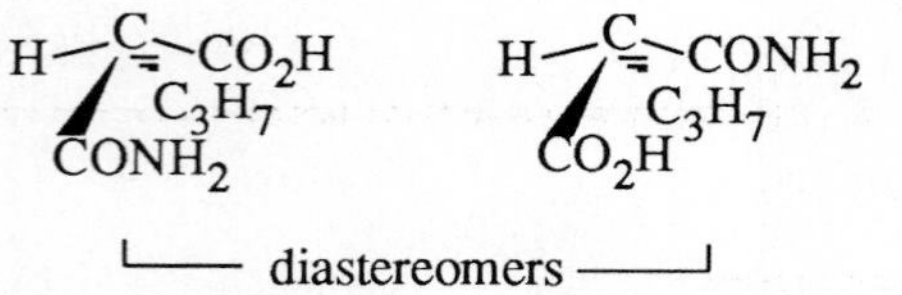

$$H-C(CO_2H)(C_3H_7)(CONH_2) \qquad H-C(CONH_2)(C_3H_7)(CO_2H)$$

|——— diastereomers ———|

Given the assumption of pyramidal geometry, Fischer had no way of knowing which stereoisomer he began with (notice from the previous problem that there are three possibilities). Thus, the conversion of one enantiomer into another could have been the result of two things occurring simultaneously: (1) pyramidal geometry and (2) the fortuitous choice of a stereoisomer in which the CO_2H and $CONH_2$ groups are in opposite positions. Fischer's result, then, was also consistent with pyramidal geometry.

38. Either result alone does not rule out pyramidal geometry, because Fischer might have fortuitously chosen to relate two groups that are on opposite corners.

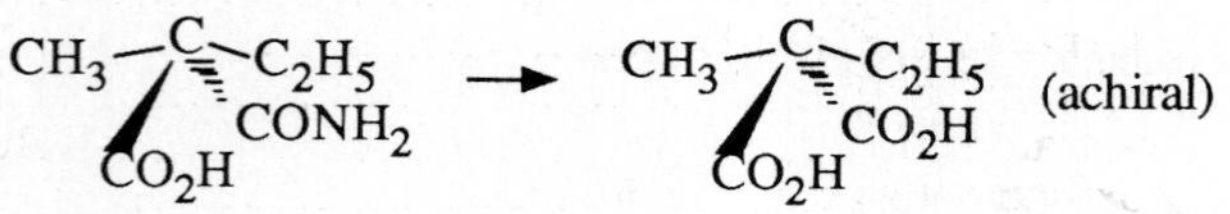

$$CH_3-C(C_2H_5)(CONH_2)(CO_2H) \rightarrow CH_3-C(C_2H_5)(CO_2H)(CO_2H) \quad \text{(achiral)}$$

However, if he happened to choose two groups on opposite corners for the *first* experiment, then in the second experiment with the same starting material, the two groups *must* be adjacent. If the compound had pyramidal geometry, then the transformation must yield a chiral substance!

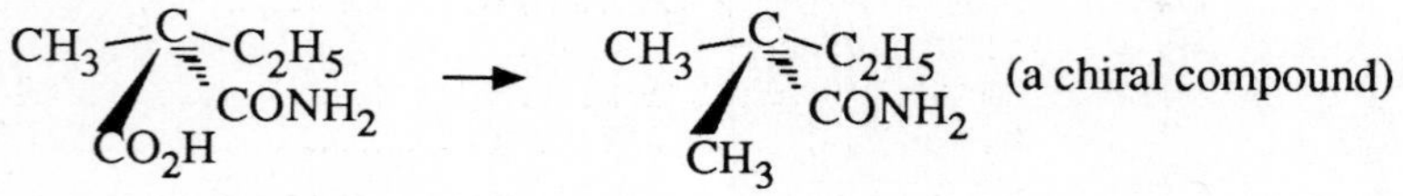

$$CH_3-C(C_2H_5)(CONH_2)(CO_2H) \rightarrow CH_3-C(C_2H_5)(CONH_2)(CH_3) \quad \text{(a chiral compound)}$$

(Be sure you see that the compound on the right is chiral. Show that its mirror image is indeed nonsuperimposable.) On the other hand, if the starting material had tetrahedral geometry, making *any* two groups identical would give an achiral compound. Since this was the experimental result, pyramidal geometry was ruled out, and tetrahedral geometry, as the only remaining possibility, was demonstrated.

➤ This but one of Emil Fischer's many beautiful contributions to the field of stereochemistry. We shall study others in Chapter 27, when we deal with Fischer's proof of the stereochemistry of the sugar glucose.

Chapter 7 / Cyclic Compounds. Stereochemistry and Chemical Reactions

---

CHAPTER 7 TERMS

angle strain 7.1
angular methyl group 7.7D
anti addition 7.10A
axial group 7.2
backside attack 7.10C
"banana"-shaped bond 7.6B
bicyclic alkane 7.7A
boat conformation 7.2
Bredt's rule 7.7C
bridged bicyclic compound 7.7A
bridgehead carbon 7.7A
bromination 7.10C
bromonium-ion mechanism 7.10C
catalytic hydrogenation 7.10D
chair conformation 7.2
circularly polarized light 7.8C
cis-decalin 7.7B
cis-disubstituted cycloalkane 7.4
cis ring fusion 7.7B
conformational analysis 7.3
conformational diastereomer 7.3
conformational enantiomer 7.4
cycloalkane 7.1
decalin 7.7B
1,3-diaxial interaction 7.3
envelope conformation 7.6
equatorial group 7.2

flagpole group 7.2
fused bicyclic compound 7.7A
gauche interaction 7.3
glycol formation 7.10D
half-chair conformation 7.2
hydroboration 7.10A
inversion of configuration 7.10B
left circularly polarized light 7.8C
loss of configuration 7.10B
monocyclic alkane 7.1
optical resolution 7.9
osmate ester 7.10D
oxymercuration 7.10D
oxymercuration-reduction 7.10D
polycyclic compound 7.7A
regioselective reaction 7.10B
retention of configuration 7.10B
right circularly polarized light 7.8C
spirocyclic alkane 7.7A
stereoselective reaction 7.10B
steroid 7.7D
strained ring 7.1
syn addition 7.10A
trans-decalin 7.7B
trans-disubstituted cycloalkane 7.4
trans ring fusion 7.7B
twist-boat conformation 7.2

CHAPTER 7 CONCEPTS

I. Cycloalkanes:

    A. <u>Monocyclic Compounds</u>:

        1. A compound that contains a single ring is called a **monocyclic compound**.

        2. The **monocyclic alkanes** have the same empirical formula: CH_2.

            a) Heats of formation can be compared by dividing by the number of CH_2 groups.

            b) The compound with the smallest heat of formation per CH_2 group is the most stable.

        3. Cyclohexane is the most stable **cycloalkane**.

4. Cyclic alkanes larger than cyclodecane do not differ very much in stability.
5. Cyclohexane has the same stability as a typical *n*-alkane (–4.9 kcal/mol per CH_2 group).
6. Cyclopropane has a planar carbon skeleton.
7. As ring size decreases, cyclic alkanes become increasingly like alkenes in their chemical behavior, especially cyclobutane and cyclopropane.
8. Rings larger than cyclopropane are puckered.

B. Bicyclic and Polycyclic Compounds:
　　1. When two rings share two or more common atoms, the compound is called a **bicyclic compound**.
　　　　a) When a bicyclic compound contains two rings joined at adjacent carbons, it is classified as a **fused bicyclic compound**.

　　　　　　bridgehead carbons　　　　　　　　　　　　　　bicyclo[4.2.0]octane

　　　　b) When the two rings are joined at nonadjacent carbons, the compound is classified as a **bridged bicyclic compound**.

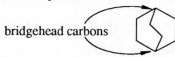

　　　　　　bridgehead carbons　　　　　　　　　　　bicyclo[2.2.2]octane

　　2. When two rings share one common atom, the compound is called a **spirocyclic compound**.

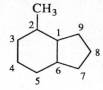

　　　　spiro carbon　　　　　　　　　　　　　　spiro[4.3]octane

　　3. Nomenclature:
　　　　a) The substituents and their positions are indicated as in monocyclic compounds.
　　　　b) The prefix **bicyclo** indicates the number of rings present.
　　　　c) The length of each carbon bridge connected to the **bridgehead carbon** atoms is indicated in decreasing value within a pair of brackets.
　　　　d) The number of atoms in the entire ring system is then indicated.

　　　　　　　　　　　　　　　　　2-methylbicyclo[4.3.0]nonane

　　4. *Cis* and *trans* ring fusion:
　　　　a) The two rings in a bicyclic compound can be fused in more than one way.
　　　　b) There are two stereoisomers of **decalin** (bicyclo[4.4.0]decane).
　　　　　　(1) In **cis-decalin**, the two —CH_2— groups on ring *B* (indicated by dots) are *cis* substituents on ring *A* and vice versa.

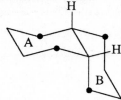

　　　　　　(2) In **trans-decalin**, the two —CH_2— groups on ring *B* (indicated with dots) are *trans* substituents on ring *A* and vice versa.

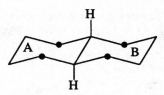

c) Each cyclohexane ring in *cis*-decalin can undergo the chair–chair interconversion.

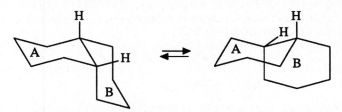

d) In *trans*-decalin, the six-membered rings can assume **twist-boat conformations,** but they cannot flip into their alternate **chair conformations.**

e) *Cis*-decalin is less stable than *trans*-decalin because of the greater number of *gauche* **interactions.**

f) Two rings may be fused in a *cis*- or *trans*-arrangement.

g) When the rings are small, only *cis* fusion is observed because *trans* fusion introduces too much ring strain.

h) In larger rings, both *cis*- and *trans*-fused isomers are well known, but the *trans*-fused ones are more stable because *gauche* interactions are minimized.

C. *Trans*-cycloalkenes:

    1. The *trans*-cycloalkenes with six or fewer carbons have never been observed.

    2. The medium-ring *trans*-cycloalkenes are considerably less stable than their *cis* isomers.

    3. A small bridged bicyclic compound is unstable if it has a double bond at a bridgehead carbon (**Bredt's rule**).

D. Steroids:

    1. **Steroids** are important naturally occurring compounds containing fused rings.

    2. All ring fusions are *trans*.

    3. The all-*trans* **ring fusion** causes a steroid to be conformationally rigid and relatively flat.

    4. Methyl groups attached to bridgehead carbons are called **angular methyl groups**.

        a) The angular methyls occupy axial positions.

        b) The top face of the steroid is called the β-face.

        c) The bottom face of the steroid is called the α-face.

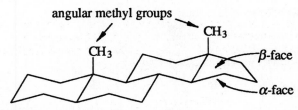

    5. Two medically important classes of steroids are:

        a) Sex hormones.

        b) Corticosteroids.

E. Planar Representation of Cyclic Compounds:

    1. The structures of nonplanar cyclic compounds can be represented by planar polygons; the stereochemistry of substituents can be indicated by dashed lines or wedges.

        a) If a substituent is up (towards the observer), it is represented with a wedge.

b) If a substituent is down (away from the observer), it it represented with a dashed line or a dashed wedge.

2. The same planar structure describes any conformation of the ring, provided that all conformations are viewed from the same face of the molecule.
   a) The chair–chair conformational change does not interchange the dashed lines and wedges.

   b) The chair–chair conformational change does not change the up or down relationship of groups on the ring.

3. Planar representations are *not* the same as Fischer representations.

II. Conformations of Cyclohexane:

A. <u>Chair Conformations</u>:
   1. The most stable conformations of cyclohexane are the chair forms.
      a) Opposite sides of the chair are parallel.
      b) The ring carbons and the substituent groups are staggered.
      c) **Axial groups** are perpendicular to the average plane of the chair conformation.
         (1) Three axial groups are above the ring.
         (2) Three axial groups are below the ring.
      d) **Equatorial groups** radiate outward from the ring carbons.

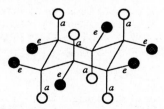

   2. When a cyclohexane molecule undergoes internal rotation, the result is a change in the conformation of the ring.
   3. There are two chair conformations.
      a) The equatorial hydrogens become axial hydrogens through a chair–chair interconversion.
      b) The axial hydrogens become equatorial hydrogens through a chair–chair interconversion.
      c) The chair–chair interconversion is rapid at room temperature.
      d) The rapid interconversion causes the axial and equatorial hydrogens to become equivalent and indistinguishable.

B. <u>Half-chair Conformations</u>:
  1. The **half-chair conformations** of cyclohexane are *not* stable.
     a) The hydrogens are eclipsed.
     b) There is **angle strain**.
  2. The half-chair conformations have five of the ring carbons in the same plane.
  3. The half-chair conformations lie at an energy maximum (10.1 kcal/mol higher in standard free energy than the chair conformations).

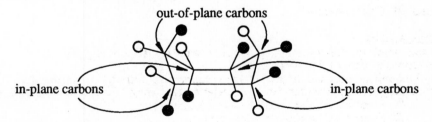

C. <u>Boat Conformations</u>:
  1. **Boat conformations** of cyclohexane are *not* stable.
     a) There is no angle strain.
     b) Several C—H bonds are eclipsed.
     c) The flagpole hydrogens experience some van der Waals repulsion.
  2. A boat conformation has two opposite ring carbons, tilted in the same direction, out of the plane containing the remaining four ring carbons.

out-of-plane carbons

in-plane carbons   in-plane carbons

D. <u>Twist-boat Conformation</u>:
  1. Twist-boat conformations of cyclohexane lie at energy minima.
  2. The twist-boat conformations are *stable* forms of cyclohexane, but not as stable at the chair forms.
     a) The flagpole interactions present in the boat forms are somewhat relieved in the twist-boat forms.
     b) The eclipsing interactions present in the boat forms are somewhat relieved in the twist-boat forms.

III. Conformational Analysis:

A. <u>Monosubstituted Cyclohexanes</u>:
   1. The analysis of molecular conformations and their relative energies is called **conformational analysis**.
   2. Methylcyclohexane is a mixture of two **conformational diastereomers** at room temperature.
      a) Diastereomers have different energies.
      b) Equatorial methylcyclohexane is more stable than axial methylcyclohexane by two *gauche* interactions.

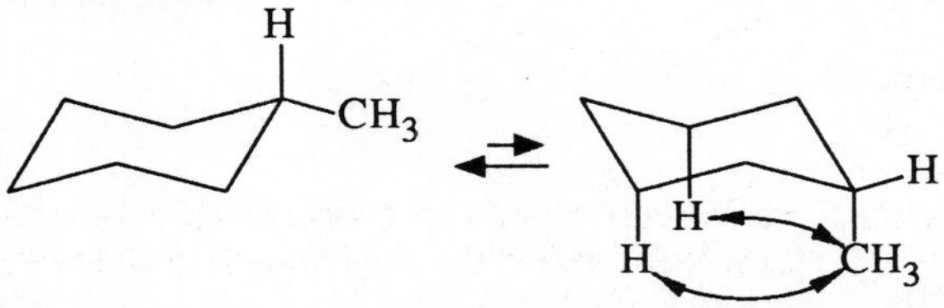

gauche interactions

   3. An axial group has a **1,3-diaxial interaction** with each axial group on the same face of the ring.
   4. Each 1,3-diaxial interaction consists of two *gauche* interactions.
   5. The larger the substituent group, the more the equilibrium favors the equatorial conformation.

B. <u>Disubstituted Cyclohexanes — *Cis-Trans* Isomerism in Cyclic Compounds</u>:
   1. A *trans*-**disubstituted** cyclohexane is one in which the substituent groups have an up–down relationship.
      a) Some *trans*-disubstituted cyclohexanes are a mixture of conformational diastereomers.
      b) Some *trans*-disubstituted cyclohexanes are a mixture of **conformational enantiomers**.
      c) The conformations of some *trans*-disubstituted cyclohexanes are identical.

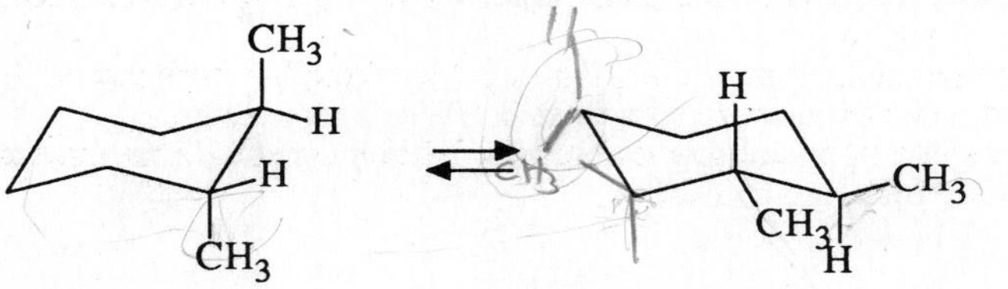

conformational diastereomers

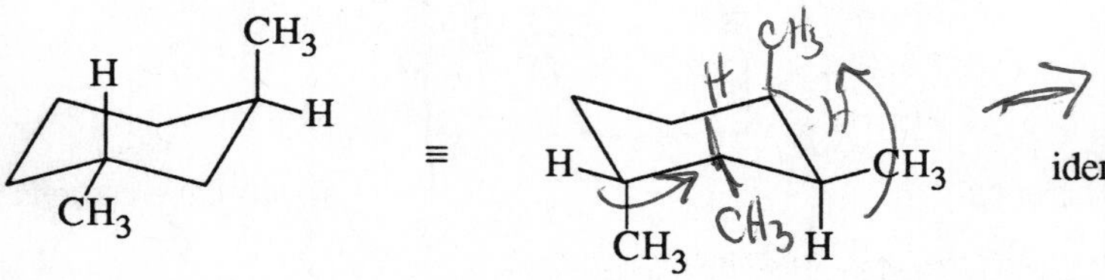

identical

   2. A *cis*-**disubstituted** cyclohexane is one in which the substituent groups have an up–up or a down–down relationship.
      a) Some *cis*-disubstituted cyclohexanes are a mixture of conformational diastereomers.

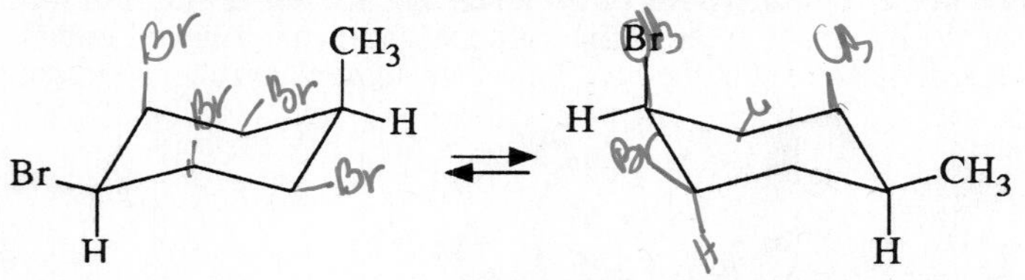

conformational diastereomers

      b) Some *cis*-disubstituted cyclohexanes are a mixture of conformational enantiomers.

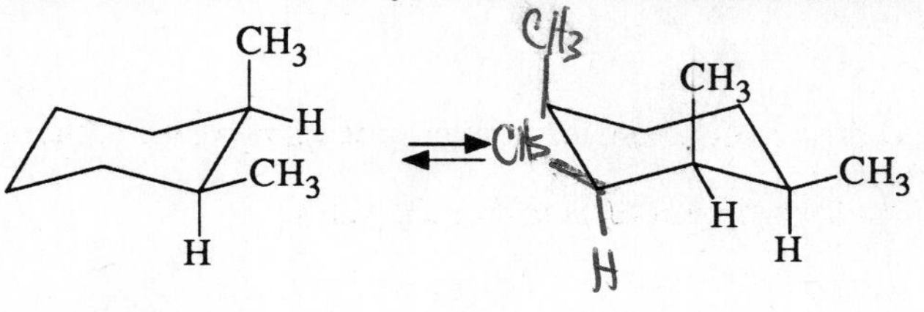

conformational enantiomers

c) The conformations of some *cis*-disubstituted cyclohexanes are identical.

3) In the diequatorial form of disubstituted cyclohexanes:
   a) There are no *gauche* interactions of the substituent groups with the carbon ring.
   b) For 1,2-disubstituted cyclohexanes, there is a *gauche* interaction between the two groups themselves.

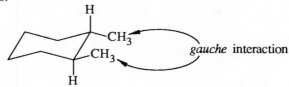

4. In the diaxial form of disubstituted cyclohexanes:
   a) There are two *gauche* interactions for each of the substituent groups with the carbon rings.
   b) For 1,2-disubstituted cyclohexanes, there are no *gauche* interactions between the two groups themselves.

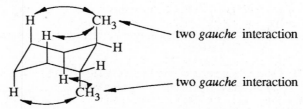

5. When two groups on a substituted cyclohexane conflict in their preference for the equatorial position, the preferred conformation can usually be predicted from the relative conformational preferences of the two groups.

6. A 1,3-diaxial interaction between two methyl groups is considerably more severe than a 1,3-diaxial interaction between a methyl and a hydrogen.

7. The *t*-butyl group is so large that its conformational preference dominates the conformational equilibrium.

C. Cyclopentane:
   1. Cyclopentane exists in a nonplanar conformation.
   2. The puckered form of the five-membered ring is called the **envelope conformation**.
   3. The envelope conformation relieves some of the eclipsed-hydrogen interactions that would be present in fully planar cyclopentane; hydrogens at three of the five carbon atoms assume axial or equatorial positions.

   4. Cyclopentane undergoes rapid conformational changes in which each carbon successively alternates as the point of the envelope.

D. Cyclobutane:
   1. Cyclobutane exists in a puckered conformation that relieves eclipsing interactions between the hydrogens on adjacent carbons.
   2. Two equivalent puckered conformations are in rapid equilibrium.

3. Cyclobutane is highly strained.

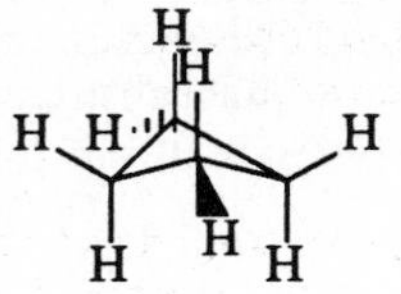

E. Cyclopropane:
    1. Cyclopropane has a planar carbon skeleton.
    2. Cyclopropane has significant angle strain.
    3. The carbon–carbon bonds of cyclopropane are bent in a "banana" shape around the ring periphery.
    4. The angle between the orbitals is about 104°.

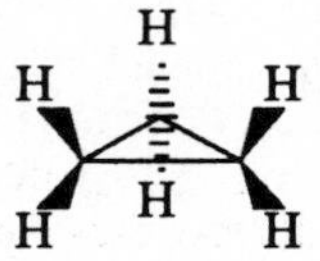

IV. Stereochemistry and Chemical Reactions:

A. General:
    1. When chiral products are formed from achiral starting materials, both enantiomers of a pair are always formed at the same rate.
        a) Reactions that give a pair of enantiomeric products occur through enantiomeric transition states.
            (1) Enantiomers have equal energies.
            (2) Both transition states have the same standard free energy.

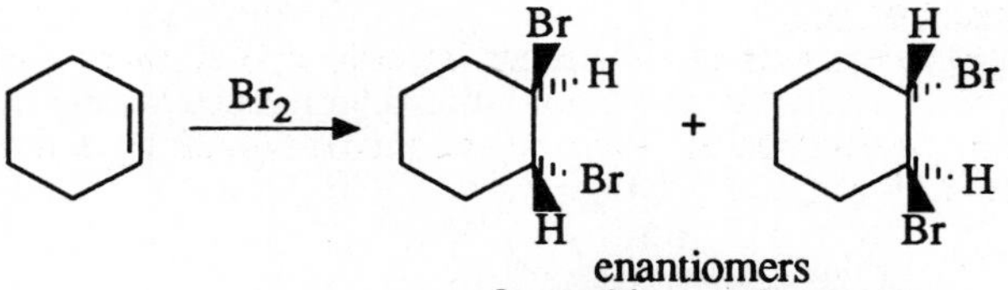

enantiomers
formed in equal amounts

        b) The product is always the racemate.
        c) Optical activity never arises spontaneously in the reaction of achiral compounds.
    2. When diastereomeric products can be formed in a reaction, they are always formed at different rates.
        a) Different amounts of each product are always formed although the difference may not be detectable.
        b) Reactions that give a pair of diastereomeric products occur through diastereomeric transition states.
            (1) Diastereomers have different energies.
            (2) One transition state has lower standard free energy than its diastereomer.

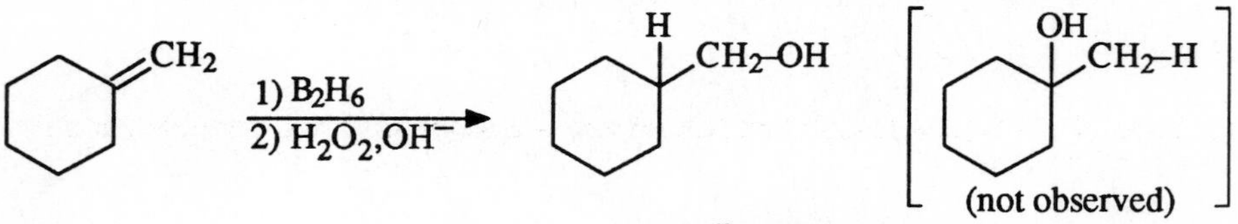

diastereomers
formed in different amounts

            (3) When the starting materials are achiral, each diastereomer of the product will be formed as a pair of enantiomers (the racemate).
    3. Enantiomers differ in their chemical or physical behavior only when they interact with other chiral objects or forces.
        a) A pair of enantiomers react at the same rate with an achiral reagent.
        b) The two enantiomers of a pair react at different rates with a chiral reagent.

B. <u>Chirality in Nature</u>:
    1. Nature is a source of optically active compounds.
    2. All enzymes are optically pure chiral compounds.

C. *Syn* and *Anti* Addition:
    1. The addition of any reagent to an alkene π-bond can occur in two stereochemically different ways.
        a) In **syn addition**, two groups add to the double bond from the same face.
            (1) In *syn* addition to a cycloalkene, these groups have a *cis* relationship in the product.
            (2) *Syn* addition can occur from above or below the π-bond of the alkene.

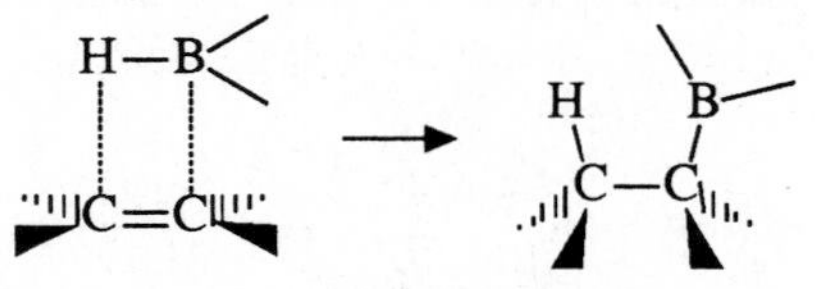

        b) In **anti addition**, two groups add to the double bond from opposite faces.
            (1) In *anti* addition to a cycloalkene, these groups have a *trans* relationship in the product.
            (2) *Anti* addition can occur with the first group adding from above and the second from below the alkene π-bond, or vice versa.

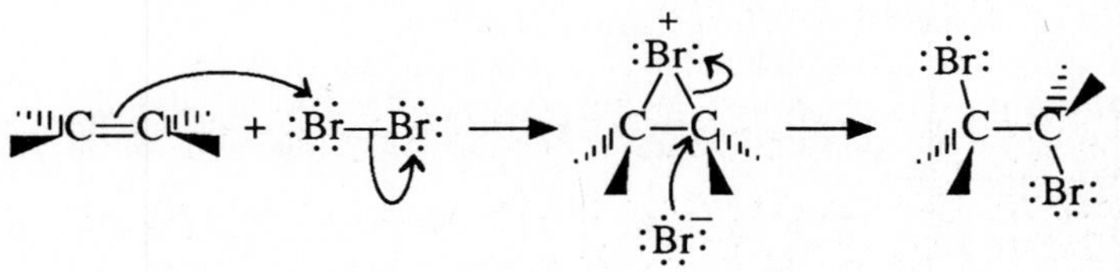

D. <u>Reactions at Asymmetric Carbons</u>:
    1. Substitution of one group for another at an asymmetric carbon can occur in two stereochemically different ways.
        a) **Retention of configuration** occurs when there is no change in the stereochemistry of the asymmetric carbon.

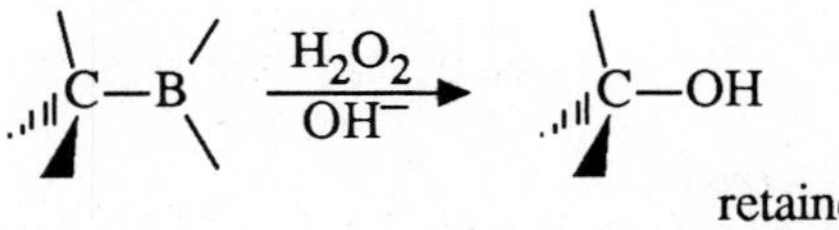

retained stereochemistry

        b) **Inversion of configuration** occurs when there is a change in the stereochemistry of the asymmetric carbon.

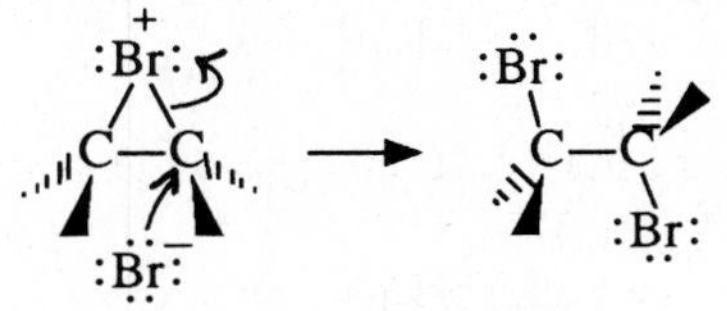

inverted stereochemistry

        c) **Loss of configuration** occurs when there is a mixture of both retention and inversion of configuration.

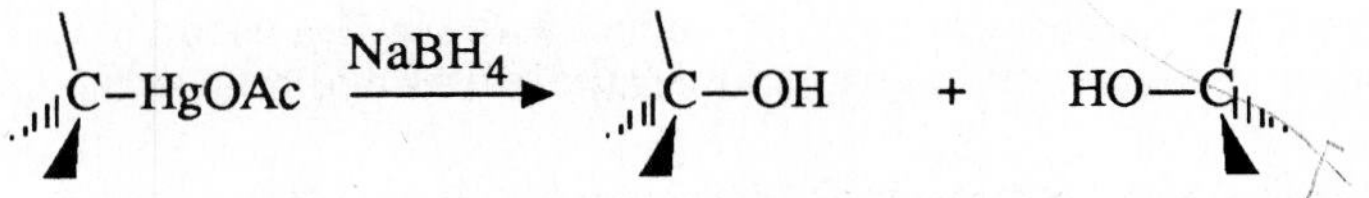

retained
stereochemistry

inverted
stereochemistry

    2. A reaction that gives a large predominance of one stereoisomer over another is called a **stereoselective reaction**.

V. Alkene Addition Reactions:

A. Hydroboration–Oxidation of Alkenes:
1. **Hydroboration–oxidation** is a stereoselective reaction.
2. Hydroboration–oxidation is a **regioselective reaction**.
3. The addition of H—B to an alkene π-bond is a *syn* addition.
4. The oxidation of an organoborane occurs with retention of configuration.
5. Hydroboration–oxidation of an alkene brings about the net *syn* addition of the elements of H–OH to the double bond.
6. Hydroboration–oxidation gives an overall anti-Markovnikov addition of H–OH across the double bond.

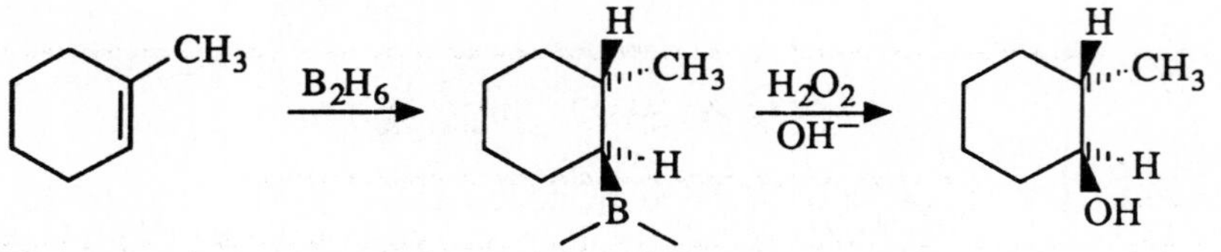

B. Bromination of Alkenes:
1. **Bromination** of alkenes is a stereoselective reaction.
2. The addition of bromine to an alkene π-bond is an *anti* addition.
     a) A **bromonium ion** is formed on either face of the alkene π-bond.
     b) The formation of a bromonium ion at one face of an alkene is followed by attack of bromide from the opposite face.
        (1) The attack of the bromide ion occurs with inversion of configuration.
        (2) For *cis*-2-butene, attack of the bromide ion at one carbon yields one enantiomer; attack at the other carbon yields the other enantiomer.

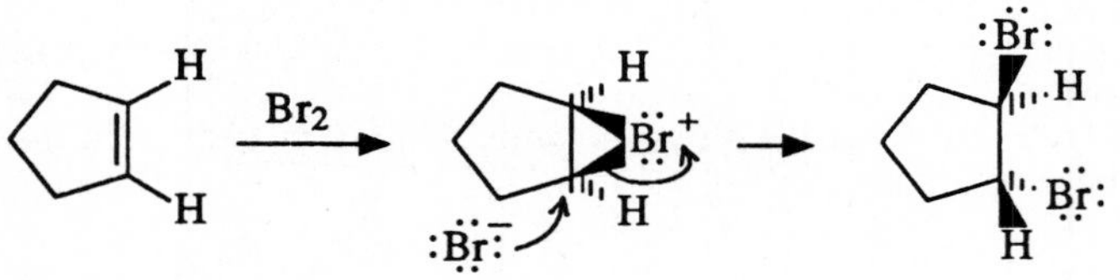

C. Catalytic Hydrogenation of Alkenes:
1. **Catalytic hydrogenation** is a stereoselective reaction.
2. Catalytic hydrogenation of most alkenes is a *syn* addition.

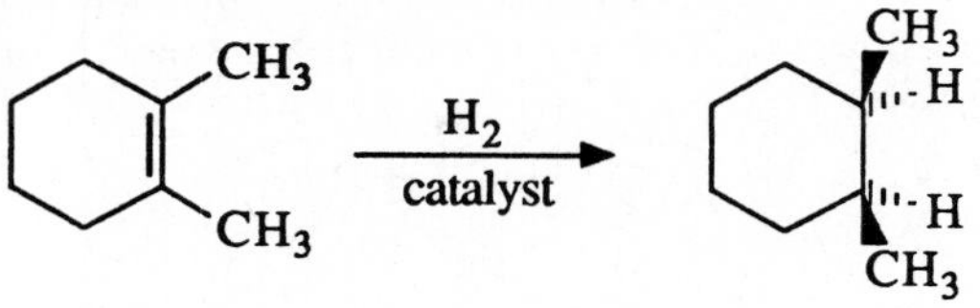

D. Oxymercuration–Reduction of Alkenes:
1. **Oxymercuration–reduction** of alkenes is a regioselective reaction.
2. Oxymercuration–reduction of alkenes is *not* a stereoselective reaction.
     a) Oxymercuration of alkenes is a stereoselective reaction.
     b) Reduction of the organomercury compound is *not* a stereoselective reaction.
3. Oxymercuration of alkenes is an *anti* addition.
4. The reduction of the mercury-containing product with $NaBH_4$ occurs with loss of configuration.
5. Oxymercuration–reduction gives an overall Markovnikov addition of H—OH across the double bond.

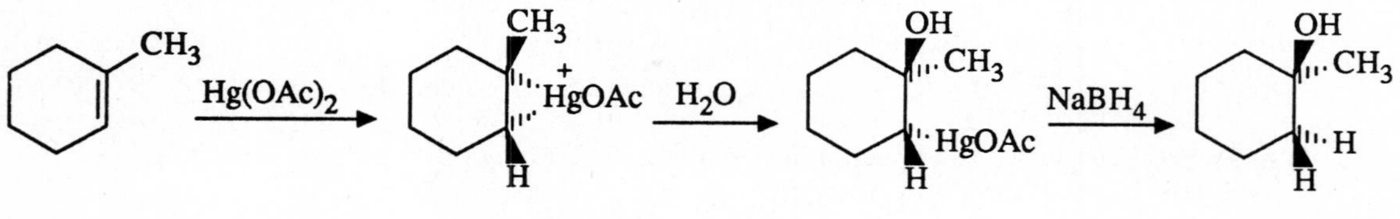

E. Formation of Glycols from Alkenes:
    1. The formation of glycols from alkenes with either alkaline $KMnO_4$ or OsO_4 is a stereoselective reaction.
    2. The formation of glycols from alkenes with either alkaline $KMnO_4$ or OsO_4 is a *syn* addition.

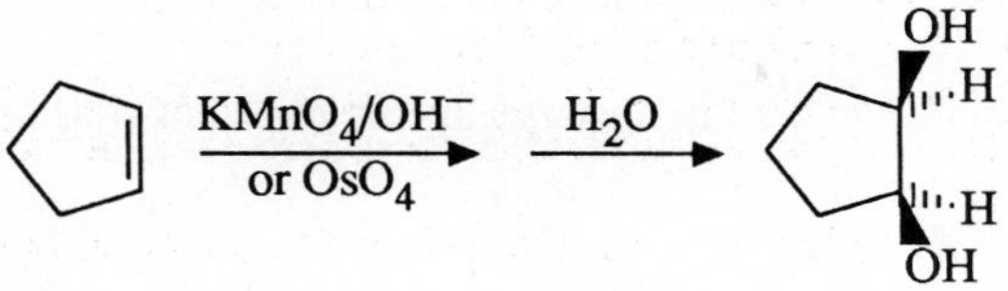

===========================

CHAPTER 7 RULES

Bredt's Rule: Small bridged bicyclic compounds are unstable if they have a double bond at a bridgehead carbon.

CHAPTER 7 SOLUTIONS

Solutions to In-Text Problems

1. We use the relationship between standard free energy and equilibrium constant:

   $$\Delta G^\circ = -2.303RT\log K_{eq}$$

   Taking antilogs, we have

   $$K_{eq} = 10^{-\Delta G^\circ/2.303RT} = 10^{-3.8/1.364} = 1.64 \times 10^{-3} \text{ at 25 °C (or 298 K).}$$

   This equilibrium constant is simply the ratio [boat]/[chair], which is the relative amount we are seeking.

2. This problem uses the same relationship as Problem 1.

   $$K_{eq} = 10^{-\Delta G^\circ/2.303RT} = 10^{-1.74/1.364} = 0.053.$$

   This is the ratio [axial]/[equatorial] for methylcyclohexane.

3. In one rotational form (form A below), the ethyl group indeed should behave as if it is larger. However, it can rotate so that the methyl group is away from the axial hydrogens of the ring (form B), in which case its interactions with the ring hydrogens resemble those in methylcyclohexane (C).

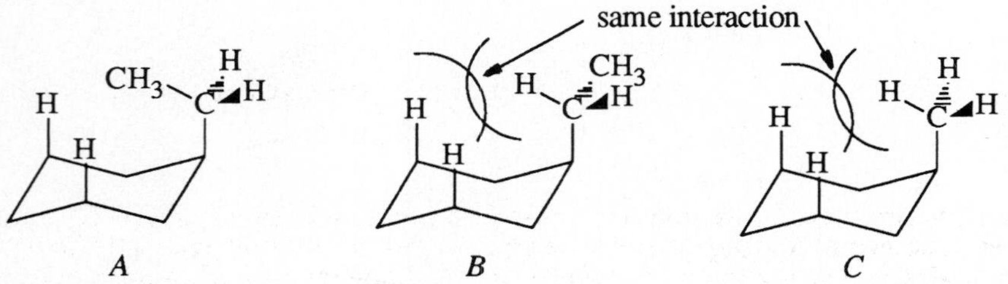

4.

   (a)

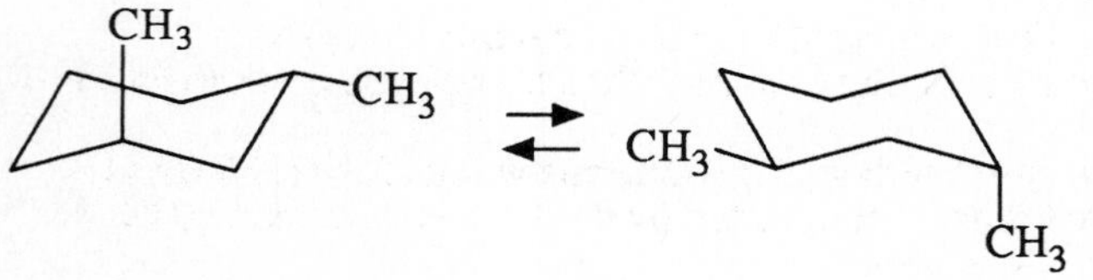

   (b)

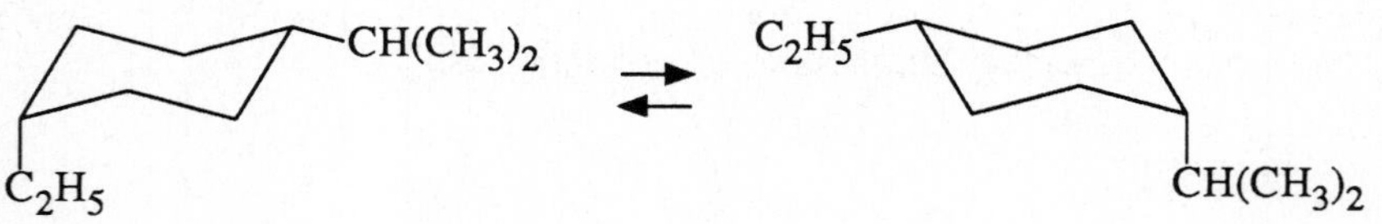

   A boat form of (b):

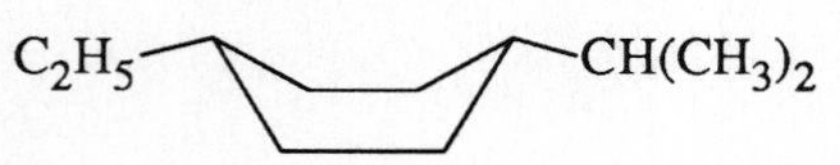

5. Compound (a) is ruled out, because there is no other *trans* isomer. Compound (e) is ruled out, because there is no other 1,3-dimethylcyclohexane. Compounds (b) and (c) are identical. Compounds (b) and (d) are the

conformational isomers, as we can see by flipping (b), then turning it 180°:

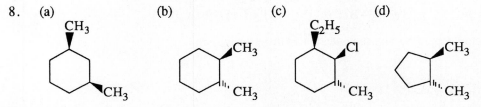

compound (b)   compound (d)

(This, of course, makes (c) and (d) conformational isomers as well.)

6.   (a) The two chair forms are identical. Let us demonstrate this rigorously.

(b) The two chair forms are conformational diastereomers. This case is relatively easy to see, because flipping changes both the chlorine and the methyl from equatorial to axial; if the two forms were enantiomeric or identical, the chlorine or methyl would have to be in the same type of position (equatorial or axial) in both conformers. Since these two possibilities are immediately ruled out, the only remaining possibility — conformational diastereomers — is the correct answer.
(c) The two chair forms are conformational diastereomers, for the same reason as in (b).
(d) The two chair forms are identical. (Use models, flip one form, then manipulate it to show identity to the other form.) DON'T SKIP THIS EXERCISE!
(e) If the *sec*-butyl groups did not contain a chiral carbon, the two forms would be conformational enantiomers; however, the chirality of these groups is unaffected by the flip. Hence, the two forms are conformational diastereomers.

7.   The *cis* compound has no *gauche* (1,3-diaxial) interactions; the *trans* compound has two, for a total of 1.74 kcal/mol. This is the enthalpy difference between the two compounds.

8.   (a)   (b)   (c)   (d)

In (a), the two bonds could both be drawn as dashed wedges. In (b) and (d), the solid and dashed wedges could be interchanged.

9. (a)

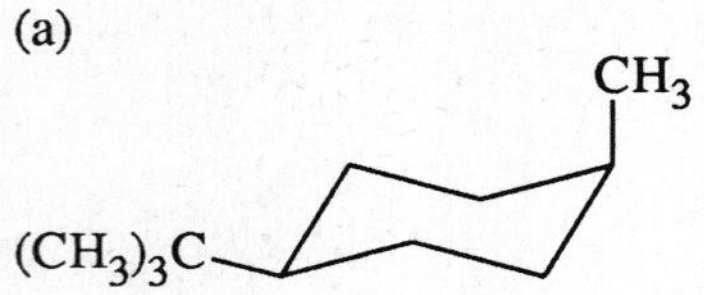

(b)

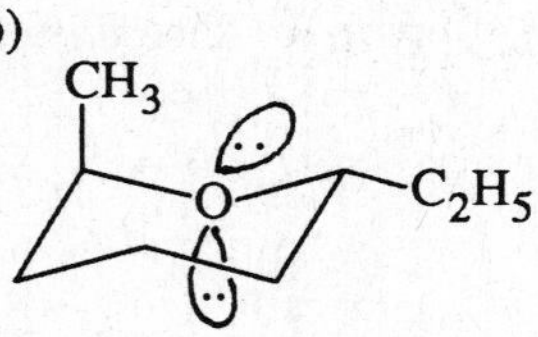

In (b), one electron pair on the oxygen is in an equatorially oriented sp^3 orbital, and the other is in an axially oriented sp^3 orbital.

10. We do not need to draw out three-dimensional projections in order to answer this question. We can treat the ring *as if it were planar*. Why? Because the two chair conformations *average* over time to be planar. For example, a mirror-image (enantiomeric) relationship in (a) is clear if we simply rotate the second structure 180° in the plane of the paper:

(a)

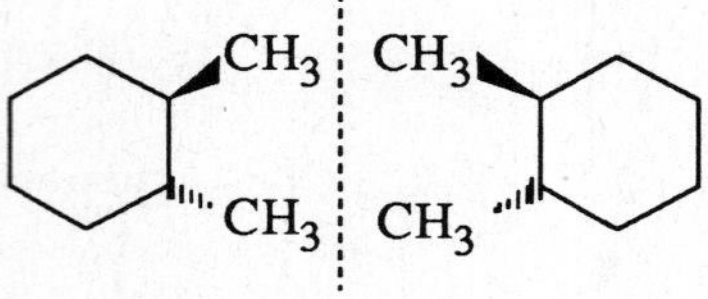

mirror plane

(b) Enantiomers (c) Identical

11. The way to handle this problem is to construct diagrams for the dipole-moment vectors of each type of *trans*-1,3-dibromocyclobutane:

puckered:

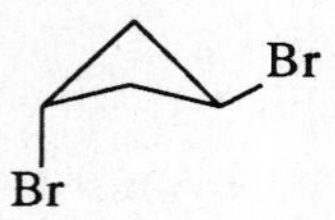

planar:

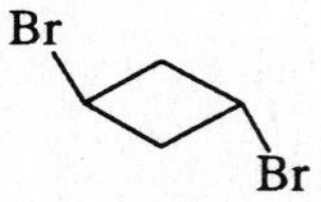

vector diagrams:

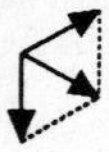

resultant is not zero

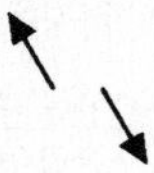

(zero resultant)

The orientations of the two bromines in the puckered compound is such that their dipole-moment vectors do not cancel; puckered 1,3-dibromocyclobutane is therefore predicted to have a nonzero dipole moment. In contrast, planar 1,3-dibromocyclobutane is predicted to have zero dipole moment. Hence, the data are in accord with the puckered form.

12. Products with cyclopropane:

(a) $CH_3CH_2CH_3$ (b) Br—$CH_2CH_2CH_2$—Br (c) Br—$CH_2CH_2CH_3$

In the case of methylcyclopropane, the ring can open in two different ways:

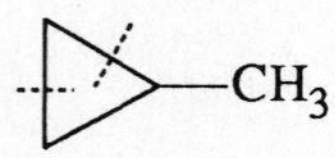

The corresponding products are:

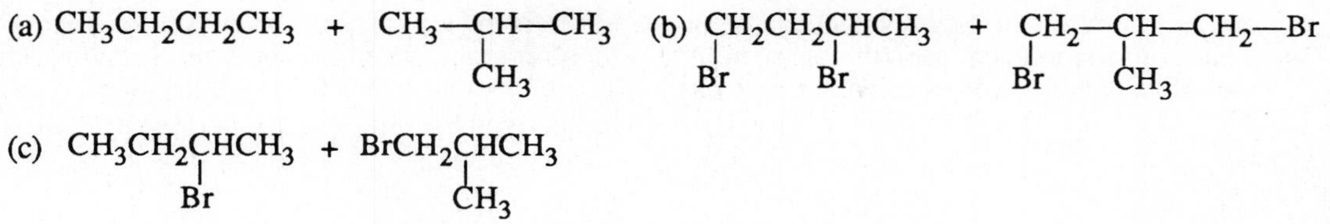

(a) $CH_3CH_2CH_2CH_3$ + $CH_3{-}\underset{\underset{CH_3}{|}}{CH}{-}CH_3$ (b) $\underset{\underset{Br}{|}}{CH_2}CH_2\underset{\underset{Br}{|}}{CH}CH_3$ + $\underset{\underset{Br}{|}}{CH_2}{-}\underset{\underset{CH_3}{|}}{CH}{-}CH_2{-}Br$

(c) $CH_3CH_2\underset{\underset{Br}{|}}{CH}CH_3$ + $BrCH_2\underset{\underset{CH_3}{|}}{CH}CH_3$

If we assume that the mechanism of HBr addition to cyclopropanes resembles that for alkenes, then in (c), the first product, *sec*-butyl bromide, would predominate because a more stable carbocation would be involved in its formation:

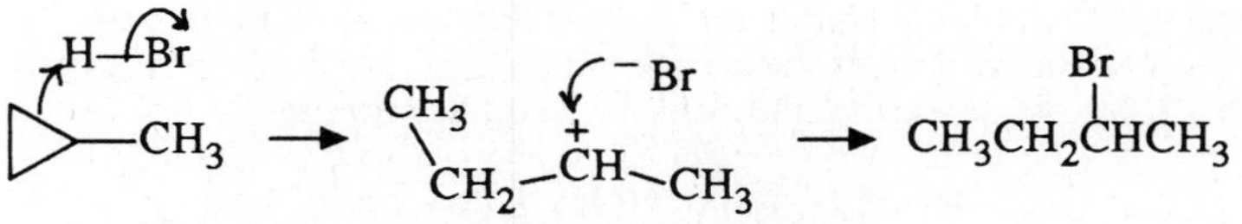

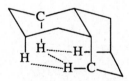 $\rightarrow$ ... $\rightarrow$ $CH_3CH_2\underset{\underset{Br}{|}}{CH}CH_3$

a secondary carbocation

In contrast, formation of the second product, isobutyl bromide, would involve formation of a primary carbocation.

13. (a) Bicyclo[2.2.2]octane   (b) Bicyclo[4.4.0]decane

14. The two labeled carbons in the diagram of *cis*-decalin below are axial substituents, and the hydrogens on these carbons are involved in 1,3-diaxial interactions (dashed lines). There are, as in other axially-substituted alkylcyclohexanes, two 1,3-diaxial interactions per axial carbon, except that one is common to both carbons; hence, there are a total of three 1,3-diaxial interactions. Except for the interactions of ring carbons with each other (which are the same as in *cis*-decalin), *trans*-decalin has no *gauche* interactions. Hence, *trans*-decalin is more stable than *cis*-decalin by 2.7 kcal/mol, a number that is verified experimentally by heats of combustion.

15. (a) The model of *cis*-bicyclo[3.1.0]hexane is much more easily built.
(b) The models of *both* stereoisomers are built with about equal ease. The reason for the difficulty in (a) is that *trans* bonds in six-membered rings cannot be compressed to a dihedral angle smaller than 50-60° without introducing considerable ring strain. In order to fuse a three-membered ring, this dihedral angle must be nearly zero. In larger rings, as in (b), *trans* bonds can be compressed to the required 0° without introducing significant ring strain.

strain in this ring decreases with increasing ring size

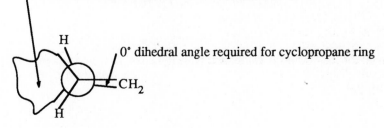

0° dihedral angle required for cyclopropane ring

16. (a) Any one conformation of *trans*-cyclooctene is chiral. Conversion into its enantiomer is slow [see (b)].
(b) When one conformation converts into its enantiomeric conformation, the alkene unit must turn in such a way that one of the alkene hydrogens passes very close to one of the hydrogens four carbons away.

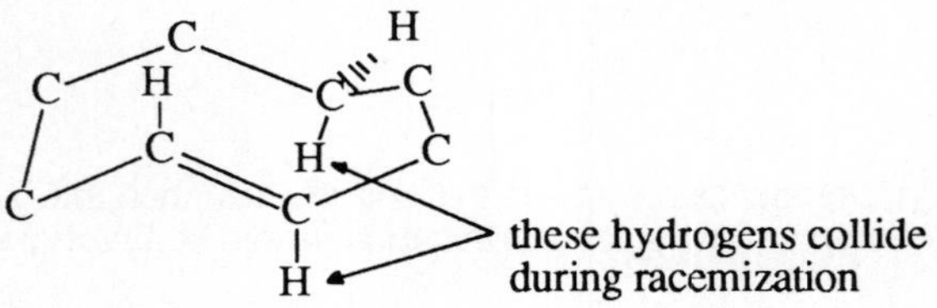

these hydrogens collide during racemization

This raises the energy of the transition state for interconversion, and makes the interconversion slow. This means that *trans*-cyclooctene can be separated into enantiomeric conformations that are not interconverted at room temperature. This, then, is another example of a chiral molecule without asymmetric atoms (Sec. 6.8A).

17. The less stable compound has the higher heat of formation. Compound (b) is less stable because the *trans* double bond is incorporated in a seven-membered ring, whereas in (a), it is incorporated in a ten-membered ring.

18. Driving a nail has no chiral elements; hence, our right and left hands (assuming equal strength) would not differ in their ability to drive a nail. However, driving a screw involves a helical motion (twisting plus forward motion of the screw). Since helices are chiral and hands are chiral, the two hands would differ in their ability to drive a screw. In other words, enantiomeric objects differ in their ability to perform chiral actions.

19. Premeds could take out their stethoscopes and find out which side of each person the heart is on. Mr. D's heart, like our hearts, should be on the left; Mr. L's heart would be on what we call the right. Another approach would be to shake hands with each gentleman. Mr. L should extend what we consider to be his left hand. Or we could have them write their names. (How would this distinguish the two?)

20. We write all possible diastereomers, which are in principle formed in different amounts:

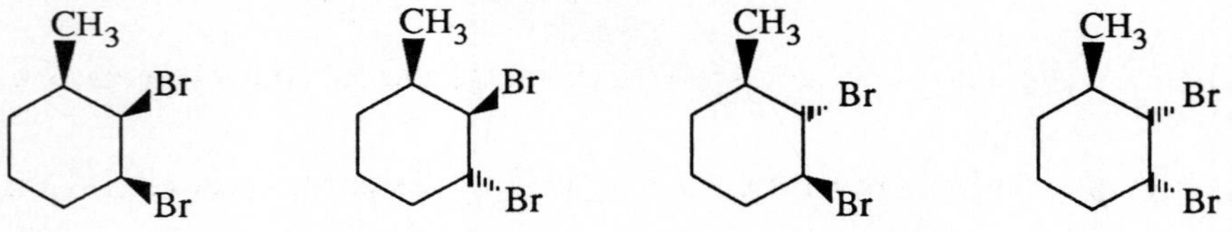

Each of these has an enantiomer:

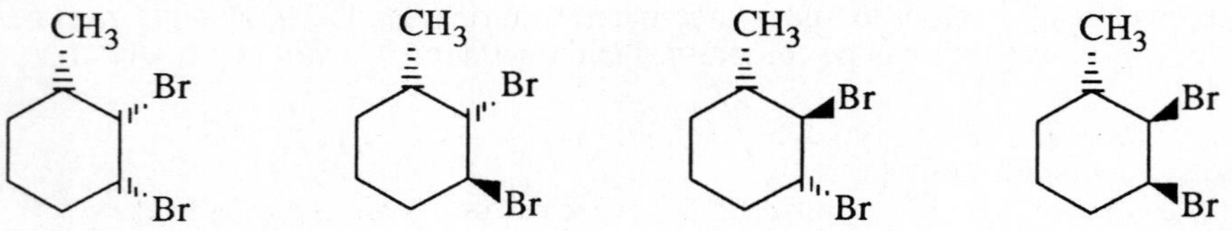

Enantiomers are formed in the same amounts. Suppose, for example, A, B, C, and D were formed in 5%, 10%, 15%, and 20% yield, respectively. Then their enantiomers A', B', C', and D' would be formed in 5%, 10%, 15%, and 20% yield, respectively.

21. *Syn* addition:

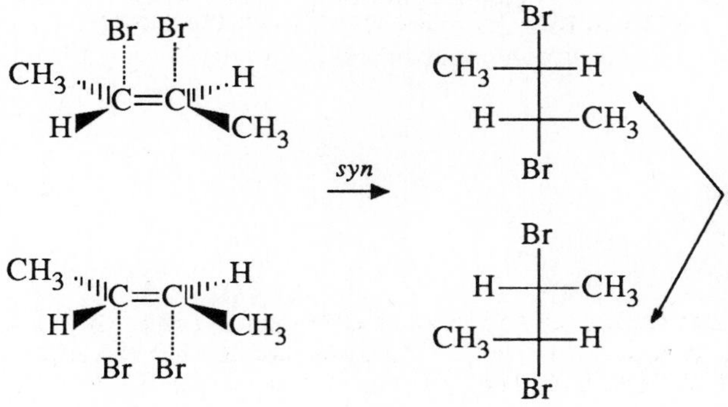

racemate

Anti addition:

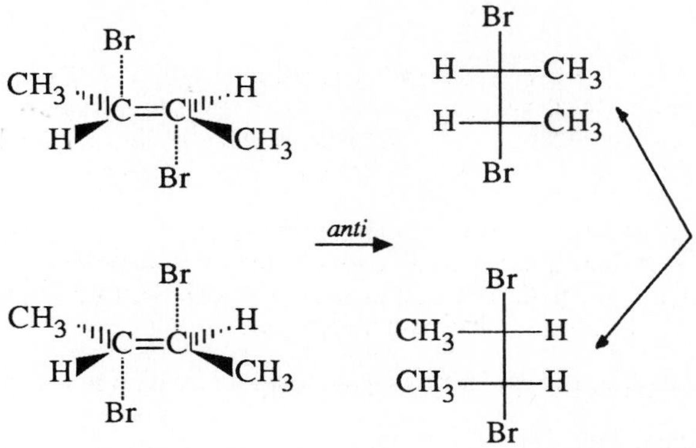

identical *meso* compounds

From the data given on page 257, the *meso* stereoisomer is obtained; hence, the addition of bromine to *trans*-2-butene is *anti*.

22. (a) The bromonium-ion mechanism implies *anti* addition. *Anti* addition of bromine to cyclohexene gives *trans*-1,2-dibromocyclohexane:

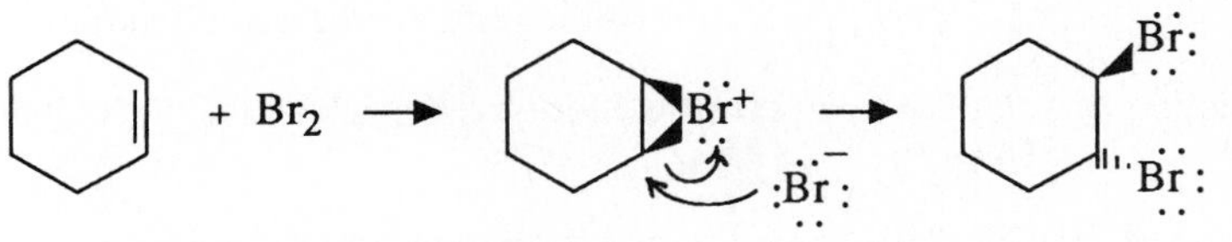

(b) The products with the bromines *trans* are most likely; these are products *B*, *C*, *B'*, and *C'*.

23. The mercurinium-ion mechanism of oxymercuration is analogous to the bromonium-ion mechanism for bromination. That is, the group that attacks the cyclic ion (Br^- in bromination, OH_2 in oxymercuration) enters from the side of the molecule opposite to that of the positively charged Br or Hg. As we can see in Eq. 7.35, text page 260, the —OH and —HgOAc groups in the product are *trans*, as required by this mechanism.

24. (a)

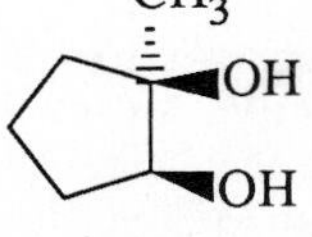

(racemate)

(b)

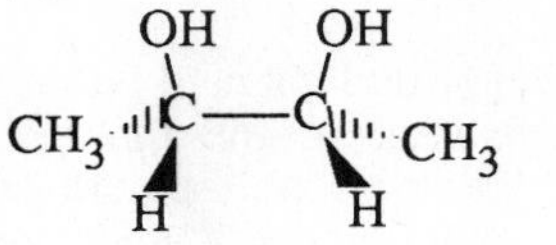

meso

(c)

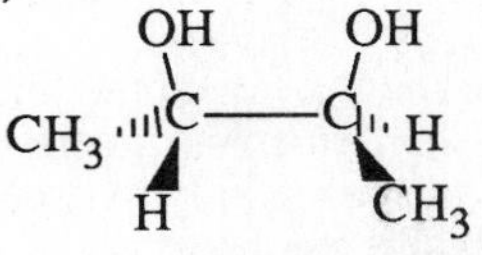

(racemate)

In bromination of the same alkenes, the products would differ from those above in two ways. First, and most obviously, the —OH groups would be replaced by —Br groups; and second, the products would differ in their stereochemistry. In the product derived from (a), the two —Br groups would be *trans*. The product derived from (b), as we have seen in the text, would be racemic 2,3-dibromobutane; and the product derived from (c) would be *meso*-2,3-dibromobutane.

Solutions to Additional Problems

25. (a) There are many correct answers to this problem. Two are:

bicyclo[3.1.0]hexane   bicyclo[2.1.1]hexane

(b)

26. The two compounds are structural isomers; one is an alkene, and the other is a cycloalkane, which will not undergo typical alkene reactions.
(a) A molecular weight determination will *not* distinguish between isomers.
(b) The alkene will take up hydrogen (Sec. 5.7A); the cycloalkane will not.
(c) The alkene will give a positive Baeyer test for unsaturation; the cycloalkane will not react. (See Sec. 5.4.)
(d) Both compounds, as isomers, have the same empirical formula (CH_2).
(e) Structural isomers in general differ in their physical properties. Indeed, we expect the cyclohexane derivative to have a smaller heat of formation than the alkene. (See the data at the bottom of text page 239; alkenes have considerably larger heats of formation than even cyclobutanes and cyclopropanes. This is reasonable if we consider them to be "cycloethanes.")
(f) The alkene is chiral and the cycloalkane is not. Hence, the alkene can in principle be separated into enantiomers.
(g) The alkene would decolorize a solution of bromine in carbon tetrachloride (Sec. 5.1A); the cycloalkane will not react with this reagent.

27. The problem tells us that [equatorial]/[axial] = 2.07. This, then, is equal to the equilibrium constant for interconversion of the two forms. Knowing the equilibrium constant, calculation of the standard free-energy difference is straightforward:

$$\Delta G° = -2.303RT \log K_{eq} = -1.364 \log (2.07) = 0.43 \text{ kcal/mol at } 25 °C \text{ (298 K)}.$$

The compound present in greatest amount at equilibrium is more stable; hence, equatorial chlorocyclohexane is more stable. This is also what we would expect from the general observation that equatorial substitution is favored over axial substitution for most cyclohexane substituent groups.

28. There are two requirements that a compound must meet in order to be separated into enantiomeric forms. First, it obviously must be chiral. Second, the two enantiomeric forms must not interconvert rapidly. A trick that can be used to test both points simultaneously is simply to draw the *planar* representation and see whether its mirror image is superimposable. If not, it can be resolved into enantiomers. (We leave it to you to figure out why this works.)

(a) *Cis*-1,3-dimethylcyclopentane is not chiral, and therefore cannot be separated into enantiomers.

(b) *Trans*-1,3-dimethylcyclopentane is indeed chiral; its mirror image is not superimposable:

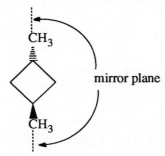

mirror images do not
superimpose

Hence, this compound can in principle be resolved into enantiomers.

(c) 1,2,2-Trimethylcyclopropane is chiral and can be resolved into enantiomers.

(d) *Trans*-1,3-dimethylcyclobutane has an internal mirror plane and is therefore not chiral:

29. (1) (a) Structure of the product:

$$C_3H_7\!-\!\underset{\displaystyle \underset{C_2H_5}{|}}{\overset{\displaystyle \overset{Br}{|}}{C}}\!-\!CH_3$$

(b) The product is formed as a pair of enantiomers.
(c) Because the reagents are achiral, the two enantiomers are formed in equal amounts.
(d) Enantiomers (including these) have the same boiling points, melting points, etc.

(2) (a) Structures of the products:

(b) The products are diastereomers.
(c) Diastereomers are formed in principle in different amounts.
(d) The products, like other diastereomerically related compounds, in principle have different melting points, boiling points, etc.

(3) (a) Structure of the product:

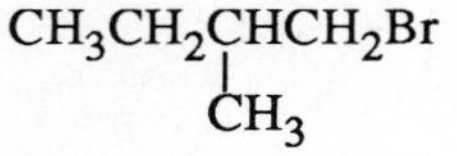

$$CH_3CH_2\underset{\underset{CH_3}{|}}{C}HCH_2Br$$

  (b), (c), and (d): The answers are the same as for (1).

(4) (a) Structures of the products:

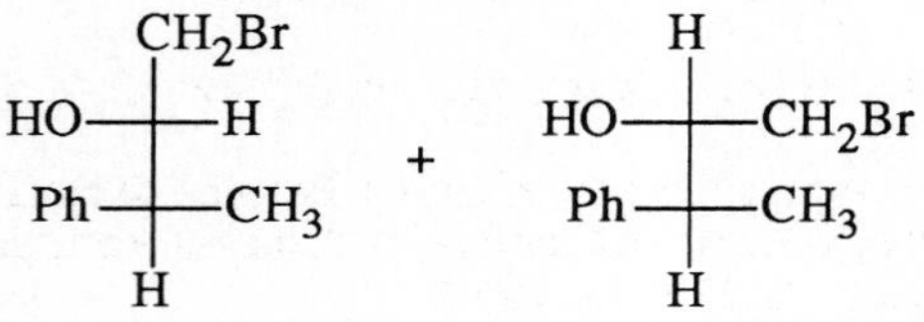

  (b), (c), and (d): The answers are the same as for (2).

(5) (a) Structures of the products: The products of (4) are formed, and, in addition, their enantiomers are also formed. In other words, a total of four products are formed — the complete set of four stereoisomers.

  (b) Let the two products from (4) be *A* and *B*, respectively. Let their two enantiomers be *A'* and *B'*, respectively. All *A-B* pairs are diastereomers (*A-B, A'-B', A-B', A'-B*); *A* and *A'* are enantiomers; and *B* and *B'* are enantiomers.

  (c) Since the starting material is a racemate — an exactly equimolar mixture of enantiomers — enantiomeric products originate from their respective enantiomeric starting materials, and are therefore formed in identical amounts; thus *A* and *A'* are formed in identical amounts, and *B* and *B'* are formed in identical amounts. Diastereomers are formed in different amounts.

  (d) Enantiomers have the same melting and boiling points; diastereomers have different melting and boiling points. Thus, in the mixture of *A, A', B*, and *B'*, *A* cannot be separated from *A'*, nor can *B* be separated from *B'*. However, the mixture of *A* and *A'* could in principle be separated from the mixture of *B* and *B'*, because these mixtures are diastereomerically related.

(6) (a) Structures of the products:

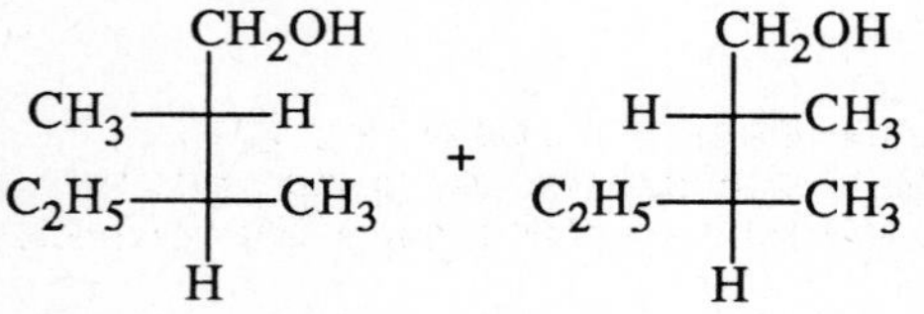

  (b), (c), and (d) The answer is the same as for (2).

(7) (a)–(d): The answers are the same as for (5), except that (6) is substituted for (4) in the comparisons.

(8) (a) The following products are obtained from the *S* enantiomer:

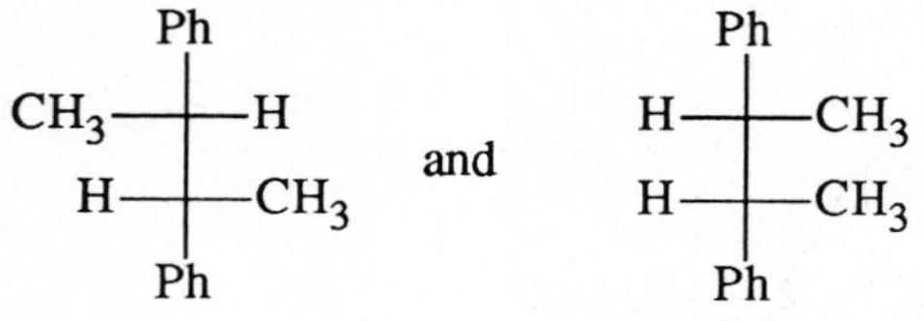

and the following products are obtained from the *R* enantiomer:

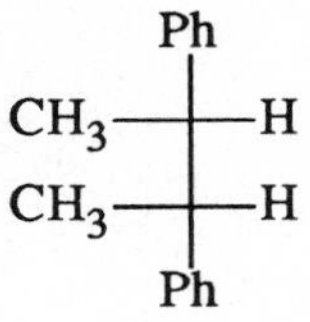

B

and

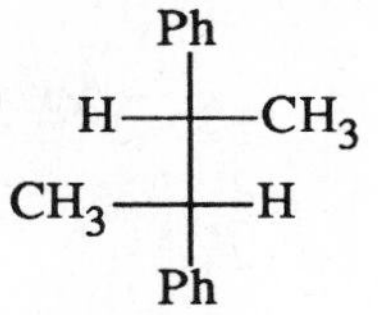

C

Notice that isomer *B*, a *meso* compound, is obtained from both enantiomers of the starting material.

(b) Compounds *A* and *C* are enantiomers; compounds *A* and *B* are diastereomers; and compounds *B* and *C* are diastereomers.

(c) The starting materials for compounds *A* and *C* are present in equimolar amounts, because the starting material is a racemate; hence, the enantiomers *A* and *C* are formed in equal amounts. Compounds *A* and *B* are formed in different amounts, and compounds *B* and *C* are formed in different amounts.

(e) The enantiomers *A* and *C* have identical melting points and boiling points; the diastereomeric pairs *A*,*B* and *B*,*C* have different melting points and boiling points. Hence, what we would obtain from this reaction is a compound *B*, a pure stereoisomer, which could be separated from a racemic mixture of *A* and *C*.

30. Compounds (a) and (d) can be synthesized free of structural isomers and diastereomers. Compound (a) comes from hydroboration–oxidation of *cis*- or *trans*-3-hexene:

$$CH_3CH_2CH{=}CHCH_2CH_3 \xrightarrow[\text{2) } H_2O_2/^{-}OH]{\text{1) } B_2H_6} CH_3CH_2\overset{\displaystyle OH}{\overset{|}{C}}HCH_2CH_2CH_3$$

Compound (d) comes from hydroboration–oxidation of 1-methyl-1-cyclopentene:

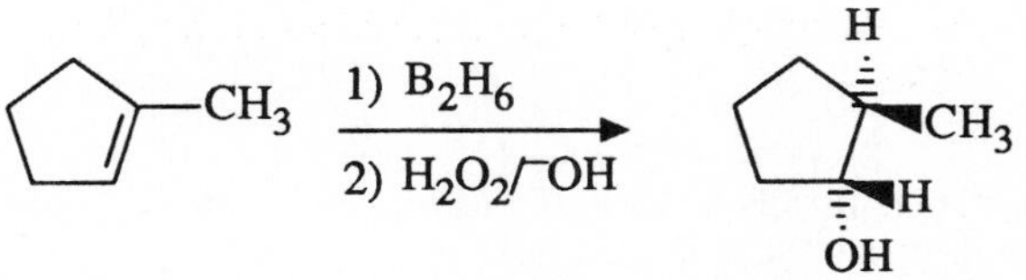

There is no alkene that would give pure (b). For example, hydroboration–oxidation of 1-methyl-1-cyclopentene gives (d), not (b), as we have just seen. Any alkene that might serve as a starting material for compound (c) would, on hydroboration–oxidation, give an alcohol with the —OH group at a less substituted carbon.

31. The answers below are not the only correct ones.

(a)

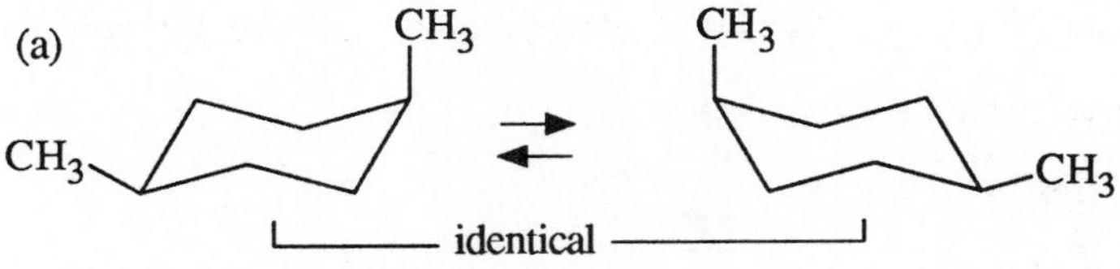

(b)

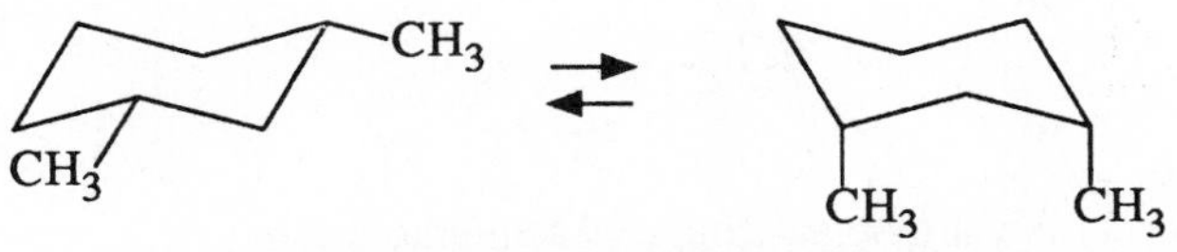

conformational diastereomers, both achiral

(c)

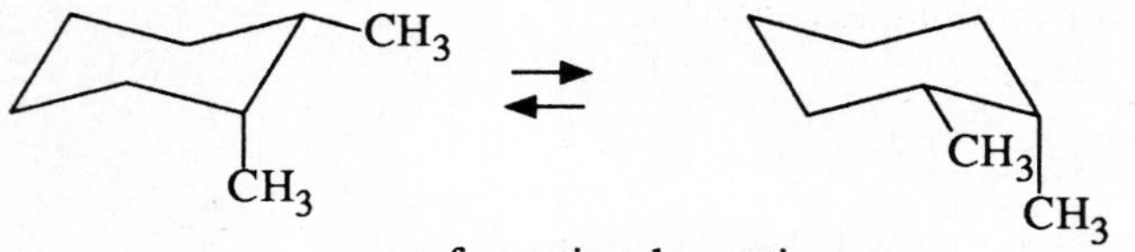

conformational enantiomers

32.

(a)

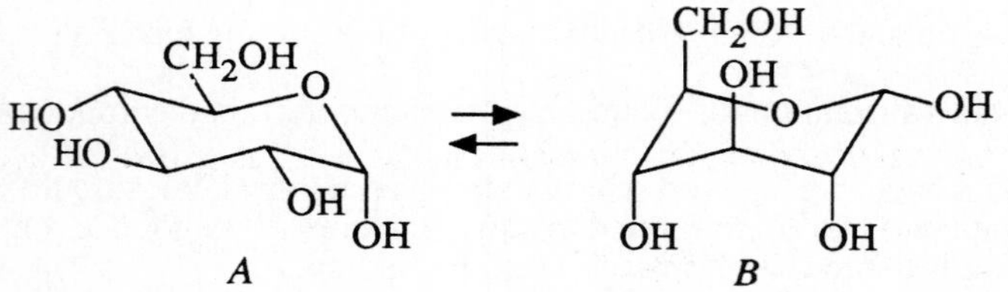

Form A predominates at equilibrium because it has fewer axial groups. In particular, the CH_2OH group is equatorial in form A.

(b)

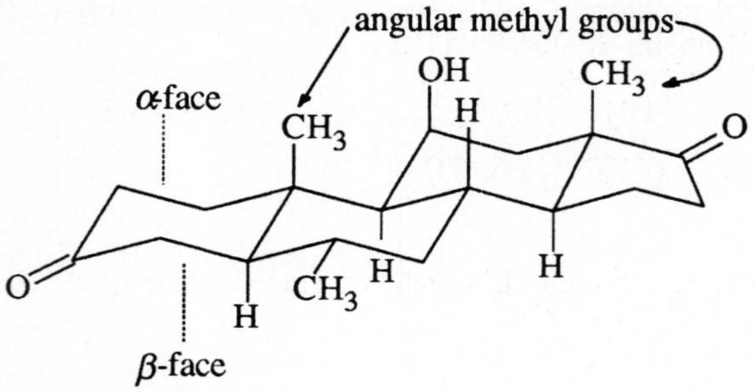

33. Properties (a), (b), (d), (e), and (g) would be the same, because they do not involve a chiral measurement. Enantiomers are differentiated by the way they rotate the plane of polarized light [property (c)]. Because enantiomers interact differently with chiral species or forces, they would differ in their solubility in a chiral solvent [property (f)], and in the way they interact with a chiral taste bud [property (h)].

34. (a) Water attacks the bromonium-ion intermediate from the backside, just as bromide ion does in ordinary bromination, to give the products of *anti* addition:

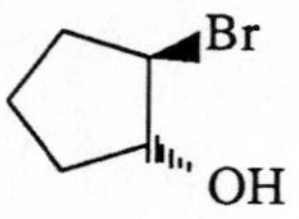

(obtained as the racemate)

(b)

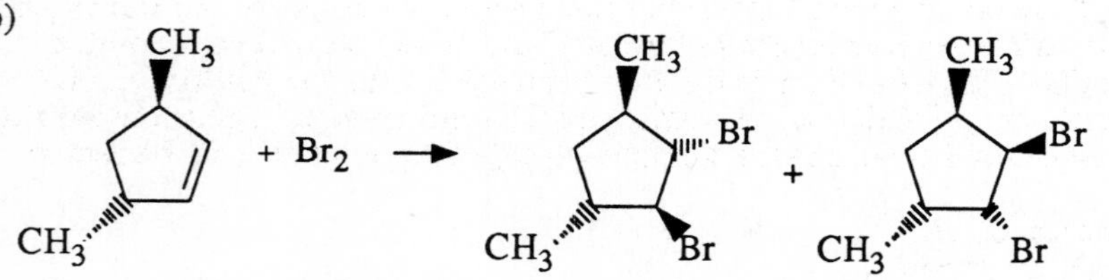

Since these two compounds are diastereomers, they are obtained in different amounts.

35.   The two dibromides are the two possible *trans*-disubstituted decalins:

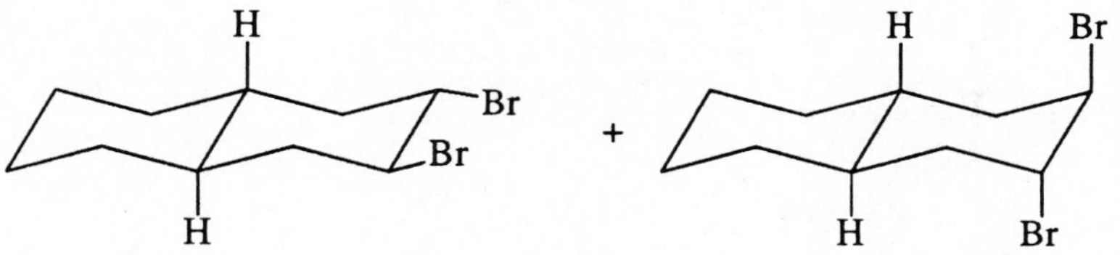

36.   In this compound, both chair-chair interconversion and amine inversion can occur. This gives four species in equilibrium:

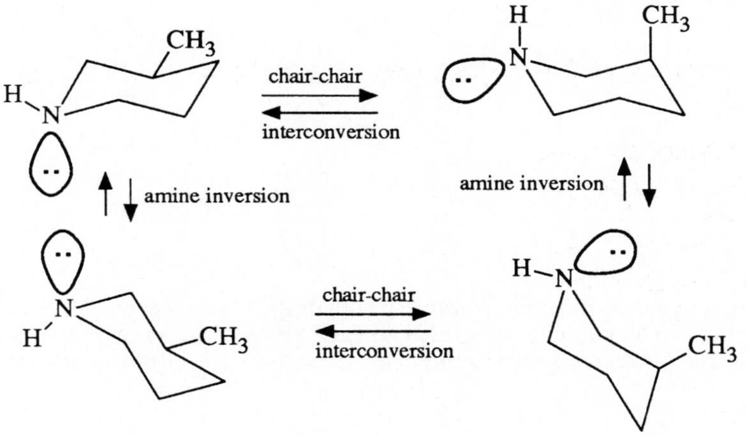

Any one of these species, of course, could be used as the answer to the first part of the question.

37.   The *cis*-isomer of the starting alkene was used. Representing our alkene as R—CH=CH—R:

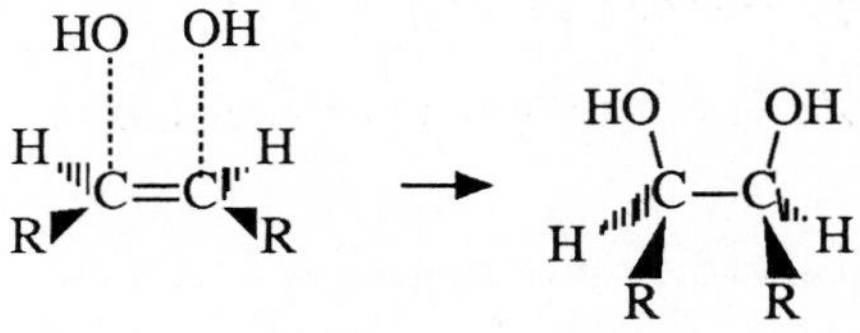

meso

➤ As this problem illustrates, there is a definite relationship among the *stereochemistry of a starting alkene,* the *stereochemistry of addition,* and the *stereochemistry of the product.* When we are dealing with a symmetrical alkene of the form R—CH=CH—R, as in the above example, these relationships can be represented by the following table, in which the stereochemistry of the starting material is on the left side, the stereochemistry of the product is along the top, and the stereochemistry of the addition is in the center:

	racemate	*meso* compound
cis	*anti*	*syn*
trans	*syn*	*anti*

38.   First, we convert our Fischer projection of the product into a three-dimensional perspective. (You can build a model.) We then rotate about the central bond until the two —CO_2 groups have a dihedral angle of 180°, as they do in the starting material. Finally, we examine the relationship of the —D and —OD groups:

With the $—CO_2^-$ groups in this *anti* arrangement, it is now clear that the $—D$ and $—OD$ groups must have entered from opposite faces of the alkene. Hence, the addition is an *anti* addition.

39. A systematic way to work this problem is to start with all $—CH_3$ groups in a *cis* arrangement; then change the stereochemistry of one group in all possible ways.

(*Meso* compounds are indicated by showing their planes of symmetry with dashed lines.) We could go on to change the stereochemistry of two groups in all possible ways, then all three groups; but, since all groups are identical, an easier way to get the remaining structures is to simply draw the mirror images of the structures already drawn.

Now we eliminate identities. First, all *meso* compounds are identical to their mirror images, since *meso* compounds are achiral. This eliminates compounds E and G. We check the other compounds by turning each one over and seeing whether it superimposes on another compound. We immediately find that compounds B and D are enantiomers. Thus, their mirror images F and H must not be new compounds; indeed, F is identical to D, and H is identical to B. Hence, all possible stereoisomers are represented by compounds $A, B, C,$ and D.

40. In order for a compound to exist in a relatively high-energy boat conformation, there must be a good reason for it to avoid the chair. Indeed, compounds (b) and (d) have very severe 1,3-diaxial interactions between a *t*-butyl group and a methyl group. Now, compound (d), a *cis*-decalin derivative, can avoid its 1,3-diaxial interaction by undergoing a chair-chair interconversion. However, compound (b), a *trans*-decalin derivative, cannot undergo the chair-chair interconversion. Hence, it has no choice but to assume a boat conformation if the 1,3-diaxial interaction is to be relieved. (Actually, it assumes a *twist*-boat conformation.)

41. Only (c) and (d) are true.

42. Compound (a) cannot be resolved into enantiomers, because the only asymmetric atom is nitrogen. Since the very rapid amine inversion interconverts enantiomers, no single enantiomer would survive long enough to be isolated. Compound (b) cannot be resolved either, because its two enantiomers are rapidly interconverted by a combination of amine inversion and chair-chair interconversion:

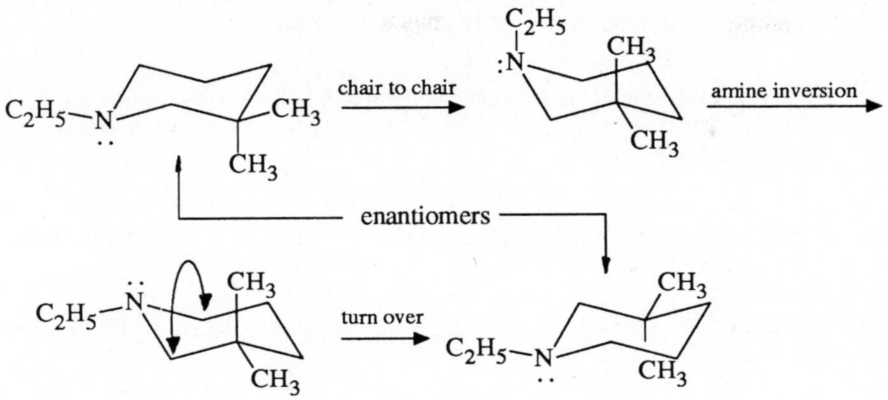

Compound (c) has two asymmetric nitrogens which are prevented from inverting by the constraints imposed by the ring. (Inversion of both nitrogens would turn the molecule "inside out"; during the inversion process some atoms would have to pass on top of other atoms.)

43. (a) N: The two are identical, as we can see by turning one of the structures over top-to-bottom.
     (b) D   (c) CE   (d) CE   (e) Identical molecules. Let us show in detail the identity of these two molecules:

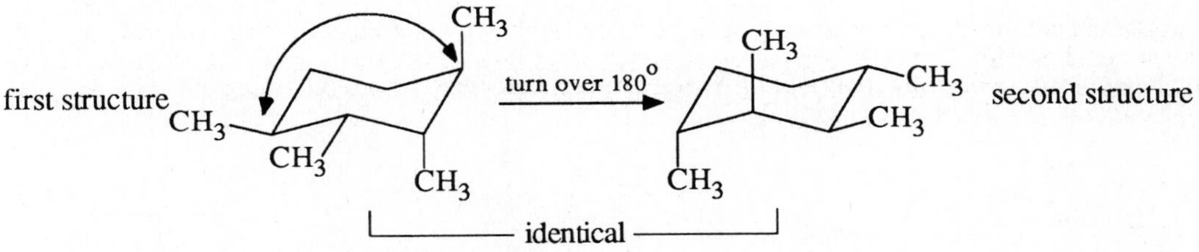

44. In the transition state for inversion, the C—N—C bond angles approximate 120°, because nitrogen is sp^2-hybridized in this transition state. This 120° angle is much more difficult to achieve with the three-membered ring, which has an optimal C—N—C angle of 60°. Hence, there is more angle strain in the transition state for inversion of 1-methylaziridine than in the transition state for inversion of 1-methylpyrrolidine. For this reason, the transition state for inversion of the aziridine derivative has a very high energy, and the inversion of this derivative is very slow. (This is a very unusual situation, since inversion of most amines is very rapid; see Sec. 6.8B.)

45. The accepted mechanism for hydration involves carbocation intermediates. A carbocation can be attacked at either face by a nucleophile:

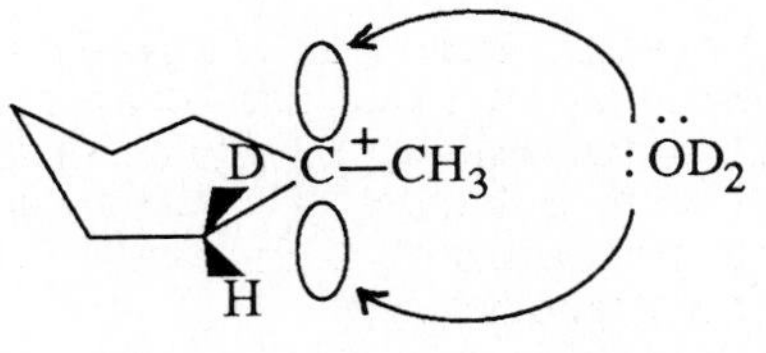

Attack at one face gives one product, and attack at the other face gives the other product. (The enantiomers are formed by having the deuterium enter from below the alkene rather than above, with the same two options for attack of D_2O.)

➤ Notice that use of D_2O is required in order to investigate the stereochemistry of the hydration reaction of 1-methyl-1-cyclohexene. Had H_2O been used, a single achiral product would form regardless of the stereochemistry of the reaction.

46. There are two distinguishable ways in which the organoborane can approach a *cis*-2-butene molecule. Approach from the top face gives a transition state in which there is steric interference between a methyl group of the alkene and a methyl group on the organoborane:

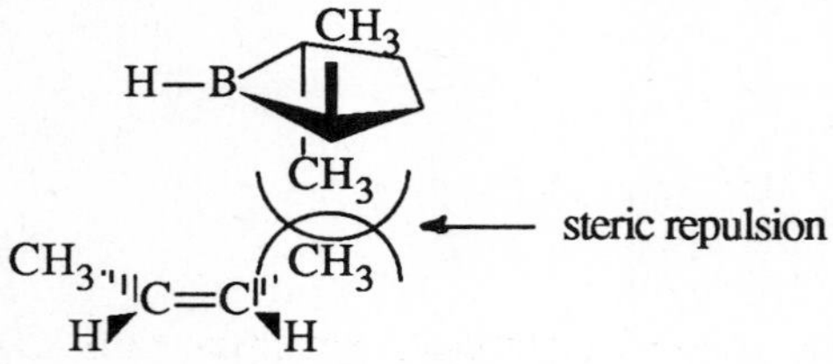

Approach from the bottom face gives a transition state in which the steric repulsion is less severe:

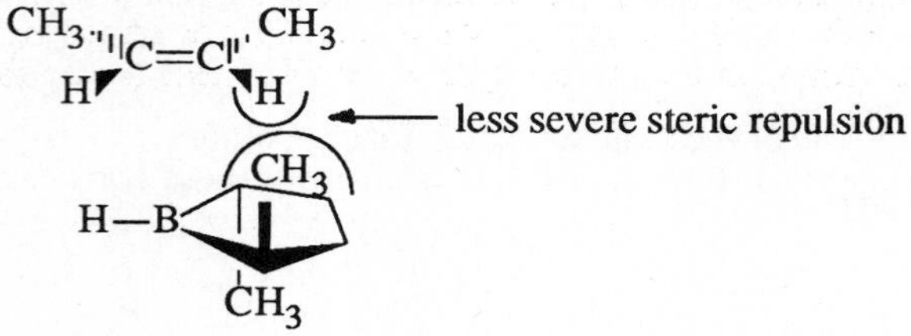

Hence, the reagent reacts from the bottom to give the product that results from the transition state of least energy. As a result, (*S*)-2-butanol is formed:

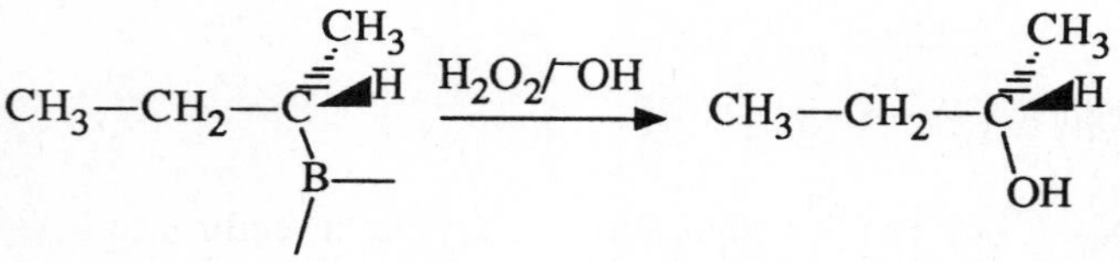

(*S*)-2-butanol

➤ The formation of a chiral compound with one of two possible configurations from an achiral starting material (*cis*-2-butene) and a chiral reagent (the organoborane) is sometimes called *asymmetric induction*.

47. In one sense, this question is much like the previous one in that a chiral compound and an achiral compound react to give a chiral product. However, in this case, the alkenes are chiral, and the borane is achiral. As a result of the reaction, new asymmetric centers appear in the products derived from the alkenes. Diborane approaches the alkenes from the face *opposite* the methyl group. As a result, the product alcohols have their —OH groups *trans* to the respective angular methyl groups:

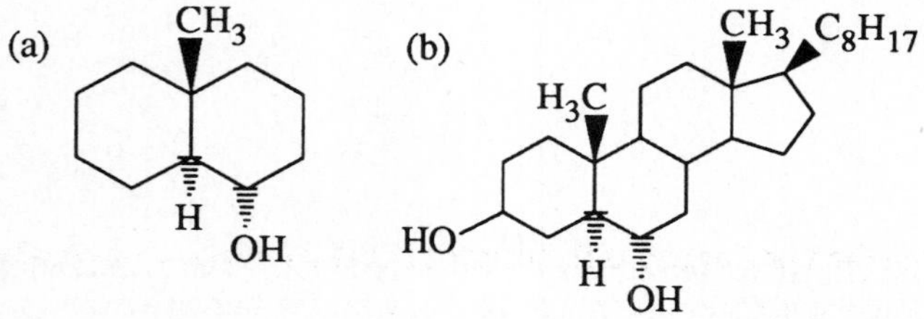

48. (a) *Trans*-decalin is more stable than *cis*-decalin (see Problem 14), which is more stable than bicyclo[6.2.0]decane, the compound in the center. The more stable compounds have the smaller heat of formation. Hence, the heats of formation are in the order *trans*-decalin < *cis*-decalin < bicyclo[6.2.0]decane.
(b) Methylcyclohexane has no *gauche* interactions; *trans*-1,2-dimethylcyclopentane has one *gauche* interaction;

and *cis*-1,2-dimethylcyclopentane has three *gauche* interactions:

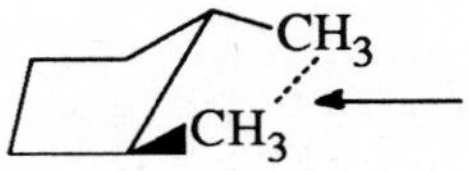

gauche interaction

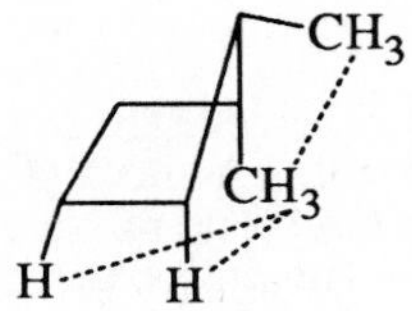

three *gauche* interactions (dotted lines)

Hence, heats of formation are in the order methylcyclohexane < *trans*-1,2-dimethylcyclopentane < *cis*-1,2-dimethylcyclopentane.

(c) The compound on the left incorporates a bridgehead double bond in a six-membered ring, and is least stable; the one in the center incorporates a cyclobutane ring, and is next most stable; and the one on the right incorporates six-membered rings, and is most stable. Although it has a bridgehead double bond, the double bond is *trans* in a ten-membered ring, and is thus unstrained.

49. (a) The two chiral forms, which are an enantiomeric pair:

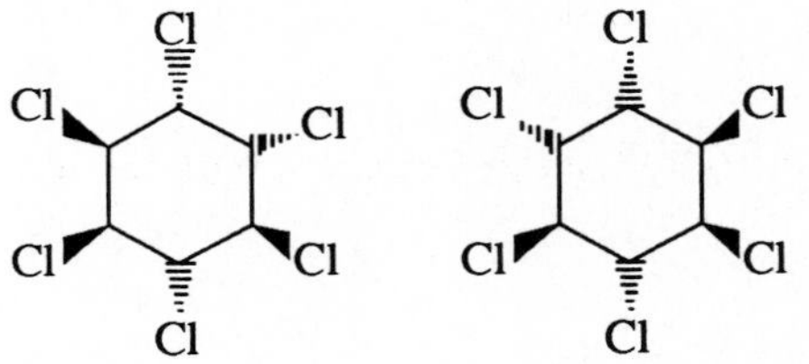

(b) The stereoisomers with two identical chair forms:

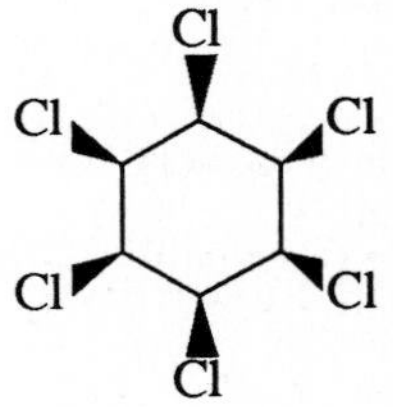

or

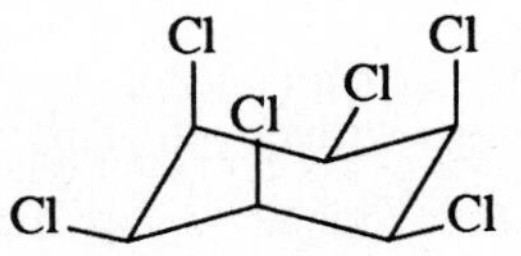

and

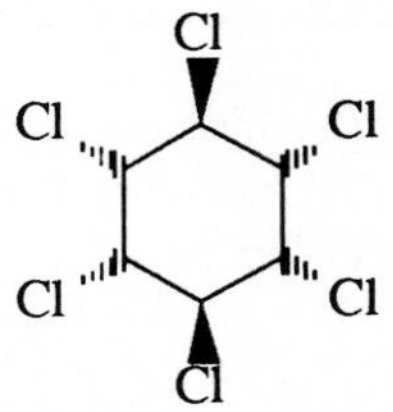

or

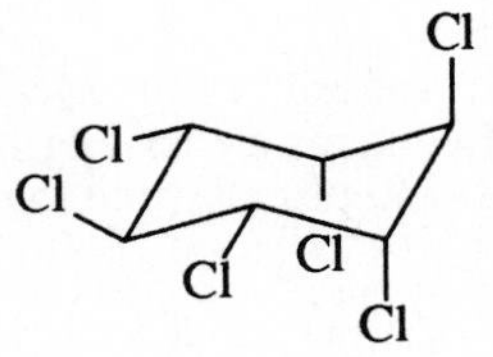

(The only candidate structures are those in which the number of axial chlorines equal the number of equatorial chlorines; why?)

50. Considering the structure on the left, there are two *gauche*-butane interactions (one for each methyl group) for a total of 1.74 kcal/mol. The methyl-methyl 1,3-diaxial interaction shown is the difference, (5.5 - 1.74) kcal/mol = 3.76 kcal/mol. (The all-equatorial form has no 1,3-diaxial interactions.)

51. Given that addition of Br$_2$ to the double bonds is *anti*, there are two possible diastereomers formed:

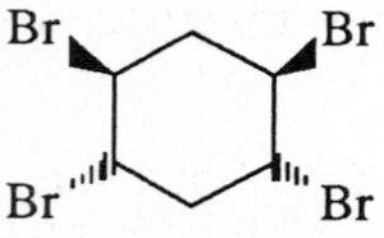

Compound *A* is a *meso* compound, and compound *B* is a mixture of enantiomers. Since diastereomers have different properties, it is expected that compounds *A* and *B* should have different melting points and solubilities. (Of course, we can't tell which is which merely from their melting points.) The mixture (which we might call *ABABABAB*. . .) is the diastereomer of either pure solid (which we can call *AAAAAA*. . . and *BBBBBB*. . . , respectively). Hence the mixture has a melting point different from that of either pure solid.

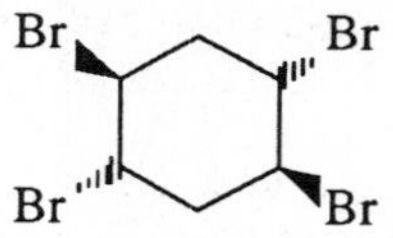

52. *Cis*-1,3-di-*t*-butylcyclohexane can exist in a chair form (*A*) in which both *t*-butyl groups are equatorial. However, in either chair form of *trans*-1,3-di-*t*-butylcyclohexane (*B*), there is an axial *t*-butyl group. The axial *t*-butyl group can be avoided if compound *B* exists in a twist-boat form *C*.

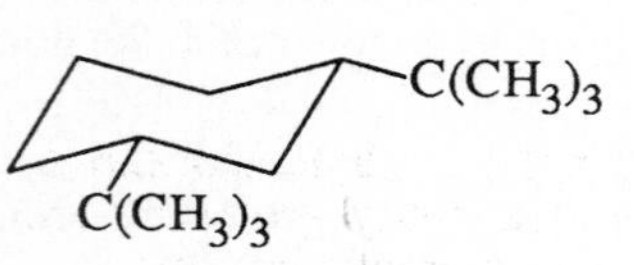

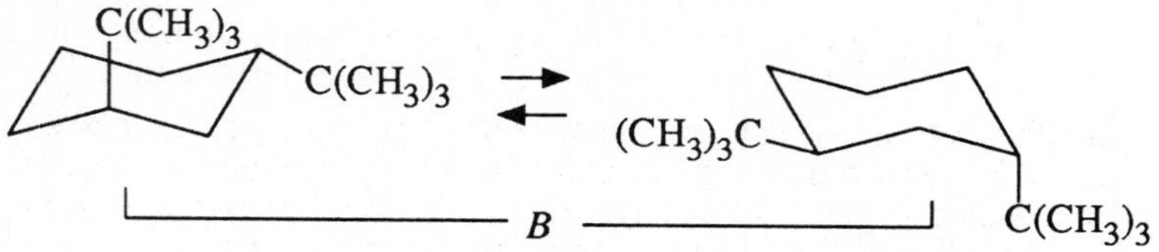

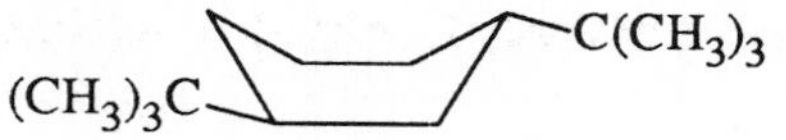

If in fact compound *B* exists in the twist-boat, then clearly the energy difference between *A* and *C* is the energy difference between a chair and twist-boat; the two *t*-butyl groups are axial in each case, and to a first approximation have the same interactions with neighboring hydrogens.

53. First, let us be sure that we know what the structure of the starting material is. (Did you try to work this without first writing down this structure? This is like trying to drive with your eyes closed!)

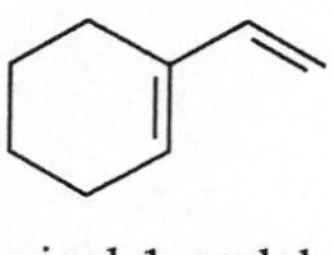

1-vinyl-1-cyclohexene

This is a diene, and can in principle be hydroborated twice. Indeed, the product following oxidation, we are told, has two —OH groups. Furthermore, "thexylborane" contains a —BH$_2$ group that can be used for two "rounds" of hydroboration. Hence, a reasonable hydroboration product, and the resulting diol, are:

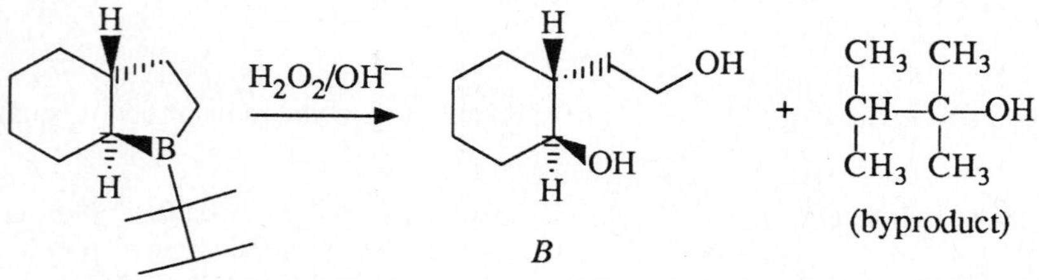

Notice the stereochemistry: once hydroboration has occurred at a given face of one double bond, it must occur at the same face of the other double bond. Of course, the enantiomers of the above compounds are formed in equal amounts.

➤ Construction of a model will show you that compound *A*, which contains a five-membered ring trans-fused to a six membered ring, is rather strained. The borane is such a reactive electrophilic species that the trans-ring fusion, required by the stereochemistry of hydroboration, will form despite the strain so introduced. In addition, once one of the double bonds has been hydroborated, hydroboration of the second is an *intramolecular* reaction. As we shall learn in Section 11.6, intramolecular reactions can be particularly rapid, even when strain is introduced.

54. (a) On the assumption that the larger group has the greater preference for the equatorial position, the phenyl group behaves as if it is larger: the chair form containing the axial phenyl group is present in smaller amount. This is reasonable merely from a comparison of the structures of methyl and phenyl: phenyl is a considerably larger, more highly branched group.
(b) The form of 4-phenyl-1-methylcyclohexane on the left contains a destabilizing contribution from an axial methyl group (1.74 kcal/mol). Hence, to estimate the $\Delta G°$ for Eq. (1), we have to add in this destabilizing contribution:

$$\Delta G°(\text{Eq. 1}) = +1.13 + 1.74 = 2.87 \text{ kcal/mol}$$

In other words, were the methyl group not present, the equilibrium for 4-phenyl-1-methylcyclohexane would favor the form containing the equatorial phenyl group even more than it does; the methyl group in effect serves as a *counterpoise* to the phenyl group, bringing the two forms more closely into energetic balance.
The $\Delta G°$ for Eq. 2 is a composite of the phenyl effect plus the effect of two methyl groups converting between axial and equatorial positions. (The phenyl effect stabilizes the form on the right; the methyl group preferences stabilize the form on the left.) The phenyl effect is derived from the $\Delta G°$ for Eq. 1, –2.87 kcal/mol. The methyl effect is derived from the $\Delta G°$ for *trans*-1,2-dimethylcyclohexane (Fig. 7.8), and is +2.61 kcal/mol. Together, these two effects give

$$\Delta G°(\text{Eq. 2}) = 2.61 - 2.87 = -0.16 \text{ kcal/mol}$$

55. In form *A*, there is a severe interaction of the methyl group with the axial hydrogen on the other ring:

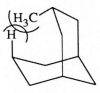

In the twist-boat form *B*, the offending interaction is absent.

56. There are no asymmetric carbons in the spirocyclic compound. Yet the compound is chiral. This can be readily demonstrated by constructing the mirror image and attempting to superimpose it on the original. This is another example of a chiral compound without asymmetric atoms. The chirality of this molecule is like that in 2,3-pentadiene, discussed on text page 203.

Chapter 8 / Introduction to Alkyl Halides, Alcohols, Ethers, Thiols, and Sulfides

CHAPTER 8 TERMS

absolute ethanol 8.9C
alcohol 8.1B
alkoxide 8.6
alkyl halide 8.1A
alkylmagnesium halide 8.8A
allyl group 8.1A
antibiotic 8.4C
apolar solvent 8.4A
aprotic solvent 8.4A
autoxidation 8.9D
benzyl group 8.1A
carbanion 8.8B
common nomenclature 8.1
covalent interaction 8.8B
crown ether 8.4C
denatured alcohol 8.9C
deuterium 8.8B
dissociation constant 8.5A
donor interactions 8.4B
donor solvent 8.4A
epoxide 8.1C
ether 8.1C
ethylene glycol 8.9C
ethylene oxide 8.9C
flash point 8.9D
free-radical substitution reaction 8.9A
glycol 8.1B
Grignard reagent 8.8A
^{2}H 8.8B
^{3}H 8.8B
heterocyclic compound 8.1C
hydride ion 8.6A
hydrogen bonding 8.3B
hydrogen-bond acceptor 8.3B
hydrogen-bond donor 8.3B
hydroxy group 8.1B
inductive effect 8.6B

intermolecular hydrogen bonding 8.3B
intramolecular hydrogen bonding 8.3B
ion–dipole attraction 8.8B
ion pair 8.4B
ionophore 8.4C
ionophorous antibiotic 8.4C
K_a 8.5A
mercaptan 8.1B
mercaptide 8.6
mercapto group 8.1C
miscible 8.4A
noncovalent interaction 8.8B
organolithium reagent 8.8A
organometallic 8.8A
perhalo compound 8.1A
pK_a 8.5A
polar effect 8.6B
polar molecule 8.3A
polar solvent 8.4A
principal chain 8.1A
principal group 8.1A
protic solvent 8.4A
protonolysis 8.8B
solvate 8.4B
solvent cage 8.4B
solvent shell 8.4B
sulfhydryl group 8.1C
sulfide 8.1C
systematic nomenclature 8.1
tetrahydrofuran (THF) 8.4B
thioether 8.1C
thiol 8.1B
thiolate 8.6
tritium 8.8B
vicinal glycol 8.1B
vinyl group 8.1A

CHAPTER 8 CONCEPTS

I. Nomenclature of Alkyl Halides, Alcohols, Ethers, Thiols, and Sulfides:

A. <u>General</u>:
1. The two most widely used systems for the nomenclature of organic compounds are **common nomenclature** and **systematic nomenclature**.
2. Common nomenclature is typically used for simple unbranched compounds.
3. Systematic nomenclature is more often used for more complex structures.
   a) The functional group on which the name is based is called the **principal group**.
      (1) The relative priorities of the principal groups are:

$$-OH > -SH$$

   b) The **principal chain** is the longest continuous carbon chain that contains the greatest number of principal groups.
   c) Steps for naming compounds systematically:
      (1) Identify the principal group.
      (2) Identify the principal carbon chain.
      (3) Number the carbon chain consecutively from one end so that the principal group receives the lowest number.
      (4) Construct the name using the appropriate numbers for the substituents.
      (5) In numbering cyclic compounds, precedence is given first to the principal group, then to double bonds, and last to substituents.
   d) Cyclic compounds with rings that contain more than one type of atom are called **heterocyclic compounds**.
4. Common and systematic nomenclature should never be mixed.

B. <u>Alkyl Halides</u>:
1. In the **alkyl halides**, a halogen atom is bonded to an alkyl group.
2. Alkyl halides are classified as methyl, primary, secondary, or tertiary.
   a) A methyl halide has no alkyl branches at the carbon bearing the halide (the α-carbon).
   b) A primary alkyl halide has one alkyl branch at the α-carbon.
   c) A secondary alkyl halide has two alkyl branches at the α-carbon.
   d) A tertiary alkyl halide has three alkyl branches at the α-carbon.

CH$_3$F	primary	secondary	tertiary
methyl			

3. Common nomenclature:
   a) The common name of an alkyl halide is constructed from the name of the alkyl group followed by the name of the halide as a separate word.
   b) Compounds in which all hydrogen atoms are formally replaced by halogen are called **perhalo compounds**.

isopropyl bromide   perfluoroethane

4. Systematic nomenclature:
   a) The systematic name of an alkyl halide is constructed by applying the rules of alkane and alkene nomenclature.

b) The principal chain is the longest continuous carbon chain containing the greatest number of double bonds.

c) If a double bond is present, it receives the lowest number.

d) If no double bond is present, the substituents receive the lowest number possible.

e) The halogen substituents are named **fluoro**, **chloro**, **bromo**, or **iodo**, respectively.

3-iodo-2-methylpentane   3-chloro-1-cyclohexene

C. Alcohols and Thiols:

1. In the **alcohols**, a **hydroxy group**, —OH, is bonded to an alkyl group.

2. In **thiols**, a **sulfhydryl group** (**mercapto group**), —SH, is bonded to an alkyl group; thiols (mercaptans) are the sulfur analogs of alcohols.

$$CH_3\text{-}\underset{\underset{CH_3}{|}}{\overset{\overset{CH_3}{|}}{C}}\text{-}OH \qquad\qquad CH_3\text{-}\underset{\underset{CH_3}{|}}{CH}\text{-}CH_2\text{-}SH$$

t-butyl alcohol   isobutyl mecraptan
2-methyl-2-propanol   2-methylpropanethiol

3. Alcohols are classified as **methyl, primary, secondary,** or **tertiary.**

a) A methyl alcohol has no alkyl branches at the carbon bearing the —OH group (the α-carbon).

b) A primary alcohol has one alkyl branch at the α-carbon.

c) A secondary alcohol has two alkyl branches at the α-carbon.

d) A tertiary alcohol has three alkyl branches at the α-carbon.

CH_3—OH   methyl   primary   secondary   tertiary

4. Alcohols that contain two hydroxy groups are called **glycols.**

5. Alcohols that contain two hydroxy groups on adjacent carbons are called **vicinal glycols.**

$$\underset{CH_2\text{-}CH_2}{\overset{HO\qquad OH}{|\qquad|}} \qquad\qquad \underset{CH_3\text{-}CH\text{-}CH_2}{\overset{HO\qquad OH}{|\qquad|}}$$

ethylene glycol   propylene glycol

6. Common nomenclature:

a) The common name of an alcohol is derived by specifying the alkyl group to which the —OH group is attached, followed by the word **alcohol.**

b) The common name of a thiol is derived by specifying the alkyl group to which the —SH group is attached, followed by the word **mercaptan.**

cyclohexyl alcohol CH_3—SH   methyl mercaptan

7. Systematic nomenclature:
   a) The systematic name of an alcohol is constructed by *dropping* the final *e* from the name of the parent alkane and adding the suffix *ol*.
      (1) The —OH group receives the lowest number in the carbon chain.
      (2) To name an alcohol containing more than one —OH group, the suffixes *diol, triol,* etc., are added to the name of the appropriate alkane *without dropping* the final *e*.
   b) The systematic name of a thiol is constructed by adding the suffix *thiol* to the name of the parent alkane *without dropping* the final *e*.

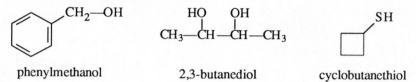

    phenylmethanol   2,3-butanediol   cyclobutanethiol

D. <u>Ethers and Sulfides</u>:
   1. In an **ether**, an oxygen is bonded to two carbon groups; two carbon groups may or may not be the same.
   2. In a thioether (**sulfide**), a sulfur is bonded to two carbon groups; two carbon groups may or may not be the same.

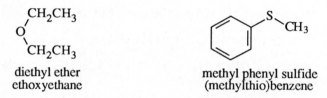

     diethyl ether   methyl phenyl sulfide
     ethoxyethane   (methylthio)benzene

   3. **Epoxides** are a special class of heterocyclic ethers that contain three-membered rings.
   4. Common nomenclature:
      a) The common name of an ether is constructed by naming the two groups on the ether oxygen, followed by the word *ether*.
      b) The common name of a thioether is constructed by naming the two groups on the sulfide (thioether) sulfur, followed by the word *sulfide*.

              CH$_3$
                \
  CH$_3$CH$_2$—O—CH$_3$ CH—S—CH$_2$CH$_3$
                /
              CH$_3$

    ethyl methyl ether   ethyl isopropyl sulfide

   c) Some epoxides are named as oxides of alkenes.

           O
          / \
     Ph—CH—CH$_2$

       styrene oxide

   5. Systematic nomenclature:
      a) If an ether or sulfide contains a principal group cited as a suffix, such as —OH or —SH, this group receives precedence in the name.
      b) In systematic nomenclature, alkoxy groups (RO—) or alkylthio groups (RS—) are cited as substituents.
         (1) An RO— group is named by adding the suffix *oxy* to the name of the R group and the final *yl* is dropped.
         (2) An RS— group is named by adding the suffix *thio* to the name of the R group and the final *yl* is not dropped.
      c) If double bonds are present, the rules of alkene nomenclature apply; the principal chain is the one that contains the greatest number of double bonds.

3-methoxy-1-cyclohexene   2-(ethylthio)butane

d) Oxirane is the parent compound of a special class of heterocyclic ethers called epoxides, which contain three-membered rings; most epoxides are named systematically as derivatives of oxirane.

cis-2-ethyl-3-methyloxirane

or (2S,3R)-2-ethyl-3-methyloxirane

II. Physical Properties of Alkyl Halides, Alcohols, Ethers, Thiols, and Sulfides:

A. <u>Structures</u>:
1. The bond angles about carbon are very nearly tetrahedral in saturated alkyl halides, alcohols, thiols, ethers, and sulfides.
2. The bond angle at the heteroatom further defines the shape of the molecule in an alcohol, thiol, ether, or sulfide.
   a) The angle at oxygen is generally found to be close to 109°.
   b) The angle at sulfur is generally found to be close to 90°.
3. Unshared electron pairs can be considered as a bond without an atom at the end.
   a) The oxygen or sulfur has four groups:
      (1) two electron pairs.
      (2) two alkyl groups.
   b) The unshared electron pairs on sulfur occupy more diffuse orbitals that take up more space.
4. The lengths of bonds between carbon and other atoms increase down the periodic table (larger atoms).
5. The lengths of bonds between carbon and other atoms increase across a given row to the left (less electronegative atoms).

B. <u>Boiling Points</u>:
1. Intermolecular forces that increase the boiling points of organic compounds are:
   a) Attractive van der Waals forces, which are influenced by:
      (1) Molecular size: larger size $\Rightarrow$ greater attractions, higher boiling points.
      (2) Molecular shape: more extended (less spherical) shape $\Rightarrow$ greater attractions, higher boiling point.
      (3) Polarizabilty of electrons: more polarizable (less tightly held) electrons $\Rightarrow$ greater attractions, higher boiling point.
   b) Attractive interactions between permanent dipoles.
   c) Association of molecules by **hydrogen bonding**.
2. Most alkyl halides, alcohols, and ethers are **polar molecules**.
3. The polarity of a compound affects its boiling point.
   a) In many cases, the more polar molecule has the higher boiling point, other things being equal.
   b) A higher boiling point results from greater attraction between two molecules in the liquid state.
   c) Polar molecules are attracted to each other because they can align in such a way that the negative end of one dipole is attracted to the positive end of the other.
4. Alkyl halides:
   a) For a given molecular weight, alkyl halides are smaller molecules than alkanes.
   b) Attractive van der Waals forces between alkane molecules are greater than those between alkyl halide molecules.
   c) Alkyl chlorides have about the same boiling points as alkanes of the same molecular weight; the effects of size and polarity essentially cancel in the case of alkyl chlorides.
   d) Alkyl bromides and iodides have lower boiling points than the alkanes of the same molecular weight; alkanes are so much larger than alkyl bromides and iodides of the same molecular weight that alkanes have considerably higher boiling points.

e) The boiling points of perfluoro compounds are quite low for compounds of their molecular weight.
  (1) Perfluoro compounds are not polar molecules.
  (2) Their overall dipole moments are about zero.
  (3) The electron clouds around electronegative fluorine atoms are held very tightly and are much more difficult to polarize than the electron clouds in an alkane.

5. Alcohols:
  a) The boiling points of alcohols, especially of lower molecular weight, are unusually high in comparison to those of other organic compounds.
  b) The unusual trends in the boiling points of alcohols are the result of a phenomenon called **hydrogen bonding.**

C. Hydrogen Bonding:
  1. Hydrogen bonds are the combination of two factors:
    a) A weak **covalent interaction** between a hydrogen on the donor atom and unshared electron pairs on the acceptor atom of another molecule.
    b) An electrostatic attraction between oppositely charged ends of two dipoles.
  2. The best **hydrogen-bond donor** atoms in neutral molecules are oxygens, nitrogens, and halogens.
    a) All strong proton acids are good hydrogen-bond donors.
    b) The ammonium ion, $^+NH_4$, is a good hydrogen-bond donor but not an acceptor.
  3. The best **hydrogen-bond acceptors** in neutral molecules are the electronegative first-row atoms: oxygen, nitrogen, and fluorine.
    a) All Brønsted bases are good hydrogen-bond acceptors.
    b) The oxygen atom of an ether is a hydrogen-bond acceptor but not a donor.
  4. Sometimes an atom can act as both a donor and an acceptor of hydrogen bonds; for example, the oxygen atom in water or an alcohol can act as both a donor and an acceptor of hydrogen bonds.
  5. The energy required to break hydrogen bonds is manifested as an unusual high boiling point.
  6. Hydrogen bonding:
    a) Can affect the solubility of organic compounds.
    b) Can occur between molecules (**intermolecular hydrogen bonding**).
    c) Can occur within the same molecule (**intramolecular hydrogen bonding**).

intermolecular hydrogen bonding   intramolecular hydrogen bonding

    d) Is a very important phenomenon in biology.

D. Safety Hazards of Ethers:
  1. Two safety hazards are generally associated with the use of ethers:
    a) peroxide formation
    b) high flammability
  2. On standing in air, ethers slowly undergo a reaction called **autoxidation**, which leads to contamination with dangerously explosive peroxides and hydroperoxides.
    a) These peroxides can form by free-radical processes in samples of anhydrous diethyl ether or THF within two weeks.
    b) Because peroxides are particularly explosive when heated, it is a good practice not to distill ethers to dryness.
  3. The **flash point** of a material is the minimum temperature at which it is ignited by a small flame under certain standard conditions; diethyl ether has a low flash point.
  4. Diethyl ether vapor is denser than air.
  5. Good safety practice demands that open flames or sparks are not permitted anywhere in a laboratory in which ether is in active use.

III. Solvents in Organic Chemistry:

    A. <u>Classification of Solvents</u>:
        1. Solvents can be classified according to three properties:
            a) Proticity:
                (1) **Protic solvents** consist of molecules that *can act* as hydrogen-bond donors.
                (2) **Aprotic solvents** consist of molecules that *cannot act* as hydrogen-bond donors.
            b) Polarity:
                (1) **Polar solvents** consist of molecules that have a relatively *high* dielectric constant ($\varepsilon > 20$).
                (2) **Apolar solvents** consist of molecules that have a relatively *low* dielectric constant ($\varepsilon < 20$).
            c) Electron-donor ability:
                (1) **A donor solvent** consists of molecules that can act as Lewis bases.
        2. Some polar solvents are protic (for example, water and methanol).
        3. Some polar solvents are aprotic (for example, acetone).

    B. <u>Solubility</u>:
        1. Three solvent properties contribute to the solubility of ionic compounds:
            a) Polarity (dielectric constant), by which solvent molecules separate ions of opposite charge.
            b) Proticity (hydrogen-bond donor capability), by which solvent molecules **solvate** anions.
            c) Electron-donor ability, by which solvent molecules solvate cations through Lewis–base and ion–dipole interactions.
        2. One role of a solvent is simply to dissolve compounds of interest.
        3. A good solvent usually has some of the molecular characteristics of the compound to be dissolved—like dissolves like.
        4. Ionic compounds in solution can exist as:
            a) **Ion pairs**, in which each ion is closely associated with an ion of opposite charge.
            b) Dissociated (solvated) ions, in which each ion is surrounded by several solvent molecules, collectively called the **solvent shell** or **solvent cage**.
        5. A solvent dissolves an ionic compound by separating the ions of opposite charge and solvating the separated ions.
        6. The ability of a solvent to separate ions is measured quantitatively by its dielectric constant, ε.
        7. Solvents interact with ions to form solvation shells in several ways:
            a) Many anions are solvated by hydrogen bonding.
            b) Solvation of cations takes place through donor interactions.
            c) There are two types of donor interactions:
                (1) In a covalent interaction, atoms of solvent with unshared electron pairs act as Lewis bases towards an electron-deficient cation.
                (2) In **noncovalent interactions**, the dipole moments of the solvent molecules align themselves around a solute cation so that the negative ends of the H—O—H dipole point towards the positive ion (an **ion–dipole attraction**).
        8. The best solvents for dissolving ionic compounds are polar protic donor solvents.
        9. Some ionic compounds have appreciable solubilities in polar aprotic solvents such as acetone or DMSO.
            a) The donor capacities of polar aprotic solvents solvates cations, and their polarity separates ions of opposite charge.
            b) Salts dissolved in polar aprotic solvents exist to a greater extent as ion pairs.

    C. <u>Crown Ethers</u>:
        1. **Crown ethers** are heterocyclic ethers containing a number of regularly spaced oxygen atoms.
        2. The crown ethers have some selectivity for metal ions according to size.
        3. Crown ethers have significant solubilities in hydrocarbon solvents.
        4. Crown ethers can cause inorganic salts to dissolve in hydrocarbons.

[4]-crown-12 metal complex

　　D. Ionophorous Antibiotics:
　　　　1. **Ionophorous antibiotics** are closely related to the crown ethers.
　　　　　　a) An **antibiotic** is a compound found in nature (or a synthetically prepared analog) that interferes
　　　　　　　　with the growth or survival of one or more microorganisms.
　　　　　　b) An **ionophore** is a compound that binds ions very tightly.
　　　　2. The ionophorous antibiotics form strong complexes with metal ions in much the same way as crown
　　　　　　ethers.

IV. Review of Brønsted Acidity and Basicity:

　　A. Dissociation Constants and pK_as:
　　　　1. Alcohols and thiols can act as both Brønsted acids and bases.
　　　　2. Ethers and sulfides can act as Brønsted bases.
　　　　3. The relative strengths of acids are determined by how well they transfer a proton to a standard base; the
　　　　　　standard base traditionally used for comparison is water.
　　　　4. The equilibrium constant for transfer of a proton from an acid HA to water is called the **dissociation
　　　　　　constant, pK_a**.
　　　　　　a) Each acid has its own unique dissociation constant.
　　　　　　b) The larger the dissociation constant of an acid, the more H_3O^+ ions are formed when the acid is
　　　　　　　　dissolved in water at a given concentration.
　　　　5. The strength of an acid is measured by the magnitude of its dissociation constant.
　　　　　　a) Stronger acids have larger K_a values.
　　　　　　b) Stronger acids have smaller pKa values.
　　　　6. Base strength is conveniently expressed for a base A:$^-$ in terms of the pK_a of its conjugate acid HA; the
　　　　　　stronger base has the conjugate acid with the higher pK_a.
　　　　7. The equilibrium in the reaction of an acid and a base *always* favors the side with the weaker acid and
　　　　　　weaker base.

　　B. Factors that Determine Acid Strength:
　　　　1. Two factors that govern acidity are:
　　　　　　a) The H—A bond strength; a weaker H—A bond contributes to strong acidity.
　　　　　　b) The electronegativity of the group A in H—A; electronegative groups in an acid contribute to
　　　　　　　　enhanced acidity.
　　　　2. The bond-strength effect dominates down a column in the periodic table.
　　　　3. Because bond strengths change less drastically, electronegativity differences determine the trend in
　　　　　　acidity across a row in the periodic table.
　　　　4. For the simple acids H—A, stronger Brønsted acids are derived from the elements A nearest the
　　　　　　bottom and right side of the periodic table.

　　C. Alcohols and Thiols:
　　　　1. Alcohols and water have about the same acidity; they are both weak acids.
　　　　2. The conjugate bases of alcohols are generally called **alkoxides**.
　　　　　　a) The common name of an alkoxide is constructed by deleting the final *yl* from the name of the
　　　　　　　　alkyl group and adding the suffix *oxide*.
　　　　　　b) The systematic name of an alkoxide is constructed by adding the suffix *ate* to the end of the alkyl
　　　　　　　　group.
　　　　3. The conjugate bases of thiols are called **thiolates** or **mercaptides**.
　　　　　　a) The common name of a mercaptide is constructed by placing the word *mercaptide*, as a separate
　　　　　　　　word, after the name of the alkyl group.
　　　　　　b) The systematic name of a thiolate is constructed by adding the suffix *thiolate* to the end of the
　　　　　　　　alkyl group.
　　　　　　c) Thiols are more acidic than alcohols.
　　　　　　d) Thiols have pK_a values near 10.
　　　　　　e) The S—H bond is weaker than the O—H bond.

　　D. Inductive Effects on Alcohol Acidity:
　　　　1. The exact acidity of an alcohol depends on its structure.
　　　　　　a) Alcohols containing electronegative substituent groups have enhanced acidity.
　　　　　　b) The acidity of an alcohol is increased by stabilizing its conjugate-base alkoxide.

2. For the ionization of an alcohol with dissociation constant K_a, the pK_a is directly proportional to $\Delta G°$, the standard free-energy difference between the reactants and products.
3. Electronegative substituent groups increase the acidities of alcohols by stabilizing their corresponding alkoxides; alcohols with electronegative substituents are more acidic than unsubstituted alcohols.
4. The interaction of positive and negative charges to lower the energy of a system is called an **inductive effect** or **polar effect.**
5. The inductive effect on alcohol acidity diminishes as the distance between the —OH and the electronegative substituent group is increased.

E. Effect of Branching on Alcohol Acidity. Role of Solvent in Acidity:
1. The acidities of alcohols in solution are in the order:

methyl > primary > secondary > tertiary

2. The relative order of acidity of different types of alcohols is reversed in solution compared to the relative order of acidity in the gas phase.
   a) In the gas phase, the electron clouds of the alkyl groups distort so that electron density moves away from the negative charge on the alkoxide oxygen.
   b) In solution there is hydrogen bonding of the alkoxide oxygen with the surrounding solvent molecules.
3. Alcohols with unbranched carbon chains near the —OH group are stronger acids in solution.
4. Highly branched alkoxides are more basic than unbranched ones in solution.

F. Basicity of Alcohols and Ethers:
1. Alcohols and ethers can be protonated by Brønsted acids.
2. Ethers are important Lewis bases and form, in many cases, stable Lewis acid–base complexes.

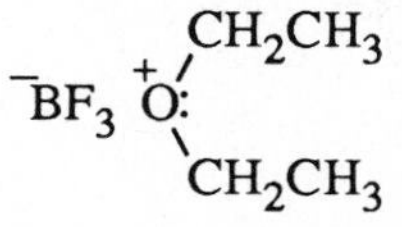

$$\text{BF}_3 \ \overset{+}{\underset{\diagdown}{\overset{\diagup}{\text{O}}}} \begin{matrix} \text{CH}_2\text{CH}_3 \\ \\ \text{CH}_2\text{CH}_3 \end{matrix}$$

3. Water and alcohols are excellent Lewis bases.

CHAPTER 8 REACTIONS

I. Substitution Reaction of Alkyl Halides:

A. <u>Free Radical Halogenation of Alkanes:</u>
1. When an alkane such as methane is treated with Cl_2 or Br_2 in the presence of heat or light, a mixture of alkyl halides is formed.
2. The reaction of alkanes with halogens is a type of free-radical reaction called a **free-radical substitution reaction**; it is a substitution because a halogen atom is substituted for an alkane hydrogen.
3. The mechanism of this reaction follows the typical pattern of other free-radical chain reactions:
    a) Initiation—the reaction is initiated when the halogen molecule absorbs energy from the heat or light and dissociates homolytically into halogen atoms.
    b) Propagation—the ensuing chain reaction forms the major reaction products.
    c) Termination—termination steps result from the recombination of radical species.

$$X_2 \xrightarrow[\text{or heat}]{\text{light}} X\cdot + X\cdot \qquad (X = Cl \text{ or } Br) \qquad \text{initiation step}$$

$$R-H + X\cdot \longrightarrow R\cdot + H-X$$

$$\left.\begin{array}{c} \\ \\ \end{array}\right\} \text{propation steps}$$

$$R\cdot + X_2 \longrightarrow R-X + X\cdot$$

$$R\cdot + X\cdot \longrightarrow R-X \qquad\qquad\qquad \text{termination step}$$

4. Halogenation with fluorine is violent.
5. Halogenations with chlorine and bromine proceed smoothly.
6. Halogenation with iodine does not occur.

B. <u>Formation of Grignard and Organolithium Reagents:</u>
1. Compounds that contain carbon–metal bonds are called **organometallic compounds**.
2. **Alkylmagnesium halides** are known as **Grignard reagents**.
    a) A Grignard reagent contains a carbon–magnesium bond.
    b) Grignard reagents are soluble in ether solvents because the magnesium is coordinated to the ether oxygen in a Lewis acid–base interaction.
    c) Ether solvents are generally required for the formation of Grignard reagents because of the importance of the coordination of the magnesium of the reagent with the solvent.
3. Reactions that form Grignard and **organolithium reagents** occur on the surface of the insoluble metals.
4. Reactions that form Grignard and organolithium reagents are heterogeneous reactions.

$$R-X + Mg \xrightarrow{\text{ether}} R-MgX \qquad (X = Cl, Br, \text{ or } I)$$

$$R-X + 2 Li \xrightarrow{\text{hexane}} R-Li + LiX \qquad (X = Cl, Br, \text{ or } I)$$

    a) Formation of Grignard and organolithium reagents has been shown to involve radical intermediates.
    b) Many organolithium reagents are sufficiently soluble in hexane or other hydrocarbons that ether need not be used.
5. Grignard and organolithium reagents react violently with oxygen and also with water.

C. Protonolysis of Grignard and Organolithium Reagents:
   1. The metal is the more electropositive partner in the metal–carbon bond.
      a) The carbon atom has a partial negative charge.
      b) The carbon reacts as if it were a **carbanion** (carbon anion).
      c) The carbon in the carbon–metal bond of a Grignard or organolithium reagent is expected to
         behave as a strong Brønsted base.
         (1) R—MgX acts much like $R:^-{}^+MgX$.
         (2) R—Li acts much like $R:^-{}^+Li$.
   2. Any Grignard or organolithium reagent reacts vigorously with even relatively weak acids such as water
      and alcohols.
      a) Grignard and organolithium reagents react with water or alcohols to give the conjugate-base
         hydroxide or alkoxides and the conjugate acid of the carbanion, a hydrocarbon.

$$R\text{—}MgX + H_2O \longrightarrow R\text{—}H + Mg(OH)X$$

$$R\text{—}Li + R'\text{—}OH \longrightarrow R\text{—}H + R'\text{—}OLi$$

      b) Grignard and organolithium reagents must be prepared in the absence of moisture.
   3. A **protonolysis** is a reaction with the proton of an acid that breaks chemical bonds.
      a) Protonolysis is a method for the preparation of hydrocarbons from alkyl halides.
      b) A particularly useful variation of protonolysis is the preparation of hydrocarbons labeled with the
         hydrogen isotopes **deuterium** (**D**, or ^2H) or **tritium** (**T**, or ^3H) using labeled water (D_2O or
         HTO, respectively).

$$R\text{—}Li + D_2O \longrightarrow R\text{—}D + LiOD$$

II. Acid-Base Reactions of Alcohols and Thiols:

A. Formation of Alkoxides and Mercaptides:
   1. Sodium metal reacts with an alcohol to afford a solution of the sodium alkoxide; hydroxide is not a
      sufficiently strong base to convert an alcohol completely into its conjugate-base alkoxide.

$$R\text{—}OH + 2\,Na \longrightarrow R\text{—}\ddot{\underset{..}{O}}{:}^-\;Na^+ + H_2$$

   2. Thiols can be converted completely into their conjugate-base mercaptide anions by reaction with one
      equivalent of hydroxide or alkoxide; thiols form insoluble mercaptides with many heavy-metal ions,
      such as Hg^{2+}, Cu^{2+}, and Pb^{2+}.

$$R\text{—}SH + NaOH \longrightarrow R\text{—}\ddot{\underset{..}{S}}{:}^-\;Na^+ + H_2O$$

$$2\,R\text{—}SH + Hg^{2+} \longrightarrow RS\text{—}Hg\text{—}SR + 2\,H^+$$

CHAPTER 8 SOLUTIONS

Solutions to In-Text Problems

1. (a) Isobutyl fluoride (b) hexyl iodide (or *n*-hexyl iodide) (c) Cyclohexyl chloride

2. (a)   (b) 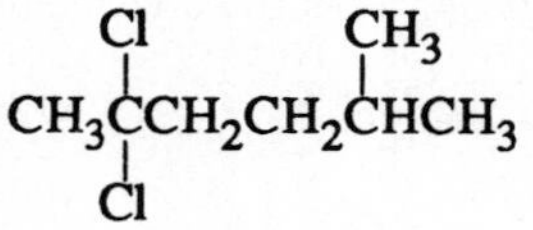   (c) 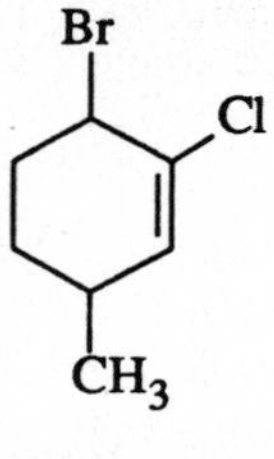   (d)

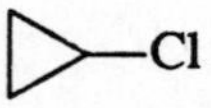

3. (a) 3-bromo-3-chloro-1-methyl-1-cyclopropene (b) (*Z*)-3-chloro-2-pentene
    (c) 3-bromo-1,1,1-trichloro-2-fluorobutane (d) trichloromethane
    (e) 2-chloro-5-methylhexane (f) 1-bromo-2,2-dimethylpropane

4. (a)   (b) 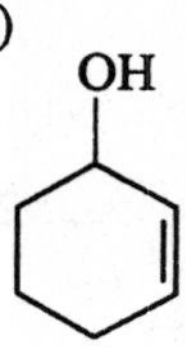   (c)

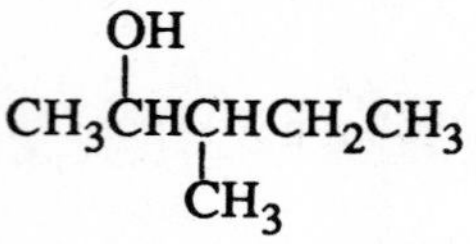

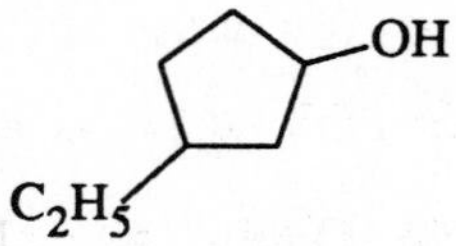

    (d) 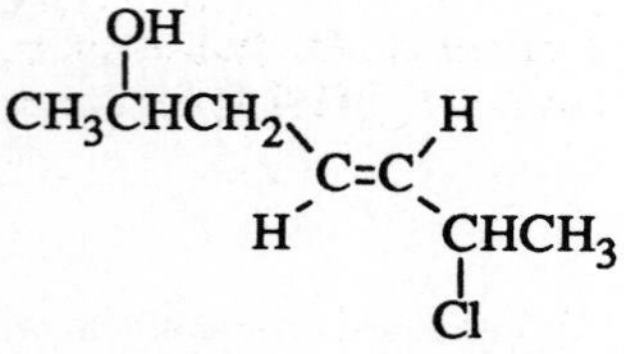   (e) 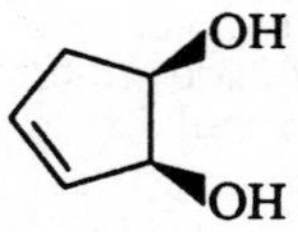   (f) $(CH_3)_2CHCH_2OH$

5. (a) 1-butanol (b) 3-bromo-1-butanol (c) (*E*)-1-chloro-3-methyl-3-penten-2-ol
    (d) 3-butyl-2,4-pentanediol (Don't forget that the principal chain is the one containing the greatest number of
    —OH groups.)
    (e) 2-methyl-2-propanethiol (f) 2-chloro-5-methyl-2-cyclopenten-1-ol
    (g) 2,5-cyclohexadien-1-ol (h) 1,2,3-propanetriol (i) 1-mercapto-2-pentanol

6. (a)   (b)   (c)

    C_2H_5—O—$CH_2CH_2CH_3$ $(CH_3)_2CHCH_2$—O—$CH_2CH(CH_3)_2$

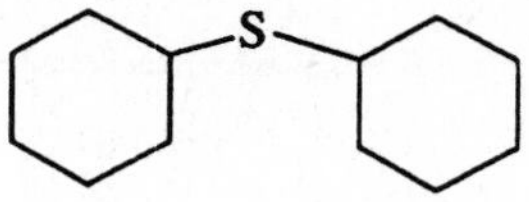

    (d)   (e) 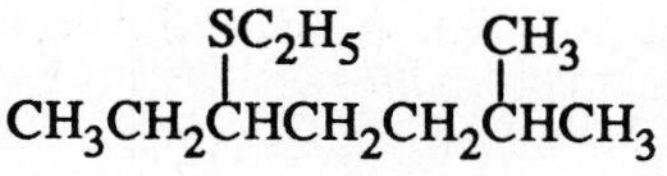   (f)

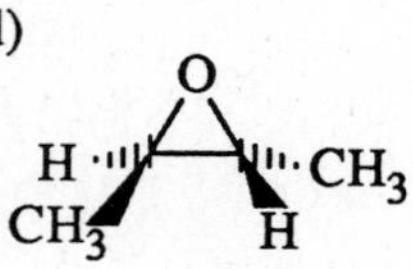

7. (a) 2-methoxy-2-methylpropane (b) 1-(isobutylthio)-2-methylpropane
    (c) 2-ethoxy-1-ethanol (d) (E)-5-methoxy-3-penten-1-ol

8. From Table 8.1, we observe from the two rightmost columns that in going from the first to the second row of
    the periodic table there is an increase in bond length of about 0.4 Å. From the last column, we see that in going
    from the second to the third row there is an increase of about 0.2 Å. Assuming the same increase for the
    column containing oxygen, sulfur, and selenium, we estimate the C—Se bond length to be about 2.0 Å.

9. (a) Donor, because H—Br is a strong acid. One might suspect that the Br, because of its unshared electrons,
    would be an acceptor. It cannot be a strong acceptor, for if it were, H—Br would be a liquid.

    (b) Donor. In addition, the fluorine is an acceptor. (H—F has a remarkably high boiling point [19°] for a
    molecule of its molecular weight.)

(c)   (d)

CH$_3$—C—OH — donor

(e)   donor and acceptor   (f)

$CH_3CH_2\overset{+}{N}H_3$ donor

10. (a) The concentration of dimer increases.
    (b) We use the usual relationship between $\Delta G°$ and K_{eq}, and assuming 25 °C (298 K):

    $$\Delta G° = -2.303RT\log K_{eq} = -1.364(\log 11) = -1.42 \text{ kcal/mol}$$

    (c) After one mole of ethanol is dissolved, let us say that x moles of ethanol have reacted to form dimer; then
    the concentration of ethanol remaining is $(1.0 - x)$, and the concentration of dimer is $x/2$. (Remember, it takes
    two ethanol molecules to form one molecule of dimer.) The equilibrium-constant expression for dimerization
    becomes

    $$K_{eq} = 11 = \frac{x/2}{(1-x)^2}$$

    Solving by the quadratic formula, we find that $x = 0.8083$ M. Thus, the concentration of dimer is $x/2 = 0.404$
    M; that of free ethanol is $(1 - x)$ or 0.102 M. Thus, about 90% of the ethanol is dimerized in a $1M$ solution.

    (d) The standard free energy change for dimerization of ethanethiol is –3.27 kcal/mol at 25°. The
    concentration of dimer is about $0.004M$, and that of free ethanethiol is about $0.992M$. Hardly any of the
    ethanethiol is dimerized. Since it is hydrogen bonding that causes dimerization, and since dimerization of
    ethanethiol is so much weaker than that of ethanol, it follows that hydrogen bonding in ethanethiol is also much
    weaker than that in ethanol.

11. Hexane should be least soluble in ethanol, because ethanol is polar and protic, whereas hexane is apolar and
    aprotic.

12. Water can accept a hydrogen bond from the hydrogen of the N—H bond, and can donate a hydrogen bond to
    the oxygen of the C=O bond. This hydrogen bonding tends to solubilize acetanilide in water. In contrast, the
    CH$_3$ group and the benzene ring cannot hydrogen bond with water, and these apolar ("greasy") groups interact
    poorly with water and tend to make acetanilide insoluble.

13. The free energy of association of K$^+$ with a crown ether is the difference between the free energy of the
    complex and that of the uncomplexed ion and ether. In water, the uncomplexed ion is stabilized by aqueous
    solvation. When the ion leaves aqueous solution, the stabilization contributed by aqueous solvation is "traded
    in" for the stabilization contributed by the oxygens of the crown ether. To a crude approximation, we can think

of this as an "even trade" — there is no increase in stabilization. In benzene, there is no solvation of the ion, and it is much less stable than it is in water. Thus, much more energy is released when the ion leaves benzene and enters the cavity of the crown ether than when the ion leaves water. Hence, the complex of potassium ion with the crown ether dissociates with more difficulty in benzene than the same complex does in water — that is, its dissociation constant is smaller in benzene.

14. The strongest base is the amide ion, $^-:NH_2$; the weakest base is the perchlorate ion, ClO_4^-.

15. We use the procedure in the text preceding the problem.

    (a)
    $$H—CN + NH_3 \rightleftarrows {}^-CN + {}^+NH_4$$
    $$pK_a = 9.4 \qquad\qquad\qquad pK_a = 9.25$$

    $$\log K_{eq} = 9.25 - 9.4 = -0.15$$

    or $K_{eq} = 10^{-0.15} = 0.71$

    Notice that the *base* on the left side of the equation is $:NH_3$; hence, the relevant pK_a is that of its *conjugate acid*, the ammonium ion. (The pK_a of ammonia itself would be used only if the relevant conjugate base were the amide ion, $^-NH_2$.)

    (b)
    $$H—CN + F^- \rightleftarrows {}^-CN + H—F$$
    $$pK_a = 9.4 \qquad\qquad\qquad pK_a = 3.2$$

    $$\log K_{eq} = 3.2 - 9.4 = -6.2$$

    or $K_{eq} = 10^{-6.2} = 6.31 \times 10^{-7}$.

16. (a) $CH_3S—H$ is a stronger acid than $CH_3O—H$ because the S—H bond is considerably weaker than the O—H bond. Because the comparison is within the same column of the periodic table, bond strength governs acidity.
    (b) H—Cl is a stronger acid than $CH_3S—H$ because chlorine is considerably more electronegative than sulfur. Because the comparison is within the same row of the periodic table, electronegativity is the overriding factor.
    (c) $(CH_3)_2P—H$ is a stronger acid than $(CH_3)_2N—H$ because the P—H bond is weaker than the N—H bond, assuming the usual trends within a column of the periodic table hold in this case (and they do!).

17. (a) $K^+ (CH_3)_3C—O^-$ (b) $Li^+ CH_3O^-$ (c) $Na^+ (CH_3)_2CH—O^-$

    (d)
    $$CH_3CH_2\overset{\overset{\displaystyle CH_3}{|}}{\underset{\underset{\displaystyle CH_3}{|}}{C}}CH_2O^- \, Na^+$$

18. (a) Calcium methoxide (calcium methanolate)   (b) Cuprous ethyl mercaptide (cuprous ethanethiolate)

19. The systematic approach to a problem such as this is to make *pairwise comparisons* — that is, a comparison within each pair of compounds. For example, in (a), let us compare the first and third compounds, each of which has one chlorine. The first compound is more acidic, because the chlorine is closer to the —OH group. Between the first and second compound, the second is more acidic because it has more chlorines. Thus we have, in order of increasing acidity:

    (a) $ClCH_2CH_2CH_2OH < ClCH_2CH_2OH < Cl_2CHCH_2OH$

    (b) $HCF_2CH_2CH_2OH < HCF_2CH_2OH < CF_3CF_2CH_2OH$

(c) Between the two chlorine-containing compounds, the thiol is more acidic, because thiols are considerably more acidic than alcohols; the alcohol containing no chlorines is least acidic:

$$CH_3CH_2OH < ClCH_2CH_2OH < ClCH_2CH_2SH$$

(d) Since oxygen is more electronegative than carbon, the order is:

$$CH_3CH_2CH_2CH_2OH < CH_3OCH_2CH_2OH$$

20. A pH of 11.0 means that the hydrogen-ion concentration is 10^{-11} M. The equilibrium expression for ionization of 2,2,2-trifluoroethanol is

$$K_a = 10^{-12.4} = \frac{[CF_3CH_2O^-][H^+]}{[CF_3CH_2OH]}$$

or $\dfrac{K_a}{[H^+]} = \dfrac{10^{-12.4}}{10^{-11}} = 10^{-1.4} = 3.98 \times 10^{-2} = \dfrac{[CF_3CH_2O^-]}{[CF_3CH_2OH]} = \dfrac{x}{0.1 - x}$

Mass balance says that

$$[CF_3CH_2OH] + [CF_3CH_2O^-] = 0.100 \ M$$

or $[CF_3CH_2OH] + 3.98 \times 10^{-2}[CF_3CH_2OH] = 0.100$

from which we obtain $[CF_3CH_2OH] = 0.096 \ M$, and $[CF_3CH_2O^-] = 0.004 \ M$.

In other words, the alcohol is about 4% ionized at pH = 11.0.

21. We use Eq. 8.17b and the data in Eq. 8.18.

    (a) $\Delta G° = 2.303RT(pK_a) = (1.364)(12.4) = 16.91$ kcal/mol
    (b) $\Delta G° = 2.303RT(pK_a) = (1.364)(15.4) = 21.01$ kcal/mol

    Evidently, it takes about 4 kcal/mol more energy to ionize 4,4,4-trifluoro-1-butanol than it does to ionize 2,2,2-trifluoro-1-ethanol. The conjugate-base anion of 2,2,2-trifluoro-1-ethanol is stabilized more by the fluorines because they are closer to the anionic oxygen than the fluorines are in 4,4,4-trifluoro-1-butanol.

22. Just as hydrogen bonding to nucleophiles decreases their reactivity with alkyl groups in alkyl halides, hydrogen bonding to bases decreases their basicity. In an aprotic solvent such as tetrahydrofuran (c), the basicity of the electron pairs on the hydroxide ion is not partially satisfied by hydrogen bonding, as it is in protic solvents. Hence, hydroxide ion is particularly basic in tetrahydrofuran.

23. We can see in Eq. 8.26 that ethers solubilize Grignard reagents by forming Lewis base-Lewis acid complexes with them. A tertiary amine is also a Lewis base, and solubilizes Grignard reagents by a similar type of interaction:

$$R_3N: \rightarrow \underset{\underset{R}{|}}{\overset{\overset{Br}{|}}{Mg}} \leftarrow :NR_3$$

24. (a) $(CH_3)_3CH$
    (b) The arrow formalism and products are as follows:

$$CH_3\text{---}Li \quad H\text{---}\overset{..}{\underset{..}{O}}CH_3 \longrightarrow CH_3\text{---}H + Li^+ \ ^-:\overset{..}{\underset{..}{O}}CH_3$$

25. Two Grignard reagents that would give propane when treated with water:

$$CH_3CHCH_3 \quad \text{and} \quad CH_3CH_2CH_2\text{—MgBr}$$
$$\quad | $$
$$MgBr$$

These compounds react with D_2O as follows:

$$CH_3CHCH_3 + D_2O \longrightarrow CH_3CHCH_3 + BrMg\text{—OD}$$
$$\quad | \qquad\qquad\qquad\qquad\quad |$$
$$MgBr \qquad\qquad\qquad\qquad\quad D$$

$$CH_3CH_2CH_2\text{—MgBr} + D_2O \longrightarrow CH_3CH_2CH_2\text{—D} + BrMg\text{—OD}$$

26. Methyl chloride (CH_3Cl) is formed as in Eq. 8.34a-c. The propagation steps for formation of methylene chloride are:

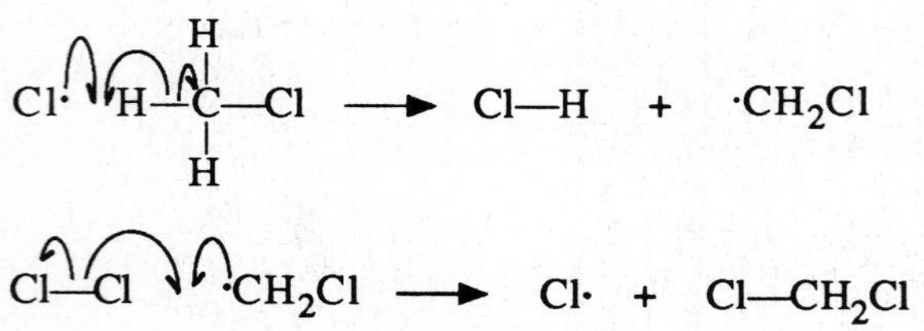

27. A recombination reaction of two methyl radicals gives ethane:

$$2 \cdot CH_3 \rightarrow CH_3\text{—}CH_3$$

Solutions to Additional Problems

28. Any alcohol with a formula $C_5H_{11}OH$ must be a saturated acyclic alcohol. The alcohols with this formula are:

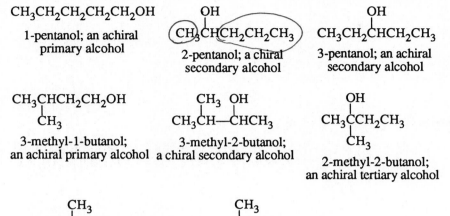

$CH_3CH_2CH_2CH_2CH_2OH$

1-pentanol; an achiral
primary alcohol

$CH_3CHCH_2CH_2CH_3$

2-pentanol; a chiral
secondary alcohol

$CH_3CH_2CHCH_2CH_3$

3-pentanol; an achiral
secondary alcohol

$CH_3CHCH_2CH_2OH$

CH_3

3-methyl-1-butanol;
an achiral primary alcohol

$CH_3CH—CHCH_3$

3-methyl-2-butanol;
a chiral secondary alcohol

$CH_3CCH_2CH_3$

CH_3

2-methyl-2-butanol;
an achiral tertiary alcohol

CH_3

$CH_3CH_2CHCH_2OH$

2-methyl-1-butanol; a
chiral primary alcohol

CH_3

CH_3CCH_2OH

CH_3

2,2-dimethyl-1-propanol;
(neopentyl alcohol); an achiral
primary alcohol

29. The systematic name for halothane is 2-bromo-2-chloro-1,1,1-trifluoroethane.

30. (a) *t*-butyl alcohol < 2-pentanol < 1-hexanol. Both molecular weight and shape determine the order; 2-pentanol has a lower molecular weight than 1-hexanol; *t*-butyl alcohol has a lower molecular weight and is more spherical than 2-pentanol.

(b) 1-hexene < 1-chloropentane < 1-hexanol. Hydrogen bonding in the alcohol is the most important effect; since alkyl halides *of a given molecular weight* have the same boiling points as the corresponding alkanes (or alkenes), and since 1-chloropentane has a *higher molecular weight* than 1-hexene, it has a higher boiling point than the alkene.

(c) propane < diethyl ether < 1,2-propanediol. The diol, because of hydrogen bonding, has a much higher boiling point than diethyl ether, a compound of about the same molecular weight that cannot donate hydrogen bonds; diethyl ether has a higher molecular weight and is more polar than propane.

(d) 1-chloropropane < 1-chlorobutane < 1-pentanol. The order of the two alkyl halides follows from their relative molecular weights; and the boiling point of the alcohol is highest, because it can undergo hydrogen bonding.

(e) 2-bromopropane < 4-ethylheptane. We have learned that alkyl bromides have lower boiling points than alkanes of about the same molecular weight; it follows, then, that an alkyl bromide has a lower boiling point than an alkane of higher molecular weight.

(f) perfluorocyclobutane < chlorocyclobutane < cyclooctane. The order of the last two compounds follows from the fact that alkanes and alkyl halides (hence, cycloalkanes and cycloalkyl chlorides) have about the same boiling points. If we can generalize from the example at the bottom of text page 283, we deduce that perfluorocyclobutane should have a lower boiling point than fluorocyclobutane, which in turn should have a lower boiling point than chlorocyclobutane.

(g) *t*-butyl alcohol < *n*-butyl alcohol. The more spherical (more highly branched) isomer has the lower boiling point.

31. There may be more than one acceptable answer for each question.
    (a) Since unsaturation number $U = 1$, the compound must contain a ring, since we are given that it has no multiple bonds.

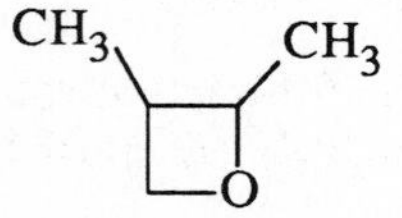

and 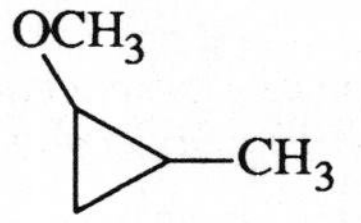   are two examples.

(b) Either rings, multiple bonds, or both are allowed in this case. Two examples are

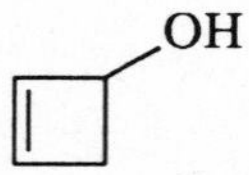

and $HC{\equiv}C-CH-OH$
                      |
                     CH_3

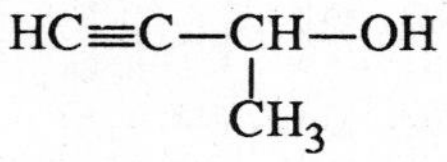

(c) The compound has $U = 2$. One example is

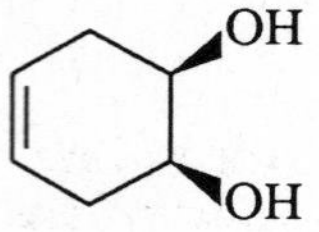

Notice that, although this compound has asymmetric carbons, it is achiral because it is *meso*.

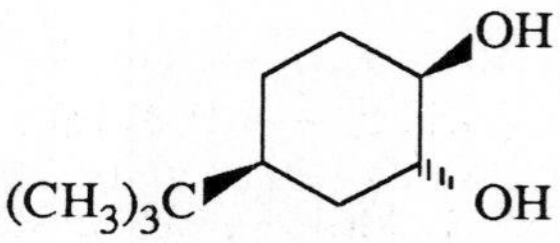

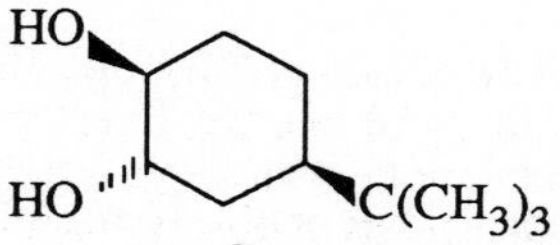

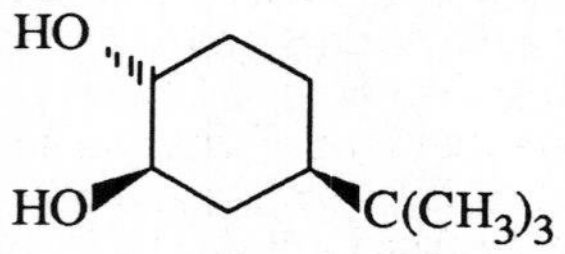

(d)

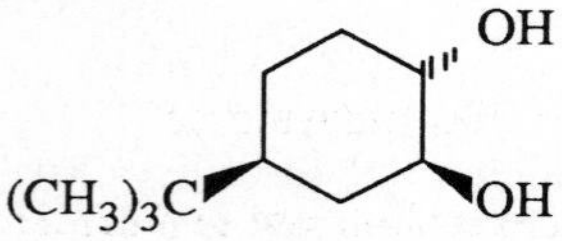

(Compounds A and D are enantiomers, as are compounds B and C.)

(e) 2,3-Butanediol exists as two enantiomers and a *meso* compound. (See Sec. 6.7, text page 199.)
(f) 1,2-Butanediol exists as two enantiomers.

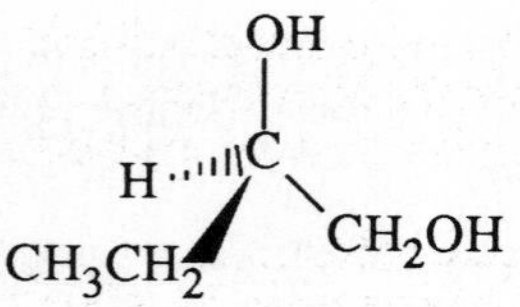

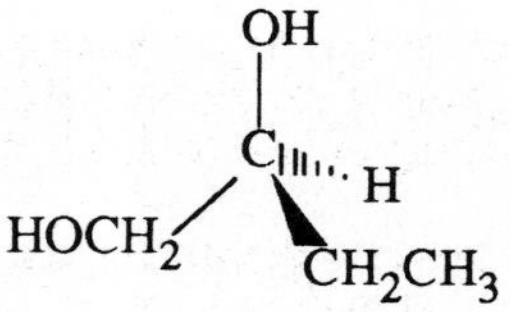

(g)

+ its enantiomer 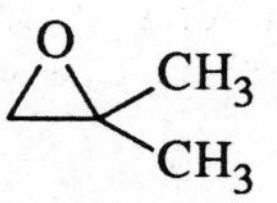 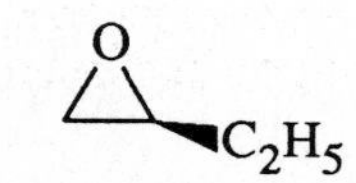   + its enantiomer

32. First, we have to know what reaction is being described in the problem. Bromine and light bring about free-radical *substitution*; see Sec. 8.9, text page 309. In this reaction, an alkyl hydrogen is replaced by a bromine.

(a) Neopentane, $(CH_3)_4C$, gives only one possible monobromination product: neopentyl bromide, $(CH_3)_3CCH_2Br$.
(b) Butane gives three monobromination products: 1-bromobutane, and the enantiomers of 2-bromobutane.
(c) Isobutane $[(CH_3)_3CH]$ gives two achiral monobromination products: isobutyl bromide, $(CH_3)_2CHCH_2Br$, and *t*-butyl bromide, $(CH_3)_3C$—Br.

33. The problem is that Flick's ether is also an alcohol. The Grignard reagent was destroyed by the —OH group of Flick's ether in a protonolysis reaction:

$$C_2H_5MgBr \ + \ H—OCH_2CH_2OCH_2CH_3 \ \longrightarrow \ C_2H_6 \ + \ BrMg^+ \ ^-OCH_2CH_2OCH_2CH_3$$

34. (a) Propyl alcohol is miscible in water because of the hydrogen bonding capabilities of its —OH group.
(b) Alcohols react with NaH to liberate hydrogen gas; hence, the compound is the alcohol 2-methylcyclohexanol.
(c) Alkenes decolorize Br_2 in CCl_4; hence, the compound is the alkene allyl methyl ether:

$$CH_2=CH—CH_2—O—CH_3 \quad \text{allyl methyl ether}$$

(d) The compound is an alkene because it decolorizes bromine; it is an alcohol, because it evolves a gas (methane) when treated with the Grignard reagent CH_3MgI; it is chiral because it is optically active. The only compound with the formula C_4H_8O that meets these criteria is 3-buten-2-ol:

$$\overset{\displaystyle OH}{\underset{\displaystyle |}{CH_2=CH—CH—CH_3}}$$

35. The compounds below are given in order of increasing acidity — that is, in order of decreasing pK_a.

(a) *t*-butyl alcohol < isopropyl alcohol < *n*-propyl alcohol. More highly branched alcohols are less acidic because their conjugate bases are more poorly solvated.

(b) cyclohexanol < cyclohexyl mercaptan. Thiols are more acidic than the corresponding alcohols because the S—H bond is much weaker than the O—H bond.

(c) 2-chloroethanol < 3-chloropropanethiol < 2-chloropropanethiol. Thiols are more acidic than alcohols for the reason given in (b). 2-Chloropropanethiol is the more acidic thiol because the electronegative chlorine is closer to the site of negative charge in the conjugate-base thiolate anion.

(d) $H_2NCH_2CH_2CH_2OH < CH_3NHCH_2CH_2OH < (CH_3)_3\overset{+}{N}CH_2CH_2OH$. The last compound is most acidic because it has a full-fledged positive charge that can stabilize a negative charge in the conjugate-base anion. In the other two compounds, the nitrogen stabilizes the conjugate-base anion by its inductive effect; in the more acidic of these compounds, the nitrogen is closer to the oxygen, which is the site of negative charge in the conjugate-base alkoxide anion.

36. Compound *A* is expected to be more soluble in hydrocarbon solvents, because of the "like-dissolves-like" rule. The alkyl groups, particularly the large cetyl $(C_{16}H_{33})$ group, interact favorably with the hydrocarbon chains of the solvent. On the other hand, there is no hydrogen bonding available in a hydrocarbon solvent to stabilize ammonium chloride.

   Although compound *A* has some solubility in hydrocarbon solvents, it exists in the solvents as ion pairs and higher aggregates rather than as free ions. The reason is that hydrocarbon solvents have a very low dielectric constant $(\varepsilon \cong 2)$, whereas a high dielectric constant is required to separate ionic aggregates into free ions. Furthermore, a hydrocarbon offers no solvation by hydrogen bonding to the bromide counter-ion. Hence, this anion remains in proximity to its positive partner at all times.

37. Water forms a Lewis acid-Lewis base complex with Cu^{2+} ion:

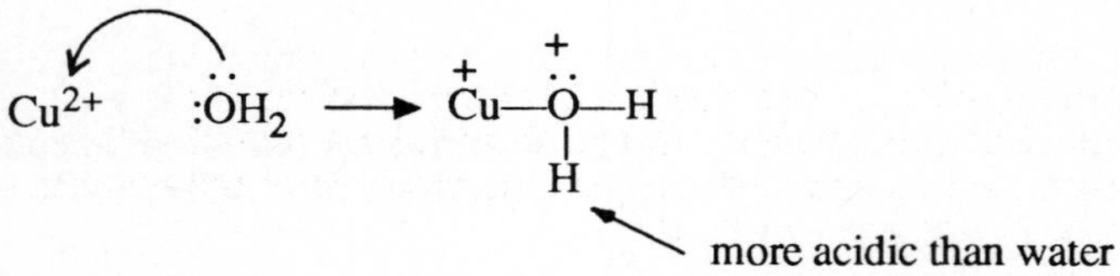

Ionization of a hydrogen of the complexed water removes a positive charge from the oxygen and eliminates the charge-charge repulsion in the complex. In water itself, ionization does not have this driving force. Hence, complexed water is more acidic.

38. In the presence of concentrated acid, dibutyl ether is protonated. The protonated ether is an ionic compound, and ionic compounds are soluble in water:

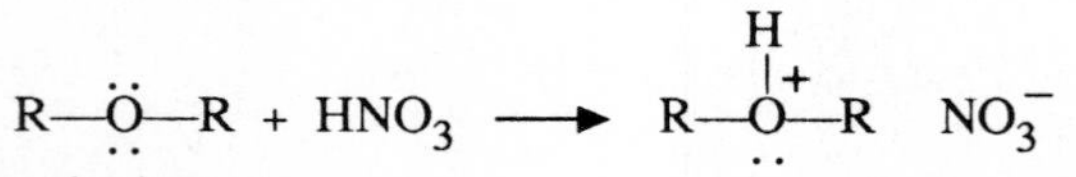

not ionic; not soluble in water

an ionic compound; water soluble

39. Since all three alkyl halides give the same protonolysis product, they have the same carbon skeleton, that of 2,4-dimethylpentane. The three alkyl halides differ only in where the bromine is located on that skeleton. Let us examine *all* the possibilities for alkyl bromides with this carbon skeleton. (For convenience, we show carbon skeletons only.)

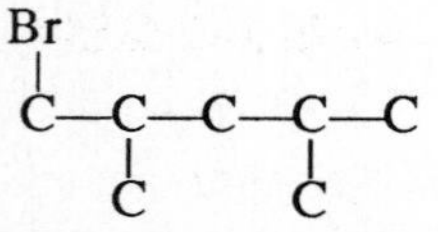

1-bromo-2,4-dimethylpentane; chiral; could be optically active

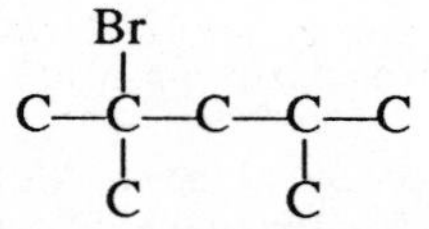

2-bromo-2,4-dimethylpentane

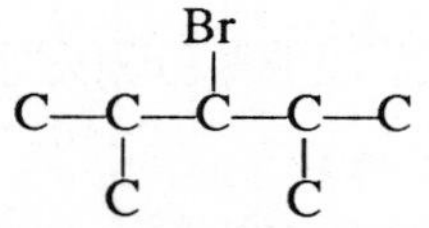

3-bromo-2,4-dimethylpentane

40. The equilibrium constant for the reaction shown, K_{eq}, is given by

$$K_{eq} = \frac{[HB][A^-]}{[HA][B^-]}$$

Following the hint, let us show that this equals K_{HA}/K_{HB}.

$$K_{HA}/K_{HB} = \frac{[A^-][H^+]}{[HA]} \times \frac{[HB]}{[H^+][B^-]} = \frac{[HB][A^-]}{[HA][B^-]}$$

or $\quad K_{eq} = K_{HA}/K_{HB}$

Now we take logarithms of this equation:

$$\log K_{eq} = \log K_{HA} - \log K_{HB} = pK_{HB} - pK_{HA}$$

Taking antilogs of both sides:

$$10^{\log K_{eq}} = K_{eq} = 10^{(pK_{HB} - pK_{HA})}$$

41. Did you try to answer any parts of this problem without first drawing the structures or making models? You MUST draw the structures or make models and examine them before you can claim to have made a reasonable attempt at a problem of this sort.

(a) In compound *A*, the equatorial position of the —OH group is preferred for the usual reason: it avoids 1,3-diaxial interactions with hydrogens on the ring. However, compound *B* prefers to have an axial —OH group because it affords the opportunity for intramolecular hydrogen bonding. Furthermore, since the ring has no hydrogens on the oxygens, the usual 1,3-diaxial interactions are absent.

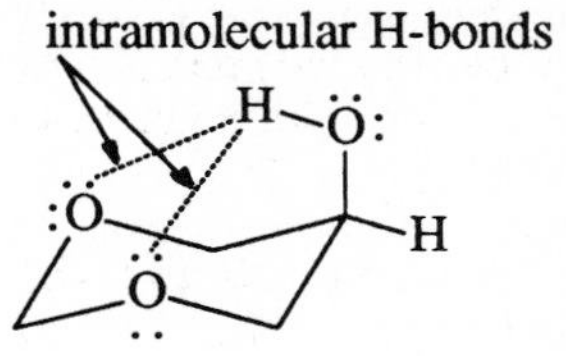

intramolecular H-bonds

axial form 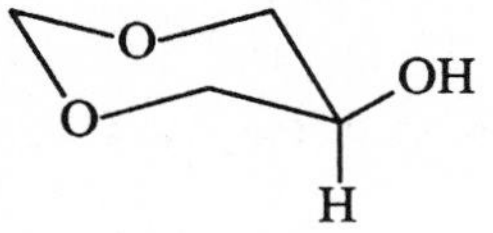   equatorial form; no
                                     intramolecular H-bonds
                                            possible

In the equatorial form, the —OH group is simply too far from the ring oxygens for effective hydrogen bonding.

➤ Why should hydrogen-bonding cause the preference for the normally less stable form? We must always remember that additional bonding provides additional stability. Hydrogen bonding is one type of additional bonding.

(b) In the *gauche* conformer, we can turn to hydrogen bonding as the source of additional stability:

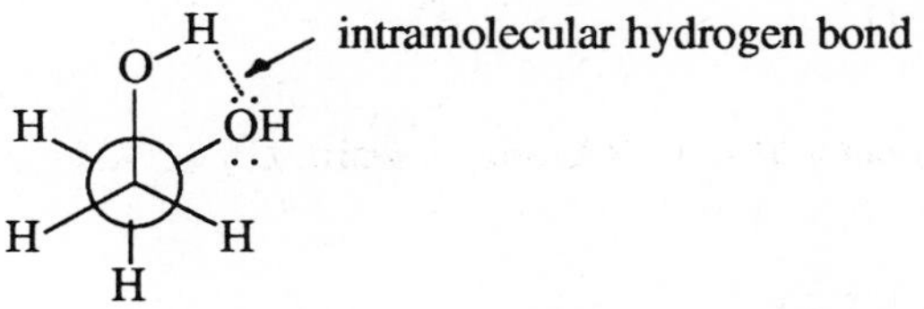

intramolecular hydrogen bond

In the *anti* form, the two —OH groups are too far apart for hydrogen bonding to occur. The solvent CCl_4 provides no hydrogen-bonding capability. Hence, intramolecular hydrogen bonding is particularly favorable in this solvent.

(c) We would expect intramolecular hydrogen bonding to stabilize both the racemate and the *meso* compound. However, in the *meso* compound, intramolecular hydrogen bonding is accompanied by a compensating, destabilizing *gauche* interaction between two *t*-butyl groups:

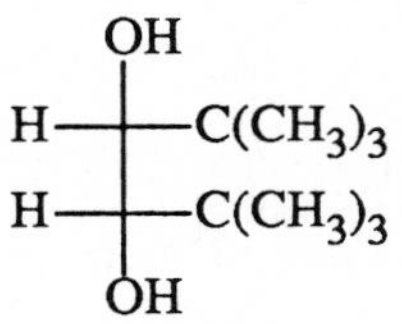

severe *gauche*
interaction

meso compound

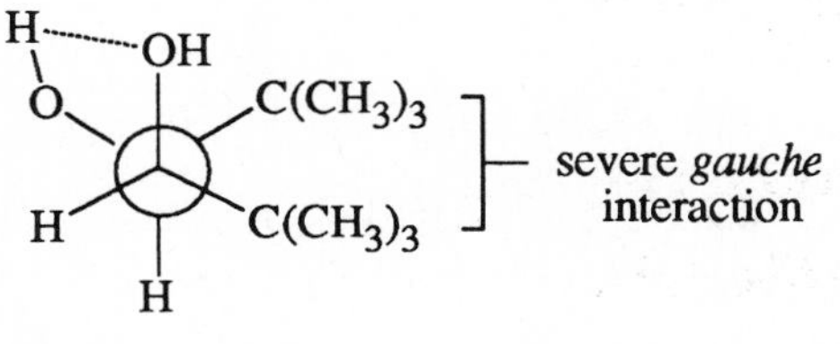

This destabilization overrides the energetic advantage of hydrogen bonding. Hence, intramolecular hydrogen bonding is not observed in the *meso* stereoisomer. The offending *gauche* interaction is not present in the hydrogen-bonded form of the racemate; hence, intramolecular hydrogen bonding in this species can occur without difficulty:

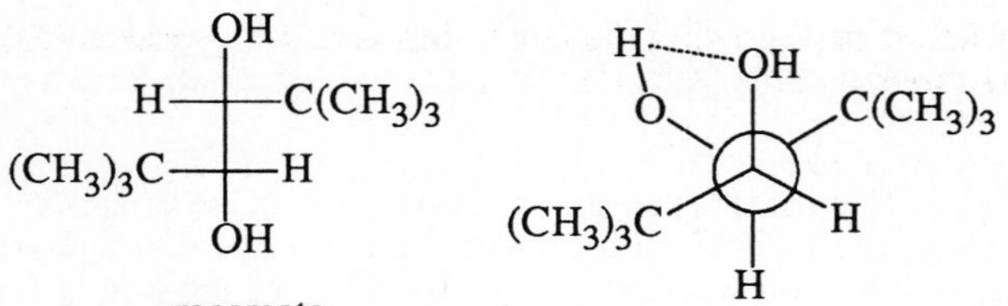

racemate

42. (a) In the chair conformation, for every C—O bond dipole in a given direction, there is another C—O bond dipole of the same magnitude pointing in the opposite direction:

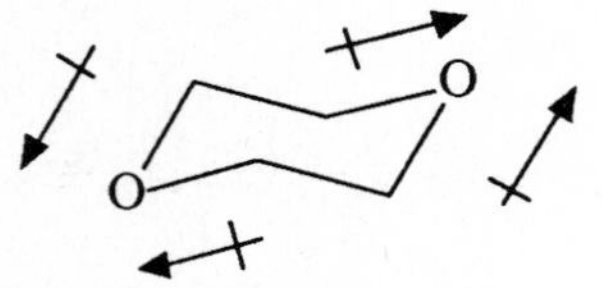

(b) To the extent that the twist-boat form is important, it will contribute a non-zero dipole moment, because the C—O bond dipoles do not cancel in this form.

resultant for entire molecule

resultants of C—O bond pairs at opposite ends of the molecule

43. As we learned on text page 307, ethers dissolve Grignard reagents by coordinating with their magnesium atoms. Ethers that cannot take part in this coordination are not good solvents for Grignard reagents. In compound *B*, the methyl groups interfere with this coordination through steric repulsions with the R— and —Br groups of Grignard reagents; hence, compound *B* is a poor solvent for these reagents.

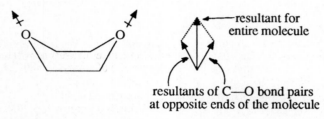

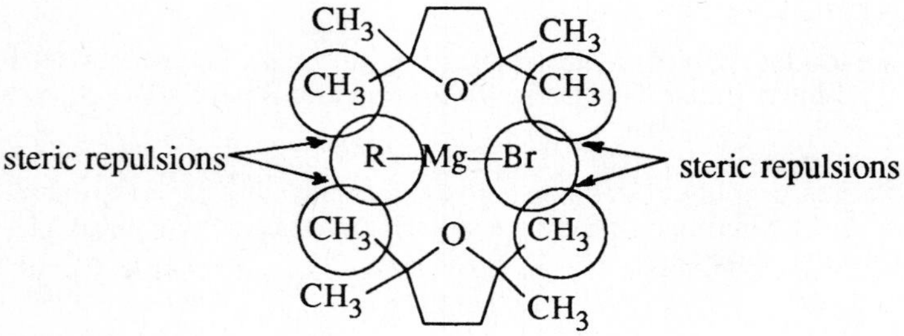

steric repulsions ⟵ ⟶ steric repulsions

44. Ethylene glycol is more acidic than ethanol because the inductive effect of the second oxygen, which ethanol lacks, stabilizes the conjugate-base anion HO—CH_2CH_2—O^-. However, this anion is also an acid, and when it ionizes, it forms a conjugate-base dianion ^-O—CH_2CH_2—O^-. The two negative charges in this dianion interact repulsively; hence, the energy of this species is relatively high, and, as a result, ionization is less favorable.

45. (a) The two monobromination products, which result from free-radical substitution, are isobutyl bromide, $(CH_3)_2CHCH_2—Br$, and t-butyl bromide, $(CH_3)_3C—Br$.

(b) The propagation steps for formation of isobutyl bromide are:

$$Br\cdot + CH_3—\overset{\overset{\displaystyle CH_3}{|}}{CH}—CH_2—H \longrightarrow HBr + CH_3—\overset{\overset{\displaystyle CH_3}{|}}{CH}—\overset{\displaystyle \cdot}{CH_2}$$
$$\qquad\qquad\qquad\qquad\qquad\qquad\qquad\qquad\qquad\qquad A$$

$$CH_3—\overset{\overset{\displaystyle CH_3}{|}}{CH}—\overset{\displaystyle \cdot}{CH_2} + Br_2 \longrightarrow Br\cdot + CH_3—\overset{\overset{\displaystyle CH_3}{|}}{CH}—CH_2—Br$$
$$\qquad A \qquad\qquad\qquad\qquad\qquad\qquad\qquad\qquad \text{isobutyl bromide}$$

The intermediate radical A is a *primary* alkyl radical. The propagation steps for the formation of t-butyl bromide are:

$$Br\cdot + (CH_3)_3C—H \longrightarrow (CH_3)_3C\cdot + H—Br$$
$$\qquad\qquad\qquad\qquad\qquad\qquad B$$

$$(CH_3)_3C\cdot + Br_2 \longrightarrow (CH_3)_3C—Br + Br\cdot$$
$$\quad B \qquad\qquad\qquad \text{t-butyl bromide}$$

In this case, the intermediate radical B is a *tertiary* free radical. By Hammond's postulate, the reaction that proceeds through the more stable intermediate is the faster reaction. Hence, formation of t-butyl bromide is favored because the tertiary free radical is formed more rapidly than the primary one.

46. (a) Both HI and HCl are much stronger acids than H_3O^+. For this reason, the following equilibrium lies well to the right for both X = Cl and X = I:

$$HX + H_2O \rightleftharpoons H_3O^+ + X^-$$

Since H_3O^+ is the major acidic species in solution in each case, and since there is, for all practical purposes, the same amount of this species present in each case, the pH is the same.

(b) Both basic species react virtually irreversibly with water to generate hydroxide ion.

$$B{:}^- + H—\overset{..}{\underset{..}{O}}H \rightleftharpoons B—H + {}^-{:}\overset{..}{\underset{..}{O}}H$$

Since the major basic species in solution is hydroxide ion, and since there is essentially 10^{-3} M hydroxide ion in each solution, the pH is about 11 in each case.

➤ In general, the most acidic species that can exist in a given solvent is the conjugate acid of the solvent itself (H_3O^+ in the case of water). The most basic species that can exist in a given solvent is the conjugate base of the solvent (^-OH in the case of water). This effect is sometimes called a *leveling effect*.

47. This is a series of reactions in which individual Lewis acid-base reactions are followed by Brønsted acid-base reactions to generate HF. The first steps are:

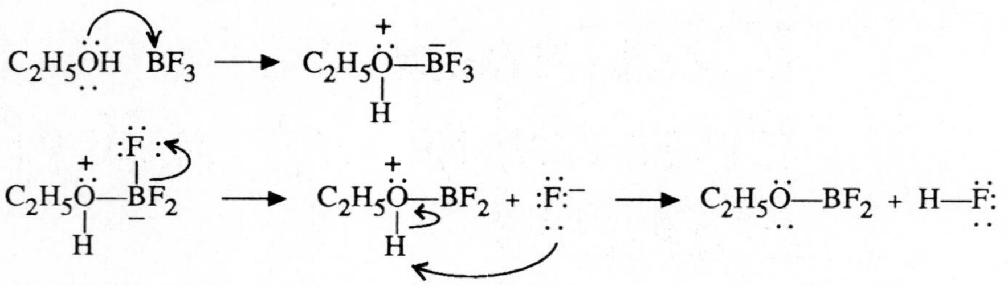

$$C_2H_5\overset{..}{\underset{..}{O}}H \quad \overset{-}{B}F_3 \longrightarrow C_2H_5\overset{+}{\underset{H}{\overset{..}{O}}}-\overline{B}F_3$$

$$C_2H_5\overset{+}{\underset{H}{\overset{..}{O}}}-\overline{B}F_2 \longrightarrow C_2H_5\overset{+}{\underset{H}{\overset{..}{O}}}{-}BF_2 + :\overset{..}{\underset{..}{F}}:^- \longrightarrow C_2H_5\overset{..}{\underset{..}{O}}-BF_2 + H-\overset{..}{\underset{..}{F}}:$$

In subsequent steps, C_2H_5OH attacks $C_2H_5O-BF_2$, fluoride is lost, and $(C_2H_5O)_2BF$ is formed along with another equivalent of H—F; the arrow formalism is completely analogous to that shown above. Then, C_2H_5OH attacks $(C_2H_5O)_2BF$, a fluoride ion is lost, and $(C_2H_5O)_3B$ is formed along with the third equivalent of H—F. (Write out the arrow formalism for these remaining steps if you were unable to do so prior to reading this answer. Use the reactions above as a guide.)

➤ This shows why some Lewis acids are destroyed by protic solvents: after forming a Lewis acid-base complex, they react further by Brønsted acid-base reactions. Since ethers lack the O—H proton, complexes of Lewis acids with many ethers are stable.

Chapter 9 / Substitution and Elimination Reactions of Alkyl Halides

CHAPTER 9 TERMS

anti addition 9.7
anti elimination 9.4E
bimolecular reaction 9.3A
carbene 9.7
α-carbon 9.4
β-carbon 9.4
α-elimination 9.7
β-elimination 9.4
elimination reaction .... Introduction
first-order reaction 9.3A
β-hydrogen 9.5B
intramolecular nucleophilic substitution reaction ... 9.1
ion pair 9.5E
kinetic order 9.3A
leaving group 9.1
LeChatelier's principle 9.2
nucleophile 9.1
nucleophilic displacement reaction .... Introduction

nucleophilic substitution reaction .... Introduction
overall kinetic order 9.3A
primary deuterium isotope effect 9.4B
product-determining step 9.5B
β-proton 9.5B
rate constant, k 9.3A
rate law 9.3A
E1 reaction 9.5B
E2 reaction 9.4A
S_N1 reaction 9.5A
S_N2 reaction 9.3A
reaction rate 9.3A
Saytzeff elimination 9.4D
second-order reaction 9.3A
solvolysis 9.1
syn addition 9.7
syn elimination 9.4E
unimolecular reaction 9.5A

CHAPTER 9 CONCEPTS

I. Nucleophilic Substitution Reactions:

A. Terminology:
  1. The group that forms the new bond to carbon is called the **nucleophile**.
    a) A nucleophile is a Lewis base.
    b) The nucleophile may be anionic, neutral, or even sometimes cationic.
  2. The group that loses its bond to carbon and take on an additional pair of electrons is called the **leaving group**.
  3. When the solvent is the nucleophile, the reaction is called **solvolysis**.

B. Equilibrium:
  1. The equilibrium in a **nucleophilic substitution reaction** favors release of the weaker base.
  2. Some equilibria that are not *too* unfavorable can be driven to completion by applying **LeChatelier's principle**.

C. Reaction Rates:
    1. A **reaction rate** describes the change in concentration of the reactants and products with respect to time and has the dimensions of concentration per unit time.
    2. The **rate law** is a mathematical statement of how the reaction rate depends on concentration.
        a) Each reaction has its own characteristic rate law.
        b) The rate law describes what species are involved in the transition state of the rate-determining step.
        c) The rate law *does not* describe how the atoms are arranged in the transition state.
        d) The rate law is determined experimentally by varying the concentration of each reactant independently.
    3. The constant of proportionality, k, is called the **rate constant**.
        a) The rate constant is a fundamental physical constant for a given reaction under particular conditions, and is related to $\Delta G^{\circ\ddagger}$.
            (1) If $\Delta G^{\circ\ddagger}$ is large for a reaction, the rate constant is small.
            (2) If $\Delta G^{\circ\ddagger}$ is small for a reaction, the rate constant is large.
        b) The dimensions of the rate constant depend on the **kinetic order** of the reaction.
        c) The rate constant is different for each reaction.
    4. The **overall kinetic order** for a reaction is the sum of the powers of all the concentrations in the rate law.
    5. The kinetic order in each reactant is the power to which its concentration is raised in the rate law.

II. S$_N$2 and E2 Reactions:

A. The S$_N$2 Reaction:
    1. The **S$_N$2 reaction** rate is second order:
        a) **First order** in the nucleophile.
        b) First order in the alkyl halide.
    2. In the transition state, the leaving group is accepting a pair of electrons.
        a) The more readily a leaving group accepts electrons, the lower is the energy of the transition state, and the greater the rate.
        b) The best electron acceptors are those groups that give the weakest bases.
        c) The best leaving groups are the weakest bases.
    3. In the transition state, the nucleophile is donating a pair of electrons.
        a) The more readily a nucleophile donates a pair of electrons, the lower is the energy of the transition state, and the greater the rate.
        b) The best electron donors are those groups that give the strongest bases.
        c) The best nucleophiles are the strongest bases.
    4. Of the solvents that dissolve salts, polar aprotic solvents give the fastest reactions.
        a) In aprotic solvents, the fastest reactions are observed with nucleophiles that are the strongest bases within a given row of the periodic table.
        b) In protic solvents, nucleophiles nearest the bottom of the periodic table give the fastest reaction because they are the most poorly solvated.
    5. Primary alkyl halides can be used to prepare substitution products in good yield.
    6. Secondary alkyl halides that are largely unbranched *near* the α-carbon can be used to prepare substitution products in good yield.

B. Stereochemistry of the S$_N$2 Reaction:
    1. In the transition state, the nucleophile and the leaving group are partially bonded to the opposite lobes of the carbon p orbital.
    2. The stereochemistry proceeds with inversion of configuration; backside attack of the nucleophile on the leaving group occurs.

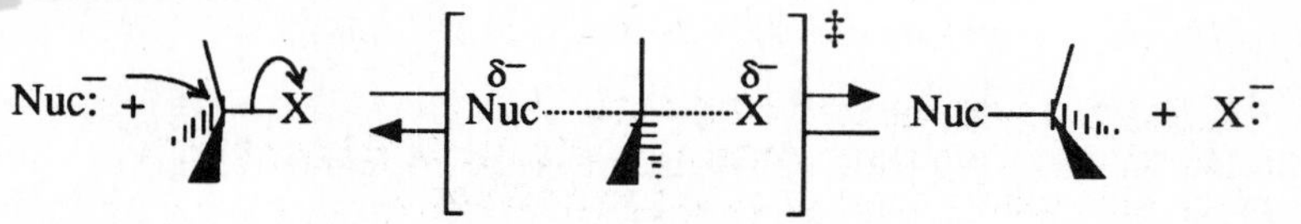

C. Effect of Alkyl Halide Structure on the S$_N$2 Reaction:
    1. Alkyl halides differ in the rates at which they undergo the S$_N$2 reaction.
        a) Methyl and primary alkyl halides react with nucleophiles by the S$_N$2 mechanism.

b) Some secondary alkyl halides react with nucleophiles by the S_N2 mechanism.
c) Tertiary alkyl halides *do not* react with nucleophiles by the S_N2 mechanism.
2. Branching at the carbon bearing the halogen retards the S_N2 reaction.
a) Secondary alkyl halides undergo S_N2 reactions more slowly than primary alkyl halides.
b) Tertiary alkyl halides *do not* undergo S_N2 reactions.
3. Increased branching near the site of substitution retards the S_N2 reaction; the steric repulsions present in the transition state raise its energy and reduce the reaction rate.

D. Solvent Effects in the S_N2 Reaction:
1. The relative reaction rates of nucleophiles from different rows of the periodic table depend on the solvent.
a) In protic solvents, the reaction rates of nucleophiles (within a given row of the periodic table) with a given alkyl halide *do not correlate* with their relative basicities.
b) In aprotic solvents, the relative reactivities of nucleophiles *do correlate* with their relative basicities.
2. Hydrogen bonding that occurs between a nucleophile and the molecules of a protic solvent affects the rate of reaction.
a) Nucleophiles act as hydrogen-bond acceptors.
(1) Anions near the top of the periodic table (the more basic anions) form stronger hydrogen bonds.
(2) At least one of its hydrogen bonds must be broken in order for a halide ion to react as a nucleophile in the S_N2 reaction.
(3) Strong hydrogen-bonding retards the rate at which a nucleophile reacts in the S_N2 reaction.
b) In solvents that *cannot* donate hydrogen bonds, the relative reactivities of the halide anions parallel their relative basicities.
3. The rate of reaction of a given nucleophile and alkyl halide is greatest in aprotic solvents; there are no hydrogen bonds that must be broken before the nucleophile can attack the alkyl halide in these solvents.

E. The E2 Reaction:
1. The **E2 reaction** rate is second order:
a) First order in the alkyl halide.
b) First order in the base.
2. An E2 reaction occurs when a strong base reacts with a tertiary alkyl halide.
a) The halide on the α-carbon and a hydrogen atom on the β-**carbon** are lost and an alkene is formed.
b) This type of reaction is called a β-**elimination** reaction.
c) An **elimination reaction** is formally the reverse of an addition reaction.
3. The rate of the reaction is greater when the leaving group is a weaker base.

F. Stereochemistry of the E2 Reaction:
1. It is found experimentally that most E2 elimination reactions are stereoselective *anti* **eliminations**; the base and leaving group are on opposite sides of the molecule.
2. *Anti* elimination occurs through a transition state in which the molecule assumes a staggered conformation.
3. *Anti* elimination involves all backside electronic displacements.

G. Effect of Alkyl Halide Structure on the E2 Reaction:
1. Alkyl halides differ in the rates at which they undergo the E2 reaction.
a) Tertiary alkyl halides can be used to prepare alkenes.
b) Branched secondary alkyl halides can be used to prepare alkenes.
c) Unbranched secondary alkyl halides can be used to prepare alkenes *only* if a tertiary alkoxide base is used.
d) Primary alkyl halides can be used to prepare alkenes *only* if a tertiary alkoxide base is used.

2. Mixtures can be expected from alkyl halides with more than one type of β-proton.
3. Elimination is favored by branching in the alkyl halide at the α- or β-carbons.

H. Effect of Base Structure on the E2 Reaction:
   1. When relatively unbranched bases are used, the predominant product is the most stable alkene isomer **(Saytzeff elimination)**.
   2. When a highly branched base is used, a smaller percentage of Saytzeff elimination is observed; more of the alkene with the least amount of branching at the double bond is formed.
   3. The branching in the base used in the E2 reaction has two consequences:
      a) It increases the relative proportion of E2 to S_N2 products.
      b) It increases the proportion of alkene with less branching at the double bonds.

I. Double-Bond Positions in E2 Reaction Products:
   1. The transition state with the most alkyl branches at its developing double bond is the one of least energy.
   2. Branching at the developing double bond stabilizes the transition state for elimination.
      a) The reaction path with this transition state has the greatest rate.
      b) The formation of the most highly branched alkene isomers is sometimes called **Saytzeff elimination.**

J. Competition Between the S_N2 and E2 Reactions:
   1. Many secondary alkyl halides react to give a mixture of products resulting from both substitution and elimination reactions.
      a) The competition is a matter of relative rates; the reaction pathway that occurs most rapidly is the one that predominates.
      b) Two variables determine the outcome of this competition:
         (1) The structure of the alkyl halide.
         (2) The structure of the base.
   2. The base (nucleophile) must attack a carbon atom in order for the S_N2 reaction to occur; when attack at carbon is retarded by steric hindrance, attack at relatively unhindered hydrogen (elimination) predominates.
   3. Branching of the alkyl halide increases the rate of the E2 reaction.
      a) Branching stabilizes the transition state of the E2 reaction.
      b) Branching reduces the rate of substitution; steric repulsions raise the energy of the transition state for substitution.
   4. A highly branched base increases the proportion of the E2 product at the expense of the S_N2 product.

K. Primary Deuterium Isotope Effect:
   1. A compound in which a proton is replaced by deuterium will react more slowly in the same reaction when the proton is transferred in the rate-determining step of a reaction.
   2. The effect of isotopic substitution on the reaction rates is called a **primary deuterium isotope effect**.
      a) The primary deuterium isotope effect is the ratio k_H/k_D.
      b) Typical primary deuterium isotope effects are in the range 2.5–8.
   3. The primary deuterium isotope effect is observed *only* when the hydrogen that is transferred in the rate-determining step is substituted by deuterium; substitution of other hydrogens with deuterium usually has little or no effect on the rate of the reaction.
   4. The rates of E2 reactions show substantial primary deuterium isotope effects.

III. S_N1 and E1 Reactions:

A. The S_N1 Reaction:
   1. The **S_N1 reaction** rate is first order in the alkyl halide.
   2. The first step of the S_N1 reaction mechanism is the rate-determining step and involves the ionization of the alkyl halide to a carbocation.
      a) A strong base is not required.
      b) The best leaving groups are those that form the weakest bases.
   3. The second step of the S_N1 reaction mechanism involves the typical reactions of carbocations:
      a) Reaction with a nucleophile.
      b) Rearrangement to a more stable carbocation.

       c) Loss of a *β*-**hydrogen** (*β*-elimination).
4. In any reaction involving carbocations as reactive intermediates, the products will reflect the occurrence of one or more of these processes.
      a) The fate of the carbocation intermediate is determined by the **product-determining steps** (the steps that follow the rate-determining step).
      b) The rates of the product-determining steps have nothing to do with the rate at which the starting material disappears.
5. The rate law for the S_N1 reaction describes the overall reaction rate regardless of the products that are formed from the carbocation.

B. Stereochemistry of the S_N1 Reaction:
1. In a carbocation, the positively charged carbon and the three groups attached to it lie in a common plane.
2. The S_N1 reaction of an optically active alkyl halide gives nearly racemic substitution products because the carbocation intermediate is achiral.

3. Two types of carbocations are possible:
    a) Ion pairs in which the carbocation and the leaving group are held tightly together.
    b) Free ions in which the carbocation is completely surrounded by solvent molecules.
    c) Both types of carbocations are important intermediates in S_N1 reactions.
      (1) Ion pairs give inversion of configuration.
      (2) Free ions give racemates.

C. Solvent Effects on the S_N1 Reaction:
1. Solvents that dissolve ions well also accelerate the S_N1 reaction (polar protic donor solvents).
    a) They hydrogen-bond to the leaving-group anion.
    b) Their high dielectric constants separate oppositely charged ions.

D. The E1 Reaction:
1. The **E1 reaction** rate is first order, and first order in the alkyl halide.
2. The E1 reaction is a Saytzeff elimination.
    a) The alkene with the most branching at the alkene carbons is formed in greatest amount.
    b) The best leaving groups are those that form the weakest bases.

E. Competition Between the S_N1 and E1 Reactions:
1. The E1 and S_N1 reaction pathways are competing processes.
    a) They share common starting materials.
    b) They share a common intermediate, the carbocation.
2. The reactions differ in their product-determining steps.
    a) The product-determining step in the S_N1 reaction is attack of a nucleophile.
    b) The product-determining step in the E1 reaction is the loss of a *β*-hydrogen.
3. The most important variable in the S_N1–E1 competition is the structure of the alkyl halide.
    a) Chain branching interferes sterically with the attack of the nucleophile on the carbocation.
    b) Chain branching stabilizes the transition states leading to alkene products.

F. Effect of Alkyl Halide Structure on the S_N1 and E1 Reactions:
    1. Tertiary alkyl halides undergo nucleophilic substitution reactions with weak bases by the S_N1 mechanism.
    2. Some secondary alkyl halides undergo nucleophilic substitution reactions with weak bases by the S_N1 mechanism.
    3. Alkyl halides that contain β-hydrogens can form elimination products by the E1 mechanism.

G. Lewis Acid Catalysis of the S_N1–E1 Reaction:
    1. The alkyl halides with the least basic leaving groups react more rapidly in the S_N1–E1 reaction.
    2. Alkyl halides undergo S_N1–E1 reactions much more rapidly if a Lewis acid (Ag^+ or Hg^{2+}) is present during the reaction.
        a) The halide leaving group acts as a weak Lewis base and coordinates with the metal ion.
        b) The leaving group is a neutral species rather than a charged species, and thus is a better leaving group.
    3. Alkyl halides that ordinarily react by the S_N1–E1 mechanism react instantaneously.
        a) Primary alkyl halides require heating and/or prolonged reaction times.
        b) This is a useful diagnostic test for an alkyl halide that forms a relatively stable carbocation.

IV. Substitution and Elimination Reactions of Alkyl Halides—Summary:

A. In the absence of a strong Brønsted base:
    1. An unbranched primary alkyl halide will react very slowly unless heat is applied in a protic solvent; any reaction observed will be a substitution that occurs by the S_N2 mechanism.
    2. A secondary alkyl halide will have intermediate reactivity in a protic solvent.
        a) Reaction will generally occur by the S_N1–E1 mechanism.
        b) Elimination and rearrangement products can be expected in appropriate cases.
    3. A tertiary alkyl halide will react by the S_N1 mechanism in a protic solvent.
        a) If β-hydrogens are present, some elimination by the E1 mechanism can generally be expected.
        b) The proportion of elimination will be greater when there is more branching at the β-carbons.
        c) The most stable alkene product will form in greatest amount.
    4. The S_N2 reaction will be faster in a polar solvent.
    5. Some relatively weak bases can be used as nucleophiles.

B. In the presence of a strong Brønsted base:
    1. An unbranched primary alkyl halide will undergo substitution by the S_N2 mechanism.
        a) Increased branching at the β-carbon atom of the primary alkyl halide will give more elimination product by the E2 mechanism.
        b) Elimination will be a minor reaction if an unbranched base is used.
        c) The use of a more highly branched base will give more elimination product by the E2 mechanism.
        d) The rates of both the S_N2 and E2 reactions are increased in polar aprotic solvents.
    2. A secondary alkyl halide will give a mixture of substitution and elimination products formed by the S_N2 and E2 mechanisms.
    3. A tertiary alkyl halide invariably reacts by the E2 mechanism if it has β-hydrogens.
        a) The most stable alkene is usually the major product of an E2 reaction.
        b) If a highly branched base is used, the alkene with the least amount of branching at the double bond will be the predominant product.
    4. At zero base concentration, the S_N1 and E1 mechanisms are promoted for tertiary alkyl halides by polar protic solvents.
    5. At high base concentrations, the E2 mechanism is the dominant process for tertiary alkyl halides.

CHAPTER 9 REACTIONS

I. Divalent Carbon:

    A. Carbenes:
        1. Chloroform can react with a strong base to give its conjugate-base anion.
            a) The conjugate-base anion of chloroform can lose chloride ion to give a neutral species called **dichloromethylene**.

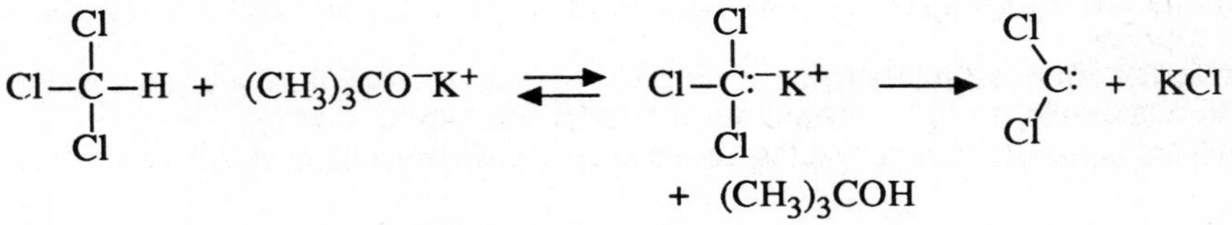

            b) The carbon atom of dichloromethylene bears three "groups," and has approximately trigonal-planar geometry.
                (1) The lone pair occupies an sp^2 orbital.
                (2) The p orbital is empty.

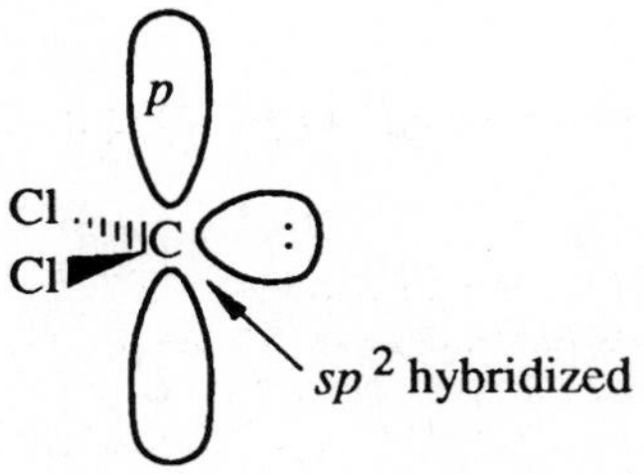

        2. An elimination of two groups from the same atom is termed an α-**elimination**.
        3. A **carbene** is a species with a divalent carbon atom.
            a) Carbenes are unstable and highly reactive species.
            b) The divalent carbon of a carbene can act as both a nucleophile and an electrophile.
        4. An important reaction of carbenes is cyclopropane formation.
            a) The addition of dichloromethylene to an alkene is a concerted pericyclic reaction.
            b) Dichloromethylene addition to an alkene is a **syn addition**.

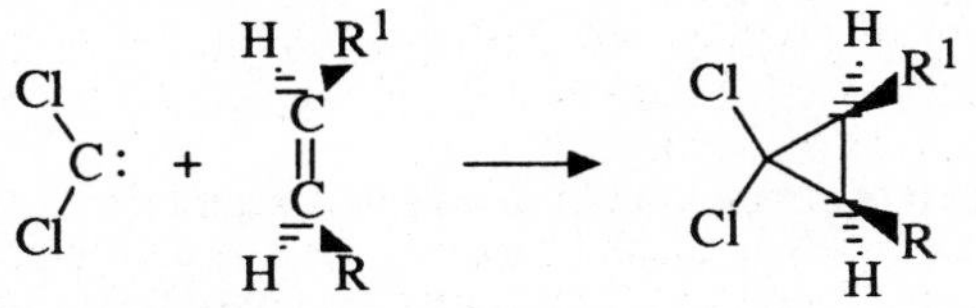

        5. In general, reaction of a haloform with base in the presence of an alkene yields a 1,1-dihalocyclopropane.

CHAPTER 9 RULES

LeChatelier's Principle: If an equilibrium is disturbed, the components of the equilibrium will react to offset the effect of the disturbance.

CHAPTER 9 SOLUTIONS

Solutions to In-Text Problems

1. Equilibrium (c) is most favorable because the corresponding acid-base reaction is most favorable:

$$HCl + CH_3O^- \longrightarrow CH_3OH + Cl^-$$

That is, the pK_a difference between CH_3OH and HCl is greater than the pK_a difference between any other pair of acids represented in the problem.

2. (a) The reaction is third order overall.
   (b) The reaction is first order in alkene and second order in bromine.
   (c) The dimensions are such that the rate has the overall dimensions of $M\text{-sec}^{-1}$.

   dimensions of k = dimensions of $\{rate/[alkene][Br_2]^2\} = M\text{-sec}^{-1}/M \cdot M^2 = M^{-2}\text{-sec}^{-1}$

3. As species A and B are depleted, the rate should decrease, approaching zero as A and B are completely consumed.

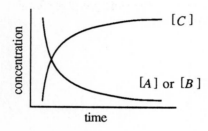

   Notice that the rate is the *slope* of the concentration *vs.* time curve. These slopes decrease in absolute value with increasing time, approaching zero at long times.

4. Any mechanism that contains the elements of both ammonia and acetic acid in the transition state is valid. The simplest one is a direct displacement:

$$CH_3-\overset{\overset{O}{\|}}{C}-\overset{..}{\underset{..}{O}}-H \quad :NH_3 \longrightarrow CH_3-\overset{\overset{O}{\|}}{C}-\overset{..}{\underset{..}{O}}:^- \quad \overset{+}{N}H_4$$

5. If the reaction is bimolecular and occurs by the direct displacement of ^-CN on ethyl bromide, we should expect a second-order rate law:

   rate = $k\,[^-CN][C_2H_5Br]$

6. The reaction should occur with inversion of configuration. Let us draw the process to be sure that we assign the R,S designation correctly.

$$HO:^- \quad H\,\text{''}C-I \longrightarrow HO-C\text{''}H \quad :I:^-$$

   As we can see from the structure of the product, it has the S configuration.

   ➤ Inversion of configuration does not ensure inversion of the R,S designation. It is possible for an

When is it SN2 & SN1?   What is k?
Do SN1 and E1 occur in same products?
Solutions to In-Text Problems   Chapter 9 / 161

(R)-starting material to react with inversion to give an (R)-product, if the relative group priorities change as a result of the reaction. In other words, when asked to give the configuration of a product, be sure to draw it and determine the R,S designation directly.

7. (a) ⁻OH (b) ⁻OH (c) CH₃S⁻ In each case, the nucleophile chosen is the more basic one. Since we are comparing nucleophiles within a *row* of the periodic table, we do not have to worry about the solvent.

8. Did you draw the starting material? If not, do so before reading further!

   Three alkenes are possible, one from each β-hydrogen atom. These are (E)- and (Z)-3-methyl-2-pentene, and 2-ethyl-1-butene:

9. (a) We would expect the reaction to be slower (and it is!), since the hydrogen that undergoes transfer is replaced by a deuterium. The product, however, would not be the same:

   Product of styrene hydration   Product of styrene hydration
   in H₂O: in D₂O:

   (b) The rate would differ little if at all, because the deuterium is not transferred in the reaction.

   ➤ There are small isotope effects associated with deuteriums that are not directly transferred, but that are bound to carbon atoms at which reaction occurs. These effects, called *secondary deuterium isotope effects*, are usually very small — much smaller than the isotope effects discussed in the text.

10. (d) > (b) > (c) > (a). The ratio follows from the degree of alkyl substitution near the α-carbon. Compound (d) is secondary; that is, it is most highly branched at the α-carbon. Compound (b) has β-branching; the branching in (c) is very far from the α-carbon; and compound (a) is a methyl halide, which has no β-hydrogens and cannot undergo elimination.

11. The more branching in the base, the more E2 elimination observed. Hence, the order is:

   (c) > (a) > (b)

12. (a) The rates of formation of the two alkenes determine the amounts that are formed. Although the data do not tell us the absolute rate, they do tell us the relative rate, which is what is required by the problem. The relative rate is 70/30, or 2.33.

   (b) There are six hydrogens that could be eliminated to give the minor product, whereas there are two that could be lost to give the major one. Hence, the minor product is (6/2) or three times as likely to form on the basis of probability. Hence, the relative rate on a per-hydrogen basis is 2.33(6/2) = 6.99. That is, the major alkene isomer, if we eliminate the number of equivalent hydrogens from consideration, is formed about seven times more rapidly.

(c)

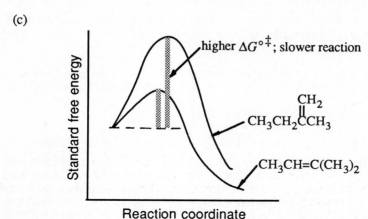

13. (a) The major product is the alkene with the more highly substituted double bond, 1-methyl-1-cyclohexene:

(b) In the presence of a more highly substituted base, the alkene with the less highly substituted double bond, methylenecyclohexane, is formed:

14. The diastereomer would be required:

15. (a) We assume that the elimination will occur with *anti* stereochemistry. First, we draw *meso*-dibromostilbene; then we draw a rotational isomer in which a hydrogen on one carbon and a bromine on an adjacent carbon are in an *anti* arrangement.

Anti elimination from a transition state in this conformation would give an alkene in which the phenyl groups are on the same side of the molecule — that is, the (*E*)-alkene:

(b) The product from (±)-dibromostilbene is the (*Z*)-alkene by a similar analysis.

16. (a) A scheme that describes the mechanism of this reaction is:

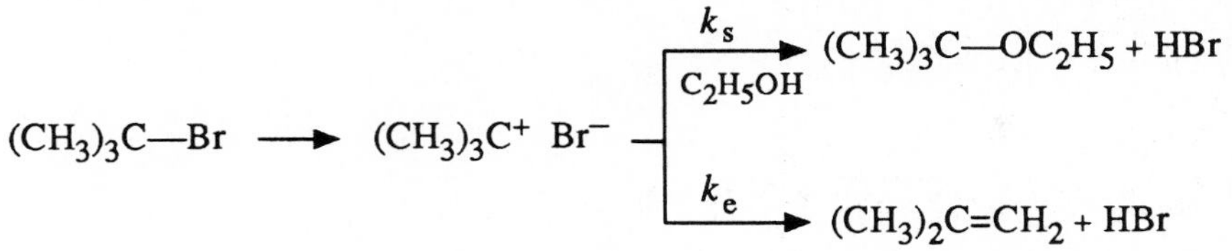

$$(CH_3)_3C\text{—}Br \longrightarrow (CH_3)_3C^+\ Br^- \begin{cases} \xrightarrow[C_2H_5OH]{k_s} (CH_3)_3C\text{—}OC_2H_5 + HBr \\ \\ \xrightarrow{k_e} (CH_3)_2C{=}CH_2 + HBr \end{cases}$$

Even though the rate of the overall reaction (the rate of disappearance of t-butyl bromide, or the total rate of appearance of products) is the rate of the first step, the relative rate at which the ether and alkene are formed is simply the ratio of rates for the steps labeled k_s and k_e. Since the proportions of ether and alkene formed reflect exactly the relative rates of these product-determining steps, the relative rate of formation of these products is the ratio $72/28 = 2.57$. That is, the ether is formed from the carbocation intermediate 2.57 times faster than the alkene is formed.

(b) If the products were to interconvert under the reaction conditions, then the percentages of products no longer reflect the relative rates of the product-determining steps, but instead also contain contributions from the rates of interconversion of the products. Indeed, if the products did interconvert under the reaction conditions, and if we let the reaction mixture sit for a very long time, the products would eventually come to equilibrium, and their ratio would be determined by the equilibrium constant for their interconversion.

17. We expect to find both S_N1 and E1 products. Since there are two nucleophiles in solution (water and ethanol), the S_N1 products will reflect displacement by both.

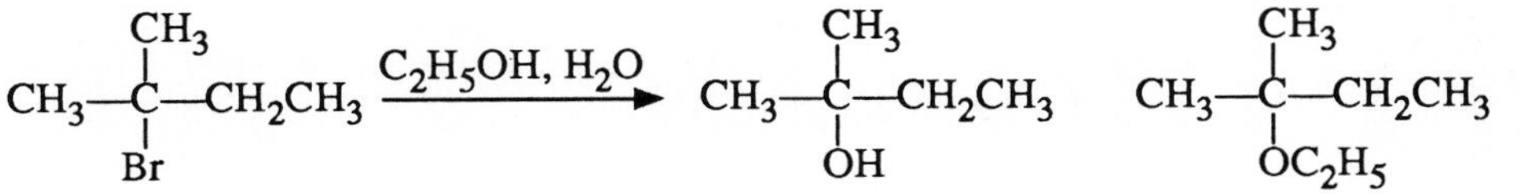

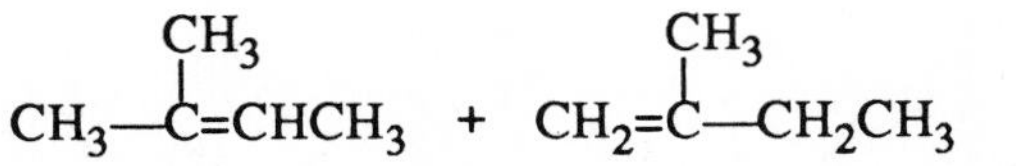

18. This is a rearrangement involving a methyl shift:

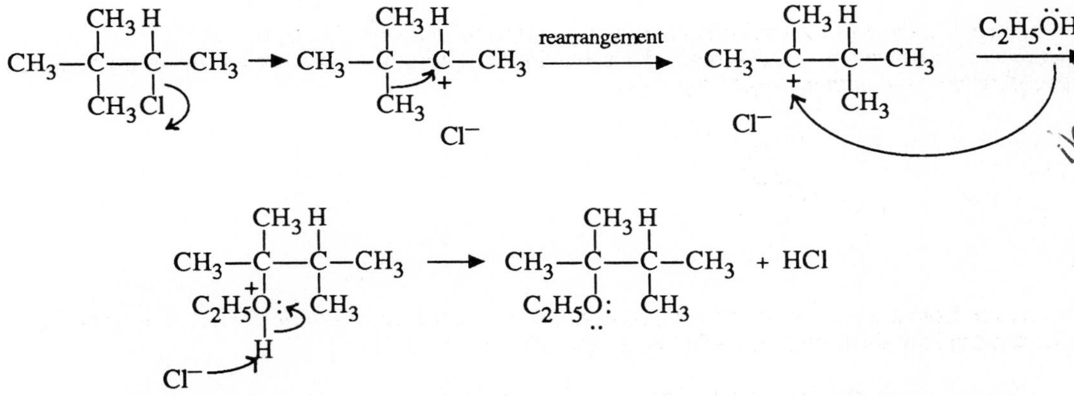

19. (c) $\ll$ (a) $<$ (b). This order corresponds to the relative rates in S_N1 reactions; $AgNO_3$ accelerates such reactions.

20. Because the carbocation intermediate can be attacked at either face, we expect to see products of both inversion and retention. The product of inversion should predominate somewhat.

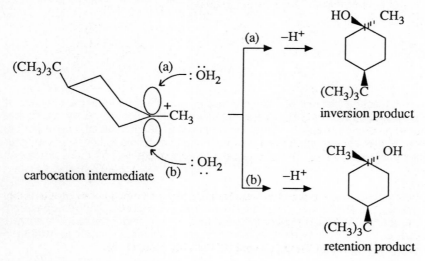

(a) inversion product

(b) retention product

The following alkene is also formed:

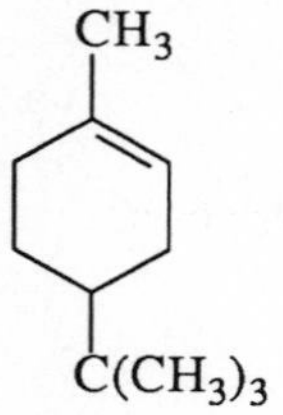

This alkene is racemic; can you see why?

21. (a)   (b) 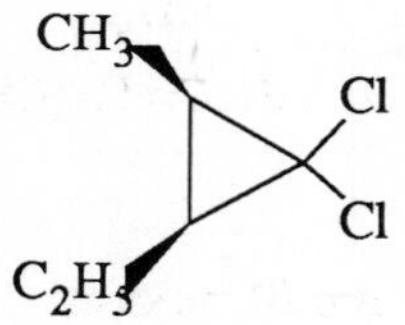   (c)

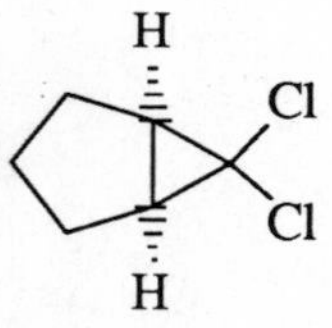

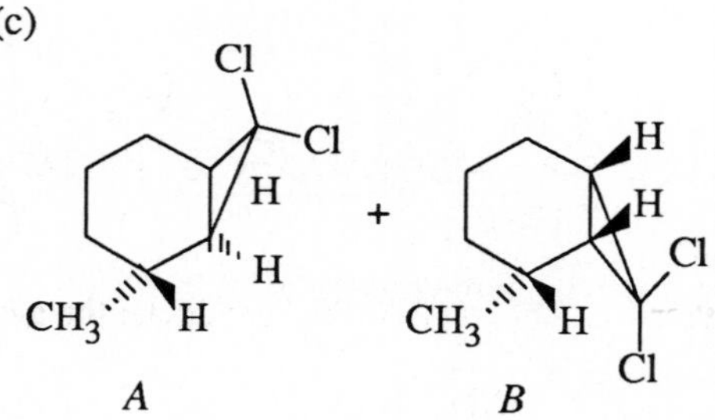

A   B

In part (c), we expect product A to predominate, since it involves addition of dichloromethylene from the side *opposite* the methyl group on the ring — the least hindered side of the ring.

22. (a) Cyclohexene and bromoform, $CHBr_3$.

(b)

Chloroform, $CHCl_3$, and norbornene,

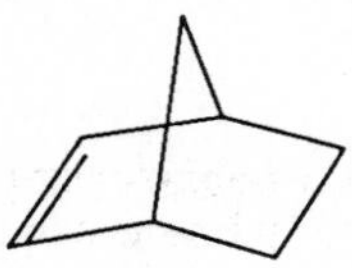

(c) 2,3-Dimethyl-2-butene, $(CH_3)_2C=C(CH_3)_2$, and benzyl chloride, $PhCH_2Cl$

Solutions to Additional Problems

23.   Before making any choices, it is important that we draw the structures!

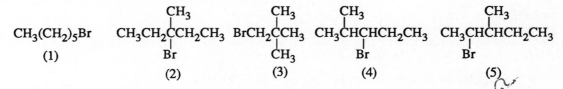

(a) Compounds (4) and (5); they have asymmetric carbons.
(b) Compound (5); it has two asymmetric carbons.
(c) Compound (1); it is an unbranched primary alkyl halide.
(d) Compound (3); it is neopentyl bromide, one of the least reactive alkyl halides.
(e) Compound (2); it is tertiary.
(f) Compound (2); it is tertiary.
(g) Compounds (4) and (5); they would ionize to secondary carbocations that can easily rearrange to tertiary carbocations.
(h) Compound (1); it has only one type of β-hydrogen.

24.   (a) $(CH_3)_2CHCH_2CH_2I$ (b) $(CH_3)_2CHCH_2CH_2OC_2H_5$ and $(CH_3)_2CHCH_2CH_2OH$

(c) $(CH_3)_2CHCH=CH_2$, and possibly some $(CH_3)_2CHCH_2CH_2$—$OC(CH_3)_3$

(d) $(CH_3)_2CHCHCH_3$ and $(CH_3)_2CCH_2CH_3$ (rearrangement product)
          | |
          Br   Br

(e)   Cl   Cl   (f) $(CH_3)_2CHCH_2CH_3$ (g) $(CH_3)_2CHCH_2CH_2OCH_3 + Na^+ Br^-$

$(CH_3)_2CH$

25.   (a)
      $CH_3\overset{CH_3}{\underset{OH}{C}}(CH_2)_3CH_3$ + $CH_3\overset{CH_3}{\underset{OC_2H_5}{C}}(CH_2)_3CH_3$ + $CH_2=\overset{CH_3}{C}(CH_2)_3CH_3$ + $CH_3\overset{CH_3}{C}=CH(CH_2)_2CH_3$

The alcohol and the ether are S_N1 displacement products; the alkenes are E1 products.

(b)
      $CH_2=\overset{CH_3}{C}(CH_2)_3CH_3$ + $CH_3\overset{CH_3}{C}=CH(CH_2)_2CH_3$
           (some)   (mostly)

(c) $BrCH_2\underset{CH_3}{\overset{|}{C}H}(CH_2)_3CH_3$ and $CH_3CH-\underset{CH_3\ Br}{CH}CH_2CH_2CH_3$

26.   Compound (d) is most reactive, because it is an unbranched primary alkyl halide. Since alkyl bromides react more rapidly than alkyl chlorides, the different halide leaving group does not affect this choice. Compound (a) is least reactive, because it is tertiary; tertiary halides do not react by an S_N2 mechanism. Compound (e) is more reactive than compound (b), because bromide is a better leaving group than chloride. Compound (c) is

more reactive than compound (b), because the branching is further from the reaction site. Putting all this together gives the following reactivity order:

$$(a) < (b) < (e) < (c) < (d)$$

➤ Notice again how the order is developed from *pairwise* comparisons.

27. To the extent that the displacement reaction which occurs is by the S_N2 mechanism, the substitution product A will have the S configuration. The alkenes B and C are formed in E2 reactions.

$$CH_3CHCH_2CH_2CH_3 \ + \ CH_2{=}CHCH_2CH_2CH_3 \ + \ CH_3CH{=}CHCH_2CH_3$$
$$\overset{|}{OC_2H_5}$$
$$A \qquad\qquad\qquad B \qquad\qquad\qquad\qquad C$$
$$(S \ \text{configuration}) \qquad\qquad\qquad\qquad\qquad (cis \ \text{and} \ trans\,)$$

28. We are letting methyl iodide react with a mixture of two nucleophiles; there will be a competition between two S_N2 reactions. Since the nucleophiles are from the same row of the periodic table, the more basic nucleophile will react most rapidly. Since cyanide is almost five pK_a units more basic than azide, the major product is expected to be "methyl cyanide," CH_3CN, better known to organic chemists as *acetonitrile*.

29. The choice is between reaction of a strong base with methyl iodide, an alkyl halide that can only react by an S_N2 mechanism, and the reaction of a strong base with *t*-butyl bromide, an alkyl halide that reacts with strong base to give E2 products, not S_N2 products. Clearly, reaction of $(CH_3)_3C{-}O^-\,K^+$ with methyl iodide is the best choice. The other reaction will give mostly isobutylene, $(CH_3)_2C{=}CH_2$.

30. Since the compound is an alkyl halide (is it ever!) with β-hydrogens, base could promote E2 reactions. One possible product is

The remaining chlorines would not be lost by elimination under ordinary conditions. Can you see why? (*Hint:* See Sec. 7.7C.)

31. Because it is a tertiary alkyl halide without β-hydrogens, trityl chloride can react only by the S_N1 mechanism. A characteristic feature of this mechanism is that the first step is rate-determining, whereas attack of the nucleophile(s) occurs on the carbocation intermediate in the second step. Hence, the rate of reaction of trityl chloride is *independent of the nucleophile concentration,* and therefore independent of its identity.

$$Ph_3C{-}Cl \xrightarrow{\text{rate-determining step}} Ph_3C^+ \ Cl^-$$

However, the product-determining steps for the various reactions are different. In this step, a nucleophile attacks the carbocation. The more basic nucleophile will react more rapidly with the carbocation intermediate; hence, the major product will be derived from the more basic nucleophile.

    For example, in reaction (1), the only nucleophile available is water. The pK_a of its conjugate acid, H_3O^+, is -1.7. After attack of water on the carbocation to give $Ph_3C{-}\overset{+}{O}H_2$, a proton is lost to give trityl alcohol as the solvolysis product. Azide ion is much more basic than water; the pK_a of HN_3 is 4.7. When, in reaction (2), sodium azide is added to the reaction mixture, trityl chloride reacts at the same rate, but the carbocation intermediate reacts preferentially with azide ion.

    When hydroxide ion (whose conjugate acid, H_2O, has a pK_a of 15.7) is added, it is the more basic nucleophile and reacts preferentially with the carbocation to give trityl alcohol directly.

32. Potassium fluoride, an ionic compound, has zero solubility in hydrocarbon solvents; benzene is a hydrocarbon, and therefore does not dissolve potassium fluoride. The crown ether dissolves KF as a complex between the crown ether and the potassium ion; the fluoride goes into solution to maintain electrical neutrality. Because the fluoride ion is unsolvated, it is particularly reactive, and reacts with $PhCH_2Br$ to give benzyl fluoride, $PhCH_2F$. The resulting bromide ion then exchanges with insoluble KF to give more dissolved "naked" fluoride, which then reacts rapidly with more benzyl bromide. To summarize:

$$PhCH_2\text{—}Br + K^+(\text{crown complex}) + F^- \longrightarrow PhCH_2\text{—}F + K^+(\text{crown complex}) + Br^-$$

$$K^+(\text{crown complex}) + Br^- + KF(\text{solid}) \rightleftharpoons K^+(\text{crown complex}) + F^- + KBr(\text{solid})$$

Because this crown ether selectively complexes potassium ion (Sec. 8.4C), it does not dissolve LiF. Because LiF does not dissolve, it does not react.

33. The first reaction is the reaction of a fairly strong base (hydroxide ion) with a primary alkyl halide; the reaction that does occur goes by the S_N2 mechanism, which does not involve carbocation intermediates, and which therefore shows no rearrangement. Little reaction occurs because neopentyl halides are very unreactive in the S_N2 reaction (see Table 9.2 and Figure 9.2). Silver ion, however, promotes ionization. An S_N1 reaction ensues in which an initially formed primary carbocation rearranges to a tertiary carbocation. The solvolysis product is derived from the rearranged cation:

silver complex of
neopentyl iodide

34. On standing, the secondary alkyl halide ionizes to a carbocation intermediate, which rearranges to a more stable tertiary carbocation. This more stable cation reacts with bromide ion to give the tertiary alkyl halide product.

35. In the S_N2 transition state, the α-carbon is sp^2-hybridized; as a result, the bond angles at this carbon prefer to be 120°. In compound (b), there is no problem achieving this angle; in compound (a), however, the angle strain in the starting material is increased in the transition state, because incorporating a 120° bond angle in a three-membered ring is very difficult. This strain raises the energy of the transition state for compound (a); as a result, it reacts more slowly.

36. The desired product can be obtained by the following E2 elimination reaction using a highly branched alkoxide base:

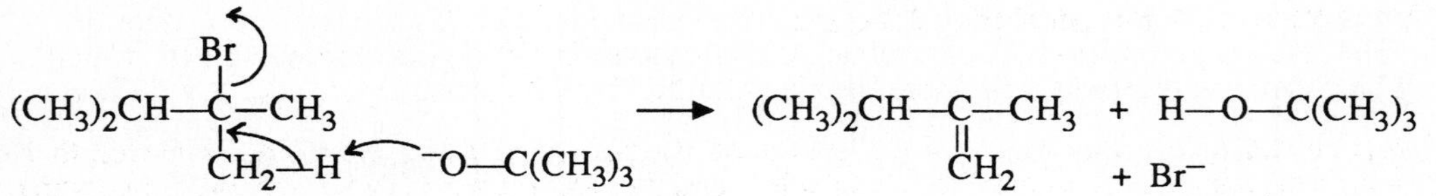

And the starting alkyl halide can be prepared by HBr addition to 2,3-dimethyl-2-butene, the starting alkene in the problem:

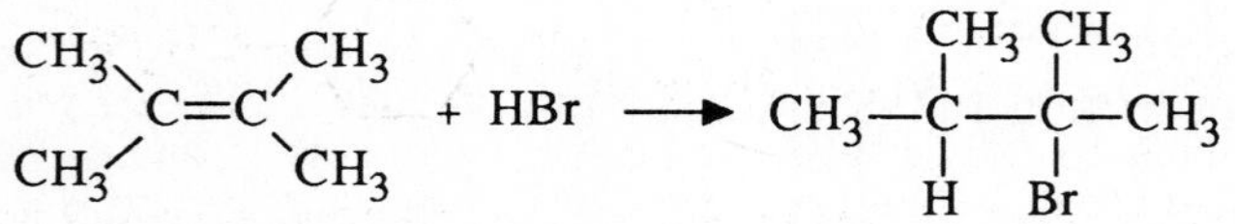

➤ Notice in this type of problem that we start at the compound we wish to make and *work backward*. This type of approach is generally useful for attacking problems in synthesis. We shall consider synthesis problems and how to solve them in more detail in the next chapter.

37. The usual stereochemistry of E2 eliminations requires that we must have an *anti* arrangement of the hydrogen and chlorine that are eliminated. In menthyl chloride, this is possible only if (a) the compound undergoes a chair-chair interconversion, and (b) a hydrogen at the unsubstituted β-carbon is lost, since this is the only axial β-hydrogen:

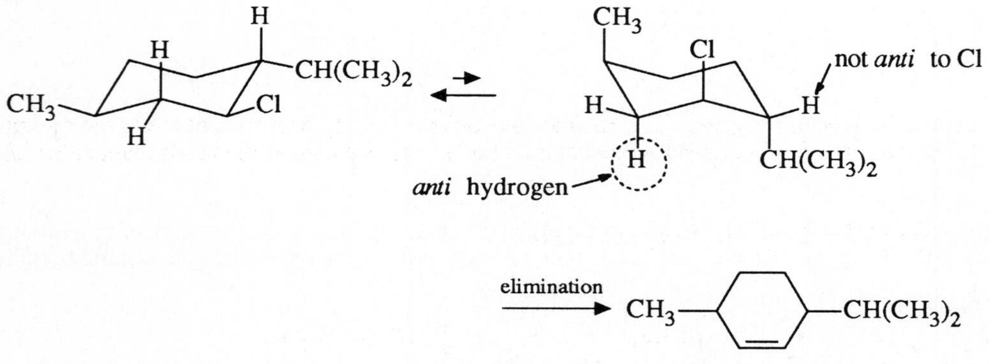

In contrast, neomenthyl chloride has two *anti* β-hydrogens (labeled H^a and H^b) that can be eliminated to give the corresponding two alkenes:

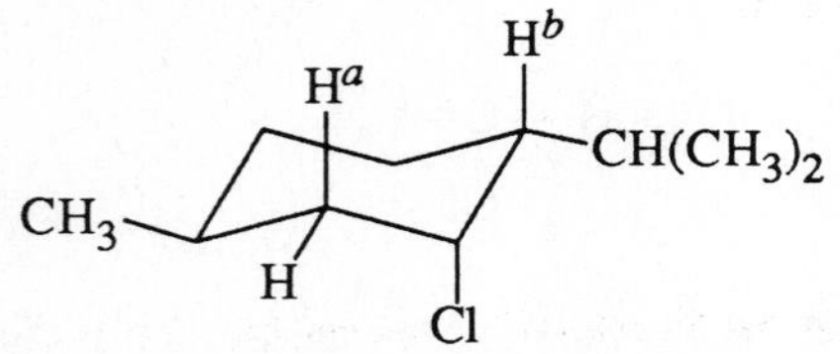

Loss of H^a and Cl gives 2-menthene; loss of H^b and Cl gives 3-menthene. 3-Menthene predominates because it is the alkene with the more highly substituted double bond (the Saytzeff product). This product cannot form from menthyl chloride because the hydrogen that would have to be lost has the wrong stereochemistry relative to the Cl.

38. First, let us be sure we know the structure of the starting material.

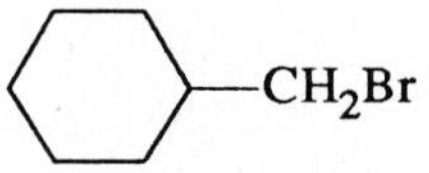

—CH$_2$Br   (bromomethyl)cyclohexane

(a) At first sight, attack of $^-$OH to give the alcohol directly might seem like a good route. However, this alkyl halide, although primary, has considerable β-branching, and the displacement product would be accompanied by a considerable amount of elimination product. So why not prepare the alkene and then convert it into the alcohol using a regiospecific reaction? The following route uses this strategy:

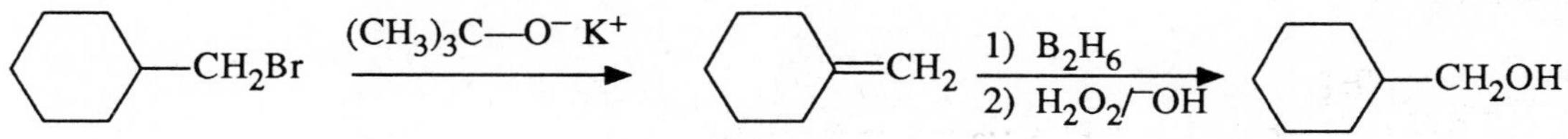

(b) and (c) The same alkene that we "prepared" in (a) can be used as a starting material for both (b) and (c):

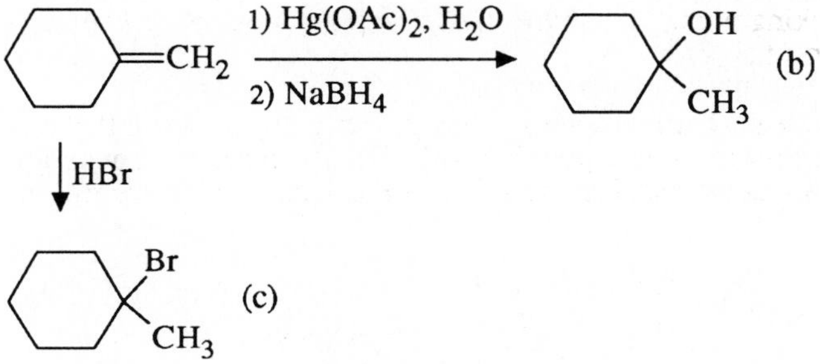

39. (a) The conditions of the reaction suggest a free-radical mechanism. Letting R· represent the initiating radical derived from AIBN (see Sec. 5.8C), and Bu represent the butyl group, we can write the mechanism as follows:

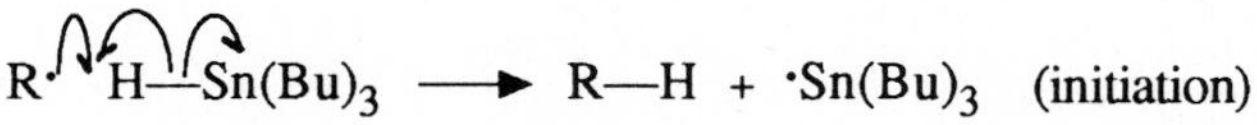

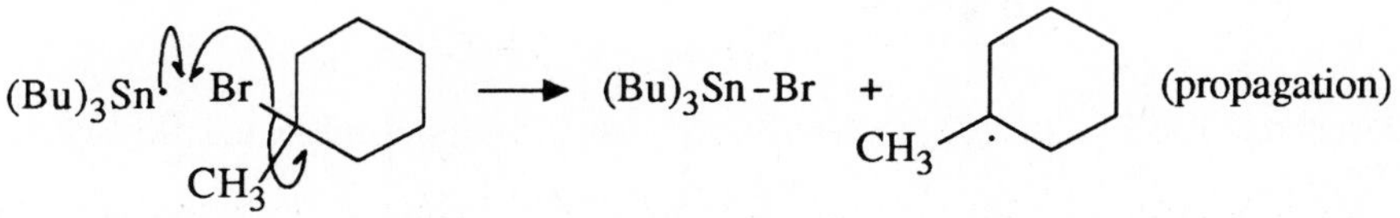

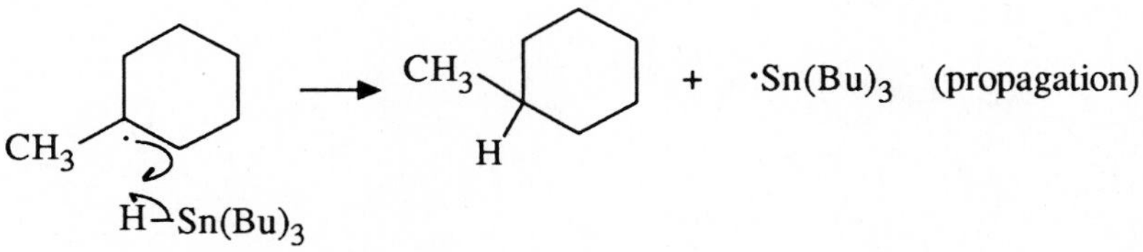

R· H—Sn(Bu)$_3$ ⟶ R—H + ·Sn(Bu)$_3$ (initiation)

(Bu)$_3$Sn· Br ... CH$_3$ ⟶ (Bu)$_3$Sn–Br + CH$_3$ · (propagation)

CH$_3$ · ... H—Sn(Bu)$_3$ ⟶ CH$_3$ H + ·Sn(Bu)$_3$ (propagation)

(b) We need two sequences that would replace —Br by —H. The most direct is the following:

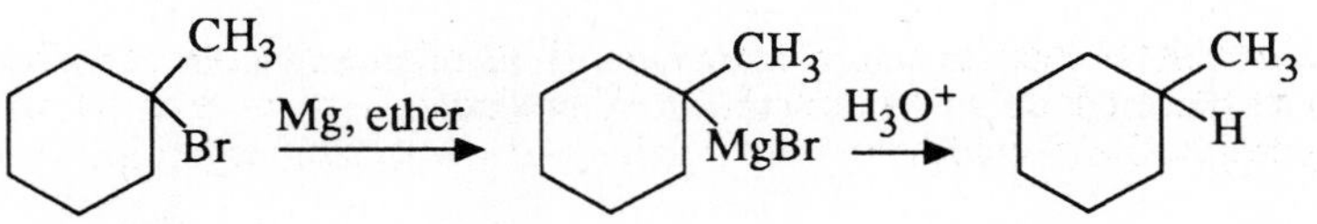

Alternatively, we could hydrogenate an alkene formed by an E2 elimination:

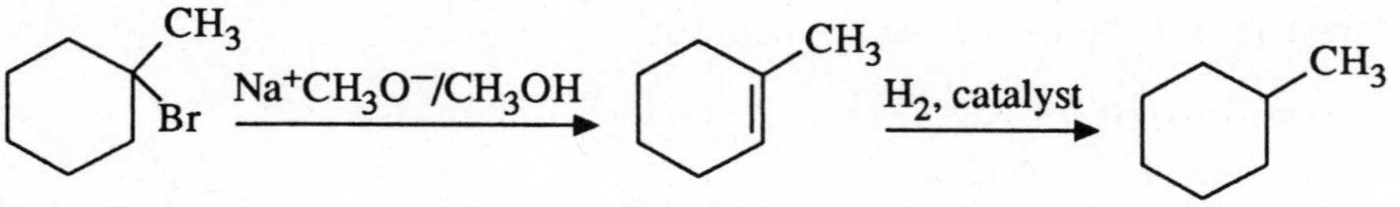

(Even if a mixture of alkenes formed in the elimination, all would hydrogenate to the same product.)

40. Compound A is an alkyl halide that undergoes elimination to an alkene B. The identity of B can be immediately deduced from the ozonolysis product:

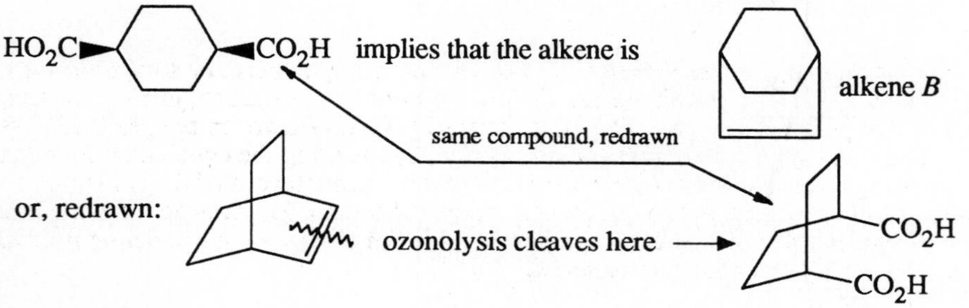

Compound A is an alkyl halide that can give this alkene by elimination:

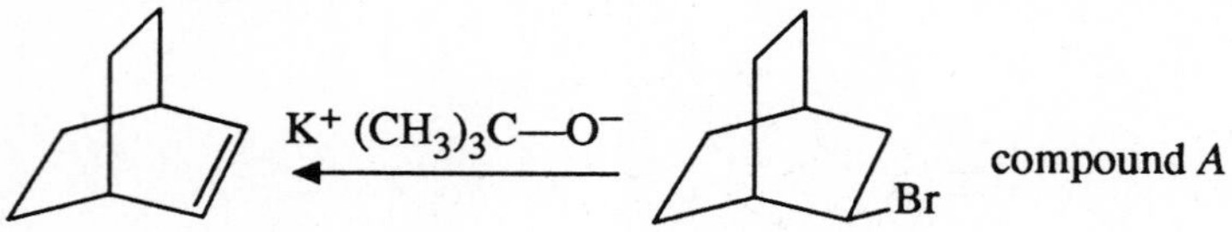

The elemental composition of this alkyl halide is $C_8H_{13}Br$. We can easily verify that it has the elemental analysis given in the problem.

41. (a) Both reactions are direct displacements. The first is a typical S_N2 reaction:

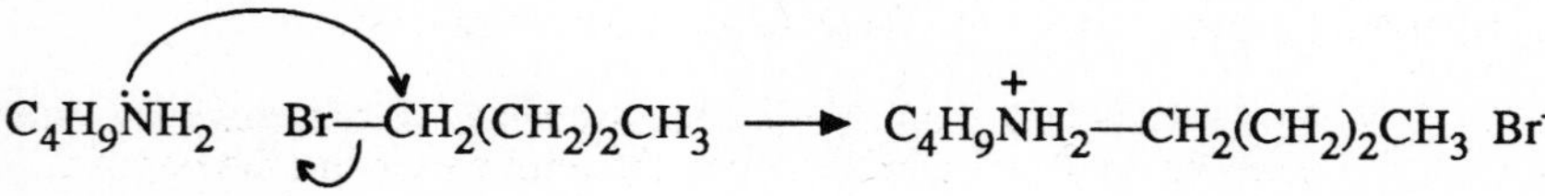

The second is also a displacement. It is like an S_N2 reaction, except that it is unimolecular; the displacement occurs within the same molecule:

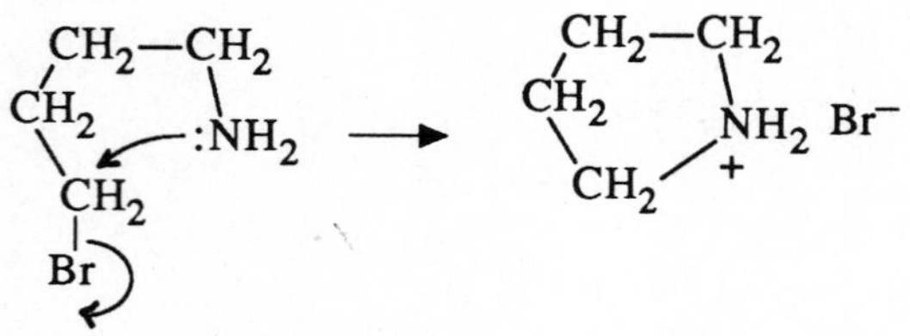

Because it is unimolecular, this reaction has a first-order rate law.

(b) In this case, we have a competition: product C is formed by an *intramolecular*, unimolecular route, and product D is formed by a bimolecular displacement between two different molecules.

(c) If the rate law for formation of C is

$$\text{rate of formation of } C = k_C[B],$$

and if the rate law for formation of D is

$$\text{rate of formation of } D = k_D[B]^2,$$

then the ratio of rates is

$$\frac{\text{rate of formation of } C}{\text{rate of formation of } D} = \frac{k_C}{k_D}\frac{[B]}{[B]^2} = \frac{k_C}{k_D}\frac{1}{[B]}$$

We can see that the rate of formation of C relative to that of D will be maximized when $[B]$ is as small as possible.

➤ Let us see why this conclusion makes sense intuitively. The rate of a reaction between two molecules is related to the probability that they will collide; this probability goes up with concentration, just as the probability that two people will collide in an airport increases with the number of people. However, the probability of an intramolecular "collision" doesn't change with concentration. Hence, by lowering the concentration of the starting material, the probability of the intermolecular reaction decreases, while the probability of the intramolecular reaction stays the same. At a low enough concentration, the intramolecular reaction will dominate completely. This leads to the general rule that *to favor an intramolecular reaction over a competing intermolecular reaction, lower the concentration of the starting material.*

42. The rate law requires that two molecules of bromine are present in the transition state. It does *not*, however, tell us how they are arranged. We can use our imagination!

Either step 1 or step 2 could be rate-determining, as both involve the *elements* of alkene and two bromine molecules. There are many reasonable mechanisms one could write. In the absence of evidence to distinguish among them, one is as good as another, provided that each is consistent with the rate law.

43. (a) One way to approach this problem is to assume a particular stereochemistry for the elimination. If this gives the correct product, the assumed stereochemistry is correct; if not, the elimination has the opposite stereochemistry. For reaction (1), if we place the two bromines in an *anti* arrangement, we see that the two methyl groups end up *cis* in the product.

Since this is the observed product, we conclude that the elimination is *anti*. A similar analysis leads to the conclusion that reaction (2) is a *syn* elimination.

(b) The mechanism shown for reaction (1) above is consistent with both the stereoselectivity of the reaction and the rate law.

(c) The reaction is a *syn* elimination. One attractive mechanism for this *syn* elimination is for the leaving acetate to "remove its own proton" in a pericyclic reaction. This requires that the acetate and proton depart from the same face of the molecule.

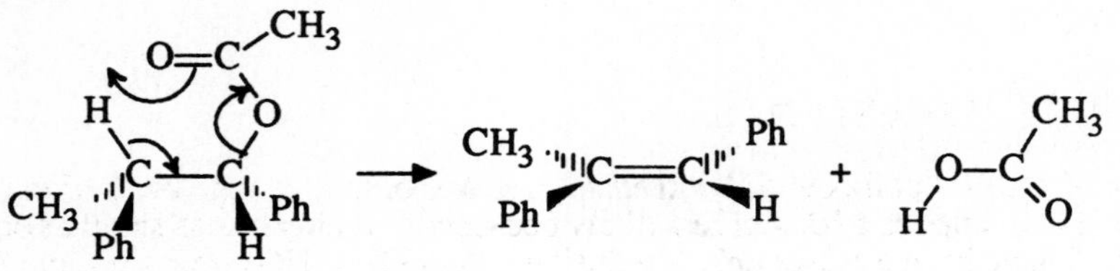

44. Consider first compound *A*. If we place an H *anti* to the Br leaving group, the deuterated (*Z*)-alkene is formed:

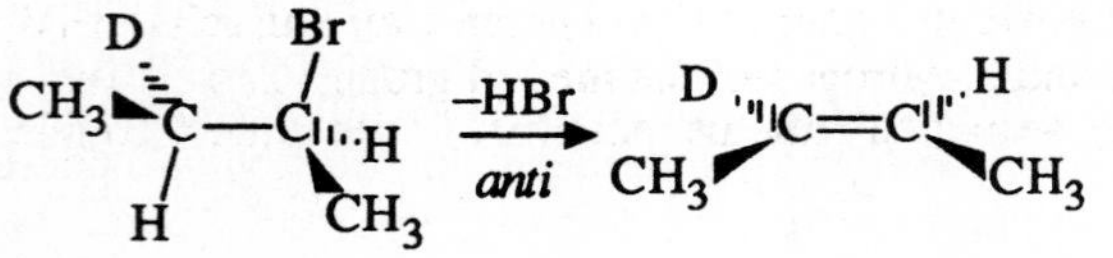

And if we place a D *anti* to the Br leaving group, the D is lost and an undeuterated (*E*)-alkene is formed:

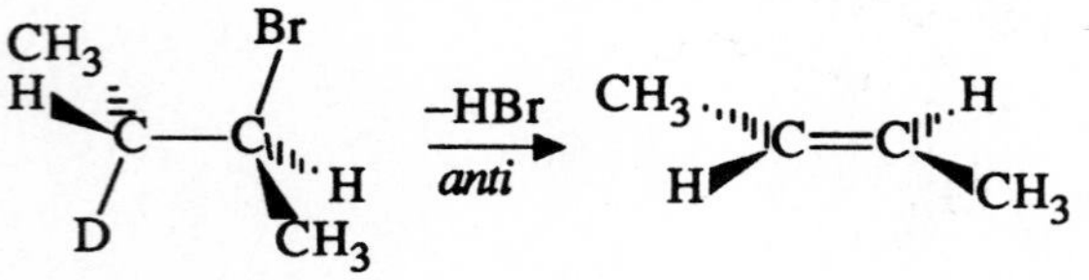

A similar analysis shows why opposite results are obtained from *B*, the diastereomer of *A*. If you didn't get the first part of this problem, be sure to work through the elimination from *B*.

45. The fact that protonolysis of the corresponding Grignard reagents gives the same hydrocarbon tells us that the two compounds have the same carbon skeleton. Since compound *A* reacts rapidly with AgNO$_3$, it must be an alkyl halide that forms a relatively stable, probably tertiary, carbocation. Since the two alkyl halides give the same ether, the product from *B* must be rearranged. The only tertiary alkyl halide with the formula C$_5$H$_{11}$Br is 2-bromo-2-methylbutane:

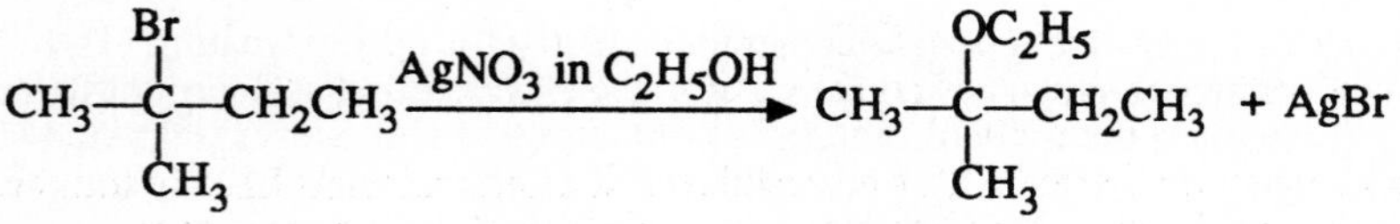

There are two possible alkyl halides with the same carbon skeleton as *A* that could rearrange in respective S$_N$1 reactions to give the same carbocation, and hence the same ether product as *A*; these are labeled *B1* and *B2* below:

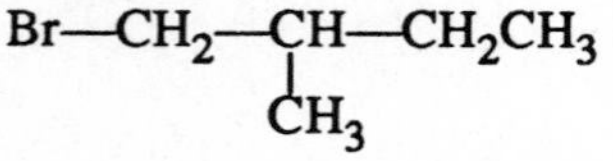

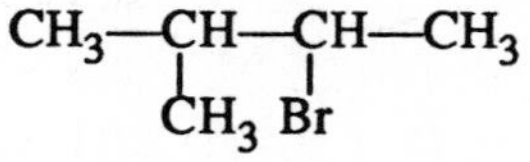

However, only *B2* can react in an E2 reaction to give an alkene that furnishes acetone on ozonolysis:

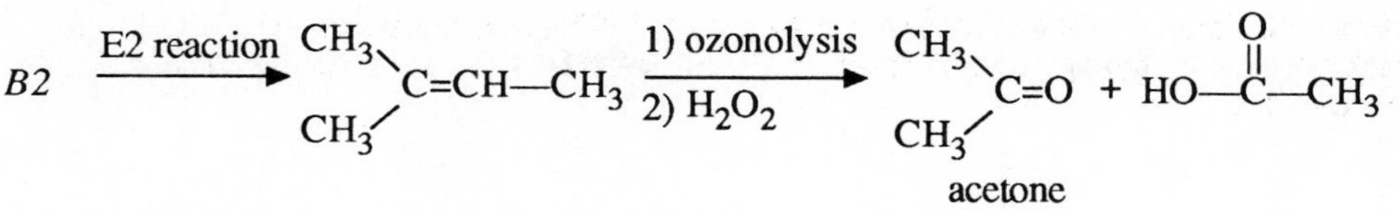

Hence, the structure for compound *B* is that shown for *B2*.

➤ Notice that we drew out *all possibilities* for compound *B* and eliminated one of them on the basis of the evidence. You may have concluded that compound *B1* was less likely because it is primary and should not undergo an S_N1 reaction. This would have been a reasonable conclusion, although $AgNO_3$ does promote S_N1 reactions and rearrangements even in some primary halides. The ozonolysis data, however, removes all doubt that *B2* is the correct answer.

46. In the first compound, there are two possible β-protons that either have or could assume an *anti* relationship to the bromine; these are the hydrogen at the ring junction and a hydrogen of the methyl group. Loss of the hydrogen at the ring junction is favored because it gives the alkene with the more highly substituted double bond.

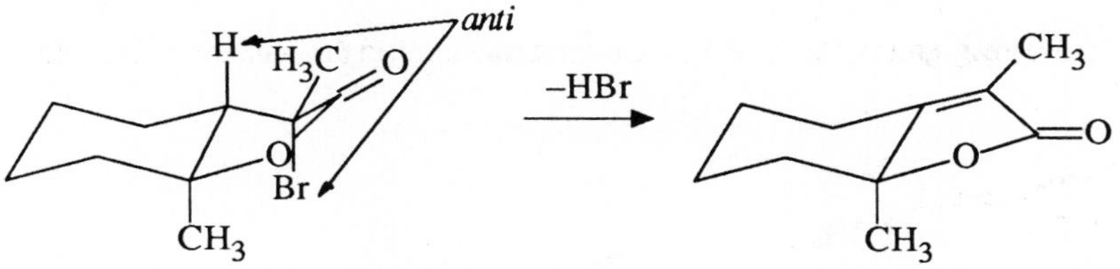

In the second compound, the only β-hydrogen that can assume an *anti* relationship to the bromine is a hydrogen on the methyl group; hence, elimination occurs from this position:

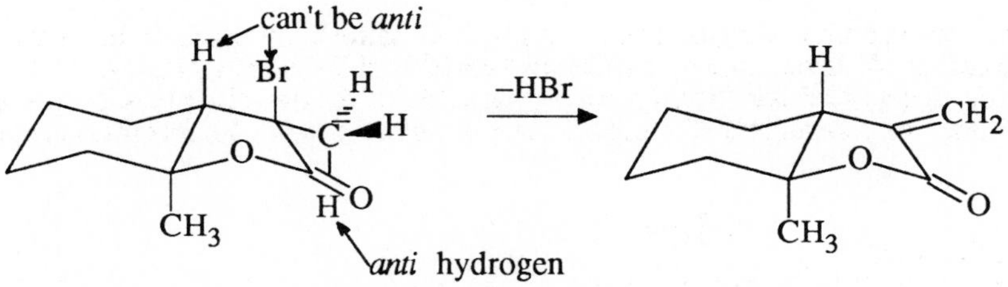

47. (a) Product *A* is the product of an E2 reaction. Since both stereoisomeric starting materials have hydrogens that can assume an *anti* relationship to the chlorine, the formation of some E2 product in each case is reasonable. Product *B* comes from ionization of the —OH group followed by isomerization to a boat form and internal displacement:

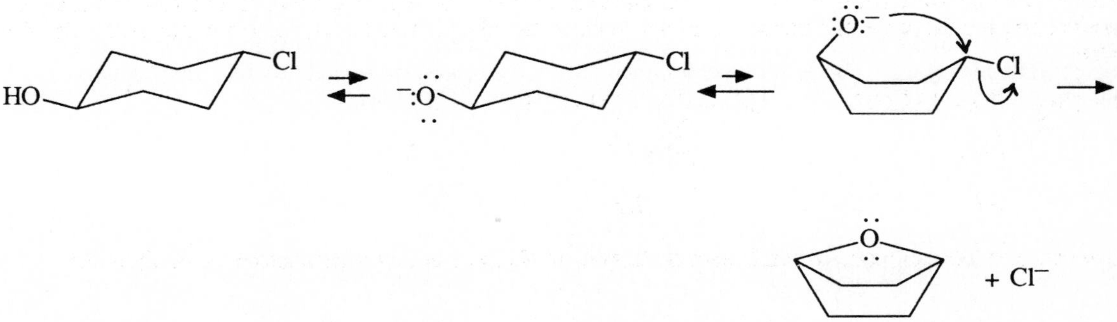

An ordinary S_N2 reaction occurs with inversion of configuration to give product *C*:

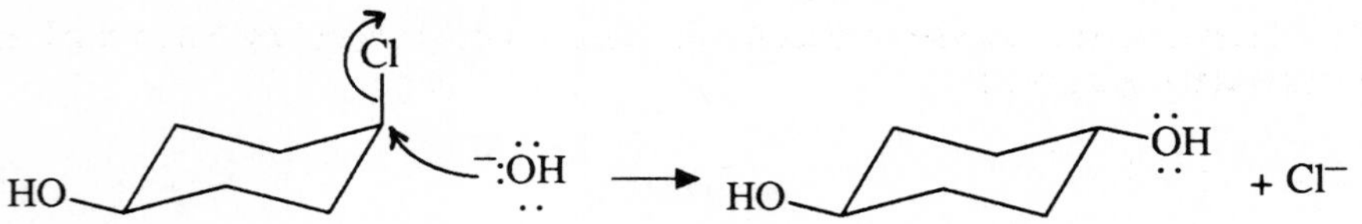

(b) In the boat form of *trans*-4-chlorocyclohexanol, the —O⁻ group can attack the chlorine-bearing carbon from the backside, as shown above. This *intramolecular* displacement gives product *B*. However, in *cis*-4-chlorocyclohexanol, the —O⁻ group cannot attack backside in *any* conformation. Hence, the *intermolecular* reaction — attack of ⁻OH — is observed instead.

48. The products are separated ions; hence, the equilibrium will lie furthest to the right in solvents that promote separation and solvation of ions: protic, polar, donor solvents:
(a) Ethanol is protic and is more polar than diethyl ether; hence, the equilibrium lies furthest to the right in ethanol.
(b) The equilibrium lies furthest to the right in a protic solvent — the water-methanol mixture — because it can solvate the anion.

49. (a) We expect bromination to occur with *anti* stereochemistry:

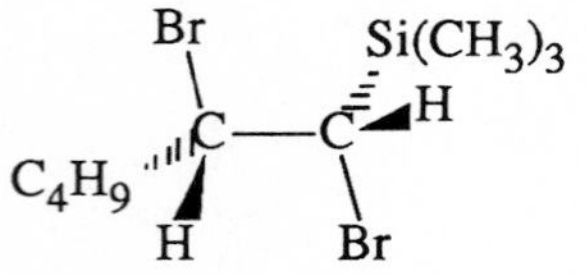

(and its enantiomer) is the *anti* bromination product

Notice that the —Br and —Si(CH₃)₃ are eliminated. If these groups are eliminated with *anti* stereochemistry, the (*E*)-alkene is formed:

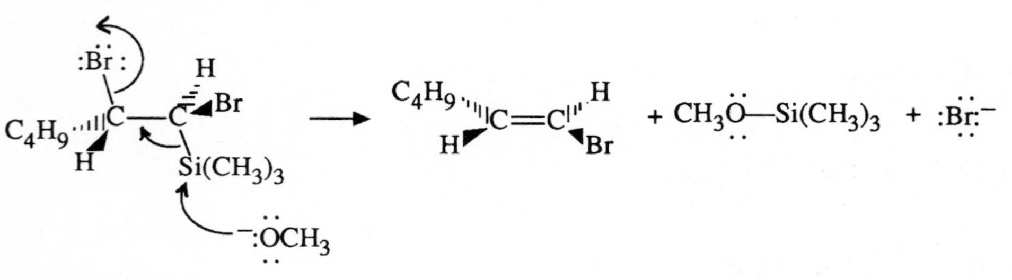

Since this is the observed product, the elimination must occur with *anti* stereochemistry.

(b) If we start with an alkene of opposite stereochemistry — the *E* isomer — then an alkene of opposite stereochemistry, (Z)-1-bromo-1-hexene, should be formed. (You should verify this by drawing the appropriate structures for yourself!)

50. (a) We know that when chloroform is treated with base, a carbene, dichloromethylene, is formed (see Eqs. 9.60a and 9.60b in the text). Since dichloromethylene is an electrophile, it can react simply with the nucleophilic iodide ion. The resulting anion then removes a proton from water to give the product:

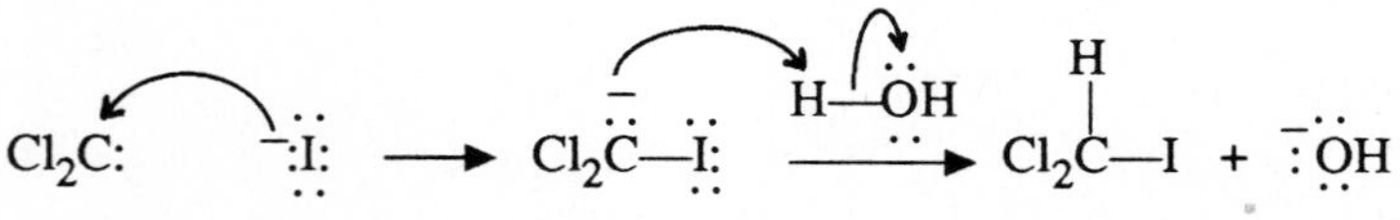

(b) The starting alkyl halide, benzyl chloride, undergoes an α-elimination brought about by the strong base butyllithium to give phenylmethylene, a carbene:

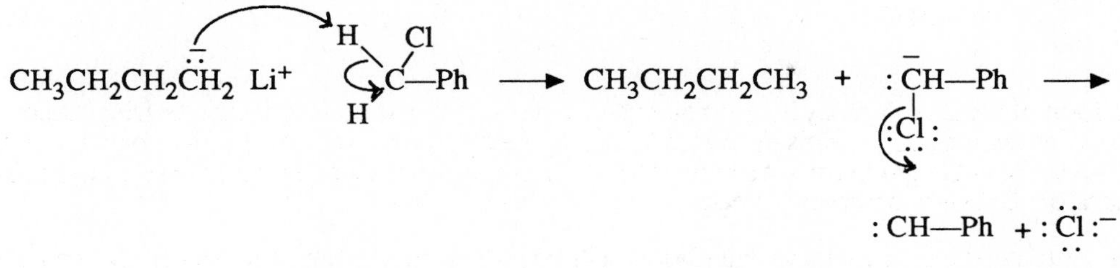

phenylmethylene

This carbene then reacts with cyclohexene to give the product cyclopropane.

51. Compound A is an achiral alkyl halide. Since compounds B and C differ from A by loss of the elements of HBr, it appears that these compounds are elimination products. The unsaturation number of A is 2; that of B and C is 3. Since compound A undergoes ozonolysis, it has at least one double bond, and, from its ozonolysis product, it has the part-structure

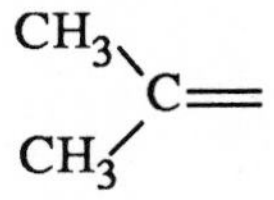

Compound A, from its reaction with $AgNO_3$, is a tertiary alkyl halide. Finally, the carbon skeleton of all compounds, from the hydrogenation results, is that of 4-methyl-1-isopropylcyclohexane:

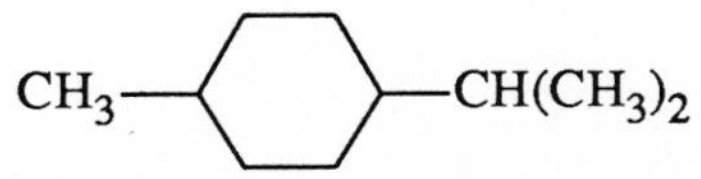

The only structure for A that fits all these data is

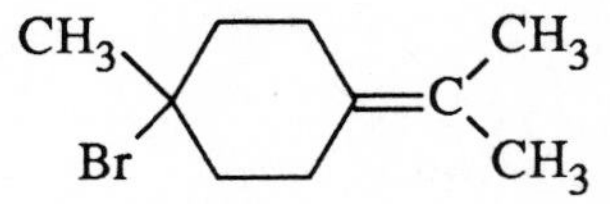

compound A

It follows that compounds D and E are the stereoisomeric bromination products of A: since both are *meso*, they are achiral.

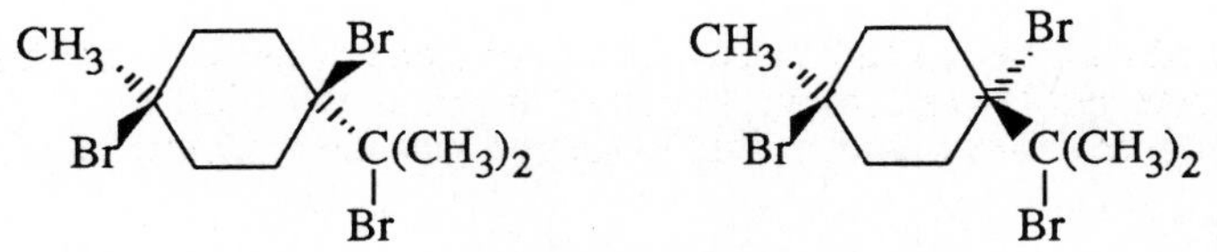

compounds D and E

Chapter 10 / Chemistry of Alcohols, Glycols, and Thiols

CHAPTER 10 TERMS

anaerobic fermentation 10.7
carbonyl compound 10.6A
chlorosulfite ester 10.4
chromate ester 10.6A
coenzyme 10.7
connectively equivalent 10.8B
dehydration 10.1A
diastereotopic 10.8B
diastereotopic groups 10.8B
disulfide 10.9
enantiotopic 10.8B
enantiotopic groups 10.8B

homotopic 10.8B
homotopic groups 10.8B
oxidation 10.6B
oxidation level 10.6B
oxidizing agent 10.6B
pinacol rearrangement 10.1B
principle of microscopic reversibility 10.1A
reducing agent 10.6B
reduction 10.6B
sulfonate ester 10.3A
sulfonic acid 10.9
target molecule 10.10B

CHAPTER 10 CONCEPTS

I. Oxidation–Reduction Reactions:

    A. <u>Oxidation-Level Assignment</u>:
        1. The **oxidation state** of a molecule is determined from the oxidation states of the individual carbon atoms.
            a) **Oxidation** is the *loss* of electrons.
                (1) In an oxidation, the change in oxidation number is positive and is equal to the number of electrons lost.
                (2) When an organic compound is oxidized, the reagent that brings about the transformation is called an **oxidizing agent**.
            b) **Reduction** is the *gain* of electrons.
                (1) In a reduction, the change in oxidation number is negative and is equal to the number of electrons gained.
                (2) When an organic compound is reduced, the reagent that brings about the transformation is called a **reducing agent**.
            c) Whenever something is oxidized, something else is reduced.
            d) By considering the change in oxidation number for a transformation, it can be determined whether an oxidizing or reducing agent is required to bring about the reaction.
        2. The oxidation level of a particular carbon is assigned by considering the relative electronegativities of the groups bound to the carbon:
            a) Assign a −1 for:
                (1) Every bond to an element less electronegative than carbon (including hydrogen).
                (2) Every negative charge on the carbon.

b) Assign a 0 (zero) for:
    (1) Every bond to another carbon atom.
    (2) Every unpaired electron on the carbon.
c) Assign a +1 for:
    (1) Every bond to an element more electronegative than carbon.
    (2) Every positive charge on the carbon.
d) Total the numbers assigned to obtain the oxidation level for the carbon atom under consideration.
e) Assign an oxidation level to *each* carbon atom in the organic reactant(s) and product(s) that undergoes some chemical *change* during the transformation.

3. The oxidation number N_{ox} for each compound is computed by adding the oxidation level of all carbons that undergo some chemical change during the transformation.
4. Subtract the N_{ox} of the reactant from the N_{ox} of the product.
    a) A *positive* difference indicates that the transformation is an *oxidation*.
    b) A *negative* difference indicates that the transformation is a *reduction*.
    c) A difference of *zero* indicates that *neither* an oxidation nor a reduction has taken place.
5. Two points help determine whether an oxidation or a reduction is occurring:
    a) In most oxidations of organic compounds, either hydrogen in a C—H bond or a carbon in a C—C bond is replaced by a more electronegative element.
    b) In most reductions of organic compounds, either hydrogen in a C—H bond or a carbon in a C—C bond is replaced by a less electronegative element.
6. The oxidation number concept can be used to organize organic compounds into functional groups with the same oxidation level; compounds with identical oxidation levels are generally interconverted by reagents that are neither oxidizing nor reducing agents.

B. <u>Biological Oxidation of Ethanol</u>:
1. Oxidation and reduction reactions are extremely important in living systems.
2. The oxidation of ethanol to acetaldehyde is catalyzed by an enzyme called **alcohol dehydrogenase**; the oxidizing agent is **nicotinamide adenine dinucleotide**, NAD+ (see structure, text page 395).
    a) NAD+ is reduced to NADH.
    b) NAD+ is an example of a **coenzyme**.

II. General Chemical Concepts:

A. <u>Chemical and Stereochemical Group Equivalence</u>:
1. Chemically equivalent groups cannot be distinguished.
    a) They behave the same towards a chemical reagent.
    b) One group does not react in preference to the other.
2. Groups within a molecule are **connectively equivalent** when they have the same connectivity relationship to all other atoms in the molecule.
    a) Whether two connectively equivalent groups are chemically equivalent depends on their stereochemical relationship.
    b) Connectively nonequivalent groups are *never* chemically equivalent.
3. The stereochemical relationship between connectively equivalent groups becomes very easy to see by making a simple substitution test—substitute each connectively equivalent group in turn with a fictitious circled group.
    a) When the substitution test gives identical molecules, the connectively equivalent groups are said to be **homotopic**; **homotopic groups** are chemically equivalent and indistinguishable under all circumstances.

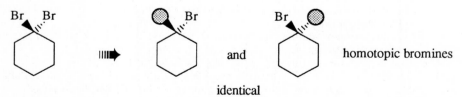

identical

b) When the substitution test gives enantiomers, the connectively equivalent groups are said to be **enantiotopic**.
    (1) **Enantiotopic groups** are chemically equivalent toward achiral reagents.
    (2) Enantiotopic groups are chemically nonequivalent toward chiral reagents.

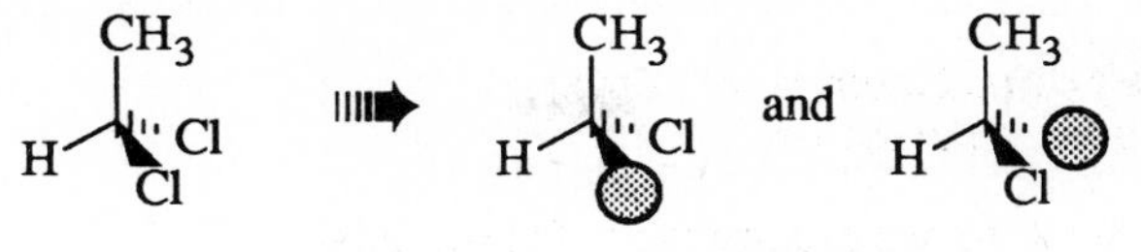

enantiomers

enantiotopic chlorines

    c) When the substitution test gives diastereomers, the connectively equivalent groups are said to be **diastereotopic**.
        (1) **Diastereotopic groups** are chemically nonequivalent under *all* conditions.
        (2) There are two situations in which diastereotopic groups are easily recognized at a glance:
            (*a*) When two connectively equivalent groups are present in a molecule that contains an asymmetric carbon.
            (*b*) When two groups on one carbon of a double bond are the same and the two groups on the other carbon are different.

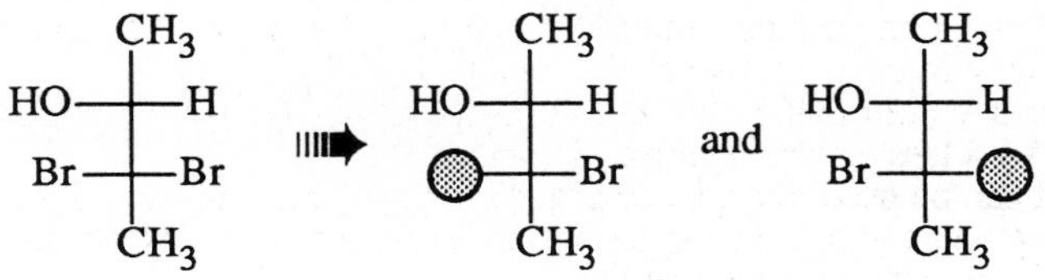

diastereomers

diastereotopic bromines

B. <u>Design of Organic Synthesis</u>:
    1. The preparation of an organic compound by the use of one or more reactions is called an **organic synthesis**.
    2. In order to assess the best route to the **target molecule** from the starting material, work backward from the target toward the starting material.
    3. Continue to work backward from this precursor step–by–step until the route from the starting material becomes clear; sometimes more than one synthetic route will be possible.
    4. Working problems in organic synthesis is one of the best ways to master organic chemistry.

CHAPTER 10 REACTIONS

I. Substitution and Elimination Reactions of Alcohols:

A. General Principles:
   1. In order to break the carbon–oxygen bond, the —OH group must first be converted into a good leaving group by:
      a) Protonation with a strong mineral acid.
      b) Conversion into **sulfonate esters** or inorganic esters.
      c) Reaction with thionyl chloride or phosphorus tribromide.

B. Synthesis of Alkyl Halides and Sulfonate Esters from Alcohols:
   1. Alcohols react with hydrogen halides to give alkyl halides.
      a) The reaction of a primary alcohol is an S_N2 reaction in which water is the leaving group; the reaction requires a Lewis-acid catalyst ($ZnCl_2$ in their reaction with HCl).
      b) Secondary alcohols can react by either the S_N1 or S_N2 mechanism, or both, and many require a Lewis-acid catalyst ($ZnCl_2$ in their reaction with HCl).
      c) The reaction of a tertiary alcohol is essentially an S_N1 reaction with H_2O as the leaving group and is much faster than the reactions of primary alcohols.
      d) Carbocation intermediates may lead to rearrangements.
      e) Alkyl halide formation and **dehydration** to alkenes are alternate branches of a common mechanism.

   2. Sulfonate esters are prepared from alcohols and **sulfonic acid** derivatives called **sulfonyl chlorides**.
      a) Pyridine catalyzes the reaction and neutralizes the HCl formed in the reaction.
      b) Sulfonate esters react like alkyl bromides or alkyl iodides in substitution and elimination reactions.
         (1) Sulfonate anions are excellent leaving groups (weak bases).
         (2) In the presence of strong base, primary alkyl sulfonate esters undergo S_N2 reactions.

$$CH_3CH_2\text{—}OH + TsCl \xrightarrow{\text{pyridine}} CH_3CH_2\text{—}OTs \xrightarrow[\text{acetone}]{\text{NaI}} CH_3CH_2\text{—}I + NaOTs$$

$$\left[Ts\text{—} \ = \ CH_3\text{—}\left\langle\bigcirc\right\rangle\text{—}SO_2\text{—} \right]$$

         (3) Tertiary alkyl sulfonate esters undergo E2 reactions in the presence of strong base.
   3. When an alcohol reacts with thionyl chloride, **a chlorosulfite ester** intermediate is formed.
      a) The chlorosulfite group is a good leaving group.
      b) The chlorosulfite ester reacts readily with nucleophiles, including Cl^- present in the reaction mixture.
         (1) The reaction mechanism is S_N2 for primary and some secondary alcohols.
         (2) Stereochemical inversion at the site of substitution is generally observed.
         (3) The displaced $^-O\text{—}SO\text{—}Cl$ ion is unstable and decomposes to SO_2 and Cl^-.
      c) The thionyl chloride method is a considerably milder technique for synthesis of alkyl chlorides than the HCl method—some secondary alcohols give somewhat less rearrangement than in the HCl method.

a chlorosulfite ester

4. Alkyl bromides can be synthesized from alcohols with phosphorus tribromide.
   a) The bromophosphite group is a good leaving group.
   b) The bromophosphite ester is displaced by bromide.
      (1) The reaction mechanism is S_N2.
      (2) Stereochemical inversion at the site of substitution is generally observed.

a bromophosphite ester

5. Summary of methods for preparing alkyl halides from alcohols:
   a) Primary alcohols—just about any method can be used to prepare primary alkyl halides.
   b) Secondary alcohols—the reaction of simple secondary alcohols with hydrogen halides in some cases is accompanied by rearrangement.
      (1) Rearrangements are avoided by converting the alcohol into a sulfonate ester followed by S_N2 displacement with halide ion.
      (2) Some unbranched secondary alcohols also react with $SOCl_2$ or PBr_3 to give the corresponding alkyl halide without rearrangement.
   c) Tertiary alcohols:
      (1) Simple tertiary alcohols react rapidly with HCl or HBr under mild conditions to give the corresponding alkyl halide.
      (2) The sulfonate ester method *does not* work.

C. Dehydration of Alcohols:
   1. Reactions in which the elements of water are lost from the starting material are called **dehydration reactions.**
   2. Mineral acids catalyze β-elimination of water from alcohols to give alkenes.
      a) Most acid-catalyzed dehydrations of alcohols are reversible reactions.
      b) These reactions can easily be driven toward alkene formation by applying LeChatelier's principle.
      c) Lewis acids and/or heat can also catalyze dehydration reactions.
   3. The most common mechanism for the dehydration of alcohols is the reverse of the mechanism for hydration of alkenes (see Chapter 10 Rules).
      a) The first step is protonation of the alcohol oxygen.
      b) A carbocation intermediate is involved.

4. The relative rates of alcohol dehydration are in the order:

   tertiary > secondary >> primary

5. If more than one type of β-proton is present in the alcohol, then a mixture of alkene products can be expected; the more stable alkenes usually predominate in the mixture (Saytzeff elimination).
6. Alcohols that react to give rearrangement-prone carbocation intermediates yield rearranged alkenes.

D. Pinacol Rearrangement:

1. Vicinal glycols also undergo acid-catalyzed dehydration.
   a) The acid-catalyzed dehydration of glycols is always accompanied by rearrangement.
   b) The acid-catalyzed dehydration of glycols is called the **pinacol rearrangement**.
2. The mechanism of the pinacol rearrangement involves:
   a) Protonation of the —OH group is followed by loss of water to give a carbocation.
   b) Rearrangement of the carbocation to another carbocation that is resonance stabilized.
   c) Loss of a proton from the oxygen to give the product.

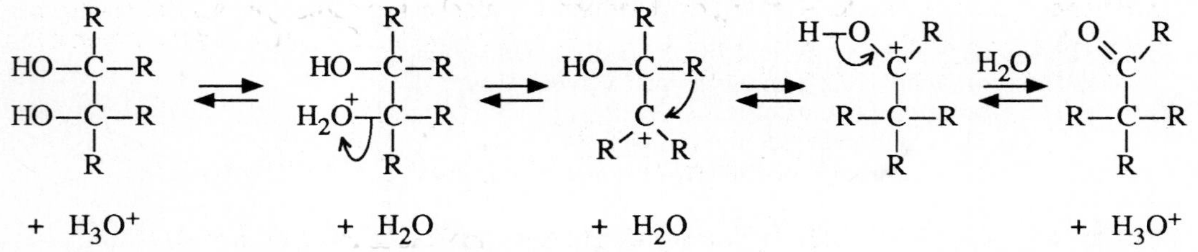

3. The most rapid pinacol rearrangements are those that involve relatively stable carbocations.
4. More than one pinacol rearrangement are possible for some glycols.

II. Oxidation Reactions of Alcohols and Thiols:

A. Oxidation of Alcohols:

1. Primary and secondary alcohols react with reagents containing chromium in the +6 oxidation state to give **carbonyl compounds.**
   a) Several forms of Cr(VI) can be used to convert alcohols into carbonyl compounds:
      (1) Chromate (CrO_4^{2-}) in strongly acidic solution.
      (2) Dichromate ($Cr_2O_7^{2-}$) in strongly acidic solution.
      (3) Chromic anhydride (chromium trioxide, CrO_3) in pyridine.
   b) The mechanism involves:
      (1) An acid-catalyzed displacement of water from chromic acid by the alcohol to form a **chromate ester**.
      (2) Decomposition of the chromate ester in a β-elimination reaction after protonation.

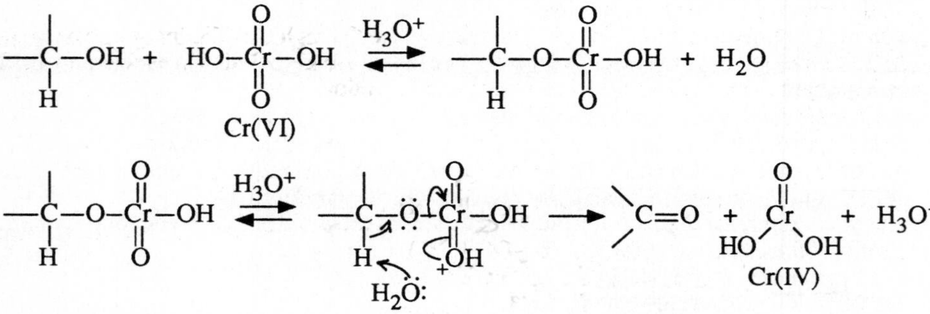

2. Primary alcohols react with Cr(VI) reagents to give aldehydes.
   a) Aldehydes in the *presence* of water react further with Cr(VI) reagents to give carboxylic acids.
   b) Aldehydes in the *absence* of water *do not* react further with Cr(VI) reagents to give carboxylic acids (CrO_3 in pyridine).

$$CH_3CH_2{-}OH \xrightarrow[\text{pyridine}]{CrO_3} CH_3\overset{O}{\overset{\|}{C}}{-}H$$

$$CH_3CH_2{-}OH \xrightarrow[H_3O^+]{Cr_2O_7^{2-}} CH_3\overset{O}{\overset{\|}{C}}{-}OH$$

3. Secondary alcohols react with Cr(VI) reagents to give ketones—ketones *do not* react further with Cr(VI) reagents under usual conditions.

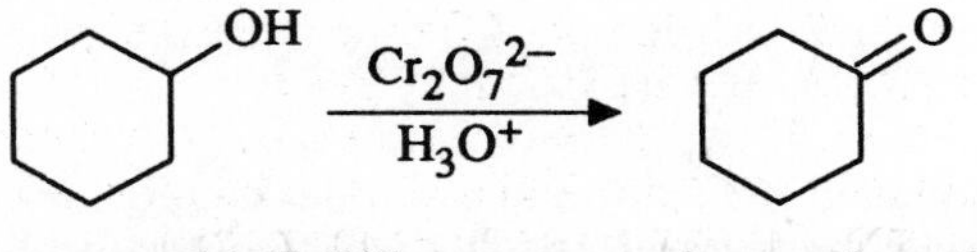

4. Tertiary alcohols *do not* react with Cr(VI) reagents under usual conditions.
5. Potassium permanganate, $KMnO_4$, oxidizes primary alcohols to carboxylic acids; because $KMnO_4$ reacts with carbon–carbon double or triple bonds, chromium(VI) is preferred for the oxidation of alcohols that contain double or triple bonds.

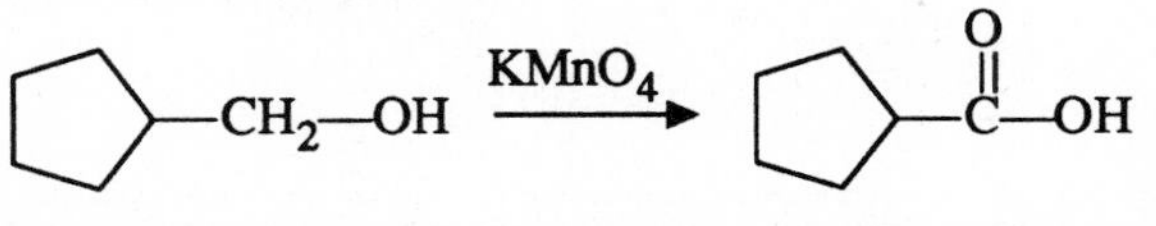

6. Nitric acid is used for oxidizing primary unsaturated alcohols to carboxylic acids.
   a) Under mild conditions, nitric acid selectively oxidizes both primary alcohols and aldehydes, but not secondary alcohols.

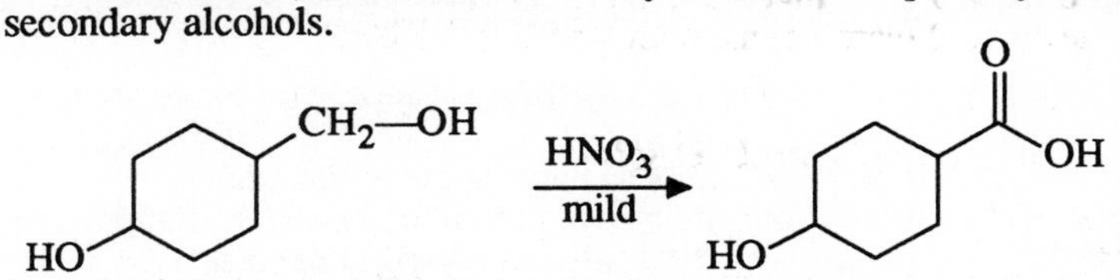

   b) Under vigorous conditions, nitric acid oxidizes secondary alcohols and cleaves a carbon-carbon bond adjacent to the —OH group.

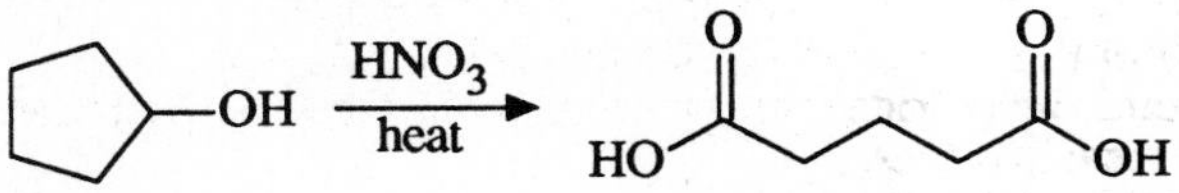

B. Oxidative Cleavage of Glycols:
   1. The carbon-carbon bond between the —OH groups of a vicinal glycol can be cleaved with periodic acid to give two carbonyl compounds.
   2. The cleavage of glycols with periodic acid takes place through a cyclic inorganic ester intermediate.
      a) The inorganic ester intermediate is formed when the glycol displaces water from H_5IO_6.
      b) The cyclic ester breaks down in a pericyclic reaction.

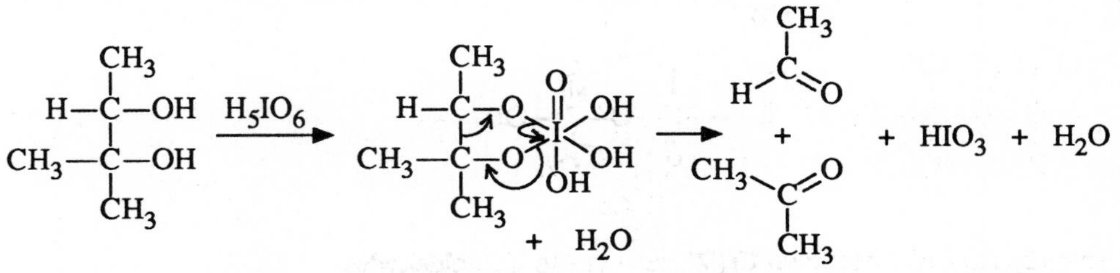

3. A glycol that cannot form a cyclic ester intermediate is not cleaved by periodic acid.

C. Oxidation of Thiols:
   1. Oxidation of a thiol occurs at the sulfur atom; the most commonly occurring oxidation products of thiols are disulfides and sulfonic acids.
   2. Sulfur can accommodate more than eight valence electrons:
      a) It has $3s$ and $3p$ orbitals.
      b) It has unfilled $3d$ orbitals of relatively low energy.

3. Thiols can be converted into disulfides by mild oxidants (I_2 and base or Br_2 in CCl_4).
    a) These reactions can be viewed simply as a series of S_N2 reactions on halogen and sulfur.

$$2\ CH_3\!-\!SH\ \xrightarrow[\text{NaOH}]{I_2}\ CH_3\!-\!S\!-\!S\!-\!CH_3\ +\ 2\ NaI$$

    b) Many thiols spontaneously oxidize to disulfides merely on standing in air (O_2).
4. Sulfonic acids are formed by vigorous oxidation of thiols or disulfides with $KMnO_4$ or HNO_3.

$$CH_3\!-\!SH\ \xrightarrow{\ KMnO_4\ }\ CH_3\!-\!\overset{\overset{\displaystyle O}{\|}}{\underset{\underset{\displaystyle O}{\|}}{S}}\!-\!OH$$

CHAPTER 10 RULES

Principle of Microscopic Reversibility: A reaction and its reverse proceed by the forward and reverse of the same mechanism.
    a) The forward and reverse reactions must have the same intermediates.
    b) The forward and reverse reactions must have the same rate-determining transition states.
    c) Any reaction catalyzed in one direction is also catalyzed in the other.

CHAPTER 10 SOLUTIONS

Solutions to In-Text Problems

1. (a) This reaction involves a rearrangement. As in ordinary dehydrations, the first step involves protonation of the alcohol, then loss of water to give a carbocation. This cation then rearranges. The rearranged carbocation loses a proton to give the alkene product.

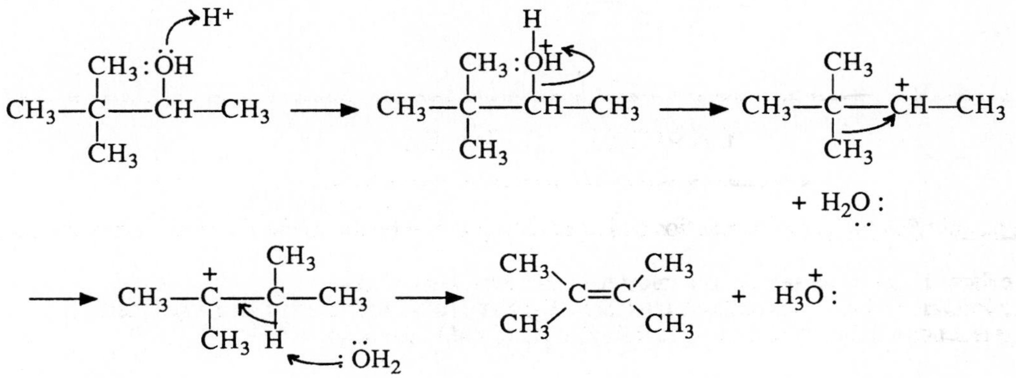

(b) The rearrangement is energetically favorable because the strain of the four-membered ring is relieved when it is converted into a five-membered ring.

2. (a)   (b)

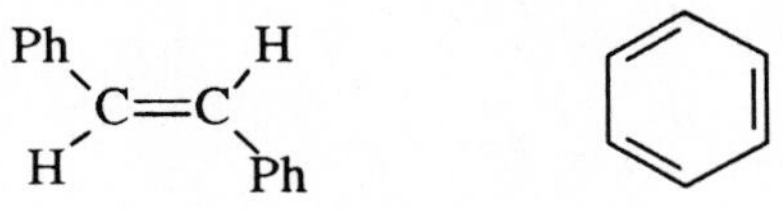

   trans-stilbene   benzene

3. Three alcohols that could in principle give 1-methyl-1-cyclohexene as a major dehydration product are those with the —OH group at or adjacent to the ring carbon bearing the CH_3— group:

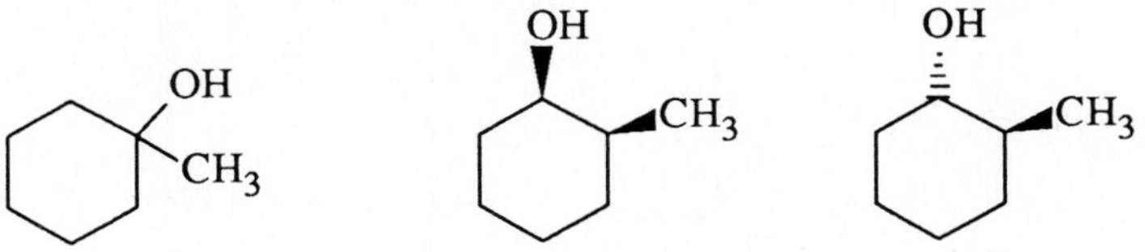

   A   B   C

   Compound A dehydrates most rapidly because it gives a tertiary carbocation.

4. (a) The answer follows directly from the mechanism for the pinacol rearrangement:

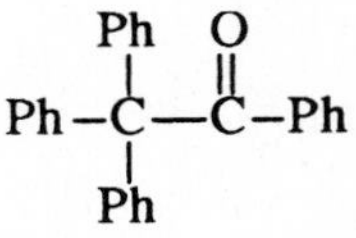

(b) The pinacol rearrangement involves in this case migration of a ring —CH_2— group — that is, a ring expansion.

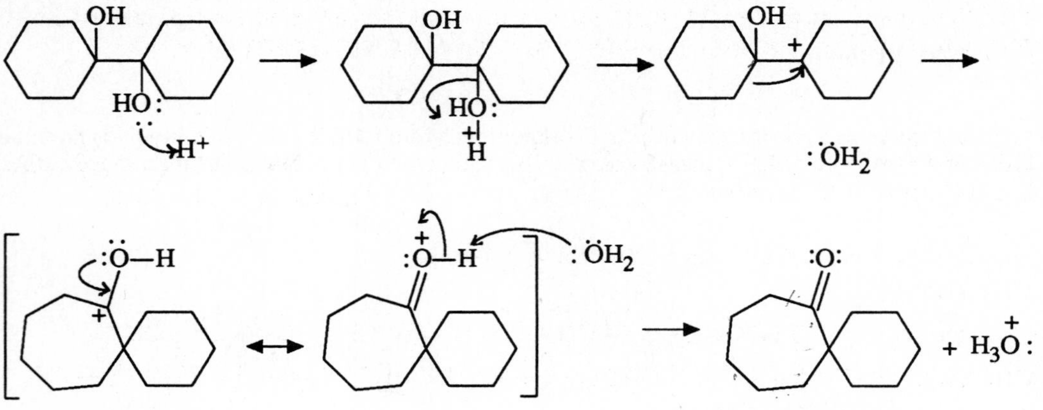

product

5. (a)

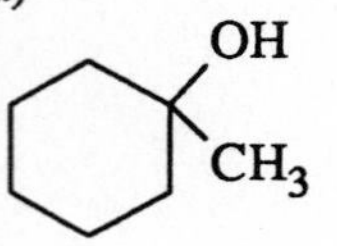

HCl →

(b)

$HOCH_2CH_2CH_2CH_2CH_2OH$
or $I—CH_2CH_2CH_2CH_2CH_2—OH$ + H—I →

6. This is a rearrangement reaction involving a hydride migration:

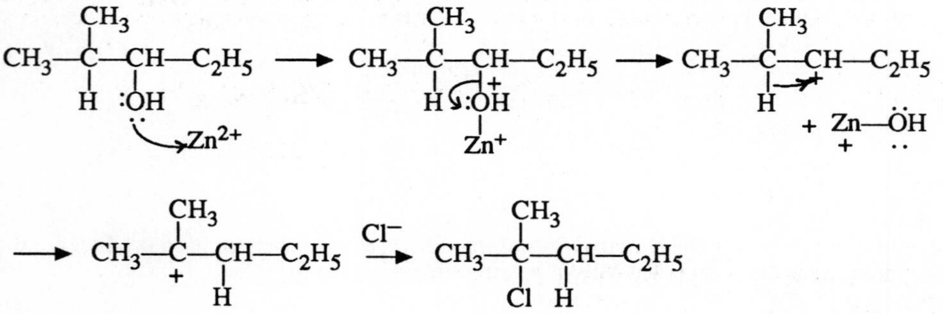

7. (a) $Br—CH_2CH_2CH_2—Br$

(b)

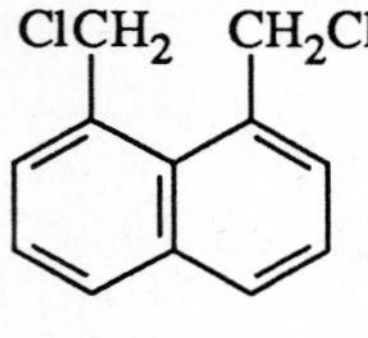

(c) No reaction. (Neopentyl compounds do not undergo S_N2 reactions under ordinary conditions.)

(d) A rearrangement is involved in this reaction:

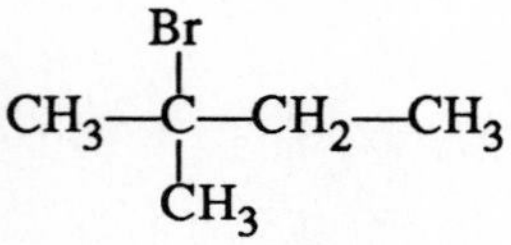

(If you can work Problem 6, you should be able to see what is happening here.)

➤ How do we know when to expect rearrangements? When a secondary alkyl halide or alcohol is subjected to S_N1 conditions (protic solvents for alkyl halides, acid for alcohols), and when a carbocation intermediate can rearrange to a more stable carbocation, we can be fairly sure that a rearrangement will occur.

8. (a)   (b) 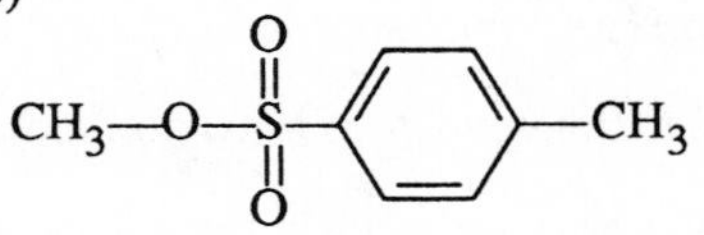   (c)

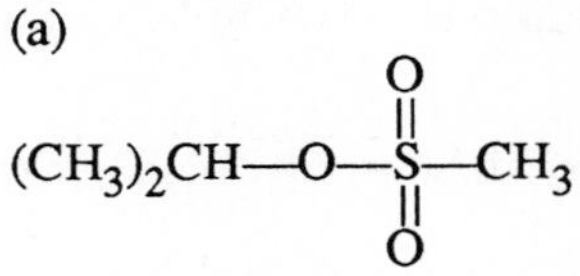

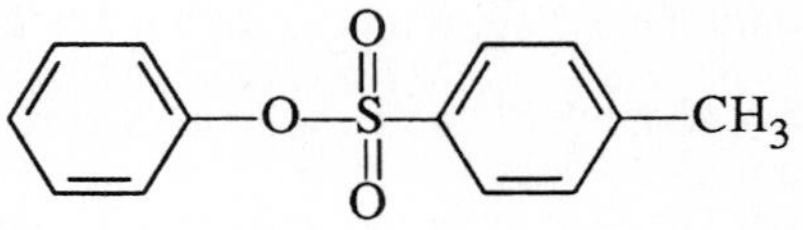

(d) The structure is given in the answer to Problem 9(b), below.

9. (a)

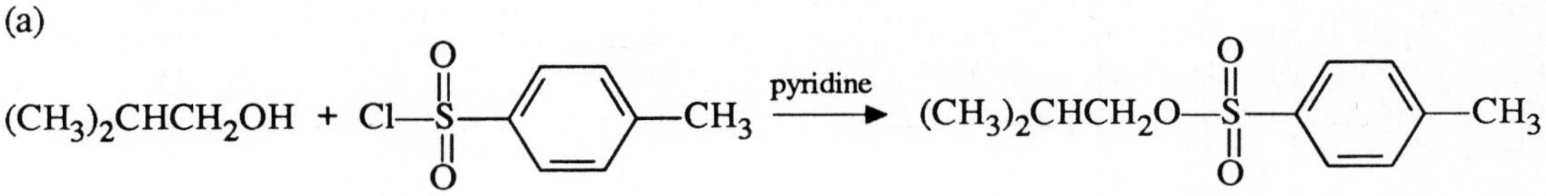

isobutyl tosylate

(b)

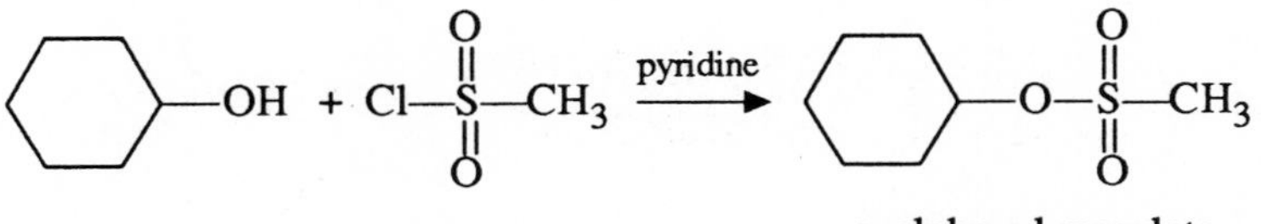

cyclohexyl mesylate

10. In the first step, a tosylate of the alcohol is formed. In the second step, the tosylate leaving group is displaced by the nucleophile cyanide under S_N2 conditions (polar aprotic solvent) to give an organic cyanide, or *nitrile*.

$$(CH_3)_2CHCH_2CH_2OH \xrightarrow{TsCl} (CH_3)_2CHCH_2CH_2OTs \xrightarrow{^-CN} (CH_3)_2CHCH_2CH_2CN$$

$$+ \ ^-OTs$$

11.

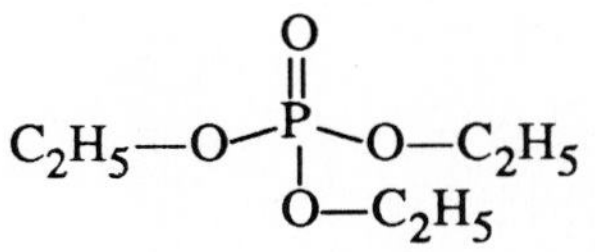

triethyl phosphate

12. In each reaction, the nucleophilic species displaces the leaving group from a methyl group. In (a), we show the complete mechanism. In the other parts, we give only the product derived from the nucleophile; you should write out the mechanism if the origin of the product is not clear.

(a)

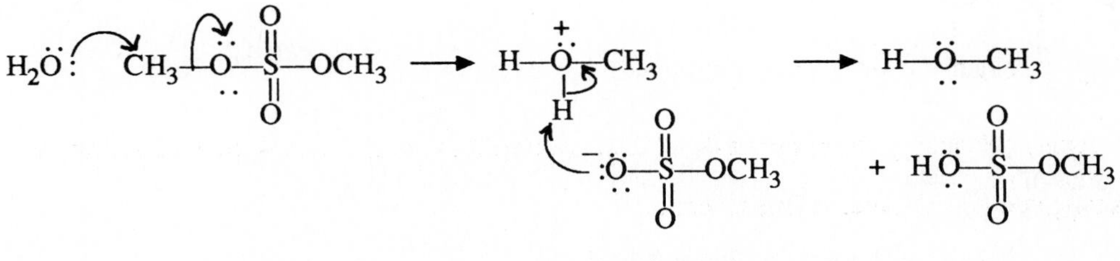

leaving group

(b) C_2H_5O—CH_3 (c) $CH_3CH_2CH_2$—S—CH_3 (d) CH_3—$\overset{+}{N}H_2$—CH_3 $\overset{..}{-\!:\!O}$—SO_2—CH_3 (If you

wrote dimethylamine, $CH_3\overset{.}{N}HCH_3$, as the product of this reaction, you have the right idea. It happens that dimethylamine is more basic than the leaving group; hence, the product remains as the salt.)

13. (a) HBr   (b) PBr_3 (c) Tosyl chloride in pyridine to give the tosylate; then displacement of the tosylate with Br⁻ (for example, KBr) in a polar aprotic solvent, such as acetone.

14. (a) Virtually any method will work, since rearrangement is not a problem. We could use $HCl/ZnCl_2$, or we could use $SOCl_2$.
(b) Since we want to avoid rearrangement in this unbranched secondary system, we use an S_N2 reaction: convert the alcohol to a tosylate, then displace the tosylate with NaBr in acetone. PBr_3 would also probably give a satisfactory yield of the desired alkyl bromide.
(c) Here a rearrangement is desired! Hence, we use conditions that promote rearrangement: concentrated HBr and heat. In the rearrangement, an unstrained tertiary carbocation is formed from a strained secondary one; hence, we can be fairly sure that the reaction will proceed as indicated.

15. The reaction is:

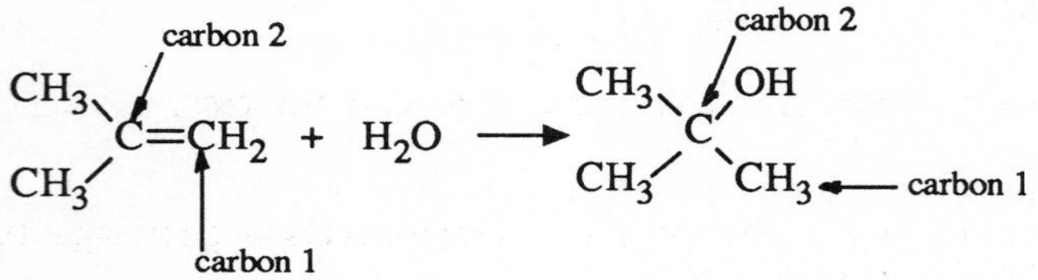

The carbons that change are carbons 1 and 2; these are the only carbons whose oxidation numbers must be considered. In the starting material, carbon 1 has an oxidation number of –2, and carbon 2 has an oxidation number of 0, for a total oxidation number of –2. In the product, carbon 1 has an oxidation number of –3, whereas carbon 2 has an oxidation number of +1, for a total of –2. The change in oxidation number is $-2 - (-2) = 0$. Hence, neither an oxidation nor a reduction has occurred. Notice, however, that carbon 1 has been reduced, and carbon 2 has undergone a compensating oxidation.

16. (a) A two-electron oxidation. We can tell this most easily by computing oxidation numbers. The carbon of the starting material has an oxidation number of –4; that of the product is –2. Net change: $-2 - (-4) = +2$.
(b) A six-electron oxidation. We can apply the oxidation-number formalism to get this result. However, in this case, let us balance the half-reaction:

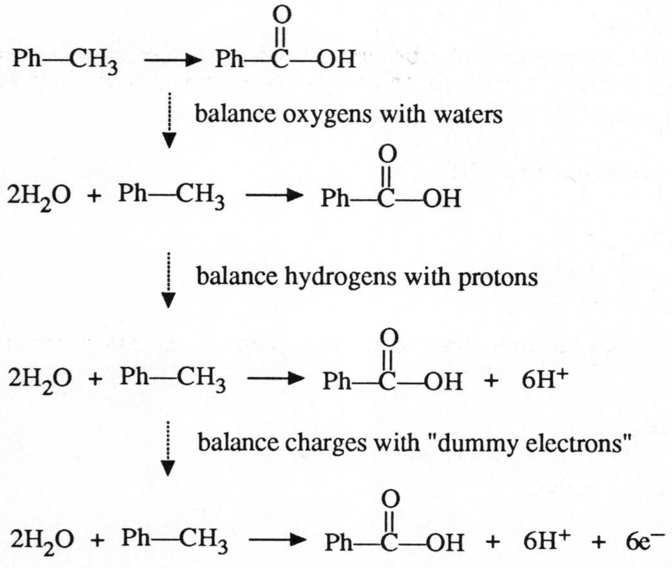

The $6e^-$ required to balance shows that this reaction is a six-electron oxidation.

(c) A two-electron reduction.
(d) A two-electron oxidation.
(e) Neither an oxidation nor a reduction.
(f) A four-electron oxidation.
(g) A two-electron reduction. Notice that the negative charge is assigned a contribution of –1 to the oxidation number.

17. (a) Ethylene undergoes a two-electron reduction; hydrogen is oxidized.
(b) The alkyl halide undergoes a two-electron reduction; the aluminum is oxidized.
(c) The organic compound (cumene) undergoes a two-electron oxidation; oxygen is reduced.
(d) Propylene undergoes a two-electron oxidation; bromine is reduced.

18. Let us first balance the half-reactions:

$$\text{Ph—CH}_3 + 2\text{H}_2\text{O} \longrightarrow \text{Ph—CO}_2\text{H} + 6\text{H}^+ + 6e^- \qquad (1)$$

$$4\text{H}^+ + \text{MnO}_4^- + 3e^- \longrightarrow \text{MnO}_2 + 2\text{H}_2\text{O} \qquad (2)$$

In order for the electrons lost to equal the electrons gained, two equivalents (which, in this case, means two moles) of MnO_4^- are required.

19. (a) Oxidation of the corresponding primary alcohol by virtually any of the usual methods — permanganate, chromic acid, or nitric acid — would work. We'll use permanganate.

$$(\text{CH}_3)_2\text{CHCH}_2\text{CH}_2\text{CH}_2\text{CH}_2\text{OH} \xrightarrow{\text{KMnO}_4} (\text{CH}_3)_2\text{CHCH}_2\text{CH}_2\text{CH}_2\text{CO}_2\text{H}$$

(b) Since this is a ketone, we'll want to avoid permanganate, which oxidizes ketones further. Since ketones are formed from secondary alcohols, we'll also reject nitric acid, which is selective for primary alcohols. A Cr(VI) reagent is the proper choice:

$$\text{CH}_3\text{CH}_2\overset{\overset{\text{OH}}{|}}{\text{C}}\text{HCH}_2\text{CH}_3 \xrightarrow{\text{CrO}_3\text{/pyridine}} \text{CH}_3\text{CH}_2\overset{\overset{\text{O}}{\|}}{\text{C}}\text{CH}_2\text{CH}_3$$

(Acidic chromate or dichromate would also work.)

(c) The carboxylic acid group is formed from a primary alcohol; however, the secondary alcohol group already in the molecule must not be oxidized. A reagent that is selective for primary alcohols would work — and that reagent is dilute nitric acid.

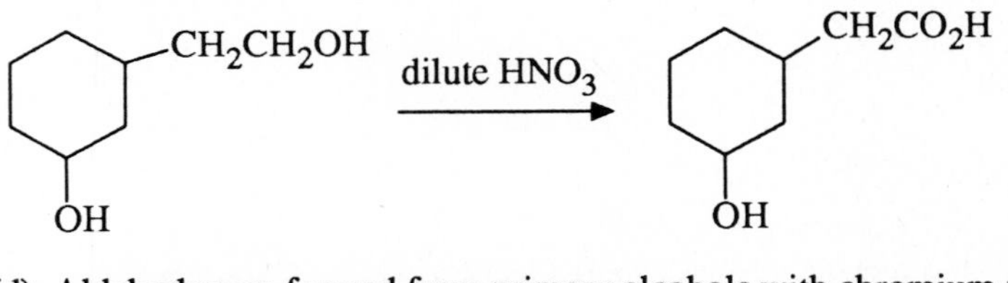

(d) Aldehydes are formed from primary alcohols with chromium trioxide in pyridine. This reagent does not oxidize the carbon-carbon double bond:

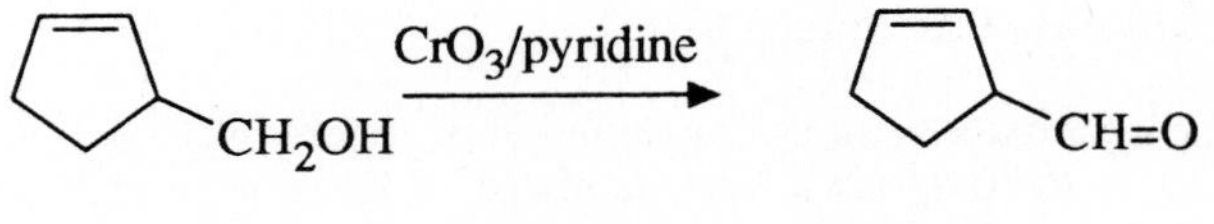

(e) Here we again have to form an aldehyde from an alcohol, a transformation that calls for Cr(VI) reagents. However, we must avoid acidic reagents because they will dehydrate the tertiary alcohol group. CrO_3 in pyridine is the logical choice:

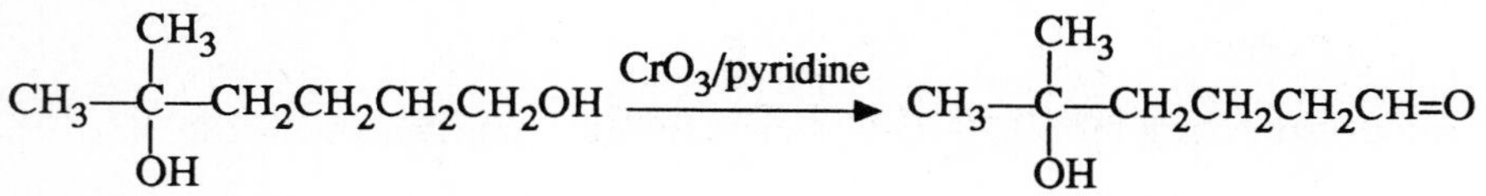

20. Nitric acid cleaves carbon-carbon bonds on either side of the —OH group:

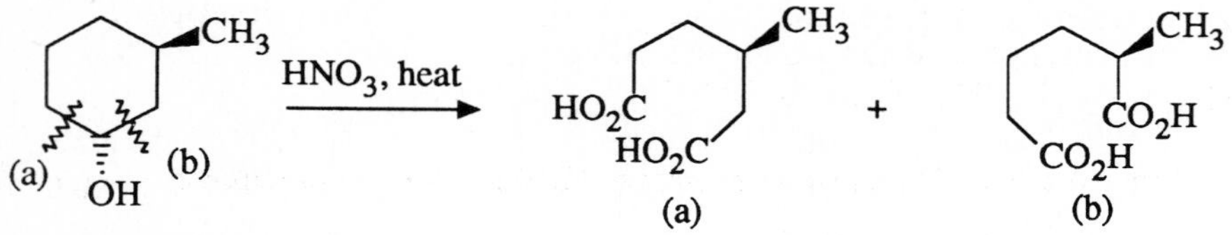

21. (a) $CH_2=O$ + $O=CH—CH_2Ph$

(b)

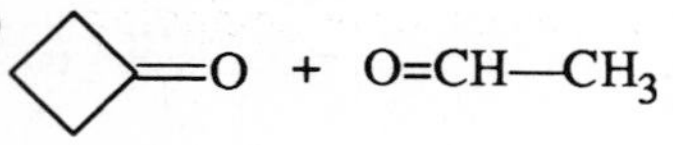

(c) and (d) Both compounds give the same product, $O=CH—CH_2CH_2CH_2CH_2—CH=O$. Even though the —OH groups in compound (d) are *trans*, they can assume a diequatorial arrangement in which they are close enough together that they can form the periodate ester intermediate.

22. The issue here is whether the two —OH groups are too far apart to form the periodate ester intermediate. The sure-fire way to tell is to draw conformational structures for the glycols:

(a)

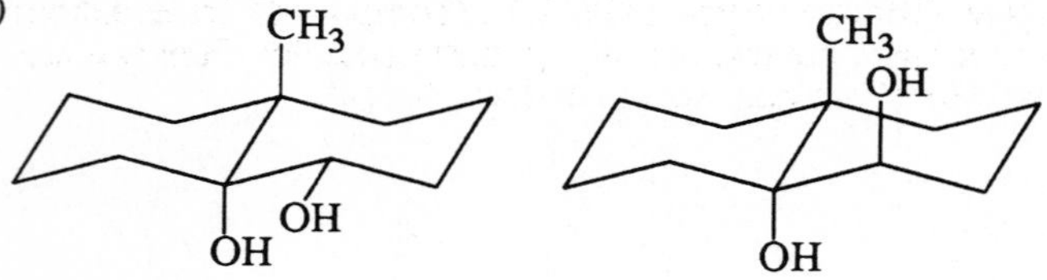

A   B

In compound B, the —OH groups are *anti*, and therefore are too far apart to form the periodate ester.

(b) The *t*-butyl group must occupy an equatorial position because of its size. This constraint fixes the positions of the —OH groups.

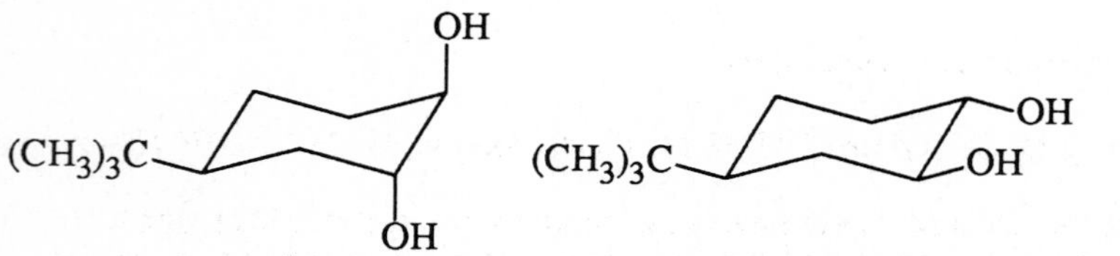

A   B

In compound A the —OH groups are too far apart to form the periodate ester.

If you cannot see why the two compounds cited above or the example on page 393 of the text are unable to form periodate esters, use your models to try to construct a five-membered ring containing the diaxial —OH groups.

23. Using the mechanism of NAD^+-promoted oxidation of ethanol as a cue, we can imagine that a hydride ion is removed by the triphenyl cation:

$$OH$$
$$CH_3\overset{|}{\underset{|}{C}}(CH_2)_4CH_3 \longrightarrow \left[\begin{array}{ccc} \overset{..}{\underset{}{:}}O-H & & \overset{+}{:}O\overset{\curvearrowright}{}H \\ CH_3\overset{|}{\underset{+}{C}}(CH_2)_4CH_3 & \longleftrightarrow & CH_3\overset{||}{C}(CH_2)_4CH_3 \end{array} \right] \begin{array}{c} {}^-BF_4 \\ \xrightarrow{} \\ -H^+ \end{array}$$
$$H$$
$$\overset{\searrow}{{}^+CPh_3} \qquad\qquad\qquad + \quad H-CPh_3$$

$$\overset{:O:}{\overset{||}{CH_3C(CH_2)_4CH_3}} \ + \ H^+ \ {}^-BF_4$$

Notice that the first step is removal of *a hydrogen with its bonding electron pair* — not removal of a proton.

24. In all cases, we use the result that the hydrogen delivered to acetaldehyde becomes the pro-(R)-hydrogen of ethanol, and that the hydrogen delivered from NADH is the one above the plane of the page. This follows from Eqs. 10.58 and 10.59 and the principle of microscopic reversibility: If the forward reaction has a given mechanism (including stereochemistry), then a reverse reaction has the same mechanism (including stereochemistry) in reverse.

(a)   (b) and (c)   (d)

$$\begin{array}{c} D \\ CH_3 \overline{|} OH \\ H \end{array} \qquad\qquad \begin{array}{c} H \\ CH_3 \overline{|} OH \\ D \end{array} \qquad\qquad \begin{array}{c} CH_3-CD_2-OH \\ \text{(achiral)} \end{array}$$

25. It is important in this exercise to use models, at least at first. Build a model in which one of the two connectively equivalent groups has a different color; then build another model in which the colors of these two groups are reversed. Now view your models as different compounds. If the compounds are enantiomers, the two groups are enantiotopic; if they are diastereomers, the two groups are diastereotopic; if the two are identical, the two groups are homotopic. We'll illustrate this process in detail for (a).

(a)

each connectively equivalent
group marked in turn (circle)

This shows that the two indicated hydrogens are *enantiotopic*.

(b) Don't forget that we always relate groups in *pairs*. H^a, H^b are diastereotopic; H^a, H^c and H^b, H^c are connectively nonequivalent.
(c) The two fluorines are diastereotopic. (Notice that the molecule contains an asymmetric carbon.)
(d) The two protons are diastereotopic. However, over time, the two protons become equivalent because of the chair–chair interconversion.

(e) Again, we relate groups in pairs. The relationships here are particularly easy to see in Fischer projections.

CH$_3$ ... CH$_3$ — enantiomers; the circled hydrogens are enantiotopic

CH$_3$ ... CH$_3$ — rotation 180° in the plane of the page shows that the structures are enantiomers; the circled hydrogens are enantiotopic

CH$_3$ ... CH$_3$ — rotation 180° in the plane of the page shows that the structures are identical; the circled hydrogens are homotopic.

(f) H^a and H^b are diastereotopic; H^c and H^d are diastereotopic; H^a and H^c are enantiotopic; H^b and H^d are enantiotopic; H^a and H^d are diastereotopic; H^b and H^c are diastereotopic; C2 and C4 are enantiotopic.

➤ The enantiotopicity of C2 and C4 is important in biology. When you study biochemistry, you will learn that one carbon is the preferred site of reaction in the citric acid cycle, or Krebs cycle. That is, a chiral enzyme can differentiate between the enantiotopic branches of citrate.

26. They are diastereotopic. That is, performing an imaginary replacement of each in turn gives diastereomers. (There are asymmetric carbons in the R-group; were this R-group not chiral, the two Hs would be enantiotopic.)

27. The relevant half-reaction is

$$R{-}\overset{..}{\underset{..}{S}}H + 3H_2O \rightarrow RSO_3H + 6H^+ + 6e^-$$

Hence, the reaction is a six-electron oxidation. (We could reach the same conclusion by applying the oxidation-number formalism to sulfur; the oxidation number of sulfur in the starting material is -1, and in the product is $+5$, for a change of $+6$.)

28. The importance of base suggests that thiolate anions are involved in the reaction; and, indeed, they are much better nucleophiles than neutral thiols:

$$C_2H_5\overset{..}{\underset{..}{S}}{-}H \; + \; {}^-{:}\overset{..}{O}C_2H_5 \longrightarrow C_2H_5\overset{..}{\underset{..}{S}}{:}^- \; + \; C_2H_5\overset{..}{O}H \tag{1}$$

$$C_2H_5\overset{..}{\underset{..}{S}}{:}^- \quad \underset{\overset{|}{C_3H_7}}{S}{-}S{-}C_3H_7 \longrightarrow C_2H_5\overset{..}{\underset{..}{S}}{-}S{-}C_3H_7 + {}^-{:}\overset{..}{\underset{..}{S}}{-}C_3H_7 \tag{2}$$

If we assume that reaction (2) is bimolecular, then its rate, like that of more conventional S$_N$2 reactions, should be increased by increasing the concentration of the nucleophile. Ethoxide increases the nucleophile concentration by reaction (1), and thus increases the rate of reaction (2) and other similar reactions.

29. (a) We know that we can form hydrocarbons from alkyl halides by protonolysis of the corresponding Grignard reagents:

$$CH_3(CH_2)_4CH_2Br \xrightarrow{Mg} CH_3(CH_2)_4CH_2MgBr \xrightarrow{H_3O^+} CH_3(CH_2)_4CH_3$$

And primary alkyl halides are formed from primary alcohols with concentrated HBr:

$$CH_3(CH_2)_4CH_2OH \xrightarrow{HBr} CH_3(CH_2)_4CH_2Br$$

(b) 2-Methyl-3-pentanol could be formed from an alkene by hydroboration-oxidation:

$$CH_3CH_2CH=C\begin{smallmatrix}CH_3\\CH_3\end{smallmatrix} \xrightarrow[\text{2) } H_2O_2/OH^-]{\text{1) } B_2H_6} CH_3CH_2\overset{\overset{\text{OH}}{|}}{CH}-CH\begin{smallmatrix}CH_3\\CH_3\end{smallmatrix}$$

And the alkene could be formed from the starting alcohol by dehydration:

$$CH_3CH_2CH_2\overset{\overset{\text{OH}}{|}}{\underset{\underset{CH_3}{|}}{C}}CH_3 \xrightarrow[-H_2O]{H_2SO_4} CH_3CH_2CH=C\begin{smallmatrix}CH_3\\CH_3\end{smallmatrix}$$

(c) Working backwards from the target:

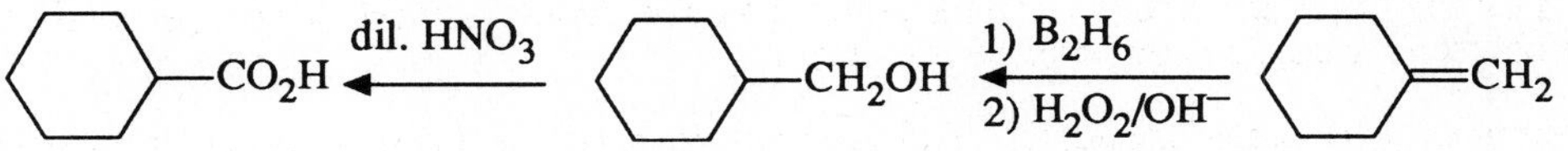

30. This is an S_N2 reaction; hence, it proceeds with inversion of stereochemistry. One limitation of this reaction is that, like all S_N2 reactions, it is restricted to primary and a few secondary alkyl halides. The reasons for both of these answers has to do with the mechanism of the reaction. In the mechanism, the nucleophile attacks the alkyl halide from the back side — thus the inversion. When the nucleophile approaches, branching in the alkyl halide restricts access of the nucleophile to the α-carbon; this is the reason for the restriction on alkyl halide structure.

Solutions to Additional Problems

31. For simplicity, we'll write the $CH_3CH_2CH_2CH_2$— group as R—.

    (a) R—Br   (b) $CH_3CH_2CH_2CO_2H$ (c) Protonation: R—$\overset{+}{O}H_2$ (d) $CH_3CH_2CH_2CH=O$

    (e) R—$\ddot{O}$:⁻ Na⁺ + H_2 (f) R—OTs   (g) In this case, the Grignard reagent acts as a strong base and simply undergoes protonolysis; the products are $CH_3CH_2CH_3$ and R—$\ddot{O}$:⁻ ⁺MgBr.

    (h) R—Cl   (i) R—MgBr   (j) $CH_3CH_2CH=CH_2$ + $(CH_3)_3C$—OH + KBr

    (k)

    $$\underset{CH_3CH_2\overset{\overset{\displaystyle OH}{|}}{C}H-\overset{\overset{\displaystyle OH}{|}}{C}H_2}{}$$

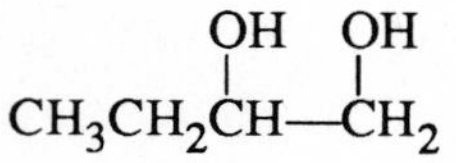

32. For simplicity, we'll write the $(CH_3)_3C$— group as R—.

    (a) R—Br   (b) No reaction; tertiary alcohols are inert to mild oxidizing conditions.

    (c) $(CH_3)_2C=CH_2 + H_2O$ (d) No reaction   (e) R—$\ddot{O}$:⁻ K⁺ + H_2 (f) R—OMs

    (g) $(CH_3)_2C=CH_2 + Na^+$ ⁻OMs + H_2O (h) $(CH_3)_2C=CH_2$ + R—OH + KBr

    (i)   (j) A pinacol rearrangement: $(CH_3)_2CH$—CH=O + H_2O

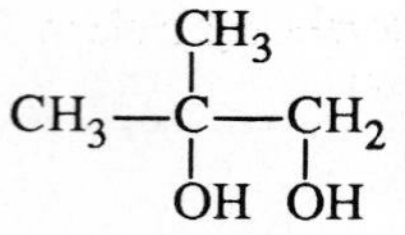

    $$CH_3-\overset{\overset{\displaystyle CH_3}{|}}{\underset{\underset{\displaystyle OH}{|}}{C}}-\overset{}{\underset{\underset{\displaystyle OH}{|}}{C}}H_2$$

    (k) $(CH_3)_2C=O$ + $CH_2=O$

33. (a) $(CH_3CH_2)_3C$—OH

    (b)

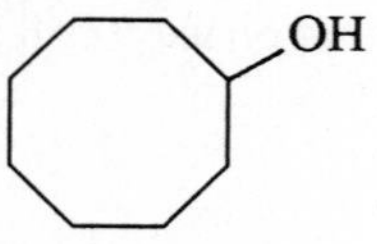

    (c)
    $$Ph-\overset{\overset{\displaystyle OH}{|}}{C}H-CH_2-Ph$$

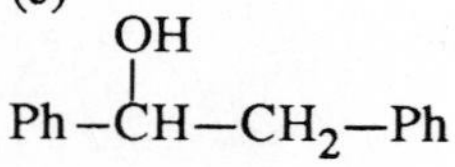

    (d)

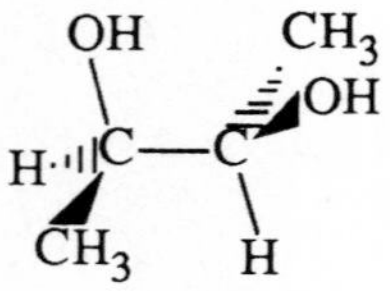

      or its enantiomer

    (e) The stereoisomeric 4-methyl-1-cyclohexanols:

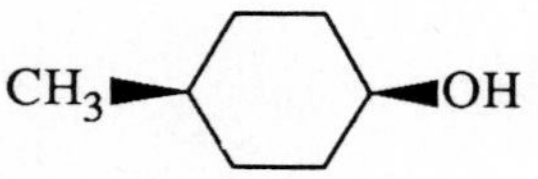

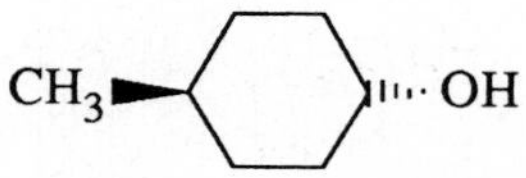

(f) Ozonolysis of 3,6-dimethyl-4-octene:

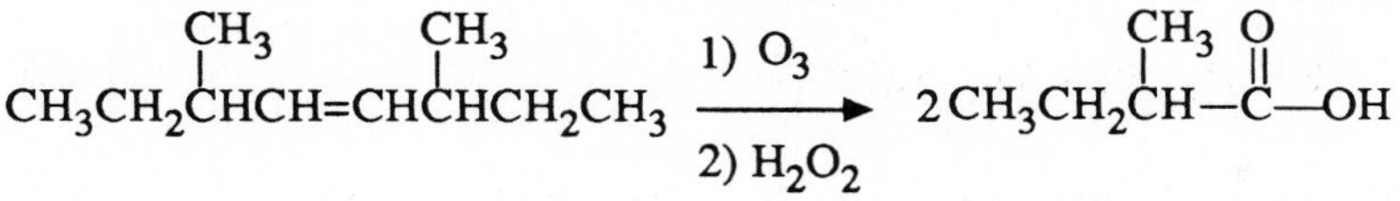

$$CH_3CH_2\overset{\overset{\displaystyle CH_3}{|}}{C}HCH=CH\overset{\overset{\displaystyle CH_3}{|}}{C}HCH_2CH_3 \quad \xrightarrow[\text{2) } H_2O_2]{\text{1) } O_3} \quad 2\,CH_3CH_2\overset{\overset{\displaystyle CH_3}{|}}{C}H-\overset{\overset{\displaystyle O}{\|}}{C}-OH$$

The alcohol that would give the same product on oxidation is 2-methyl-1-butanol:

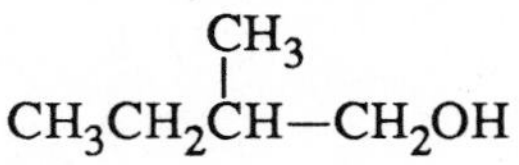

$$CH_3CH_2\overset{\overset{\displaystyle CH_3}{|}}{C}H-CH_2OH$$

(g)

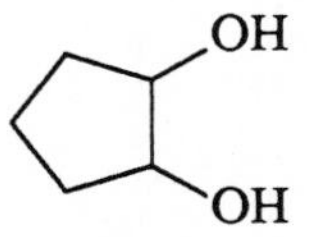

1,2-cyclopentanediol

34. This compound is derived from nitric acid (H—O—NO$_2$) and glycerol:

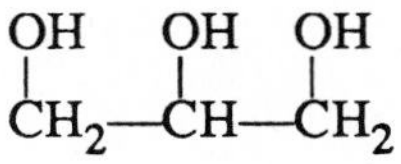

$$\overset{\overset{\displaystyle OH}{|}}{C}H_2-\overset{\overset{\displaystyle OH}{|}}{C}H-\overset{\overset{\displaystyle OH}{|}}{C}H_2$$

This compound is commonly called *nitroglycerin.*

35. If two groups are either homotopic, enantiotopic, or diastereotopic, they are connectively equivalent. Thus, in each of the structures below, fluorines with the same letter are connectively equivalent.

(a)

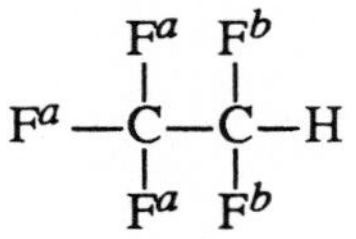

$$F^a-\overset{\overset{\displaystyle F^a}{|}}{\underset{\underset{\displaystyle F^a}{|}}{C}}-\overset{\overset{\displaystyle F^b}{|}}{\underset{\underset{\displaystyle F^b}{|}}{C}}-H$$

The fluorines F^a are homotopic; the fluorines F^b are enantiotopic; F^a and F^b are connectively nonequivalent.

(b)

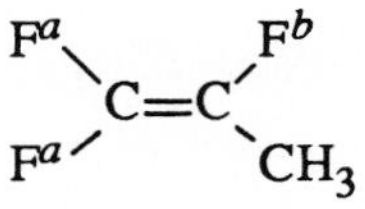

Fluorines F^a are diastereotopic; fluorine F^b is connectively nonequivalent to fluorines F^a.

(c)

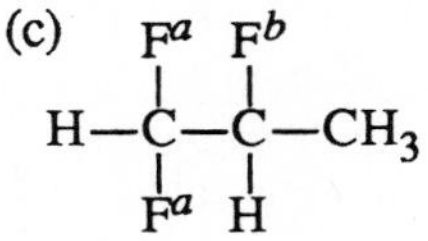

$$H-\overset{\overset{\displaystyle F^a}{|}}{\underset{\underset{\displaystyle F^a}{|}}{C}}-\overset{\overset{\displaystyle F^b}{|}}{\underset{\underset{\displaystyle H}{|}}{C}}-CH_3$$

Fluorines F^a are diastereotopic; fluorines F^a and F^b are connectively nonequivalent.

36. The oxygen of the alcohol is protonated, and water is lost to give the *t*-butyl cation.

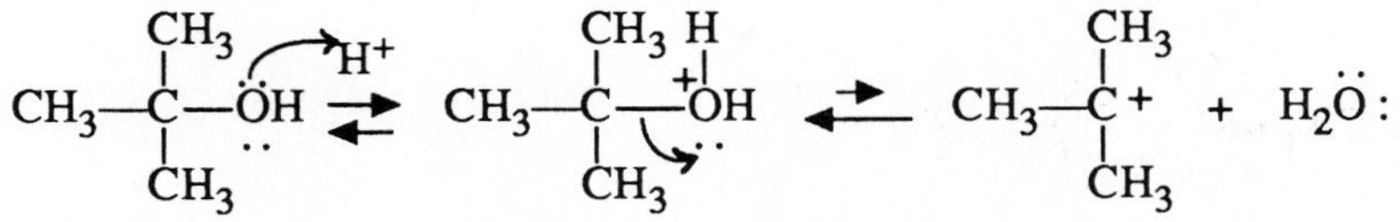

This water becomes part of the large pool of labeled water. When isotopically enriched water reattacks the carbocation to re-form *t*-butyl alcohol, the alcohol becomes labeled. This process occurs simply by the reverse of the above equation, with isotopic water replacing ordinary water.

37. (a) A two-electron reduction.
     (b) Neither an oxidation nor a reduction.
     (c) A two-electron oxidation.
     (d) Neither an oxidation nor a reduction.
     (e) A two-electron oxidation.

38. We'll work backward from the target compound in each case.

(a)

$$CH_3CHCH_2CH_2CH_3 \xleftarrow{D_2O} \xleftarrow{\text{Mg, ether}} CH_3CHCH_2CH_2CH_3 \xleftarrow{\text{HBr}} CH_2=CH-CH_2CH_2CH_3 \longleftarrow$$

$$\underset{D}{|} \qquad\qquad\qquad\qquad\qquad \underset{Br}{|}$$

$$HO-CH_2CH_2CH_2CH_2CH_3 \xrightarrow{\text{TsCl, pyridine}} TsO-CH_2CH_2CH_2CH_2CH_3 \xrightarrow{K^+ \, (CH_3)_3C-O^-}$$

(b)

$$D-(CH_2)_4CH_3 \xleftarrow{D_2O} \xleftarrow{\text{Mg, ether}} Br-(CH_2)_4CH_3 \xleftarrow{\text{HBr}} HO-(CH_2)_4CH_3$$

(c)

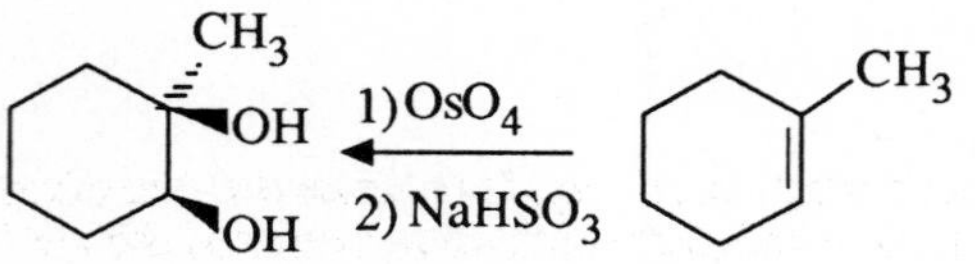

$$\xleftarrow{\substack{1)\,OsO_4 \\ 2)\,NaHSO_3}}$$

(d)

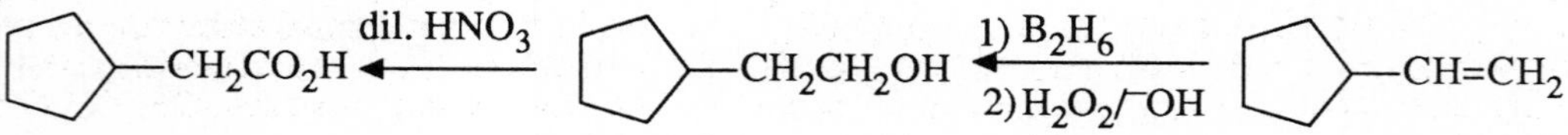

$$\xleftarrow{\text{dil. HNO}_3} \qquad \xleftarrow{\substack{1)\,B_2H_6 \\ 2)\,H_2O_2/^-OH}}$$

(e)

$$\xleftarrow{\substack{1)\,O_3 \\ 2)\,H_2O_2}}$$

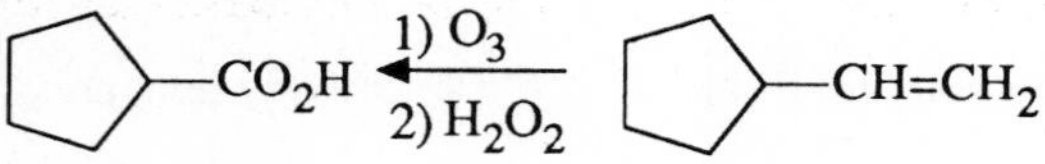

(f) This compound can be obtained by CrO₃/pyridine oxidation of the primary alcohol prepared in part (d):

(g)

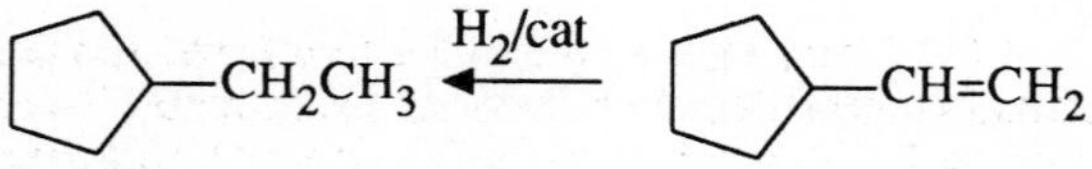

$$\xleftarrow{\text{H}_2/\text{cat}}$$

(h) Notice that a rearrangement is required in this reaction. One rearrangement we have studied that gives ketone products is the *pinacol rearrangement*. In fact, preparation of the target compound is shown in Eq. 10.8. This problem, then, reduces to the preparation of pinacol from the required starting material.

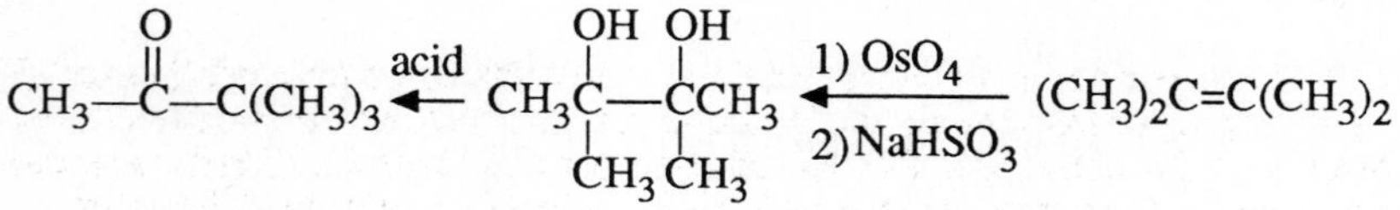

$$\underset{\underset{}{\overset{\overset{O}{\|}}{}}}{CH_3-C-C(CH_3)_3} \xleftarrow{\text{acid}} \underset{\underset{CH_3\,CH_3}{|\quad|}}{\overset{\overset{OH\ OH}{|\quad|}}{CH_3C-CCH_3}} \xleftarrow{\substack{1)\,OsO_4 \\ 2)\,NaHSO_3}} (CH_3)_2C=C(CH_3)_2$$

(i) From the hint, we can make this compound by an S_N2 reaction of cyanide ion with an alkyl halide or tosylate.

$$CH_3CH_2CH_2CH_2\!-\!CN \xleftarrow[\text{DMSO}]{Na^+ \ ^-CN} CH_3CH_2CH_2CH_2\!-\!Br \xleftarrow{\text{HBr, peroxides}} CH_3CH_2CH\!=\!CH_2$$

with concd HBr and
$$\downarrow \begin{array}{l} 1)\ B_2H_6 \\ 2)\ H_2O_2/ ^-OH \end{array}$$
$$CH_3CH_2CH_2CH_2\!-\!OH$$

We could also have prepared the tosylate or mesylate from the alcohol and allowed it to react with cyanide ion.

39. Before answering this question, we have to know what reaction we're considering. Since ethoxide ion is a good nucleophile, and ethyl mesylate reacts much like ethyl bromide, we expect that the reaction in question is an S_N2 reaction in which the sulfonate ester is displaced from the ethyl group by ethoxide:

$$CH_3CH_2\!-\!\overset{..}{\underset{..}{O}}SO_2CH_3 \longrightarrow CH_3CH_2\!-\!\overset{..}{O}\!-\!CH_2CH_3 \ + \ ^-\!:\!\overset{..}{\underset{..}{O}}SO_2CH_3$$

$$^-\!:\!\overset{..}{\underset{..}{O}}\!-\!CH_2CH_3$$

Now we have to decide which of the two given compounds reacts more rapidly. Since the two compounds *differ only in their leaving groups*, the problem reduces to determining which compound has the best leaving group. What makes a good leaving group? Recall from Chapter 9 that the best leaving groups in displacement reactions are the ones that give the weakest bases. The problem then becomes: Which is the weaker base, the mesylate ion, $^-OSO_2CH_3$, or the triflate ion, $^-OSO_2CF_3$? We should expect inductive effects to operate in these anions much as they do in alkoxide anions (see Sec. 8.6B, text page 301). Since fluorine stabilizes anions, then the triflate anion is the weaker base, just as $CF_3CH_2O^-$ is a weaker base than $CH_3CH_2O^-$. We thus arrive at the conclusion that ethyl triflate is much more reactive.

40. Answering this question is not difficult once we have a balanced reaction. Using the method of half-reactions:

$$6e^- + 14H^+ + Cr_2O_7^{2-} \longrightarrow Cr^{3+} + 7H_2O$$

$$\overset{\displaystyle OH}{\underset{\displaystyle |}{CH_3\!-\!CH}}\!-\!(CH_2)_3CH_3 \longrightarrow \overset{\displaystyle O}{\overset{\displaystyle ||}{CH_3\!-\!C}}\!-\!(CH_2)_3CH_3 \ + \ 2H^+ \ + \ 2e^-$$

Electrons lost ($2e^-$) are in balance with electrons gained ($6e^-$) when three moles of alcohol are used per mole of dichromate. That is, for every mole of alcohol oxidized, we need one-third mole of dichromate. The moles of 2-heptanol in 10 g of this alcohol are $10/116.2 = 0.086$ mol. Thus, we need 0.0287 mole of potassium dichromate (molecular weight = 294.2), or 8.44 g.

41. Since thiols and disulfides readily equilibrate to give a mixture of all possible thiols and disulfides (text pages 405-406, and Eq. 10.67), Stench has evidently obtained just such a complex mixture in which the desired compound is but a minor component.

42. Since compounds *C* and *D* give the same periodate oxidation product, they must be compounds (2) and (3). Since compound (2) is a *meso* compound, it cannot be optically active, and is therefore compound *D*. By process of elimination, then, compound *C* = compound (3). Since compound *B* gives a different periodate oxidation product, it must be compound (4), because it is the only vicinal glycol remaining. Therefore, compound (1) is compound *A*.

43. Preliminary information: compound *A* is an alkene, and thus compound *B* is an alcohol. Since compound *B* can be oxidized to a carboxylic acid, it is a *primary* alcohol. The information leading us to a structure is the oxidation data. Oxidation of 3-hexanol with chromic acid gives 3-hexanone:

$$\underset{\text{OH}}{\overset{\underset{|}{}}{CH_3CH_2CHCH_2CH_2CH_3}} \xrightarrow{\text{chromic acid}} \underset{\overset{\overset{\text{O}}{\|}}{}}{CH_3CH_2CCH_2CH_2CH_3}$$

compound *D*

This, we are told, is an ozonolysis product of alkene *A*. Since this compound has one fewer carbon than alkene *A*, it follows that *A* can only be

$$\underset{\overset{\overset{\text{CH}_2}{\|}}{}}{CH_3CH_2CCH_2CH_2CH_3}$$

The structures of the remaining compounds follow from the reactions:

$$\underset{\overset{|}{}}{\overset{\text{CH}_2\text{O}}{}}{CH_3CH_2CHCH_2CH_2CH_3} \qquad \underset{\overset{|}{}}{\overset{\text{CO}_2\text{H}}{}}{CH_3CH_2CHCH_2CH_2CH_3}$$

     compound *B*   compound *C*

44. (a) The first reaction forms a tosylate ester, which is then displaced by bromide ion to give the following alkyl halide:

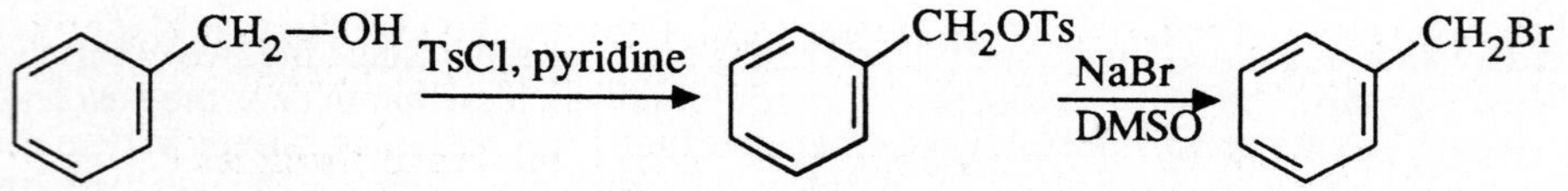

(b)

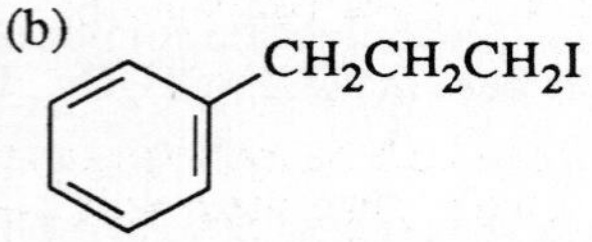

(c) The mercaptide anion, formed in the first reaction by ionization of the thiol, reacts with dimethyl sulfate to give the sulfide $(CH_3)_2CH—S—CH_3$.

(d)   (e)

$$\underset{\overset{|}{}}{\overset{\text{Br}}{}}{CH_3CHCH_2CH_2Ph}$$

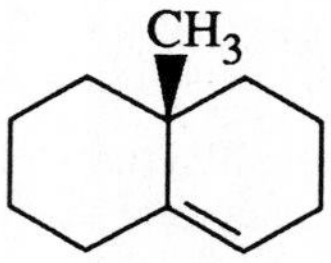

(f) In the first reaction, bromocyclohexane is formed; in the second, an E2 reaction ensues to give cyclohexene:

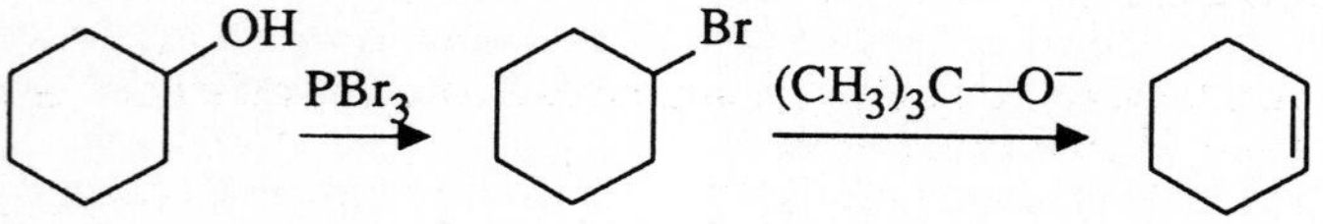

(g) The first step is formation of a glycol; in the second step, the primary alcohol group is oxidized by nitric acid, leaving the secondary alcohol unaffected.

$$(CH_3)_2CHCH=CH_2 \xrightarrow[\text{2) NaHSO}_3]{\text{1) OsO}_4} (CH_3)_2CH\underset{\overset{|}{}}{\overset{\text{OH}}{C}}H—CH_2OH \xrightarrow{\text{HNO}_3} (CH_3)_2CH\underset{\overset{|}{}}{\overset{\text{OH}}{C}}H—CO_2H$$

(h) In this case, the reagents for two successive reactions are present together in the reaction mixture. The OsO_4 brings about the formation of a glycol; the resulting glycol is then cleaved by periodate to give a dialdehyde.

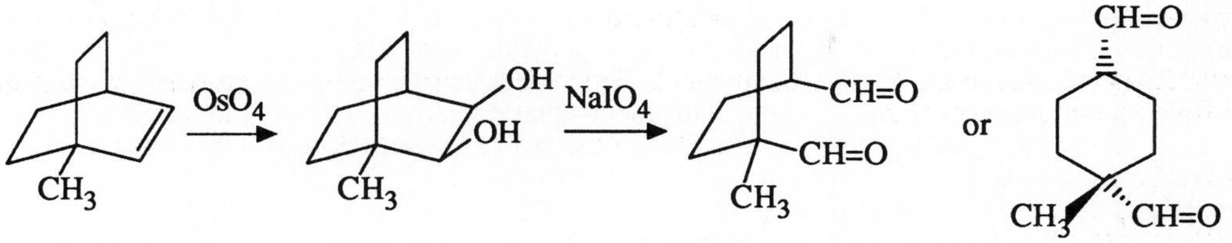

(i) This reaction is a variation of the pinacol rearrangement. Silver promotes rapid ionization of the halide to give exactly the same carbocation that is involved in the rearrangement of pinacol (see last structure, Eq. 10.9). From that point on, the reaction follows the course of the pinacol rearrangement.

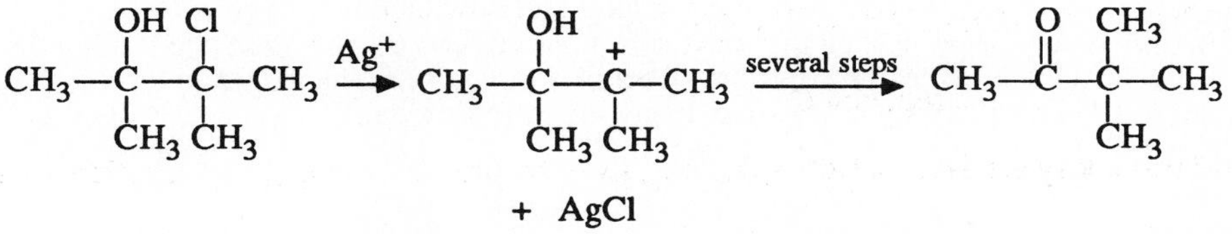

(Notice that the carbocation can be generated in two different ways: from the alkyl halide, as in this problem, and from pinacol in acid. However it is formed, it ultimately reacts to give the same product.)

(j) Like Mr. Stench Thiall in Problem 41, we get a mixture of all possible thiols and disulfides:

$(CH_3)_2CHCH_2CH_2S$—SC_2H_5, $(CH_3)_2CHCH_2CH_2S$—$SCH_2CH_2CH(CH_3)_2$, C_2H_5SH, and starting materials.

45. The structural information we have in this problem tells us that alkenes *B* and *C* can both be hydrogenated to give methylcyclohexane, and that both are chiral. Compound *A* is evidently an alcohol, and the reaction of its tosylate derivative with potassium *t*-butoxide is an elimination. Since the hydrogenation data show that compounds *B* and *C*, and by inference, compound *A*, contain cyclohexane rings, the ring completely accounts for the unsaturation number of compound *A*. Thus, compounds *B* and *C* contain a single double bond. It is not difficult to write the structures of *all* alkenes that would give methylcyclohexane on hydrogenation:

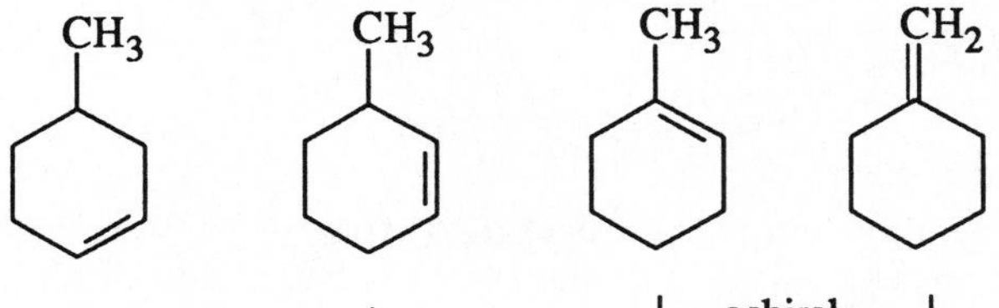

chiral (compounds *B* and *C*) — achiral (cannot be *B* and *C*)

A chiral alcohol whose tosylate would be eliminated to a mixture of compounds *B* and *C* is either *cis*- or *trans*-3-methyl-1-cyclohexanol. Either compound could be compound *A*.

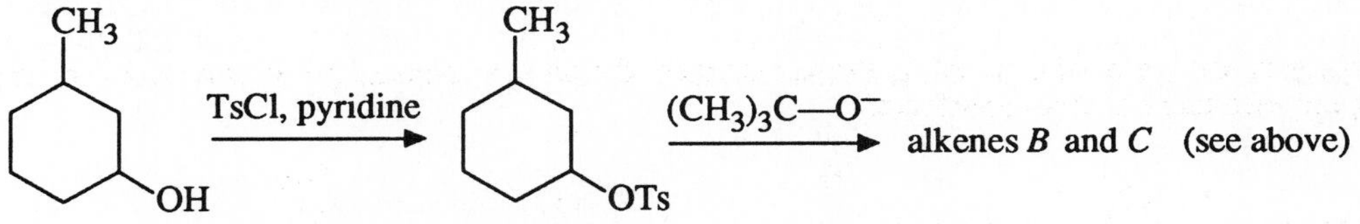

A

46. (a) The *primary deuterium isotope effect* indicates that transfer of the labeled hydrogen is the rate-determining step. This means that the step in which the chromate ester is eliminated, analogous to Eq. 10.39c, is the rate-determining step.

    (b) The experimental result with CrO_3 in pyridine indicates that there is a discrimination in favor of hydrogen removal rather than deuterium removal; hence, the product acetaldehyde (CH_3—CD=O) is largely deuterated. Because of the isotope effect considered in part (a), CrO_3/pyridine removes a hydrogen much faster (about seven times faster) than it removes a deuterium. This means that deuterium is left in the product aldehyde. The isotope effect exists whether the hydrogen removed is in the pro-(R) or pro-(S) position, because CrO_3, an *achiral reagent*, cannot distinguish between enantiotopic hydrogens.
        In contrast, because alcohol dehydrogenase is chiral, it distinguishes between enantiotopic groups. That is, the enantiotopic hydrogens of ethanol are *chemically nonequivalent* in the presence of the chiral enzyme. The enzyme removes the pro-(R) "hydrogen," whether it is hydrogen or a deuterium. If there is an isotope effect in the enzyme-catalyzed reaction, it would show up only in the relative reaction rates of (R)-2-deuterioethanol and (S)-2-deuterioethanol, because in the former compound, D is removed, whereas in the latter, H is removed. The stereochemical discrimination between enantiotopic hydrogens by the enzyme is so complete that the isotope effect, if there is one, doesn't have an effect on which hydrogen is removed. To look at the situation more quantitatively, suppose that the enzyme removes a pro-(R) hydrogen one million times faster than it removes the pro-(S) hydrogen. An isotope effect of 7 in favor of a hydrogen in a pro-(S) position would not tilt the balance in favor of hydrogen removal to any measurable extent.

47. In the first reaction a rearrangement has occurred; hence, the reaction must take place by an S_N1 mechanism. Indeed, the very acidic conditions are precisely those that promote loss of the —OH group of the alcohol as water.

    In the first step of the second equation, the alcohol is converted into a tosylate. Displacement of the tosylate by bromide is carried out under conditions that favor an S_N2 reaction: a polar aprotic solvent. This displacement, like other S_N2 reactions, occurs without rearrangement.

48. The enzyme-catalyzed reaction is completely specific in a stereochemical sense. Since the (2S)-alcohol is formed in the forward reaction, only the (2S)-alcohol reacts in the reverse reaction, by microscopic reversibility. Hence, compound (c) is inert to fumarase, because it has the 2R configuration. Derivatives (a) and (b) do react, however. From the reaction given, we can see that the groups added are those that are on the left of the Fischer projection, one of which must be the —OH group at carbon-2. Hence, it follows that the groups lost in the reverse reaction are those on the left of the Fischer projection:

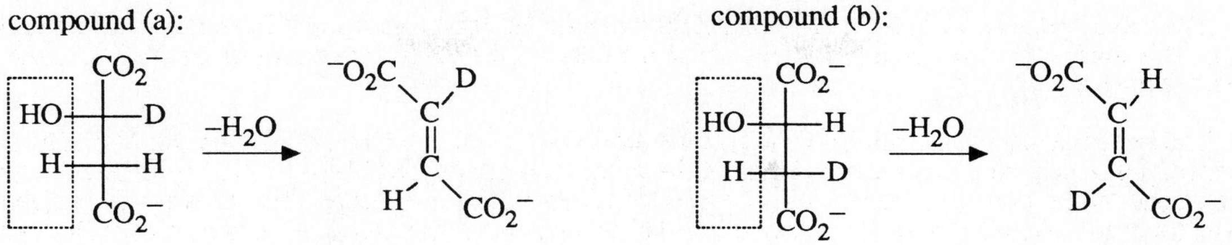

compound (a):   compound (b):

49. Unlike HBr, HCN is a rather weak acid ($pK_a = 9.4$), and it provides only a very low concentration of the nucleophilic cyanide ion because it is poorly ionized. In the absence of added acid, HCN is also not a strong enough acid to protonate the alcohol to any reasonable extent. Hence, the —OH group of the alcohol cannot act as a leaving group. With a very low nucleophile concentration and a poor leaving group, what chance is there for a reaction? None!

       Addition of acid to the reaction mixture will bring about the protonation of the alcohol. However, the same acid suppresses ionization of HCN, and reduces the concentration of cyanide ion even further. Hence, with no source of a good nucleophile, the reaction is doomed.

50. Loss of chloride in an S_N1 ionization affords a relatively stable carbocation, which can lose a proton to give acetophenone:

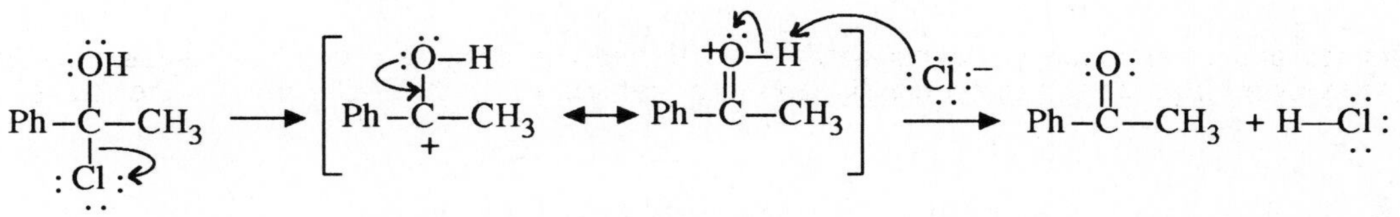

51. (a) This reaction involves protonation of the double bond, and rearrangement of the resulting carbocation by ring expansion.

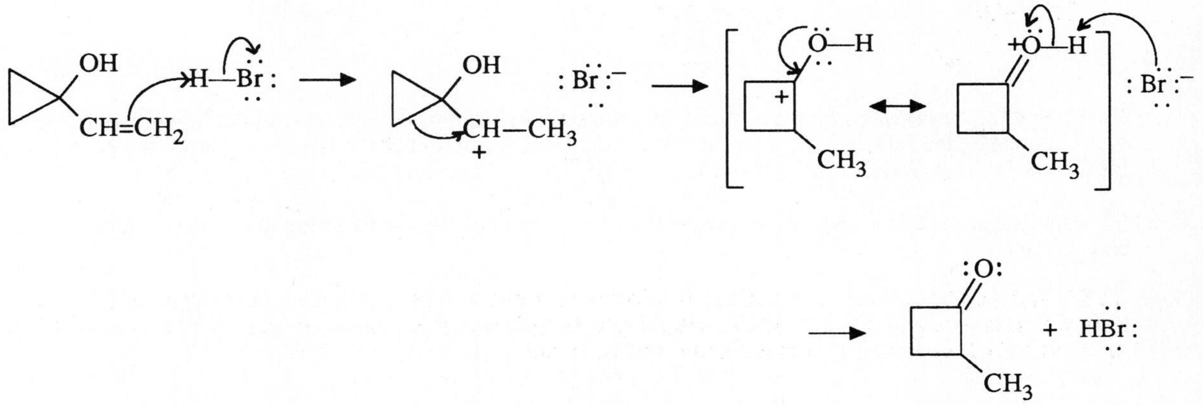

Why isn't the —OH group protonated? It probably is! But it is not lost as H_2O because a very unstable carbocation would be formed. (Cyclopropyl cations are unstable because they are very strained; their sp^2 hybridization demands a bond angle of 120°, whereas they are constrained to an angle of 60°.) In contrast, the pathway shown above involves a relatively stable carbocation and relieves some of the strain in the cyclopropane through the ring expansion.

(b) This is a pinacol rearrangement in which a ring expansion occurs.

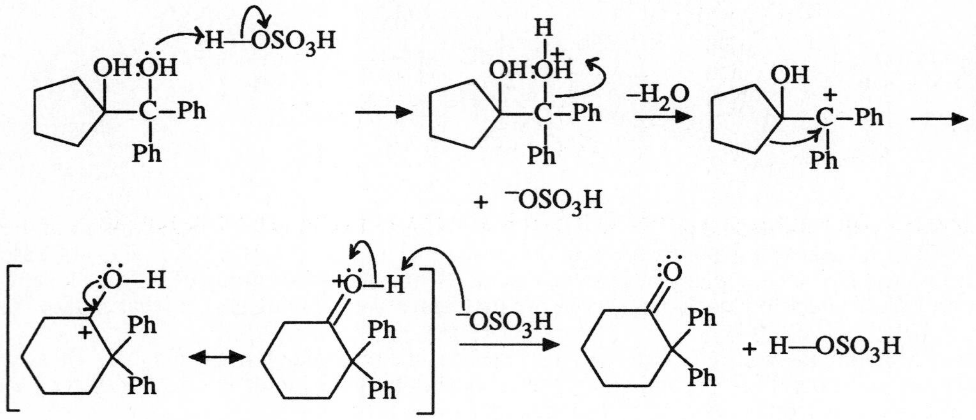

(c) The alcohol is protonated; water is lost to give a carbocation; and rearrangement by ring expansion takes place. The rearranged carbocation is captured by bromide ion.

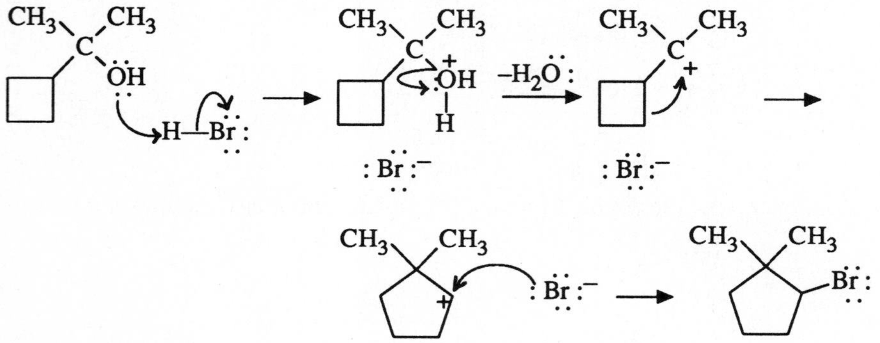

Notice that the carbocation rearrangement involves transformation of a tertiary carbocation into a secondary one. Evidently, the relief of angle strain that results from formation of the larger ring more than compensates for the energy required for this otherwise unfavorable transformation.

(d) The first step in formation of all products is protonation of the —OH group and loss of water to give a carbocation:

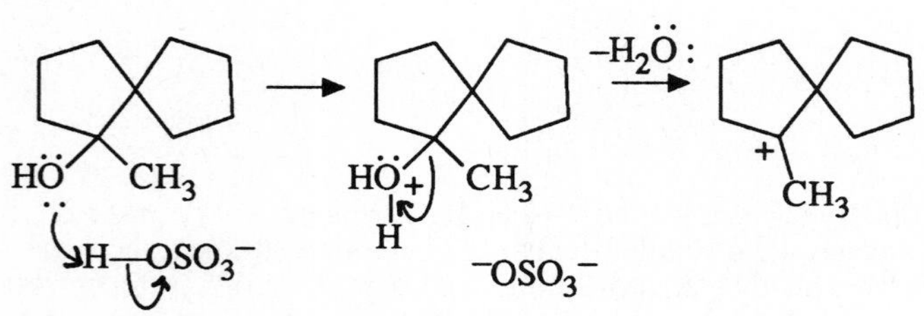

The carbocation can lose either of two β-protons to give the first two products. (We leave it to you to show this in detail; see Eq. 10.2a-c if necessary.) The remaining product comes from a rearrangement by ring expansion, followed by loss of a β-proton from the new carbocation.

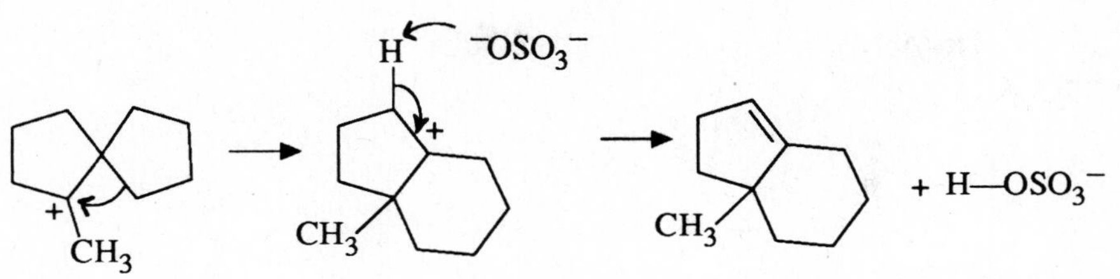

(Although the product alkene is drawn differently than it is in the text, it is the same compound.)

Chapter 11 / Chemistry of Ethers, Epoxides, and Sulfides

CHAPTER 11 TERMS

alkoxymercuration 11.1B
anchimeric assistance 11.6
episulfonium ion 11.6
epoxidation 11.2B
functional group transformation 11.8
halohydrin 11.2B
hydrolysis 11.4A
intermolecular reaction 11.6
intramolecular reaction 11.6

neighboring-group participation 11.6
oxonium salt 11.5A
peroxyacid 11.2A
peroxycarboxylic acid 11.2A
Raney nickel (RaNi) 11.3B
sulfone 11.7
sulfonium salt 11.5A
sulfoxide 11.7
Williamson ether synthesis 11.1A

CHAPTER 11 CONCEPTS

I. General Synthetic Concepts:

A. Neighboring-Group Participation:
1. The covalent involvement of neighboring groups in chemical reactions has been termed **neighboring-group participation** or **anchimeric assistance**.
2. A neighboring-group mechanism is:
   a) An intramolecular reaction.
   b) In competition with ordinary bimolecular mechanisms.
3. For a neighboring-group mechanism to operate, it must give a faster reaction than other competing mechanisms.
   a) An **intramolecular reaction** has a greater probability of occurring than an **intermolecular reaction**.
   b) The probability of an intramolecular reaction is balanced against the instability of the cyclic intermediate that is formed.
4. Neighboring-group participation in nucleophilic substitution reactions is common for cases involving three-, five-, and six-membered rings.

B. Organic Synthesis, Continued:
1. It is helpful to classify organic reactions into three fundamental types of operations:
   a) **Functional group transformations**.
   b) Control of stereochemistry.
   c) Formation of carbon-carbon bonds.
2. Most reactions represent combinations of these three fundamental operations.

CHAPTER 11 REACTIONS

I. Synthesis of Ethers, Epoxides, and Sulfides:

A. Williamson Ether Synthesis:

1. The **Williamson ether synthesis** is an example of the S_N2 reaction in which an ether (sulfide) is formed through displacement of a leaving group by an alkoxide (thiolate).

   a) Methyl, primary, and a few secondary halides or sulfonate esters react with alkoxides (thiolates) to give ethers (sulfides).

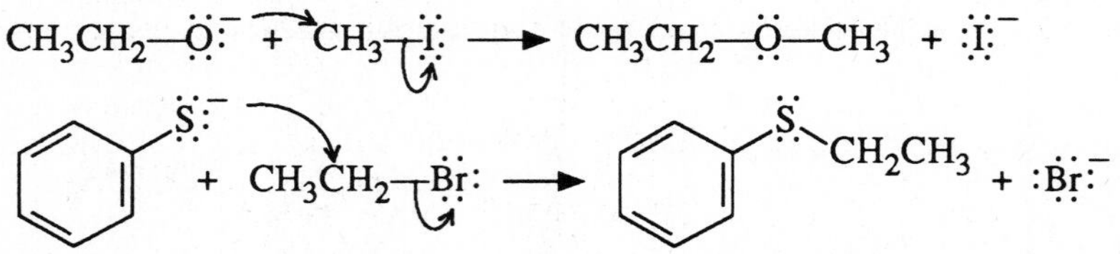

$$CH_3CH_2\overset{..}{\underset{..}{O}}{:}^- + CH_3\text{---}\overset{..}{\underset{..}{I}}{:} \longrightarrow CH_3CH_2\text{---}\overset{..}{\underset{..}{O}}\text{---}CH_3 + :\overset{..}{\underset{..}{I}}{:}^-$$

   b) Tertiary alkyl halides and most secondary alkyl halides *cannot* be used.

2. In principle there are *two different* Williamson syntheses for any ether with two different alkyl groups.

   a) The preferred synthesis is usually the one that involves the alkyl halide with the greater S_N2 reactivity.

   b) If one of the alkyl groups is tertiary, it should be derived from the alkoxide.

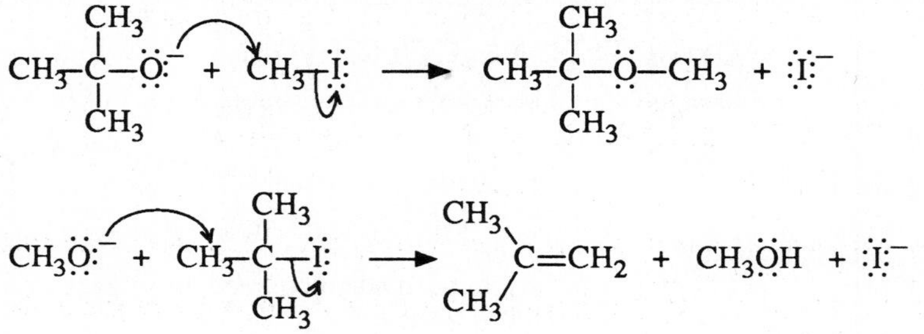

B. Alkoxymercuration-Reduction of Alkenes:

1. **Alkoxymercuration-reduction** is a variation of the oxymercuration-reduction reaction in which an alcohol is used as the solvent instead of water.

2. The mechanism of this reaction is completely analogous to the mechanism of oxymercuration.

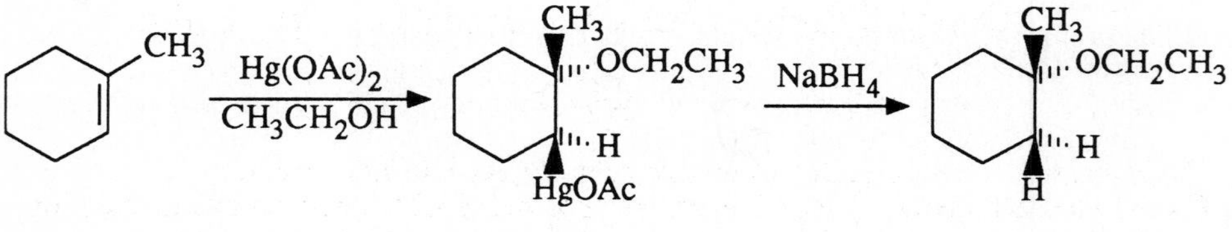

C. Synthesis of Epoxides with Peroxyacids:

1. Epoxides can be formed by the direct oxidation of alkenes using a **peroxycarboxylic acid (peroxyacid)**.

   a) A peroxyacid is a peroxide analog of a carboxylic acid.

   b) Many peroxyacids are unstable.

   c) *Meta*-chloroperoxybenzoic acid (MCPBA) is widely used for the synthesis of epoxides.

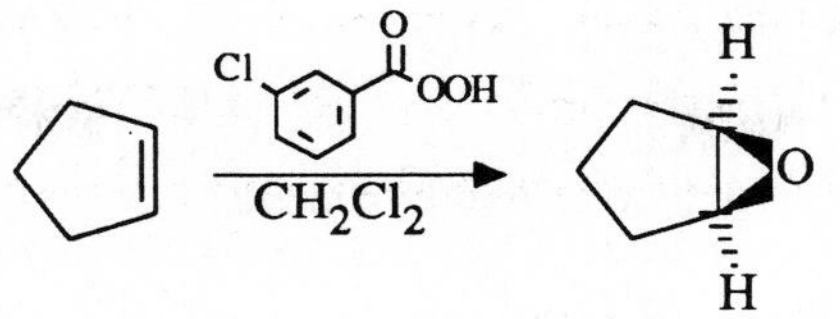

2. The formation of an epoxide with a peroxyacid is another example of electrophilic addition to alkenes.
    a) The electrophile is the —OH group of the peroxyacid.
    b) The O—O bond is very weak and easily broken.
    c) The oxygen is transferred to the alkene in a concerted fashion.
3. The mechanism is similar to that for formation of a bromonium ion.
4. The formation of epoxides with peroxyacids is a stereoselective reaction.
    a) The reaction proceeds with complete retention of the alkene stereochemistry.
    b) The oxygen from the peroxyacid must bond to both alkene carbons at the same face.

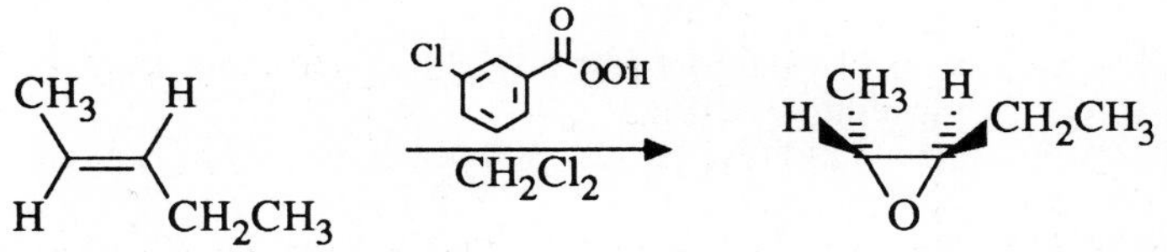

D. Synthesis of Epoxides by Cyclization of Halohydrins:
    1. Epoxides can be synthesized by the treatment of **halohydrins** with base.
        a) This reaction is an intramolecular variation of the Williamson ether synthesis.
        b) The alkoxide anion is formed reversibly by reaction of the alcohol with NaOH.
        c) The alkoxide displaces the halide ion from the neighboring carbon.

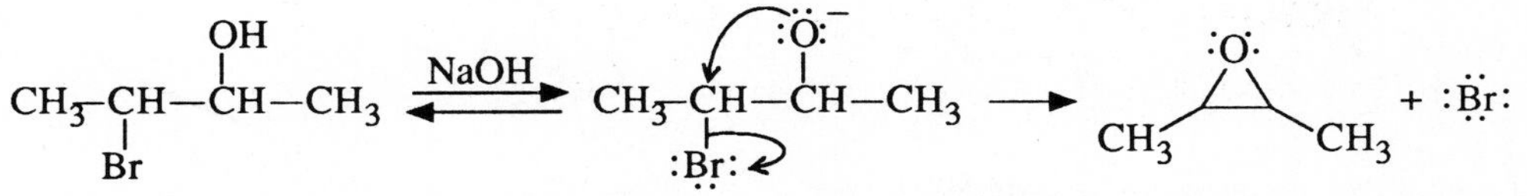

    2. Like other S_N2 reactions, this reaction takes place by backside attack of the nucleophilic oxygen anion at the halide-bearing carbon.
    3. An *anti* relationship between the alkoxide oxygen and the leaving halogen in the transition state of the reaction is required.
        a) This relationship can be achieved through a simple bond rotation for noncyclic halohydrins.
        b) Halohydrins derived from cyclic compounds *must* be able to assume the required *anti* relationship through a conformational change.

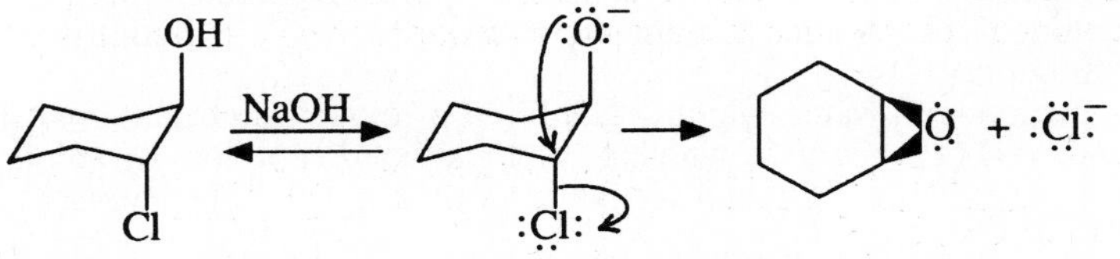

    4. The formation of epoxides from halohydrins is a stereoselective reaction.
    5. The net reaction, alkene → bromohydrin → epoxide, proceeds with complete retention of the alkene stereochemistry.
        a) Bromohydrin formation is an *anti* addition that involves a stereochemical inversion of configuration.
        b) Epoxide formation from the bromohydrin involves a second inversion of configuration.
        c) The two inversions have the same overall effect as retention.

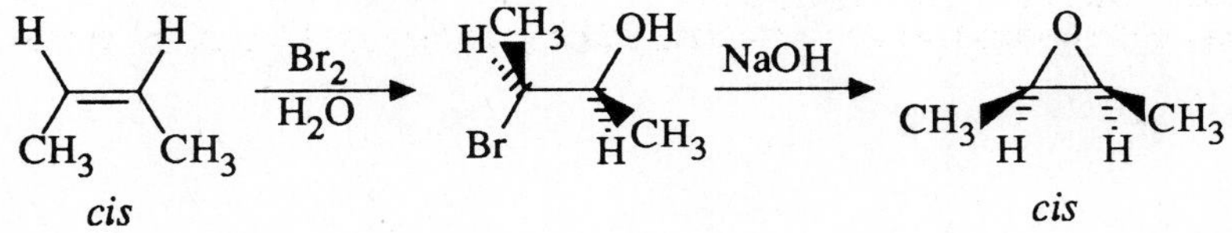

II. Reactions of Ethers, Epoxides, and Sulfides:

A. <u>Cleavage of Ethers</u>:
    1. The ether linkage is relatively inert to many reagents.
    2. High concentrations of strong acids (HI or HBr) promote the cleavage of the ether linkage to give
        alcohols and alkyl halides.
        a) The mechanism of this reaction involves protonation of the ether oxygen.
            (1) Attack of the halide ion occurs by the S_N2 mechanism on the more reactive alkyl group if
                the only alkyl groups in the ether are methyl or primary.

            (2) Cleavage occurs by the S_N1 pathway if the protonated ether can cleave to give a relatively
                stable carbocation.
            (3) The cleavage reactions of tertiary ethers are generally faster and occur at lower acid
                concentrations.
        b) The alcohols initially formed in the ether cleavage reaction can react further to give alkyl halides.

B. <u>Cleavage of Sulfides by Raney Nickel</u>:
    1. Sulfides, disulfides, and even some thiols are readily cleaved by hydrogenation over **Raney nickel** (a
        finely divided nickel catalyst prepared from a nickel-aluminum alloy).
    2. The sulfur is completely removed from the molecule and is replaced by two hydrogen atoms derived
        from the hydrogen absorbed on the metal.

    3. The mechanism is not known definitively.
        a) It is thought that absorption of the sulfide on the nickel leads to the formation of radicals.
        b) The radical intermediates abstract hydrogen atoms from the surface of the metal or sometimes
            undergo typical free-radical reactions.

C. <u>Hydrolysis of Epoxides</u>:
    1. Epoxides undergo a variety of nucleophilic substitution reactions that involve the opening, or cleavage,
        of the epoxide ring at one of the carbon–oxygen bonds.
        a) Opening an epoxide relieves the strain in the three-membered ring.
        b) Unsymmetrical epoxides contain two nonequivalent C—O bonds that can break when ring
            opening occurs.
        c) The reaction with water, which is catalyzed by either dilute acid or base, is an example of a
            hydrolysis (a reaction in which a chemical bond is broken by reaction with water).
    2. Hydrolysis of epoxides is a stereoselective reaction; ring opening occurs with inversion of
        configuration.
    3. Epoxides react with a variety of nucleophiles under acidic conditions.
        a) Consider the protonated epoxide as a resonance hybrid that has some carbocation character.
        b) Nucleophiles attack protonated epoxides preferentially at the more substituted carbon.
        c) In many cases inversion of stereochemistry occurs at the point of nucleophilic attack.

4. Like other S_N2 reactions, ring opening of epoxides by bases involves backside attack of the nucleophile on the epoxide carbon.
   a) Inversion of configuration occurs.
   b) Basic reagents attack an epoxide at the less substituted carbon atom.

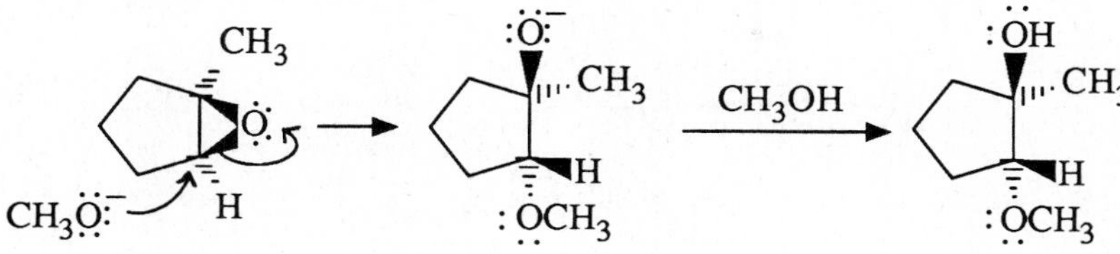

D. Reaction of Ethylene Oxide with Grignard Reagents:
   1. Grignard reagents react with ethylene oxide to give, after protonolysis, primary alcohols.
      a) This reaction is an epoxide ring-opening reaction.
      b) The Grignard reagent has carbanion character and is therefore very basic.
      c) The Grignard reagent attacks the epoxide as a nucleophile.
   2. After the Grignard reagent has reacted, the alkoxide is converted into the alcohol product in a separate step by addition of water or dilute acid (protonolysis).

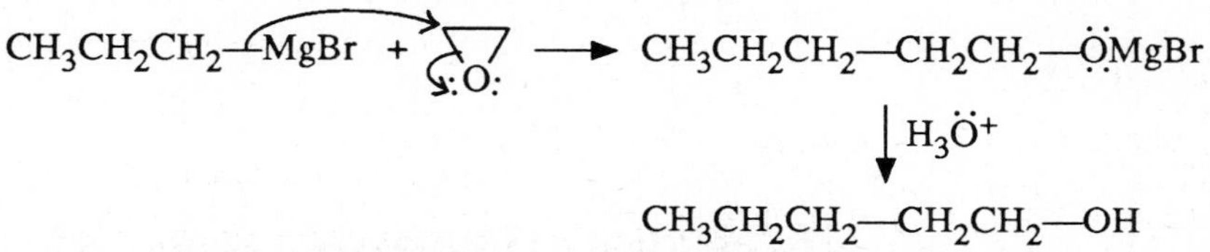

   3. The reactions of many other epoxides are unsatisfactory because they yield troublesome mixtures of products caused by rearrangements and other side reactions.

E. Oxonium and Sulfonium Salts:
   1. **Oxonium (sulfonium) ions** are formed by formally replacing the proton of a protonated ether (sulfide) with an alkyl group.
   2. Oxonium and sulfonium salts react with nucleophiles in S_N2 reactions.
      a) Oxonium salts react very rapidly with most nucleophiles; oxonium salts are stable only when they contain non-nucleophilic counter-ions such as $^-BF_4$.
      b) Sulfonium salts are considerably less reactive; sulfonium salts are somewhat less reactive than the corresponding alkyl chlorides in S_N2 reactions.

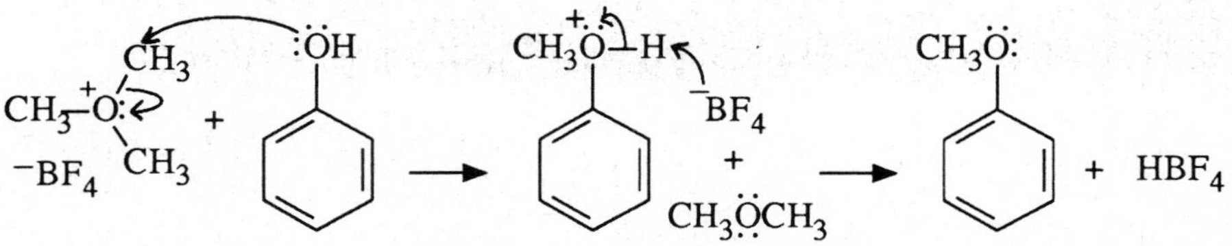

   3. The sulfonium salt S-adenosylmethionine (SAM) is used in nature to deliver methyl groups to biological nucleophiles; SAM reacts with nucleophiles at the methyl carbon to liberate a sulfide leaving group.

F. Oxidation of Ethers and Sulfides:
   1. Ethers undergo slow autoxidation to peroxides; the sulfur analog of a peroxide is a disulfide, which is the oxidation product of a thiol.

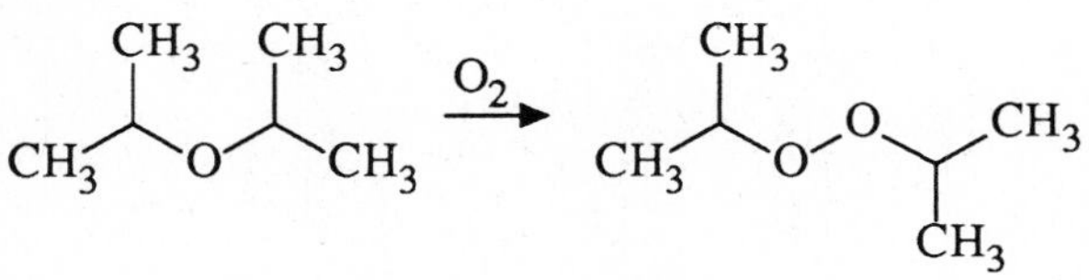

2. Sulfides oxidize at sulfur rather than carbon when they react with common oxidizing agents.
   a) Sulfides can be oxidized to **sulfoxides** and **sulfones**.
   b) Sulfoxides and sulfones can be prepared by the direct oxidation of sulfides with one and two equivalents, respectively, of hydrogen peroxide.

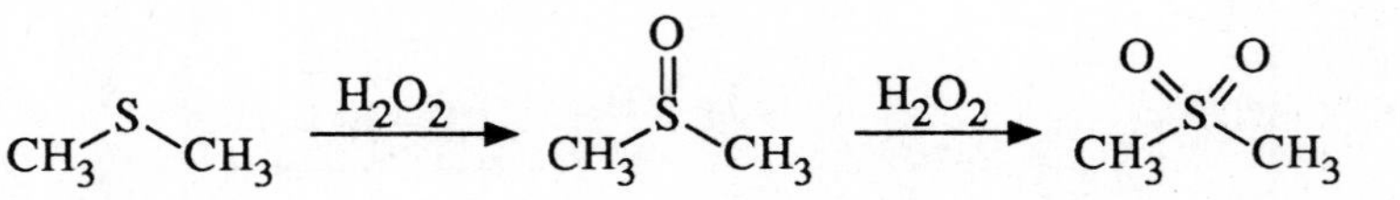

$$CH_3 \overset{S}{\diagup} CH_3 \xrightarrow{H_2O_2} CH_3 \overset{\overset{O}{\|}}{\underset{S}{\diagup}} CH_3 \xrightarrow{H_2O_2} CH_3 \overset{O \underset{\|}{\diagdown} \overset{O}{\diagup}}{\underset{S}{}} CH_3$$

$$\qquad \text{a sulfide} \qquad\qquad\qquad \text{a sulfoxide} \qquad\qquad\qquad \text{a sulfone}$$

CHAPTER 11 SOLUTIONS

Solutions to In-Text Problems

1. (a) $(CH_3)_2CH{-}O{-}CH_3$
(b) $CH_2{=}CH{-}CH_2{-}S{-}CH_3$
(c) $(CH_3)_2C{=}CH_2$ An E2 elimination occurs because the alkyl halide is tertiary and does not undergo S_N2 reactions.
(d) This is neopentyl tosylate which, like neopentyl halides, does not undergo the S_N2 reaction. Because it has no β-hydrogen, it also cannot undergo an elimination. Hence, there is no reaction.

2. Williamson ether syntheses are possible for compounds (a) and (b):

(a)

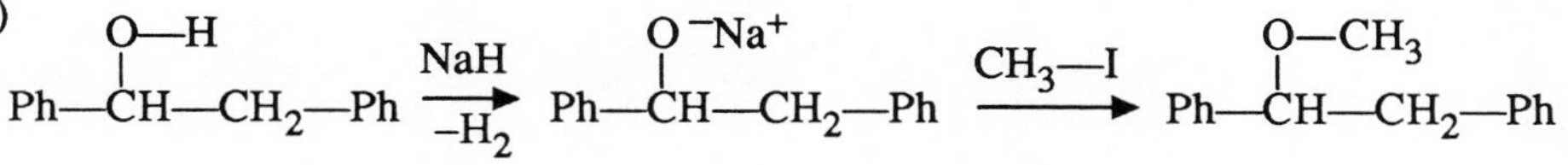

(b)

$$PhCH_2CH_2SH \xrightarrow{NaOC_2H_5} PhCH_2CH_2S^- \xrightarrow{Br{-}CH_2CH(CH_3)_2} PhCH_2CH_2{-}S{-}CH_2CH(CH_3)_2$$

A Williamson ether synthesis is not possible for compound (c); the strongly basic conditions required (*t*-butoxide and *t*-butyl halide) would bring about elimination.

3. The mechanism is identical to the mechanism of oxymercuration, except that an alcohol rather than water attacks the mercurinium ion. We'll abbreviate the $CH_3CH_2CH_2CH_2{-}$ group as R—. The first step is formation of a mercurinium ion:

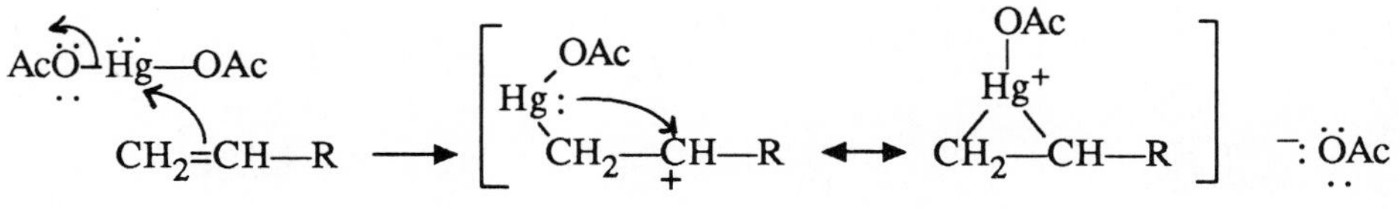

Attack of the alcohol on the mercurinium ion and loss of a proton gives the alkoxymercuration adduct. (This is subsequently transformed into an ether by treatment with $NaBH_4$.

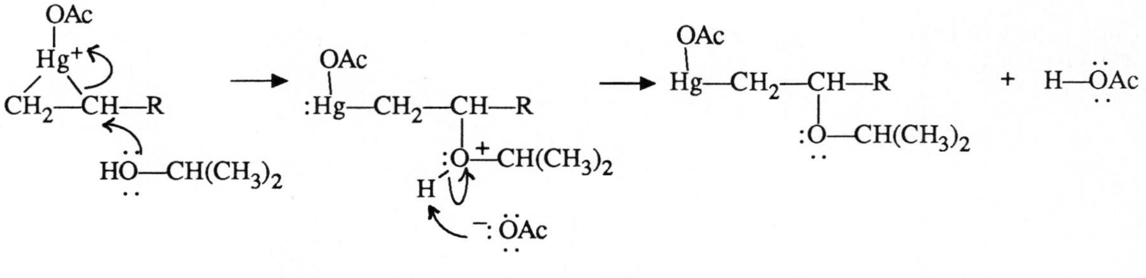

A Williamson ether synthesis would afford a significant amount of elimination product.

4. (a)

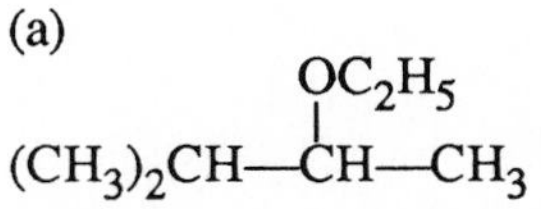

(b)

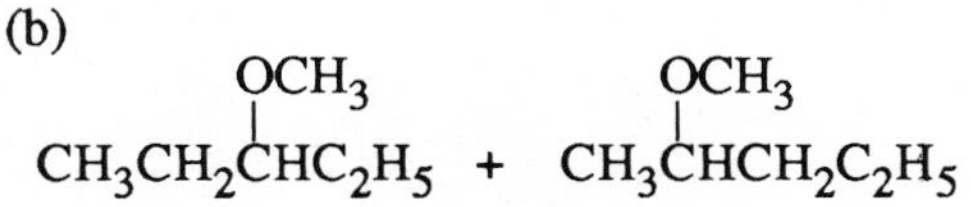

A mixture is formed in (b) because both carbons of the alkene double bond bear the same number of alkyl substituents.

5.   This ether can be prepared by alkoxymercuration-reduction of isobutylene in isobutyl alcohol:

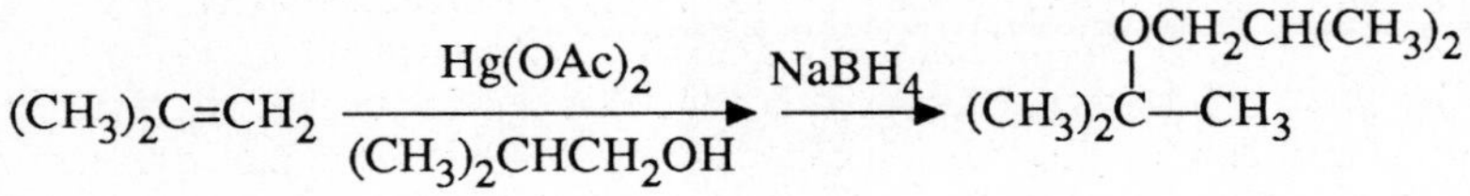

$$(CH_3)_2C=CH_2 \xrightarrow[\text{(CH}_3)_2\text{CHCH}_2\text{OH}]{\text{Hg(OAc)}_2} \xrightarrow{\text{NaBH}_4} (CH_3)_2\overset{\overset{\displaystyle OCH_2CH(CH_3)_2}{\displaystyle |}}{C}-CH_3$$

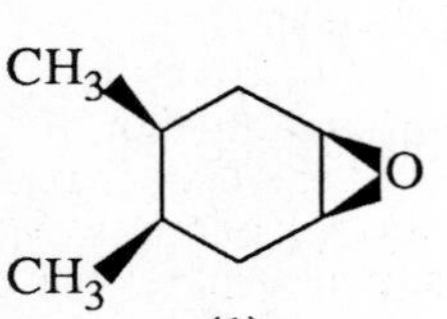

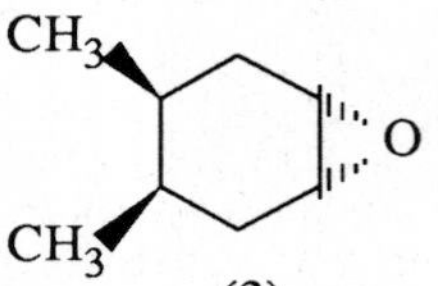

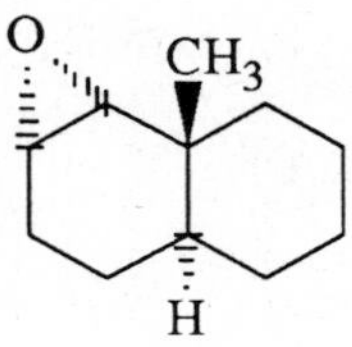

6.   (a) 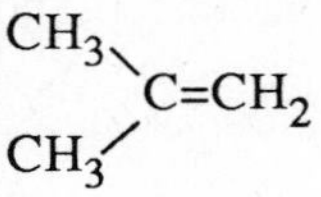   (b) 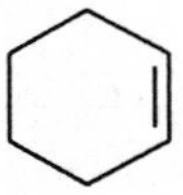   (c)

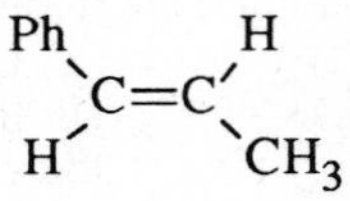

7.   (a)   (b)

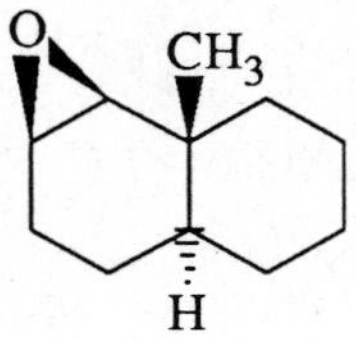

We expect the second epoxide to predominate in each case, because it is formed from the least hindered side of the ring system (the side opposite the —CH₃ group in each case).

8.   We first draw the compounds with the —OH and —Br in an *anti* arrangement. When we do so, we find that stereoisomer *B* has methyl groups in a *gauche* relationship, whereas isomer *A* has its methyls in an *anti* relationship. The *gauche* methyls impart strain to the transition state for the reaction of *A*, and therefore the rate at which *B* reacts is reduced.

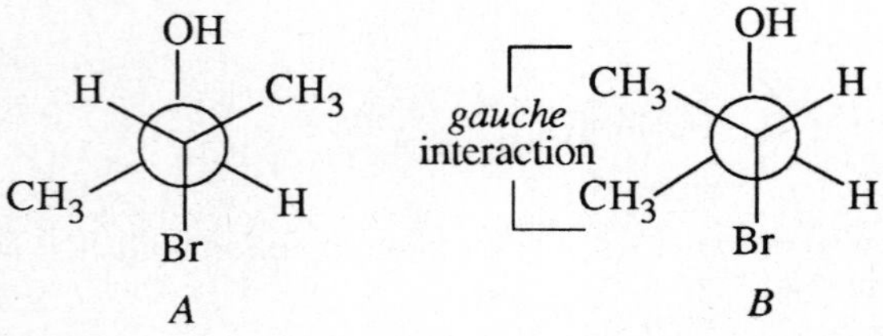

9.   Only in the *trans* isomer can the —Cl and —OH groups achieve the required *anti* relationship by a chair-chair interconversion:

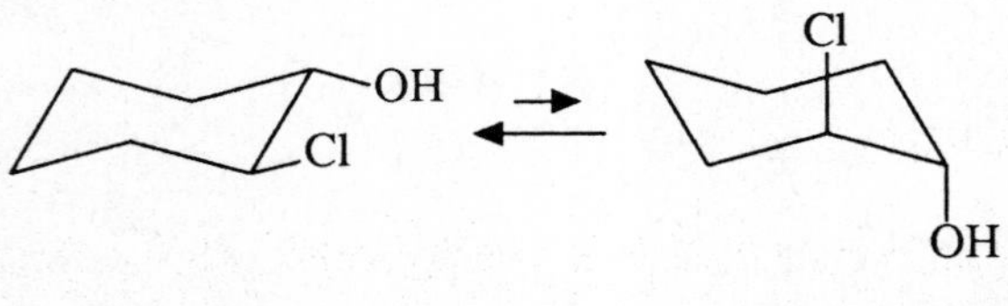

trans isomer   *anti* —Cl and —OH

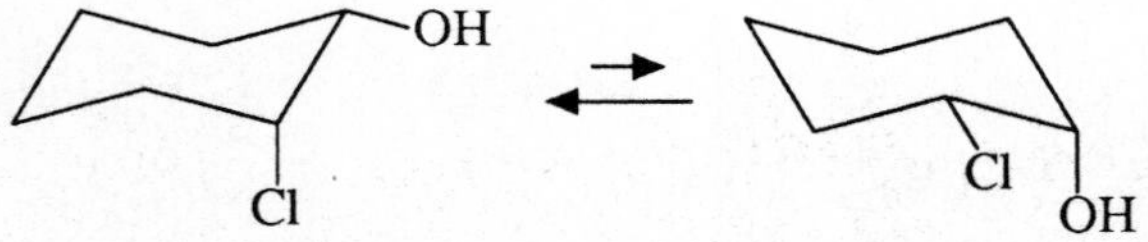

cis isomer   cannot achieve *anti* relationship of
                                        —Cl and —OH

10. Because the alkyl groups are respectively primary and methyl in butyl methyl ether, the reaction occurs by an S_N2 mechanism. Iodide attacks the protonated ether at the alkyl group that is most reactive in the S_N2 reaction — namely, the methyl group — to give CH_3—I and butyl alcohol. In the case of *t*-butyl methyl ether, the reaction occurs by an S_N1 pathway to give a *t*-butyl cation intermediate along with methyl alcohol. This cation is attacked by iodide to give *t*-butyl iodide. (See Eq. 11.23b.) Notice that when a choice exists between an S_N2 reaction and an S_N1 reaction of a tertiary group, the S_N1 reaction is faster and is the reaction observed.

11. (a)   (b)

$(CH_3)_2CH$—I and $(CH_3)_2CH$—OH

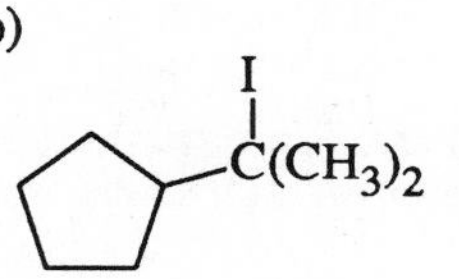

➤ Notice in part (b) that the product is derived from attack of iodide at the tertiary alkyl group, as indicated in the previous problem. The reaction occurs by an S_N1 mechanism. (Write out this mechanism!)

12. In acid-promoted ether of sulfide cleavage, the protonated form of the ether or sulfide is the form that undergoes a displacement reaction. Since sulfides are much less basic in solution than ethers, there is much less of the protonated sulfide present at a given acid concentration. Since the rate of cleavage of the sulfide should be proportional to the amount of protonated sulfide present, it is reasonable that the sulfide is much less reactive.

13. The radical formed by loss of sulfur can react *intermolecularly* with hydrogen from the metal to give pentane, or it can react *intramolecularly* in a recombination reaction to give cyclopentane:

$\cdot CH_2CH_2CH_2CH_2CH_2\dot{C}H_2 + H_2$ (or $2H\cdot$) → H—$CH_2CH_2CH_2CH_2CH_2CH_2$—H

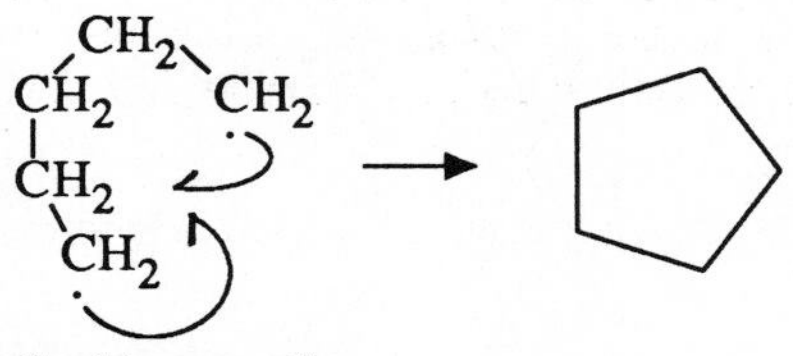

radical intermediate

14. To get the products, we break the bonds to sulfur and replace the carbon-sulfur bonds with carbon-hydrogen bonds.

(a)   (b)

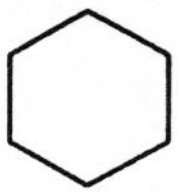

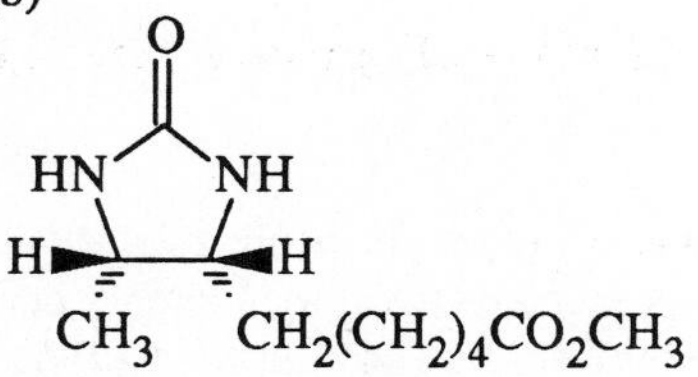

15. The epoxide is attacked from the backside of either asymmetric carbon by the nucleophilic hydroxide ion:

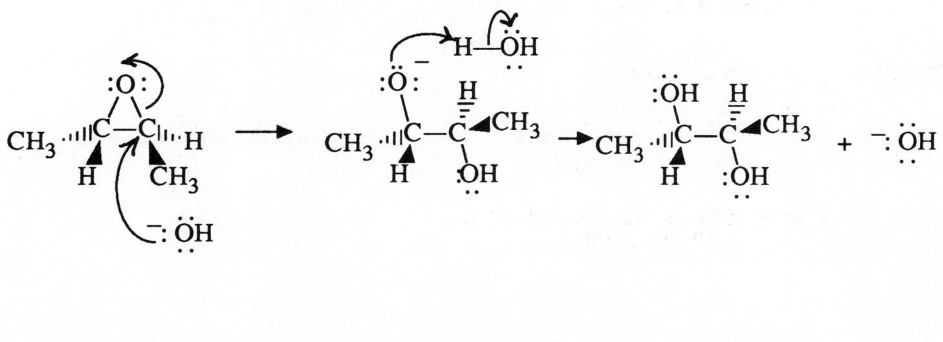

The product is *meso*-2,3-butanediol, an achiral compound. (The same product is obtained by attack at the other epoxide carbon.) Because the product is achiral, it cannot be optically active.

16. (a)

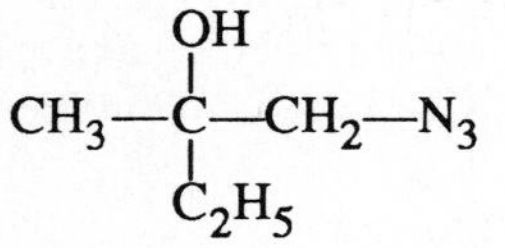

$$CH_3-\underset{\underset{C_2H_5}{|}}{\overset{\overset{OH}{|}}{C}}-CH_2-N_3$$

(b)

$$CH_3-\underset{\underset{CH_3}{|}}{\overset{\overset{OH}{|}}{C}}-\underset{\underset{}{}}{\overset{\overset{CH_3}{|}}{CH}}-OCH_3$$

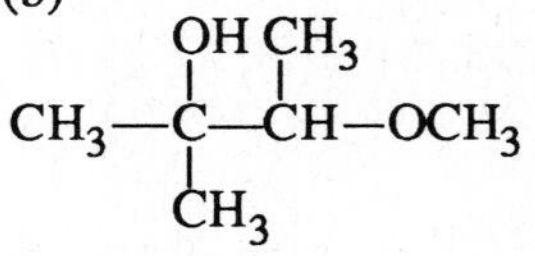

In (a), azide acts as a nucleophile in an S_N2 reaction and attacks the less substituted epoxide carbon. In (b), methoxide ion is the nucleophile, and also attacks the less substituted epoxide carbon.

17. (a)

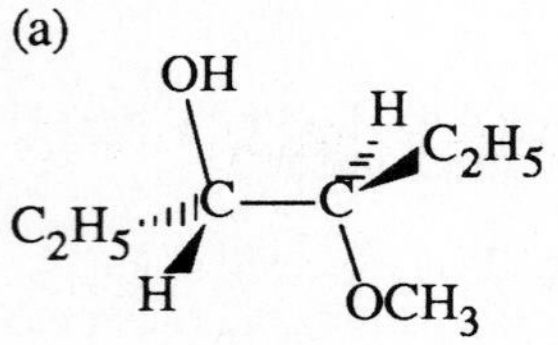

(b)

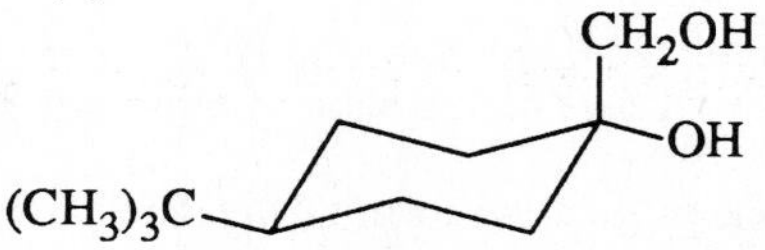

(c)

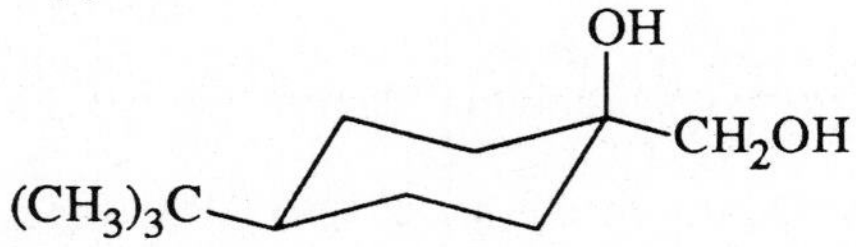

In (a), attack of methoxide at either epoxide carbon is equally likely; attack at the other carbon gives the enantiomer. The product is the racemate. In (b), the acidic conditions dictate that attack of the nucleophile water occurs at the more substituted epoxide carbon. In (c), the base hydroxide ion attacks at the less substituted epoxide carbon.

(d)

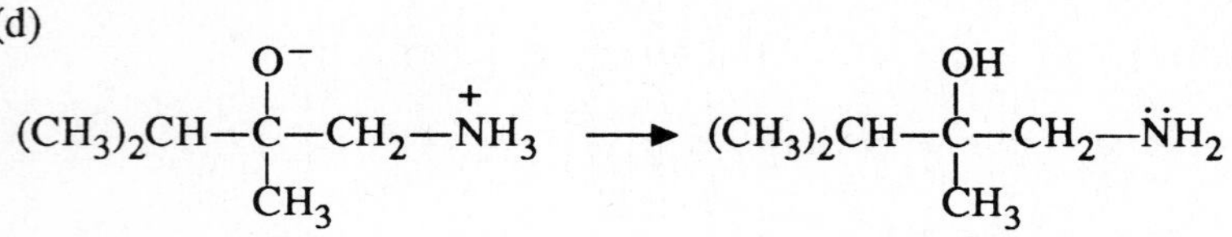

$$(CH_3)_2CH-\underset{\underset{CH_3}{|}}{\overset{\overset{O^-}{|}}{C}}-CH_2-\overset{+}{N}H_3 \longrightarrow (CH_3)_2CH-\underset{\underset{CH_3}{|}}{\overset{\overset{OH}{|}}{C}}-CH_2-\ddot{N}H_2$$

In this case, the initially formed product undergoes proton transfer as shown, because the alkoxide ion is more basic than the amino (—NH$_2$) group.

(e)

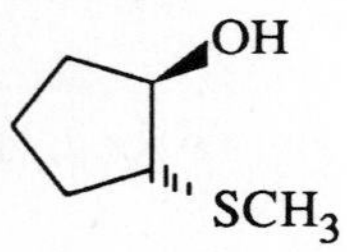

Hydroxide ion deprotonates CH$_3$SH to give CH$_3$S$^-$ because thiols are more acidic than water. The CH$_3$S$^-$ ion is the nucleophile that reacts with the epoxide. Both enantiomers of the product are formed in equal amount, because attack may occur at either epoxide carbon.

18. In acid, attack of water on the epoxide occurs at the more substituted carbon — the asymmetric carbon. In base, attack of ⁻OH occurs by an S_N2 mechanism at the primary carbon; the configuration of the asymmetric carbon is unaffected. Thus, we can deduce the configuration of the epoxide from that of the (R)-(–)-product.

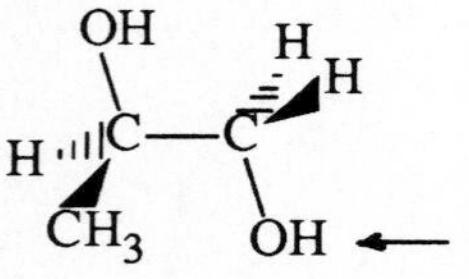

epoxide has the following configuration:

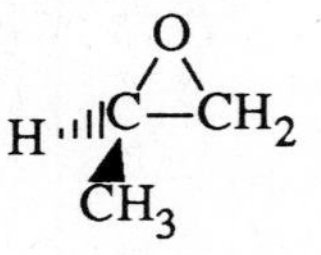

Evidently, the epoxide also has the R configuration. Attack of water in the acid-catalyzed reaction occurs with inversion of configuration at the asymmetric carbon.

19. (a) Let us work backward from the target compound:

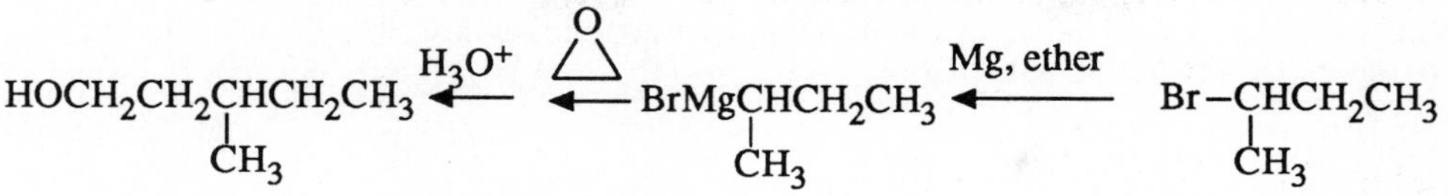

$$HOCH_2CH_2\underset{CH_3}{CH}CH_2CH_3 \xleftarrow{H_3O^+} \triangle \xleftarrow{} BrMg\underset{CH_3}{CH}CH_2CH_3 \xleftarrow{Mg,\ ether} Br-\underset{CH_3}{CH}CH_2CH_3$$

(b) Hydroboration-oxidation of 3-methyl-1-pentene would afford the same compound:

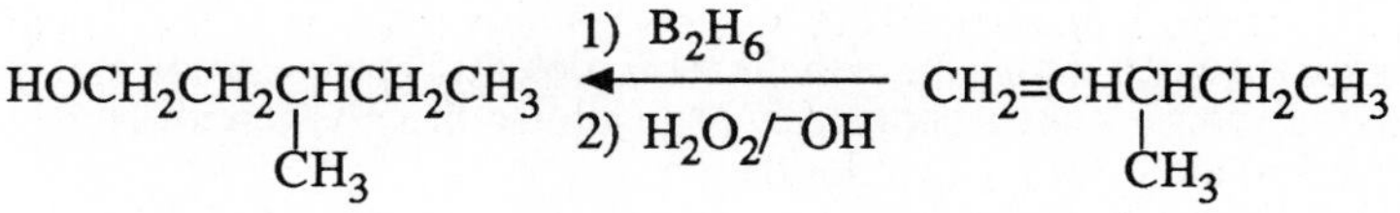

$$HOCH_2CH_2\underset{CH_3}{CH}CH_2CH_3 \xleftarrow[\text{2) } H_2O_2/^-OH]{\text{1) } B_2H_6} CH_2=CH\underset{CH_3}{CH}CH_2CH_3$$

20. Trimethyloxonium ion reacts with its counter-ion, iodide. This means that the salt is unstable, and therefore cannot be isolated:

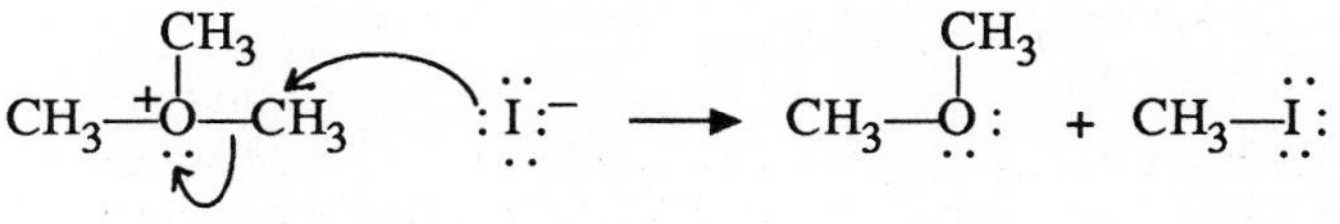

$$CH_3-\overset{\overset{CH_3}{|}}{\overset{+}{O}}-CH_3 \quad :\ddot{I}:^- \longrightarrow CH_3-\overset{\overset{CH_3}{|}}{\ddot{O}}: + CH_3-\ddot{I}:$$

21. In each case, a nucleophile reacts, S_N2-fashion, with the trimethyloxonium ion:

(a)

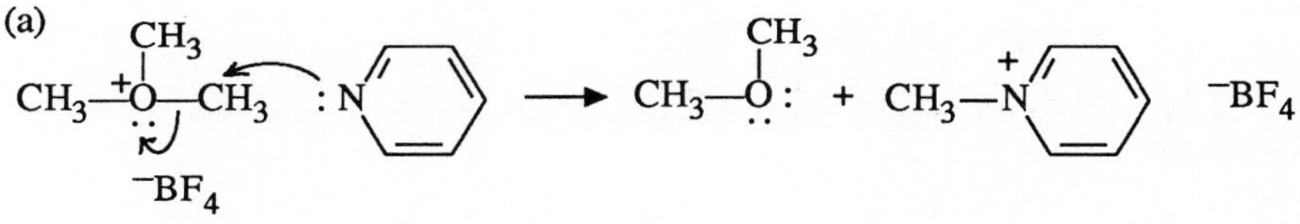

$$CH_3-\overset{\overset{CH_3}{|}}{\overset{+}{O}}-CH_3 \quad :N\langle\text{pyridine}\rangle \longrightarrow CH_3-\overset{\overset{CH_3}{|}}{\ddot{O}}: + CH_3-\overset{+}{N}\langle\text{pyridine}\rangle \quad {}^-BF_4$$
$$^-BF_4$$

(b)

$$CH_3-\overset{\overset{CH_3}{|}}{\overset{+}{O}}-CH_3 \quad :\overset{\overset{}{\underset{CH_3}{|}}}{\ddot{S}}-CH_3 \longrightarrow CH_3-\overset{\overset{CH_3}{|}}{\ddot{O}}: + CH_3-\overset{+}{\underset{\underset{CH_3}{|}}{\ddot{S}}}-CH_3 \quad {}^-BF_4$$
$$^-BF_4$$

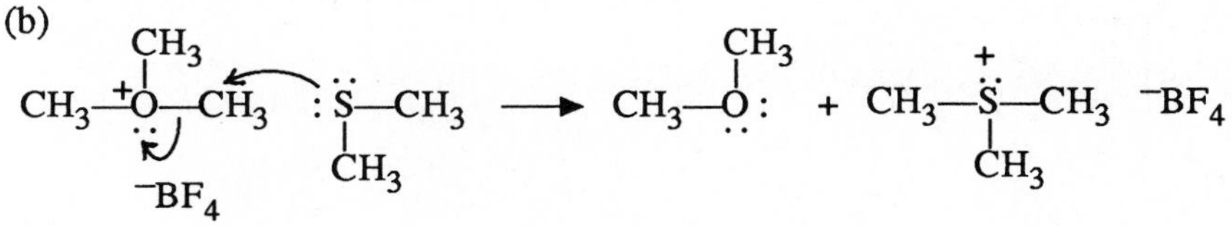

22. (a) If neighboring-group participation does *not* occur, $C_2H_5SCH_2\overset{*}{C}H_2OH$ is the only product formed; that is, radioactivity is *not* distributed between the —CH_2— carbons.

(b) Neighboring-group participation would give a mixture of products because attack of water on the episulfonium ion can occur at either carbon:

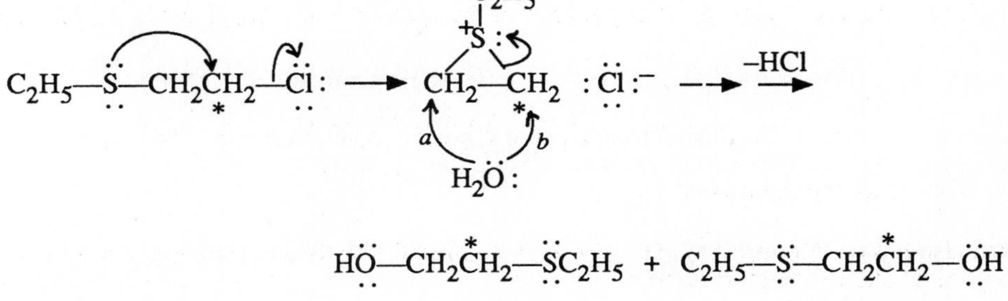

$$C_2H_5-\ddot{S}-CH_2\overset{*}{C}H_2-\ddot{C}l: \longrightarrow \underset{\underset{H_2\ddot{O}:}{a\qquad b}}{\overset{\overset{C_2H_5}{\underset{\overset{+}{S}:}{|}}}{CH_2-CH_2}} \quad :\ddot{C}l:^- \xrightarrow{-HCl}$$

$$H\ddot{O}-CH_2\overset{*}{C}H_2-\ddot{S}C_2H_5 + C_2H_5-\ddot{S}-CH_2\overset{*}{C}H_2-\ddot{O}H$$

product of pathway *a*   product of pathway *b*

That is, the radioactivity is distributed 50% at each —CH_2— carbon.

➤ This problem brings up an issue of terminology that will arise again. When compounds in a mixture differ only in the position of an isotopic label, we can write a single structure that describes the mixture. For example, the mixture in part (b) can be written as

$$C_2H_5\overset{..}{\underset{..}{S}}-\overset{*}{C}H_2\overset{*}{C}H_2-OH$$

in which we say that 50% of the radioactivity is at each carbon.

23. This is really a different type of labeling experiment; in this case, the label is a methyl group, which makes the two carbons in the episulfonium ion nonequivalent. Like a comparably substituted bromonium ion, the episulfonium ion is attacked at the more substituted carbon by chloride ion:

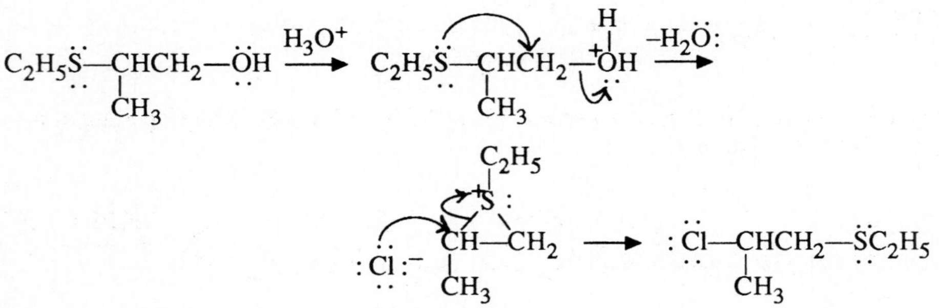

                                    episulfonium ion

The same episulfonium ion is formed from the other starting material. (Be sure to demonstrate this for yourself!) Hence, the same products are also formed.

24. (a) Intramolecular product:

intermolecular product: HOCH₂CH₂OCH₂CH₂Br or HOCH₂CH₂OH (from attack of ⁻OH).

(b) Intramolecular product:

intermolecular product: HO(CH₂)₄—O—(CH₂)₄Br or HO(CH₂)₄OH (from attack of ⁻OH).

(c) Intramolecular product:

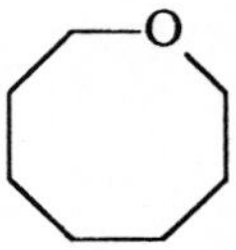

intermolecular product: HO(CH₂)₇—O—(CH₂)₇Br or HO(CH₂)₇OH (from attack of ⁻OH).

The starting material in (c) would give the most intermolecular product. When three- and five-membered rings can form, as in (a) or (b), intramolecular reactions are more favorable.

25. (a) The carboxylic acid is prepared by oxidation of a primary alcohol with KMnO₄ or HNO₃:

$$(CH_3)_2CHCH_2CH_2CH_2OH \xrightarrow{\text{KMnO}_4} (CH_3)_2CH_2CH_2CH_2CO_2H$$

The alcohol is prepared by reaction of a Grignard reagent with ethylene oxide; this step also adds two carbons:

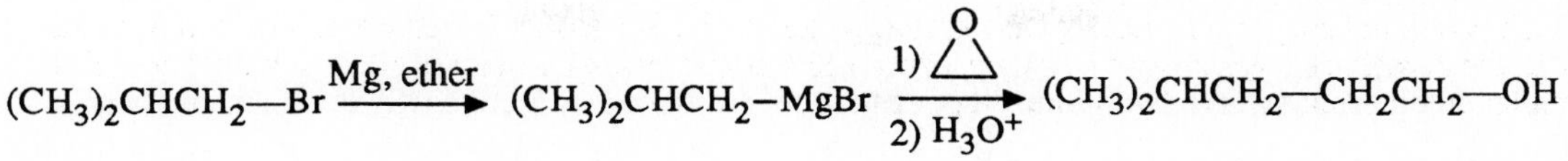

$(CH_3)_2CHCH_2-Br \xrightarrow{\text{Mg, ether}} (CH_3)_2CHCH_2-MgBr \xrightarrow[\text{2) } H_3O^+]{\text{1) } \triangle O} (CH_3)_2CHCH_2-CH_2CH_2-OH$

Finally, the required alkyl halide can be made by addition of HBr to isobutylene in the presence of peroxides:

$(CH_3)_2C=CH_2 \xrightarrow{\text{HBr, peroxides}} (CH_3)_2CH-CH_2Br$

(b) In this case, the carboxylic acid can be prepared by oxidation of the alcohol formed by hydroboration-oxidation of isobutylene itself:

$(CH_3)_2CHCO_2H \xleftarrow{\text{dilute HNO}_3} (CH_3)_2CHCH_2OH \xleftarrow[\text{2) } H_2O_2/^-OH]{\text{1) } B_2H_6} (CH_3)_2C=CH_2$

(c) This reaction scheme is very similar to the one shown in Eq. 11.59, and involves ring-opening of an epoxide followed by a Williamson synthesis:

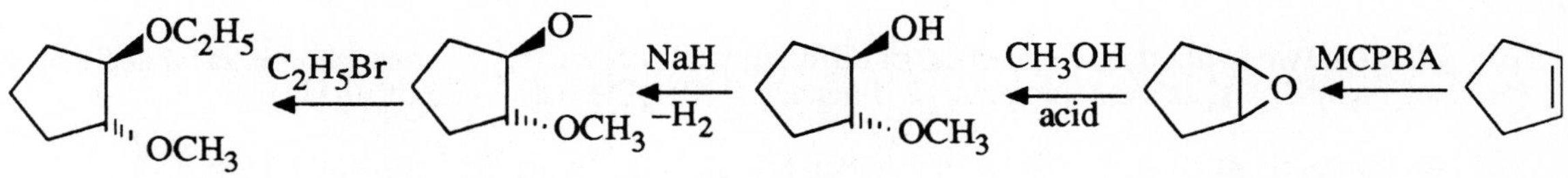

(MCPBA = *m*-chloroperbenzoic acid; see text page 420.) The same compound could be prepared by opening the epoxide with ethoxide, then carrying out a Williamson synthesis with CH_3I.

(d) The key is to recognize that a carbon-sulfur bond must be formed. This can be realized by an S_N2 reaction of a sulfide anion with an alkyl halide.

Solutions to Additional Problems

26. (a) Such an ether must have two groups that cannot be introduced by S_N2 reactions. Such an ether is

$$CH_3—\underset{\underset{\displaystyle CH_3}{|}}{\overset{\overset{\displaystyle CH_3}{|}}{C}}—O—\underset{\underset{\displaystyle CH_3}{|}}{\overset{\overset{\displaystyle CH_3}{|}}{C}}—CH_2CH_3$$

Another such ether is *t*-butyl neopentyl ether.

(b) Such an ether must contain only propyl groups: $CH_3CH_2CH_2OCH_2CH_2CH_3$.

(c) Since the alkyl halide product has two alkyl halide groups, the ether oxygen must be attached at each end of the carbon chain — that is, the ether is cyclic. Tetrahydrofuran is the ether that would give this product:

(d) Since the two methods give products of differing stereochemistry, we must choose an alkene whose glycol product cannot exist as diastereomers. 1-Butene, $CH_3CH_2CH=CH_2$, is such an alkene.

(e) Now we need an alkene that gives diastereomeric glycols. Either *cis*- or *trans*-2-butene, $CH_3CH=CHCH_3$, is a satisfactory answer.

(f) The alkene has an unsaturation number of 3, and since it forms a di-epoxide, it must have two double bonds. Hence, the alkene also has one ring.

![diagrams] gives ... and ... + ...

Notice that 1,3-cyclohexadiene is not correct, because it gives two stereoisomeric mono-epoxides and three stereoisomeric di-epoxides.

27. As usual, let us be sure we know the structure of the starting material:

$$\overset{O}{\triangle}\!\!\!\!<\!\!\begin{array}{l} CH_3 \\ C_2H_5 \end{array}$$

(a)
$$HO—CH_2—\underset{\underset{\displaystyle C_2H_5}{|}}{\overset{\overset{\displaystyle OH}{|}}{C}}—CH_3$$

(b)
$$CH_3O—CH_2—\underset{\underset{\displaystyle C_2H_5}{|}}{\overset{\overset{\displaystyle OH}{|}}{C}}—CH_3$$

(c)
$$CH_3O—CH_2—\underset{\underset{\displaystyle C_2H_5}{|}}{\overset{\overset{\displaystyle Br}{|}}{C}}—CH_3$$

In the case of (c), the tertiary alcohol group reacts more rapidly than the ether group because a much more stable carbocation is formed. Cleavage of an ordinary ether requires heat.

(d)
$$CH_3O—CH_2—\underset{\underset{\displaystyle C_2H_5}{|}}{\overset{\overset{\displaystyle MgBr}{|}}{C}}—CH_3$$

(e)
$$CH_3O—CH_2—\underset{\underset{\displaystyle C_2H_5}{|}}{\overset{\overset{\displaystyle CH_2CH_2—OH}{|}}{C}}—CH_3$$

(f)
$$CH_3O—CH_2—\underset{\underset{\displaystyle C_2H_5}{|}}{\overset{\overset{\displaystyle OCH_3}{|}}{C}}—CH_3$$

(g)

$$CH_2=O \ + \ CH_3\overset{\overset{\displaystyle O}{\|}}{\underset{}{C}}\!-\!C_2H_5$$

(h) $O=CH\!-\!\underset{\underset{\displaystyle CH_3}{|}}{CH}\!-\!C_2H_5$ (pinacol rearrangement)

28. The reason that cyclopropanes do not open easily in base is that the leaving group would have to be a *carbanion*, which is too basic to be a good leaving group. (Recall that alkanes have pK_a values of about 55–60.)

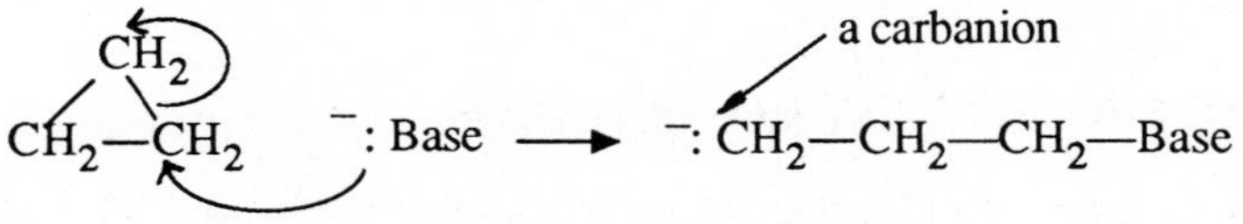

a carbanion

29. (a) Reaction of the alcohol with Na, NaH, or CH_3—MgI will give a gas (H_2, H_2, or CH_4, respectively).

(b) 3-Ethoxypropene is an alkene and will decolorize Br_2 in CCl_4.

(c) The second compound is a tertiary alkyl halide as well as an ether; tertiary alkyl halides give precipitates of AgCl with acidic $AgNO_3$ solution.

30. Propylene oxide reacts with HCl in a ring-opening reaction:

31. (a) Sodium ethoxide reacts with water to give NaOH:

$$C_2H_5\ddot{\underset{\cdot\cdot}{O}}\!:^- \ + \ H\!-\!\ddot{\underset{\cdot\cdot}{O}}H \ \rightleftharpoons \ C_2H_5\ddot{\underset{\cdot\cdot}{O}}\!-\!H \ + \ ^-\!:\ddot{\underset{\cdot\cdot}{O}}H$$

Although ethanol and water have similar pK_a values, the equilibrium above lies to the right when water is the solvent and is in excess. Thus, $^-$OH will be the nucleophile, and the likely product will be $(CH_3)_2CHCH_2CH_2OH$.

(b) The intent of this reaction is to use the Grignard reagent to open the epoxide; however, the starting material contains not only an epoxide group, but an —OH group, which reacts instantaneously to destroy the Grignard reagent by protonolysis.

32. The formula of the product implies one degree of unsaturation; this observation, together with the hint, suggests that a ring is formed. That is, the nucleophile is an alcohol group within the molecule, rather than an alcohol added as solvent, as in a conventional alkoxymercuration. (See Problems 45a and 45c, Chapter 5, for similar situations.)

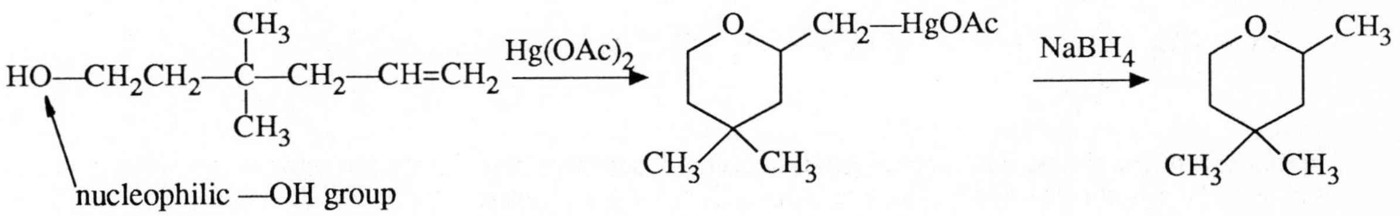

➤ The intramolecular reaction of the —OH group with the mercurinium ion is faster than the intermolecular reaction of water with the same species.

33. Given the structures of products C and D, which contain rings, the one degree of unsaturation in compound A is a ring. Because compound A liberates gas on treatment with sodium or with C_2H_5MgBr (H_2 in the former case, ethane in the latter), it has at least one —OH group; and because it forms a di-tosylate, it must be a diol. Reaction of the di-tosylate with sodium sulfide evidently leads to a second ring, because the unsaturation number of compound B is 2. From the products C and D we can infer that compound B is

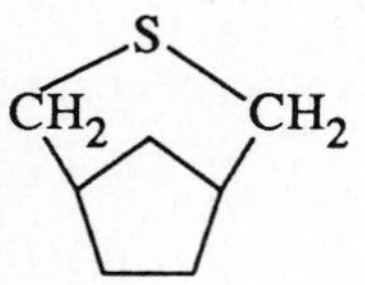

compound B

Raney-nickel cleavage then takes place by a combination of intermolecular and intramolecular pathways (see Problem 13) to give compounds C and D.

The formation of compound B is by two successive displacements: an S_N2 reaction with sulfide as the nucleophile, followed by an intramolecular displacement, in which an ionized thiol is the nucleophile.

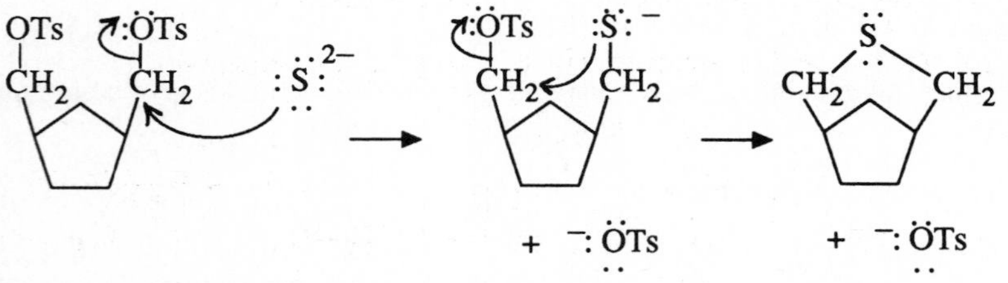

34. (a) $CH_3CH_2CH_2$—O—C_2H_5 (a simple S_N2 reaction).

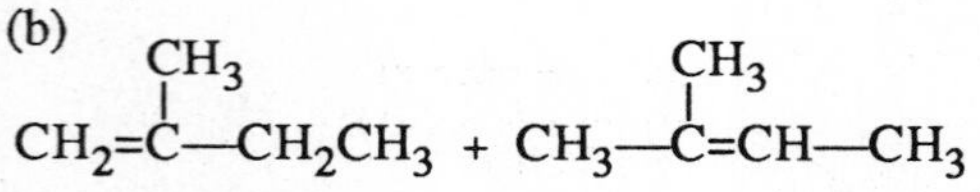

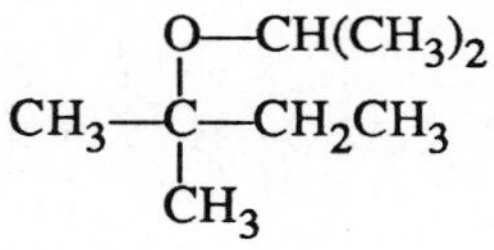

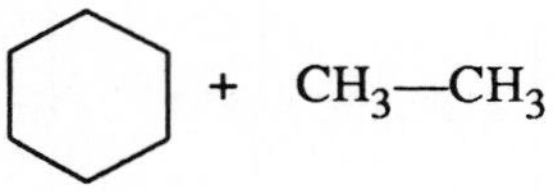

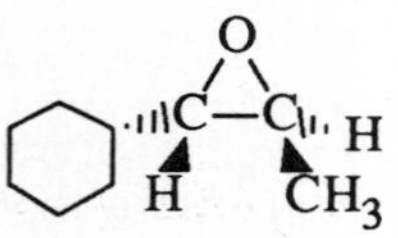

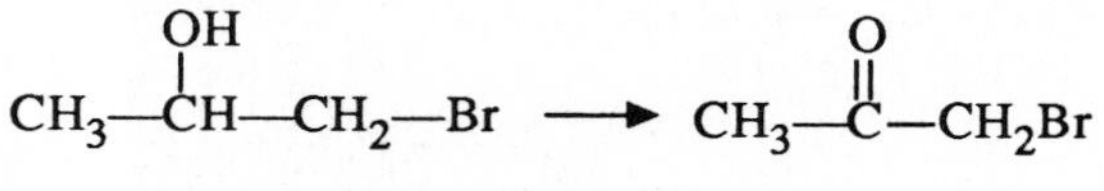

(g) The aqueous acidic conditions first cause hydrolysis of the epoxide; the resulting glycol is cleaved by periodate to give $BrCH_2CH_2CH_2CH=O + CH_2=O$.

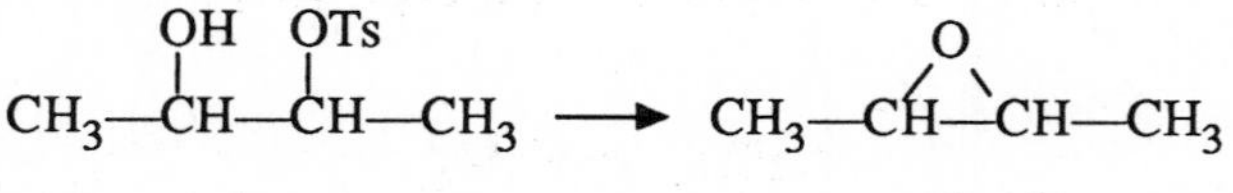

In part (j), the intermediate is the tosylate analog of a bromohydrin; and, like a bromohydrin, it forms an epoxide in base. (Write out the detailed mechanism if you have not already done so!)

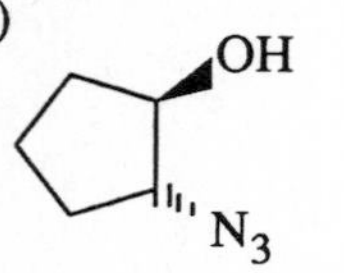

35. (a) The reaction is a double S_N2 reaction:

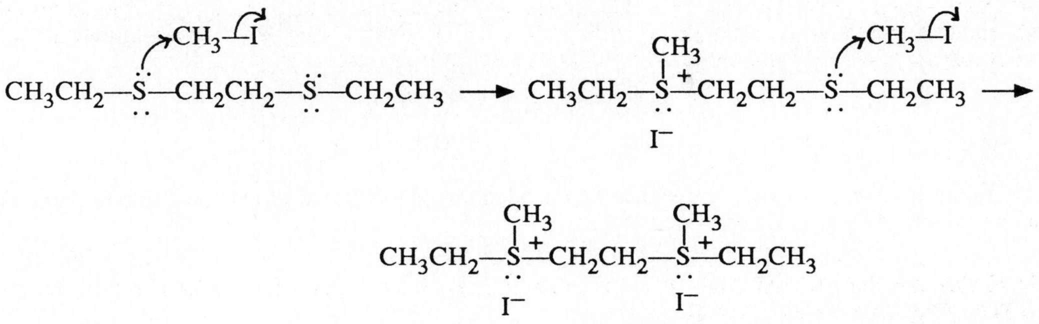

$$CH_3CH_2-\overset{..}{\underset{..}{S}}-CH_2CH_2-\overset{..}{\underset{..}{S}}-CH_2CH_3 \longrightarrow CH_3CH_2-\overset{\overset{CH_3}{|}}{\underset{\underset{I^-}{..}}{S^+}}-CH_2CH_2-\overset{..}{\underset{..}{S}}-CH_2CH_3 \longrightarrow$$

$$CH_3CH_2-\overset{\overset{CH_3}{|}}{\underset{\underset{I^-}{..}}{S^+}}-CH_2CH_2-\overset{\overset{CH_3}{|}}{\underset{\underset{I^-}{..}}{S^+}}-CH_2CH_3$$

(b) The two compounds are diastereomers that differ in their configurations at *sulfur*. One diastereomer is the *meso*, or (R,S) stereoisomer; the other is the racemate, a 1:1 mixture of the (R,R) and (S,S) stereoisomers. Evidently, sulfonium ions do not undergo rapid inversion of the type found in amines.

36. (a) The rate acceleration suggests a mechanism that involves neighboring-group participation:

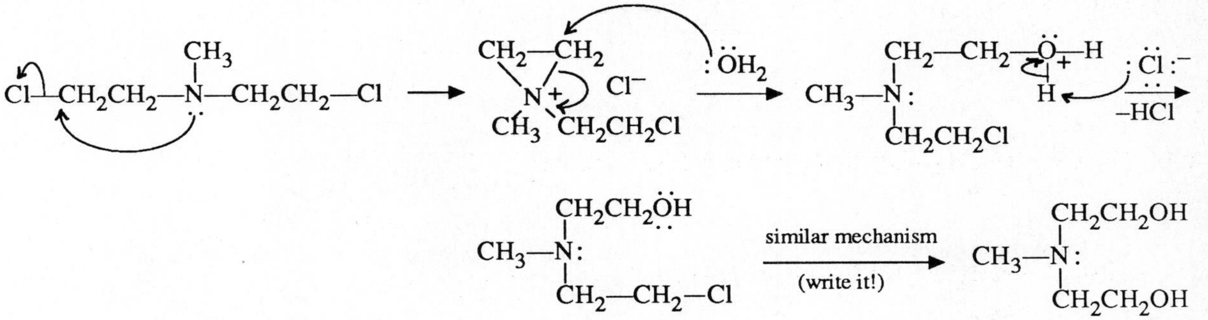

(b) We would expect another nucleophile to react with the cyclic intermediates in the above scheme, just as water does:

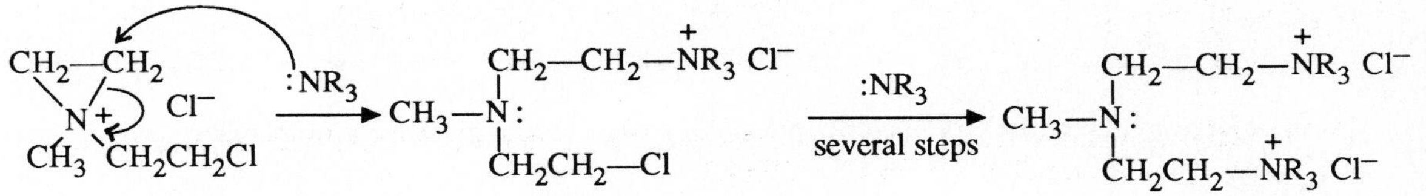

37. In each case, we'll work backward from the target compound.

(a)

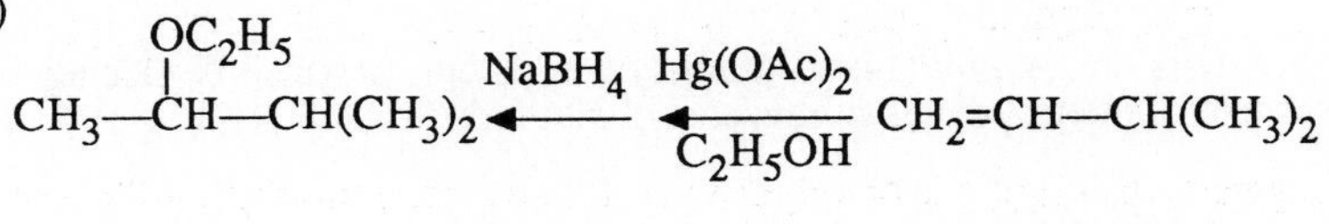

$$CH_3-\overset{\overset{OC_2H_5}{|}}{CH}-CH(CH_3)_2 \xleftarrow[C_2H_5OH]{NaBH_4\ Hg(OAc)_2} CH_2=CH-CH(CH_3)_2$$

(b)

$$C_2H_5S-CH_2CH_2-SC_2H_5 \xleftarrow{2\ C_2H_5S^-} Br-CH_2CH_2-Br$$

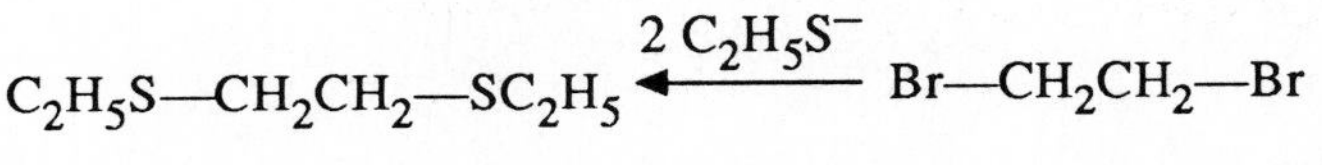

The mercaptide $C_2H_5S^-$ is formed by adding the thiol C_2H_5SH to one equivalent of sodium ethoxide in ethanol.

(c)

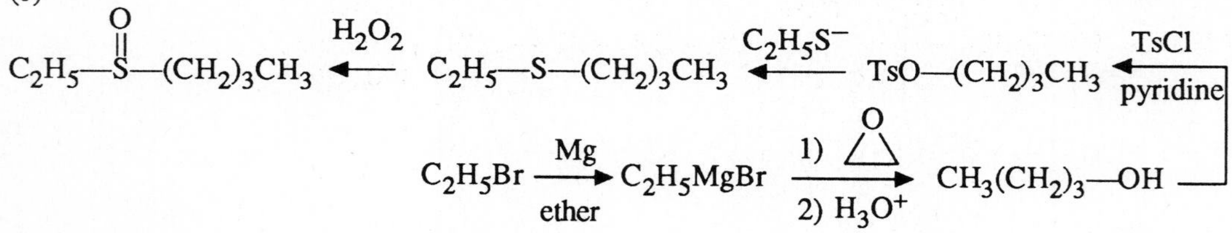

$$C_2H_5\overset{\overset{\displaystyle O}{\|}}{S}\!-\!(CH_2)_3CH_3 \xleftarrow{H_2O_2} C_2H_5\!-\!S\!-\!(CH_2)_3CH_3 \xleftarrow{C_2H_5S^-} TsO\!-\!(CH_2)_3CH_3 \xleftarrow[\text{pyridine}]{TsCl}$$

$$C_2H_5Br \xrightarrow[\text{ether}]{Mg} C_2H_5MgBr \xrightarrow[\text{2) } H_3O^+]{\text{1) } \triangle O} CH_3(CH_2)_3\!-\!OH$$

(d) The key to this synthesis is to recognize that the introduction of functional groups on adjacent carbons can often be accomplished by use of an epoxide.

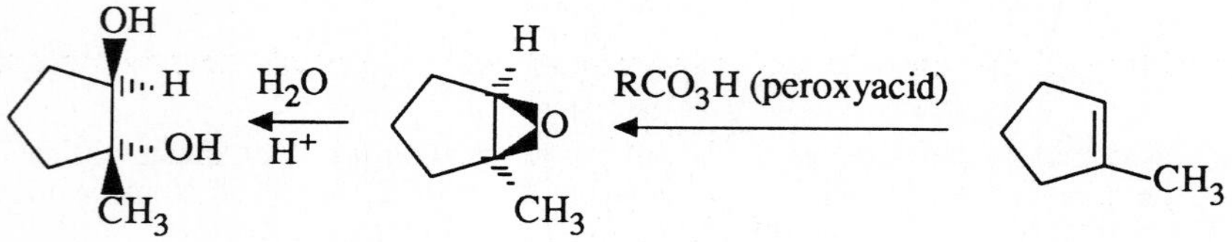

(e)

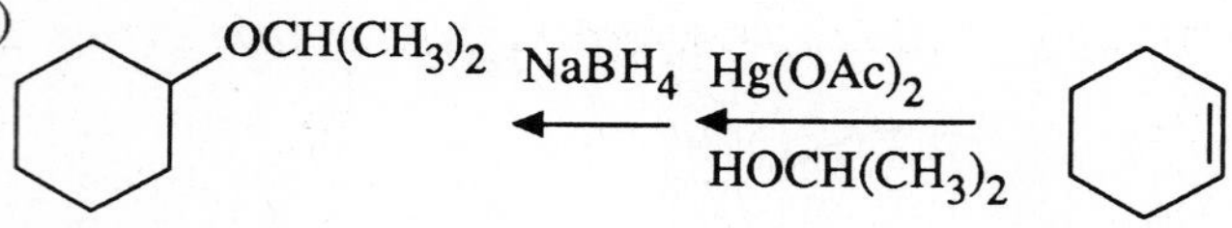

(f)

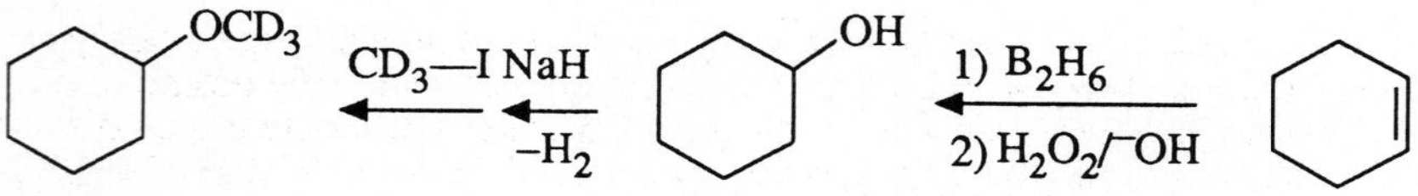

Cyclohexanol could also have been prepared from cyclohexene by oxymercuration–reduction.

(g)

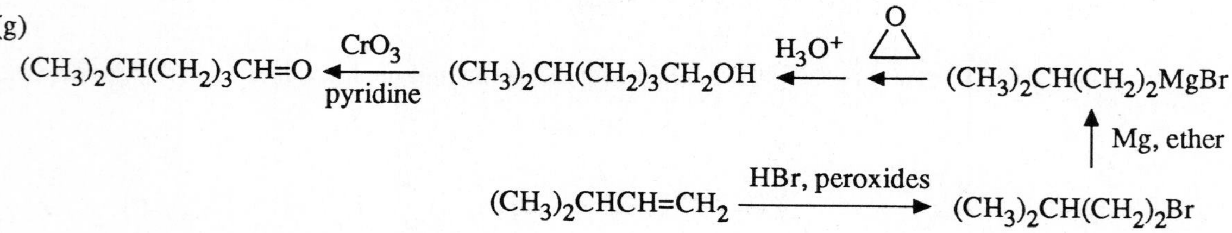

$$(CH_3)_2CH(CH_2)_3CH=O \xleftarrow[\text{pyridine}]{CrO_3} (CH_3)_2CH(CH_2)_3CH_2OH \xleftarrow{H_3O^+} \xleftarrow{\triangle O} (CH_3)_2CH(CH_2)_2MgBr$$

$$\big\uparrow \text{ Mg, ether}$$

$$(CH_3)_2CHCH=CH_2 \xrightarrow{\text{HBr, peroxides}} (CH_3)_2CH(CH_2)_2Br$$

(h) Since Br_2/H_2O gives the bromohydrin, by analogy Br_2/CH_3OH gives the bromo ether.

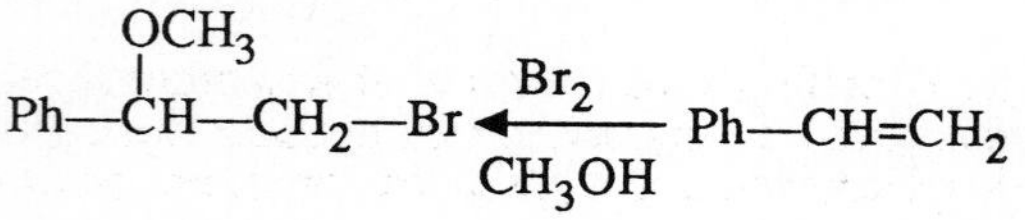

$$Ph\overset{\overset{\displaystyle OCH_3}{|}}{-CH}\!-\!CH_2\!-\!Br \xleftarrow[\text{CH}_3OH]{Br_2} Ph\!-\!CH=CH_2$$

(i) In the target molecule, we see that there are two functional groups on adjacent carbons. Notice again [see part (d)] that epoxides often serve as useful intermediates in this sort of situation.

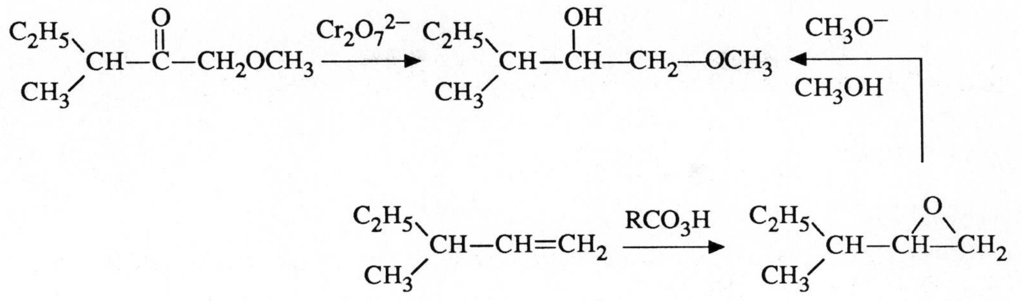

38. In this reaction the ion formed from displacement on one ethylene oxide molecule attacks another molecule:

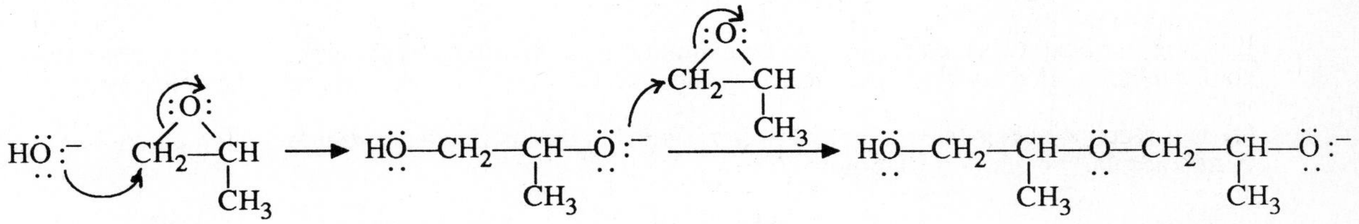

The reaction continues indefinitely in this same fashion.

39. Compound A is an alkene — an octene. There can be no branches in the carbon chain, since catalytic hydrogenation gives octane. Compounds C and D are stereoisomeric glycols. The only octene that would give an achiral glycol is the one that can give a *meso* isomer — namely, 4-octene. The 4-octene stereoisomer that gives *meso*-4,5-octanediol with OsO_4 is *cis*-4-octene. To summarize, with R— = $CH_3CH_2CH_2CH_2$—:

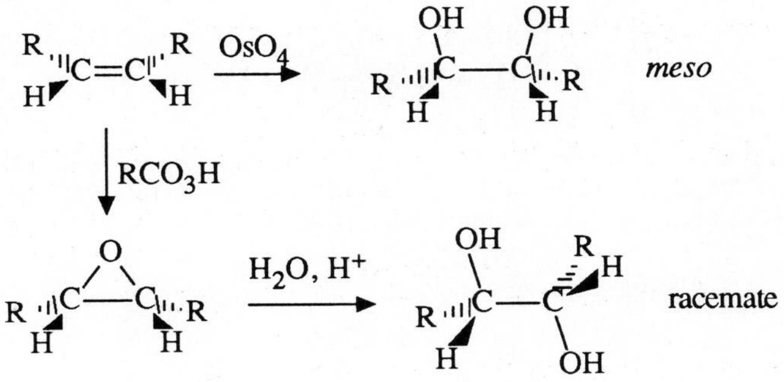

40. The principles to be used here are that the *t*-butyl group strongly prefers to be axial; and that in order to react, the chloro and hydroxy groups must be able to achieve an *anti*, and thus diaxial, conformation. Thus, compound (1) reacts fastest, because the —OH and —Cl groups are *anti* in the preferred conformation of the compound:

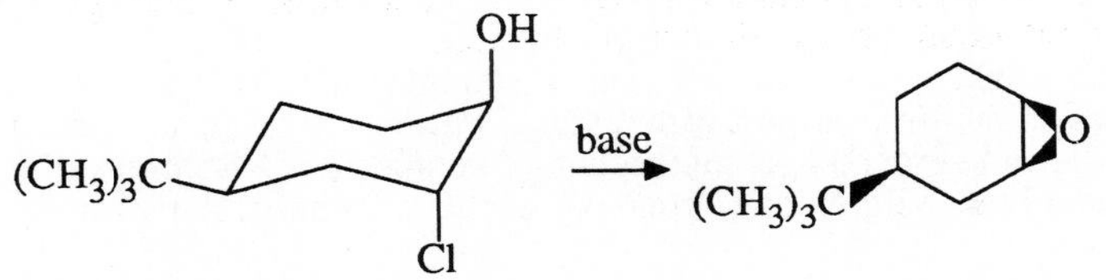

compound B = (1)   epoxide D

Hence, B is compound (1). Compound (2) can achieve a conformation with the —OH and —Cl group in an *anti* arrangement, but only at the energetic cost of either placing a *t*-butyl group in an axial position, or switching into a twist-boat:

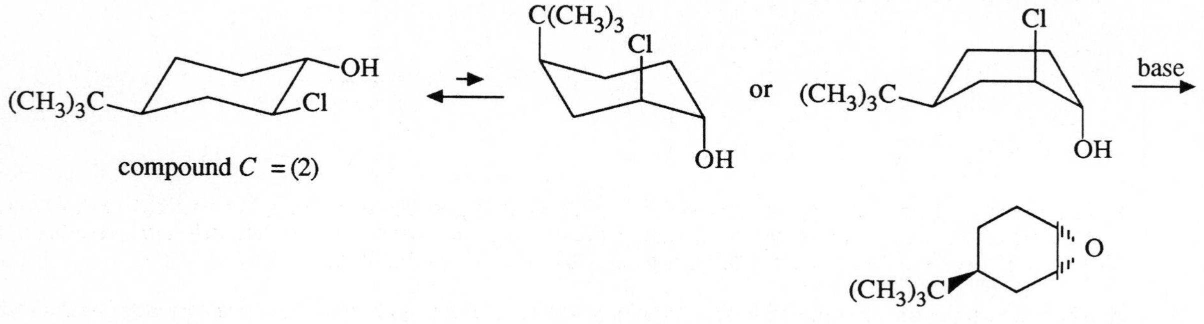

compound C = (2)

epoxide E

Hence, compound C is compound (2). Compound A is thus compound (3), which cannot achieve the proper conformation under any circumstances. (For the —OH and —Cl groups to be *anti*, they must be *trans*.)

41. (a) This reaction begins like bromohydrin formation, but the intermediate bromonium ion is attacked intramolecularly by the —OH group:

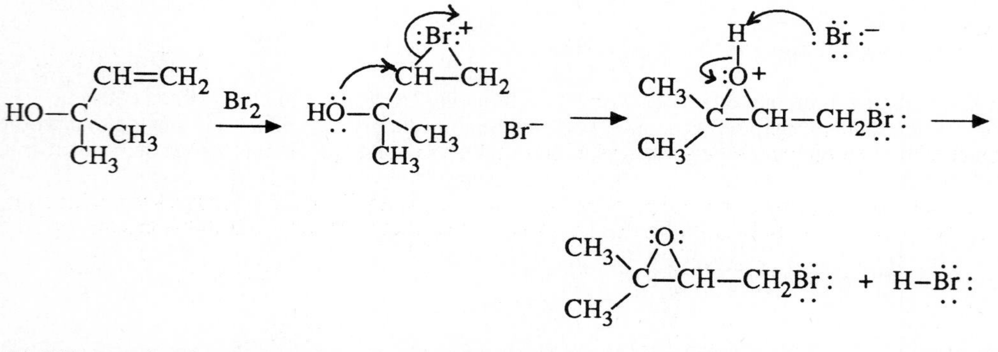

(b) This reaction is an intramolecular S_N2 reaction in which the sulfide anion, formed by ionization of the starting material, internally displaces the tosylate group through a boat conformation:

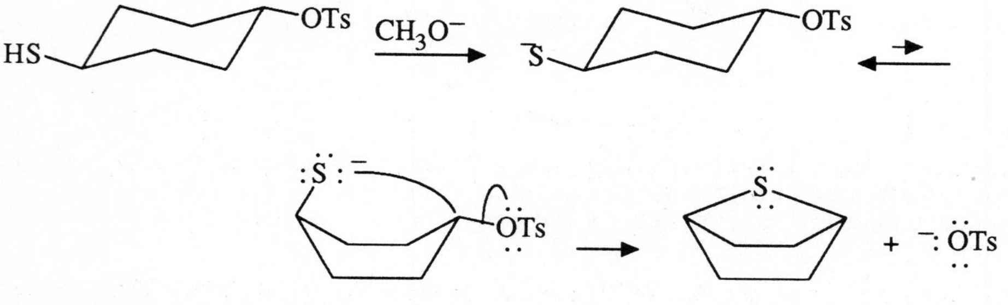

Why doesn't methoxide attack the tosylate? There are two reasons. The most important is that thiols are much more acidic than alcohols. Hence, the thiol anion forms almost irreversibly. Furthermore, such proton-transfer reactions are generally very fast — they happen before competing reactions can take place. Secondly, the intramolecular reaction, like all reactions involving neighboring-group participation, is particularly rapid.

(c) In this reaction, the radical formed in the desulfurization process "bites back" onto the double bond. (Recall that radicals add to double bonds.)

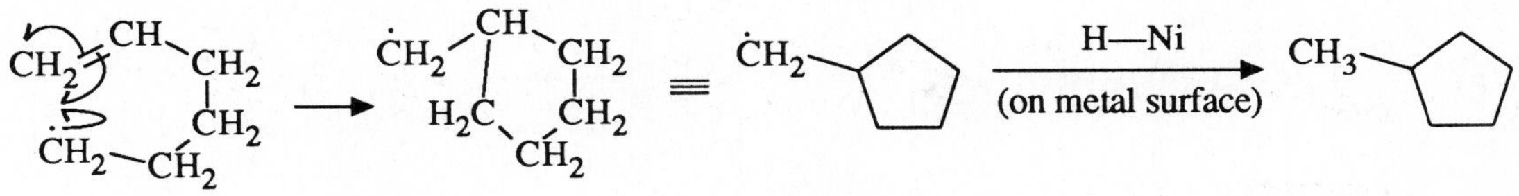

➤ It is interesting that the radical adds to the double bond to give the *less substituted* radical. Formation of the five-membered ring is more probable than formation of a six-membered one, and primary radicals do not differ enough in stability from secondary ones to overcome this probability.

(d) Since E2 reactions compete with S_N2 reactions of alkyl halides, perhaps it is not surprising that a similar competition exists with epoxides:

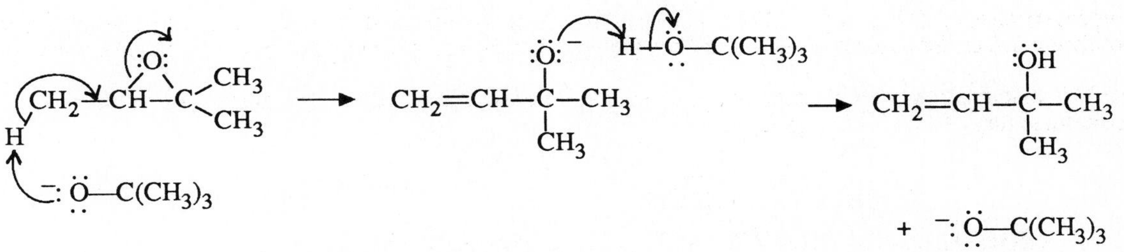

(This is the mechanism for the major product; write the one for the minor product.)

(e) This is a variation of the pinacol rearrangement. BF_3 is a Lewis acid. In many cases, we can think of a Lewis acid as a "fat proton" — that is, we can treat it more or less like a proton — and this case is typical:

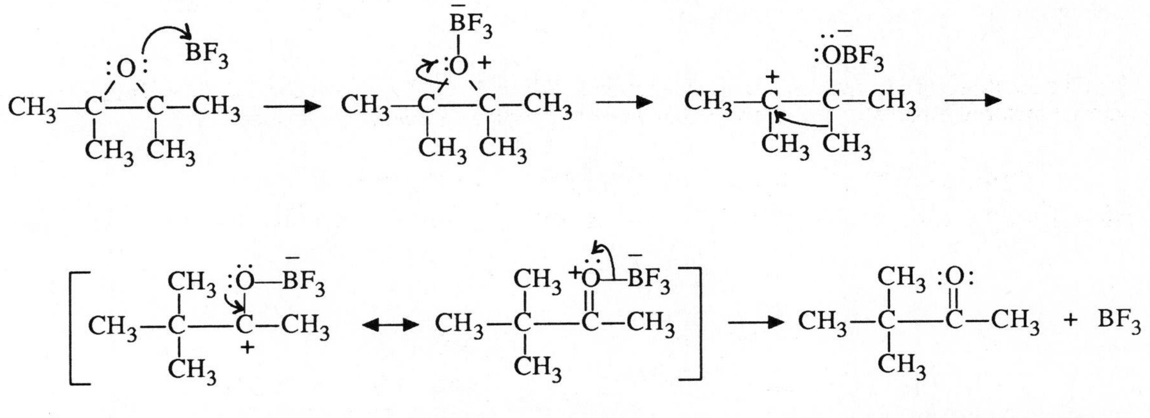

(f) Notice that a bond has been formed between sulfur and one carbon of the double bond. The other carbon of the double bond has added a proton. (Of course, we don't see the proton explicitly because hydrogens are not shown in skeletal structures.) Hence, this reaction is nothing more than an addition to a double bond in which the nucleophile is within the same molecule:

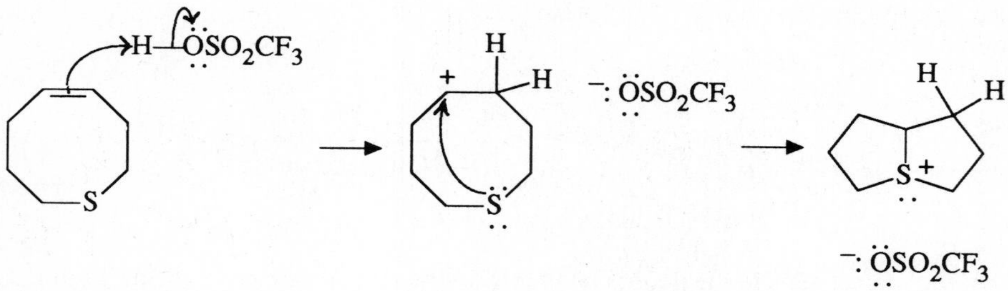

(g) This is an interesting (and relatively rare) case of neighboring-group participation involving a four-membered ring. Sulfur displaces the tosylate group, and methanol displaces the sulfur by attack at the more substituted carbon of the sulfonium ion.

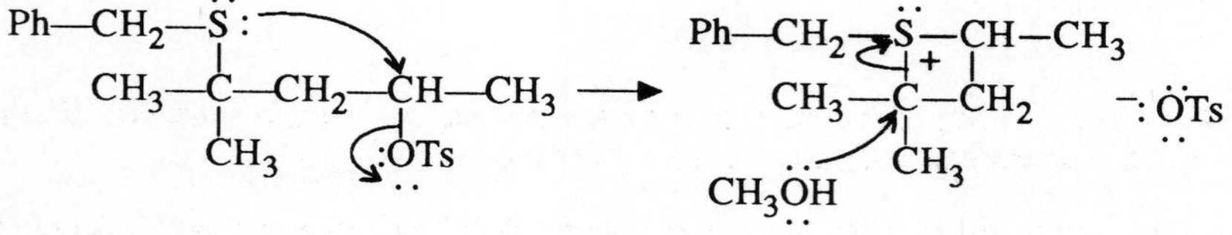

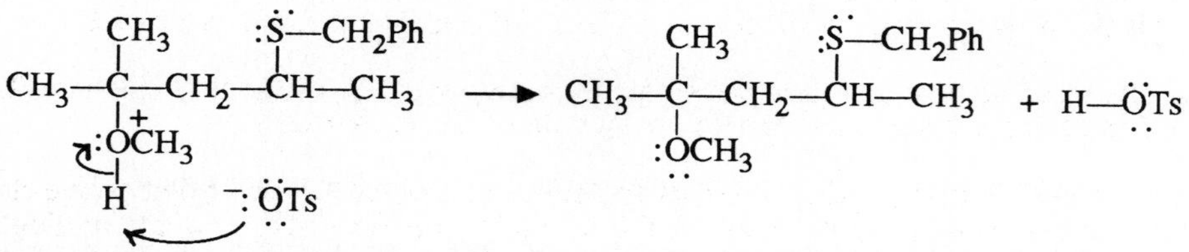

(h) This is a multiple rearrangement. This fact, and the acidic reaction conditions, suggest the involvement of carbocation intermediates. The first carbocation is generated by epoxide ring opening. (See remarks in (e) about treating Lewis acids as "fat protons.")

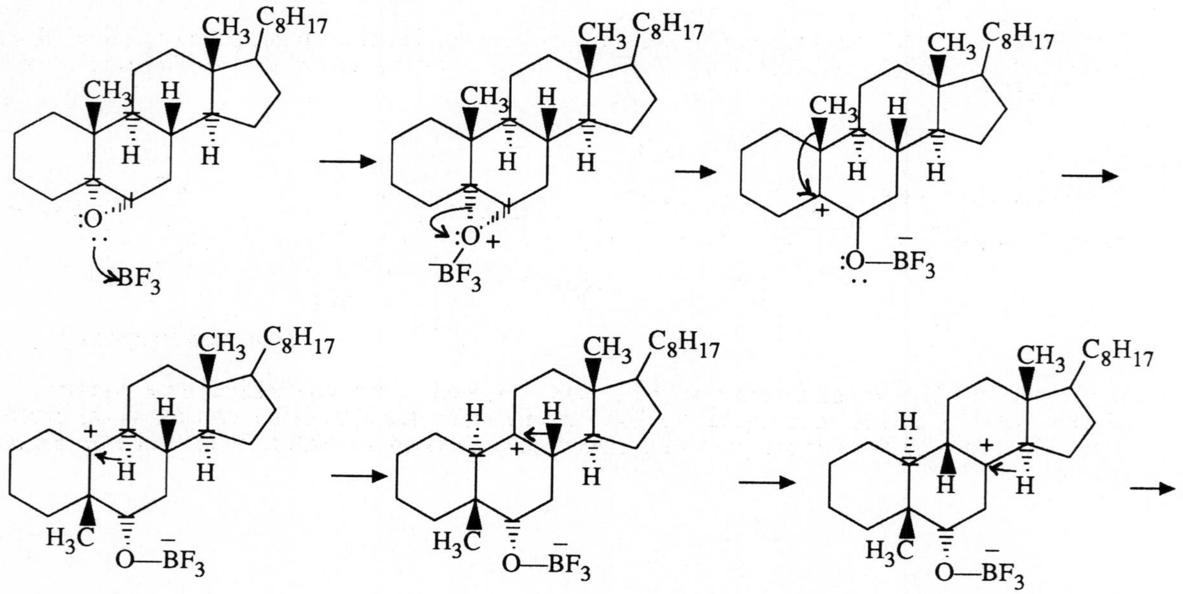

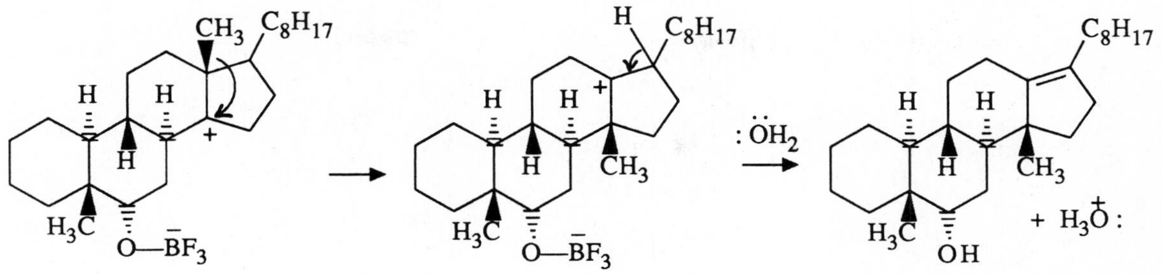

(Addition of water liberates the BF_3, with which it reacts further.) Notice that each group has migrated to an adjacent carbon, and remains on the same face of the ring. Migration to an opposite face of the ring would be stereochemically impossible.

42. To solve this problem we must examine the charge situation in the transition state of each reaction relative to that in the starting materials, and how solvent affects the relative free energies of the two.

    (a) In this reaction, ions of opposite charge must come together; the products have zero charge. Solvents that promote *separation* of charge and solvation of ions will retard this reaction. Since water is the best solvent for ions, it is the worst solvent for this reaction. Thus, this reaction is faster in ethanol.

    (b) In this reaction, ions of opposite charge must be separated; this is an S_N1 reaction. The best solvent is one that separates and solvates ions. Hence, this reaction is faster in water.

    (c) In this reaction, both starting materials and transition state contain a single positive charge, because the leaving group is neutral. Hence, to a first approximation, the free energies of the starting materials and transition state should be affected in the same way by a change of solvent, and the reaction rate has little dependence on solvent.

43. Fact #3 tells us that the reaction of compound *A* involves neighboring-group participation by sulfur. Since sulfur displaces chloride, the groups must be able to assume an *anti* conformation in *A*. This is achieved by a chair-chair flip:

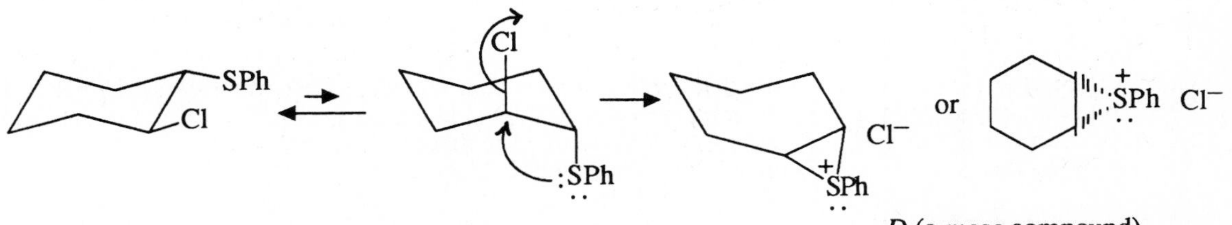

D (a *meso* compound)

    Notice that the sulfonium-ion intermediate *D* is a *meso* compound. It can be attacked at either carbon by ethanol. Attack at the two carbons gives the respective enantiomers, and these are formed in equal amounts. (Recall that achiral reagents cannot generate optically active compounds.) Hence, the product is the racemate (Fact #2).

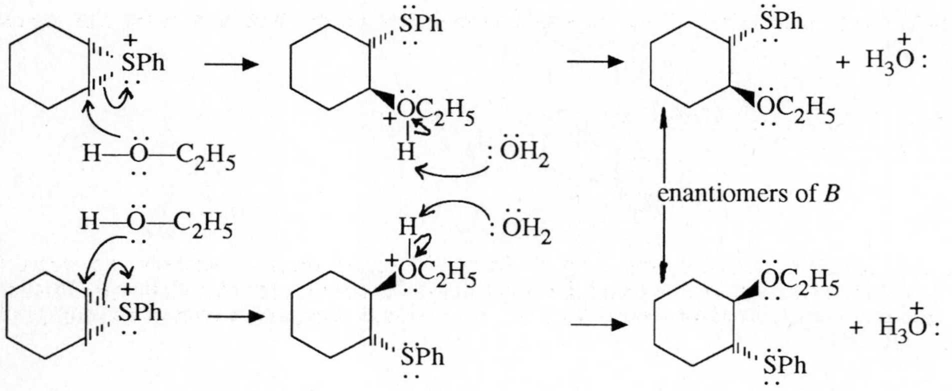

Since attack of ethanol must occur at the backside of the carbon-sulfur bond, only the *trans* isomer *B* is formed (Fact #1).

44. The key to this problem is to consider the stereochemical aspects of the problem after we have determined how to make the appropriate bonds.

(a)

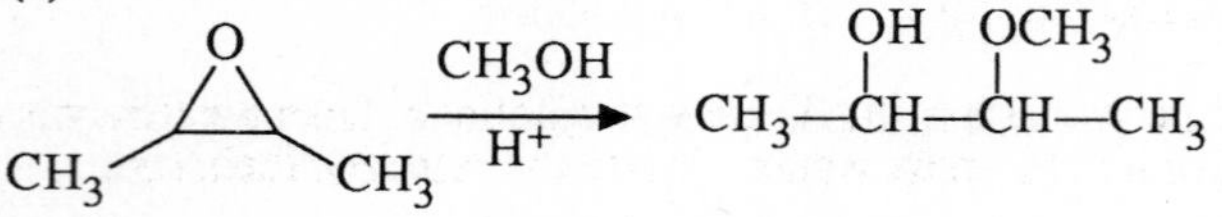

This is the desired product. But does it have the correct stereochemistry? Such a reaction would occur with inversion of configuration:

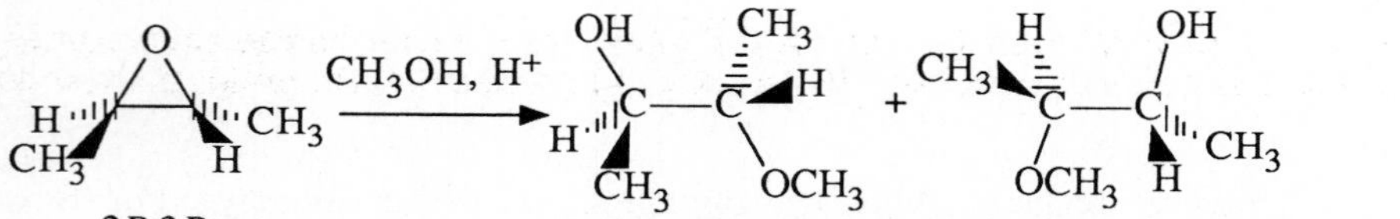

2*R*,3*R*

(from attack of CH_3OH at carbon-3) (from attack of CH_3OH at carbon-2)

same compound

The "two" products are indeed the same compound, and this compound has the correct stereochemistry; it is 2*R*,3*S*. In other words, the carbon at which the methanol molecule attacks becomes carbon-3 in the product; because it is inverted, this carbon has the *S* configuration. The other carbon, because it bears the —OH group, is carbon-2, and its configuration is unaffected; it has the *R* configuration.

(b) The product has the *S* configuration, like the product in (a). Hence, all we have to do is to oxidize the secondary alcohol formed as the product of (a):

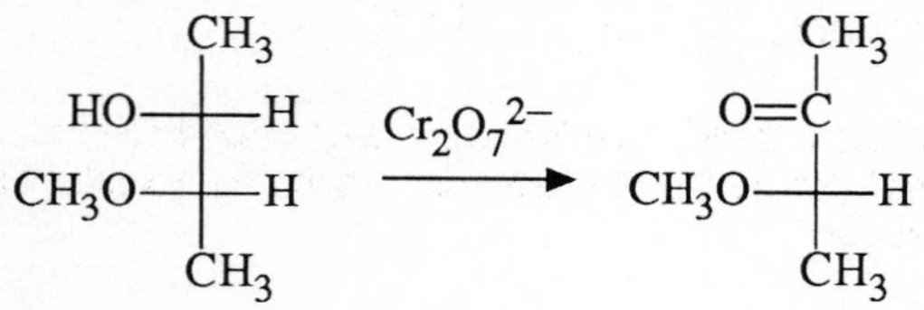

(c) This compound is the product of a Williamson synthesis in which the product of (a) is the starting material:

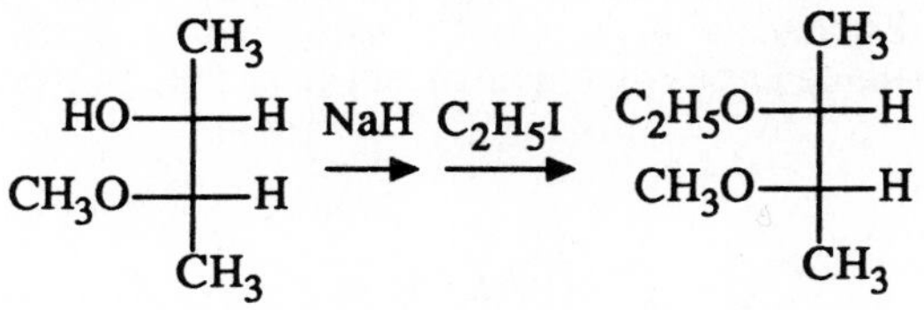

(d) This compound is the enantiomer of the one prepared in (c). The temptation is somehow to manipulate (c) to get this compound, but in fact we have to go all the way back to the starting epoxide. We open this epoxide with ethanol rather than methanol, and then carry out a Williamson ether synthesis with methyl iodide rather than ethyl iodide.

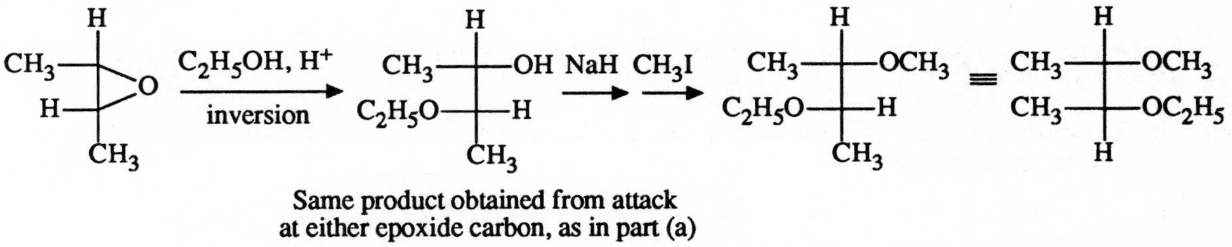

Same product obtained from attack
at either epoxide carbon, as in part (a)

➤ We worked (a) using conformational projections and (d) using Fischer projections. Use whatever method is easier. Fischer projections are easier to draw if you are careful not to violate the rules for their use.

45. The result is explained if the loss of water from the protonated alcohol involves neighboring-group participation by the bromine to give a bromonium-ion intermediate. We start the mechanism with the protonated alcohol:

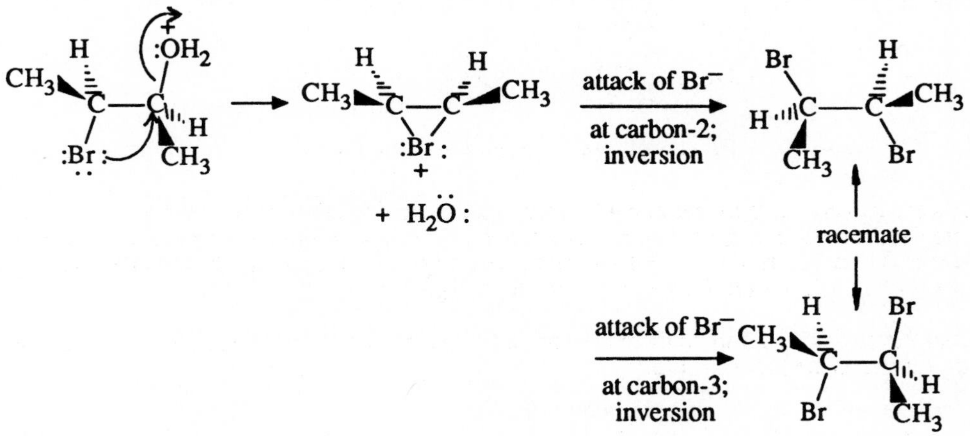

Because the bromonium-ion intermediate is *meso*, and therefore achiral, attack at carbon-2 or carbon-3 is equally probable; the product is the racemate. Now you should show that an identical mechanism applied to the other stereoisomer of the starting material gives the *meso* product.

➤ What stereochemical result would we expect if bromonium-ion intermediates were not involved, and carbocation intermediates were involved instead?

46. In general, we expect diastereomeric products to be formed in different amounts. But the issue is why compound B is the *particular* diastereomer that is formed. The stereochemical requirement of epoxide ring opening is that attack of the nucleophile occurs from the back side. When this happens, the attacking group and leaving group have an *anti* relationship. We further require that the *t*-butyl group be locked into an equatorial position. Attack at one carbon of the epoxide while maintaining these two requirements gives the conjugate base of compound B (which protonates to form B itself):

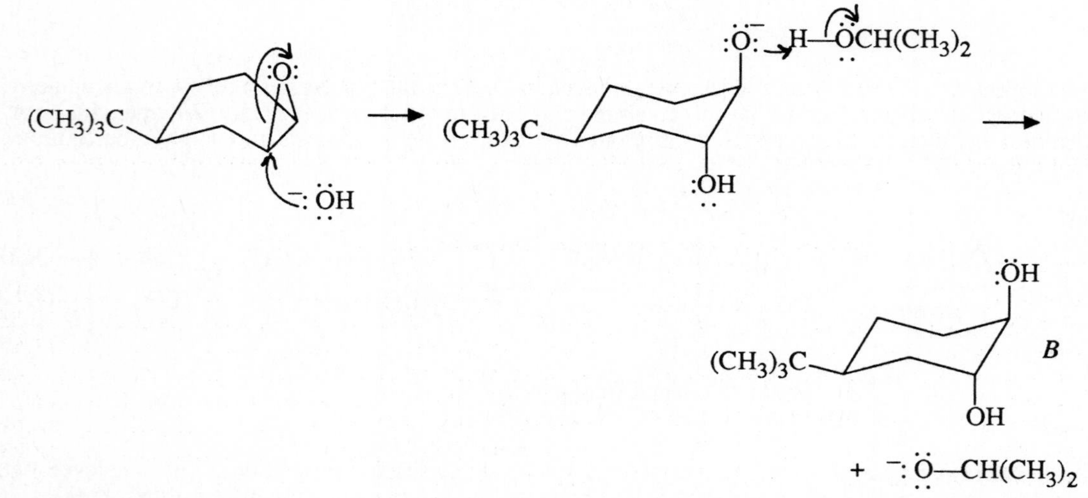

Attack at the other carbon of the epoxide gives the conjugate base of compound C; however, the required *anti* relationship of attacking and leaving group can only be achieved if the ring adopts a *boat conformation*.

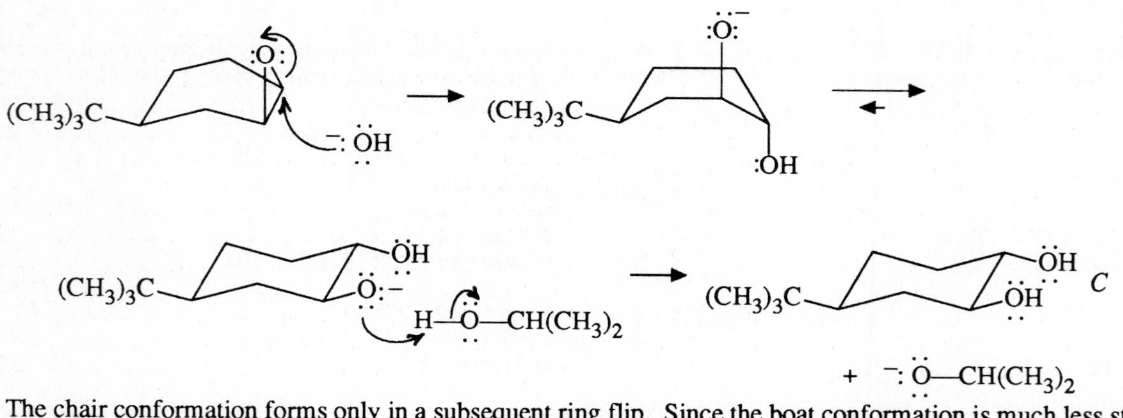

The chair conformation forms only in a subsequent ring flip. Since the boat conformation is much less stable than the chair, the transition state for formation of B has lower energy and is therefore formed more rapidly.

➤ Notice that product B is actually a less stable product than product C (why?), yet B is formed more rapidly. It is the stability of the *transition state*, not the stability of the product, that determines the rate. The requirement that the transition state for formation of C adopt a boat conformation makes this transition state less stable, even though a more stable product is formed in the end.

Chapter 12 / Infrared Spectroscopy and Mass Spectrometry

CHAPTER 12 TERMS

α-cleavage 12.5C
absorption spectroscopy 12.1B
β-scission 12.5C
base peak 12.5A
bending vibration 12.2D
chemical-ionization mass spectrometry (CI) 12.5D
cycles per second (cps) 12.1A
electromagnetic radiation 12.1A
electromagnetic spectrum 12.1A
electron-impact mass spectrometry (EI) 12.5D
even-electron ion 12.5C
exact mass 12.5E
fast-atom bombardment (FAB) 12.5E
fishhook arrow formalism 12.5A
force constant 12.2D
fragment ion 12.5A
fragmentation reaction 12.5A
free-radical arrow formalism 12.5A
frequency (ν) 12.1A
gauss 12.5E
hertz (Hz) 12.1A
high-resolution mass spectrometer 12.5E
inductive cleavage 12.5C
infrared active 12.2E
infrared inactive 12.2E
infrared (IR) spectrophotometer 12.2A
in-the-plane vibration 12.2D

isotopic peak 12.5B
magnetic field, **H** 12.5E
mass spectrometer 12.5A
mass spectrometry 12.5
mass spectrum 12.5A
mass-to-charge ratio (m/e) 12.5A
micrometer (micron), μm 12.2A
nominal mass 12.5E
normal vibrational mode 12.2D
odd-electron ion 12.5C
out-of-the-plane vibration 12.2D
parent (molecular) ion (p) 12.5A
photon 12.1A
Planck's constant (h) 12.1A
radical cation 12.5A
reciprocal centimeters (cm^{-1}) 12.2A
relative abundance 12.5A
resolution 12.5E
scissoring 12.2D
spectrometer 12.1B
spectrophotometer 12.1B
spectroscopy 12.1
stretching vibration 12.2D
symmetrical vibration 12.2D
unsymmetrical vibration 12.2D
wavelength (λ) 12.1A
wavenumber ($\bar{\nu}$) 12.2A

CHAPTER 12 CONCEPTS

I. **Introduction to Spectroscopy:**

    A. <u>Electromagnetic Radiation:</u>

        1. The total range of electromagnetic radiation, called the **electromagnetic spectrum**, is given in Fig. 12.2 of the text; several important forms of electromagnetic radiation are:

            a) Ultraviolet radiation.

            b) Infrared radiation.

            c) Visible light.

2. Electromagnetic radiation can be characterized by its wavelength, λ.
   a) The **wavelength** of a wave is the distance between successive peaks or successive troughs.
   b) The **frequency** v of a wave is defined by the equation

$$v = \frac{c}{\lambda}$$

   in which c = the velocity of light, and frequency has the dimensions of sec^{-1} [cycles per second (cps) or hertz (Hz)].
   c) The frequency increases as the wavelength decreases.
   d) All forms of electromagnetic radiation are fundamentally the same; they differ only in energy.
3. Light shows particlelike behavior.
   a) The light particle is called a **photon**.
   b) The relationship between the energy of a photon and the wavelength or frequency of light is a fundamental law of physics:

$$E = hv = h\frac{c}{\lambda}$$

   where h is Plank's constant.

B. Absorption Spectroscopy:
   1. The study of the interaction of matter and electromagnetic radiation is called **spectroscopy**.
      a) Spectroscopy can be used to determine unknown molecular structures.
      b) The most common type of spectroscopy used for structure determination is **absorption spectroscopy**.
         (1) Matter can absorb energy from certain wavelengths of electromagnetic radiation.
         (2) This absorption is determined as a function of wavelength, frequency, or energy in an instrument called a **spectrophotometer** or **spectrometer**.
   2. The components of a spectroscopy experiment include:
      a) A source of electromagnetic radiation.
      b) The sample.
      c) A detector.
      d) A recorder.
   3. The graph recorded by a spectrometer is commonly called a **spectrum** (plural: **spectra**).
   4. The three types of spectroscopy of greatest use to organic chemists for structure determination are:
      a) Nuclear magnetic resonance (NMR).
      b) Infrared (IR).
      c) Ultraviolet-visible (UV-VIS).
   5. **Mass spectrometry** is a fourth physical technique used for structure determination; however, it is *not* a type of absorption spectroscopy.

II. Infrared Spectroscopy:

A. The Infrared Spectrum:
   1. An infrared spectrum is a record of the radiation absorbed by a substance as a function of wavelength.
   2. Another way to express the frequency of the radiation, and a way used widely in IR spectroscopy, is by **wavenumber** ($\tilde{v}$), in the units of **reciprocal centimeters** (cm^{-1}).
      a) Wavenumber is inversely proportional to the wavelength λ.

$$\tilde{v} = \frac{10^4}{\lambda}$$

   where λ is in micrometers (μm).
      b) Wavenumber is directly proportional to energy and frequency:

$$E = \frac{hc}{\lambda} = hv = hc\tilde{v}$$

   where $\tilde{v}$ is in cm^{-1} and λ is in cm.
   3. Percent transmittance is plotted on the vertical axis of the spectrum.
      a) This is the percentage of the radiation falling on the sample that is transmitted to the detector.
      b) Absorptions in the IR spectrum are registered as downward deflections.

    4. Intensities are often expressed qualitatively:
        a) vs—very strong.
        b) s—strong.
        c) m—moderate.
        d) w—weak.

B. Infrared Absorption and Chemical Structure:
    1. The absorptions observed in an IR spectrum are the result of vibrations within a molecule.
        a) Atoms in chemical bonds vibrate with characteristic frequencies.
        b) Absorption of energy from infrared radiation can occur *only* when there is a match between the
            wavelength of the radiation and the wavelength of the bond vibration.
    2. Each peak in the IR spectrum of a molecule corresponds to absorption of energy by the vibrations of a
       bond or group of bonds.
        a) In all compounds, a given type of functional group absorbs in the same general region of the IR
            spectrum.
        b) The IR spectrum serves as a fingerprint of the functional groups present in the molecule.
    3. Two aspects of IR absorption peaks are particularly important:
        a) Position (the wavenumber or wavelength at which it occurs).
        b) Intensity.
    4. Factors that govern the position of an IR absorption are:
        a) Strength of the bond.
        b) Masses of the atoms involved in the bond.
        c) The type of vibration being observed.
    5. Factors that govern the intensity of an IR absorption are:
        a) Number of bonds of the type being observed.
        b) Concentration of the sample.
        c) The dipole-moment change in the molecule resulting from the bond vibration of interest.

C. Factors Determining IR Absorption Positions:
    1. The vibration of a stronger bond occurs at higher wavenumber (lower wavelength) than the vibration
       of a weaker bond.
        a) Bond dissociation energies give information about bond strengths and **force constants**.
            (1) The higher the bond dissociation energy, the greater the bond strength.
            (2) The stronger the bond, the greater the force constant.
    2. Vibrations of heavier atoms occur at lower frequency or wavenumber than vibrations of lighter atoms.
    3. There are two general types of vibrations:
        a) **Stretching vibrations**—vibrations along the line of the chemical bond.
        b) **Bending vibrations**—any vibration that does not occur along the line of the chemical bond.
    4. Bending vibrations occur at lower frequencies (higher wavelengths) than stretching vibrations of the
       same group.
    5. There are two types of bending vibrations:
        a) In the plane of the vibrating atoms.
        b) Out of the plane of the vibrating atoms.
    6. Stretching and bending vibrations can be symmetrical or unsymmetrical with respect to a symmetry
       plane.
    7. The only possible type of vibration in a diatomic molecule is the stretching vibration.

D. Factors Determining IR Absorption Intensities:
    1. The different peaks in an IR spectrum typically have very different intensities.
    2. The intensity of an infrared absorption depends on:
        a) The number of bonds present of the type being observed.
        b) The size of the dipole-moment change associated with the vibration in question.
    3. A more concentrated sample gives a stronger spectrum than a less concentrated one.
    4. A vibration must result in a dipole-moment change in the molecule if it is to be observed in the IR
       spectrum.
        a) Dipole moments change during vibrations because a dipole moment is the product of both charge
            separation and distance.
        b) A vibration that causes a change in the dipole moment gives rise to an IR absorption peak and is
            said to be **infrared active.**
        c) A vibration that *does not* cause a change in the dipole moment and *cannot* give an IR absorption
            peak is said to be **infrared inactive.**

E. Experimental Aspects of Infrared Spectroscopy:
  1. An IR spectrum is determined in an infrared spectrometer.
  2. The major features of an infrared spectrometer are:
    a) A source of infrared radiation.
    b) A mirror system to split the IR beam into:
      (1) A sample beam.
      (2) A reference beam.
    c) A monochromator (a device that sorts the IR beam into various wavelengths).
    d) A detector.
    e) A recorder.

III. Introduction to Mass Spectrometry:

  A. The Mass Spectrum:
    1. The **mass spectrum** can be determined for any molecule that can be vaporized in a high vacuum.
    2. The utility of mass spectrometry is:
      a) It can be used to determine the molecular weight of an unknown compound.
      b) An analysis of the **fragment ions** in the spectrum can be used to determine the structure of an unknown compound.
    3. Only *ions* are detected by the **mass spectrometer**.
    4. Some ions formed in the mass spectrometer are **radical cations**—cations with an unpaired electron. These are designated by the symbol $^{+}_{\cdot}$.
      a) Radical cations decompose in a series of reactions called **fragmentation reactions**.
      b) Further decomposition reactions give fragments of progressively lower mass.
      c) These fragment ions are separated according to their **mass-to-charge ratio**, m/e.
    5. A mass spectrum is a graph of the relative amount of each ion (**relative abundance**).
      a) The **parent ion** or **molecular ion** (p) is the ion derived from electron ejection before any fragmentation takes place.
      b) The molecular ion occurs at an m/e value equal to the molecular weight of the sample molecule.
      c) The **base peak** is the ion of greatest relative abundance.
        (1) The base peak is arbitrarily assigned a relative abundance of 100%.
        (2) The other peaks in the mass spectrum are scaled relative to the base peak.

  B. Isotopic Peaks:
    1. Most compounds are mixtures whose components contain the various isotopes of their constituent atoms.
      a) Each isotopic compound contributes a peak with a relative abundance in proportion to its amount.
      b) The amount of each isotopic compound is directly related to the natural abundance of isotope involved.
      c) Not only the parent peak, but every other peak in the mass spectrum, has **isotopic peaks**.
      d) The mixture of isotopes leaves in the mass spectrum a characteristic trail that indicates the elements present.
      e) The presence of chlorine or bromine is particularly easy to detect with isotopic peaks.
        (1) A single chlorine gives two isotopic peaks of about 3:1 relative intensity.
        (2) A single bromine gives two isotopic peaks of about equal intensity.
    2. Isotopes provide a specific label at particular atoms without changing their chemical properties.
      a) Isotopes can be used to determine the fate of specific atoms in deciding between two mechanisms.
      b) When a compound has been isotopically enriched, isotopic peaks become much larger than they normally are.

  C. Fragmentation:
    1. The molecular ion is formed by loss of an electron from a parent molecule.
      a) A stable molecular ion decomposes slowly and is detected as a peak of large relative abundance.
      b) An unstable molecular ion decomposes into smaller pieces called **fragment ions**.
    2. The relative abundances of the various fragments in a mass spectrum depend on their relative lifetimes.
      a) The most stable ions have the longest lifetimes.
      b) The most stable ions are detected as the largest peaks in a mass spectrum.
    3. The simplest way to analyze a mass spectrum is to think of fragment ions as coherent pieces that result from the breaking of chemical bonds in the molecular ion.

a) It takes less energy to eject an electron from an unshared electron pair or a π-bond than it does from a σ-bond.

b) Unshared electrons and π-electrons are held less tightly than σ-electrons.

c) **Inductive cleavage** is very common in compounds containing a very electronegative element.

d) α-**Cleavage** (also called β-**scission**) is a common fragmentation mode at double bonds and at atoms with unshared electrons.

4. The masses of *both* the fragments lost and the fragments observed can be used to postulate the structure of the fragments.

a) The observed fragment *must* be charged.

b) Fragmentation is not random.

c) Fragmentation is a consequence of the rules of carbocation or free-radical stability.

(1) Ions with *no* unpaired electrons are called **even-electron ions**.

(2) Ions with an unpaired electron are called **odd-electron ions**.

(3) Hydrogen-atom transfer followed by loss of a stable neutral molecule is a common mechanism for the formation of odd-electron ions.

5. A molecule containing only C, H, and O has an even mass.

a) Radical cations of even mass in many cases fragment to give separate radical and cation species having odd masses.

(1) The unpaired electron is carried off in the radical fragment.

(2) The carbocation fragment detected has no unpaired electrons.

b) When a compound contains only C, H, and O, its fragment ions of odd mass must be even-electron ions.

c) When a compound contains only C, H, and O, its fragment ions of even mass must be odd-electron ions.

D. Identifying the Molecular Ion:

1. The molecular ion is the most important peak in the mass spectrum.

a) It provides the molecular weight of the molecule under study.

b) It is the basis for calculating the losses involved in fragmentation.

c) All compounds containing only the elements C, H, and O have molecular ions of even mass.

2. In some mass spectra, the abundance of the molecular ion is so small it is undetectable.

3. One way to determine the mass of the molecular ion is by chemical derivatization.

E. Types of Mass Spectrometry:

1. **Electron-impact mass spectrometry** employs electron bombardment to ionize a molecule.

2. **Chemical-ionization mass spectrometry** uses protons to protonate the most basic site of a molecule.

a) The molecular ion appears at one mass unit higher than the molecular weight of the unprotonated molecule.

b) A much higher percentage of molecular ion is usually obtained.

c) Different fragmentation patterns are observed containing fewer peaks.

3. **High-resolution mass spectrometers** can resolve ions that are separated in mass by only a few thousandths of a mass unit, and permit the distinction between ions of different composition that have the same **nominal mass**.

4. **Fast-atom bombardment** converts compounds directly into gas-phase ions by subjecting them to a beam of heavy atoms that have been accelerated to high velocities.

F. The Mass Spectrometer:

1. Within the mass spectrometer the sample is ionized and fragment ions are formed, separated, and detected. A sample *must* be vaporized before it can be analyzed by mass spectrometry.

2. Ions of different mass are differentiated in the mass spectrometer by their different interactions with a **magnetic field**.

CHAPTER 12 SOLUTIONS

Solutions to In-Text Problems

1. We apply Eq. 12.1 and obtain:

    for blue light,
    $v = (3 \times 10^{10} \text{ cm/sec})/(4800 \times 10^{-8} \text{ cm}) = 6.25 \times 10^{14} \text{ sec}^{-1}$

    for infrared light,
    $v = (3 \times 10^{10} \text{ cm/sec})/(900 \times 10^{-6} \text{ cm}) = 3.33 \times 10^{13} \text{ sec}^{-1}$

2. We apply Eq. 12.3 and obtain:

    for blue light,
    $E = (9.532 \times 10^{-14} \text{ kcal-sec-mol}^{-1})(6.25 \times 10^{14} \text{ sec}^{-1}) = 59.6 \text{ kcal/mol}$

    for infrared light,
    $E = (9.532 \times 10^{-14} \text{ kcal-sec-mol}^{-1})(3.33 \times 10^{13} \text{ sec}^{-1}) = 3.2 \text{ kcal/mol}$

3. X-rays have much shorter wavelength, since wavelength and energy are inversely related (Eq. 12.3).

4. (a) $\tilde{v}$ = wavenumber = $10^4/6.0 = 1667 \text{ cm}^{-1}$
    (b) λ = wavelength = $10^4/1720 = 5.81 \ \mu$

5. From Eq. 12.1 and 12.7a,

    $$E = hc/\lambda = hc\tilde{v}; \text{ since } v = c/\lambda, \text{ then } hv = hc\tilde{v}, \text{ or } v = c\tilde{v}.$$

6. From Eq. 12.7b,

    $$\tilde{v} = v/c = (9 \times 10^{13} \text{ sec}^{-1})/(3 \times 10^{10} \text{ cm/sec})$$
    $$= 3000 \text{ cm}^{-1}$$

    The peak at 3000 cm^{-1} in the IR spectrum of nonane is due to the C—H stretching vibration.

7. The force constants for the C—H and C—D bonds are the same. Hence, the wavenumbers of the two vibrations are in the ratio of factors

    $$\sqrt{\frac{m + M}{mM}}$$

    for each atom, where M = the mass of carbon, and m = the mass of hydrogen or deuterium. Thus, we have

    $$\frac{\tilde{v}(\text{C—H})}{\tilde{v}(\text{C—D})} = \sqrt{\frac{1.083}{0.583}} = \sqrt{1.858} = 1.36$$

    Therefore, $\tilde{v}(\text{C—D}) = 3000 \text{ cm}^{-1}/1.36 = 2205 \text{ cm}^{-1}$. This number is actually quite close to the C—D stretching frequency.

8. From Table 5.2, text page 164, we see that bond strengths increase in the given series to the right; therefore, bond strength is more important. Were atomic mass more important, frequencies would decrease to the right.

9. The guiding principle here is whether the vibration in question changes the dipole moment of the molecule. Remember, dipole moment is the product of charge separation times *length*. A change in bond length can also bring about a change in dipole moment if charge separation is increased.

   (a) Active.
   (b) Active; the vibration imparts a nonzero dipole moment to CO_2:

   (c) Active.

   (d) Inactive; both the molecule and its stretched form have zero dipole moment.

   (e) Virtually inactive. Because alkyl groups have similar electronic properties, the molecule and its stretched form have almost zero dipole moment.

   (f) Inactive.

   (g) Active.

   (h) Active; stretching both N—O groups simultaneously increases the dipole moment of the molecule.

   (i) Inactive; both the molecule and its stretched form have zero dipole moment.

10. Spectrum (b) has the characteristic *trans*-alkene absorption at 965 cm^{-1}, and lacks a C=C stretching absorption, as we would expect for a symmetrical or nearly symmetrical alkene; hence, spectrum (b) is that of *trans*-2-heptene. Spectrum (a) shows the characteristic terminal C=CH$_2$ absorption near 900 cm^{-1} as well as a strong C=C absorption.

11. The =C—H stretch absorbs at higher frequency than the alkyl C—H stretch. The stronger the bond, the greater its stretching frequency.

12. The spectrum lacks O—H stretch and C=C stretch, and therefore is neither the alkene nor the alcohol. Our diagnosis that this compound is the ether is confirmed by the strong C—O stretching absorption near 1200 cm^{-1}.

13. The two absorptions are due to symmetrical and unsymmetrical stretching absorptions:

    R—O—R $\xrightarrow{\text{stretch}}$ R—O—R   unsymmetrical stretch

    R—O—R $\xrightarrow{\text{stretch}}$ R—O—R   symmetrical stretch

14. This is simply a mass-action effect. If we consider the hydrogen bonding of two alcohol molecules as an equilibrium, we have:

    $$2RO-H \rightleftharpoons RO-H\cdots\cdots O-R$$

    free   hydrogen bonded

    When the alcohol concentration is high, the reaction is driven to the right; there is a larger amount of hydrogen-bonded alcohol. If we take our IR spectrum under conditions of high concentration, we see a preponderance of hydrogen-bonded species. Conversely, when the alcohol concentration is very low, there is more free alcohol; this is the species that we see in the IR spectrum.

15. There will be two peaks: one at $m/e = 50$, corresponding to CH_3—^{35}Cl; and one at $m/e = 52$, corresponding to CH_3—^{37}Cl. From the relative abundances in Table 12.2, we see that the peak at $m/e = 52$ will be about one-third as intense as the peak at $m/e = 50$. There will also be very small peaks at $m/e = 51$ and 53 due to $^{13}CH_3$—^{35}Cl and $^{13}CH_3$—^{37}Cl, respectively.

16. (a) This peak is due to the t-butyl cation, which is formed as follows:

$$CH_3\text{—}\underset{\underset{CH_3}{|}}{\overset{\overset{CH_3}{|}}{C}}CH_2CH_2\underset{\underset{CH_3}{|}}{\overset{\overset{CH_3}{|}}{C}}\text{—}CH_3 \xrightarrow{-e^-} CH_3\text{—}\underset{\underset{CH_3}{|}}{\overset{\overset{CH_3}{|}}{C}}{}^+ CH_2CH_2\underset{\underset{CH_3}{|}}{\overset{\overset{CH_3}{|}}{C}}\text{—}CH_3 \longrightarrow CH_3\text{—}\underset{\underset{CH_3}{|}}{\overset{\overset{CH_3}{|}}{C}}{}^+ \quad + \quad \cdot CH_2CH_2\text{—}\underset{\underset{CH_3}{|}}{\overset{\overset{CH_3}{|}}{C}}\text{—}CH_3$$

(b) This ion is particularly stable, and therefore occurs in great abundance, because it is a tertiary carbocation.

17. 2-Methyl-2-pentanol has molecular weight = 102. The indicated fragments correspond to losses of 15 mass units (a methyl group) and 43 mass units (a propyl group), respectively. Both groups can be lost by α-cleavage mechanisms:

$$CH_3\text{—}\underset{\underset{CH_3}{|}}{\overset{\overset{:\ddot{O}H}{|}}{C}}\text{—}CH_2CH_2CH_3 \xrightarrow{-e^-} CH_3\text{—}\underset{\underset{CH_3}{|}}{\overset{\overset{+\ddot{O}H}{|}}{C}}CH_2CH_2CH_3 \longrightarrow CH_3\text{—}\underset{\underset{CH_3}{|}}{\overset{\overset{:\ddot{O}\text{—}H}{|}}{C}}{}^+ \quad + \quad \cdot CH_2CH_2CH_3$$
$$m/e = 59$$

$$CH_3\text{—}\underset{\underset{CH_3}{|}}{\overset{\overset{+\ddot{O}H}{|}}{C}}\text{—}CH_2CH_2CH_3 \longrightarrow CH_3\text{—}\overset{\overset{+}{:\ddot{O}\text{—}H}}{\underset{\|}{C}}\text{—}CH_2CH_2CH_3 \quad + \quad \cdot CH_3$$
$$m/e = 87$$

➤ Be sure not to confuse the fragments lost as uncharged *radicals* with the fragment *ions*.

18. The mass of the fragment corresponds to some type of propyl group, and there is an isopropyl group attached to oxygen. The inductive cleavage mechanism can yield an isopropyl cation:

$$CH_3CH_2\underset{\underset{CH_3}{|}}{\overset{+}{CH}}\text{—}\overset{..}{\underset{..}{O}}\text{—}CH(CH_3)_2 \longrightarrow CH_3CH_2\underset{\underset{CH_3}{|}}{CH}\text{—}\overset{..}{\underset{..}{O}}: \quad + \quad {}^+CH(CH_3)_2$$
$$m/e = 43$$

19. There is no reason why the inductive cleavage mechanism of the previous problem should occur at only one of the secondary alkyl groups; cleavage at the other side of the oxygen gives the fragment at $m/e = 57$:

$$CH_3CH_2\underset{\underset{CH_3}{|}}{CH}\text{—}\overset{..+}{\underset{..}{O}}\text{—}CH(CH_3)_2 \longrightarrow CH_3CH_2\underset{\underset{CH_3}{|}}{\overset{+}{CH}} \quad + \quad :\overset{.}{\underset{..}{O}}CH(CH_3)_2$$
$$m/e = 57$$

20. (a) The fragment at $m/e = 57$ is an even-electron ion; the fragmen at $m/e = 56$ is an odd-electron ion.

(b) HCl can be lost to give the ion at $m/e = 56$.

$$
\overset{\overset{\displaystyle +\ddot{C}l:}{|}}{CH_3-\underset{}{CH}-CH_2CH_3} \xrightarrow{\text{inductive cleavage}} CH_3-\overset{+}{\underset{}{CH}}-CH_2CH_3 \ + \ :\ddot{\dot{C}}l:
$$

A mechanism analogous to the one in Eq. 12.22 gives the ion at $m/e = 56$. The latter mechanism involves loss of H—Cl, as suggested by the answer to part (b):

$$
\underset{\overset{\displaystyle H}{CH_2}-CH-CH_2CH_3}{\overset{\overset{\displaystyle \ddot{C}l:^+}{|}}{}} \longrightarrow \underset{\dot{C}H_2-CH-CH_2CH_3}{\overset{\overset{\displaystyle H-\ddot{C}l:^+}{|}}{}} \longrightarrow \overset{+}{CH_2}-CH-CH_2CH_3 + H-\ddot{\dot{C}}l:
$$

Solutions to Additional Problems

21. The three factors that determine the position of an infrared absorption are: strength of the bonds involved, masses of the atoms involved, and the type of vibration.

22. The intensity of an infrared absorption is affected by (a) the number of absorbing groups and (b) the size of the dipole moment change when the molecule undergoes the bond vibration. The number of absorbing groups, in turn, depends on (a) the number of groups of interest within a given molecule and (b) the concentration of molecules in the sample.

23. (a) Use a branched alkoxide base such as K^+ $(CH_3)_3C$—O^- to bring about an E2 elimination. Follow the appearance of the alkene C=C stretch at about 1655 cm^{-1}.

    (b) Carry out a Williamson ether synthesis:

$$
CH_3(CH_2)_5-OH \xrightarrow{NaH} \xrightarrow{CH_3-I} CH_3(CH_2)_5-OCH_3
$$

Follow the loss of the O—H stretch of the alcohol in the 3200-3400 cm^{-1} region of the spectrum.

    (c) Allow the epoxide to react with C_2H_5—MgBr, followed by H_3O^+. Follow the appearance of the alcohol by its O—H stretch [see part (b)].

    (d) Catalytically hydrogenate the alkene. Follow its disappearance by loss of the C=C stretching absorption at 1660-1675 cm^{-1}.

24. (a) Since neopentane has molecular weight = 72, the indicated fragment with $m/e = 57$ corresponds to a loss of 15 units, which typically corresponds to a methyl group. Indeed, loss of a methyl group gives the relatively stable t-butyl cation:

$$
\underset{\overset{\displaystyle CH_3}{CH_3}}{\overset{\overset{\displaystyle CH_3}{|}}{CH_3-C-CH_3}} \xrightarrow{-e^-} \underset{\overset{\displaystyle CH_3}{CH_3}}{\overset{\overset{\displaystyle CH_3}{|}}{CH_3-C+\ CH_3}} \longrightarrow \underset{\overset{\displaystyle CH_3}{CH_3}}{\overset{\overset{\displaystyle CH_3}{|}}{CH_3-C+}} \ + \ \cdot CH_3
$$

$$m/e = 57$$

    (b) 3-Methyl-3-hexanol has molecular weight = 116; hence a fragment with $m/e = 73$ corresponds to loss of 43 mass units, which equals the mass of a propyl group. Indeed, there is a propyl group that can be lost by α-cleavage:

$$m/e = 73$$

(c) This must be an odd-electron ion, because it is an ion of even mass in a compound containing only C, H, and O. This ion is formed by a loss of 18 mass units, which corresponds to loss of water (see Eq. 12.22):

$$m/e = 70$$

(d) The observed fragment corresponds to loss of 43 mass units — again, a propyl group — by α-cleavage. This transformation is closely analogous to that in (b).

$$m/e = 72$$

➤ As we shall see in Problem 38, compounds containing one nitrogen have odd masses; and even-electron ions containing one nitrogen have even masses.

25. (a) H_2O
    (b) $CH_2=CH_2$
    (c) The isotopic information implies the presence of a chlorine. Hence, a reasonable fragment is HCl.

26. The principle used in working this problem is that structural isomers and diastereomers have different physical properties; hence, they have different spectra. Enantiomers have the same physical properties and thus have the same spectra (provided, of course, that chiral solvents or other chiral elements are not involved in the spectroscopy experiment).

    (a) 3-Pentanol and 2-pentanol are structural isomers and thus have different spectra.

    (b) (R)- and (S)-2-pentanol are enantiomers and have identical spectra.

    (c) The axial and equatorial forms of cyclohexanol are conformational diastereomers and have different IR spectra. In fact, the IR spectrum of cyclohexanol contains contributions from both compounds, because cyclohexanol is a mixture of both compounds.

27. Only spectrum 4 has an O—H stretching absorption. Of the two possible alcohols (c) and (g), we choose (c) because this spectrum also shows C=C stretching absorption. Hence, there is no spectrum corresponding to (g). The other two spectra with alkene absorption are spectra 2 and 5. Spectrum 2 contains all the earmarks of —CH=CH$_2$ bending absorptions and is therefore 1,5-hexadiene. Spectrum 5 lacks the strong 965 cm^{-1} absorption characteristic of *trans*-alkenes (see Fig. 12.8b) and is therefore compound (b). Of the two compounds left to assign, spectrum 1 is that of (d) because it has C—O stretching absorption at 1100 cm^{-1}. Hence, spectrum 3 is that of compound (f), cyclohexane. This spectrum has comparatively few peaks because the compound has no functional groups and because the compound is quite symmetrical. Such symmetry means that a number of absorptions are infrared inactive.

28. Spectrum 2 is that of 2-methoxybutane. The peaks at $m/e = 73$ and 59 correspond to losses of 15 and 29 units, respectively (methyl and ethyl groups). 2-Methoxybutane contains methyl and ethyl branches that can be lost as radicals by an α-cleavage mechanism. The two losses in spectrum 1, which is the spectrum of 1-methoxybutane, correspond to loss of propyl radical by α-cleavage and loss of methanol by a mechanism analogous to the one involved in loss of water from a primary alcohol:

$$CH_3CH_2-\overset{\underset{H\curvearrowright\overset{+}{\ddot{O}}CH_3}{|}}{CH}-CH_2 \longrightarrow CH_3CH_2-\overset{H-\overset{\cdot+}{\ddot{O}}CH_3}{\underset{\curvearrowleft}{CH}}-CH_2 \longrightarrow CH_3CH_2-\overset{\cdot}{CH}-\overset{+}{CH_2} + H\ddot{O}CH_3$$

29.   The three peaks correspond to compounds with isotopic distributions of two ^{79}Br, one each of ^{79}Br and ^{81}Br, and two ^{81}Br. Since there are two ways to distribute one ^{79}Br and one ^{81}Br, the situation with one of each isotope is twice as probable.

Br #1	Br #2	
79	79	relative probability 1
79	81	relative probability 2
81	79	
81	81	relative probability 1

30.   From Table 12.2, we see that Si has the following abundances: ^{28}Si, 92.21; ^{29}Si, 4.70; and ^{30}Si, 3.09. These abundances will cause the $m/e = 74$ and 75 peaks to have the following relative intensities:

$m/e = 74$ relative intensity $(4.70)/(92.21) = 0.0510$
$m/e = 75$ relative intensity $(3.09)/(92.21) = 0.0335$

To this we have to add the contribution due to ^{13}C. From the molecular weight of $(CH_3)_4Si$ (88), we see that the base peak results from loss of CH_3. Hence, this peak will have a contribution from three isotopic carbons equal to $3(1.12)/(92.21) = 0.0364$. We add this contribution to the $m/e = 74$ peak to get the final value for this peak:

$m/e = 74$ relative intensity $= 0.0510 + 0.0364 = 0.0874$

The contribution of ^{13}C to the $m/e = 75$ peak is negligible. Hence, the $m/e = 74$ peak has a relative intensity of 8.74%, and the $m/e = 75$ peak has a relative intensity of 3.35%.

31.   Spectrum 2 is that of compound A, because it contains C=C stretching absorption and =C—H stretching absorption. Spectrum 1 is that of compound B.

32.   First, we should ask what products we expect from the reaction. Indeed, two structural isomers are anticipated:

$$\underset{\text{2-pentanol}}{CH_3\overset{\overset{\displaystyle OH}{|}}{C}HCH_2CH_2CH_3} \quad \text{and} \quad \underset{\text{3-pentanol}}{CH_3CH_2\overset{\overset{\displaystyle OH}{|}}{C}HCH_2CH_3}$$

Spectrum (b) is consistent with compound B; the base peak corresponds to loss of C_2H_5, and there are two ethyl groups in this compound that could be lost by α-cleavage. Spectrum (a) has a base peak at $m/e = 45$ that corresponds to loss of 43 units, or propyl. And sure enough, compound A has a propyl branch that could be lost as a radical by α-cleavage.

➤ In postulating structures we always use what we know about chemical reactions.

33.   (a) The relative abundance of the $p + 1$ peak is $(2.5/38) \times 100 = 6.5\%$; this is about what we would expect for six carbons $(6 \times 1.12\% = 6.72\%)$. Six carbons contribute 72 units to the molecular weight. With ten mass units left, the formula for the compound could be C_6H_{10}.

(b) The relative abundance of the $p + 1$ peak is $(1.06/19) \times 100 = 5.58\%$, which is about what we would expect for five carbons. Five carbons contribute 60 mass units. The remaining mass cannot be due solely to hydrogens (why?). Therefore, let's add an oxygen, which gives us 76 mass units, leaving ten mass units for hydrogen. A possible formula is $C_5H_{10}O$.

34. Evidently the O—O stretching frequency is infrared inactive. This is what we would expect if the molecule has a zero dipole moment. A zero dipole moment is expected if peroxides adopt the following conformation:

bond dipoles of R—O bonds are opposed.

35. Since absorption frequency increases with increasing force constant, which, in turn, increases with bond strength, we must conclude that methylenecyclopropane with its absorption frequency of 1781 cm^{-1} has the strongest double bond.

36. The ions at $m/e = 110$ and 108 are the parent ions corresponding to each isotope of bromine. The ions at $m/e = 81$ and 79 are the masses of the two isotopes of bromine and correspond to loss of C_2H_5:

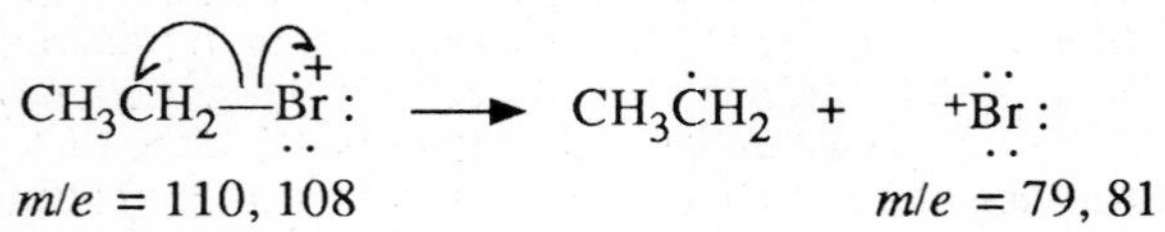

The ion at $m/e = 29$ corresponds to loss of Br by inductive cleavage:

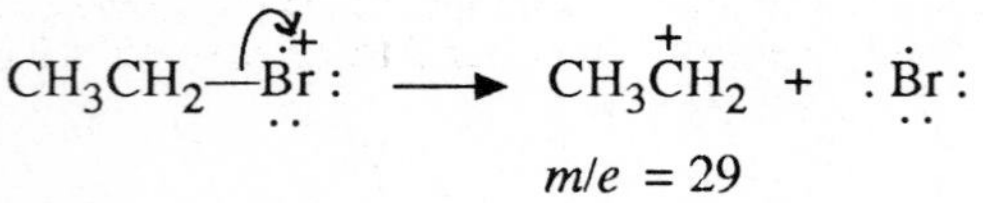

The ion at $m/e = 28$ is an odd-electron ion corresponding to loss of the neutral HBr:

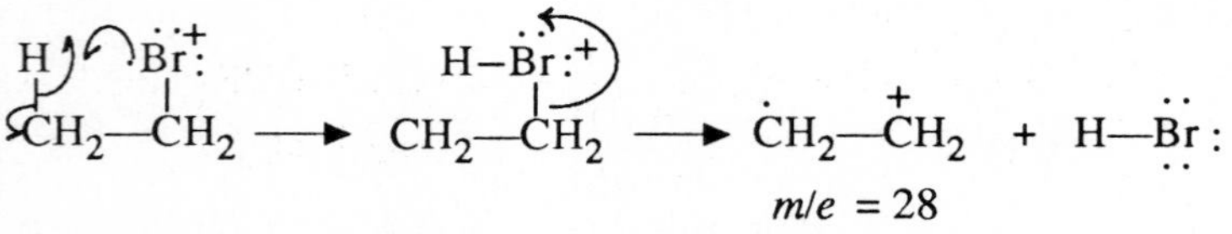

And the ion at $m/e = 27$ could arise through elimination of H· from the $m/e = 28$ ion by a β-scission mechanism:

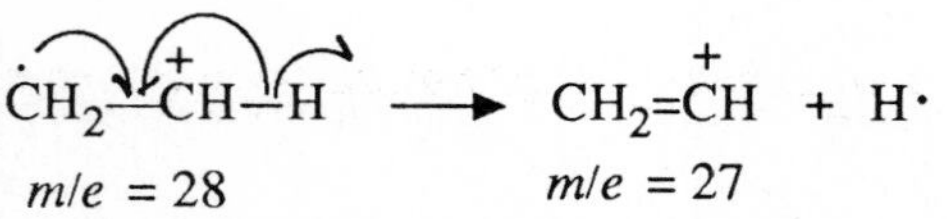

➤ Although in general it is not possible to rationalize the entire mass spectrum for most compounds, it is possible for simple compounds, as we have just demonstrated.

37. (a) We would expect the dipole moment of the S—H bond to be much less than that of the O—H bond because sulfur is less electronegative than oxygen. As a result, the S—H vibration is less active in the infrared, and the corresponding absorption is less intense. The S—H absorption occurs at lower frequency mostly because the S—H bond is much weaker than the O—H bond, and to a lesser extent because the mass of sulfur is greater than the mass of oxygen.

(b) Compound B has a strong O—H stretching absorption, and therefore is $(HOCH_2CH_2)_2S$. Compound A lacks this absorption, and is therefore $(SHCH_2CH_2)_2O$. Notice the absorption at 2250 cm^{-1}: this is the S—H absorption. As suggested in (a), it is considerably weaker than the O—H absorption.

(c) Titrate the compounds. The thiols should have a pK_a near 10, whereas the alcohol will not titrate below pH 14. We could also treat the compounds with lead salts (see Eq. 8.16); the thiol should precipitate as a lead mercaptide.

38. Compounds with an odd number of nitrogens have odd molecular weights. This means that parent ions and other odd-electron ions containing an odd number of nitrogens also have odd mass. Even-electron ions containing an odd number of nitrogens have even mass. Thus:

    (a) The parent ion (like all parent ions) is an odd-electron ion.
    (b) An even-electron ion.
    (c) An odd-electron ion.

    ➤ Some examples illustrate the correctness of these generalizations:

    $$\overset{\cdot\,+}{C_2H_5{-}NH_2} \qquad\qquad CH_2{=}\overset{+}{N}H_2$$

    | odd mass; | even mass; |
    | odd-electron ion | even-electron ion |

39. Both compounds have the same absorptions, except that several absorptions of compound 1 (the compound whose spectrum is at the top of the page) are displaced to lower frequency, an observation that implies a higher mass for the absorbing group (Eq. 12.9). In particular, a peak at 3000 cm^{-1} in compound 2, undoubtedly a C—H stretching absorption, is displaced to 2250 cm^{-1} in compound 2. This is a factor of 1.33; the factor derived from Eq. 12.8 (Problem 7) is 1.36. Hence, compound 1 is $CDCl_3$. The two compounds could be distinguished by mass spectrometry on the basis of the masses of their parent ions. $CDCl_3$ has four parent ions (why?), each of which lies at one unit higher mass than the corresponding parent ion of $CHCl_3$.

40. (a) σ-Electrons are held closer to the nucleus than π-electrons; by the electrostatic law, there is a greater energy of attraction of the nucleus for σ-electrons. This means that more energy must be used to remove a σ-electron.

    (b)

    $$CH_2{=}CH{-}CH_2{-}CH_2{-}C_3H_7 \xrightarrow{-e^-} \left[\overset{\cdot}{C}H_2{-}\overset{+}{C}H{-}CH_2{-}CH_2{-}C_3H_7 \longleftrightarrow \right.$$

    $$\left. \overset{+}{C}H_2{-}\overset{\cdot}{C}H{-}CH_2{-}CH_2{-}C_3H_7 \right] \longrightarrow \overset{+}{C}H_2{-}CH{=}CH_2 + \overset{\cdot}{C}H_2{-}C_3H_7$$
    $$m/e = 41$$

    The resonance structures shown above are somewhat unusual. When there is an unpaired electron on one carbon, and an empty p orbital on an adjacent carbon, there is overlap between the two. Both the unpaired electron and the electron deficiency are shared between the two carbons.

    ➤ It is common that fragments with $m/e = 41$ in mass spectra turn out to be allyl cations, as in this case. Allyl cations are particularly stable, as we shall learn in Chapter 15.

    (c) From Eq. 12.22, the structure of the ion derived from the loss of water from the parent ion of 1-heptanol is

    $$CH_3(CH_2)_3\overset{\cdot}{C}H{-}\overset{+}{C}H_2$$

    Loss of a π-electron from 1-heptene gives precisely the same ion:

    $$CH_3(CH_2)_3CH{=}CH_2 \xrightarrow{-e^-} CH_3(CH_2)_3\overset{\cdot}{C}H{-}\overset{+}{C}H_2$$

    Since both compounds give the same ion, then the same (or nearly the same) fragmentation pattern should be expected.

    ➤ As suggested by this problem, primary alcohols and the corresponding 1-alkenes in many cases give very similar mass spectra.

41. (a) If we replace the hydrogens involved in the vibration with deuteriums, the 3086 cm^{-1} absorption should be displaced to considerably lower frequency (higher wavelength). (See some related examples in Problem 39.) Hence, a useful analog would be

$$CD_2{=}C{-}CH_2CH_2CH_3$$
$$\ \ \ \ \ |$$
$$\ \ \ \ CH_3$$

(b) In principle, replacement of the CH_2 carbon with ^{13}C should also give a shifted absorption. However, Eq. 12.9 shows that the frequency depends on the square root of the mass. Replacement of H by D would give a frequency shift in the approximate ratio $\sqrt{2}$ (=1.4), whereas replacement of ^{12}C by ^{13}C would give a shift in the ratio $\sqrt{1.08}$ (=1.04), which is so small that it would be difficult to detect.

42. Let us assume as a crude approximation that the C—C bond is about half as strong as a C=C bond; that is, the force constant of the single bond is about half that of the double bond. Eq. 12.9 suggests that the frequency ratio should be equal to the square root of the force-constant ratio. Since a C=C bond absorbs at about 1650 cm^{-1}, a C—C single bond should absorb at about $(1650/\sqrt{2}) = 1178$ cm^{-1}. Likewise, a C≡C bond should absorb at about $(1178)(\sqrt{3}) = 2041$ cm^{-1}. (In fact, C≡C absorption occurs at about 2150 cm^{-1}.)

Chapter 13 / Nuclear Magnetic Resonance Spectroscopy

CHAPTER 13 TERMS

allylic protons 13.5A
applied magnetic field, H_0 .... 13.2A
carbon-13 NMR spectroscopy (CMR) 13.1
chemical exchange 13.5C
chemical shift 13.2A
complex multiplet 13.4
coupled proton 13.3A
coupling constant, J 13.3A
d (doublet) 13.3D
deshielded 13.2D
deuterochloroform (chloroform-*d*, $CDCl_3$) 13.6
doublet of doublets 13.3C
downfield 13.2A
effective shift contribution, σ_G 13.2B
first-order spectrum 13.4
fluorine NMR 13.5C
Fourier-transform NMR (FT-NMR) 13.10
gauss 13.1
geminal splitting 13.5A
high-field spectrum 13.4
induced magnetic field, H_e 13.2D
induced magnetic field, H_i 13.5A
integral 13.2A
leaning 13.3A
m (multiplet) 13.3D
magnetic field, H_p 13.1
magnetic-resonance imaging (MRI) 13.10
magnetogyric ratio ($\gamma_H, \gamma_C, \gamma_F,...$) 13.1
$n + 1$ rule 13.3A

NMR spectrometer 13.1
NMR spectroscopy 13.1
NMR tomography 13.10
nuclear spin 13.1
off-resonance decoupled spectrum 13.8
off-resonance proton spin decoupling 13.8
operating frequency (v_0) 13.2A
parts per million (ppm), δ 13.2A
proton-decoupled carbon NMR spectrum 13.8
proton NMR spectroscopy 13.1
proton spin decoupling 13.8
q (quartet) 13.3D
radiofrequency (rf) 13.1
resonance line 13.2A
rf oscillator 13.10
s (singlet) 13.3D
shielded 13.2D
solid-state NMR 13.10
spin magnetic field, H_s 13.3B
spin state 13.1
splitting 13.3
splitting diagram 13.3C
sweep coil 13.10
t (triplet) 13.3D
tetramethylsilane (TMS) 13.2A
time-average spectrum 13.7
triplet of triplets 13.3C
vinylic protons 13.5A

CHAPTER 13 CONCEPTS

I. NMR Spectroscopy:

    A. <u>Introduction</u>:

        1. Some nuclei have spin that is analogous to the electron spin.

            a) The hydrogen nucleus ^1H has a **nuclear spin** that can assume either of two values ($+\frac{1}{2}$ and $-\frac{1}{2}$).

            b) These nuclei act like tiny magnets; hydrogen nuclei respond to a **magnetic field**.

                (1) In the absence of a magnetic field, the nuclear magnetic poles are oriented randomly.

(2) After a magnetic field is applied, the magnetic poles of nuclei with spin of $+\frac{1}{2}$ are oriented parallel to the magnetic field.

(3) Those of nuclei with spin of $-\frac{1}{2}$ are oriented antiparallel to the field.

2. Any nucleus with a spin can be detected by NMR.

3. One of the most important uses of NMR spectroscopy is to examine the hydrogens in organic compounds.

B. Physical Basis of NMR Spectroscopy:

1. The presence of a magnetic field causes the two **spin states** to have different energies; the energy difference between two spin states, ΔE, depends on the intensity of the magnetic field at the nucleus, $\mathbf{H_p}$.

$$\Delta E = \frac{h \gamma_H}{2\pi} \mathbf{H_p}$$

where γ_H (the **magnetogyric ratio**) is a fundamental constant of the proton related to its magnetic properties (26,753 radians gauss^{-1} sec^{-1}) and h is Planck's constant.

a) In the absence of the field, the two spin states have the same energy.

b) Nuclei in the two spin states are in rapid equilibrium.

c) The spin equilibrium favors the state with lower energy.

2. The absorption of energy corresponds physically to the flipping of nuclear spins from the $+\frac{1}{2}$ to the $-\frac{1}{2}$ spin state.

a) This energy absorption by nuclei in a magnetic field is termed **nuclear magnetic resonance (NMR)**.

(1) NMR can be detected in a type of absorption spectrophotometer called a **nuclear magnetic resonance spectrometer (NMR spectrometer)**.

(2) The study of NMR absorption is called **NMR spectroscopy**.

b) For nuclei to absorb energy, they must have a nuclear spin and must be situated in a magnetic field.

C. Instrumentation:

1. The basic components of an NMR instrument are:

a) Sample.

b) Magnetic field provided by an electromagnet.

c) Sweep generator and coils that vary the magnetic field.

d) Radiofrequency energy source.

e) Receiving coils and rf detector with amplifier.

f) Recorder to plot the spectrum.

II. The NMR Spectrum—Chemical Shift and Integral:

A. The NMR Spectrum:

1. The NMR instrument is fixed at a convenient frequency (60 MHz) called the **operating frequency**, ν_0.

2. The **applied magnetic field**, $\mathbf{H_0}$, is slowly and continuously changed over a very narrow range.

3. The protons absorb energy from the rf source when they experience a magnetic field $\mathbf{H_p}$ equal to $2\pi\nu_0/\gamma_H$.

a) The resulting absorption (resonance) is registered as a peak in the NMR spectrum.

b) The strength of the applied field $\mathbf{H_0}$ is plotted on the horizontal axis and increases to the right.

4. Peak positions are always cited relative to the resonance position of a standard compound.

a) **Tetramethylsilane (TMS)** is commonly added to the sample as a reference.

b) The position of a peak relative to a standard is called its **chemical shift**.

(1) The chemical shift in Hz varies directly with the operating frequency.

(2) The chemical shift in ppm (**parts per million**, δ) is defined by the ratio:

$$\delta = \frac{\text{chemical shift (Hz)}}{\text{operating frequency (MHz)}} = \frac{\nu_{\text{sample}} - \nu_{\text{TMS}}}{\nu_0}$$

(3) The chemical shift in ppm is independent of the operating frequency.

5. In most organic molecules, protons give NMR absorptions over a chemical shift range of about 0–10 ppm **downfield** from TMS.
6. The intensity (size) of an NMR absorption is governed almost entirely by the number of protons contributing to it.
   a) The exact intensity of an NMR absorption is given by the total area under the peak, called the **integral**.
   b) The relative height of the integral is proportional to the number of protons contributing to the peak.
   c) Values of the intergal give the *relative* numbers of hydrogens under the NMR peaks.

B. Relationship of Chemical Shift and Integral to Structure:
   1. The chemical shift and integral can be used to determine the types of chemically distinguishable protons, as well as the number of protons of each type, in an unknown compound.
      a) Protons in different chemical environments have different chemical shifts.
      b) For two sets of protons to be chemically equivalent, they must be connectively equivalent; they must be either homotopic or enantiotopic.
      c) Diastereotopic groups are in principle chemically distinguishable; they have different chemical and spectroscopic behavior.
   2. One of the most important factors that affect proton chemical shifts is the electronegativities of the groups in a molecule that are near the protons of interest.
      a) Factors that increase the proton chemical shift are:
         (1) Increasing electronegativity of nearby groups.
         (2) Increasing number of nearby electronegative groups.
         (3) Decreasing distance between the proton and nearby electronegative groups.
      b) A β-halogen or β-oxygen adds about 0.5 ppm to the chemical shift.
      c) The effect of electropositive groups is opposite to the effect of electronegative groups.
   3. The chemical shifts of carbon protons are of the order:

   tertiary > secondary > primary

   4. The chemical shift contributions of different groups are approximately additive.
   5. Chemical-shift contributions of various groups can be found in Table 13.2, text page 499 or in Appendix III, text page A-4.

C. Physical Basis of the Chemical Shift:
   1. Chemical shifts are observed because the field H_p is different for protons in different chemical environments.
      a) A greater electron density about the proton indicates:
         (1) A greater induced electron current.
         (2) A greater induced field, H_e.
      b) The smaller is this electron density, the smaller is H_e.
      c) Nearby electronegative groups reduce the electron density at a proton.
   2. Protons that absorb in the NMR spectrum at a lower value of H_0 are imbedded in a smaller induced field H_e and are **deshielded**.
   3. Protons that absorb at a higher value of H_0 imbedded in a larger induced field H_e and are **shielded**.

D. The $n + 1$ Splitting Rule:
   1. **Splitting** arises from the effect that one set of protons has on the NMR signal of neighboring protons.
   2. The number of lines in the NMR splitting pattern for a given set of equivalent protons depends on the number of adjacent protons.
      a) If there are n equivalent protons in adjacent positions, a **proton NMR** signal is split into $n + 1$ lines.
      b) Protons that split each other are coupled.
         (1) The spacing between adjacent peaks of a splitting pattern (in Hz) is called the **coupling constant**, J.
         (2) The coupling constant between any two protons does not vary with operating frequency.
   3. The relative intensities of the lines within a split signal follow a well-defined pattern (see Table 13.3, text page 504).
      a) The chemical shift of a split line occurs approximately at the midpoint of the splitting pattern.

b) The departure from the normal intensity ratios is called **leaning**.
   (1) Leaning is most severe when two signals that split each other are very close together in chemical shift.
   (2) Leaning is less pronounced when the two signals are very far apart.
4. Splitting between protons is usually not observed if the protons are separated by more than two saturated atoms.
5. No splitting is observed between protons with identical chemical shifts.

E. Physical Basis of Splitting:
   1. Splitting occurs because the magnetic field due to the spin of a neighboring proton adds to or subtracts from the applied magnetic field and affects the total field experienced by an observed proton.
   2. When a proton resonance is split separately by more than one other proton, each splitting is applied successively.
      a) Multiple splitting may occur any time one set of protons is split by two or more nonequivalent sets.
      b) When applying successive splittings to a proton signal and each has about the same coupling constant, the signal is the same as that predicted by the $n + 1$ rule.
   3. In a **splitting diagram**:
      a) NMR signals are approximated as vertical lines, and the effect of each splitting is shown separately.
      b) It makes no difference which splitting is applied first.

F. Solving Unknown Structures with NMR:
   1. First use the information inherent in the molecular formula; note the saturation number.
   2. The NMR spectrum tells the chemically different types of hydrogens; determine the number of each type of chemically different protons.
      a) The chemical shift gives information about functional groups that are near an observed proton.
         (1) Use a table of chemical shift values (Table 13.2 of the text) to evaluate the types of hydrogens present.
         (2) Use the chemical shift information to place functional groups at the appropriate carbons.
      b) The integral gives information about the relative number of protons contributing to a given signal.
      c) The splitting pattern gives information about the number of protons adjacent to an observed proton.
      d) Abbreviations used to indicate splitting patterns:
         (1) s—singlet.
         (2) d—doublet.
         (3) t—triplet.
         (4) q—quartet.
         (5) m—multiplet.
   3. Construct partial structures suggested by the integration and splitting patterns; when multiple possibilities exist, write them all.
   4. Assemble the individual parts.
   5. Write out all structures that seem to fit the data.
      a) Decide what to look for in the NMR spectrum to distinguish between them.
      b) Eliminate as many candidates as possible.
      c) Consult the spectrum to see whether such a feature is present.
      d) Double check the possible structures with the observed spectrum.

G. Interpreting Complex NMR Spectra. High-Field NMR:
   1. Spectra that conform to the $n + 1$ rule are called **first-order spectra**.
      a) First-order NMR spectra are generally observed when the chemical shift difference (in Hz) between **coupled protons** is much greater than their coupling constants.
      b) First-order behavior can be expected when the chemical shift difference between coupled protons is more than about 60 Hz, or 1 ppm at 60 MHz operating frequency.
   2. When the chemical shift difference of coupled protons is substantially less than this, non-first-order spectra usually can be anticipated.
      a) Most complex spectra can be simplified by running them at a greater operating frequency ν_0.
      b) Such spectra are sometimes called **high-field spectra**.
         (1) Chemical shifts (in Hz) increase with increasing ν_0.
         (2) Coupling constants do not change.

III. Functional-Group NMR Absorption:

A. NMR Spectra of Alkanes and Cycloalkanes:
   1. The splitting in such spectra shows extensive non-first-order behavior.
   2. Protons on a cyclopropane ring typically absorb at rather high field.

B. NMR Spectra of Alkenes:
   1. The protons attached to double bonds are called **vinylic protons.**
      a) The chemical shifts of these protons are considerably greater than predicted from the electronegativity of the C=C functional group.
      b) The applied field induces a circulation of the π-electrons in closed loops above and below the plane of the alkene.
      c) An **induced magnetic field** that opposes the applied field at the center of the loop occurs.
      d) The induced field augments the applied field at the vinyl protons.
         (1) The applied field necessary for resonance is reduced by the induced field.
         (2) The vinyl protons are deshielded and absorb at lower field.
   2. Splitting between vinylic protons in alkenes depends strongly on the geometric relationship of the coupled protons.
      a) Vinyl protons of a *cis*-alkene have smaller coupling constants than those of their *trans*-isomers.
      b) The very weak splitting (called **geminal splitting**) between vinylic protons on the *same* carbons stands in contrast to the much larger *cis*- and *trans*-splitting.
   3. Protons on carbons adjacent to double bonds are called **allylic protons**; these protons have greater chemical shifts than ordinary alkyl protons, but not so great as vinylic protons.
   4. Splitting in alkenes may sometimes be observed between protons separated by more than three bonds.
   5. The long-distance interactions between protons are transmitted by the π-electrons.

C. NMR Spectra of Alkyl Halides and Ethers:
   1. Protons at the α-carbons of ethers and alkyl halides have chemical shifts in the δ 3–4 range.
   2. Epoxides have considerably smaller chemical shifts than their open-chain analogs.
   3. Proton signals are split by neighboring fluorine in the same general way that they are split by neighboring protons; the splitting rule is the same.
      a) Values of H—F coupling constants are larger than H—H coupling constants.
      b) Coupling between protons and fluorines can sometimes be observed over as many as four single bonds.
   4. The common isotopes of chlorine, bromine, and iodine do not cause detectable proton splittings.

D. NMR Spectra of Alcohols:
   1. Protons of the α-carbons of primary and secondary alcohols have chemical shifts generally in the same range as ethers.
   2. Since tertiary alcohols have no α-protons, absence of the —CH—O— absorption in the NMR spectrum of an alcohol is good evidence for a tertiary alcohol.
   3. The chemical shift of the —OH proton in an alcohol depends on the degree to which the alcohol is involved in hydrogen bonding under the conditions that the spectrum is determined.
      a) The presence of water, acid, or base causes a collapse of the —OH resonance to a single line.
         (1) This phenomenon is a consequence of **chemical exchange**—an equilibrium involving chemical reactions that take place very rapidly as the NMR spectrum is being determined.
         (2) This type of behavior is quite general for alcohols, amines, and other compounds with protons bonded to an electronegative atom.
      b) Rapidly exchanging protons do not show spin-spin splitting with neighboring protons.
         (1) Acid and base catalyze this exchange reaction, accelerating it enough that splitting is no longer observed.
         (2) In the absence of acid or base, this exchange is much slower and splitting of the —OH protons and neighboring protons is observed.

E. Use of Deuterium in Proton NMR:
   1. Deuterium NMR and proton NMR require different operating frequencies.
      a) The coupling constants for proton-deuterium splitting are very small.
      b) Deuterium NMR signals are not detected under the conditions used for proton NMR.
      c) Deuterium substitution can be used to simplify NMR spectra and assign resonances.

        d) An important practical application of this fact is the use of deuterated solvents in NMR experiments.

               (1) **Deuterochloroform (CDCl₃)** has no proton-NMR absorption, but has all the desirable solvent properties of chloroform.

               (2) Carbon tetrachloride (CCl_4) is a useful solvent because it has no protons.

    2. With a few drops of D_2O, the rapid exchange of the —OH protons for deuterium causes the disappearance of the —OH resonance.

F. NMR Spectroscopy of Dynamic Systems:

    1. The NMR spectrometer is intrinsically limited in its capacity to resolve events in time.

    2. When a spectrum is taken of a compound that is involved in a rapid equilibrium, a single spectrum is observed that is the time-average of *all* species involved in the equilibrium.

    3. The spectra of molecules undergoing any rapid process, such as a chemical reaction, are also averaged by NMR spectroscopy.

IV. NMR of Nuclei other than Hydrogen:

A. Carbon-13 NMR:

    1. Any nucleus with a nuclear spin can be studied by NMR spectroscopy.

    2. Splitting in the NMR spectra of these nuclei conforms to the same $n + 1$ rule than we learned for protons; however, the size of the coupling constants vary with the nuclei involved.

    3. There are two special problems associated with NMR experiments on nuclei other than protons.

        a) Instrumentation.

               (1) Each nucleus requires a special operating frequency.

               (2) Instruments designed for the NMR of other nuclei must provide the proper operating frequency for each nucleus of interest.

        b) Detection

               (1) Different nuclei give NMR signals with different intrinsic intensities.

               (2) Some nuclei of interest have low natural abundance.

    4. Coupling (splitting) between carbons generally is not observed.

        a) The reason is the low natural abundance of carbon-13.

        b) Two ^{13}C atoms almost never occur together within the same molecule.

    5. $^{13}C-^1H$ coupling is large.

        a) Carbon NMR signals are also split by protons farther away.

        b) Splitting is eliminated by a special technique called **proton spin decoupling.**

        c) Spectra in which proton coupling has been eliminated are called **proton-decoupled carbon NMR spectra.**

               (1) A special instrumental technique known as **off-resonance proton spin decoupling** can be used to decrease all $^{13}C-^1H$ coupling constants to the point that only the coupling of directly attached protons is observed.

               (2) Off-resonance decoupled spectra readily distinguish primary, secondary, tertiary, and quaternary carbons.

    6. The range of chemical shifts is large compared to that in proton NMR; trends in most carbon chemical shifts parallel those for proton chemical shifts.

    7. CMR spectra are generally not integrated.

B. Newer Uses of NMR:

    1. In **Fourier-transform NMR,** a large number of spectra are recorded and stored in a computer.

        a) The background noise is averaged to nearly zero.

        b) The signals from the spectra are added together to give a much stronger spectrum.

    2. **Solid-state NMR** is used to study the properties of important solid substances.

    3. Phosphorus-31 NMR is used to study biological processes.

    4. **NMR tomography,** or **magnetic-resonance imaging (MRI)**, monitors the proton magnetic resonances in signals from water in various parts of the body; clinical scientists can achieve organ imaging without using X-rays or other harmful techniques.

CHAPTER 13 SOLUTIONS

Solutions to In-Text Problems

1. (a) We apply Eq. 13.3 and solve for H_p:

$$\Delta E/h = v_0 = 100 \times 10^{-6} \text{ Hz} = \gamma_H H_p/2\pi = \frac{26,753 \text{ rad/gauss-sec}}{2\pi \text{ rad}} \quad H_p = 23,486 \text{ gauss}$$

(b) In this case we solve for v_0, which equals $\Delta E/h$:

$$v_0 = \frac{(51,671)(26,753)}{2\pi} = 220 \text{ MHz}$$

2. Using Eq. 13.4, the chemical shift in Hz relative to TMS, $v_{sample} - v_{TMS}$, is the operating frequency, v_0, times the chemical shift δ. Hence, the chemical shift *in Hz* is $(90)(4.40) = 386$ Hz at 90 MHz, and $(360)(4.40) = 1584$ Hz at 360 MHz (see Fig. 13.2).

3. Let us call the two signals 1 and 2. Applying Eq. 13.4,

$$\delta(1) - \delta(2) = \frac{v(1) - v(TMS)}{v_0} - \frac{v(2) - v(TMS)}{v_0} = \frac{v(1) - v(2)}{v_0} = 45/60 = 0.75 \text{ ppm}$$

4. (a) Letting the resonance position, in Hz, of the —CH_3 protons be $v(1)$, and that of TMS be $v(TMS)$; and letting the corresponding positions, in gauss, be $H(1)$ and $H(TMS)$, respectively, we use an equation analogous to Eq. 13.3:

$$v(1) = \frac{\gamma_H}{2\pi} H(1) \quad \text{and} \quad v(TMS) = \frac{\gamma_H}{2\pi} H(TMS)$$

The difference $v(1) - v(TMS)$ at $v_0 = 60$ MHz is 194 Hz, from Fig. 13.2. Subtracting these two equations, we have:

$$v(1) - v(TMS) = 194 \text{ Hz} = \frac{\gamma_H}{2\pi} [H(1) - H(TMS)], \text{ or}$$

$$H(1) - H(TMS) = \frac{2\pi}{\gamma_H} [v(1) - v(TMS)] = 0.0456 \text{ gauss}$$

5. (a)-(c): The answers to these parts are discussed below the problem in the text.
   (d) Just as electronegative atoms *increase* the chemical shifts of nearby protons, electropositive atoms *decrease* these chemical shifts. Because Si is more electropositive than the other atoms in the table, protons near Si should absorb at *higher* field, as observed. We would expect $(CH_3)_2Mg$ to absorb at higher field than TMS, because Mg is more electropositive than Si. (See also the answer to Problem 6c.)

6. (a) CH_2Cl_2 has the greatest chemical shift, because Cl is more electronegative than I, and because CH_2Cl_2 has the largest number of these electronegative atoms.
   (b) Cl_2CH—$CHCl_2$. The two chlorines on the α-carbon give a chemical-shift contribution of about 5.3 ppm (Table 13.1); we add to this the effect of two β-chlorines, 1.0 ppm, for a chemical shift of *at least* 6.3 ppm. The compound Cl_3C—CH_3 has a contribution of about 1.5 ppm for three β-chlorines.
   (c) $(CH_3)_4Sn$, because Sn is more electronegative (less electropositive) than Si.

7. (a) Since there is one type of hydrogen, there is one absorption.
    (b) There are two types of hydrogens; hence, there are two absorptions.
    (c) There are two types of hydrogens and hence, two absorptions.

8. To make the required estimates, we apply Eq. 13.5 and the data in Table 13.2.

    (a) $0.2 + 0.5 + 0.5 = \delta\,1.2$

    (b) $\delta\,2.3$

    (c) $0.2 + 2.2 + 2.3 = \delta\,4.7$
    (d) The two sets of protons are equivalent, and have the same chemical shift:
    $0.2 + 2.4 + 0.5 = \delta\,3.1$

    (e) $0.2 + 0.5 + 0.5(\beta\text{-halogen}) + 1.3 = \delta\,2.5$

    (f) $0.2 + 0.5 + 2.3 = \delta\,3.0$

    (g) $0.2 + 0.5 + 0.5 + 0.5(\beta\text{-halogen}) = \delta\,1.7$

    (h) An α-Br contributes 2.3, a β-Br 0.5; so a γ-bromine contributes, by extrapolation, perhaps 0.1 ppm. The chemical shift should be a little greater than $\delta\,0.8$.

9. (Solved in the text.)

10. (a)   (b)

$$CH_3\!-\!\overset{\overset{\displaystyle CH_3}{|}}{\underset{\underset{\displaystyle CH_3}{|}}{C}}\!-\!\overset{\overset{\displaystyle CH_3}{|}}{\underset{\underset{\displaystyle CH_3}{|}}{C}}\!-\!Cl \qquad\qquad Cl_2CH\!-\!\overset{\overset{\displaystyle CH_3}{|}}{\underset{\underset{\displaystyle CH_3}{|}}{C}}\!-\!CH_2Cl$$

11. (a) The line at $\delta\,1.8$ is that of t-butyl bromide, and the line at $\delta\,2.20$ is that of methyl iodide. (These assignments follow from Table 13.2 and Eq. 13.5.) The ratio of methyl iodide to t-butyl bromide is 15:1. This follows from the fact that there are three times as many protons in the t-butyl bromide molecule as in the methyl iodide molecule; thus, for a given concentration, the t-butyl bromide gives a signal that is three times as intense as methyl iodide. Rigorously,

$$\frac{5 \text{ protons } CH_3I \times 1/3 \text{ molecule/proton}}{1 \text{ proton } (CH_3)_3CBr \times 1/9 \text{ molecule/proton}} = \frac{15 \text{ molecules } CH_3I}{1 \text{ molecule } (CH_3)_3CBr}$$

The mole fraction methyl iodide is then $\dfrac{15}{15 + 1} = 15/16 = 0.938$

Thus, the sample contains 93.8 mole per cent methyl iodide.

(b) The $(CH_3)_3CBr$ impurity in CH_3I is more easily detected, because a given mole fraction of $(CH_3)_3CBr$ gives a three times stronger signal than the same amount of CH_3I, as we have just seen in part (a) of this problem.

12. All protons absorb when they sense the same field H_p. The external field, H_0, at which a proton absorbs is equal to $H_p + H_e$. Since the field H_0 at which TMS absorbs is higher than the field at which a $\delta\,5.50$ proton absorbs, then TMS must have a greater value of H_e. In other words, the protons of TMS are more shielded.

13. (a) Applying Eq. 13.5, we have $0.2 + 0.5 + 0.5 + 0.5 = \delta\,1.7$ for the shift of the methyl protons. This set of protons thus gives rise to a doublet at about $\delta\,1.7$. The $-CHCl_2$ proton absorbs at about $\delta\,(5.30 + 0.5)$, or about $\delta\,5.8$. This proton is therefore a quartet at about $\delta\,6$.

(b) From Table 13.1, leaning would cause the inner lines of the two signals to be taller than the outer lines.

14. There are four possibilities for the spin of three neighboring equivalent protons b:

All up (probability = 1)
Two up, one down (three ways, probability = 3)
One up, two down (three ways, probability = 3)
All down (probability = 1)

In other words, the signal for proton a would be split by the three protons b into a quartet whose lines are in the intensity ratio 1:3:3:1.

15. Protons H^c and H^a will be doublets at their respective chemical shifts. Proton H^b will be split into a quartet (J = 6 Hz) by proton H^c, and each line of this quartet will be split into a doublet hy H^a:

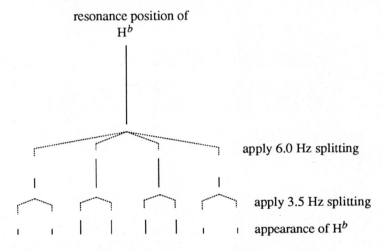

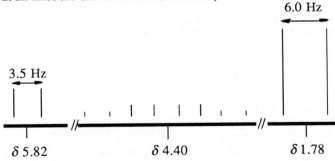

The appearance of the spectrum: (Compared to the diagram above, the horizontal scale has been compressed, but all lines are drawn on the same scale.)

16. (a) A six-proton doublet at about δ 1.4, and a one-proton septet at about δ 3.
    (b) A two-proton doublet at about δ 4.2, and a one-proton triplet at about δ 6.
    (c) A six-proton singlet at about δ 1.2, and a two-proton singlet at about δ 3.5.
    (d) A four-proton triplet at about δ 3.6, and a two-proton quintet at about δ 2.2.
    (e) Like (d); but add a six-proton singlet at about δ 3.5.

17. (Solved in the text.)

18. (a) $CH_3CH_2CH_2Br$ (b) $ClCH_2\underset{|}{\overset{}{C}}HCl$ (c)

$$BrCH_2\overset{\overset{\textstyle CH_2Br}{|}}{\underset{\underset{\textstyle CH_2Br}{|}}{C}}CH_2Br$$

19. (a) From what we know about the peroxide effect on HBr addition to alkenes, we expect A to be the anti-Markovnikov HBr addition product:

$$\delta\ 3.60$$

$$BrCH_2CH{=}CH_2\ +\ H{-}Br\ \xrightarrow{\text{peroxides}}\ BrCH_2CH_2CH_2Br$$

$$\delta\ 1.38$$

(b) The chemical shifts and splittings are indeed consistent with this structure.

20. An alkyl halide A with the formula C_4H_9Cl that gives a single line in its NMR spectrum can be only t-butyl chloride, $(CH_3)_3C{-}Cl$. For compound B, the total integral is 37 spaces, and the low-field sextet integrates for 4 of these spaces; this signal is therefore caused by 4/37, or about 1/9, of the protons in B, or one proton. This defines the following partial structure:

sextet

$$-CH_2-\underset{\underset{\textstyle Cl}{|}}{CH}-CH_3$$

A compound C_4H_9Cl with this part structure can be only sec-butyl chloride:

$$CH_3-CH_2-\underset{\underset{\textstyle Cl}{|}}{CH}-CH_3 \qquad \text{compound } B$$

21. The integral is 38 spaces, or, with 14 protons, about 2.71 spaces/proton. The signal at $\delta\,4.6$, in the vinylic proton region, accounts for about 2 protons; the signal at $\delta\,1.8$, in the allylic proton region, accounts for about 3 protons; and the singlet at $\delta\,1.05$ accounts for 9 protons (aha! a t-butyl group). The only two possible structures that could give these chemical shifts are A and B:

$$\underset{CH_3}{\overset{(CH_3)_3C}{\diagdown}}C{=}C\underset{\diagdown H}{\overset{\diagup H}{}} \qquad\qquad (CH_3)_3C{-}CH{=}CH{-}CH_3$$

$$A \qquad\qquad\qquad B\ (cis\text{- or }trans\text{-isomer})$$

If the structure were B, the —CH_3 group would be a doublet with a typical splitting of about 6-8 Hz, and the vinylic protons would be very complex (cis- or $trans$-splitting plus a quartet for the splitting by the —CH_3 group). This splitting is not observed. On the other hand, structure A (the correct structure) is consistent with the spectrum. The vinylic protons are weakly split by each other (geminal splitting) and by the —CH_3 group (allylic splitting); the —CH_3 group shows the same type of weak allylic splitting by the vinylic protons.

22. The spectrum of ethyl fluoride would look very much like that of ethyl chloride, which, in turn, would resemble that of ethyl bromide (Fig. 13.5), except that the quartet would be at lower field. In ethyl fluoride, the methyl group would be a *triplet of doublets*. (Splitting by —CH_2— group gives three lines; each of these are split into two by the fluorine for a total of six.) The —CH_2— group would be a *doublet of quartets*. (Splitting by the fluorine gives a widely spaced doublet; each line of the doublet is split into a quartet by the —CH_3 group.)

23. (a) This triplet-quartet pattern screams "ethyl group!" Since there appears to be *only* ethyl resonances, the spectrum is that of diethyl ether, $C_2H_5{-}O{-}C_2H_5$.

(b) The large splittings suggest nearby fluorines; there seem to be no smaller splittings, a fact suggesting that the two sets of protons are separated by at least one carbon. A structure that meets all these requirements is CH_3—CF_2—CH_2—Cl. Notice that the coupling constant of each set of protons caused by the fluorines is similar; this is reasonable, since each set of protons is separated from the fluorine by the same number of bonds.

24. A greater concentration of ethanol pushes the hydrogen-bonding equilibrium toward the hydrogen-bonded form. Hence, there is more of the hydrogen-bonded form of ethanol in the $2M$ solution. Since the hydrogen-bonded form of ethanol has a greater chemical shift, the $2M$ solution of ethanol has the greater chemical shift.

25. (a) *t*-butyl alcohol, $(CH_3)_3C$—OH

    (b) The resonance at $\delta\,5.41$ is a vinylic proton coupled to two other protons, and the resonance at $\delta\,4.41$ arises from two protons adjacent to an oxygen with nearby electronegative functionality. The following structure is consistent with the data:

    $(CH_3)_2C=CH$—CH_2OH

26. First, we could prepare $CH_3CD_2CH_2CD_2Cl$. The protons of the CH_3— and —CH_2— groups would appear as singlets, whose positions would give their chemical shifts directly. Then we could prepare $CD_3CH_2CD_2CH_2Cl$, which would show two other singlets whose chemical shifts could be readily assigned. In each pair of singlets, the one further downfield would be assigned to the protons nearer the chlorine.

27. The methyl group at room temperature would appear as a singlet. When the temperature is lowered, we would see two singlets for this methyl group, one for the form of 1-chloro-1-methylcyclohexane in which the methyl group is axial, and one for the form in which the methyl group is equatorial. The relative integrals of the two singlets would be proportional to the relative amounts of the two forms. Since chlorine and methyl are about the same size, we would expect to see about equal amounts of the two forms.

28. Any changes observed would be related to the separate observation of the different rotational isomers. There are three such isomers, two of which are enantiomers:

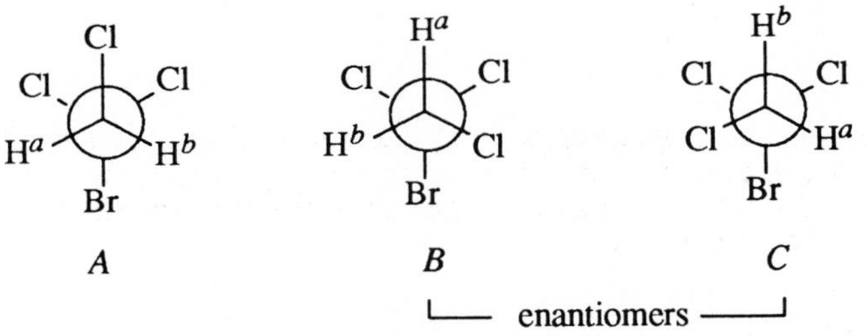

A   *B*   *C*

└── enantiomers ──┘

In rotational isomer A, protons H^a and H^b are equivalent and have the same chemical shift. In any one of the enantiomers, H^a is split by H^b and is therefore a doublet; likewise, H^b is split by H^a and is also a doublet. Hence, the signal from isomer B should consist of four lines of equal intensity, assuming no overlap. Similarly, the signal from isomer C should also consist of four lines; but since the signal from H^a in B should have the same chemical shift as the signal from H^b in A, and vice versa, the spectrum of form C will be identical to that of form B. Hence, we should see one line for form A, and four lines for forms B and C, for a total of five lines at low temperature, assuming no overlaps. The relative integrals depend on the amount of form A relative to the amounts of forms B and C.

29. We apply Eq. 13.14, using the magnetogyric ratios of the different nuclei given in Table 13.6:

$$\nu_0 = (\gamma/2\pi)(46{,}973)$$

    (a) proton: $\nu_0 = 200$ MHz
    (b) ^{13}C: $\nu_0 = 50.3$ MHz
    (c) ^{31}P: $\nu_0 = 81.0$ MHz

30. (a) The sensitivity of ^{19}F relative to ^1H is the ratio of the cubes of the magnetogyric ratios:

relative sensitivity = $(\gamma_F/\gamma_H)^3$ = $(25,179/26,753)^3$ = 0.834

The sensitivity of ^{31}P relative to ^1H is

$(\gamma_P/\gamma_H)^3$ = $(10,840/26,753)^3$ = 0.0665

➤ We can see from this calculation that phosphorus NMR is much less sensitive than fluorine or proton NMR.

(b) Given that 1.21 = $(\gamma_T/\gamma_H)^3$, then (γ_T/γ_H) = $\sqrt[3]{1.21}$ = 1.066.

Using the value of γ_H, and solving for γ_T, we have

γ_T = (1.066)(26,753) = 28,510 rad/gauss-sec

Two problems are likely to be encountered in tritium NMR: First, there is a safety hazard, since tritium is radioactive. Second, synthesis of compounds substantially enriched in tritium is expensive.

➤ Despite these problems, tritium NMR has been developed and used.

31. Because of its symmetry, 4-heptanol has only four sets of distinguishable carbons, and hence has four lines. 3-Heptanol has seven lines.

32. In 1-chlorobutane (Fig. 13.24), the carbon at lowest field is a triplet, because it is bound to two protons. In 2-chlorobutane, the carbon at lowest field is a doublet, because it is bound to one proton. (The carbon at lowest field in each case is the one to which the chlorine is bound).

33. (Solved in the text.)

34. (Solved in the text.)

35. (a) Among other reasons, there are not enough vinylic hydrogens to fit the integral; also, the Cl—CH$_2$— group would be a triplet and would integrate for two protons.
(b) Again, there are not enough vinylic hydrogens to account for the integral. Further, because the chlorine-bearing carbon has no protons, there would be no signals in the —CHCl— region.

36. (a) This compound would have only two lines in its CMR spectrum and would have only two types of protons in its proton NMR spectrum.
(b) This compound would have too many lines in its CMR spectrum and only one exchangeable proton.

Solutions to Additional Problems

37. The three pieces of information and their significance are:
(a) Chemical shift, which gives information about the functional groups that are near the proton of interest;
(b) Integral, which tells how many protons of a given type there are; and
(c) Splitting, which tells how many protons are *adjacent* to the proton of interest.

38. (a) The spectrum of cyclohexane is a singlet; the alkene would show a much more complex spectrum, including signals in the vinylic proton region.
(b) The two could be distinguished by integration of the vinylic proton region; 1-hexene has 25% vinylic protons, whereas *trans*-3-hexene has 17% vinylic protons.
(c) Each spectrum would consist of a singlet; however, the singlet in 1,1,2,2-tetrabromoethane would occur at lower field.
(d) 1,1-Dichlorohexane would show a one-proton triplet at lowest field; this absorption would be at a chemical shift of at least δ 5.7. 1,6-Dichlorohexane would show a four-proton triplet at lowest field, but this would be at a chemical shift of about δ 3.2. 1,2-Dichlorohexane would show a more complex spectrum at lowest field: a two-proton doublet at about δ 3.7, and a one-proton multiplet (or quintet) at a chemical shift of at least δ 4.2.
(e) The spectrum of *t*-butyl methyl ether consists of two singlets; that of isopropyl methyl ether is a singlet for the methoxy group, but a more complex doublet/septet pattern for the isopropyl group.
(f) The first compound, $Cl_3CCH_2CH_2CHF_2$, has the absorption at lowest field; furthermore, this absorption will show the typically large H—F splitting.
(g) The *cis* and *trans* isomers will have the absorptions at lowest field because they contain protons that are both vinylic and α to the halogens. The *cis* isomer will have smaller proton-proton splitting than the *trans* isomer. The remaining compound will show very small (geminal) splitting.

39. (a) Chemical shift in Hz is proportional to operating frequency.
(b) Coupling constant J is independent of operating frequency.
(c) The chemical shift in ppm does not change with operating frequency because it is *defined* to be independent of operating frequency (see Eq. 13.4).
(d) NMR spectroscopy requires that the sample be situated in a magnetic field before absorption of electromagnetic radiation can occur. Other forms of absorption spectroscopy do not require the presence of a magnetic field. The field establishes the energy difference between proton spins.
(e) The differences in chemical shift between all signals, in Hz, must be greater than their coupling constants.
(f) Some of the protons change from a lower-energy spin to a higher-energy spin.

40. (a)   (b)   (c)   (d)

(e) The chemical shifts suggest a cyclopropane. A structure consistent with the evidence is 1,1,2,2-tetramethylcyclopropane:

41. (a)   (b)

(c)-(d) The hydrogenation data define the carbon skeleton. The NMR spectra indicate that both compounds are alkenes. The only two possibilities for alkenes with the carbon skeleton of 2,2,4-trimethylpentane are:

(c)

$$CH_3-\underset{\underset{CH_3}{|}}{C}=CH-\underset{\underset{CH_3}{|}}{\overset{\overset{CH_3}{|}}{C}}-CH_3$$

and

(d)

$$CH_2=\underset{\underset{CH_3}{|}}{\overset{\overset{CH_3}{|}}{C}}-CH_2-\underset{\underset{CH_3}{|}}{\overset{\overset{CH_3}{|}}{C}}-CH_3$$

Compound (c) has one vinylic proton, and therefore matches the spectrum in Figure 13.28a; compound (d) has two vinylic protons, and therefore matches the spectrum in Figure 13.28b.

➤ How do we know the number of vinylic protons in each spectrum? Consider the spectrum in Fig. 13.28b, for example. The molecular formula is given as C_8H_{16}; thus, the total integral of 47 spaces gives 2.94 spaces/proton. The integral of the vinylic region is 5.5 spaces, very close to the 5.8 predicted for two protons. Thus: two vinylic protons. A similar analysis shows that the spectrum in Figure 13.28a has one vinylic proton.

(e)

$$Br-\underset{\underset{Cl}{|}}{CH}-\underset{\underset{Cl}{|}}{CH}-Br$$

(We can't tell from the spectrum whether this is the racemate or the *meso* compound.)

(f) The total integral is 41.7 spaces, or 3.5 spaces/proton. Thus, the signal at δ 1.07 accounts for nine protons; that at δ 2.28 accounts for two protons; and that at δ 5.77 accounts for one proton. There is one degree of unsaturation; the vinylic proton signal at δ 5.77 indicates that this is probably an alkene. The nine-proton signal at δ 1.07 suggests (what else?) a *t*-butyl group. A structure that is consistent with these observations is:

$$(CH_3)_3C-CH_2 \underset{H}{\overset{}{\diagdown}} C=C \overset{Cl}{\underset{Cl}{\diagup}}$$

(g) The two protons are evidently equivalent (a single chemical shift), and they must be very close to the fluorines (large splitting). The compound is 1,2-dibromo-1,1-difluoroethane, $Br-CF_2-CH_2-Br$.

(h) The integral is 6.80 spaces/proton; the doublet at δ 3.9 accounts for two protons next to an electronegative group, probably the bromine. The remaining signals are a complex pattern in the vinylic region accounting for three protons. The only structure with three vinylic protons and two protons next to a bromine split into a triplet is allyl bromide, $CH_2=CH-CH_2Br$.

(i) The compound is dichloromethyl methyl ether, $CH_3-O-CHCl_2$.

(j) There is one type of proton split by three fluorines. The compound is 1,1,1-trifluoro-2-iodoethane, $I-CH_2-CF_3$.

(k) Since there are sixteen protons, the integrals account for two, twelve, and two protons, respectively. The compound is

$$\overset{CH_3O}{\underset{CH_3O}{\diagdown \diagup}} CH-CH_2-CH \overset{OCH_3}{\underset{OCH_3}{\diagup \diagdown}}$$

What makes this problem tricky — and the whole point of the problem — is that not all equivalent protons of a given type are on the same carbon. For example, the two CH protons are equivalent and therefore have exactly the same chemical shift; they are split into a triplet by the adjacent CH_2 protons. Likewise, the CH_2 protons are split by the two adjacent protons into a triplet. We could just as well view this splitting as two doublets (2 × 2) whose inner lines exactly overlap. (See Fig. 13.12 and the accompanying discussion.)

42. Compound *A* can be only 2,3-dimethyl-2-butene (see Problem 40b):

$$CH_3 \diagdown \qquad \diagup CH_3$$
$$\qquad C{=}C$$
$$CH_3 \diagup \qquad \diagdown CH_3$$

The IR spectrum of compound *B* indicates a $CH_2{=}C$ group. The NMR spectrum shows a typical isopropyl pattern: a septet/doublet pattern ($\delta\, 2.20$, $\delta\, 1.07$, respectively); the isopropyl CH group is allylic. The presence of two vinylic hydrogens ($\delta\, 4.60$) is in agreement with the IR spectrum, and the three equivalent hydrogens remaining probably correspond to a methyl group. The isopropyl group must be attached to a carbon that bears no protons, since the CH is split only by its adjacent methyls. The structure is:

$$CH_3 \diagdown \qquad\qquad H$$
$$\qquad CH{-}C{=}C \diagup$$
$$CH_3 \diagup \qquad | \qquad \diagdown H$$
$$\qquad\qquad CH_3$$

Although the two vinylic hydrogens are not exactly equivalent, they accidentally have the same chemical shift. This is reasonable, since both are surrounded by very similar functional groups. Because they have the same chemical shift, they do not split each other. The methyl groups and the vinylic hydrogens show allylic splitting of 1.5 Hz.

Compound *C* shows the now familiar nine-proton singlet: a *t*-butyl group. The remaining three protons are vinylic. Don't worry about the splitting (although it *is* very similar to that in Figures 13.10 and 13.11); the structure is completely specified as 3,3-dimethyl-1-butene: $(CH_3)_3C{-}CH{=}CH_2$.

Compound *D* is not an alkene, a point clear from both the chemical data and the NMR absorption. A six-carbon hydrocarbon that is a singlet in the NMR and has one degree of unsaturation can be only cyclohexane. [See Problem 41(b) for a similar case.]

➤ Perhaps by now you are beginning to recognize common group patterns in NMR spectra. Let us review some of these. An ethyl group attached to an atom bearing no protons (as in OCH_2CH_3) is a three-proton triplet accompanied by a two-proton quartet; the chemical shift of the quartet indicates the attached functionality. An isopropyl group [as in $OCH(CH_3)_2$] is a six-proton doublet accompanied by a one-proton septet; a *t*-butyl group is a nine-proton singlet; a methyl group attached to a CH is a three-proton doublet. Splittings between adjacent protons of saturated groups are almost always in the 6-8 Hz range.

43. At (c), 10 MHz. Chemical shifts *in hertz* decrease with decreasing operating frequency. At the lowest operating frequencies, the chemical shift difference between two signals *in hertz* is smallest; however, their coupling constant does not change with frequency. At a sufficiently low frequency, the condition for first-order spectra in Eq. 13.10 will not hold, and the spectrum will be non-first order. The chemical shift difference between the two signals of ethyl iodide is about the same as that between the two signals of ethyl bromide (Table 13.2, Fig. 13.5). This difference is about 1.2 ppm, or 12 Hz at 10 MHz operating frequency. The coupling constant is about 7 Hz. Clearly, the condition of Eq. 13.10 no longer holds at 10 MHz.

44. (a) The vinylic signals of the starting material will disappear; the spectrum of the product will be a single line near $\delta\, 1$.
(b) The NMR spectrum of the starting material is a single line (see the solution to Problem 42); that of the product is more complex. In particular, the product will have a six-proton doublet at highest field, and a six-proton doublet at somewhat lower field.
(c) The *t*-butyl singlet of the starting material absorbs at nearly the same place as that of the product. However, the starting material has a singlet for the O—H proton that exchanges out in D_2O; the product lacks this signal.

45.   Let us first write the reaction in question. (We have seen a very similar reaction in Eq. 4.26.)

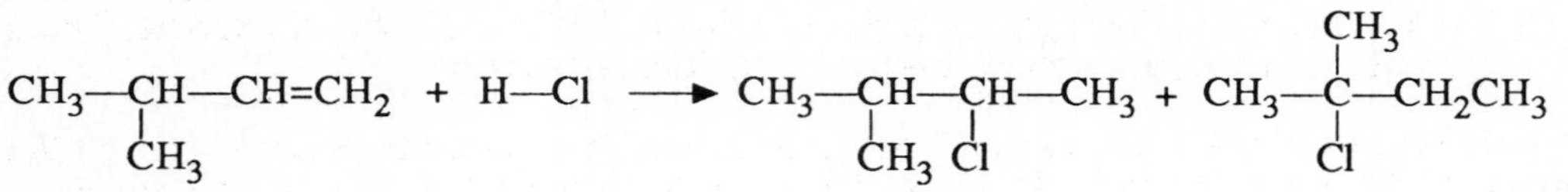

$$CH_3\!-\!\underset{\underset{CH_3}{|}}{CH}\!-\!CH\!=\!CH_2 \; + \; H\!-\!Cl \; \longrightarrow \; CH_3\!-\!\underset{\underset{CH_3}{|}}{CH}\!-\!\underset{\underset{Cl}{|}}{CH}\!-\!CH_3 \; + \; CH_3\!-\!\overset{\overset{CH_3}{|}}{\underset{\underset{Cl}{|}}{C}}\!-\!CH_2CH_3$$

Markovnikov product *A*   rearrangement product *B*

In the Markovnikov product, there should be a six-proton methyl doublet (for the isopropyl methyls) and a three-proton methyl doublet at somewhat lower field. In the rearrangement product, there should be a six-proton singlet for the two methyl groups, and a typical ethyl pattern (triplet at high field, quartet at lower field.)

46.   From the integral of the —CH_2Cl protons of 1-chlorobutane, we can deduce that there are 12.5 chart spaces/proton attributable to this compound. Thus the seven remaining protons account for $(7 \times 12.5) = 87.5$ spaces. Thus, the remaining signal of $(113 - 87.5) = 25.5$ spaces is due to the *t*-butyl chloride. Thus, the total integral for 1-chlorobutane is $(25 + 87.5) = 112.5$ spaces; the total integral for *t*-butyl chloride is 25.5 spaces. Since both have the same number of protons, we can compare their integrals directly. The mole fraction of *t*-butyl chloride present is $25.5/(25.5 + 112.5) = 0.184$, or 18.5 mole percent.

47.   The analysis is consistent with the formula C_7H_{12}, which corresponds to an unsaturation number of 2. From the hydrogenation data, the compound has the carbon skeleton of methylcyclohexane. Therefore, the additional unsaturation is accounted for by one double bond. Indeed, the proposed structures are consistent with these deductions.
       The methyl doublet ($J = 7$ Hz) in the NMR spectrum is consistent only with 3-methyl-1-cyclohexene; in 1-methyl-1-cyclohexene, the methyl group should be unsplit or, at best, should show small allylic splitting.

48.   From the chemical shift of the —CH_2— quartet, the compound contains at least one ethoxy group. Hence, we can rule out compounds (a) and (c). Furthermore, the ethyl group(s), if there are more than one, are equivalent, since there is only one triplet and one quartet. This rules out compound (b), which has two nonequivalent ethyl groups. We now come to a choice between compounds (d) and (e). In compound (d), the two CH protons are equivalent and hence, should not split each other. Since this rules out (d), we are left with (e) as the structure of the compound. The CH groups are nonequivalent and split each other into doublets, and the ethoxy groups are equivalent.

49.   (a) The first compound, isopropyl chloride, will have a typical isopropyl pattern: a six-proton methyl doublet at high field, and a one-proton septet at lower field. In the second compound, the septet will be missing, and the signal for the methyls will be a singlet, but at the same chemical shift as the methyls in the first compound.
       (b) The two compounds are enantiomers, and therefore have the same physical properties, including NMR spectra.
       (c) The spectrum of the first compound will consist of two two-proton triplets; that of the second compound will consist of a four-proton triplet and a two-proton quintet at higher field.
       (d) The first two compounds are diastereomers and should have different NMR spectra, although they may not be *detectably* different. The compound on the right is a different compound, and is not an isomer of the other two; hence, its NMR spectrum will be different. In particular, the —CH_2— protons, if they have different chemical shifts, should appear as two doublets, because they are nonequivalent and split each other. (In the language of Sec. 10.8, they are *diastereotopic*.)

50.   (a) The nitrogen can take on three values of spin with equal probability: +1, 0, and –1. Hence, we expect to see three lines of equal intensity for the *protons*.
       (b) The two deuteriums can have the following values of spin:

Total spin = +2:   +1, +1
Total spin = +1:   0, +1 and +1, 0   (two ways)
Total spin = 0:   0, 0; +1, –1; and –1, +1   (three ways)
Total spin = –1:   0, –1 and –1, 0   (two ways)
Total spin = –2:   –1, –1

Each value of the total deuterium spin makes a different contribution to the position of the proton resonance; thus, there are five lines, with relative intensities proportional to the relative probabilities of deuterium spin: 1:2:3:2:1.

(c) The sample of CH_2D—I should be a triplet whose three lines are in the intensity ratio 1:1:1; the sample of CHD_2—I should be a quintet whose five lines are in the intensity ratio 1:2:3:2:1. Mass spectrometry could, of course, easily distinguish the two species on the basis of their differing masses.

(d) The reason the carbon-13 NMR spectrum of $CDCl_3$ is a 1:1:1 triplet is the same reason that the proton NMR spectrum of $^+NH_4$ is a 1:1:1 triplet; deuterium, like nitrogen, has a spin of +1, 0, −1, and splits carbon-13 signals just as it splits proton signals.

51. (a) The spectrum of *t*-butyl fluoride (dashed lines) shows that the methyl groups are split by the fluorine. The species produced upon reaction with the Lewis acid has evidently lost the fluorine, because the splitting has disappeared. In fact, this new species is the *t*-butyl cation, which, when added to H_2O, forms *t*-butyl alcohol:

$$(CH_3)_3C\text{—F} \quad SbF_5 \longrightarrow (CH_3)_3C^+ + F\text{—}\bar{S}bF_5$$

$$H_2\ddot{O}:$$

$$(CH_3)_3C\text{—}\overset{+}{\underset{..}{\ddot{O}}}H \longrightarrow (CH_3)_3C\text{—}\ddot{O}H + H\text{—}F + SbF_5$$

(b) The signal for the two methyl groups would appear at approximately the same place that the methyls of *t*-butyl fluoride appear; however, these signals would be a doublet of doublets: they would be split by the CH proton *and* the fluorine. The CH proton would appear further downfield as a doublet of septets: This proton is split into a doublet with a very large coupling constant by the fluorine, and each line of the doublet is split into a septet by the six methyl protons. On ionization of isopropyl fluoride to the isopropyl cation, the signals for the septets would collapse into one septet at a more downfield position (this proton is at the carbon bearing the positive charge); and the CH_3 signals would collapse into a single doublet and move to about the same position as the methyls in the *t*-butyl cation. When this solution is added to ice water, we would expect isopropyl alcohol to be formed. (Write the equation for this reaction.)

➤ The NMR experiments described in this problem, performed in the 1960s by Professor George Olah, now of University of Southern California, were the first direct observations of simple carbocations.

52. (a) The IR spectrum indicates that the compound is both an alcohol (broad absorption near 3400 cm^{-1}) and an alkene (absorption near 1640 cm^{-1}). The alcohol functional group is confirmed in the NMR spectrum by the signal for the exchangeable hydrogen at δ 1.8. The integration of the vinylic proton region in the NMR spectrum is for three protons; hence, there is a CH_2=CH— (terminal vinyl) group. Furthermore, there can be no other unsaturation in the molecule. Given that the compound is chiral, there are only two possible structures:

$$\underset{\text{OH}}{CH_2=CH\text{—}\overset{|}{CH}\text{—}CH_2CH_3} \quad \text{and} \quad \underset{\text{OH}}{CH_2=CH\text{—}CH_2\text{—}\overset{|}{CH}\text{—}CH_3} \quad \text{(correct structure)}$$

The integral for the protons in the allylic region (δ 2.2) is for two protons, and this signal is a triplet. This evidence clearly shows that the second structure is correct. (You should rationalize the rest of the spectrum, and show why it is inconsistent with the first structure.)

(b) A peak at $m/e = 45$ corresponds to a loss of 41 mass units and corresponds to the following fragmentation (an α-cleavage):

$$CH_2=CH\text{—}CH_2\text{—}\overset{\overset{+..}{\ddot{O}H}}{CH}\text{—}CH_3 \longrightarrow CH_2=CH\text{—}\dot{C}H_2 + CH_3\text{—}\overset{\overset{+}{\ddot{O}H}}{CH}$$
$$\text{allyl radical} \qquad m/e = 45$$

53. (a) Protons H^a and H^b are diastereotopic.

$$\underset{\begin{array}{cc} & \end{array}}{CH_2=CH\!-\!\underset{\displaystyle OH}{\overset{\displaystyle |}{CH}}\!-\!\underset{\displaystyle CH_3^a}{\overset{\displaystyle |}{CH}}\!-\!CH_3^b}$$

Therefore, each should appear in the proton NMR spectrum as a doublet; in other words, these protons appear as two three-proton doublets. Were these protons *not* diastereotopic, they would be a single six-proton doublet.

(b) It is useful to draw the compound in a Fischer projection:

$$
\begin{array}{c}
CH_3 \\
H^a \!\!-\!\!-\!\!|\!\!-\!\!-\!\! H^b \\
O \;\; H^c \\
H^e \!\!-\!\!-\!\!|\!\!-\!\! C\!-\!Br \\
O \;\; H^d \\
H^b \!\!-\!\!-\!\!|\!\!-\!\!-\!\! H^a \\
CH_3
\end{array}
$$

Protons with the same label are equivalent. Protons H^a and H^b are diastereotopic; and protons H^c and H^d are diastereotopic. Protons H^a and H^b are *each* a one-proton quartet of doublets; each is split by the other (two lines) and by the adjacent methyl group (four more lines; eight lines total for each). Protons H^c and H^d are *each* a one-proton doublet of doublets; each is split by the other (two lines) and by H^e (two more lines; four lines total for each). This analysis assumes that the splitting is first-order; however, it may be more complex, because the chemical shifts of diastereotopic protons are usually very similar.

54. The structures of the compounds in the problem are as follows:

$$CH_3\!-\!\underset{\displaystyle OH}{\overset{\displaystyle |}{CH}}\!-\!CH_2\!-\!\underset{\underset{\displaystyle b}{\displaystyle CH_3}}{\overset{\displaystyle |}{CH}}\!-\!\overset{a}{CH_3} \qquad\qquad HOCH_2CH_2CH_2\underset{\underset{\displaystyle b}{\displaystyle CH_3}}{\overset{\displaystyle |}{CH}}\!-\!\overset{a}{CH_3}$$

$$\text{4-methyl-2-pentanol} \qquad\qquad\qquad \text{4-methyl-1-pentanol}$$

Carbons *a* and *b* in 4-methyl-2-pentanol are diastereotopic and hence are nonequivalent; that is, they give distinguishable NMR signals. All other carbons are connectively nonequivalent. Hence, there are six lines — a separate line for each carbon. Carbons *a* and *b* in 4-methyl-1-pentanol are enantiotopic and therefore are indistinguishable in the NMR spectrum. Hence these carbons together give a single line, and the CMR spectrum of the compound consists of five lines.

55. The odd mass and the loss of 12 mass units to give the peak at $m/e = 87$ cast serious doubt that the $m/e = 99$ peak is the parent ion of compound *A*. Treatment of compound *A* with acid gives a compound with a peak of highest mass at $m/e = 98$. The absorption near 3400 cm^{-1} in the IR spectrum of compound *A* indicates that *A* is an alcohol. If so, it must be a *tertiary alcohol*, because there are no peaks in the proton NMR spectrum near $\delta\, 3.5$. The CMR spectrum suggests a high degree of symmetry (only three carbon signals). Treatment of tertiary alcohols with acid gives alkenes; hence, it seems reasonable that compound *B* is an alkene. If, as its mass spectrum suggests, its molecular weight is 98, then the molecular weight of the tertiary alcohol *A* is 98 + one water molecule, or $(98 + 18) = 116$. Indeed, we see peaks for $116 - OH$ and $116 - H_2O$ ($m/e = 98$ and 99, respectively) in the mass spectrum of compound *A*. A reasonable formula for an alcohol with molecular weight = 116 is $C_7H_{16}O$, and the only possible alcohol of this formula with three distinguishable

carbons is 3-ethyl-3-pentanol:

$$CH_3CH_2 \overset{\overset{\displaystyle OH}{|}}{\underset{\underset{\displaystyle CH_2CH_3}{|}}{C}} CH_2CH_3$$

The large peak at m/e = 87 corresponds to loss of 29 mass units (an ethyl group), and is easily rationalized by an α-cleavage fragmentation mechanism:

$$CH_3\overset{\displaystyle \cdot}{CH_2} \overset{\overset{\displaystyle +\overset{..}{O}H}{\|}}{\underset{\underset{\displaystyle CH_2CH_3}{|}}{C}} CH_2CH_3 \longrightarrow CH_3\overset{\displaystyle \cdot}{CH_2} + \overset{\overset{\displaystyle +\overset{..}{O}-H}{\|}}{\underset{\underset{\displaystyle CH_2CH_3}{|}}{C}} CH_2CH_3$$

$$m/e = 87$$

The alkene *B* is the dehydration product 3-ethyl-2-pentene:

$$CH_3CH_2 \overset{\overset{\displaystyle OH}{|}}{\underset{\underset{\displaystyle CH_2CH_3}{|}}{C}} CH_2CH_3 \xrightarrow{H_3PO_4} CH_3CH=\overset{\overset{\displaystyle}{}}{\underset{\underset{\displaystyle CH_2CH_3}{|}}{C}}CH_2CH_3 + H_2O$$

3-ethyl-2-pentene

56. The double parent ion in the mass spectrum suggests the presence of one bromine. The NMR spectrum accounts for seven protons. After subtracting the hydrogens and the bromine from the parent, we are left with 66 mass units to account for. The typical ethyl pattern in the NMR, with the —CH_2— chemical shift of δ 3.91, suggests an ethyl ether, CH_3CH_2O—. If the compound contains an oxygen, then the 66 mass units can be accounted for by four carbons and the oxygen; a formula of C_4H_7OBr would fit the facts. The IR spectrum shows strong C=C absorption at 1644 cm^{-1}, but shows no *trans*-alkene, —CH=CH$_2$, or =CH$_2$ absorptions; hence, a *cis*-alkene is reasonable. Indeed, there appear to be two vinylic hydrogens; the small coupling constant of 4 Hz also suggests a *cis*-alkene. A reasonable structure that fits all these facts is:

$$\underset{H}{\overset{CH_3CH_2O}{\diagdown}}C=C\underset{H}{\overset{Br}{\diagup}}$$

57. The ^{17}O NMR signal is split into a triplet by the two protons of water. The splitting pattern suggests that, in the presence of acid, the ^{17}O signal is split by *three* protons. Evidently, this signal is due to the hydronium ion, H_3O^+.

58. Let us label the protons for ease of discussion:

$$Cl—\overset{a}{C}H_2—\overset{b}{C}H_2—\overset{c}{O}H$$

If the sample is very dry, the signal for proton H^c should be a triplet; that for proton H^b should be a doublet of triplets (six lines); and that for H^a should be a triplet. If the sample is wet, the O—H proton will be exchanging rapidly, and its resonance will be a singlet; the resonances of both H^a and H^b will be triplets. (There is a good chance that both spectra will be more complex than first order, because the chemical shifts of the resonances for both H^a and H^b should be similar. The conclusions above assume that the spectrum is taken at high enough field that the spectrum is first order.)

59. The different species present, and their relative abundances, will be as follows:

$\overset{*}{C}H_3$—$\overset{*}{C}H_2$—Br   Relative probability = (0.5)(0.5) = 0.25   two doublets

CH_3—$\overset{*}{C}H_2$—Br   Relative probability = (0.5)(0.5) = 0.25   one singlet

$\overset{*}{C}H_3$—CH_2—Br   Relative probability = (0.5)(0.5) = 0.25   one singlet

CH_3—CH_2—Br   Relative probability = (0.5)(0.5) = 0.25   no ^{13}C signal

Each line will show an apparent "triplet" pattern: the line from the singly-enriched species will be in the center of a doublet for the doubly-enriched species. Each line of the doublet will have half the total intensity of the doublet, and therefore half the intensity of the singlet. A diagram of the spectrum is as follows:

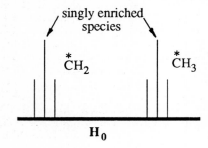

60. (a) Using Eq. 13.3, we have

$$v_0 = \frac{\gamma_{electron}}{2\pi} H_0 = \frac{(658)(26,753)}{2\pi}(14,092) = 39 \times 10^9 \text{ Hz}$$

This frequency lies in the microwave region; and, indeed, ESR spectrometers operate in this region.

(b) The resonance of the unpaired electron is split into four lines by the three neighboring protons according to the same $n + 1$ rule that applies to splitting between nuclei.

➤ ESR cannot be used for compounds without unpaired electrons; paired electrons — electrons that cohabit a given orbital — have opposite spin, and therefore have no net spin. When there is no net spin, there is no interaction with a magnetic field, and no magnetic resonance.

61. (a) At 25 °C, the spectrum is the average of rapidly equilibrating torsional isomers. However, at lower temperature, the individual isomers are separately observable:

enantiomers; methyl groups are equivalent

The first of these two isomers is the conformational diastereomer of the other two, which are a pair of conformational enantiomers. The first isomer contributes one line; the pair of enantiomers contributes another.

(b) The lines have different intensities because the enantiomers, taken together, have twice the probability of occurrence (there are two of them); furthermore, each of the enantiomers should have an energy that is different from that of the remaining isomer, and should therefore be present in general in a different amount.

Chapter 14 / Chemistry of Alkynes

CHAPTER 14 TERMS

acetylene 14.1
acetylide anion 14.7A
aldehyde 14.5A
alkyne 14.1
alkynyl group 14.1
amide ion ($^-NH_2$) 14.7A
carbonyl group 14.5A
catalyst poison 14.6A
dianion 14.8
enol 14.5A
ketone 14.5A

Lindlar catalyst (Pd/CaCO$_3$) 14.6A
monoanion 14.8
pheromone 14.9
poisoned catalyst 14.6A
propargyl group 14.1
radical anion 14.6B
sp hybrid orbital 14.2
transmetallation 14.7A
vinylic anion 14.7A
vinylic cation 14.5A
vinylic radical 14.6B

CHAPTER 14 CONCEPTS

I. Introduction to Alkynes:

A. General:
  1. **Alkynes (acetylenes)** are compounds with carbon–carbon triple bonds; the simplest member of this family is **acetylene** (ethyne), H—C≡C—H.
  2. The chemistry of the carbon–carbon triple bond is similar in many respects to that of the carbon–carbon double bond.

B. Common Nomenclature of Alkynes:
  1. In common nomenclature, simple alkynes are named as derivatives of the parent compound acetylene.

  —C≡C—CH$_2$CH$_3$ cyclopentyl ethyl acetylene

  2. In the common system, compounds containing the **propargyl group** (H—C≡C—CH$_2$—) are named as derivatives of this group.

  H—C≡C—CH$_2$—OH   propargyl alcohol

C. Systematic Nomenclature of Alkynes:
  1. The systematic nomenclature of alkynes is very much like that of alkenes.
     a) The suffix *ane* in the name of the corresponding alkane is replaced by the suffix *yne*.
     b) The triple bond is given the lowest possible number.
  2. When double bonds and triple bonds are present in the same molecule, the principal chain is the carbon chain containing the greatest number of double and triple bonds.
  3. The numerical precedence of a double bond or triple bond within the principal chain is decided by the first point of difference rule.

    a) Precedence is given to the bond that gives the lowest number in the name of the compound, whether it is a double or triple bond.

    b) The double bond is always cited *first* in the name by dropping the terminal *e* from the *ene* suffix.

$$\overset{7}{C}H_3 - \overset{6}{C}H_2 \quad CH_3$$

(*E*)-4-methylhept-4-en-1-yne

4. When the foregoing rules do not completely specify the name, the double bond takes precedence in numbering.

5. Substituent groups that contain a triple bond are named by replacing the final *e* in the name of the corresponding alkyne with the suffix *yl* (the alkynyl group is numbered from the point of attachment to the main chain).

          $-CH_2CH_2C\equiv CH$ 1-(3-butynyl)-1-cyclohexanol

6. Groups that can be cited as principal groups are given numerical precedence over the triple bond.

$$CH_3 - C\equiv C - CH_2 - \overset{\overset{\displaystyle OH}{|}}{C}H - CH_2 - CH_3$$ 5-heptyn-3-ol

II. Physical Properties of Alkynes:

  A. <u>Structure and Bonding in Alkynes</u>:

    1. The bonding in alkynes involves the hybridization of the 2s orbital with *one* 2p orbital to form *two sp* **hybrid orbitals.**

      a) *sp* Orbitals:

        (1) Resemble sp^2 or sp^3 orbitals in shape (one small lobe, one large lobe).

        (2) Are more compact than sp^2 or sp^3 orbitals.

      b) The *sp* hybridization state is inherently less stable than the sp^2 hybridization state.

    2. The acetylene molecule is linear.

      a) One bond between the carbon atoms is a σ-bond resulting from the overlap of two *sp* hybrid orbitals.

      b) Two π-bonds are formed by the side-to-side overlap of the *p* orbitals.

        (1) These bonding π-molecular orbitals are mutually perpendicular, and each contains two electrons.

        (2) The total electron density of the π electrons lies in a cylinder about the axis of the σ-bond.

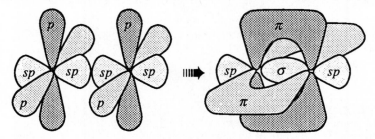

      c) There is no *cis–trans* isomerism at a triple bond.

      d) Cycloalkynes smaller than cyclooctyne cannot be isolated under ordinary conditions.

    3. Carbon–carbon triple bonds are shorter than carbon–carbon double bonds or single bonds.

    4. Heats of formation show that alkynes are less stable than isomeric dienes.

    5. A triple bond prefers energetically to be on the interior of a carbon chain rather than at the end.

B. <u>Boiling Points and Solubilities</u>:
    1. The boiling points of most alkynes are not very different from those of analogous alkenes and alkanes.
    2. Alkynes have much lower densities than water.
    3. Alkynes are insoluble in water.

C. <u>Acidity of 1-Alkynes. Acetylenic Anions</u>:
    1. 1-Alkynes are the most acidic of all the aliphatic hydrocarbons.
       a) The electronegativity of the $C\equiv C$ group is responsible for their enhanced acidity.
       b) The electronegativities of carbon groups increase in the order:

$$\text{alkyl} < \text{alkenyl} < \text{alkynyl}$$

       c) The source of this electronegativity effect is the hybridization of carbons involved in triple bonds.
          (1) The anion derived from the ionization of a 1-alkyne (acetylide anion) has an electron pair in an sp orbital.
          (2) Electrons are drawn closer to the nucleus when they occupy sp orbitals; this is a stabilizing effect.
          (3) Free electron pairs prefer to be in orbitals with the *most* s-character.
    2. Alkynes are sufficiently acidic that their conjugate-base acetylide anions can be formed with strong bases.
       a) This reaction (transmetallation) is another Brønsted acid–base reaction.
       b) Alkynes with an internal triple bond do not react because they lack an acidic alkyne hydrogen.

III. Spectroscopy:

A. <u>IR Spectroscopy of Alkynes</u>:
    1. Alkynes have a $C\equiv C$ stretching absorption in the 2100-2200 cm^{-1} region of the infrared spectrum; this is absent in many symmetrical, or nearly symmetrical, alkynes because of the dipole moment effect.
    2. A useful absorption of 1-alkynes is due to the $\equiv C$—H stretching vibration, and occurs at about 3300 cm^{-1}.

B. <u>NMR Spectroscopy of Alkynes</u>:
    1. The chemical shifts of acetylenic protons are much less than those of vinylic protons.
       a) An induced electron circulation is set up in the cylinder of π-electrons that encircles the alkyne molecule.
       b) The resulting induced field H_i opposes the applied field along the axis of this cylinder.
          (1) The net field at this proton is reduced.
          (2) This proton is shielded by the induced H_i.
    2. Acetylenic protons show NMR absorptions at higher field than they would if H_i were not present.

CHAPTER 14 REACTIONS

I. Addition Reactions of Alkynes:

A. Hydration of Alkynes:

1. Water adds to the triple bond of an alkyne in an acid-catalyzed addition reaction.
2. The mechanism of hydration is analogous to that of alkenes; the Markovnikov rule is obeyed.
   a) Protonation of the triple bond gives a carbocation in which the electron-deficient carbon is part of a double bond (a **vinylic cation**).
   b) Attack of water on the vinylic cation and subsequent loss of a proton forms an **enol**.
   c) The enol double bond is protonated to give another carbocation.
   d) This ion loses a proton to give the ketone or aldehyde.

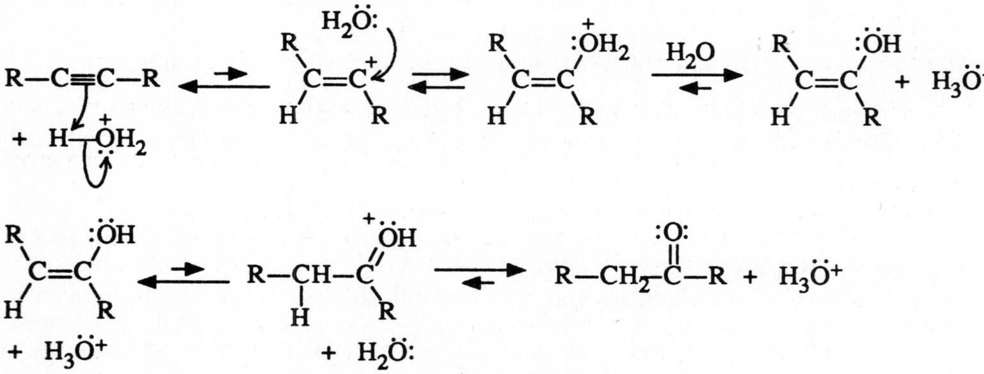

3. The hydration of alkynes can be carried out under milder conditions when it is catalyzed by mercuric ion, Hg^{2+}.
   a) The first step in this reaction is probably oxymercuration of the triple bond.
   b) Protonation of the organomercury compound leads to loss of mercuric ion and formation of the enol.
   c) Oxymercuration of alkynes does not require $NaBH_4$ for the removal of mercury.

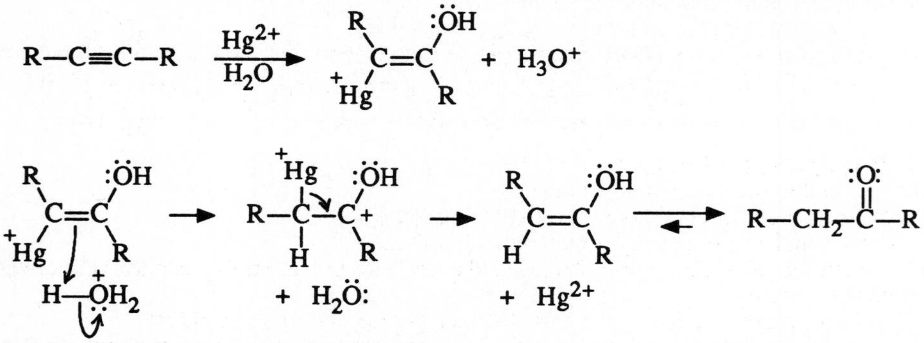

4. The hydration of alkynes is a useful preparative method for ketones provided that the starting material is a 1-alkyne or a symmetric alkyne; other alkynes give difficult-to-separate mixtures of isomers.

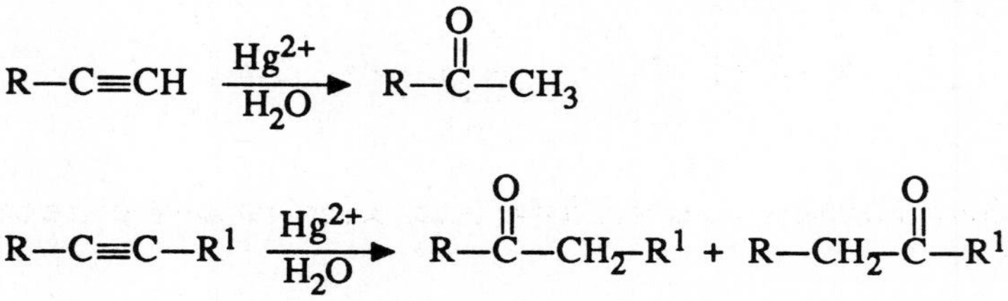

B. Hydroboration of Alkynes:
  1. When alkynes react with diborane (B_2H_6), the elements of BH_3 are added to the triple bond.
       a) Oxidation of the organoborane with alkaline hydrogen peroxide yields the corresponding enol.
       b) A second addition of BH_3 is possible and cannot be prevented in the reaction of 1-alkynes.
  2. Boron adds to the least hindered carbon atom of the triple bond.

$$R_2CH-C\equiv C-R \xrightarrow{B_2H_6} \left[R_2CH-\underset{H}{\overset{R}{C}}=\overset{C-B}{} \right]_3$$

$$\left[R_2CH-\underset{H}{\overset{R}{C}}=\overset{C-B}{} \right]_3 \xrightarrow[NaOH]{H_2O_2} R_2CH-CH=\underset{R}{\overset{OH}{C}} \longrightarrow R_2CH-CH_2-\overset{O}{\underset{\|}{C}}-R$$

  3. It is possible to control the addition to internal alkynes so that addition stops after the addition of one equivalent of BH_3.
  4. The hydroboration of 1-alkynes can be stopped after the first addition provided that a highly branched borane is used.
       a) One reagent developed for this purpose is called disiamylborane.
       b) Since hydroboration is sensitive to steric effects, only one equivalent of the very large disiamylborane molecule adds to the triple bond of the 1-alkyne.

$$R-C\equiv C-H \xrightarrow[\text{2) } H_2O_2/OH^-]{\text{1) } (\rule{6pt}{0.5pt}\llcorner)_2BH} R-CH_2-\overset{O}{\underset{\|}{C}}-H$$

C. Addition of Hydrogen Halides and Halogens:
  1. HCl and HBr add *slowly* to alkynes in accordance with the Markovnikov rule; in the presence of free-radical initiators, such as peroxides, anti-Markovnikov addition of HBr is observed.
  2. The stereochemistry of addition of hydrogen halides or halogens can be *syn* or *anti*, which can lead to *E* or *Z* adducts, respectively, and in some cases can give a mixture of stereoisomers.
  3. A second addition can follow the first.

$$R-C\equiv C-R \xrightarrow{Br_2}{CCl_4} \underset{R}{\overset{Br}{C}}=\underset{R}{\overset{Br}{C}} + \underset{Br}{\overset{R}{C}}=\underset{R}{\overset{Br}{C}} \xrightarrow{Br_2}{CCl_4} R-\underset{Br}{\overset{Br}{C}}-\underset{Br}{\overset{Br}{C}}-R$$

D. Catalytic Hydrogenation of Alkynes:
  1. Alkynes undergo catalytic hydrogenation.
       a) The first addition of hydrogen yields an alkene.
       b) A second addition of hydrogen gives an alkane.
  2. Hydrogenation of an alkyne may be stopped at the alkene stage if the reaction mixture contains a **catalyst poison.**
       a) A catalyst poison is a compound that disrupts the action of a catalyst.
       b) Useful catalyst poisons are salts of Pb^{2+}, and certain nitrogen compounds, such as pyridine or quinoline.
       c) **Lindlar catalyst** is $Pd/CaCO_3$ that has been washed with $Pb(OAc)_2$.

$$R-C\equiv C-R^1 \xrightarrow[\substack{Pd/CaCO_3 \\ Pb^{2+}}]{H_2} \underset{R}{\overset{H}{C}}=\underset{R^1}{\overset{H}{C}}$$

  3. Hydrogenation of alkynes is a stereoselective *syn*-addition and is one of the best methods to prepare *cis*-alkenes.

E. Reduction of Alkynes with Alkali Metals in Ammonia:
   1. Reaction of an alkyne with a solution of an alkali metal (usually sodium) in liquid ammonia gives a *trans*-alkene.

$$R—C≡C—R \xrightarrow[\text{NH}_3]{\text{Na}} \begin{array}{c} H \quad R \\ C=C \\ R \quad H \end{array}$$

   2. The mechanism of this reaction involves a two-electron reduction:
      a) Alkali metals in liquid ammonia are sources of electrons complexed to ammonia (**solvated electrons**).
      b) The addition of an electron to the triple bond results in a species (a **radical anion**) that has both an unpaired electron and a negative charge.
      c) The radical anion, a strong base, removes a proton from ammonia to give a **vinylic radical**.
      d) The resulting vinylic radical rapidly undergoes inversion.
         (1) The equilibrium between the *cis* and *trans* radical favors the *trans* radical for steric reasons.
         (2) Since there is much more of the *trans* radical, the ultimate product of the reaction is the *trans*-alkene.
      e) The vinylic radical accepts an electron to form a **vinylic anion**.
      f) The vinylic anion, a stong base, removes a proton from ammonia to complete the addition.

$$Na· \longrightarrow Na^+ + e^-(NH_3)_n$$
$$\text{solvated electron}$$

II. **Reactions of 1-Alkynes:**

   A. Formation of Acetylenic Anions:
      1. The sodium salt of an alkyne can be formed from a 1-alkyne quantitatively with $NaNH_2$ (sodamide).

$$R—C≡C—H + NaNH_2 \longrightarrow R—C≡C{:}^- Na^+ + NH_3$$

      2. Acetylenic Grignard reagents are prepared by the reaction of an alkylmagnesium halide with an alkyne. The formation of a gaseous product (CH_4 or C_2H_6) when CH_3MgI or C_2H_5MgI, respectively, can be used as a test for 1-alkynes.

$$R—C≡C—H + CH_3MgI \longrightarrow R—C≡C{:}^- \overset{+}{Mg}I + CH_4\uparrow$$

      3. 1-Alkynes form acetylide precipitates when they react with heavy-metal salts.

$$R—C≡C—H + CuCl \longrightarrow R—C≡C—Cu \downarrow + HCl$$

   B. Acetylenic Anions as Nucleophiles:
      1. Acetylenic anions are strong bases.
      2. Acetylenic anions can be used as nucleophiles in S_N2 reactions to prepare other alkynes.

$$R—C≡C{:}^- + R^1—Br \longrightarrow R—C≡C—R^1 + Br^-$$

      a) The alkyl halide or sulfonate use in this reaction must be a primary or unbranched secondary compound.
      b) This is another method of carbon–carbon bond formation.

CHAPTER 14 SOLUTIONS

Solutions to In-Text Problems

1. (a)   (b)   (c)   (d)

    $(CH_3)_2CHC\equiv CH$ $HC\equiv CCH_2CH(CH_3)_2$

$C\equiv C$

$C\equiv CH$ OH

    (e) $HC\equiv C-C\equiv C-CH_2CH_3$ (f) $CH_3CH_2CHCH_2C\equiv C\ CH_2CH_2CH_2CH_3$
    $OCH_2CH_2CH_2CH_2CH_3$

2. (a) dibutylacetylene   (b) 2-(3-butynyl)oxirane   (c) 2-methyl-3-pentyn-2-ol
    (d) 3-butyl-8-methoxy-6-octen-1-yne

3. The *sp* hybridization of the carbon atoms of the triple bond requires a linear arrangement for these atoms and the two attached carbon atoms. The remaining two carbon atoms cannot close a ring without excessively long bond lengths and/or unrealistic bond angles.

4. The order of carbon–carbon single bond lengths is

    propyne < propene < propane

    The reason is that there is progressively more *p* character in the single bond along this series (or progressively less *s* character). The single bond in propyne is an sp–sp^3 single bond; that in propene is an sp^2–sp^3 single bond; and that in propane is an sp^3–sp^3 single bond. The more *p* character in the bond, the longer it is; the more *s* character in a bond, the shorter it is.

5. The IR stretching frequencies increase along the series

    alkane C—H < alkene C—H < alkyne C—H

    Since the molecular masses involved in these bonds are about the same, the frequency differences must be due to differences in force constants. (See Eq. 12.8, text page 459.) Greater frequency is associated with greater force constant; and greater force constant is associated with greater bond strength. Hence, bond strength increases in the same order as the IR stretching frequencies; that is, the alkane C—H bond is the weakest bond, and the alkyne C—H bond is the strongest.

6. Since there are two sets of nonequivalent protons (the methyl protons and the $\equiv$C—H proton), the two signals for these protons must be the same by coincidence. In fact, the chemical shift of δ 1.8 is about what we would expect for both acetylenic and propargylic protons.

7. The IR spectrum shows absorptions for both a $\equiv$C—H stretch and a C$\equiv$C stretch. The NMR spectrum indicates a *t*-butyl group and an acetylenic proton. With a molecular weight of 82, the compound must be 3,3-dimethyl-1-butyne (*t*-butylacetylene):

    $$CH_3-\underset{\underset{CH_3}{|}}{\overset{\overset{CH_3}{|}}{C}}-C\equiv CH$$

8.   (a) There are two potential choices for a starting material: 4-decyne and 5-decyne. However, hydration of 4-decyne would give a *mixture* of products, while hydration of 5-decyne, $CH_3(CH_2)_3$—C≡C—$(CH_2)_3CH_3$ gives only the desired product as a pure compound. (Write out the products from hydration of 4-decyne if this point is not clear!)
     (b) The only possible starting material is *t*-butylacetylene, $(CH_3)_3C$—C≡C—H.

9.   (a) An examination of the hydration reaction shows that its overall effect is to bring about the following transformation:

$$—C≡C— \longrightarrow \overset{\overset{\textstyle O}{\|}}{—C}—CH_2—$$

That is, the carbon *adjacent* to the carbonyl group in the product must bear two protons. The structure of the product in (a) is not compatible with this type of transformation; it lacks the —CH_2— group.
     (b) In alkyne hydration, the oxygen is added to the *more substituted* carbon of the triple bond. To get the product in (b), the oxygen would have to be added to the *less substituted carbon* of propyne.
     (c) The starting material would have to be cyclohexyne, a compound that, as we learned in Problem 3, cannot be isolated. It's fairly difficult to run a reaction on a compound that cannot be isolated!

10. (a) There are two stereoisomeric enols:

$$\underset{H}{\overset{CH_3}{\diagdown}}C=C\underset{C_2H_5}{\overset{OH}{\diagup}} \quad \text{and} \quad \underset{H}{\overset{CH_3}{\diagdown}}C=C\underset{OH}{\overset{C_2H_5}{\diagup}}$$

     (b) Alkyne hydration would *not* be a good preparative method for this compound, because the alkyne required, 2-pentyne, would give a mixture of products:

$$CH_3C≡CCH_2CH_3 \xrightarrow[\text{H}_2\text{O}]{\text{Hg}^{2+}, \text{H}_2\text{SO}_4} \overset{\overset{\textstyle O}{\|}}{CH_3C}CH_2CH_2CH_3 \text{ and } CH_3CH_2\overset{\overset{\textstyle O}{\|}}{C}CH_2CH_3$$

➤ The message of this problem, and Problems 8(a) and 9(b), is that only *symmetrical* alkynes and 1-alkynes give single structural isomers of hydration products.

11. (a)   (b)

product of hydration   product of hydroboration–oxidation $CH_3\overset{\overset{\textstyle O}{\|}}{C}CH_2CH_3$

same product
obtained from
both reactions

12. (a)   (b)   (c)

$$\underset{H}{\overset{CH_3CH_2CH_2}{\diagdown}}C=C\underset{H}{\overset{(CH_2)_4CH=CH_2}{\diagup}} \quad CH_3(CH_2)_9CH_3$$

In (c), the pyridine ring is not only part of the starting material, but also acts as its own poison.

13. (a)

$$CH_3CH_2C{\equiv}CCH_2CH_3 \xrightarrow{Na/NH_3} \underset{H}{\overset{CH_3CH_2}{}}{C}{=}{C}\underset{CH_2CH_3}{\overset{H}{}} \xrightarrow[H_2/Pd]{D_2} CH_3CH_2 {-}\!\!\overset{D}{\underset{H}{C}}{-}\overset{D}{\underset{CH_2CH_3}{C}}{-}H$$

(racemate)

(b) The reaction with H_2 over Pd/C gives *cis*-2-hexene; catalytic hydrogenation with D_2 gives the *meso* stereoisomer of the product in part (a).

14. Structures of the conjugate acids:

(a) $CH_3{-}CH{=}\overset{+}{N}H_2$ (b) $CH_3{-}C{\equiv}\overset{+}{N}H$ (c) $CH_3{-}\overset{+}{N}H_3$

Basicity order: (b) < (a) < (c)

We can apply the same arguments to rationalize relative basicity that are used to understand the relative basicity of carbanions. In both $CH_3{-}C{\equiv}C:^-$ and $CH_3{-}C{\equiv}N:$, the electron pair is in an *sp* orbital. Electron pairs in orbitals with a high degree of *s* character are not very basic. In both $^-:CH_3$ and $:NH_2{-}CH_3$, the electron pair is in an sp^3 orbital. Electron pairs in orbitals with more *p* character are *more* basic. Thus, hybridization arguments apply to atoms other than carbon.

15. The acids in Eq. 14.30 have the following pK_a values:

$$R{-}C{\equiv}C{-}H \quad + \quad {}^-:\overset{..}{N}H_2 \quad \rightleftharpoons \quad R{-}C{\equiv}C:^- \quad + \quad :NH_3$$
$$pK_a = 25 \qquad\qquad\qquad\qquad\qquad\qquad\qquad pK_a = 35$$

We then apply the method discussed in Chapter 8, text page 297, and derived in Problem 40 of Chapter 8:

$$\log K_{eq} = pK_a(NH_3) - pK_a(R{-}C{\equiv}C{-}H) = 35 - 25 = 10$$

or $K_{eq} = 10^{10}$.

This equilibrium constant shows that the reaction is highly favorable to the right. In contrast, alkanes have pK_a values near 55; their reactions with sodium amide have equilibrium constants near 10^{-20} and are therefore very unfavorable.

16. (a) $CH_3C{\equiv}CC_2H_5 + Na^+ I^-$ (b) $HC{\equiv}C{-}(CH_2)_5{-}C{\equiv}CH + 2Na^+ Br^-$ (c) $Ph{-}C{\equiv}C{-}(CH_2)_3CH_3$
    (d) $CH_3C{\equiv}C{-}CH_2CH_2{-}OH$

17. Acetylide ions are strong bases. When they react with primary alkyl halides, they give displacement products by the S_N2 mechanism; but when they react with tertiary alkyl halides such as *t*-butyl bromide, they give elimination products by the E2 mechanism. Hence, Choke Fumely obtained isobutylene, $(CH_3)_2C{=}CH_2$, and methylacetylene, $CH_3C{\equiv}CH$, from his reaction.

18. We could allow methylacetylide ion to react with butyl bromide:

$$CH_3{-}C{\equiv}C:^- Na^+ + Br{-}CH_2CH_2CH_2CH_3 \rightarrow CH_3C{\equiv}CCH_2CH_2CH_2CH_3 + Na^+ Br^-$$

However, the reaction shown in Eq. 14.36 would be the better alternative for two reasons. First, methyl bromide is more reactive than butyl bromide in S_N2 reactions (see Table 9.2, text page 329); and second, competing elimination, although not likely to be a serious problem with butyl bromide, absolutely cannot occur with methyl bromide.

19. We adopt the recommended approach to multistep syntheses — to work backwards from the desired product.

(a)
$$CH_3CH_2C\equiv C(CH_2)_2CH_3 \xleftarrow{\;CH_3CH_2-I\;} {}^-\!:C\equiv C(CH_2)_2CH_3 \xleftarrow{\;NaNH_2\;} HC\equiv C(CH_2)_2CH_3$$

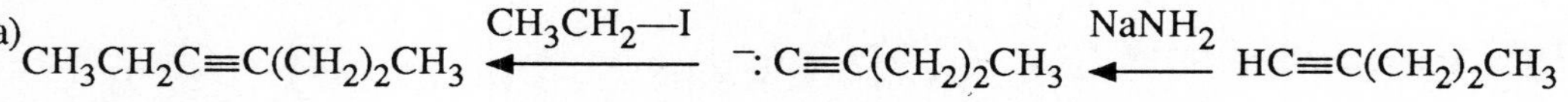

(b)

$$CH_3\!-\!\underset{\underset{CH_3}{|}}{\overset{\overset{CH_3}{|}}{C}}\!-\!C\equiv CCH_3 \xleftarrow{\;CH_3I\;} CH_3\!-\!\underset{\underset{CH_3}{|}}{\overset{\overset{CH_3}{|}}{C}}\!-\!C\equiv C:^- \xleftarrow{\;NaNH_2\;} CH_3\!-\!\underset{\underset{CH_3}{|}}{\overset{\overset{CH_3}{|}}{C}}\!-\!C\equiv C\!-\!H$$

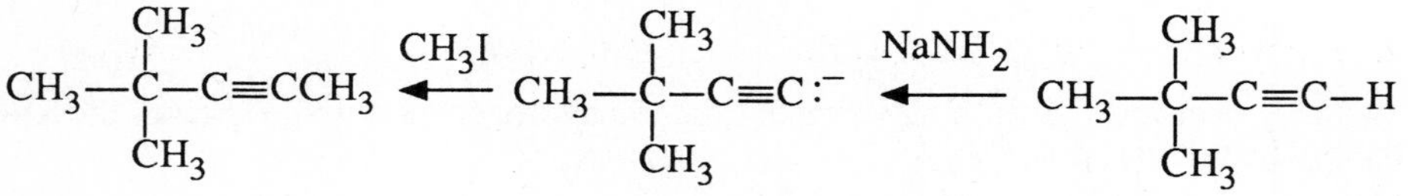

20. (Solved in the text.)

21. Working backwards from the desired products:

(a)
$$CH_3(CH_2)_6\!-\!OH \xleftarrow[\text{2) } H_2O_2/^-OH]{\text{1) } B_2H_6} CH_3(CH_2)_4CH=CH_2 \xleftarrow[\text{Lindlar cat.}]{H_2} CH_3(CH_2)_4C\equiv CH$$

$$\Big\uparrow Na^+\, {}^-\!:C\equiv CH$$

$$CH_3CH_2CH_2CH_2CH_2Br$$

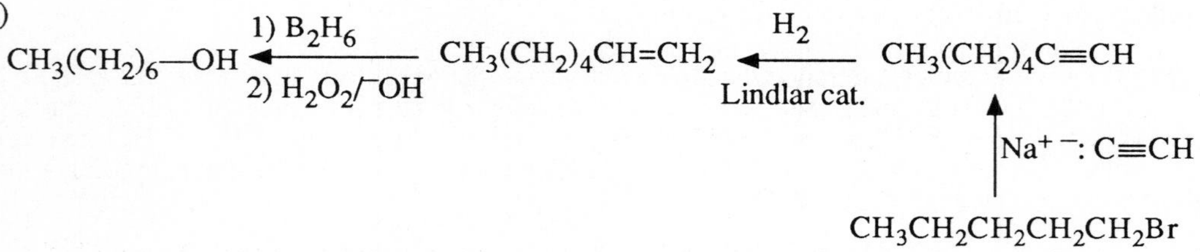

The sodium acetylide used in the first step is formed by treatment of a large excess of acetylene with sodium amide ($NaNH_2$). (The same material is also required in the following solution.)

(b)
$$\overset{\overset{\displaystyle O}{\|}}{CH_3C}(CH_2)_8CH_3 \xleftarrow[H_2O]{Hg^{2+},\, H_2SO_4} HC\equiv C(CH_2)_8CH_3 \xleftarrow{\;Na^+\, {}^-\!:C\equiv CH\;} Br\!-\!(CH_2)_8CH_3$$

$$\Big\uparrow HBr,\ \text{peroxides}$$

$$CH_3(CH_2)_6Br \xrightarrow{\;Na^+\!:C\equiv CH\;} HC\equiv CH(CH_2)_6CH_3 \xrightarrow[\text{Lindlar cat.}]{H_2} CH_2=CH(CH_2)_6CH_3$$

$$\Big\uparrow HBr,\ H_2SO_4$$

$$CH_3(CH_2)_6OH \xleftarrow{\;H_3O^+\;} \overset{O}{\triangle} \xleftarrow{} CH_3(CH_2)_4MgBr \xleftarrow{\;Mg,\ ether\;} CH_3(CH_2)_4Br$$

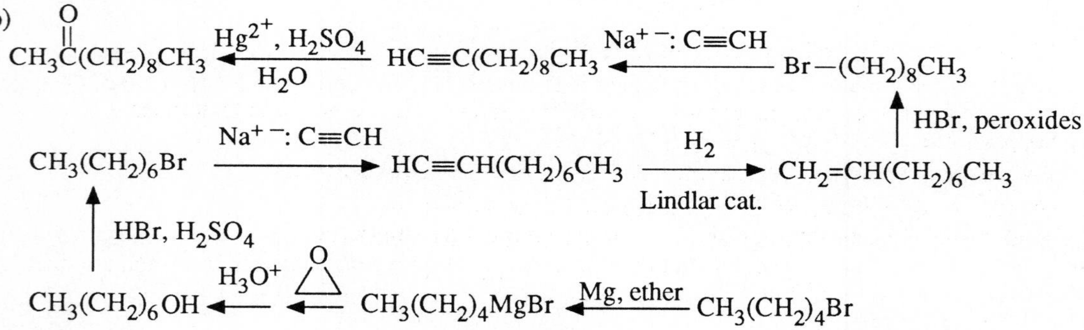

22. We'll abbreviate the alkyl halide as R—Br:

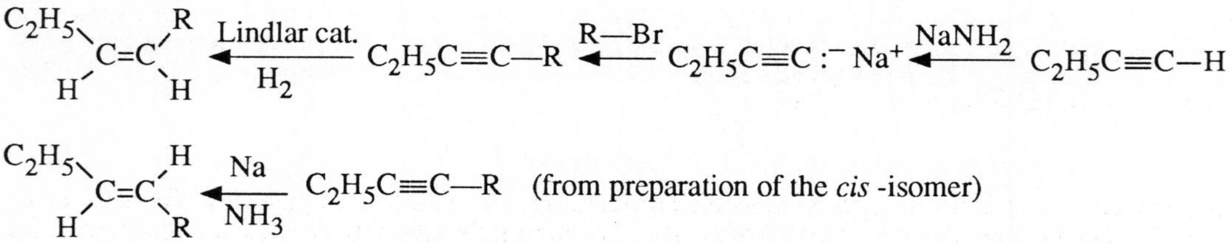

$$\underset{H}{\overset{C_2H_5}{}}\!\!\diagdown\!\!\underset{}{C}=\!\!C\!\!\diagup\!\!\overset{R}{\underset{H}{}} \xleftarrow[H_2]{\text{Lindlar cat.}} C_2H_5C\equiv C\!-\!R \xleftarrow{\;R-Br\;} C_2H_5C\equiv C:^-Na^+ \xleftarrow{\;NaNH_2\;} C_2H_5C\equiv C\!-\!H$$

$$\underset{H}{\overset{C_2H_5}{}}\!\!\diagdown\!\!\underset{}{C}=\!\!C\!\!\diagup\!\!\overset{H}{\underset{R}{}} \xleftarrow[NH_3]{Na} C_2H_5C\equiv C\!-\!R \quad (\text{from preparation of the } cis\text{-isomer})$$

Solutions to Additional Problems

23. In the following solutions, R— = $CH_3CH_2CH_2$— .

(a)

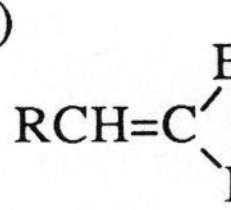

$RCH=C\overset{Br}{\underset{R}{\diagdown}}$ (*cis* and *trans*) and RCH_2CBr_2R

(b)

$CH_3(CH_2)_6CH_3$

(c)

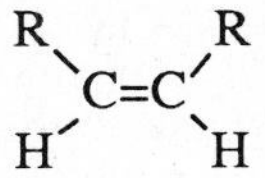

$\overset{R}{\diagup}C=C\overset{R}{\diagdown}$
$H\diagup \quad \diagdown H$

(d)

2 RCH=O

(e)

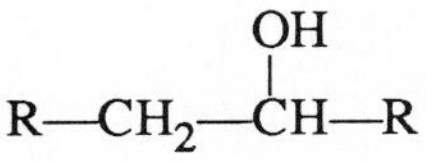

$\overset{OH}{\underset{|}{R-CH_2-CH-R}}$

(f)

$\overset{R}{\diagdown}C=C\overset{Br}{\diagup}$ + $R-\overset{Br}{\underset{Br}{\overset{|}{C}}}-\overset{Br}{\underset{Br}{\overset{|}{C}}}-R$
$Br\diagup \quad \diagdown R$

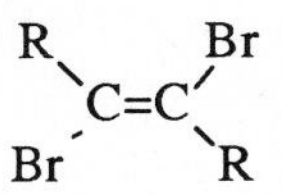

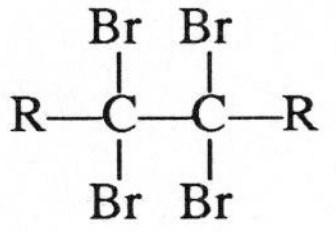

cis and *trans*

(g)

no reaction

(h)

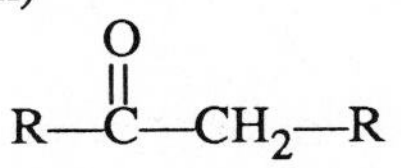

$R-\overset{O}{\overset{||}{C}}-CH_2-R$

(i)

$\overset{R}{\diagup}C=C\overset{H}{\diagdown}$
$H\diagup \quad \diagdown R$

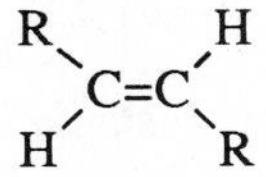

(j)

same as (e)

24. We'll draw the structure indicated by the name in the Blarneystyne catalog, and then we'll provide the correct name.

(a)

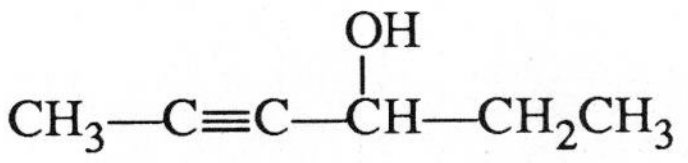

$CH_3-C\equiv C-\overset{OH}{\underset{|}{CH}}-CH_2CH_3$ 4-hexyn-3-ol

The —OH group is the principal group, and therefore receives the lowest possible number.

(b) $HC\equiv C-CH=CH_2$ 1-buten-3-yne
The double bond receives numerical precedence, and is cited first in the name.

(c) $HC\equiv C-CH_2CH_2C\equiv C-OCH_3$ 1-methoxy-1,5-hexadiyne
The methoxy substituent receives the lower of the two possible numbers.

25. (a)

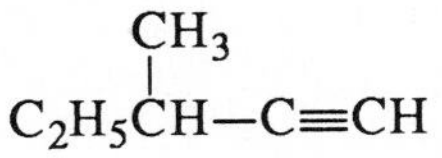

$C_2H_5\overset{CH_3}{\underset{|}{CH}}-C\equiv CH$

(b)

$CH_3CH_2C\equiv CCH_2CH_3$

(c)

$HC\equiv C-CH_2CH_2CH_2CH_3$

(d)

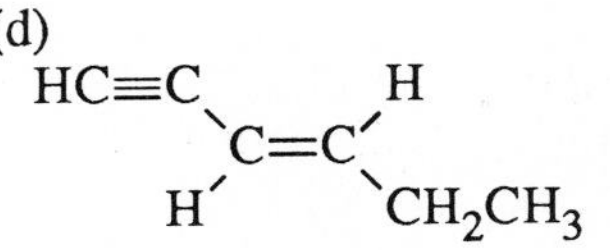

$\overset{HC\equiv C}{\diagdown}C=C\overset{H}{\diagup}$
$H\diagup \quad \diagdown CH_2CH_3$

or

$\underset{CH_3}{\overset{C\equiv CH}{\triangleleft}}$

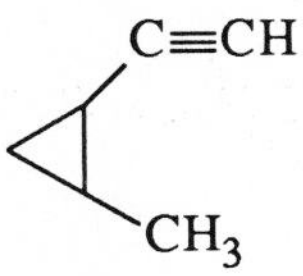

The answer given in (a) is one of several possible correct answers. The correct answer to (b) must be a symmetrical alkyne — an alkyne in which both carbons of the triple bond are identically substituted. The correct answer to (c) must be an alkyne that gives the same alkene whether the addition of hydrogen is *syn* or *anti* — that is, an alkene that cannot exist as *cis*- or *trans*-isomers.

26. (a) Acetylenic anions are less basic than vinylic anions, which are less basic than alkyl anions, for the reasons given in the text (Sec. 14.7):

$$CH_3(CH_2)_3-C\equiv C:^- < CH_3(CH_2)_3-CH=\ddot{C}H < CH_3(CH_2)_4\ddot{C}H_2$$

(b) Basicity decreases as we move to the right within a row of the periodic table. Strictly speaking, the comparison of acidities within a row of the periodic table assumes the same hybridization of the basic atoms. The oxygen and fluorine are (to our level of approximation) sp^3 hybridized, whereas the carbon of the acetylide anion is sp hybridized. However, even acetylide ions, whose conjugate acids have pK_a values of about 25, are considerably more basic than alkoxide anions, whose conjugate acids have pK_a values of about 16. The required basicity order, then, is

$$:\ddot{F}:^- < CH_3CH_2\ddot{O}:^- < HC\equiv C:^-$$

27. (a) Reaction of 1-hexyne with C_2H_5MgBr gives a gas (ethane); alkenes are not acidic enough to react with Grignard reagents.
(b) Reaction of 1-hexyne with C_2H_5MgBr gives a gas; internal alkynes do not give this reaction.
(c) The alkyne will decolorize a solution of Br_2 in an inert solvent such as CCl_4.
(d) Propyne is a gas; 1-decyne is a liquid.
(e) 5-Chloro-5-methyl-2-hexyne is a tertiary alkyl halide, and therefore instantaneously gives a precipitate of AgCl when allowed to react with acidic $AgNO_3$ solution. Because the other compound is a neopentyl-type halide, it is unreactive under normal S_N1 or S_N2 conditions.

28. According to our usual practice in working multistep synthesis problems, we work backwards from the target compound.

(a)
$$HC\equiv C-(CH_2)_3CH_3 \xleftarrow{\quad Br(CH_2)_3CH_3 \quad} Na^+{}^-:C\equiv CH \xleftarrow{\quad NaNH_2 \quad} HC\equiv CH$$

(b)

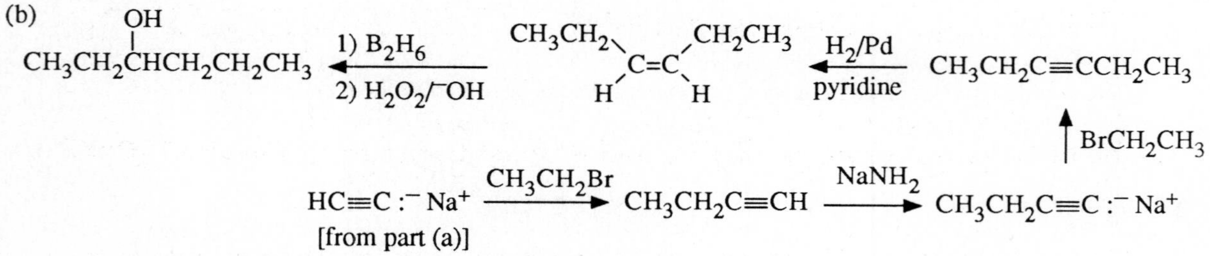

Oxymercuration–reduction would work equally well in the last step.

(c)
$$CH_3CH_2CD_2CD_2CH_2CH_3 \xleftarrow[\text{Pt/C}]{D_2} CH_3CH_2C\equiv CCH_2CH_3$$
[from part (b)]

(d)
$$CH_2=CH(CH_2)_3CH_3 \xleftarrow[\substack{\text{Pd/C}\\\text{quinoline}}]{H_2} HC\equiv C(CH_2)_3CH_3 \quad \text{[from part (a)]}$$

(e)

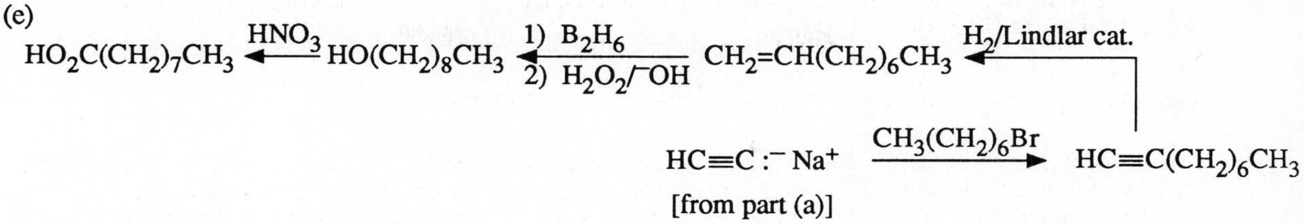

$$HO_2C(CH_2)_7CH_3 \xleftarrow{HNO_3} HO(CH_2)_8CH_3 \xleftarrow[2)\ H_2O_2/^-OH]{1)\ B_2H_6} CH_2=CH(CH_2)_6CH_3 \xleftarrow{H_2/Lindlar\ cat.}$$

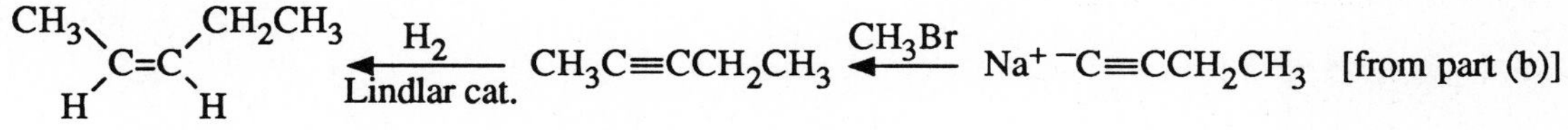

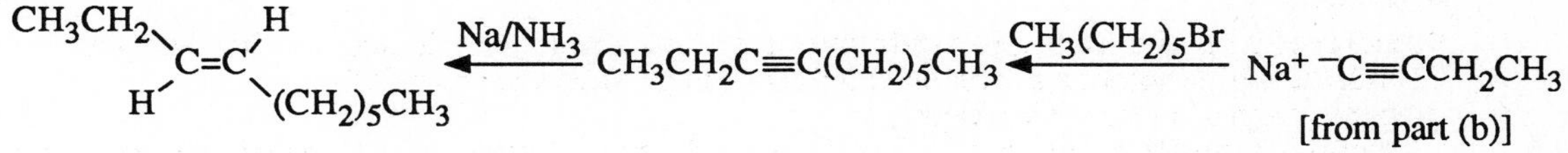

$$HC\equiv C:^- Na^+ \xrightarrow{CH_3(CH_2)_6Br} HC\equiv C(CH_2)_6CH_3$$

[from part (a)]

(f)

$$\xleftarrow[Lindlar\ cat.]{H_2} CH_3C\equiv CCH_2CH_3 \xleftarrow{CH_3Br} Na^+\ ^-C\equiv CCH_2CH_3 \quad \text{[from part (b)]}$$

(g)

$$\xleftarrow{Na/NH_3} CH_3CH_2C\equiv C(CH_2)_5CH_3 \xleftarrow{CH_3(CH_2)_5Br} Na^+\ ^-C\equiv CCH_2CH_3$$

[from part (b)]

(h)

$$(CH_3)_2CH(CH_2)_3CH=O \xleftarrow[2)\ H_2O_2/^-OH]{1)\ [\text{BH}]} (CH_3)_2CH(CH_2)_2C\equiv CH \xleftarrow{(CH_3)_2CH(CH_2)_2Br} Na^+\ ^-:C\equiv CH$$

[from part (a)]

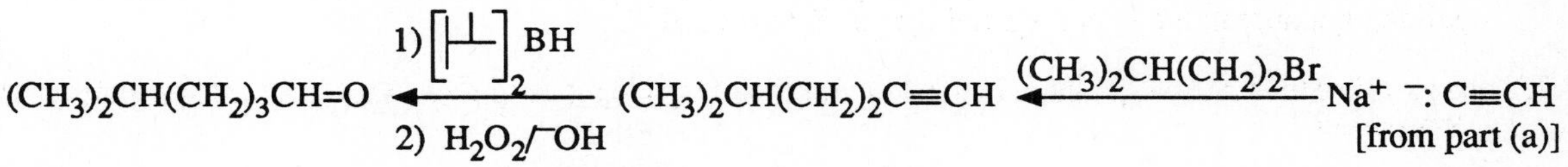

(i)

$$\xleftarrow[^-OH]{KMnO_4} CH_3CH_2CH_2\cdots C=C\cdots CH_2CH_2CH_3 \xleftarrow[quinoline]{H_2 \atop Pd/C}$$

$$HC\equiv CH \xrightarrow[2)\ CH_3CH_2CH_2Br]{1)\ NaNH_2} CH_3CH_2CH_2C\equiv CH \xrightarrow[2)\ CH_3CH_2CH_2Br]{1)\ NaNH_2} CH_3CH_2CH_2C\equiv CCH_2CH_2CH_3$$

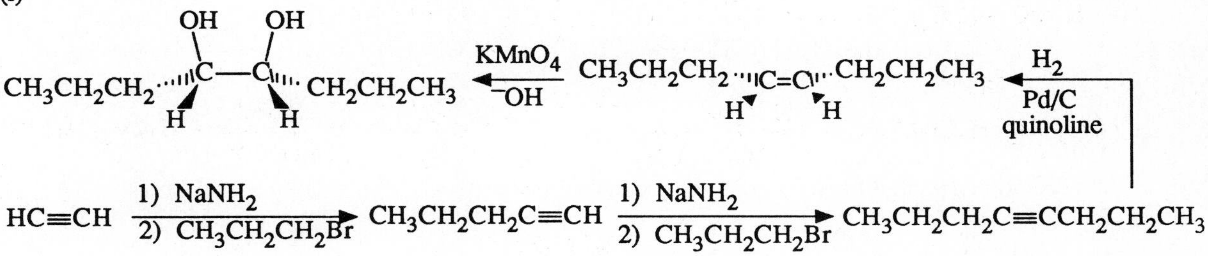

The same compound could be made by hydrolysis of the epoxide of *trans*-4-octene; the alkene, in turn, could be prepared by treating 4-octyne with Na/NH_3.

(j)

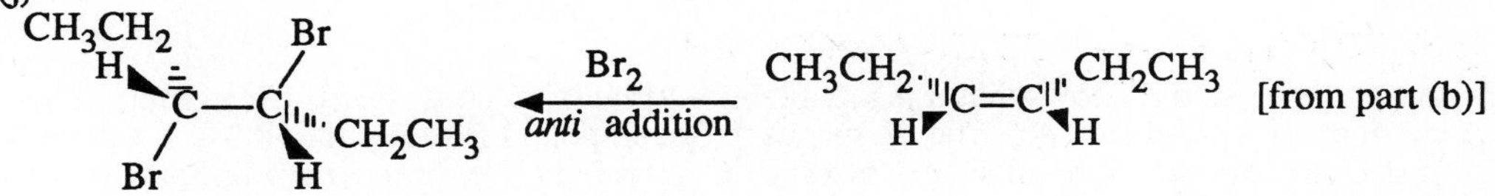

$$\xleftarrow[anti\ addition]{Br_2} CH_3CH_2\cdots C=C\cdots CH_2CH_3 \quad \text{[from part (b)]}$$

29. The ⁻OD in solution removes a proton from the alkyne; since the solvent is D_2O, the HDO that is formed is a relatively minor part of the solvent. The acetylide ion reacts with the D_2O present in large excess to form the deuterated alkyne:

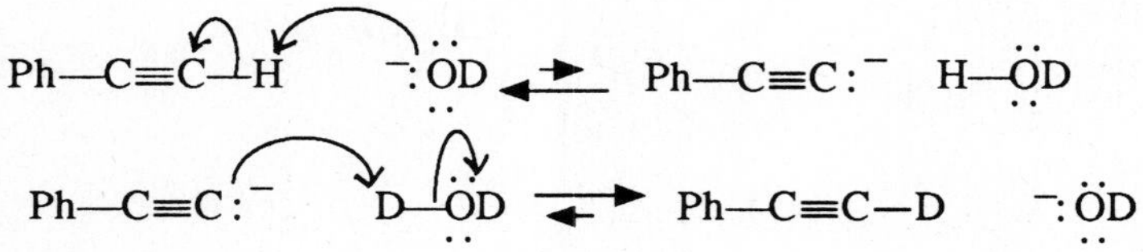

Ph—C≡C—H   :ÖD   ⇌   Ph—C≡C:⁻   H—ÖD

Ph—C≡C:⁻   D—ÖD   ⇌   Ph—C≡C—D   ⁻:ÖD

30. Once again, we work backward from the target compound:

(a)
$CH_3CH_2C≡C—D$ ⟵[D—OD] $CH_3CH_2C≡C:^-$ ⁺MgBr ⟵[C_2H_5MgBr] $CH_3CH_2C≡C—H$

(b)
$CH_3CH_2CD_2CD_3$ ⟵[D_2 / Pd/C] $CH_3CH_2C≡C—D$ [from part (a)]

(c)
$CH_3CH_2\overset{O}{\overset{||}{C}}—OH$ ⟵[1) O_3 / 2) H_2O_2] $CH_3CH_2CH=CH_2$ ⟵[H_2 / Pd/C / quinoline] $CH_3CH_2C≡CH$

(d)
$CH_3CH_2CH_2CH_2CH_2CH_2CH_2CH_3$ ⟵[H_2 / Pd/C] $CH_3CH_2C≡CCH_2CH_2CH_2CH_3$ ⟵[$CH_3CH_2CH_2CH_2—Br$]

$CH_3CH_2C≡C—H$ ⟶[$NaNH_2$] $CH_3CH_2C≡C:^- Na^+$

Butyl bromide, the alkyl halide used in the second step, is prepared from an alkyne as follows:

$CH_3CH_2CH_2CH_2Br$ ⟵[HBr / peroxides] $CH_3CH_2CH=CH_2$ [from part (a)]

(e)

$\underset{H}{\overset{CH_3CH_2}{}}C=C\underset{H}{\overset{CH_2CH_2CH_2CH_3}{}}$ ⟶[H_2 / Lindlar cat.] $CH_3CH_2C≡CCH_2CH_2CH_2CH_3$
[from part (d)]

31. The IR spectrum of compound *A* shows that it is a 1-alkene — that is, it has a —CH=CH₂ group. Therefore, compound *A* is 3-methyl-1,4-pentadiene. The IR spectrum of compound *B* shows that it is a 1-alkyne (C≡C stretch, ≡C—H stretch), and therefore must be 1-hexyne. Compound *C*, by process of elimination, must therefore be 2-hexyne.

32. There are a number of possible variations on the following synthesis:

$$CH_3(CH_2)_7 \quad (CH_2)_{12}CH_3$$
$$C=C \xleftarrow[\text{2) } Br(CH_2)_7CH_3]{\text{1) } NaNH_2} HC\equiv C(CH_2)_{12}CH_3 \xleftarrow{Na^+ \ ^-:C\equiv CH}$$
$$H \qquad H$$
$$\text{(see below)}$$

$$\xrightarrow{} HC\equiv C(CH_2)_{10}CH_3 \xrightarrow[\text{pyridine}]{H_2/cat} CH_2=CH(CH_2)_{10}CH_3 \xrightarrow[\text{peroxides}]{HBr} Br(CH_2)_{12}CH_3$$
$$HC\equiv C^- \ Na^+$$

$$CH_3(CH_2)_{10}Br \xleftarrow[\text{peroxides}]{HBr} CH_3(CH_2)_8CH=CH_2 \xleftarrow[\text{pyridine}]{H_2/cat} CH_3(CH_2)_8C\equiv CH \xleftarrow{Na^+ \ ^-C\equiv CH}$$

$$HC\equiv C:^- \ Na^+$$
$$\xrightarrow{} CH_3(CH_2)_4C\equiv CH \xrightarrow[\text{pyridine}]{H_2/cat} CH_3(CH_2)_4CH=CH_2 \xrightarrow[\text{peroxides}]{HBr} CH_3(CH_2)_6Br$$

$$CH_3(CH_2)_4Br \xleftarrow[\text{peroxides}]{HBr} CH_3(CH_2)_2CH=CH_2 \xleftarrow[\text{pyridine}]{H_2/cat} CH_3(CH_2)_2C\equiv CH$$

The synthesis of 1-bromooctane used in the last step is as follows:

$$Br(CH_2)_7CH_3 \xleftarrow[\text{peroxides}]{HBr} CH_2=CH(CH_2)_5CH_3 \xleftarrow[\text{pyridine}]{H_2/cat} HC\equiv C(CH_2)_5CH_3 \xleftarrow{HC\equiv C:^- \ Na^+}$$

$$HC\equiv C:^- \ Na^+$$
$$\xrightarrow{} HC\equiv C(CH_2)_3CH_3 \xrightarrow[\text{pyridine}]{H_2/cat} CH_2=CH(CH_2)_3CH_3 \xrightarrow[\text{peroxides}]{HBr} Br(CH_2)_5CH_3$$

$$CH_3CH_2CH_2CH_2Br \xleftarrow[\text{peroxides}]{HBr} CH_3CH_2CH=CH_2 \xleftarrow[\text{pyridine}]{H_2/cat} CH_3CH_2C\equiv CH$$

The alkyl halides could also have been prepared from the alcohols, which, in turn, are prepared from the corresponding 1-alkenes by hydroboration–oxidation:

$$BrCH_2CH_2-R \xleftarrow{\text{concd } HBr} HOCH_2CH_2-R \xleftarrow[\text{2) } H_2O_2/^-OH]{\text{1) } B_2H_6} CH_2=CH-R$$

33. (a) As a useful approximation. let us write Grignard reagents R—MgBr as R :⁻ ⁺MgBr to emphasize their basic, carbanion character, although they are not really free ions.

$$(1) \quad CH_3\ddot{C}H_2 \quad H-C\equiv C-MgBr \longrightarrow CH_3CH_3 \ + \ BrMg-C\equiv C-MgBr$$
$$^+MgBr$$

$$(2) \quad HC\equiv C:^- \quad H-C\equiv C-MgBr \longrightarrow HC\equiv CH \ + \ BrMg-C\equiv C-MgBr$$
$$^+MgBr$$

(b) The large excess of acetylene drives reaction (2) backward by mass action; and by reaction with the product of reaction (1) by the reverse of reaction (2), acetylene gives ethynylmagnesium bromide, the desired material.

(c) Were BrMg—C≡C—MgBr to precipitate, both side reactions (1) and (2) would be forced to completion. Using a solvent that avoids this precipitation thus avoids these side reactions.

34.   (a) The IR spectrum suggests a 1-alkyne, and the NMR spectrum suggests a methoxy group and two equivalent methyls. The correct structure is:

$$HC\equiv C-\underset{\underset{CH_3}{|}}{\overset{\overset{OCH_3}{|}}{C}}-CH_3$$

(b) The liberation of a gas with ethylmagnesium bromide suggests a 1-alkyne, and this is confirmed by the IR data. The correct structure is:

$$HC\equiv C-CH_2-OCH_3$$

Notice that the acetylenic proton is split by the —CH$_2$— group.

(c) The IR data again suggest a 1-alkyne, and also an alcohol. The presence of an —OH group is confirmed by the broad resonance at about δ 4.1, which exchanges with D$_2$O. The compound is 3-butyn-2-ol:

$$HC\equiv C-\underset{}{\overset{\overset{OH}{|}}{C}}H-CH_3$$

Notice that the resonance of the α-proton of the alcohol is split into a quartet by the adjacent methyl group; and each line of this quartet is split into a doublet by the acetylenic proton.

(d)
$$\begin{array}{c}CH_3O \quad\quad\quad C\equiv CH \\ \searrow \quad\quad \nearrow \\ C=C \\ \nearrow \quad\quad \searrow \\ H \quad\quad\quad\quad H\end{array}$$

Notice the 6 Hz splitting between the vinylic hydrogens; this relatively small splitting is more consistent with a *cis*-alkene than with a *trans*-alkene. Notice also that one of the vinylic hydrogens is split by the acetylenic proton, as in the previous problem.

35.   In the following solution, RCO$_3$H represents a peroxyacid such as *m*-chloroperbenzoic acid (see Sec. 11.2A).

$$\text{disparlure} \xleftarrow{RCO_3H} \begin{array}{c}CH_3(CH_2)_9 \quad\quad (CH_2)_4CH(CH_3)_2 \\ \searrow \quad\quad\quad \nearrow \\ C=C \\ \nearrow \quad\quad\quad \searrow \\ H \quad\quad\quad\quad H\end{array} \xleftarrow[\text{pyridine}]{H_2/cat} CH_3(CH_2)_9C\equiv C(CH_2)_4CH(CH_3)_2$$

$$\Big\uparrow Na^+\ {}^-C\equiv C(CH_2)_4CH(CH_3)_2$$
$$\text{(see below)}$$

$$CH_3(CH_2)_7C\equiv CH \xrightarrow[\text{pyridine}]{H_2/cat} CH_3(CH_2)_7CH=CH_2 \xrightarrow[\text{peroxides}]{HBr} CH_3(CH_2)_9Br$$

$$\Big\uparrow Na^+\ {}^-C\equiv CH$$

$$CH_3(CH_2)_7Br \quad \text{(from Problem 32)}$$

Preparation of Na$^+$ $^-$C≡C(CH$_2$)$_4$CH(CH$_3$)$_2$ is as follows:

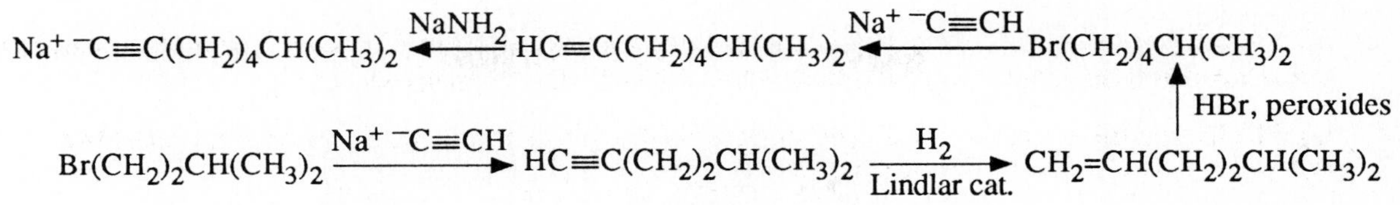

$$Na^+ \ ^-C{\equiv}C(CH_2)_4CH(CH_3)_2 \xleftarrow{\text{NaNH}_2} HC{\equiv}C(CH_2)_4CH(CH_3)_2 \xleftarrow{Na^+ \ ^-C{\equiv}CH} Br(CH_2)_4CH(CH_3)_2$$

$$\uparrow \text{HBr, peroxides}$$

$$Br(CH_2)_2CH(CH_3)_2 \xrightarrow{Na^+ \ ^-C{\equiv}CH} HC{\equiv}C(CH_2)_2CH(CH_3)_2 \xrightarrow[\text{Lindlar cat.}]{H_2} CH_2{=}CH(CH_2)_2CH(CH_3)_2$$

(See the note following the solution to Problem 32 about an alternate way to prepare the alkyl bromides.)

36. The heats of formation on text page 553 show that a molecule energetically prefers two sp^2-hybridized carbons to an sp-hybridized carbon and an sp^3-hybridized carbon. This is why the secondary carbocation is more stable.

37. (a) The organolithium reagent reacts with the alkyne to form an acetylide anion, which, in turn, acts as a nucleophile toward the silyl chloride to give the following product:

$$CH_3CH_2CH_2CH_2C{\equiv}C{-}Si{-}C(CH_3)_3$$

(b) The acetylide ion reacts as a nucleophile in an S_N2 reaction with diethyl sulfate just as it would with ethyl bromide to give $CH_3(CH_2)_6C{\equiv}C{-}CH_2CH_3$.
(c) The acetylide salt reacts with the alkyl halide, expelling the better leaving group, a chloride ion; the fluoro group remains unaffected. The product is $HC{\equiv}C{-}(CH_2)_5{-}F$.
(d) The starting material, styrene, adds bromine to give a dibromide, which then undergoes two successive E2 reactions to give phenylacetylene:

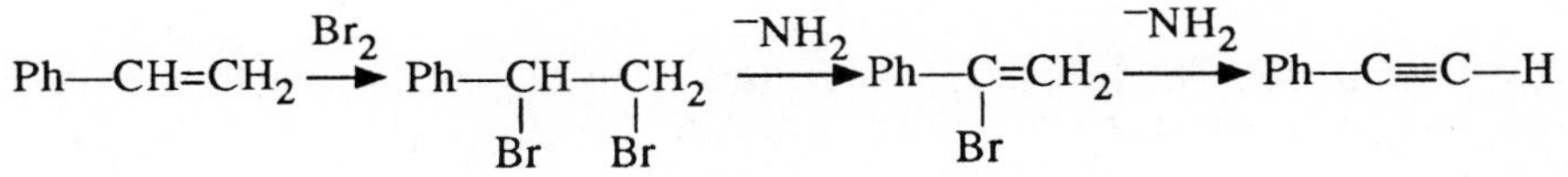

$$Ph{-}CH{=}CH_2 \xrightarrow{Br_2} Ph{-}\underset{Br}{\underset{|}{CH}}{-}\underset{Br}{\underset{|}{CH_2}} \xrightarrow{^-NH_2} Ph{-}\underset{Br}{\underset{|}{C}}{=}CH_2 \xrightarrow{^-NH_2} Ph{-}C{\equiv}C{-}H$$

(e) We know that chloroform reacts with base to give dichloromethylene, a carbene (Sec. 9.7); and we also know that carbenes add to alkenes to give cyclopropanes. They also add to alkynes to give *cyclopropenes*:

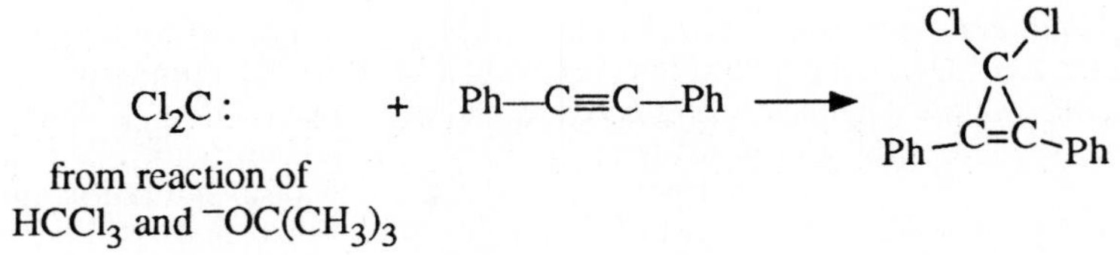

$$Cl_2C: \quad + \quad Ph{-}C{\equiv}C{-}Ph \longrightarrow$$

from reaction of
$HCCl_3$ and $^-OC(CH_3)_3$

38. (a)

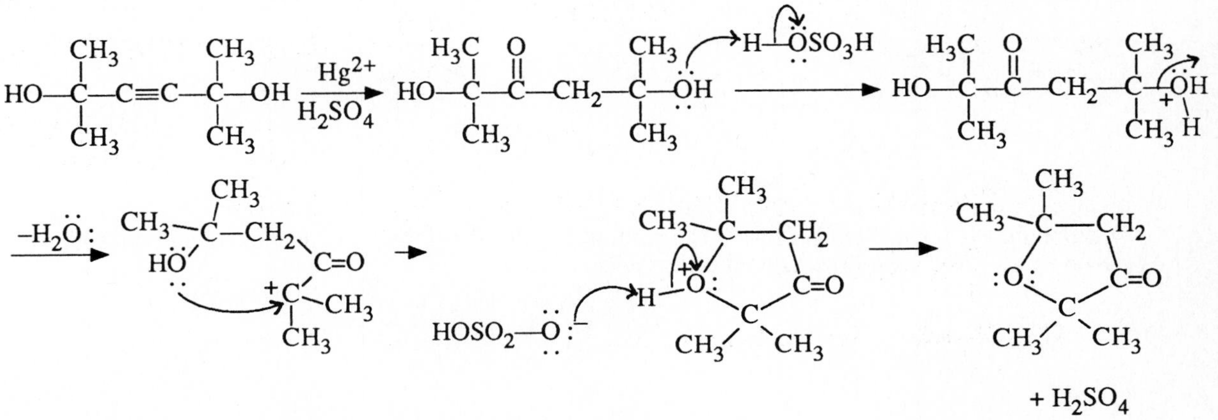

$$+ \ H_2SO_4$$

The alkyne undergoes hydration before the ether ring closes, because a five-membered ring cannot contain a triple bond.

(b) These are the conditions of bromohydrin formation (see text page 137); however, the bromohydrin product is an enol, and it therefore is spontaneously transformed into the ketone product:

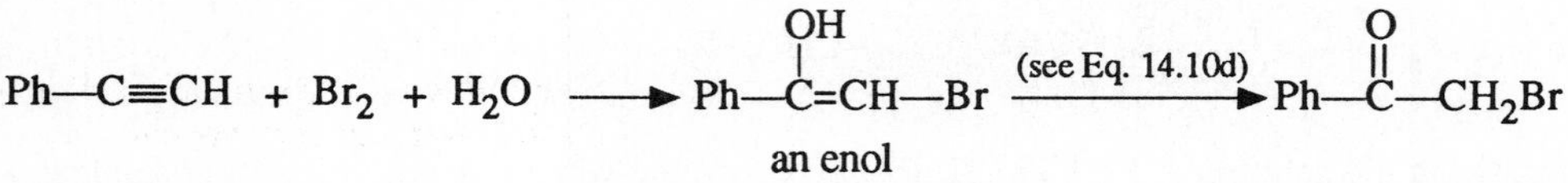

$$Ph-C\equiv CH + Br_2 + H_2O \longrightarrow Ph-\underset{\underset{\text{an enol}}{|}}{\overset{\overset{OH}{|}}{C}}=CH-Br \xrightarrow{\text{(see Eq. 14.10d)}} Ph-\overset{\overset{O}{\|}}{C}-CH_2Br$$

(c) Reaction of the alkyne with ethylmagnesium bromide gives an acetylenic Grignard reagent that, like other Grignard reagents, reacts with ethylene oxide to open the epoxide ring:

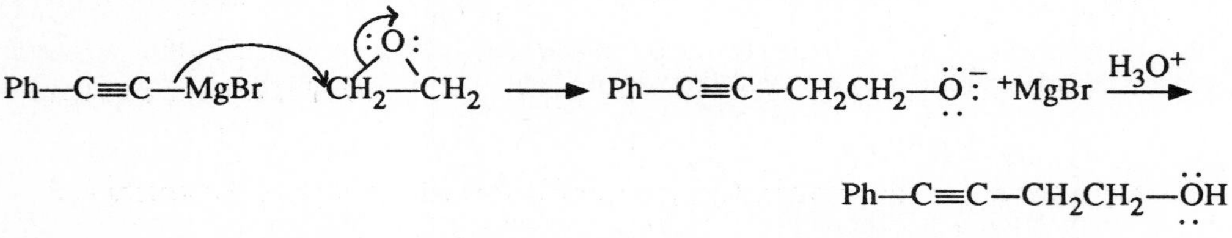

$$Ph-C\equiv C-MgBr \quad \overset{\overset{:O:}{}}{CH_2-CH_2} \longrightarrow Ph-C\equiv C-CH_2CH_2-\ddot{O}:^-{}^+MgBr \xrightarrow{H_3O^+}$$

$$Ph-C\equiv C-CH_2CH_2-\ddot{O}H$$

The second product evidently arises from protonation of the triple bond by acid present in the workup. The resulting carbocation is attacked *intramolecularly* by the —OH group:

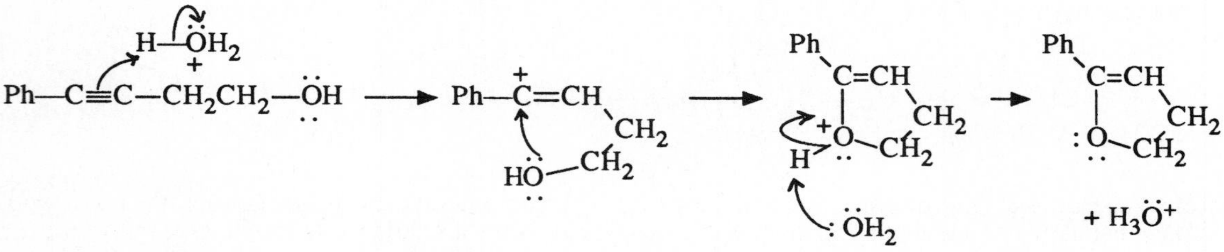

39. From the elemental analysis of compound *A* we derive the empirical formula C_5H_7. Since the hydrogenation product contains ten carbons, the molecular formula of compound *A* must be $C_{10}H_{14}$. The compound has the carbon skeleton of butylcyclohexane (an unbranched chain of four carbons on a cyclohexane ring). We are given that the compound is an alkyne, but it does not give a test for a 1-alkyne. Furthermore, the alkyne unit cannot be within the six-membered ring (why?). Since compound *A* has four degrees of unsaturation, and the ring and the triple bond account for three, there must be an additional double bond. Because ozonolysis affords a *tricarboxylic* acid, the double bond must be within the ring. Finally, ozonolysis of the hydrogenation product "carves out" two carbons; hence, the triple bond (which becomes one of the double bonds in the hydrogenation product) is two carbons from the end of the side-chain. The only possibilities for compound *A* are, then:

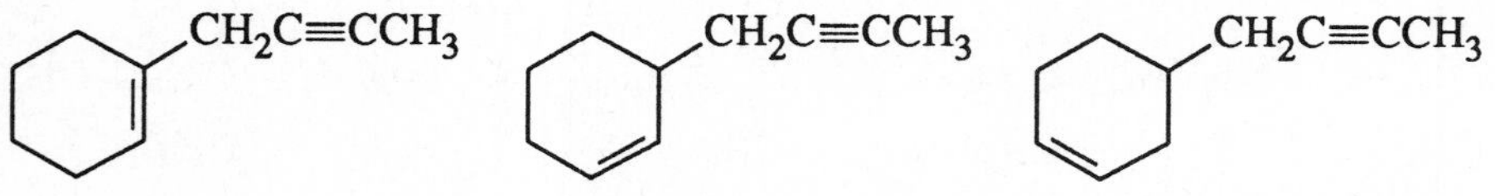

Compound *A1* is ruled out because it is not chiral. Hydrogenation of compounds *A2* and *A3*, followed by ozonolysis, gives the following predicted results:

compound *A2* $\xrightarrow[\text{quinoline}]{\text{H}_2/\text{cat}}$ [structure: cyclohexene ring with CH$_2$–CH=CH–CH$_3$ side chain, H on each alkene carbon] $\xrightarrow[\text{2) H}_2\text{O}_2]{\text{1) O}_3}$ [structure: CH$_2$–CH$_2$, CH–CH$_2$–CO$_2$H, CH$_2$, CO$_2$H, CO$_2$H branching]

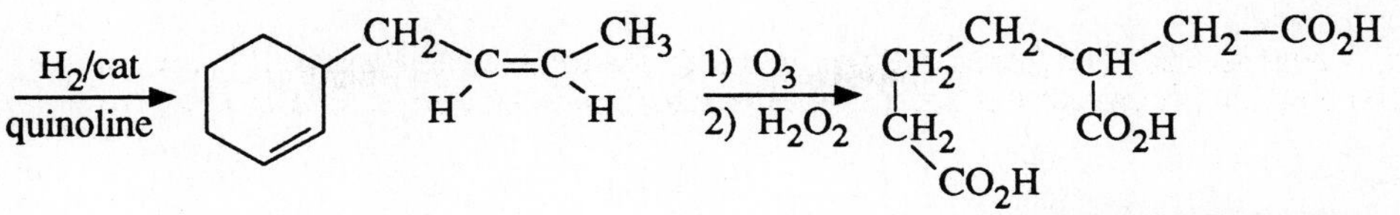

chiral; would be optically active if
A2 were optically active

compound *A3* $\xrightarrow[\text{quinoline}]{\text{H}_2/\text{cat}}$ [structure: cyclohexene ring with CH$_2$–CH=CH–CH$_3$ side chain, H on each alkene carbon] $\xrightarrow[\text{2) H}_2\text{O}_2]{\text{1) O}_3}$ [structure: CH$_2$, CH$_2$–CH–CH$_2$–CO$_2$H, CO$_2$H, CH$_2$, CO$_2$H branching]

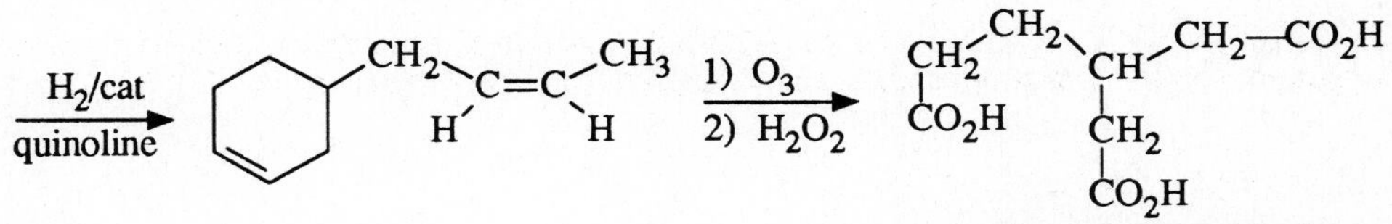

achiral; cannot be optically
active

Since optical activity is lost in the ozonolysis product, structure *A3* best fits the data as the structure of compound *A*.

Chapter 15 / Dienes, Resonance, and Aromaticity

CHAPTER 15 TERMS

absorbance (*A*) 15.2A
1,2-addition 15.4A
1,4-addition 15.3A
allyl group 15.4A
allylic cation 15.4A
allylic group 15.4A
allylic rearrangement 15.4B
antiaromaticity 15.7D
antibonding molecular orbital 15.7E
aromatic hydrocarbon 15.7A
aromaticity 15.7D
Beer's Law 15.2A
bonding molecular orbital 15.7E
chromophore 15.2B
conjugate addition 15.3A
conjugated diene .... Introduction
conjugated double bond .... Introduction
copolymer 15.5
cumulated double bond .... Introduction
cumulene .... Introduction
cycloaddition 15.3A
degenerate molecular orbitals 15.7E
Diels–Alder reaction 15.3A
diene 15
dienophile 15.3A
electronic spectrum 15.2B
empirical resonance energy 15.7C

endo-addition 15.3C
ester 15.3A
exo-addition 15.3C
Hückel 4*n* + 2 rule 15.7D
kinetic control 15.4B
λ_{max} 15.2A
millimicron (mμ) 15.2A
molar absorptivity (extinction coefficient), ε 15.2A
molecular orbital (MO) theory 15.7E
nanometer (nm) 15.2A
near ultraviolet 15.2
nitrile 15.3A
nonbonding molecular orbital 15.7E
optical density (O.D.) 15.2A
ordinary diene .... Introduction
$\pi \rightarrow \pi^*$ transition 15.2B
pericyclic reaction 15.3A
resonance stablized 15.6C
s–cis form 15.1A
s–trans form 15.1A
styrene–butadiene rubber 15.5
thermodynamic control 15.4B
transmittance 15.2A
ultraviolet–visible (UV) spectroscopy 15.2
UV spectrometer 15.2A
vinylic group 15.4A
vulcanization 15.5

CHAPTER 15 CONCEPTS

I. Structure and Reactivity of Dienes:

A. Introduction:
1. **Dienes** are compounds with two carbon–carbon double bonds.
   a) **Conjugated dienes** have two double bonds that are separated by one single bond.
   b) **Cumulenes** are compounds in which one carbon participates in two carbon–carbon double bonds.
      (1) The double bonds are called **cumulated double bonds**.
      (2) Allene is the simplest cumulene.

2. Conjugated dienes and allenes have unique structures and chemical properties.

$$CH_3—CH=CH—CH=CH—CH_3 \qquad \text{conjugated diene}$$

$$CH_3—CH=C=CH—CH_3 \qquad \text{cumulated diene}$$

3. Dienes in which the double bonds are separated by two or more saturated carbon atoms have structures and chemical properties similar to those of simple alkenes.
4. The IR and NMR spectra of conjugated dienes show only minor differences from the spectra of ordinary alkenes.

B. Conjugated Dienes:
 1. There are two reasons for the added stability of conjugated dienes.
    a) The carbon–carbon single bond between the two double bonds in a conjugated diene is derived from the overlap of two carbon sp^2 orbitals.
       (1) An sp^2–sp^2 single bond is a stronger bond than the sp^2–sp^3 single bond in an ordinary diene.
       (2) The sp^2–sp^2 single bond is shorter than the sp^2–sp^3 or sp^3–sp^3 carbon–carbon single bond.
           (*a*) Bonds with more *s* character in their component orbitals are shorter.
           (*b*) The stronger bond gives a conjugate diene greater stability.
    b) There is overlap of π-orbitals across the carbon–carbon bond connecting the two alkene units.
       (1) There is π-bonding *within* and *between* the two alkene units.
       (2) The additional bonding associated with this overlap provides additional stability to the molecule.

carbon skeleton   *p orbitals* π-orbital

 2. There are two stable conformations of 1,3-butadiene:
    a) The transoid or *s–trans* form.
    b) The cisoid or *s–cis* form.
    c) Both forms are planar, or nearly so.
       (1) The *s–trans* form of the molecule is more stable than the *s–cis* form.
       (2) The internal rotation that interconverts these two forms is very rapid at room temperature.

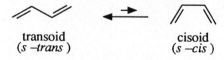

transoid   cisoid
(*s –trans*)   (*s –cis*)

C. Cumulated Dienes:
 1. The carbon skeleton of allene is linear.
    a) The central carbon of allene is *sp* hybridized.
    b) The two remaining carbons are sp^2 hybridized and have trigonal geometry.
    c) The two bonding π-molecular orbitals in allenes are mutually perpendicular; these two π-systems *do not* overlap.

 2. The bond length of each cumulated double bond is somewhat less than that of an ordinary alkene double bond.
 3. The H—C—H plane at one end of the allene molecule is perpendicular to the H—C—H plane at the other end.
    a) The perpendicularity of the two end groups can give rise to enantiomeric allenes.

b) Enantiomeric allenes can be separated and do not interconvert.

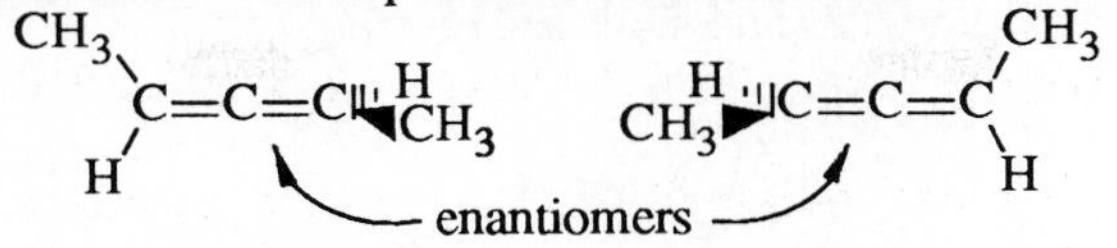

4. The cumulated arrangement is the least stable arrangement of two double bonds; allenes are somewhat less stable than their isomeric alkynes.
5. Allenes have a C=C stretching absorption in the infrared spectrum around 1950 cm^{-1}.
6. Allenes are relatively rare in nature.

II. Resonance:

A. Use of Resonance Structures:

1. Resonance structures are a symbolic way of representing additional bonding associated with orbital overlap.
2. Any species for which additional bonding (additional stability) can be indicated by resonance structures is said to be **resonance stabilized.**
3. Usually the compound with the greater number of important resonance structures is more stable.

B. Writing Resonance Structures:

1. Resonance structures can be drawn when bonds, unshared electron pairs, or single electrons can be delocalized by the arrow formalism *without* moving any atoms.
   a) Relationships between resonance structures are denoted by *single* double-headed arrows.
   b) Resonance structures are alternate electronic descriptions of a single molecule.

   c) If two structures can exist as different compounds, they are not resonance structures.

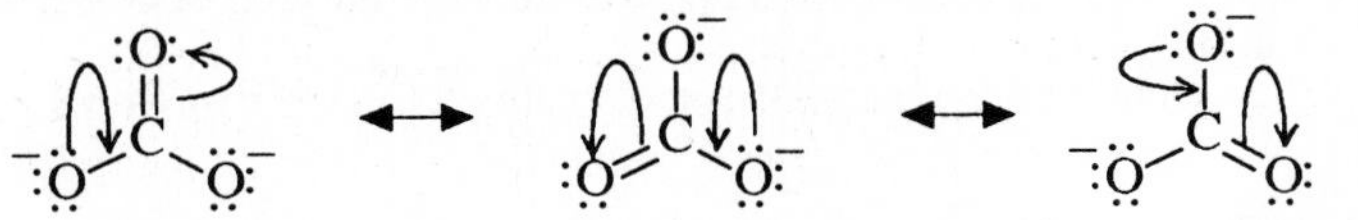

ketone — enol

tautomeric structures; *not* resonance structures

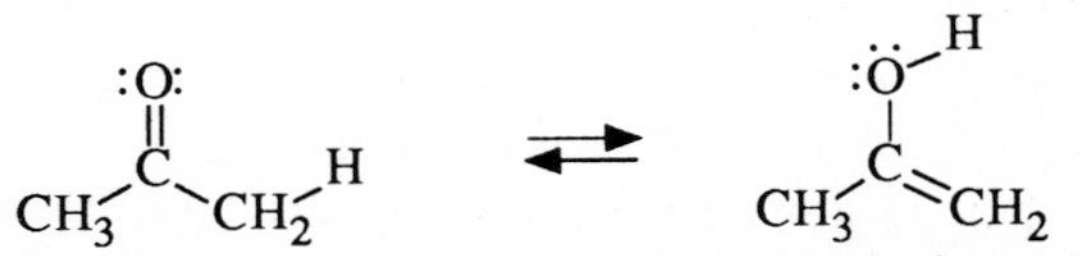

2. Some of the most common situations in which resonance structures are used involve:
   a) electron-deficient atoms
   b) electron pairs
   c) unpaired electrons next to double or triple bonds.
3. When dealing with bonds to atoms in the first row of the periodic table, the octet rule is not violated.

C. Relative Importance of Resonance Structures:

1. A molecule is an average of its contributing resonance structures; some structures are more important than others.
   a) Compare the stabilities of all the resonance structures for a given molecule as if each structure were a separate molecule.
   b) The most stable structures are the most important ones.
2. Guidelines for *important* resonance structures:
   a) Identical structures are equally important descriptions of a molecule.

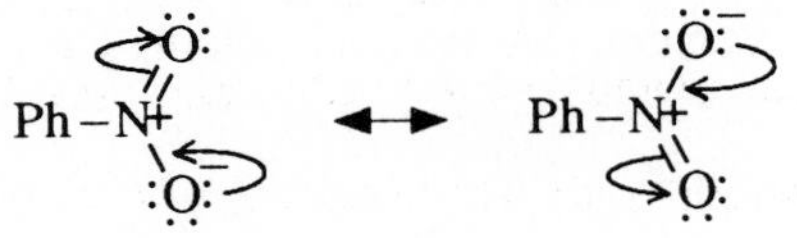

b) Structures that delocalize charge or unpaired electrons are important—delocalization of charge implies overlap of orbitals and increased bonding.

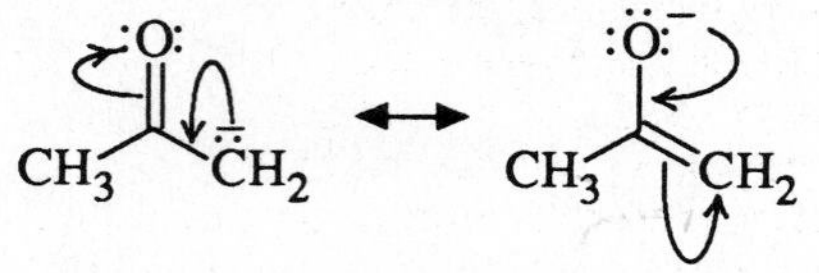

c) Structures with the greater number of formal bonds are more important—bonding is energetically favorable.

d) Structures in which charges and electron deficiency are assigned to atoms of appropriate electronegativity are more important.

(1) A resonance contributor that delocalizes charge and gives every atom an electronic octet is important even if it involves positive charge on an electronegative atom.

(2) A resonance structure that involves an electron-deficient electronegative atom is generally *not* very important.

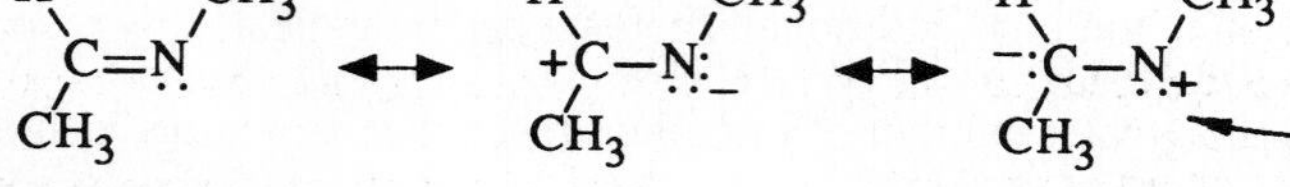

most important — least important — electron-deficient electronegative atom

3. Guidelines for *unimportant* resonance structures:

a) Structures that require the separation of opposite formal charges are less important than those that do not.

(1) When a charge is *delocalized* by resonance, charge of a given type is moved to different locations within a molecule.

(2) When charge is *separated*, two opposite charges are moved away from each other.

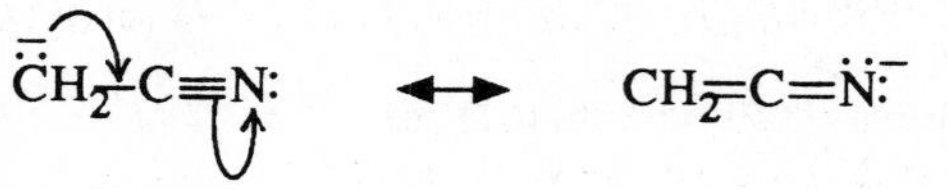

charge delocalization

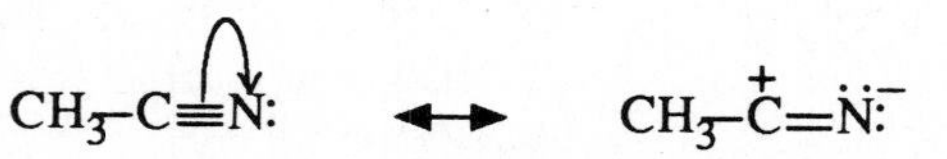

charge separation

b) Highly strained structures are unimportant.

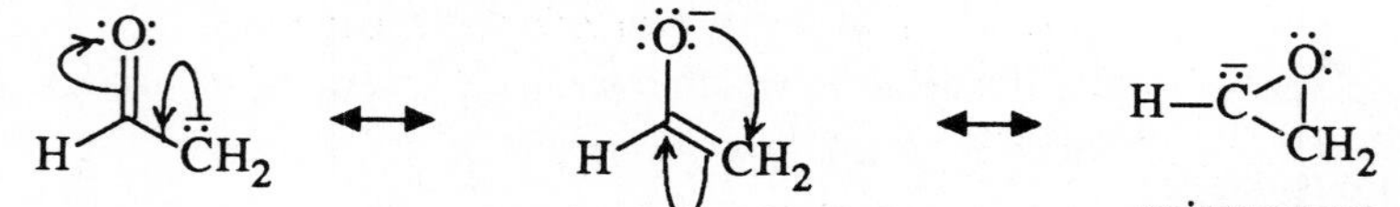

unimportant

c) If the orbital overlap symbolized by a resonance structure is not possible, the resonance structure is not important.

III. Benzene:

A. Introduction:

1. Benzene is the simplest of the **aromatic hydrocarbons**.
2. Benzene itself, as well as benzene rings in other compounds, are inert to the usual conditions of halogenation, hydroboration, hydration, or ozonolysis.
3. Resonance arguments play a central role in understanding the structure and reactivity of benzene.

B. Structure of Benzene:
1. The structure of benzene has only *one* type of carbon–carbon bond with a bond length intermediate between the lengths of single and double bonds.
    a) All atoms in the molecule lie in one plane.
    b) Each carbon atom is trigonal (sp^2 hybridized).
        (1) There is a *p* orbital on each carbon atom.
        (2) These *p* orbitals overlap to form a continuous bonding π-molecular orbital.

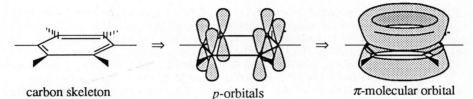

        carbon skeleton   *p*-orbitals π-molecular orbital

2. Benzene can be depicted as a hybrid (average) of two equally contributing resonance structures.

C. Stability of Benzene:
1. Benzene is more stable than a hypothetical six-carbon cyclic triene; this energy difference is called the **empirical resonance energy.**
2. It is the stability of benzene, called **aromaticity**, that is responsible for its unique chemical behavior.

IV. Aromaticity:

A. Aromaticity—The Hückel 4*n* + 2 Rule:
1. To be aromatic, a compound must conform to *all* of the following criteria (often called collectively the **Hückel 4*n* + 2 rule**):
    a) Aromatic compounds have a *cyclic* arrangement of *p* orbitals.
        (1) The cyclic arrangement of *p* orbitals in an aromatic compound must contain 4*n* + 2 π-electrons, where *n* is any integer (0, 1, 2, . . .).
        (2) Aromatic compounds have 2, 6, 10, . . . π-electrons.
    b) Aromatic compounds have a *p* orbital on *every* atom of an aromatic ring.
    c) Aromatic compounds are planar, which allows the *p* orbitals on every atom to overlap.

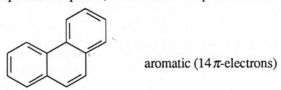

           aromatic (14 π-electrons)

2. Electron counting rules:
    a) Each atom that is part of a formal double bond contributes one π-electron.
    b) Vinylic electrons *do not* contribute to the π-electron count.
    c) Allylic electrons contribute to the π-electron count if they occupy an orbital parallel to the other *p* orbitals in the molecule.
    d) An atom with an empty *p* orbital can be part of a continuous aromatic π-electron system, but contributes *no* π-electrons.
3. There are many different types of aromatic compounds:
    a) Aromatic compounds may contain heteroatoms (aromatic heterocycles).
    b) Aromatic compounds need not be neutral species.
    c) There are some remarkable organometallic compounds that demonstrate aromaticity.
4. If the planar conformation of a molecule required for aromaticity is too strained to exist, then the molecule cannot have aromatic stability.
5. *No* compound has ever been found to be aromatic that the 4*n* + 2 rule says should *not* be aromatic.

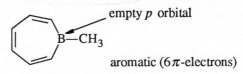

empty *p* orbital

aromatic (6 π-electrons)

B. Antiaromatic compounds:
    1. A molecule with $4n$ π-electrons is *destabilized* by resonance.
    2. Compounds containing planar, continuous rings of $4n$ π-electrons are said to be **antiaromatic** and are unstable.

               ⊡   antiaromatic (4 π-electrons)

C. Electronic Basis of the $4n + 2$ Rule:
    1. The $4n + 2$ rule comes from **molecular-orbital theory** (**MO theory**)—the application of quantum theory to cyclic π-electron systems.
        a) Aromatic stability is associated with the overlap of p orbitals.
        b) When a molecule contains a number n of p orbitals on adjacent atoms, these orbitals combine in very specific ways to give n π-molecular orbitals.
        c) π-MOs have lobes on both faces of the aromatic ring, like the p orbitals from which they are constructed.
    2. Determination of relative MO energies:
        a) A geometric figure is constructed identical to the carbon skeleton of the hydrocarbon under consideration and is drawn with one vertex down.
        b) The energy of an isolated p orbital lies across the middle of the figure.
            (1) Orbitals with energies below that of the isolated p orbital are called **bonding molecular orbitals**.
            (2) Orbitals with energies above that of the isolated p orbital are called **antibonding molecular orbitals**.
            (3) Orbitals with energies equal to that of the isolated p orbital are called **nonbonding molecular orbitals**.
                (*a*) The MO of lowest energy has no nodes.
                (*b*) MOs of progressively higher energy have more nodes.
        c) Different MOs of the same energy are said to be **degenerate MOs**.

    3. Electrons that occupy bonding MOs contribute positively to π-bonding; all molecules conforming to the $4n + 2$ rule have just enough electrons to fill exactly their bonding MOs.
    4. Electrons that occupy antibonding MOs contribute negatively to π-bonding.
    5. Electrons in nonbonding MOs contribute neither positively nor negatively to π-bonding.

V. General Concepts:

A. Allylic Cations:
    1. Allylic cations are more stable than comparably substituted nonallylic alkyl cations.
        a) The unusual stability of allylic cations lies in their electronic structures.
        b) The electron-deficient carbon and the carbons of the double bond are all sp^2 hybridized (each carbon has a p orbital).
            (1) The overlap of these p orbitals provides additional bonding in allylic cations and hence, additional stability.
            (2) Both the positive charge and the double-bond character are delocalized.

$$\overset{+}{C}H_2\!-\!CH\!=\!CH_2 \quad \longleftrightarrow \quad CH_2\!=\!CH\!-\!\overset{+}{C}H_2$$

    2. Allylic rearrangements can occur.
        a) **Allylic rearrangement** is the interconversion of two allylic isomers.
        b) Allylic rearrangement allows the two products eventually to come to equilibrium.

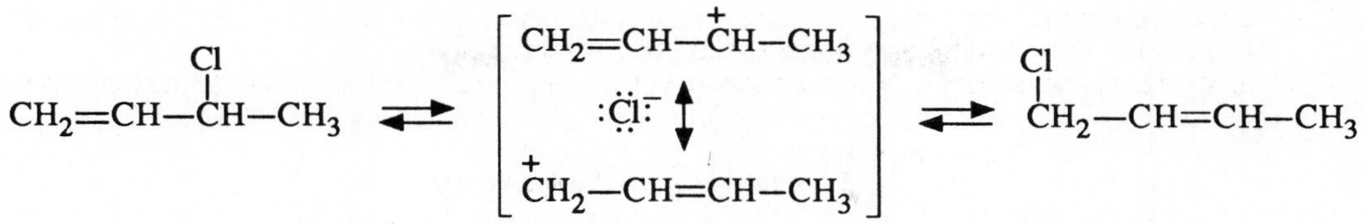

$$CH_2=CH-\underset{\underset{\displaystyle Cl}{|}}{CH}-CH_3 \;\rightleftharpoons\; \left[\begin{array}{c} CH_2=CH-\overset{+}{C}H-CH_3 \\[4pt] :\ddot{\underset{..}{C}l:^- \;\updownarrow \\[4pt] \overset{+}{C}H_2-CH=CH-CH_3 \end{array} \right] \;\rightleftharpoons\; \underset{\underset{\displaystyle CH_2-CH=CH-CH_3}{|}}{Cl}$$

3. Relative stability of carbocations:

primary vinyl ‹ secondary vinyl ≈ primary alkyl ‹ secondary alkyl ‹ secondary allylic ≈ tertiary alkyl ‹ tertiary allylic

B. <u>Kinetic and Thermodynamic Control</u>:
   1. The product distribution in hydrogen halide addition to a conjugated diene is determined by the relative rates of the two product-determining steps.
      a) The 1,2-addition product predominates in the reaction between hydrogen halides and conjugated dienes; the formation of the 1,2-addition product is rapid but reversible.
      b) When the 1,2- and 1,4-addition products come to equilibrium, the 1,4-isomer predominates.
         (1) The formation of the 1,4-addition product is slower but almost irreversible.
         (2) The 1,4-addition product is more stable than the 1,2-addition product.
      c) When Lewis acids are added, or if the products stands in solution, the 1,2-addition product is converted into the 1,4-addition product by an S_N1 reaction that goes through the same allylic cation intermediate.
   2. When the product distribution in a reaction differs substantially from the product distribution that would be observed if the products were at equilibrium, the reaction is said to be **kinetically controlled**.
   3. If the products of a reaction come to equilibrium under the reaction conditions, the product distribution is said to be **thermodynamically controlled**.
   4. The precise reason for kinetic control varies from reaction to reaction; the relative amounts of products in a kinetically controlled reaction are determined by the relative energies of the transition states for each of the product-determining steps.
   5. The most stable product is *not* always the one formed in greatest amount.

[handwritten margin notes: "differed kinetically" "same thermodynamically"]

VI. Ultraviolet Spectroscopy:

A. <u>Introduction</u>:
   1. Both UV and visible spectroscopy are considered together as one type of spectroscopy, often simply called **UV spectroscopy**.
      a) **Ultraviolet-visible spectroscopy** can be used to identify organic compounds containing conjugated π-electron systems.
      b) The part of the ultraviolet spectrum of greatest interest to organic chemists is the near ultraviolet range (200 – 400 nm).
      c) The visible spectrum is in the 400 – 750 nm range of the electromagnetic spectrum.
   2. UV spectroscopy is frequently used for quantitative analysis.
      a) The absorbance at a given wavelength depends on the number of molecules in the light path.
      b) The Beer-Lambert Law (**Beer's Law**) states that **absorbance** is proportional to the product of the path length (l) and the concentration (c).

$$A = \varepsilon l c$$

where ε, the constant of proportionality, is called the **molar extinction coefficient** or **molar absorptivity**.
      (1) The molar extinction coefficient depends on wavelength, solvent, and temperature.
      (2) There is a unique extinction coefficient for each absorption of each compound.
      (3) The larger the ε, the greater is its light absorption at a given concentration c and path length l.

3. The **UV spectrum** of a substance is the graph of radiation absorption by a substance *vs.* the wavelength of radiation that is passed through it.
    a) The absorbance (*A*) or **optical density** (O.D.) is plotted on the vertical axis of a UV spectrum; the absorbance is a measure of the amount of radiation energy absorbed.
        (1) The radiation entering a sample has intensity I_0.
        (2) The light emerging from the sample has intensity I.
        (3) The absorbance *A* is defined as the logarithm of the ratio I_0/I.

$$A = \log \frac{I_0}{I}$$

    b) The wavelength λ of the ultraviolet radiation is plotted on the horizontal axis of the UV spectrum.
    c) Absorption peaks in the UV spectra of compounds in solution are generally quite broad.
    d) Some UV spectra are presented in abbreviated form by citing the λ_{max} values of their principal peaks, the solvent used, and the extinction coefficients.
4. The instrument used to measure the UV spectrum is called a **UV spectrometer,** which is conceptually much like an IR spectrometer.
5. UV spectroscopy is limited in its application to structure determination for the most part to molecules with conjugated π-electron systems.

B. Physical Basis of UV Spectroscopy:
    1. UV and visible spectra are sometimes called electronic spectra—ultraviolet or visible radiation is absorbed by the π-electrons and, in some cases, by the unshared electron pairs in organic compounds.
        a) Intense absorption of UV radiation occurs when a compound contains π-electrons.
        b) Absorption by compounds containing only unshared electron pairs is generally quite weak.
    2. The structural feature of a molecule responsible for its UV or visible absorption is called a **chromophore**.
    3. When a chromophore absorbs radiant energy, a π-electron is elevated from a bonding molecular orbital to an antibonding π^*-molecular orbital.
        a) The radiant energy required for this absorption must match the difference in energy between the π- and π^*-orbitals (a $\pi \rightarrow \pi^*$ **transition**).
        b) UV absorptions of conjugated alkenes are also due to $\pi \rightarrow \pi^*$ transitions.

C. UV Spectroscopy of Conjugated Alkenes:
    1. UV spectroscopy is useful for the diagnosis of conjugated double or triple bonds.
    2. When UV spectroscopy is used to determine chemical structure, the most important aspect of a spectrum is the λ_{max} values.
    3. The λ_{max} is affected by:
        a) The number of double or triple bonds in conjugation.
            (1) The λ_{max} is greater for compounds containing more conjugated double bonds.
            (2) The λ_{max} of a compound that has several double bonds in conjugation will be large enough to be in the visible region of the electromagnetic spectrum, and the compound will appear colored.
        b) The presence of substituent groups on the conjugated double bonds.
        c) The conformation of the molecule—noncyclic dienes generally assume the lower energy *s–trans* conformation.
        d) Other structural characteristics of the conjugated π-electron system.
    4. Light absorption by a pigment, rhodopsin, in the rod cells of the eye triggers the series of physiological events associated with vision.

CHAPTER 15 REACTIONS

I. The Diels–Alder Reaction:

A. <u>Introduction</u>:
1. Many conjugated dienes undergo addition reactions with certain alkenes or alkynes called **Diels–Alder reactions**.
a) The conjugated diene component of this reaction is often referred to as the *diene*.
b) The alkene component of this reaction is often referred to as the *dienophile*.

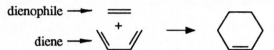

2. Some of the dienophiles that react most readily in the Diels–Alder reaction bear substituent groups such as esters ($—CO_2R$), nitriles ($—C{\equiv}N$), or certain other unsaturated, electronegative groups (some alkynes also act as dienophiles).
3. When the diene is cyclic, bicyclic products are obtained in the Diels–Alder reaction.

4. The Diels–Alder reaction is:
a) A pericyclic reaction (a reaction that occurs in one step by a cyclic flow of electrons).
b) A cycloaddition reaction (an addition reaction that forms a ring).
c) A **1,4-addition (conjugate addition)** reaction.
d) A stereoselective reaction.

B. <u>Effect of Diene Conformation on the Diels–Alder Reaction</u>:
1. In the Diels–Alder transition state, the diene component is in the *s–cis* conformation.
a) Dienes locked into *s–cis* conformations are unusually reactive.
b) Dienes locked into *s–trans* conformations are unreactive in Diels–Alder reactions.
c) Conjugated dienes that have strained *s–cis* conformations are unreactive.
2. If a steric effect destabilizes the *s–cis* form of the diene, it also destabilizes the transition states of its Diels–Alder reactions, and these reactions are slow.

C. <u>Stereochemistry of the Diels–Alder Reaction</u>:
1. When a diene and dienophile react in a Diels–Alder reaction, they approach each other in parallel planes.
a) This approach allows the π-electron clouds of the two components to overlap and form the bonds of the product.
b) Each component adds to *one face* of the other.
(1) The diene undergoes a *syn*–addition to the dienophile.
(2) The dienophile undergoes a 1,4-*syn*–addition to the diene.
2. The six-membered ring of the product is formed initially in a boat-like conformation.

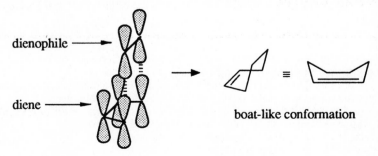

boat-like conformation

3. Alkene stereochemistry is retained in the Diels–Alder reaction; groups that are *cis* in the alkene starting material are also *cis* in the product.

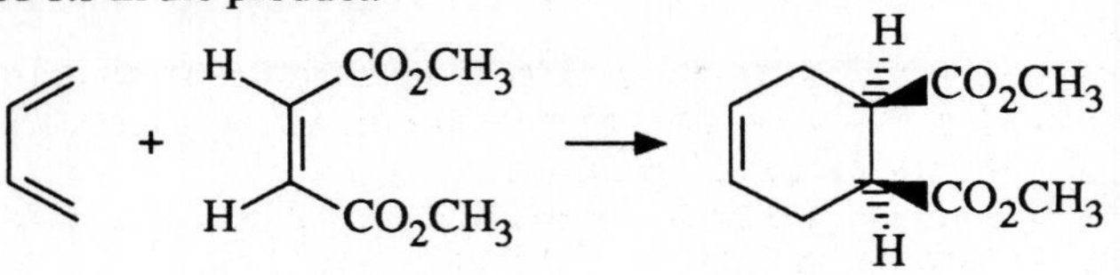

4. Diene stereochemistry is also retained in the Diels–Alder reaction.
   a) The two inner groups of the diene always end up in a *cis* relationship in the Diels–Alder product.
   b) The two outer groups of the diene always end up in a *cis* relationship in the Diels–Alder product.
   c) An inner group of one carbon of the diene always ends up *trans* to an outer group on the other in the Diels–Alder product.

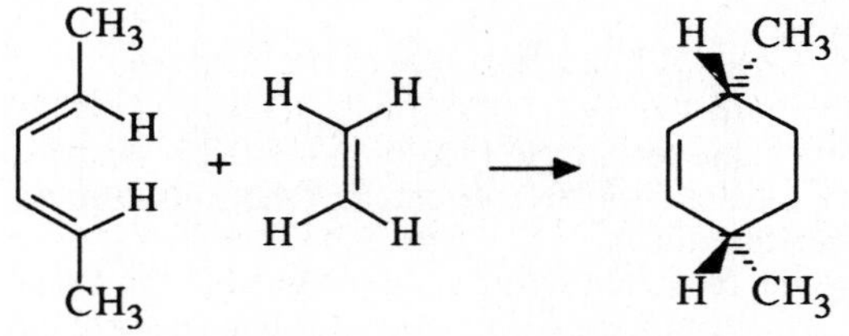

5. There are two possibilities for the stereochemical relationship between the diene substituents and those of the dienophile:
   a) *Endo*-addition involves a transition state in which the dienophile substituents groups are directly over (or under) the diene double bonds.

endo addition

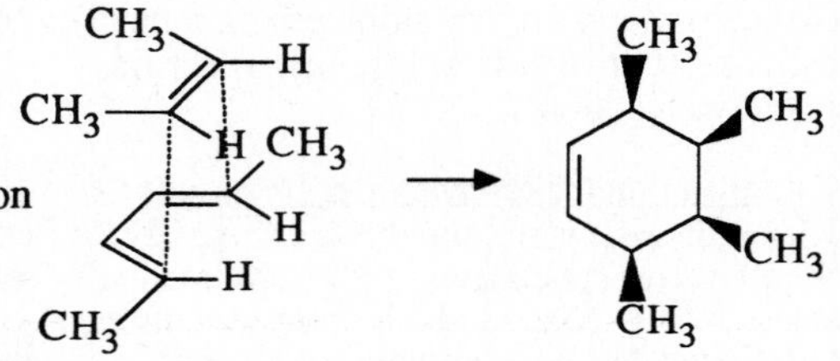

   b) *Exo*-addition involves a transition state in which the dienophile substituents project away from the diene.

exo addition

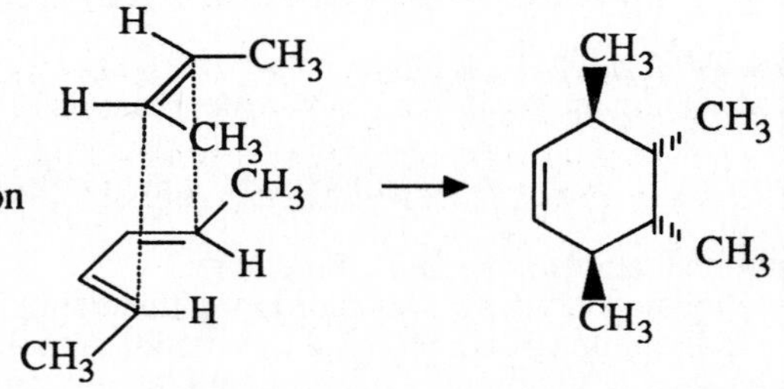

   c) In many Diels–Alder reactions, the *endo* product predominates, particularly when cyclic dienes are used.

D. Uses of the Diels–Alder Reaction:
   1. The Diels–Alder reaction is another method of forming carbon–carbon bonds and is used in the construction of carbon rings, including bicyclic compounds.
   2. The Diels–Alder reaction can be planned so that the diene and dienophile substituent groups end up in a well-defined stereochemical relationship in the Diels–Alder products.
   3. The Diels–Alder reaction can be used to trap highly reactive dienophiles that cannot be isolated in pure form, but whose existence is nevertheless of theoretical interest.
      a) This type of experiment is called a trapping experiment.
      b) Diphenylisobenzofuran is one diene used for this purpose.

II. Addition of Hydrogen Halides to Conjugated Dienes:

A. <u>1,2- and 1,4-Additions</u>:
1. Conjugated dienes react with hydrogen halides to give *two* types of addition products.
a) The major product is a **1,2-addition product**; addition is completed at the nearest site of positive charge, giving the 1,2-product.
b) The minor product results from **1,4-addition (conjugate addition)**—the hydrogen and halide add to carbons that have a 1,4-relationship.

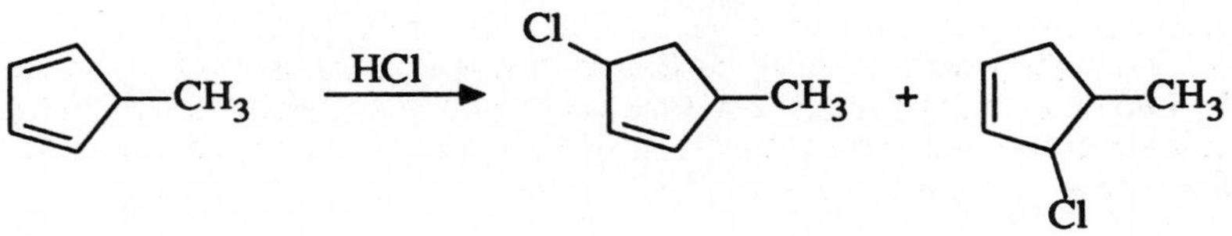

2. The mechanism:
a) Protonation of a double bond gives an **allylic cation.**
(1) The positive charge in this ion is *delocalized*; it is *shared* by two different carbons.
(2) The carbocation and halide ion are not really free—they exist as an ion pair.
(3) Allylic cations are represented as resonance hybrids.
b) Attack by a nucleophile on the two carbons gives two products.

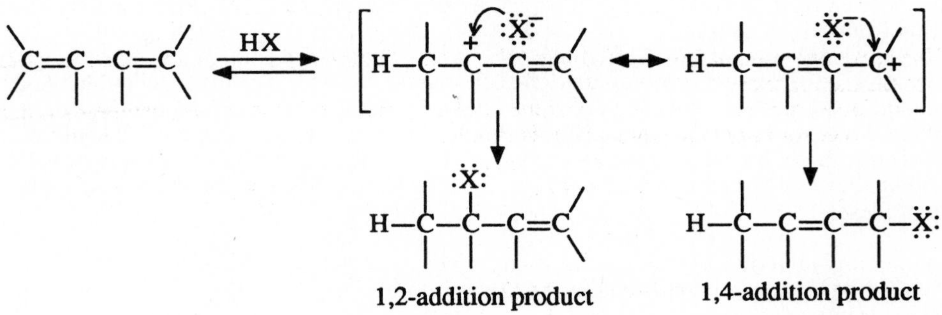

CHAPTER 15 RULES

<u>Hückel $4n + 2$ rule</u>: To be aromatic, a compound must conform to *all* of the following criteria:
a) A *cyclic* arrangement of p orbitals.
b) A p orbital on *every* atom of an aromatic ring.
c) Planarity to allow overlap of the p orbitals on every atom.
d) $4n + 2$ π-electrons

<u>Beer's Law</u>: Absorbance (A) is proportional to the product of the path length (l) and the concentration (c); the constant of proportionality (ε) is the extinction coefficient.

CHAPTER 15 SOLUTIONS

Solutions to In-Text Problems

1. In the *s–cis* form of 1,3-butadiene, the inner hydrogens are close enough to have van der Waals repulsions. These repulsions raise the energy of the *s–cis* form.

    A small rotation alleviates these repulsions at the cost of some overlap of *p* orbitals across the single bond. Evidently, the molecule compromises these opposing factors to give the lowest possible energy.

    ➤ The overlap between *p* orbitals decreases as $\cos^2 \theta$, where θ is the angle from which the π-electron system is distorted from planarity. A 15° distortion from planarity costs the molecule only 7% of its stabilization from orbital overlap.

2. When the molecule undergoes internal rotation such that the π-systems of the two double bonds are perpendicular, overlap is lost at the cost of some stabilization. Loss of π-orbital overlap is not a factor in butane internal rotation, since butane has no *p* orbitals. Notice, however, that the 3-4 kcal/mol cost of rotation about the central single bond is very modest compared with the cost of rotation about a true double bond, which is about 63 kcal/mol. In other words, the π-orbital overlap across the central single bond, while real, is relatively modest.

3. The σ-bond component of the double bond is an sp–sp^2 bond, whereas, in ordinary alkenes, it is an sp^2–sp^2 bond. That is, the bond in a cumulated diene contains more *s* character. Bonds that contain more *s* character, as we have learned, are shorter.

4. (a)

    (b) Since enantiomers have rotations of equal magnitude and opposite sign, it follows that the optical rotation of the enantiomer is +30.7°.

5. We apply Eq. 12.3, the relationship between energy and wavelength of electromagnetic radiation:

    $$E = h\nu = hc/\lambda = \frac{(9.53 \times 10^{-14}\ \text{kcal-sec-mol}^{-1})(3 \times 10^{10}\ \text{cm/sec})}{450 \times 10^{-7}\ \text{cm}} = 63.5\ \text{kcal/mol}$$

6. We use Eq. 15.2.
    (a) Setting $I_0/I = 2$, $A = \log 2 = 0.301$
    (b) Setting $A = \log (I_0/I) = 1.0$, we find that $I_0/I = 10$, or $I/I_0 = 0.10$. That is, 10% of the incident radiation is transmitted. At an absorbance of 0, 100% of the incident radiation is transmitted.

7. The thicker glass has the higher absorbance, because it transmits less of the incident light.

8. (a) The extinction coefficient is 10,750; the absorbance is 0.8. Using these numbers in Eq. 15.3, we have:

    $A = \varepsilon c l$
    $0.8 = (10,750)(c)(1.0)$ or $c = 7.44 \times 10^{-5}$ mol/L

(b) From Figure 15.3, we estimate the absorbance at 235 nm as 0.20, and use the concentration determined from part (a):

$$e = A/cl = (0.20)/(7.44 \times 10^{-5})(1.0) = 2,688$$

9. In each case, we make the assumption that the energy difference is the same as the energy of the UV radiation at the λ_{max}. This energy, in turn, is equal to $hc\lambda$:

(a) $E = (9.53 \times 10^{-14})(3 \times 10^{10})/(165 \times 10^{-7}) = 173$ kcal/mol
(b) $E = (9.53 \times 10^{-14})(3 \times 10^{10})/(222.5 \times 10^{-7}) = 128$ kcal/mol

10. (a) The —CH_2— groups of the ring attached to the double bond are considered to be alkyl substituents. Since there are two alkyl substituents, the predicted λ_{max} is 217 + 10 = 227 nm.
(b) Similarly, the predicted λ_{max} is 227 nm.
(c) In this case, there are three alkyl substituents, for a predicted λ_{max} of 232 nm.

➤ Notice that any alkyl group has the same effect, whether it is a methyl group, an ethyl group, or the —CH_2— group of a ring.

11. (a)   (b)

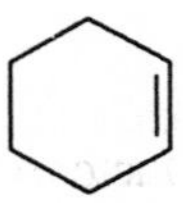

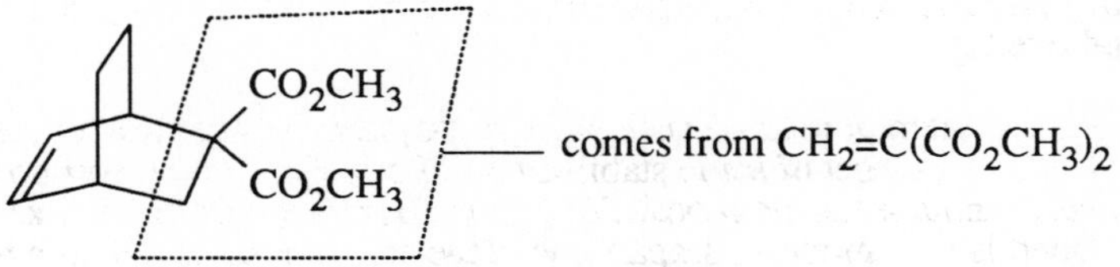

comes from $CH_2=C(CO_2CH_3)_2$

12. (a) This compound would arise from the Diels–Alder dimerization of 1,3-butadiene:

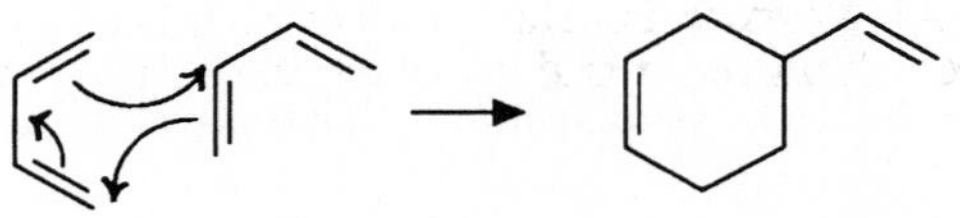

(b) 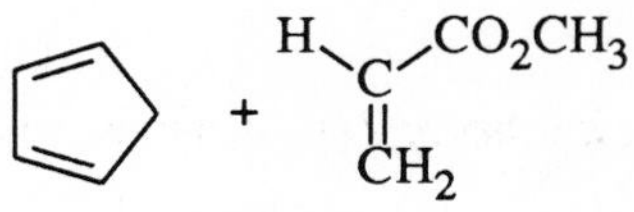   (c)

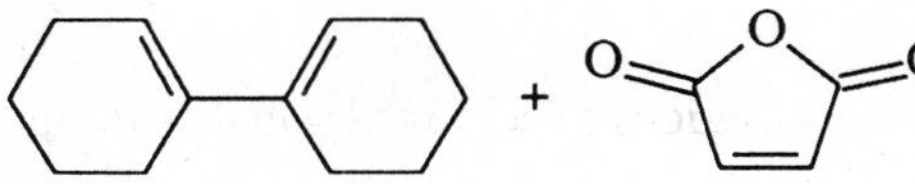

13. The diene and dienophile can be mutually oriented in two different ways:

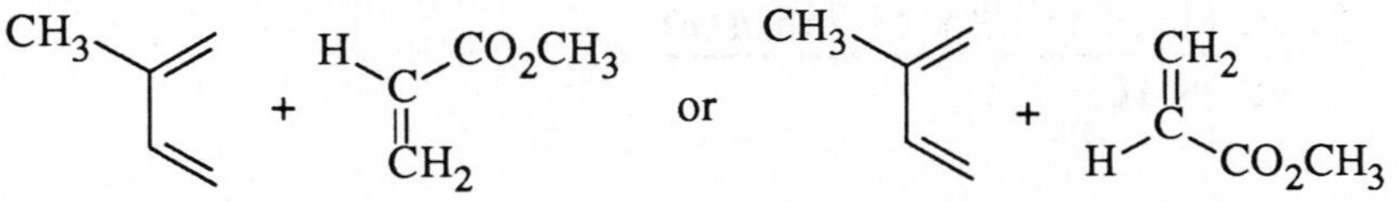

14. The Diels–Alder reaction requires that the diene assume an *s–cis* conformation in the transition state. In this conformation, the *cis–trans* diene has a methyl-hydrogen van der Waals repulsion that is absent in the all-*trans* diene:

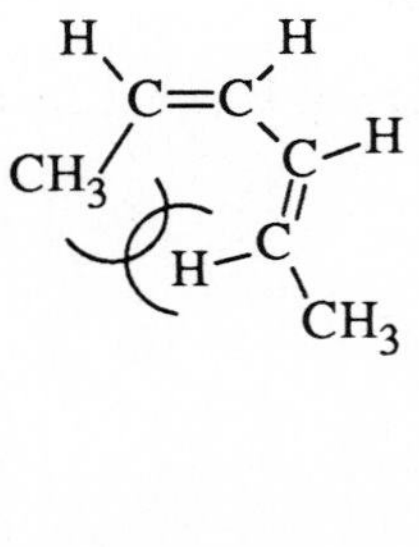

s-cis conformation
of *cis–trans* diene

This repulsion raises the energy of the Diels–Alder transition state of this diene, and therefore reduces the rate of its reaction. Since the *cis–trans* diene reacts more slowly than the all-*trans* diene, it follows that the all-*trans* diene is consumed in the reaction, and the *cis–trans* diene remains unreacted.

15. There are two conjugated diene units within the bicyclic compound; the dienophile can react only with the diene unit that is in the *s–cis* conformation.

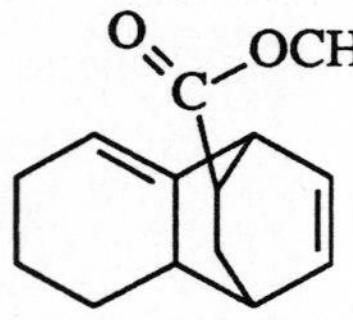

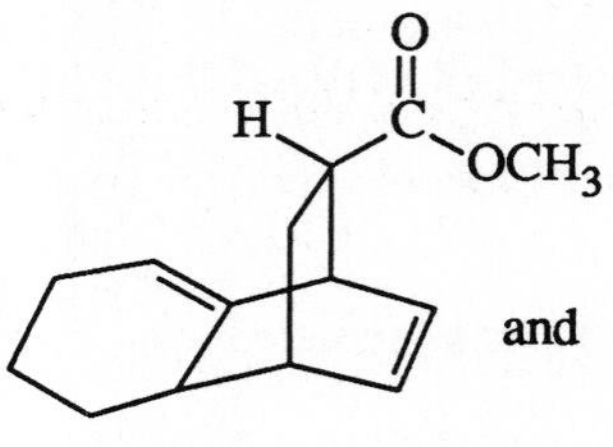

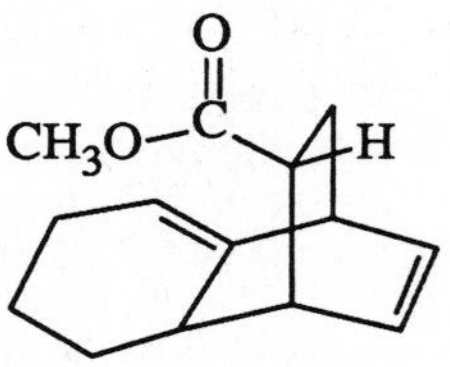

The two compounds arise from reaction of the dienophile in two possible orientations with respect to the diene; see Problem 13 for a similar situation. In addition, each product shown above can be formed as a diastereomer in which the —CO$_2$CH$_3$ and —H groups are interchanged:

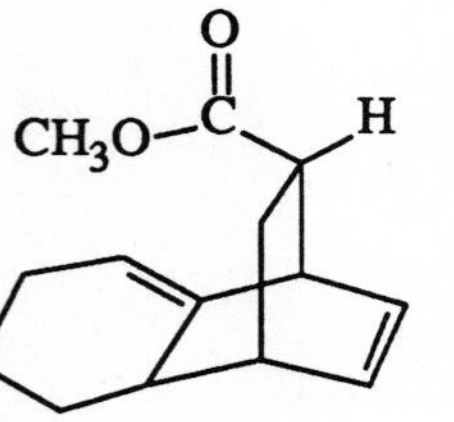

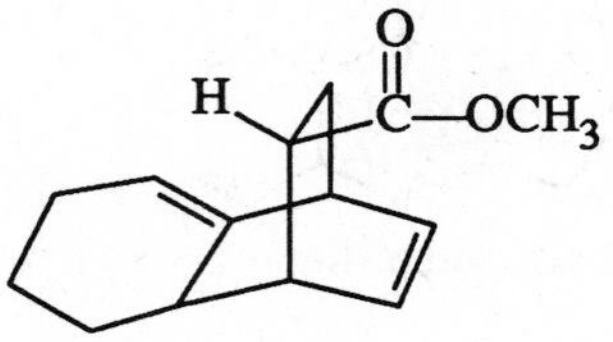

➤ Do not be terribly concerned if you did not notice the possibility of stereoisomers; this is covered in the next section of the text.

16. (a)   (b) 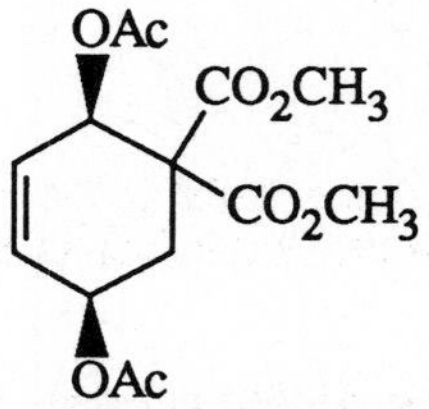   (c)

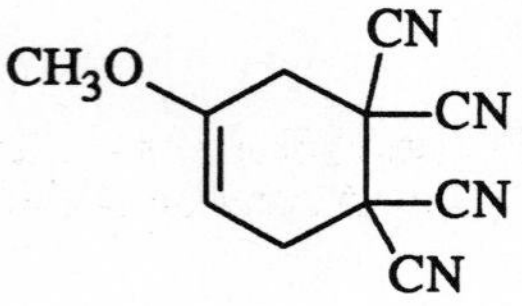

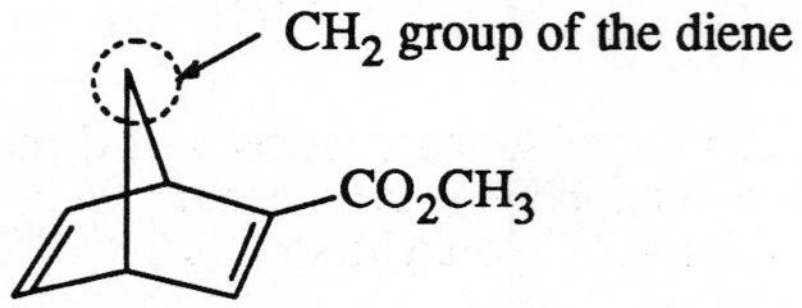

In (a), geometry is not an issue. In (b), the enantiomer of the product shown is also formed; the important point is that the acetate groups are *cis*.

17. (a)   (b)

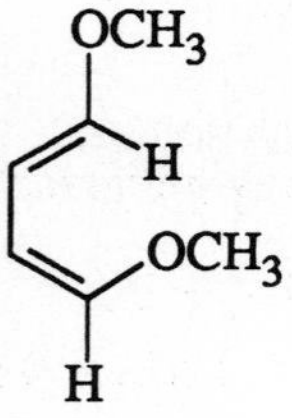

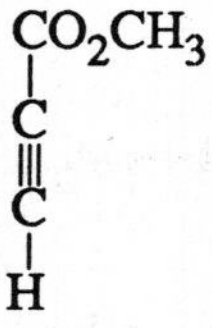

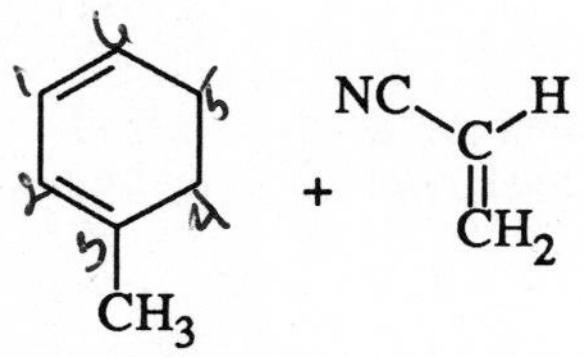

(c)

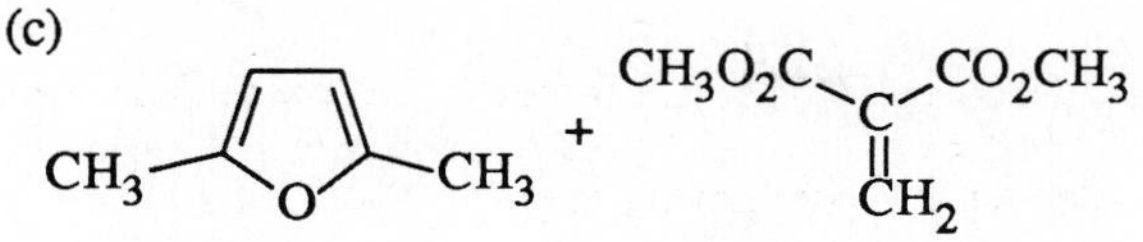

(d)

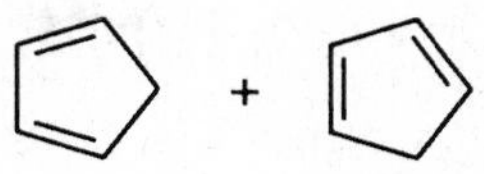

➤ Part (d) shows the dimerization of 1,3-cyclopentadiene. In fact, 1,3-cyclopentadiene, on storage, largely forms this dimer. Free 1,3-cyclopentadiene is isolated by distilling the dimer. In other words, on heating, the Diels–Alder reaction reverses!

18. It is not specified whether the product is the *endo* or *exo* adduct. Assuming operation of the *endo* rule, the following *endo* product should predominate:

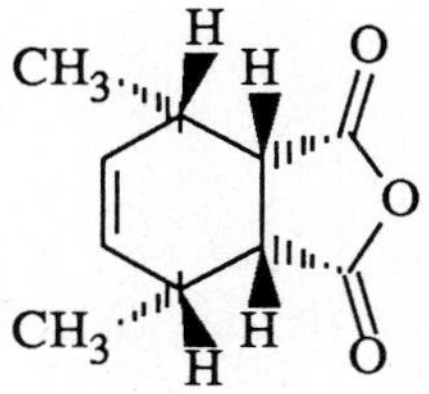

19. (a)

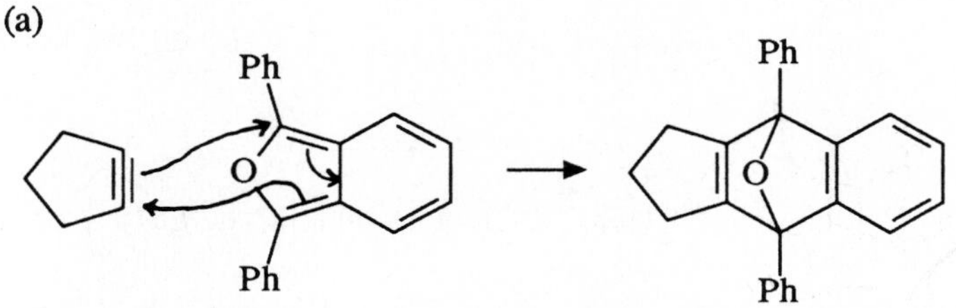

(b) This is a β-elimination reaction, in which $MgBr_2$ is lost from an α-bromo Grignard reagent:

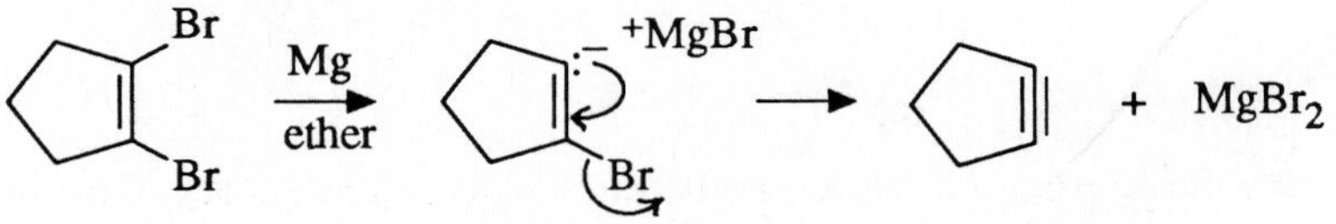

20. All-*trans* dienes tend to react fastest with dienophiles. (See Problem 14 for a similar situation.) Hence, it is likely that both double bonds are *trans*. Were one or both double bonds *cis*, the *s–cis* conformation of the diene in the transition state would be strained.

21. In each case, an allylic carbocation is formed; and this carbocation reacts with the nucleophile at all sites of positive charge.

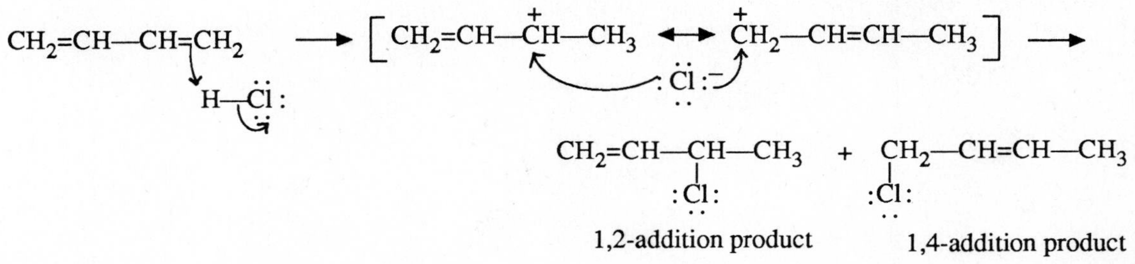

(b)

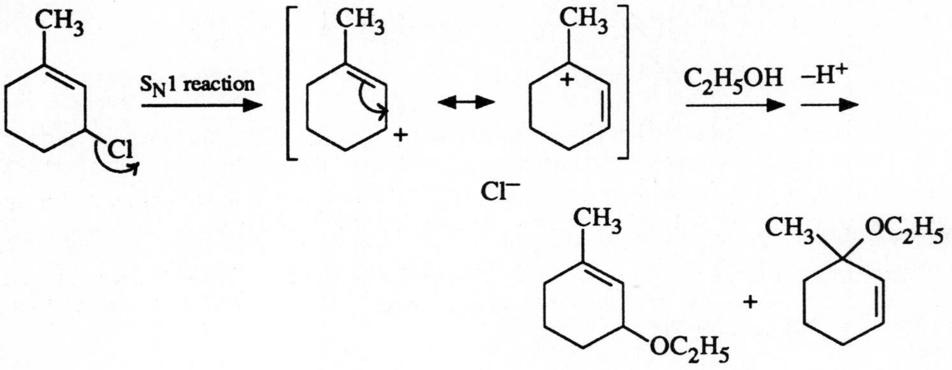

(c)

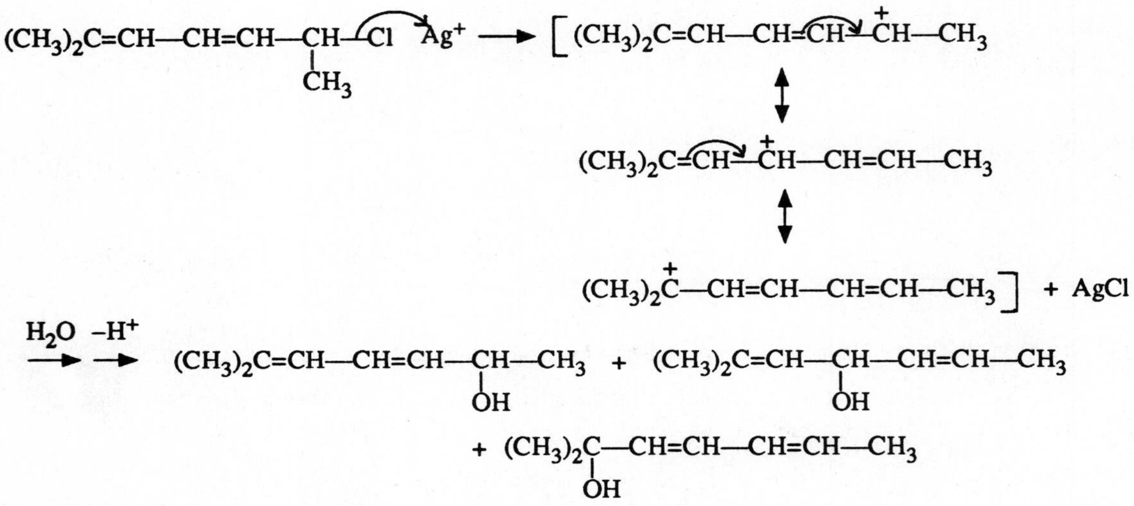

In part (c), positive charge is shared by three carbons within the carbocation intermediate; hence, three products are formed.

➤ For purposes of predicting products, we treat each resonance structure in turn as if it were the correct description of the intermediate. Thus, we expect a nucleophile to attack a carbocation with three resonance structures [such as the one in (c)] at three different positions.

➤ A word on notation: To save space (and time) in writing the answers to mechanistic problems, we have used an abbreviated reaction scheme for loss of a proton. For example, in writing the attack of ethanol on a carbocation, followed by loss of a proton [as in part (b) above], we write:

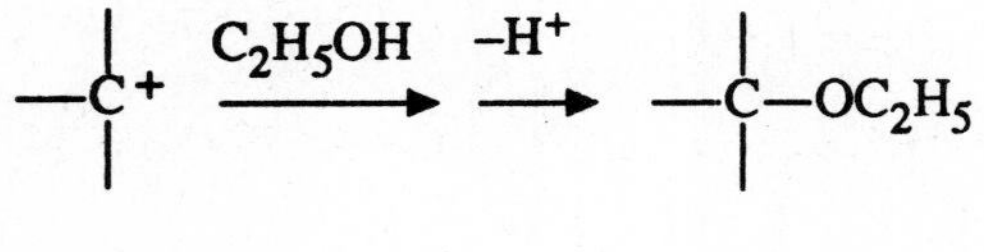

to mean:

$$
\underset{|}{\overset{|}{-C}} + :\ddot{O}C_2H_5 \quad\longrightarrow\quad \underset{\underset{\overset{\displaystyle |}{H}}{}}{\overset{|}{-\underset{|}{\overset{\displaystyle +}{C}}}-\overset{+}{\ddot{O}}C_2H_5} \quad\longrightarrow\quad \underset{|}{\overset{|}{-C}}-\ddot{O}C_2H_5 \;+\; C_2H_5\overset{+}{\ddot{O}H_2}
$$

$$
C_2H_5\ddot{O}H
$$

That is, we shall not show the proton-removal step explicitly. When using this shorthand, we must always remember that the proton does not "fall off" the product by itself; a base is required.

22. This reaction is closely related to one that we studied in Chapter 10: formation of alkyl halides from alcohols with HBr. Even though the alcohol is primary in this case, it reacts by an S_N1 mechanism because a relatively stable allylic cation intermediate is involved:

$$
CH_3CH{=}CHCH_2{-}\ddot{O}H \;\longrightarrow\; \underset{Br^-}{CH_3CH{=}CHCH_2{-}\overset{+}{\ddot{O}}H_2} \overset{-H_2\ddot{O}:}{\longrightarrow} \Big[CH_3CH{=}CH{-}\overset{+}{C}H_2
$$

H—Br

$$
\updownarrow \qquad\qquad Br^-
$$

$$
CH_3\overset{+}{C}H{-}CH{=}CH_2 \Big]
$$

$$
\longrightarrow\; CH_3CH{=}CHCH_2{-}Br \;+\; \underset{Br}{CH_3CHCH{=}CH_2}
$$

23. The 1,4-addition product has the double bond with the greater degree of alkyl substitution. (See Sec. 4.4C for a discussion of this effect.)

24. We expect 1,2- and 1,4-addition products:

$$
\underset{\underset{\text{Cl}}{|}}{Cl{-}CH_2{-}CH}{-}CH{=}CH_2 \;+\; Cl{-}CH_2{-}CH{=}CH{-}CH_2{-}Cl
$$

1,2-addition product \qquad\qquad 1,4-addition product

We expect the 1,4-addition product to predominate when the reaction is allowed to come to equilibrium, for the reason given in the solution to Problem 23.

25. Let $R\cdot$ = an initiating radical. This radical adds to 1,3-butadiene to give a resonance-stabilized radical; and this radical adds to another molecule of 1,3-butadiene to give another resonance-stabilized radical:

$$
R\cdot\; CH_2{=}CH{-}CH{=}CH_2 \;\longrightarrow\; \Big[R{-}CH_2{-}\dot{C}H{-}CH{=}CH_2 \;\longleftrightarrow\; R{-}CH_2{-}CH{=}CH{-}\dot{C}H_2 \Big]
$$

$$
R{-}CH_2{-}CH{=}CH{-}\dot{C}H_2 \;\; CH_2{=}CH{-}CH{=}CH_2 \;\longrightarrow\; \Big[RCH_2CH{=}CHCH_2{-}CH_2\dot{C}H{-}CH{=}CH_2
$$

$$
\updownarrow
$$

$$
RCH_2CH{=}CHCH_2{-}CH_2CH{=}CH{-}\dot{C}H_2 \Big]
$$

Addition of this radical to yet another 1,3-butadiene molecule occurs:

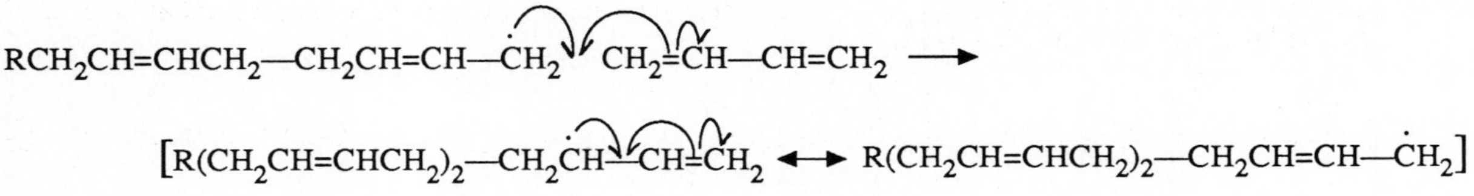

RCH₂CH=CHCH₂—CH₂CH=CH—ĊH₂   CH₂=CH—CH=CH₂ ⟶

[R(CH₂CH=CHCH₂)₂—CH₂ĊH—CH=CH₂ ⟷ R(CH₂CH=CHCH₂)₂—CH₂CH=CH—ĊH₂]

And the resulting radical adds to styrene:

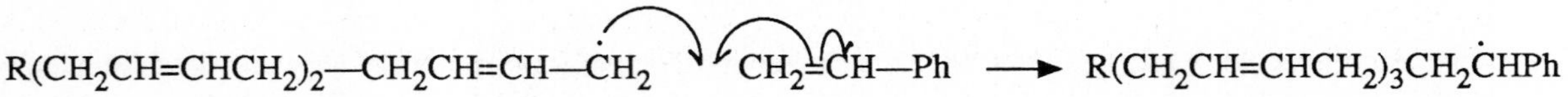

R(CH₂CH=CHCH₂)₂—CH₂CH=CH—ĊH₂   CH₂=CH—Ph ⟶ R(CH₂CH=CHCH₂)₃CH₂ĊHPh

Addition of the last radical to more 1,3-butadiene continues the polymerization.

26. (a) The first structure is most important; the others have fewer formal bonds, and involve separation of charge or separation of unpaired electrons.

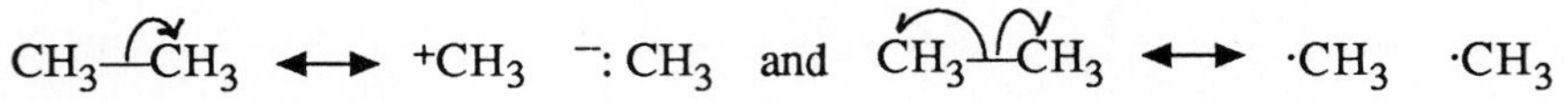

CH₃—CH₃ ⟷ ⁺CH₃   ⁻:CH₃   and   CH₃—CH₃ ⟷ ·CH₃   ·CH₃

(b) The second structure has more formal bonds than the others; the first structure assigns positive charge to the more electropositive atom, carbon. Both structures are important, and both are much more important than the third structure, in which there is separation of charge and fewer formal bonds.

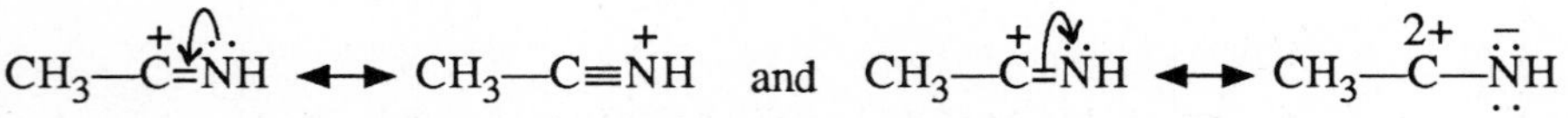

CH₃—C≐NH⁺ ⟷ CH₃—C≡NH⁺   and   CH₃—C≐NH⁺ ⟷ CH₃—C—NH²⁺ ⁻

(c) The first two structures are equivalent, and therefore equally important. The third structure is strained, and therefore much less important. In addition, conjugation of the double bonds is lost.

(d) Both structures are important, because they have the same number of formal bonds, and show delocalization of charge. The second structure is somewhat more important than the first, because in this structure, formal positive charge is on the more highly substituted carbon atom.

CH₃—CH≐CH—CH₂⁺ ⟷ CH₃—CH⁺—CH=CH₂

27. (a) The compound on the right is more stable, because is has two important resonance structures:

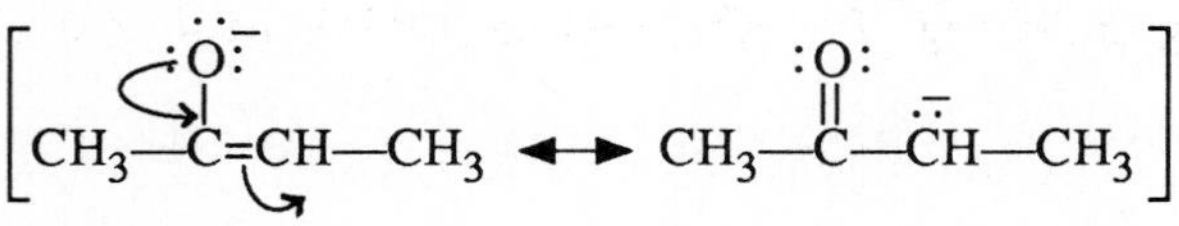

[CH₃—C=CH—CH₃   ⟷   CH₃—C—CH—CH₃]
        :O:⁻   :O:
                              ‖   ⁻

The compound on the left has only the one structure shown in the problem.

(b) The compound on the left is more stable, because the negative charge can be delocalized by both the C=O double bond and the C≡C triple bond:

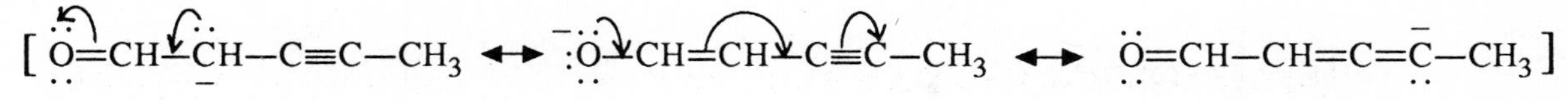

$$\left[\ddot{O}=CH-\ddot{C}H-C\equiv C-CH_3 \quad \longleftrightarrow \quad :\ddot{O}-CH=CH-C\equiv\ddot{C}-CH_3 \quad \longleftrightarrow \quad \ddot{O}=CH-CH=C=\ddot{C}-CH_3 \right]$$

In the structure on the right, the negative charge cannot be delocalized into the triple bond.

(c) The radical on the left is more stable, because the unpaired electron can be delocalized by both double bonds; there are more important resonance structures for this radical. The unpaired electron in the structure on the right can be delocalized only by one of the double bonds. (Draw these structures.)

(d) The structure in the center is least stable; it has no resonance structures. (Notice that a structure like the following:

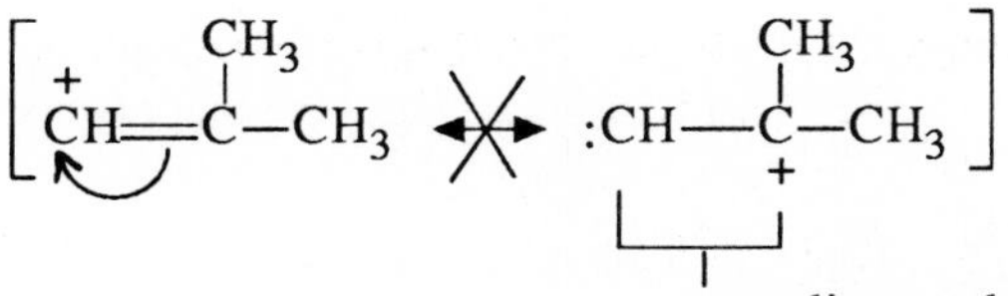

$$\left[\overset{+}{CH}=\overset{CH_3}{\underset{|}{C}}-CH_3 \quad \longleftrightarrow\!\!\!\!\times \quad :CH-\overset{CH_3}{\underset{|}{\underset{+}{C}}}-CH_3 \right]$$

two adjacent electron-deficient carbons

involves fewer formal bonds and introduces further electron deficiency into an already electron-deficient species. This is not an important structure.) Now we have to decide between the other two compounds. Each has two important resonance structures:

$$\left[CH_2=\overset{CH_3}{\underset{|}{C}}-\overset{+}{CH}_2 \quad \longleftrightarrow \quad \overset{+}{CH}_2-\overset{CH_3}{\underset{|}{C}}=CH_2 \right] \quad \text{vs.} \quad \left[CH_3-CH=CH-\overset{+}{CH}_2 \quad \longleftrightarrow \quad CH_3-\overset{+}{CH}-CH=CH_2 \right]$$

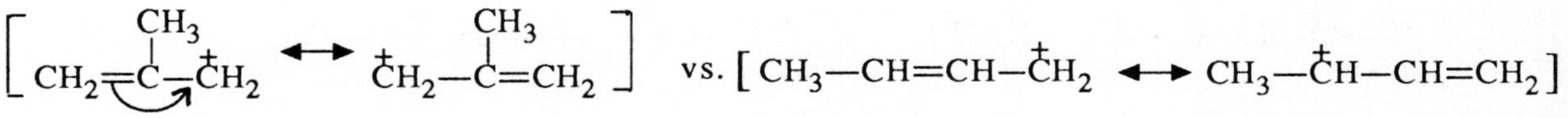

One structure for the ion on the right places positive charge on a secondary carbon, while both structures for the ion on the left are primary carbocations. Hence, the ion on the right is somewhat more stable.

28. Hammond's postulate tells to predict the relative transition-state free energies by examining the energies of the corresponding carbocation intermediates. Ionization of the first compound gives the following cation:

$$CH_3\ddot{O}-CH=CH-\overset{+}{CH}_2$$

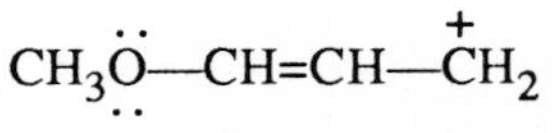

And ionization of the second compound gives the following cation:

$$CH_3\ddot{O}-\overset{\overset{CH_2}{\|}}{C}-\overset{+}{CH}_2$$

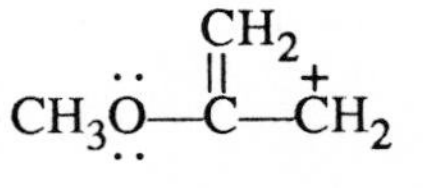

These two cations are precisely the ones whose energies were compared in Eqs. 15.44 and 15.45. Since the first ion has more resonance structures, it is more stable. It follows that the first compound reacts more rapidly in an S_N1 reaction. (We assume that the relative stabilities of the starting materials can be ignored.)

29. Given that furan is aromatic, it can have $4n + 2$ π-electrons (six electrons) if one of the electron pairs on oxygen is in a p orbital that is part of the π-electron system of the ring. The other electron pair is in an sp^2 orbital whose axis is in the plane of the ring:

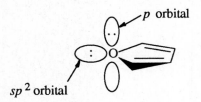

30. It is not possible to have an aromatic free radical, because $4n + 2$ must be an even number; a free radical, by definition, has an odd number of electrons.

31. (a) Not a continuous cycle of π orbitals; not aromatic.
(b) Has ten π-electrons; aromatic.
(c) Has $4n$ π-electrons (the p orbital on boron is empty); not aromatic.
(d) Has $4n$ π-electrons; not aromatic.
(e) Has fourteen π-electrons; aromatic.
(f) Has six π-electrons; aromatic. (This compound is analogous to furan; see Problem 29.)
(g) The oxygen is like that in furan; one pair of electrons is in the π-electron system, and the other is not. The pair on nitrogen is also not part of the ring π-electron system.
(h) Has six π-electrons; aromatic.
(i) Has six π-electrons. One nitrogen is like the nitrogen of pyridine; the other is like the nitrogen of pyrrole. (See Fig. 15.12.)

32. According to the $4n + 2$ rule, (a) and (c) are aromatic; (b) is antiaromatic. Let us try to understand this with the aid of energy diagrams. (In the diagrams below, the dashed line represents the energy of an electron in an isolated p orbital.)

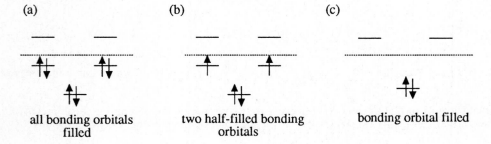

Solutions to Additional Problems

33. The structure of the starting material is:

$$\underset{H}{\overset{CH_3}{>}}C=C\underset{CH=CH_2}{\overset{H}{<}}$$

(a)

$$\underset{}{CH_3\overset{Br}{\underset{|}{C}}H-\overset{Br}{\underset{|}{C}}H-CH=CH_2} \qquad \underset{H}{\overset{CH_3}{>}}C=C\underset{\overset{|}{Br}}{\overset{H}{<}}\!\!\!\begin{array}{c}H\\CH-CH_2Br\end{array} \qquad \underset{\text{1,4-addition product}}{CH_3\overset{Br}{\underset{|}{C}}HCH=CHCH_2Br}$$

$$\underline{\qquad\qquad \text{1,2-addition products} \qquad\qquad}$$

(b)

$$\underset{H}{\overset{CH_3}{>}}C=C\underset{\underset{Br}{|}}{\overset{H}{<}}\!\!\!\begin{array}{c}\\CHCH_3\end{array} + CH_3CH_2\overset{Br}{\underset{|}{C}}HCH=CH_2 + CH_3\overset{Br}{\underset{|}{C}}HCH=CHCH_3 + CH_3CH_2CH=CHCH_2Br$$

(major)   (minor)   (major)   (minor)

$$\underline{\qquad\qquad \text{1,2-addition products} \qquad\qquad} \qquad \underline{\qquad\qquad \text{1,4-addition products} \qquad\qquad}$$

The major addition products result from the more stable of the two possible allylic cations:

$$\overset{\curvearrowleft}{Br}-H$$
$$CH_3CH\!\!=\!\!CHCH=CH_2 \longrightarrow \left[CH_3\overset{H}{\underset{|}{C}}\overset{+}{H}CHCH=CH_2 \longleftrightarrow CH_3\overset{H}{\underset{|}{C}}HCH=CH\overset{+}{C}H_2\right]Br^-$$

less stable allylic cation

$$H\!-\!Br$$
$$CH_3CH=CHCH\!\!=\!\!CH_2 \longrightarrow \left[CH_3CH=CH\overset{+}{C}HCH_2\!-\!H \longleftrightarrow CH_3\overset{+}{C}HCH=CHCH_2\!-\!H\right]Br^-$$

more stable allylic cation

(Why is the second cation more stable?)

We have not specified the stereochemistry of some of these adducts, since we have not considered stereochemistry of additions to dienes.

(c) $CH_3CH_2CH_2CH_2CH_3$

(d)

$$\underset{H}{\overset{CH_3}{>}}C=C\underset{\underset{OH}{|}}{\overset{H}{<}}\!\!\!\begin{array}{c}\\CHCH_3\end{array} \qquad CH_3CH_2\overset{}{\underset{\underset{OH}{|}}{C}}HCH=CH_2 \qquad CH_3\overset{OH}{\underset{|}{C}}HCH=CHCH_3 \qquad CH_3CH_2CH=CHCH_2OH$$

(major)   (minor)   (major)   (minor)

$$\underline{\qquad\qquad \text{1,2-addition products} \qquad\qquad} \qquad \underline{\qquad\qquad \text{1,4-addition products} \qquad\qquad}$$

(These products are exactly analogous to those in (b), except that there is an —OH group instead of a —Br.)

(e) No reaction. Base does not react with ordinary alkenes or dienes.

(f) The Diels–Alder adduct:

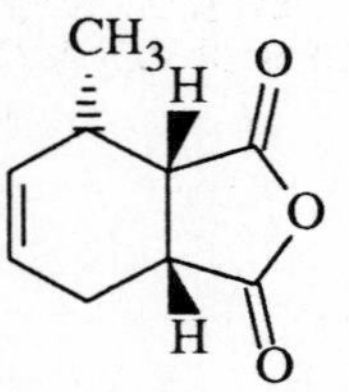

It is assumed that the *endo* adduct is formed.

34. In parts (a) and (b), we write all possible 1,2- and 1,4-addition products, as in the previous problem.

(a)

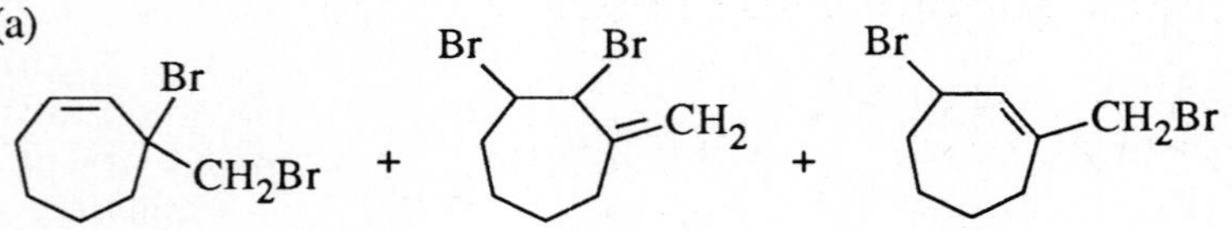

(b)

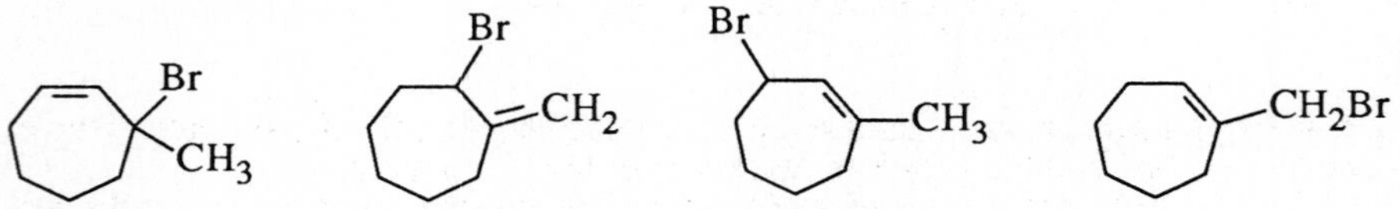

(major)   (minor)   (major)   (minor)
└──── 1,2-addition products ────┘   └──── 1,4-addition products ────┘

(c)

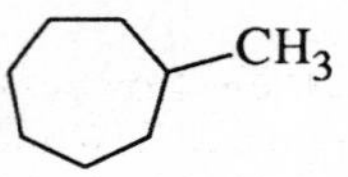

(d)

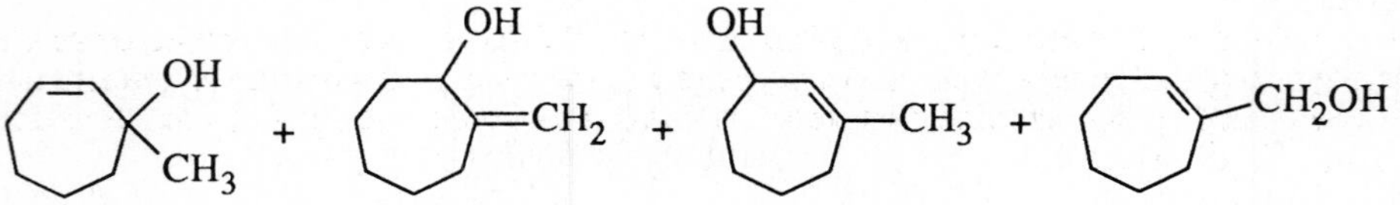

(major)   (minor)   (major)   (minor)
└──── 1,2-addition products ────┘   └──── 1,4-addition products ────┘

(e) No reaction, as in Problem 33.
(f) No reaction; dienes such as this that are locked in an *s–trans* conformation do not undergo Diels–Alder reactions.

35. 1,3-Cyclopentadiene would give the same product, 3-chloro-1-cyclopentene:

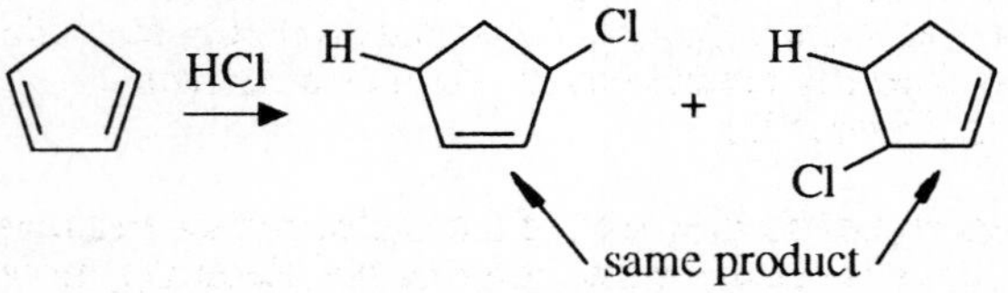

36. The answers to both (a) and (b) follow from the geometry of cumulenes. Each additional cumulated double bond results in a 90° twist of one end of a molecule with respect to the other. Thus, in alkenes, the atoms connected to the double bond are in the same plane; in allenes, the atoms connected to the double bonds are in *perpendicular* planes; in cumulenes with three contiguous double bonds, the atoms attached to the terminal double bonds are in the same plane, as they are in alkenes. Since the perpendicular relationship is necessary for chirality of a cumulene, alkenes and cumulenes with an even number of double bonds can be chiral. Indeed, 2,3-heptadiene is a chiral allene, and therefore exists as a pair of enantiomers:

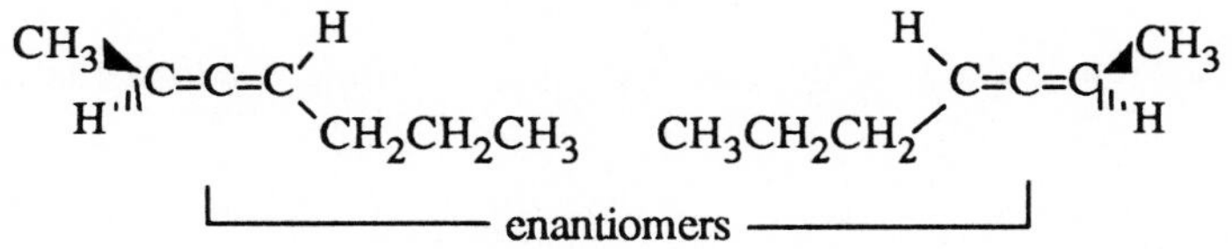

Allenes and cumulenes with an odd number of contiguous double bonds cannot be chiral (unless, of course, they contain a chiral element elsewhere in the molecule). However, like alkenes, these cumulene can exist as *cis–trans* isomers, which, of course, have a *diastereomeric* relationship:

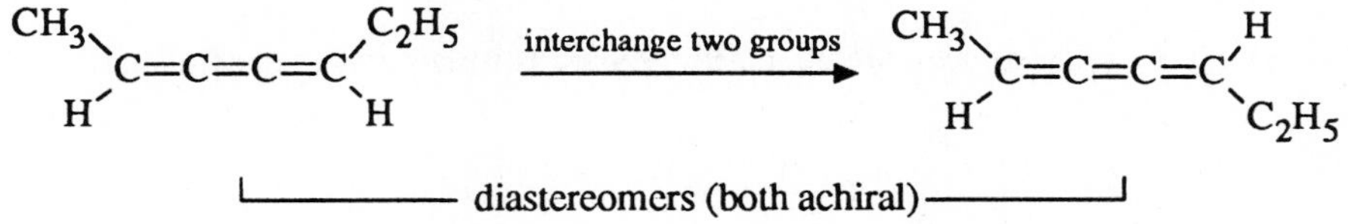

37. (a) The system as a whole is not aromatic, because it lacks a continuous cycle of *p* orbitals. However, the compound can be viewed as a substituted benzene; the benzene ring is aromatic.
(b) Each carbon of a double bond contributes one π-electron; there are fourteen π-electrons; the molecule is aromatic.
(c) The two electrons of the anion are added to eight electrons contributed by the remaining double bonds, for a total of ten; the ion is aromatic.
(d) The adjacent electron-deficient carbons bear empty *p* orbitals with zero electrons; the double bond contributes two electrons. This dication is aromatic.
(e) The nitrogens that are part of the double bonds contribute one electron each to the π-electron system; their unshared pairs are directed outward in the plane of the ring, and are not part of the π-system. The allylic nitrogen contributes two electrons to the π-electron system. Since there are six electrons in the π-system, the molecule is aromatic.
(f) The molecule contains eight π-electrons, two from each formal double bond. The molecule as a whole is not aromatic. In order to avoid being antiaromatic, the benzene ring retains its aromatic character, and the single bonds of the attached cyclobutene ring are very long; this reduces the overlap between the benzene ring and the double bond. To exaggerate:

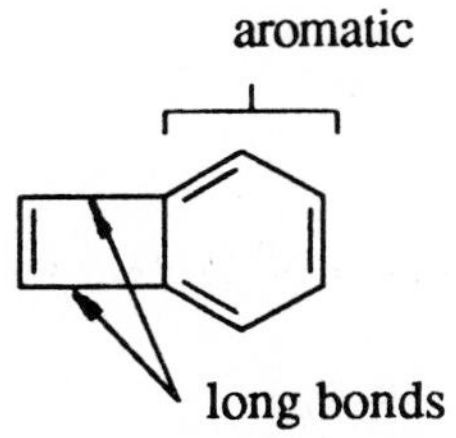

(g) If one electron pair on the oxygen and two from each double bond are part of a continuous π-electron system, the molecule has eight electrons, and is thus antiaromatic. To avoid being antiaromatic, the molecule puckers so as to reduce overlap between the oxygen and nearby double bonds. (It also undergoes intramolecular reactions of a type that we shall study in Chapter 25.)

➤ We may ask why *both* electron pairs of the oxygen cannot become part of the π-electron system to give a total of ten electrons. Remember that a given orbital can only contain a maximum of two electrons. In order for both electron pairs to be part of the π-electron system, then, would require that two orbitals occupy the same region of space. But electrons that occupy exactly the same region of space are by definition in the same orbital. This situation, as we have just indicated, is not allowed by quantum theory.

(h) Free radicals cannot be aromatic because they contain an odd number of π-electrons. (See Problem 30.)
(i) Each triple bond contains four π-electrons, but only two of these can be part of the aromatic π-electron system; the other two are in a perpendicular π orbital. Hence, each triple bond, like each double bond, contributes two electrons to the cyclic π-electron system. There are eighteen π-electrons, and the compound is aromatic.

38. In the first compound, severe van der Waals repulsions associated with the inner hydrogens shown below force the compound out of planarity:

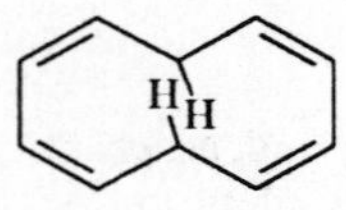

Since the compound is not planar, it is not aromatic. (In fact, it has never been prepared!)

In the case of octalene, steric interference between the indicated hydrogens forces rings out of planarity:

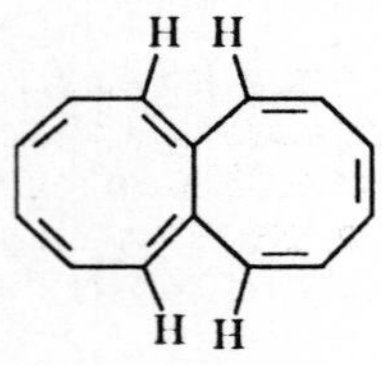

39. If naphthacene absorbs blue light, its color is the complement of blue, which is yellow or yellow-orange.

40. (a) 1,4-Cyclohexadiene is not conjugated and therefore has no UV spectrum in the useful range; 1,3-cyclo-hexadiene, an s–cis diene, has absorption at 256 nm (see text page 591). The compound with the UV spectrum is the 1,3-diene.
(b) The first compound has three alkyl substituents on conjugated double bonds; the second compound has two. Hence, λ_{max} for the first compound should be about 5 nm greater than λ_{max} for the second.
(c) The double bonds of the second compound have two more alkyl substituents than the double bonds of the first. Hence, the λ_{max} of the first compound is greater than that of the second by about 10 nm.
(d) The first compound has three conjugated double bonds, whereas the second compound has two; hence, the first compound has a considerably greater λ_{max} than the second.
(e) Although the first compound is shown in the s–$trans$ conformation, it doesn't exist that way because of severe steric repulsions between the t-butyl groups. It can avoid these repulsions by rotating into its s–cis conformation.

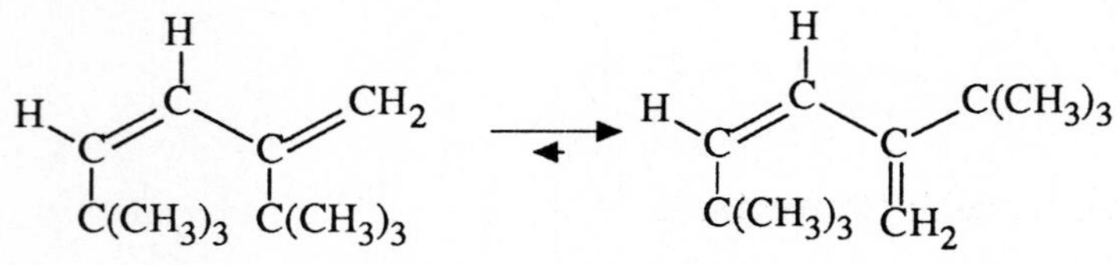

The second diene, however, has a perfectly stable s–$trans$ conformation. Since s–cis dienes have considerably greater λ_{max} values than comparable s–$trans$ dienes, the first diene will absorb at higher wavelength, but with reduced intensity.

41. First, we use Beer's Law to determine the concentration of the diene:

$A = \varepsilon cl$
$0.356 = (10,750)(c)(1.0)$ or $c = 3.312 \times 10^{-5}$ mol/L

Since the entire sample was diluted to one liter, there are 3.312×10^{-5} moles of isoprene in the entire sample.

(Notice that any hydrogenation product lacks conjugated double bonds and does not absorb.) With a molecular weight of 68.11, we calculate that the amount of isoprene present is

$(3.312 \times 10^{-5} \text{ mol/L})(68.11 \text{ g/mol}) = 2.26 \times 10^{-3} \text{ g/L}$

or 2.26 mg. Hence, the weight percent isoprene present in the sample is $(2.26/75) \times 100$, or 3.01%. Hack's hydrogenation was 97% complete.

42. Assuming addition to the triple bond occurs through an allylic-type carbocation intermediate, the structure of chloroprene is as follows:

$$CH_2\!\!=\!\!\underset{\underset{Cl}{|}}{C}\!\!-\!\!CH\!\!=\!\!CH_2$$

Following the general pattern for 1,4-addition polymerization on text page 608, the general formula for neoprene is:

$$\left[\!\!-CH_2\!\!-\!\!\underset{\underset{Cl}{|}}{C}\!\!=\!\!CH\!\!-\!\!CH_2\!\!-\!\!\right]_n$$

43. The carbon skeleton of compound A, from the hydrogenation data, is that of hexane; that is, it is an unbranched six-carbon chain. With two degrees of unsaturation, it follows that the compound is a diene or an alkyne; the IR absorption and the observation of optical activity indicate that the compound is an allene. The only possible chiral allene is 2,3-hexadiene, $CH_3\!\!-\!\!CH\!\!=\!\!C\!\!=\!\!CH\!\!-\!\!CH_2CH_3$. Indeed, partial hydrogenation of this diene would give a mixture of *cis*-2-hexene and *cis*-3-hexene.

44. (a) From the Diels–Alder product, the structure of compound A is:

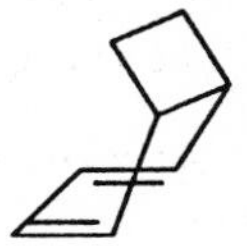

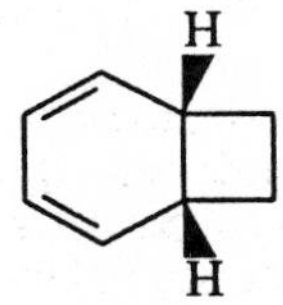

(b) This intermediate is formed in a simple pericyclic reaction:

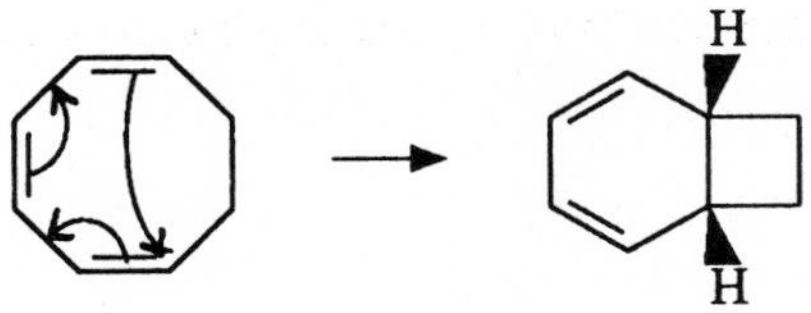

(This type of reaction is considered in more detail in Chapter 25.)

45. (a) The compound is aromatic. Each boron bears a vacant p orbital, and each nitrogen contributes two electrons to the cyclic π-electron system. There are six π-electrons in the molecule. The resemblance of the molecule to benzene is more apparent if we draw resonance structures:

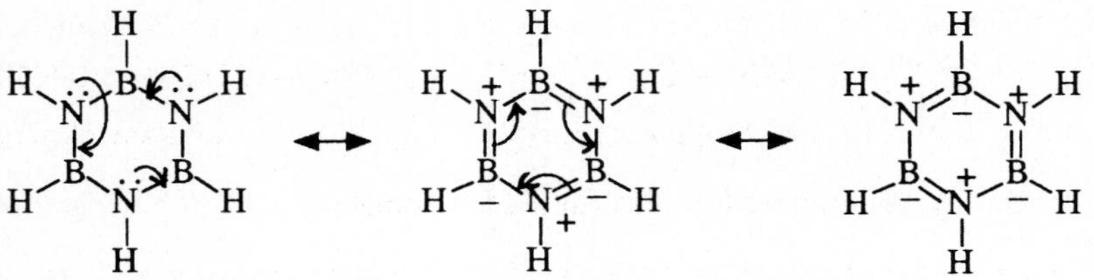

(b) Reaction with potassium forms the potassium salt of the cyclopentadienyl anion. In this anion, the five carbons are equivalent by resonance. Hence protonation can occur at any carbon. As a result, the radiolabeled carbon has a 20% chance of ending up in any one position of the molecule:

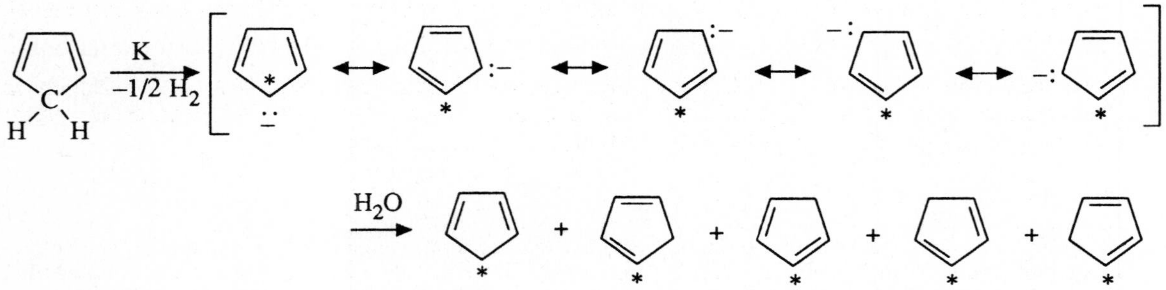

(c) Taken as a whole, the π-electron system of acenaphthylene contains twelve π-electrons, and apparently should not be aromatic. Instead, in an effort to achieve minimum energy, the naphthalene system behaves as a separate aromatic entity, and the double bond is isolated from it as an ordinary double bond. Because it is not part of the aromatic π-electron system, it reacts like ordinary double bonds, and chlorinates readily:

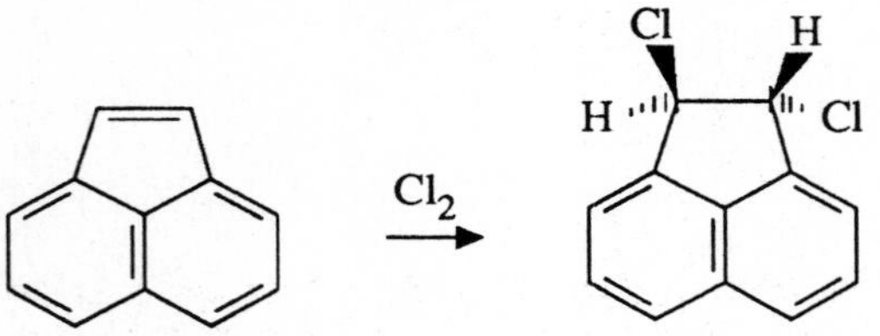

46. (a) When HBr reacts with isoprene, there are two possible allylic cations that could be formed:

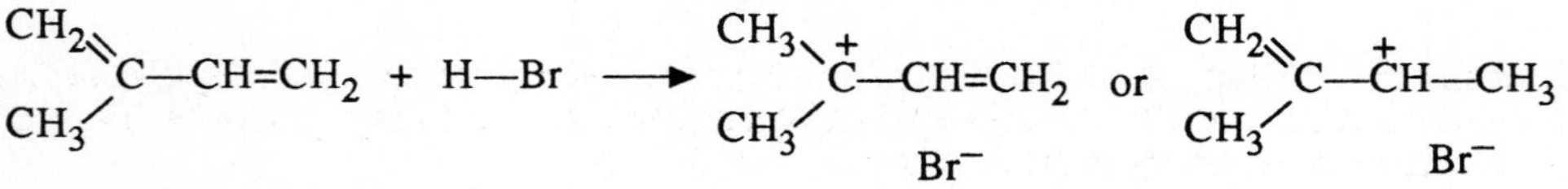

Cation *A* is preferred because it is more stable (why?). The products, then, are derived from this cation:

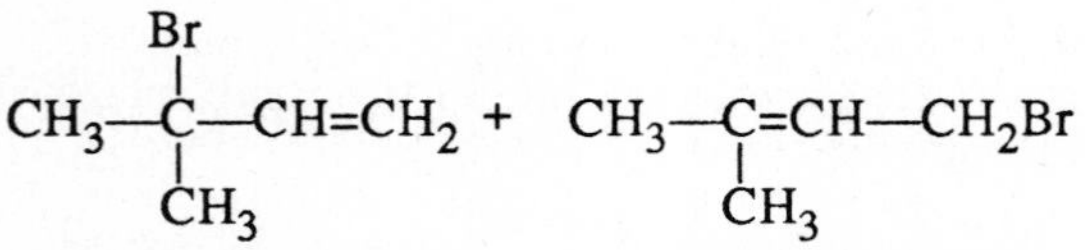

1,2-addition product   1,4-addition product

In the case of 1,3,5-hexatriene, protonation of carbon-1 gives the most stable cation, and the products are derived from this cation:

$$\underset{\text{1,2-addition product}}{CH_3-\overset{\overset{\displaystyle Br}{|}}{CH}-CH=CH-CH=CH_2} \quad + \quad \underset{\text{1,4-addition product}}{CH_3-CH=CH-\overset{\overset{\displaystyle Br}{|}}{CH}-CH=CH_2} \quad + \quad \underset{\text{1,6-addition product}}{CH_3-CH=CH-CH=CH-\overset{\overset{\displaystyle Br}{|}}{CH_2}}$$

(You should show the protonation and the structure of the carbocation intermediate.)

(b) According to the pattern discussed in the text, the 1,2-addition product should be the major kinetically controlled product in the reactions of both alkenes. In the case of isoprene, the 1,4-addition product should be favored at equilibrium, because it has the more highly substituted double bond. In the case of the triene, the 1,6-addition product should be the thermodynamic product; not only are its double bonds disubstituted, but they are also conjugated.

47. Mycomycin has no asymmetric carbons, but it does have an allene unit. Evidently, mycomycin is one of the enantiomers of this chiral allene.

48. As we learned in Secs. 4.4B and 4.4C, heats of formation measure the relative stabilities of molecules due to arrangements of their bonds. This question really asks us to arrange compounds in reverse order of stability. (Lowest heat of formation = most stable compound.)

(a)

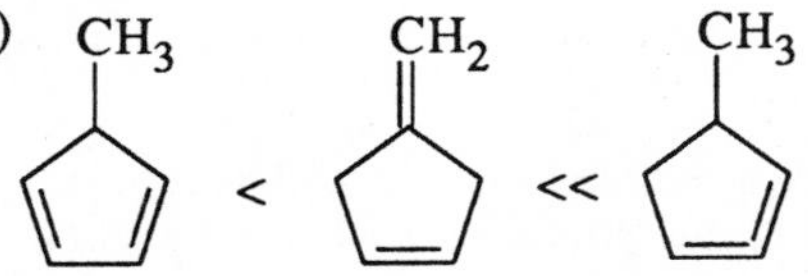

The compound with conjugated double bonds is most stable, because conjugation is a stabilizing factor. The cyclic allene should be most unstable, because, in addition to the intrinsic instability of allenes in general, the allene unit requires a linear geometry that cannot be accommodated by the five-membered ring.

(b)

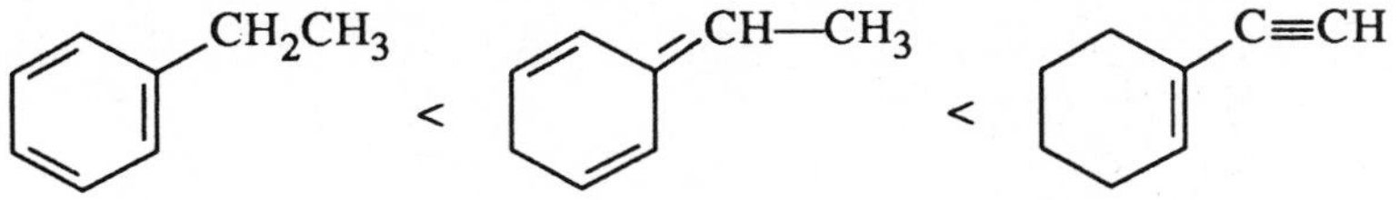

The aromatic compound is most stable; aromaticity gives it a thirty kcal/mol energetic advantage over the other compounds. All double bonds are conjugated in the next most stable compound. In the least stable compound, sp hybridization of the alkyne unit is a more unstable situation than the alternatives, in which the carbons involved in multiple bonding are sp^2 hybridized. (See data in Table 15.1; alkynes are less stable than isomeric alkenes.)

49. In the s–cis conformation of 2,3-dimethyl-1,3-butadiene, there are no severe van der Waals repulsions (steric repulsions). In the s–cis conformation of 2,3-di-t-butyl-1,3-butadiene, the two t-butyl groups are moved into proximal positions in which these groups interfere sterically:

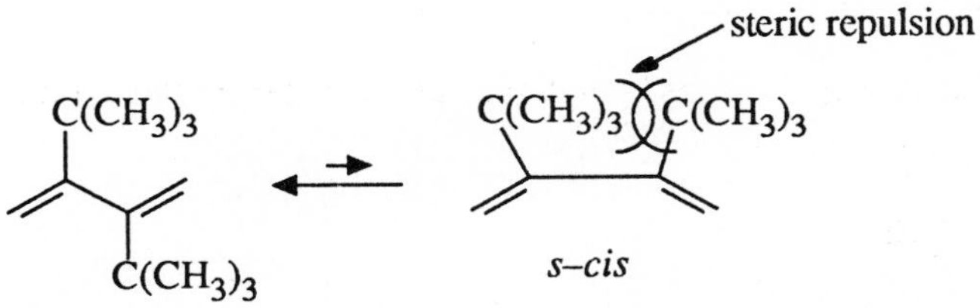

Hence, the molecule is in effect locked out of the s-cis conformation. Since this conformation is required in the transition state of the Diels–Alder reaction, 2,3-di-t-butyl-1,3-butadiene cannot react.

50. Working backward from the structures of the product and diphenylisobenzofuran, the dienophile must be a cyclic allene, formed by an E2 reaction:

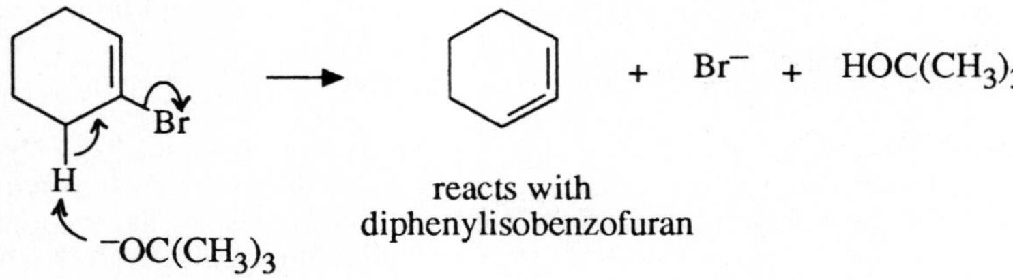

reacts with
diphenylisobenzofuran

51. The product would be most interesting:

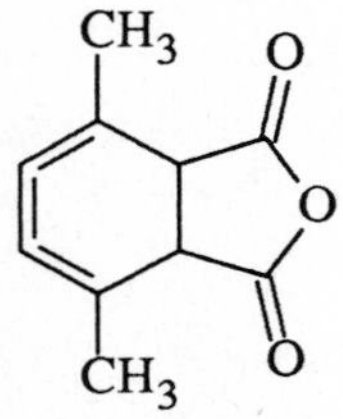

Wow! A cyclic cumulene with three cumulated double bonds. Alas, such an adduct could never form, because the requirement for linear geometry in the cumulated double bonds of the product is such that the compound would have immense angle strain. Looking at the situation another way, the *p* orbitals of maleic anhydride and those of the alkyne must overlap as in Figure 15.6. Because the alkyne is constrained to linear geometry, the transition state for such a reaction would be very strained (if the alkyne units were bent) or would contain extremely poor electronic overlap.

52. (a) This is an ordinary Diels–Alder reaction, with an alkyne as the dienophile:

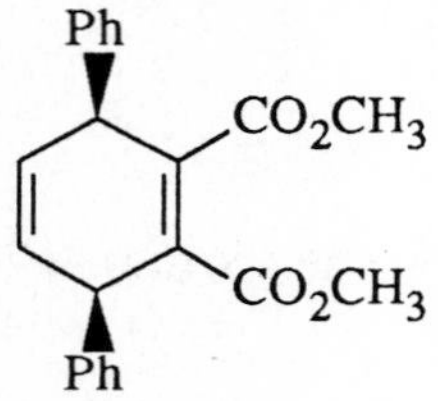

(b) This is another Diels–Alder reaction; in this case, maleic anhydride reacts with the *s–cis* diene unit, and at the face of the molecule *opposite* the angular methyl groups (for steric reasons) to give the following product:

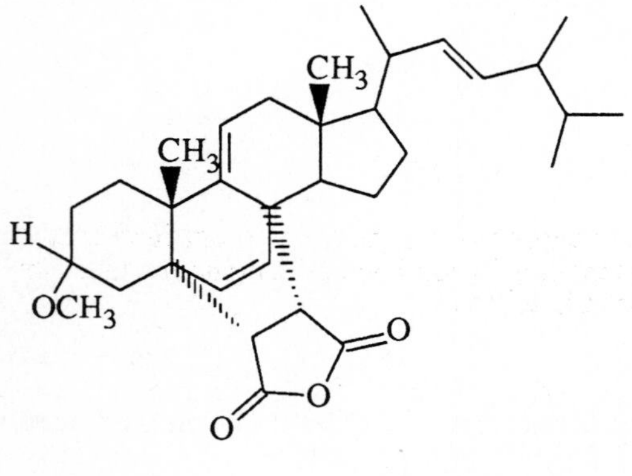

(c) Each double bond of benzoquinone acts as a dienophile in a double-Diels–Alder reaction:

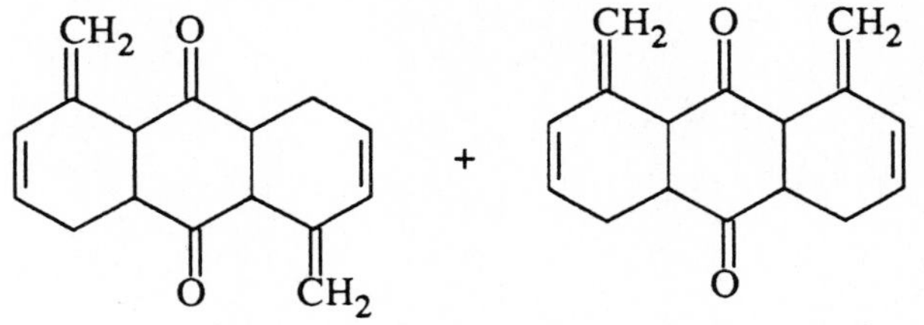

There are two products because in the second Diels–Alder reaction the triene may approach in either of two ways:

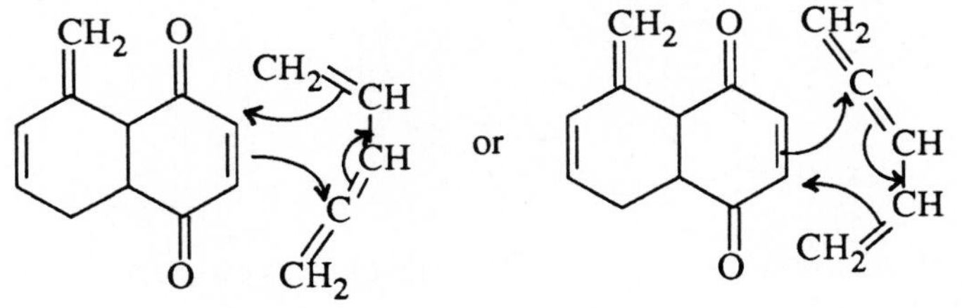

(d) The hint tells us that the reaction is intramolecular, because no carbons are gained or lost. This is an *intramolecular* Diels–Alder reaction; a model of the starting material helps!

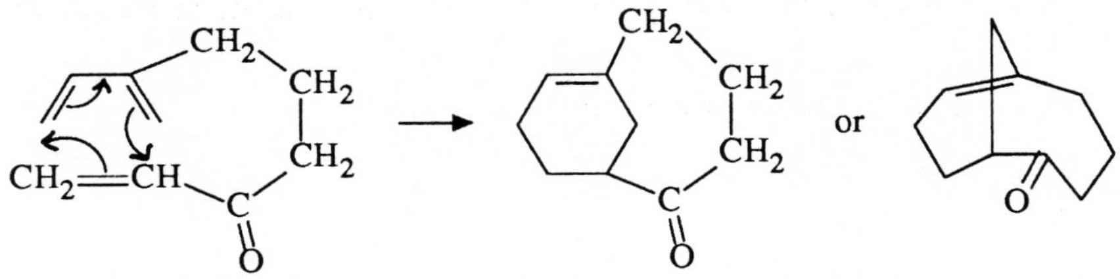

Although this product has a bridgehead double bond, it is not a severe violation of Bredt's rule (Sec. 7.7C), because a large ring is involved.

(e) The product, by analogy to the ferrocene synthesis on text page 625, is nickelocene:

Ni^{2+}

53. Evidently, a methyl group has rearranged. The way for this to happen is to generate a carbocation at an adjacent position. This can be done by protonating the adjacent double bond, after which nature takes its course. (Only the part of the molecule involved in the reaction is shown.)

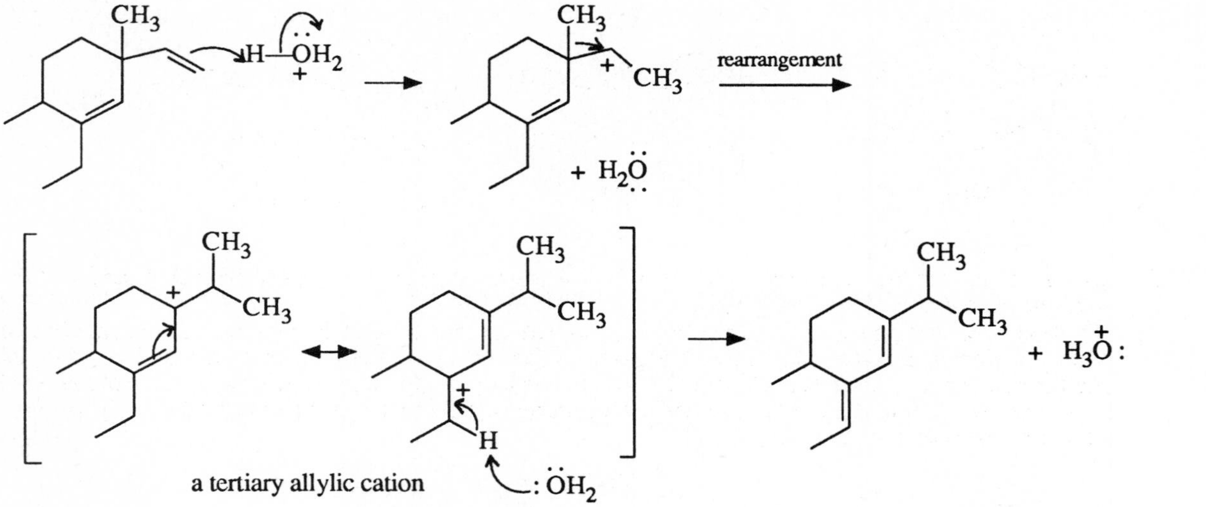

a tertiary allylic cation

54. (a) So many double bonds to protonate! We protonate the double bond that gives the most stable carbocation — the carbocation with the most resonance structures:

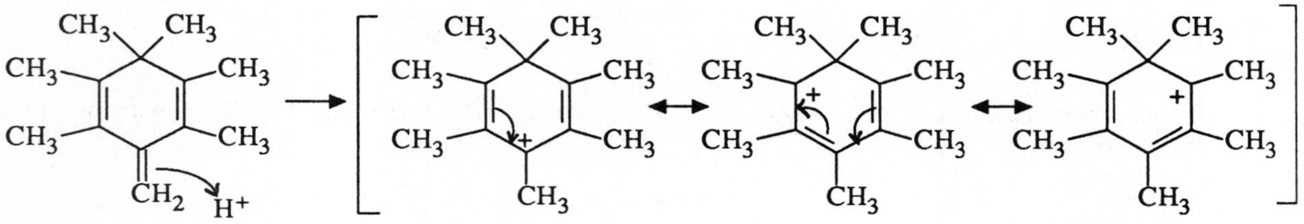

carbocation A

(b) The protons nearest the positive charge have the greatest chemical shifts. These are immediately apparent from the resonance structures above. The assignment of the methyl protons at $\delta\,2.82$ is clear from their relative integral; this methyl is the only one not equivalent to another methyl by symmetry. The two non-vinylic methyls have the smallest chemical shift. To summarize:

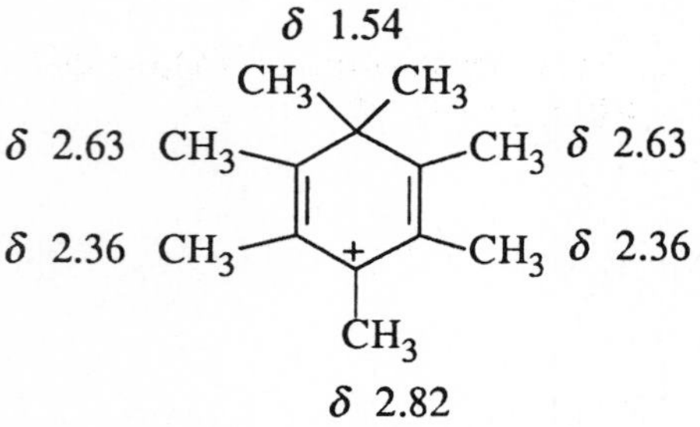

(c) Evidently, the methyl groups become equivalent because of some sort of reaction. The reaction is a "methyl walk":

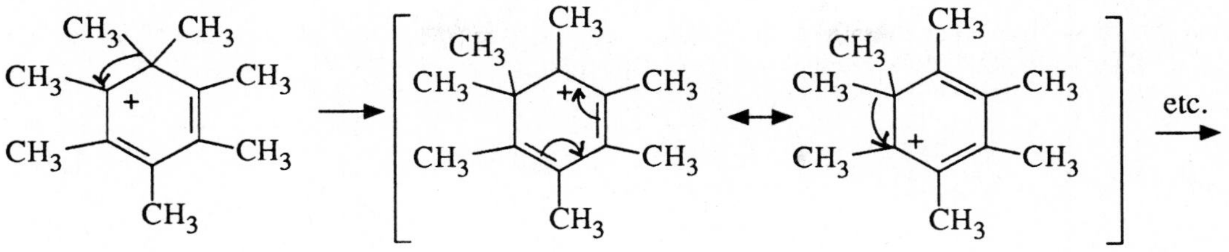

55. (a) One of the products (ethylene) is a gas; and if that is not enough, the other (benzene) is stabilized by its aromatic character.

(b) A bicyclic starting material such as the one given at the beginning of the problem has to come from a Diels–Alder reaction; and we are told that such products undergo reverse Diels–Alder reactions. Evidently, then, α-phellandrene undergoes a Diels–Alder reaction with the alkyne, which undergoes the reverse of *another* Diels–Alder reaction. Let us deduce the structure of the immediate precursor of the final products. Ignoring stereoisomers, two structures fit the bill:

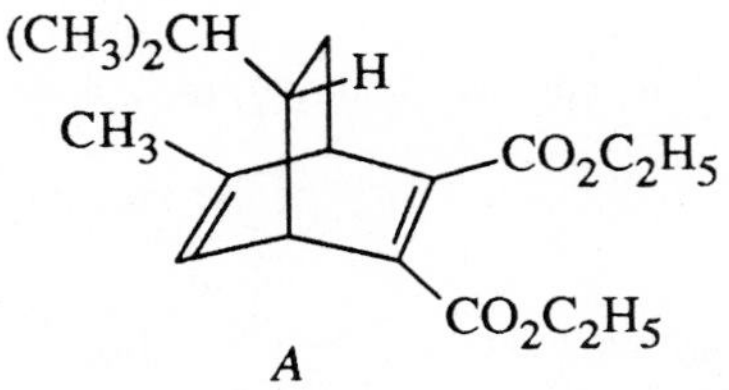

A

and

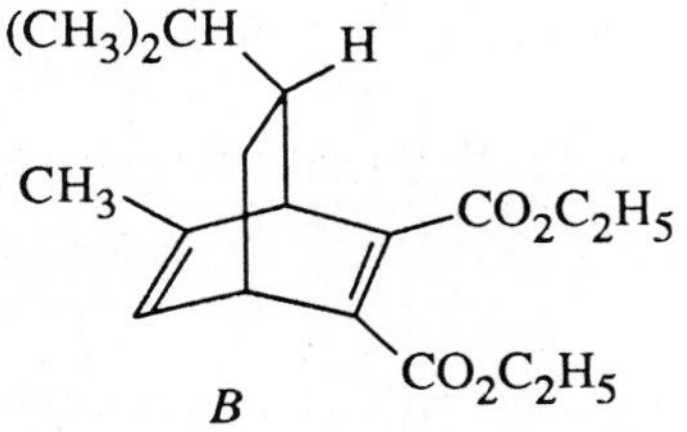

B

These compounds, in turn, would arise from Diels–Alder reactions of the following dienes with the alkyne dienophile:

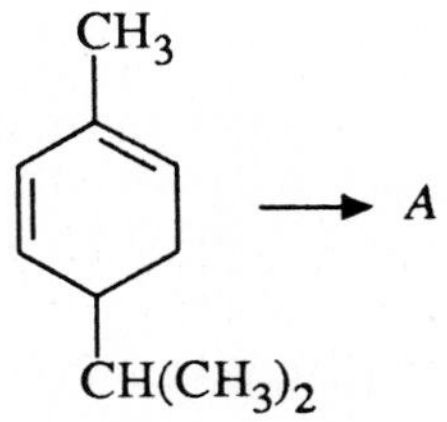

(1)

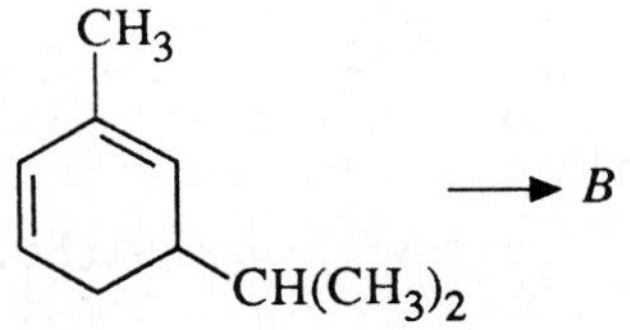

(2)

Since α-phellandrene has the same carbon skeleton as 1-isopropyl-4-methylcyclohexane, it follows that compound (1) is α-phellandrene, and compound *A* is the intermediate in the reaction.

56. The two possible dichlorides are:

$ClCH_2—CH(Cl)—CH=CH_2$ (*A*), 1,2-addition product

$ClCH_2—CH=CH—CH_2Cl$ (*B*), 1,4-addition product

Their identities are established by the ozonolysis data, together with the fact that one is likely to be a 1,2-addition product, and the other, a 1,4-addition product. Under kinetic conditions, *A* and *B* are formed in 2:1 ratio; under thermodynamic conditions, their ratio is 3:7. These ratios are quite analogous to those found in HBr and HCl addition to conjugated dienes: the 1,2-addition product predominates under kinetic conditions, and the 1,3-product under thermodynamic conditions. One thing not established by the data is whether dichloride *B* is *cis* or *trans*. We are given that the product tetrachloride *D* is achiral. Since this tetrachloride has asymmetric carbons, it must be the *meso* stereoisomer. On the assumption that chlorination of *B* is an *anti* addition, it follows that compound *B* must be the *trans*-isomer:

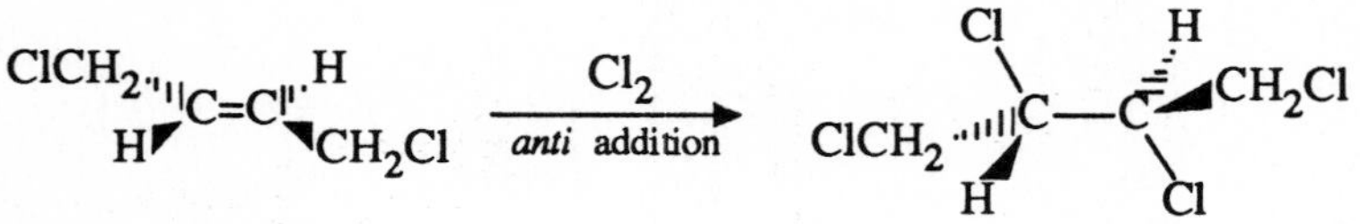

B

D

(a *meso* compound)

The remaining tetrachloride, *C*, must be the racemate:

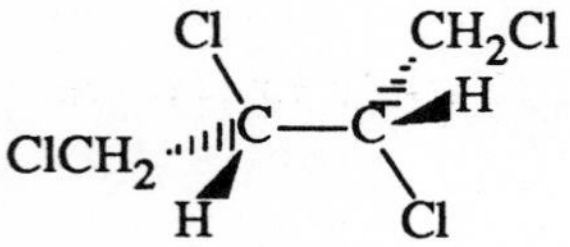

(and its enantiomer)

57. (a) This compound is achiral.
    (b) This compound is chiral. The allene unit is *not* asymmetric, however; the chirality is due to the asymmetric carbon.
    (c) This compound is chiral because of the absence of rotation, and hence, the asymmetry, of the disubstituted allene unit.

    The only way to answer (d) and (e) is to draw (or make a model of) the mirror image, and see whether it superimposes on the original.

    (d) This compound is chiral; its mirror image is nonsuperimposable.
    (e) This compound is achiral; its mirror image is superimposable.

58. (a) If this compound were strictly planar, the rings at the ends of this structure would interfere with each other sterically. Instead, one end is above the plane of the paper, and the other below. In other words, the molecule adopts a helical, or screw, configuration. A screw is chiral. Hexahelicene can be separated into a compound with a left-handed screw sense, and one with a right-handed screw sense. These compounds are enantiomers. Heating causes the ends to move past each other, thus racemizing the compound.

    (b) This compound is chiral because of restricted rotation about the bond between the two benzene rings. In order for the compound to racemize, one ring has to turn 180°. When this happens, a hydrogen on one ring is forced up against an —SO₃H group on the other. The steric repulsions of this arrangement are so great that this requires very high temperatures. At lower temperatures, the compound can be separated into enantiomers.

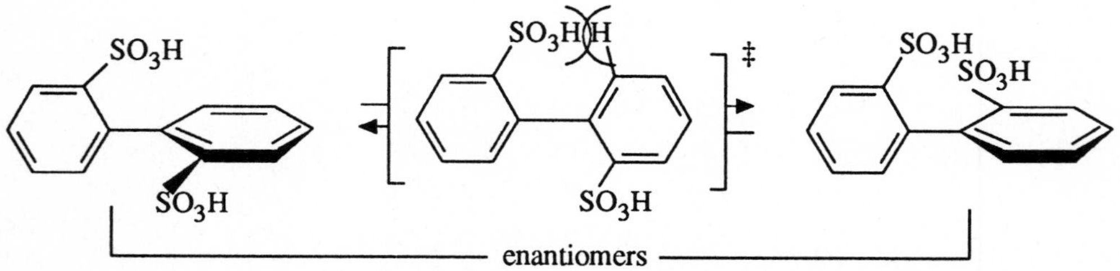

enantiomers

➤ There are now many cases known of optical activity due to restricted rotation about *single* bonds. The chirality in this situation is identical in principle to that of *gauche*-butane (Sec. 6.8A). The only difference here is that internal rotation is so slow that the enantiomeric forms of the two compounds can be separated!

(c) As we have learned (Figs. 15.10, 15.11), 1,3,5,7-cyclooctatetraene and its derivatives are nonplanar, and have a significant barrier to interconversion of the two tub forms (why?). It is a simple matter to show that the two tub forms of this compound are nonsuperimposable mirror images:

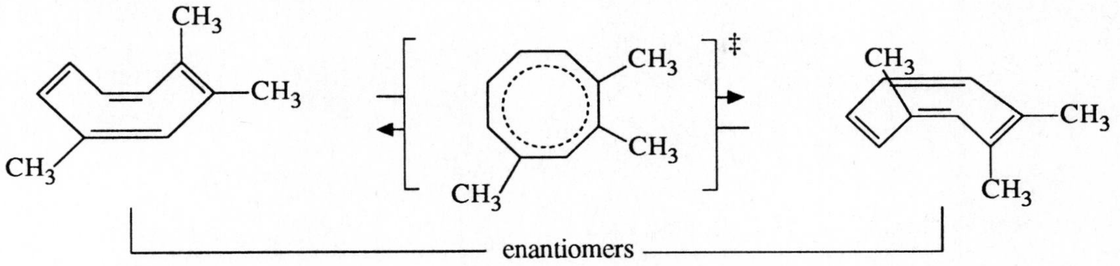

enantiomers

Like any reaction, the interconversion of these two enantiomers is accelerated by raising the temperature.

Chapter 16 / Chemistry of Benzene and Its Derivatives

CHAPTER 16 TERMS

activating group 16.5B
acyl group 16.4E
acylium ion 16.4E
aryl group 16.1
benzylic proton 16.3B
carcinogen 16.8
carcinogenicity 16.8
deactivating group 16.5B
electrophilic aromatic substitution 16.4B
Friedel–Crafts acylation 16.4E
Friedel–Crafts alkylation 16.4F
inductive effect 16.5B
meta-directing group 16.5A
meta-substitution 16.1

nitration 16.4C
nitro group 16.4C
nitronium ion 16.4C
ortho, para-directing group 16.5A
ortho-substitution 16.1
overtone and combination band 16.3A
para-substitution 16.1
phenol 16.1
phenyl group 16.1
polar effect 16.5B
resonance effect 16.5B
ring current 16.3B
sulfonation 16.4D

CHAPTER 16 CONCEPTS

I. Introduction to Benzene and Its Derivatives:

A. Nomenclature of Benzene Derivatives:

1. The nomenclature of many substituted derivatives of benzene follows the same rules used to name other substituted hydrocarbons.
2. Some monosubstituted benzene derivatives have well-established common names that must be learned.

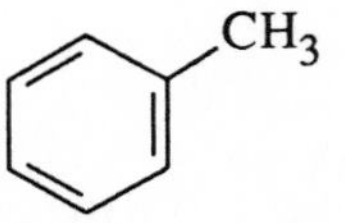

toluene 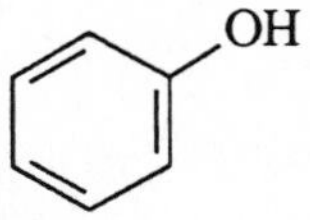   phenol 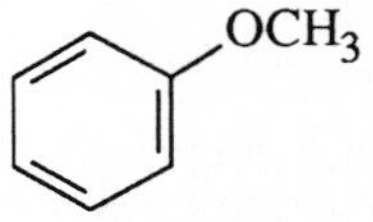   anisole

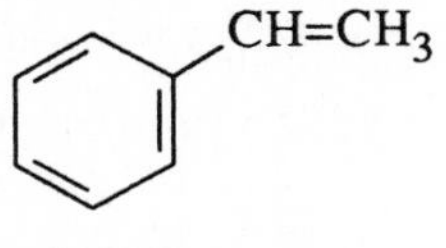

styrene 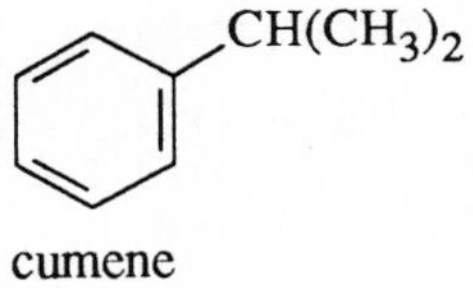   cumene

3. The substituent groups of disubstituted benzenes can be designated either by numbers or by special prefixes that can be used *only* for disubstituted benzene derivatives.
    a) *o* (*ortho*) for a 1,2 relationship.
    b) *m* (*meta*) for a 1,3 relationship.
    c) *p* (*para*) for a 1,4 relationship.

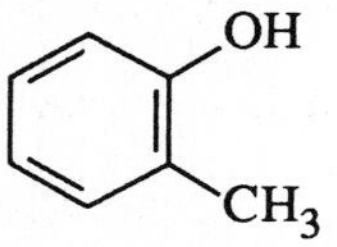

ortho -cresol
o -cresol

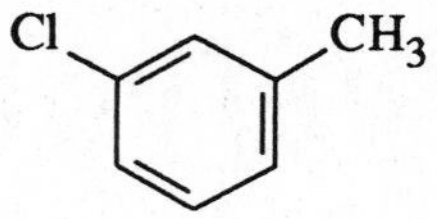

meta -chlorotoluene
m -chlorotoluene

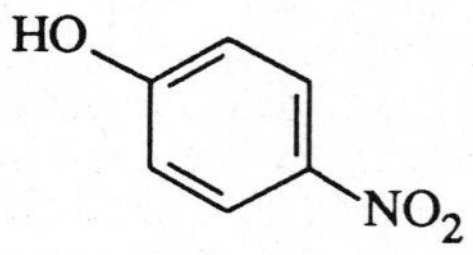

para -nitrophenol
p -nitrophenol
4-nitrophenol

4. Some disubstituted benzenes have time-honored names:
    a) The dimethylbenzenes are called xylenes.
    b) The methylphenols are called cresols.

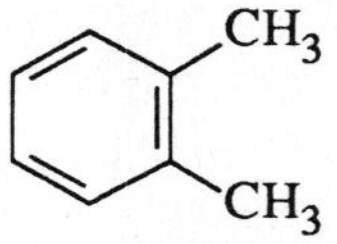

a xylene
(*o* -xylene)

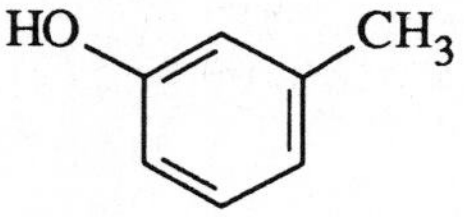

a cresol
(*m* -cresol)

    c) The hydroxyphenols are:
        (1) catechol (1,2-disubstituted).
        (2) resorcinol (1,3-disubstituted).
        (3) hydroquinone (1,4-disubstituted).

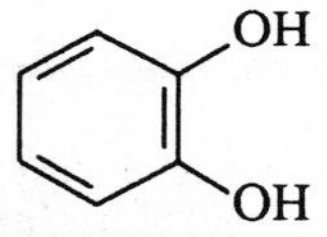

catechol

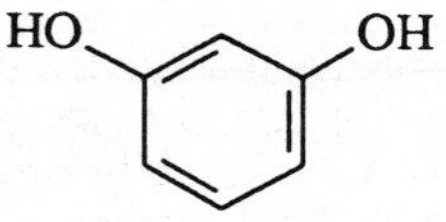

resorcinol

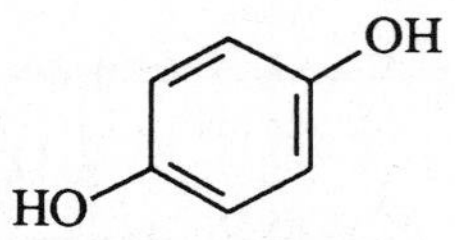

hydroquinone

5. When a benzene derivative contains more than two substituents on the ring, only numbers may be used to designate the positions of substituents.
    a) Substituents are cited and numbered in alphabetical order.
    b) If a substituent is eligible for citation as a principal group, it is assumed to be at position-1 of the ring.

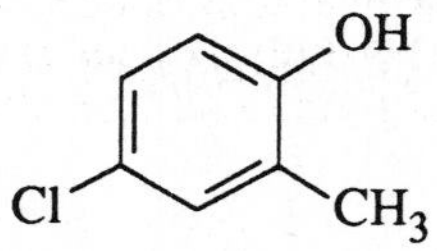

4-chloro-2-methylphenol

6. Sometimes it is simpler to name the benzene ring as a substituent group.
    a) When an unsubstituted benzene ring is a substituent, it is called a **phenyl group**.
    b) The Ph—CH₂— group is called the **benzyl group**.

Ph₃CH
triphenylmethane

Ph—CH₂—Cl
benzyl chloride

    c) A benzene ring or substituted benzene ring used as a substituent is referred to generally as an **aryl group**.

B. Physical Properties of Benzene Derivatives:
    1. Boiling points of benzene derivatives are similar to those of other hydrocarbons with similar shapes and molecular weights.
    2. Melting points of *para*-disubstituted benzene derivatives are typically higher than the corresponding *ortho* or *meta* isomers.
    3. Many *para*-substituted compounds can be separated from their *ortho* and *meta* isomers by recrystallization.
    4. Densities of benzene and other aromatic hydrocarbons are less than that of water, but greater than those of alkanes and alkenes of about the same molecular weight.
    5. Benzene and its hydrocarbon derivatives are insoluble in water; benzene derivatives with substituents that form hydrogen bonds to water are more soluble.

II. Spectroscopy of Benzene Derivatives:

A. IR Spectroscopy:
    1. The most useful absorptions in the infrared spectra of benzene derivatives are the carbon–carbon stretching absorptions of the ring near 1600 cm^{-1} and 1500 cm^{-1}.
    2. Strong absorptions below 900 cm^{-1} are characteristic of C—H bending and ring puckering.
    3. Overtone and combination bands in the $1600 - 2000 \text{ cm}^{-1}$ region can also be observed.

B. NMR Spectroscopy:
    1. Protons on aromatic rings show unusual downfield chemical shifts of about 1.5 ppm relative to those of alkenes; the NMR spectrum of benzene consists of a singlet at a chemical shift of $\delta\,7.4$.
    2. When benzene is oriented relative to the applied field, a circulation of π-electrons around the ring, called a **ring current**, occurs.
        a) The ring current induces a magnetic field that forms closed loops through the ring.
        b) The ring current produces a deshielding effect on the benzene protons and hence a larger downfield chemical shift.
        c) The basis of both the ring current and aromaticity is the overlap of *p* orbitals in a continuous cyclic array.
    3. When the ring protons in substituted benzene derivatives are nonequivalent, they split each other.
        a) Their coupling constants depend on their positional relationships.
        b) The NMR spectra of many monosubstituted benzene derivatives, especially those substituted with a strongly electronegative or electropositive group, have complex absorptions in the aromatic region.
            (1) The protons *ortho* to a very electronegative group have resonances that are further downfield.
            (2) The resonances of the protons *ortho* to less electronegative groups are further upfield.
        c) Splitting patterns in many disubstituted benzenes are complex; however, many *para*-disubstituted benzenes consist of a pair of doublets in which each doublet leans toward the other.
        d) The aromatic protons of many monoalkylbenzenes appear as a broadened singlet.
    4. The chemical shifts of benzylic protons are slightly greater than those of allylic protons.
    5. The O—H of phenols exchange in D_2O and their absorption is typically at lower field than that of alcohols.

C. UV Spectroscopy:
    1. Simple aromatic hydrocarbons have two absorption bands in their UV spectra:
        a) A relatively strong bond near 210 nm.
        b) A much weaker one near 260 nm.
    2. Substituent groups on the ring alter both the λ_{max} values and the intensities of both peaks, particularly if:
        a) The substituent has an unshared electron pair.
        b) The substituent has *p* orbitals that can overlap with the π-electron system of the aromatic ring.
    3. More extensive conjugation is associated with an increase in both λ_{max} and intensity.

III. Introduction to Electrophilic Aromatic Substitution Reactions of Substituted Benzenes:

A. Electrophilic Aromatic Substitution:
   1. Because of their aromaticity, benzene and its derivatives *do not* undergo most of the usual addition reactions of alkenes.
   2. Benzene and its derivatives undergo reactions in which a ring hydrogen is substituted by another group.
   3. **Electrophilic aromatic substitution** reactions are very typical of benzene and other aromatic compounds.
      a) Such a reaction is a substitution reaction because hydrogen is replaced by another group.
      b) Such a reaction is electrophilic because it involves the reaction of an electrophilic species with the aromatic π-electrons.
   4. All electrophilic aromatic substitution reactions have the following common steps:
      a) Generation of an electrophile.
      b) Attack of the π-electrons of the aromatic ring on the electrophile and formation of a resonance-stabilized carbocation.
      c) Loss of a proton from the carbocation intermediate at the site of substitution to generate the substituted aromatic compound.

(E^+ = electrophile)

B. Directing Effects of Substituents:
   1. It is found experimentally that electrophilic substitution reactions of substituted benzenes are regioselective.
      a) A substituent group is either an *ortho*, *para*-directing group or a *meta*-directing group in *all* electrophilic aromatic substitution reactions.
      b) When a substituted benzene undergoes further substitution mostly at the *ortho* and *para* positions, the original substituent group is called an **ortho, para-directing group**.
      c) When a substituted benzene undergoes further substitution mostly at the *meta* position, the original substituent group is called a **meta-directing group**.
   2. This regioselectivity means that the rate of reaction at one position of the benzene derivative is much faster than the rate of reaction at another position.

C. *Ortho, Para*-Directing Groups:
   1. All alkyl groups are *ortho*, *para*-directing substituents.
      a) Reaction at a position that is *ortho* or *para* to an alkyl group gives a carbocation intermediate ion that has one tertiary carbocation resonance structure.
   2. All groups that have atoms with unshared electron pairs directly attached to the benzene ring are *ortho*, *para*-directing substituents.
      a) The reaction of an electrophile at either the *ortho* or *para* positions gives a carbocation with more resonance structures; in one structure, charge can be delocalized onto the substituent.
      b) The charge *cannot* be delocalized onto the substituent when reaction occurs at the *meta* position.
   3. Resonance formalism shows that the positive charge is shared on alternate carbons of the ring; when *meta* substitution occurs, the positive charge is *not* shared by the carbon adjacent to the substituent.
   4. *Ortho* and *para* substitution are observed because the carbocation intermediate in these pathways are more stable than the intermediate involved in *meta* substitution.

D. The *Ortho:Para* Ratio:
   1. When a benzene derivative bears an *ortho*, *para*-directing group, most electrophilic aromatic substitution reactions give much more *para* than *ortho* product; the Friedel–Crafts acylation reaction of alkylbenzenes typically gives almost all *para* products and only traces, if any, of the *ortho* products.
   2. In some cases, predominance of the *para* isomer can be explained as a steric effect.
   3. The *ortho* and *para* isomers obtained in many electrophilic aromatic substitution reactions have sufficiently different physical properties that they are readily separated.

E. *Meta*-Directing Groups:
    1. The groups that act as *meta*-directing groups are all electronegative groups without an unshared electron pair on an atom adjacent to the benzene ring.
    2. All *meta*-directing groups have bond dipoles that place a substantial degree of positive charge next to the benzene ring.
    3. Reaction at the *meta* position is favored because it gives an ion in which the two like charges are farthest apart.

F. Activating and Deactivating Effects of Substituents:
    1. Different benzene derivatives have greatly different reactivities in electrophilic aromatic substitution reactions.
        a) An **activating group** is the substituent in a substituted benzene derivative that reacts more rapidly than benzene itself.
        b) A **deactivating group** is the substituent in a substituted benzene derivative that reacts more slowly than benzene itself.
    2. A given substituent group is either *activating* in *all* electrophilic aromatic substitution reactions or *deactivating* in *all* such reactions.
        a) All *meta*-directing groups are deactivating groups.
            (1) This is due to greater deactivation of the *ortho* and *para* positions.
            (2) This is *not* due to selective activation of the *meta* position.
        b) All *ortho*, *para*-directing groups except for the halogens are activating groups.
        c) The halogens are deactivating groups.
    3. Except for the halogens, there is a correlation between the activating and directing effects of substituents.
        a) Directing effects are concerned with the relative rates of substitution at different positions of the *same* compound.
        b) Activating or deactivating effects are concerned with the relative rates of substitution of *different* compounds.
    4. Properties of substituents that control activating and deactivating effects are:
        a) The **resonance effect** of the substituent—the ability of the substituent to stabilize the carbocation intermediate in electrophilic substitution by delocalization of electrons from the substituent into the ring.
            (1) The electron-donating resonance effect of a group with unshared electron pairs *stabilizes* positive charge and *activates* further substitution, provided that the substitution occurs in the *ortho* or *para* position.
            (2) When a ring substituent is electropositive (for example, an alkyl group), it pushes electrons into the ring away from itself and creates a slight excess of electrons (negative charge) in the ring.
        b) The **polar effect** (**inductive effect**)—the tendency of the substituent group by virtue of its electronegativity to pull electrons away from the ring.
            (1) The electron-withdrawing inductive effect of such an electronegative group *destabilizes* positive charge and *deactivates* further substitution.
            (2) Electronegative groups (for example, nitro, sulfonic acid, and acyl groups) destabilize positive charge in the ring; this effect is greater when substitution occurs at an *ortho* or *para* position; hence, *meta*-substitution is observed.
            (3) The deactivating, rate-retarding inductive effects of the halogens are offset somewhat by their resonance effects when substitution occurs *ortho* or *para* to the halogen.
        c) Whether a substituted derivative of benzene is activated or deactivated toward further substitution depends on:
            (1) The balance of the resonance and inductive effects.
            (2) The *position* on the ring that is being considered.
        d) Alkyl groups on the benzene ring:
            (1) Stabilize positive charge.
            (2) Activate electrophilic substitution.

G. Use of Electrophilic Aromatic Substitution Reactions in Organic Chemistry:
  1. Electrophilic aromatic substitution reactions are often important in preparing one substituted benzene from another.
  2. Directing effects of the substituents must be considered carefully when designing an organic synthesis that involves electrophilic aromatic substitution reactions.
  3. When an electrophilic substitution reaction is carried out on a benzene derivative with more than one substituent:
      a) The activating and directing effects are roughly the sum of the effects of the separate substituents.
      b) If one group is much more strongly activating than the other, the directing effect of the more powerful activating group generally predominates.
  4. Knowledge of the activating effects of substituents in an aromatic compound dictates what conditions must be used in an electrophilic substitution reaction.
      a) When a deactivating group is introduced by an electrophilic substitution reaction, it is easy to introduce one group at a time.
      b) When an activating group is introduced by electrophilic substitution, additional substitutions can occur easily under the conditions of the first substitution and mixtures of products are obtained.
      c) Deactivating substituents retard some reactions to the point that they are not useful.
          (1) Friedel–Crafts *acylation* does not occur on a benzene ring substituted *solely* with one or more *meta*-directing groups.
          (2) Friedel–Crafts *alkylation* is generally not useful on compounds that are more deactivated than benzene itself.

CHAPTER 16 REACTIONS

I. Electrophilic Aromatic Substitution Reactions of Benzene:

A. Halogenation of Benzene:
1. Benzene reacts with bromine in the presence of a Lewis acid (FeBr$_3$) to yield a product in which one bromine is substituted for a ring hydrogen.

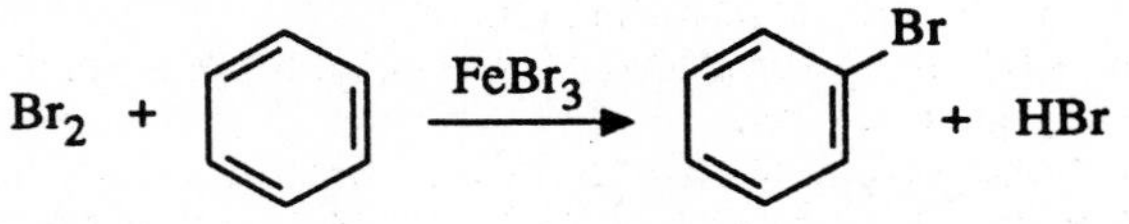

$$Br_2 \; + \; \text{(benzene)} \xrightarrow{FeBr_3} \text{(bromobenzene, Br)} \; + \; HBr$$

2. An analogous chlorination reaction using Cl$_2$ and FeCl$_3$ gives chlorobenzene.
3. Halogenation of benzene differs from the halogenation of alkenes by:
   a) The type of product obtained:
      (1) Halogenation of benzene gives substitution products.
      (2) Halogenation of alkenes gives addition products.
   b) The severity of the reaction:
      (1) Halogenation of benzene requires a Lewis acid and relatively severe reaction conditions.
      (2) Halogenation of alkenes is rapid and requires no catalyst.
4. The mechanism of the bromination of benzene contains the following steps:
   a) In the first step, bromine forms a complex with the Lewis acid FeBr$_3$.
      (1) This complexation makes one of the bromines a better leaving group.
      (2) The other bromine in this complex takes on some electron-deficient character—it acts like Br$^+$.
   b) In the second step, the electron-deficient bromine in this complex is attacked by the π-electrons of the benzene ring.
      (1) Bromination requires harsh conditions because this step disrupts the aromatic stability of the benzene ring.
      (2) The carbocation intermediate is resonance stabilized.
   c) The reaction is completed when a Br$^-$ counter-ion acts as a base to remove the ring proton and give the products; by losing a β-proton, the carbocation can form a stable aromatic compound.

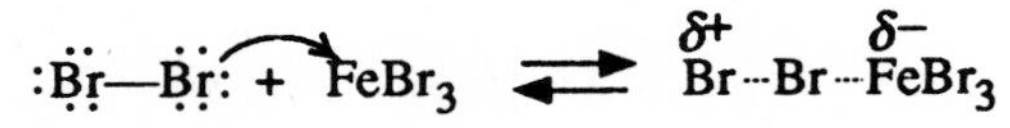

$$:\!\ddot{B}r\!-\!\ddot{B}r\!: \; + \; FeBr_3 \; \rightleftharpoons \; \overset{\delta+}{Br}\!\cdots\!\overset{}{Br}\overset{\delta-}{\cdots}FeBr_3$$

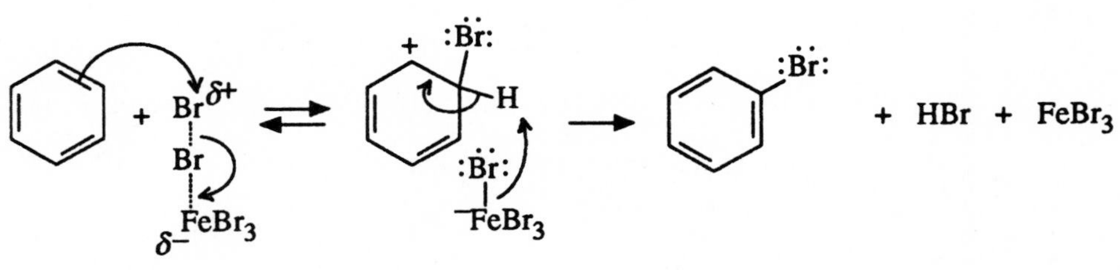

B. Sulfonation of Benzene:
1. Another electrophilic substitution reaction of benzene is its conversion into benzenesulfonic acid by a solution of sulfur trioxide in H$_2$SO$_4$.
2. In this reaction, called **sulfonation**, the electrophile is the neutral compound sulfur trioxide, SO$_3$.
3. Sulfonic acids such as benzenesulfonic acid are rather strong acids.

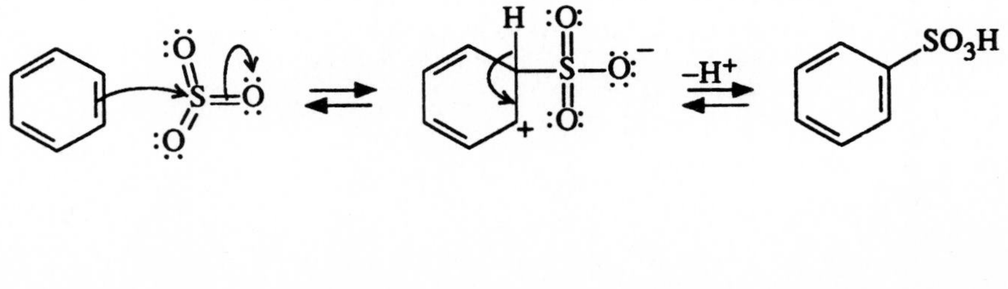

C. Nitration of Benzene:
   1. Benzene reacts with concentrated nitric acid, usually in the presence of sulfuric acid, to form nitrobenzene.

$$H_2SO_4 + HNO_3 \rightleftharpoons {}^+NO_2 \; HSO_4^- + H_2O$$

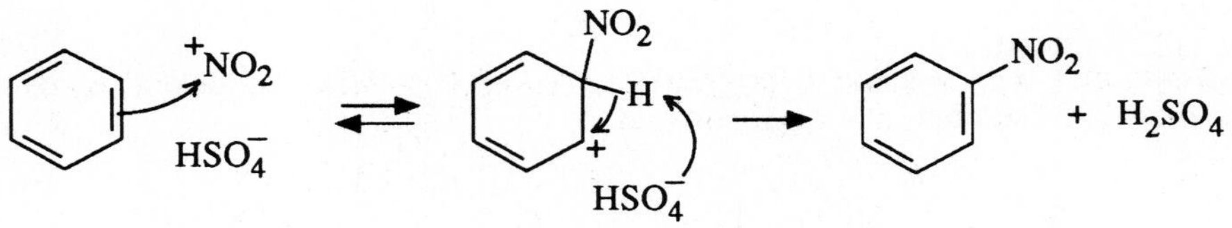

   2. In this reaction, called **nitration**, the nitro group, —NO$_2$, is introduced into the benzene ring by electrophilic substitution.

D. Friedel–Crafts Acylation of Benzene:
   1. When benzene reacts with an acid chloride in the presence of an acid such as AlCl$_3$, a ketone is formed.
      a) This reaction is called a **Friedel–Crafts acylation**.
      b) The group introduced into the benzene ring is called in general an acyl group.

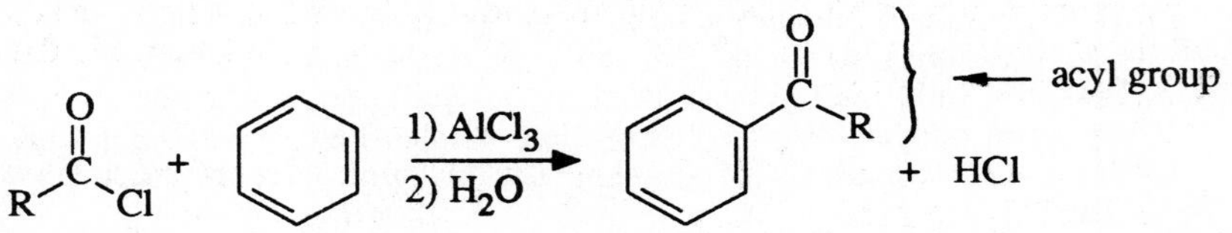

   2. The electrophile in the Friedel–Crafts acylation reaction is a carbocation called an acylium ion.
      a) This ion is formed when the acid chloride reacts with the Lewis acid AlCl$_3$.

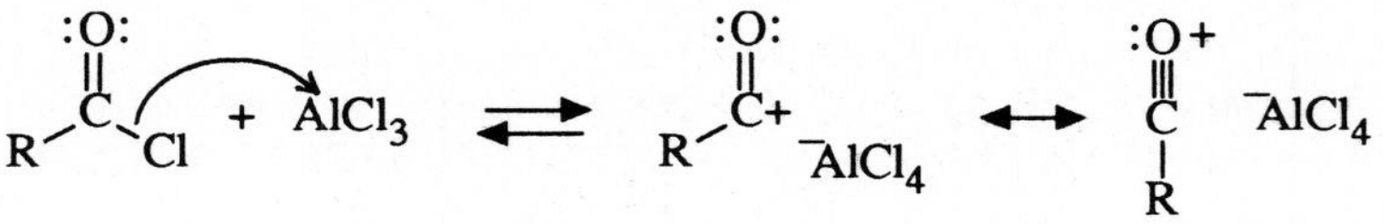

      b) The substitution occurs when the benzene π-electrons attack the acylium ion.
   3. The AlCl$_3$ forms a complex with the ketone product . Since complexed AlCl$_3$ is catalytically inactive, slightly more than one equivalent of the catalyst must be used in the Friedel–Crafts acylation.
   4. The Friedel–Crafts acylation occurs intramolecularly when the product contains a five- or six-membered ring.
      a) The intramolecular process is much faster than attack of the acylium ion on the phenyl ring of another molecule.
      b) This type of reaction can only occur at an adjacent *ortho* position.

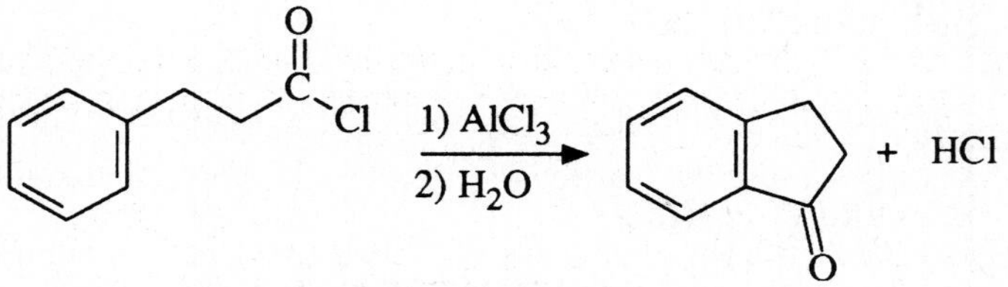

   5. The Friedel–Crafts acylation reaction is important for two reasons.
      a) It is an excellent method for the synthesis of aromatic ketones.
      b) It is another method for the formation of carbon–carbon bonds (see list on text page 655 or Appendix V, text page A-10).

E. Friedel–Crafts Alkylation of Benzene:
1. The reaction of an alkyl halide with benzene in the presence of a Lewis acid gives an alkylbenzene; this reaction is called **Friedel–Crafts alkylation.**
2. The electrophile in this reaction is formed by complexation of $AlCl_3$ with the alkyl halide.
   a) The resulting complex forms a carbocation, which is attacked by the benzene π-electrons.
   b) Rearrangements of alkyl groups are observed in some Friedel–Crafts alkylations.

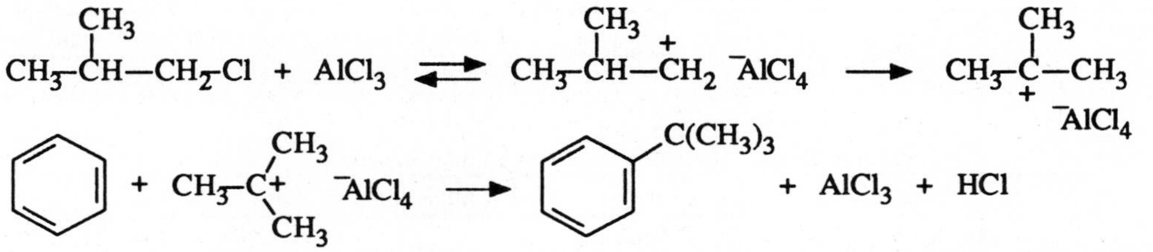

3. A catalytic amount (much less than one equivalent) of the $AlCl_3$ catalyst can be used in this reaction.
4. The alkylbenzene products are more reactive than benzene itself.
   a) Because the product itself can undergo alkylation, mixtures of products alkylated to different extents are observed.
   b) A monoalkylation product can be obtained in good yield if a large excess of the starting material is used; this strategy is practical only if the starting material is cheap, and if it can be readily separated from the product.
5. Alkenes and alcohols can also be used in Friedel–Crafts alkylation reactions; the carbocation electrophiles in such reactions are generated from alkenes by protonation, and from alcohols by protonation and loss of water.

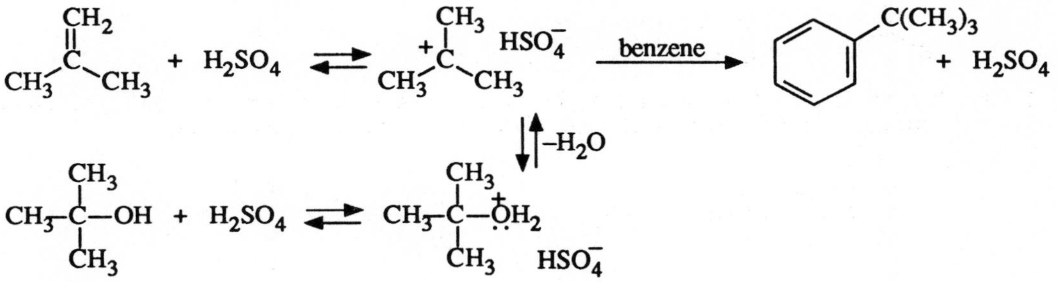

F. Review of Carbocation Reactions:
1. Reaction with nucleophiles.
2. Rearrangement to other carbocations.
3. Loss of a β-proton to give an alkene.
4. Reaction with the π-electrons of a double bond (or aromatic ring).

II. Addition Reactions of Benzene Derivatives:

A. Hydrogenation of Benzene Derivatives:
1. Aromatic rings can be hydrogenated under extreme conditions of temperature and/or pressure.
2. Catalytic hydrogenation of benzene derivatives gives the corresponding cyclohexanes, and cannot be stopped at the cyclohexadiene or cyclohexene stages.

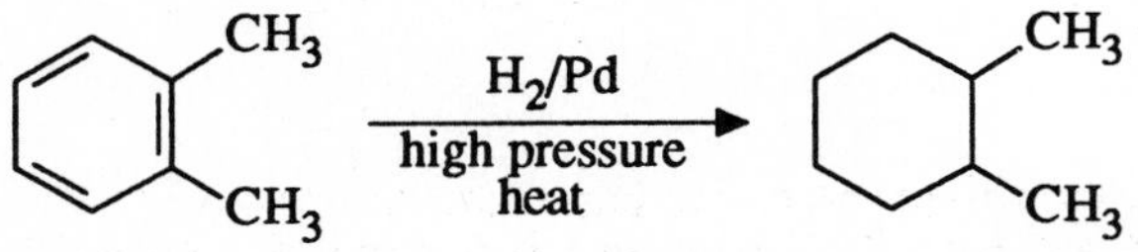

3. The reaction requires heat or pressure because hydrogenation of benzene is an endothermic reaction. That is, the reaction is thermodynamically unfavorable; energy must be added for it to occur.

ELECTROPHILIC AROMATIC
SUBSTITUTION SUMMARY

Electrophile	Reaction Name	Product
Br^+, Cl^+	halogenation	a halobenzene (bromobenzene or chlorobenzene)
SO_3 in H_2SO_4	sulfonation	benzene sulfonic acid
$^+NO_2$	nitration	nitrobenzene
$R—C≡O:^+$	Friedel–Crafts acylation	an aryl ketone
R^+	Friedel–Crafts alkylation	an alkylbenzene

CHAPTER 16 SOLUTIONS

Solutions to In-Text Problems

1. (a) 1-chloro-3-ethylbenzene, or *m*-chloroethylbenzene
    (b) 1,2-diethylbenzene, or *o*-diethylbenzene
    (c) *p*-nitrostyrene, or 4-nitrostyrene
    (d) 2-bromo-1-chloro-5-fluoro-4-iodo-3-nitrobenzene
    (e) 2,4-dichlorophenol
    (f) diphenylmethane

2. (a) OCH₃ ... (b) CH₃ ... (c) SH ... (d) CH₂—Ph ... (e) OH
    (see structures)

3. Thiophene has the NMR signals at lower field because it is aromatic. The ring current of aromatic rings causes them to have a greater chemical shift than ordinary double bonds.

4. (a) The annulene has 18 π-electrons. This meets the $4n + 2$ criterion for $n = 4$. Furthermore, the molecule is planar, and is an uninterrupted cycle of *p* orbitals.
    (b) The ring current brings about deshielding of protons outside the ring, but, from Figure 16.2, text page 643, it should have exactly the *opposite* effect on the protons *inside* the ring: these should be strongly shielded. The signal at $\delta\, 9.28$ is for the outer protons, and the resonance at $\delta\, (-2.99)$ is for the inner protons. The former protons are strongly deshielded, and the latter are strongly shielded. The relative integral is in agreement with this assignment.

5. Mesitylene would give an NMR spectrum containing only two singlets in the integral ratio 3:1 for the methyl groups and ring protons, respectively. Isopropylbenzene would have a more complex spectrum; the isopropyl resonance would be a doublet for the methyls and a septet at lower field for the CH proton; the ring protons would be nearly equivalent. The integral of alkyl to ring protons would be in the ratio 7:5.

6. Both compounds contain —OH groups; (a) has a signal for an exchangeable proton at $\delta\, 3.76$, and (b) has a broad resonance at $\delta\, 6$, plus —OH absorption in its IR spectrum. Both compounds also contain aromatic absorptions in their NMR spectra, and these absorptions suggest a *para*-disubstituted benzene ring in each case. The correct structures are:

    (a) CH₃
        CH—OH
        (structure)
        CH₃
    1-(4-methylphenyl)-1-ethanol

    (b) OH
        (structure)
        CH₂CH₃
    4-ethylphenol

7. (a) The two benzene rings are conjugated in compound *A*; because there are more formal double bonds in conjugation, the UV absorption occurs at longer wavelength than it does in ethylbenzene.
    (b) Compound *B* is like two connected molecules of compound *C* in the same sense that compound *A* is like two connected ethylbenzene molecules. We would expect the absorption of compound *B* to occur at longer

wavelength than that of compound *C* for the reason given in part (a). That this is *not* the case means that the two rings in compound *B* are not conjugated. They are not conjugated because they are not coplanar; and they are not coplanar because the *ortho* methyl groups on the two rings have severe steric repulsions that are relieved when the molecule adopts a nonplanar conformation:

planar conformation

nonplanar conformation;
not conjugated

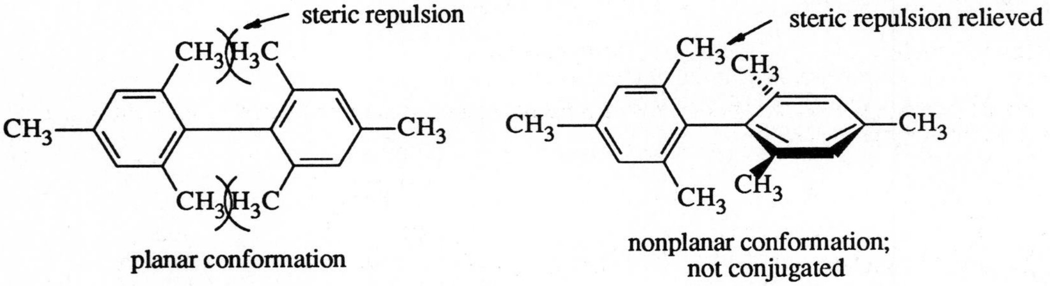

8.   *p*-Dibromobenzene is formed by bromination of the major product, bromobenzene, at the *para* position:

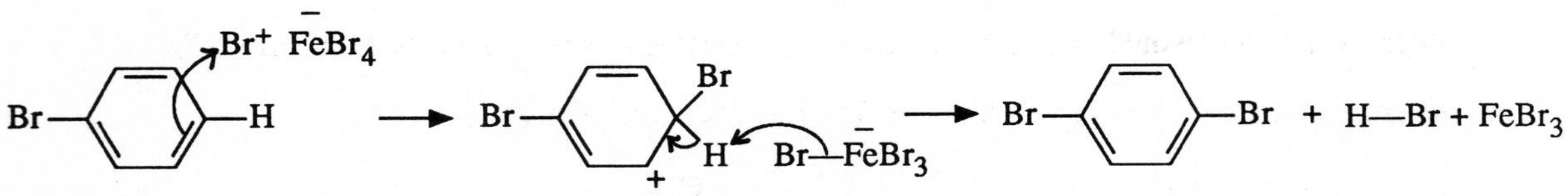

9.   In this reaction, the electrophile is D^+ derived from D_2SO_4. The mechanism follows the typical pattern of electrophilic aromatic substitution: reaction of benzene with the electrophile to form a carbocation; and loss of a proton to give the substituted benzene:

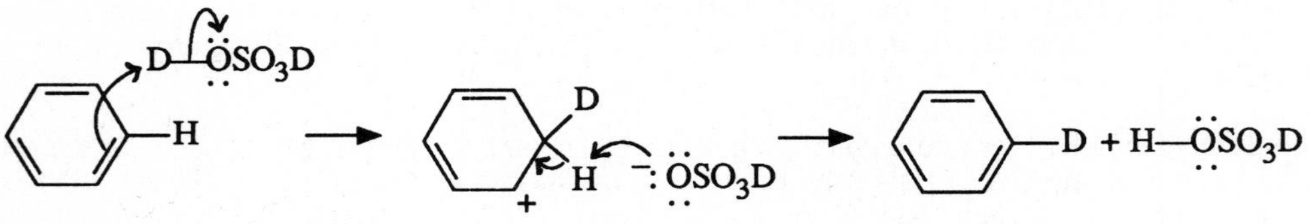

10.   In this reaction, SO_3 is attacked by the π-electron system of the benzene ring at the *para* position. The mechanism is the typical one for electrophilic aromatic substitution: formation of a carbocation, and loss of a proton at the site of substitution to give the product:

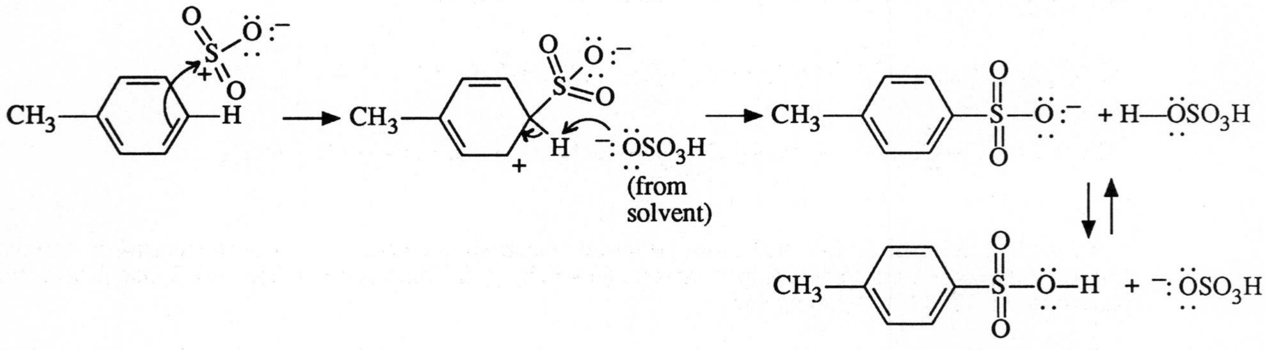

p-toluenesulfonic acid

11. (a)   (b)

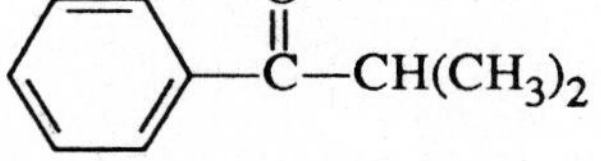

      isobutyrophenone 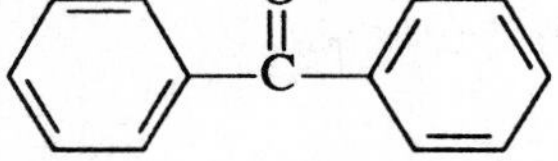   benzophenone

12. Either aromatic group could be present in the acid chloride, and the other would then be in the aromatic compound that undergoes acylation:

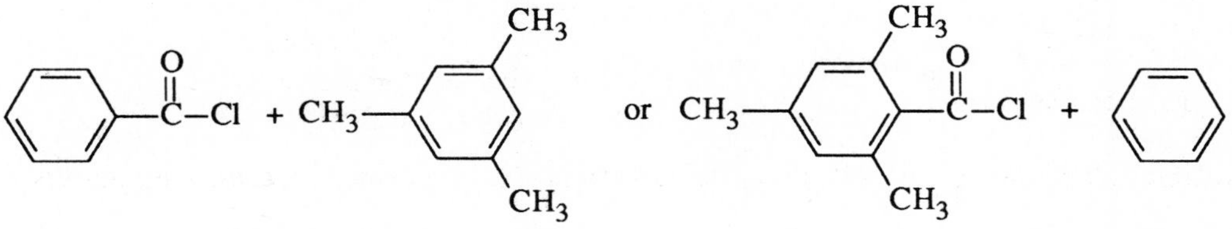

Either combination would react in the presence of a suitable Lewis-acid catalyst such as AlCl₃.

13. The product results from an *intramolecular* Friedel–Crafts acylation reaction:

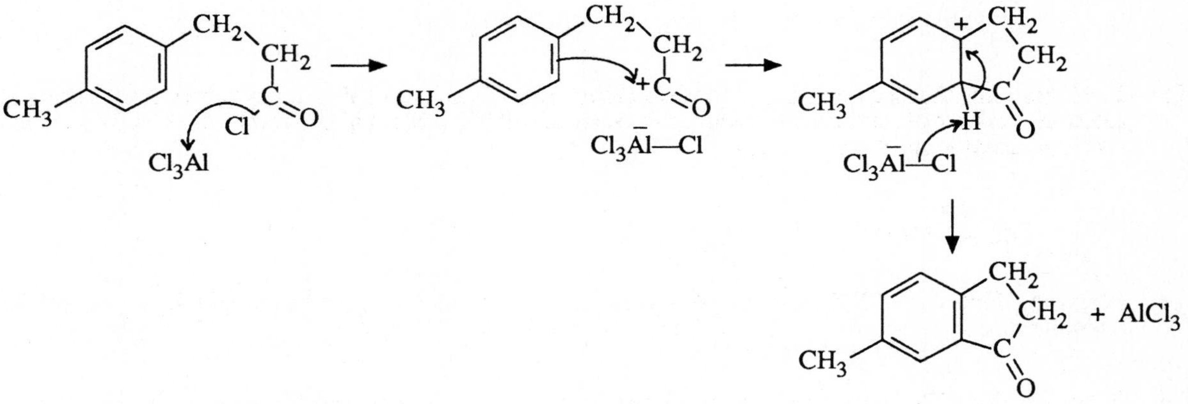

14. The mechanism involves formation and rearrangement of a carbocation, followed by attack of the benzene π-electrons on the rearranged carbocation in the usual mechanism of electrophilic aromatic substitution. Formation and rearrangement of the carbocation occur as follows:

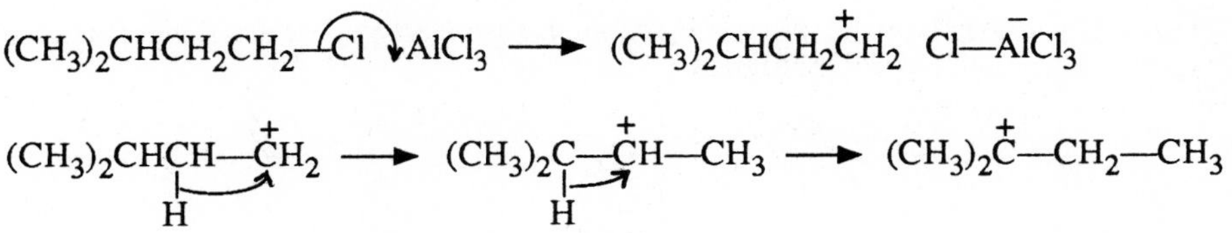

It is this carbocation that is attacked by the benzene π-electrons in an electrophilic aromatic substitution reaction. We leave it to you to complete the mechanism. (If you have difficulty, review Sec. 16.4B, and follow the pattern in Eq. 16.20b on text page 656.)

➤ Notice that there are two successive carbocation rearrangements required to generate the tertiary carbocation. If you wrote a single rearrangement in which a hydrogen moves over two carbons, you have the correct idea. It turns out that such four-center rearrangements generally do not occur for reasons that are beyond the scope of our present discussion.

15. This is an intramolecular Friedel–Crafts *alkylation* in the same sense that the reaction in Problem 13 is an intramolecular Friedel–Crafts *acylation*:

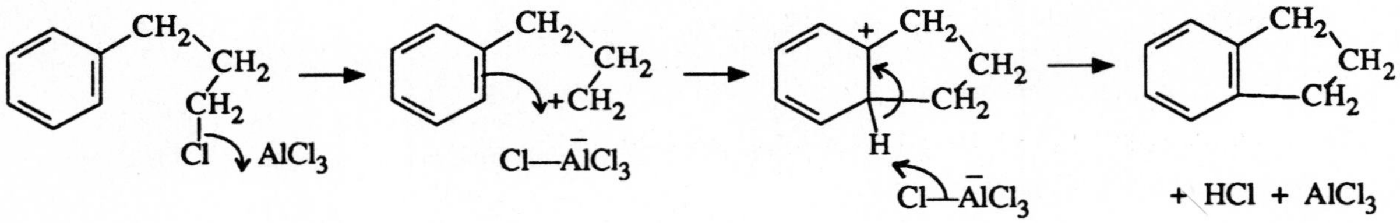

16. (a) A carbocation is generated by protonation of cyclohexene:

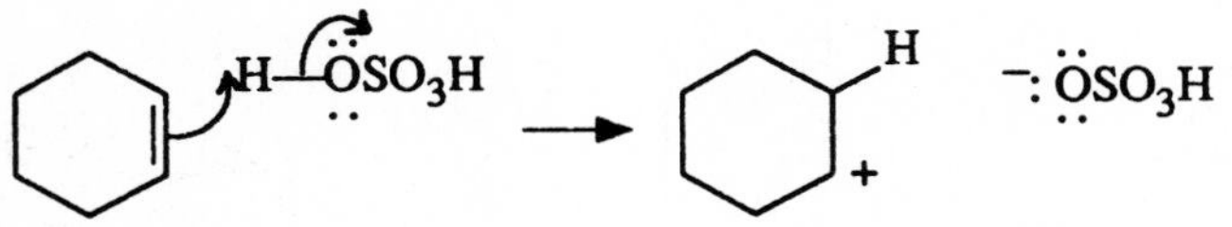

This carbocation is then attacked by the π-electrons of the benzene ring in the usual mechanism of electrophilic aromatic substitution. We leave it to you to complete the mechanism.

(b) The same product is formed because the same carbocation is formed:

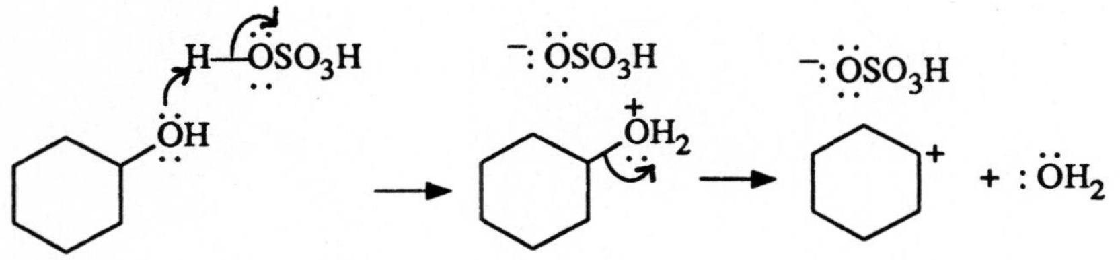

17. Following the lead of the previous two problems, we know that alkenes can be protonated to give carbocation intermediates:

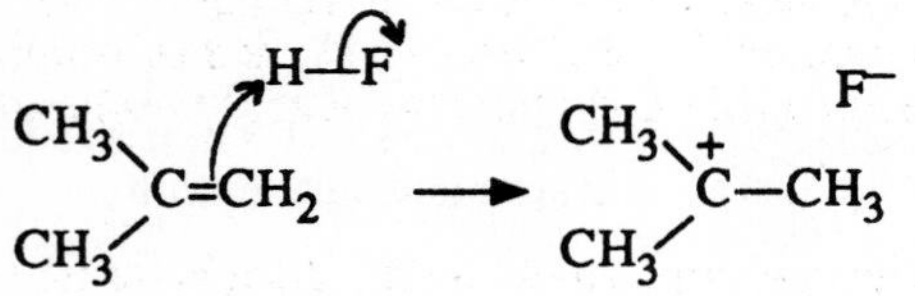

This cation, the *t*-butyl cation, is attacked by the π-electrons of the benzene ring in the usual mechanism of electrophilic aromatic substitution to give *t*-butylbenzene:

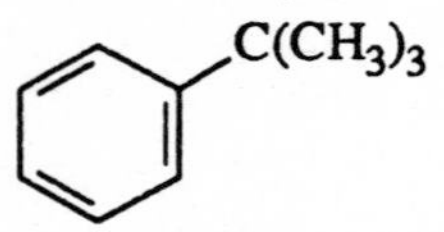

18. The third entry in Table 16.2 tells us that alkoxy (—OR) groups are *ortho, para* directors. Since the methoxy group is a type of alkoxy group, we expect that acylation of anisole will give a mixture of *ortho* and *para* acylation products:

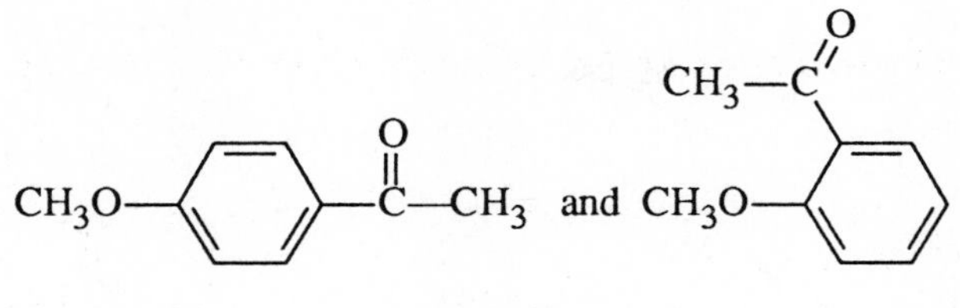

19. Let us designate a general electrophile by E^+, as in Eq. 16.28:

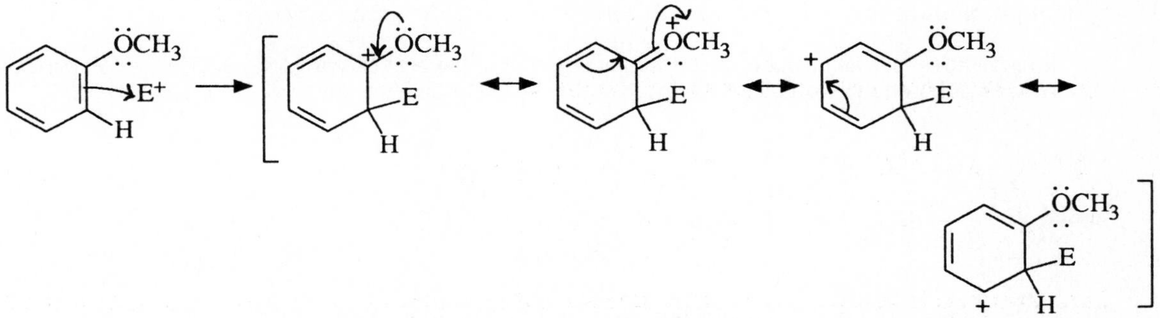

20. When the electrophile (the nitronium ion, $^+NO_2$) reacts with bromobenzene at the *ortho* or *para* position, a carbocation intermediate that results has four resonance structures; in one of those structures, the positive charge is delocalized onto the bromine:

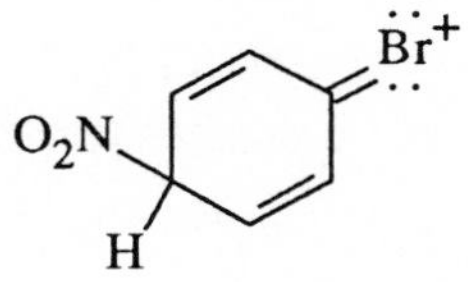

(The ion shown results from reaction at the *para* position; an analogous ion is formed by reaction at the *ortho* position.) When the nitronium ion reacts with bromobenzene at the *meta* position, an ion with only three resonance structures is formed; charge cannot be delocalized onto the bromine. Since the ions resulting from reaction at the *ortho* and *para* positions have more resonance structures, these ions are more stable. The reactions involving the more stable carbocation intermediates are faster. Hence, *ortho*- and *para*-substitution reactions of bromobenzene are faster than the corresponding *meta*-substitution reactions, and the *ortho*- and *para*-substitution products are the ones observed.

21. When an electrophile E^+ reacts at the *ortho* position of nitrobenzene, a carbocation intermediate is formed that has one resonance structure in which positive charge is adjacent to the electronegative nitro group:

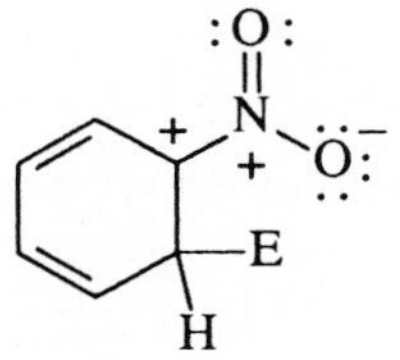

The resulting repulsion between like charges destabilizes this ion. When the electrophile reacts at the *meta* position of nitrobenzene, the two positive charges are further apart:

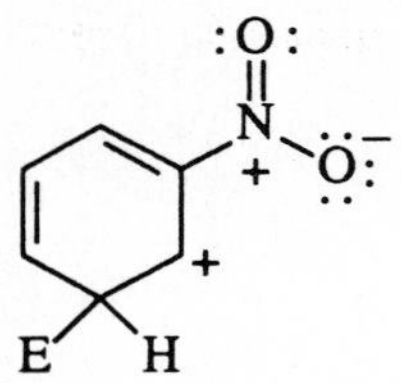

This ion is therefore more stable (or less unstable) than the previous one. The reaction that involves the more stable carbocation intermediate is the faster reaction, and therefore the reaction that is observed. Hence, *meta* substitution of nitrobenzene is observed. In other words, the nitro group is a *meta* director.

22. (a) The substituent has an unshared electron pair adjacent to the benzene ring, and is therefore an *ortho, para* director. Hence, bromine would be introduced at the *ortho* or *para* position:

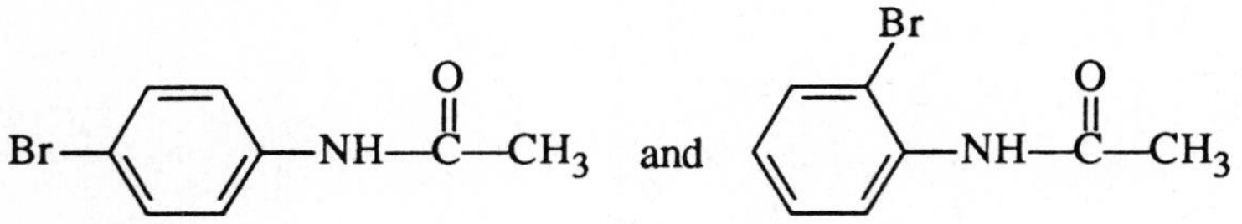

(b) For the same reason as in (a), the amino group is an *ortho, para* director:

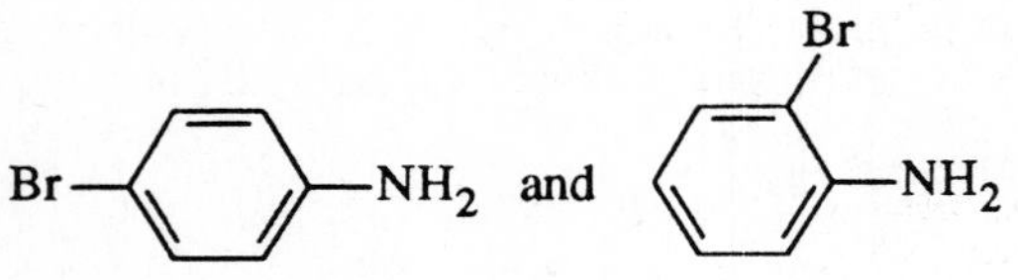

(c) Because of its positive charge, the substituent is a *meta* director; the *meta*-substitution product is formed:

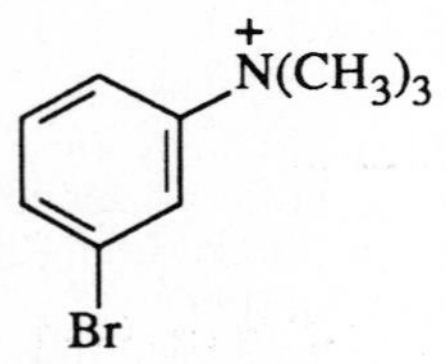

(d) Alkyl groups are *ortho, para* directors; hence, the products are *o-* and *p*-bromo-*t*-butylbenzene:

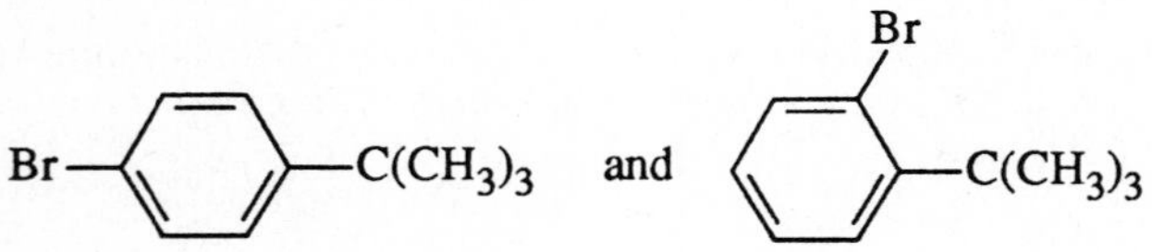

(e) The strong C—F bond dipoles place substantial positive charge on carbon; hence, the trifluoromethyl group is a *meta* director:

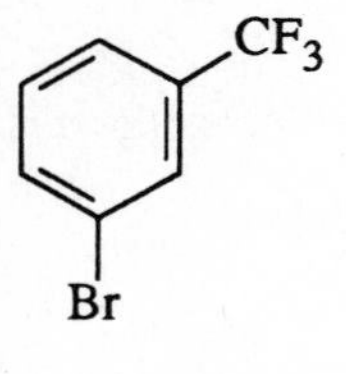

(f) The —O⁻ group has both unshared electron pairs and a negative charge with which to stabilize the carbocation intermediate; the substituent is an *ortho, para* director:

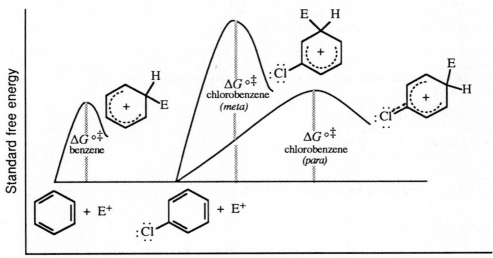

➤ If you draw the carbocation intermediate, you will see that it is not a cation at all, but a neutral species! (See Eq. 18.43, text page 741.)

23. As the alkyl substituent gets larger, there is a progressively smaller proportion of *ortho*-substitution product formed. This observation is consistent with the existence of a steric effect on substitution at the *ortho* position.

24.

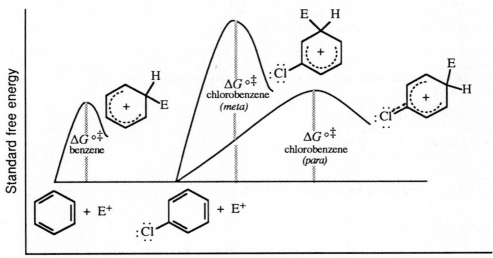

25. (a) Bromination of *N,N*-dimethylaniline is faster, because the dimethylamino group [—N(CH₃)₂] is an activating group.
(b) Nitration of anisole is faster. As we go down a column of the periodic table, the activating effect of substituents with unshared electron pairs decreases because of the involvement of orbitals with more nodes.

26. (a)   (b)

(c)

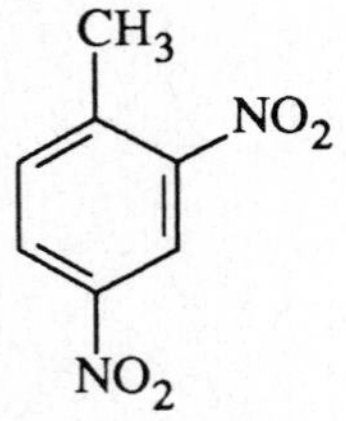

(d) 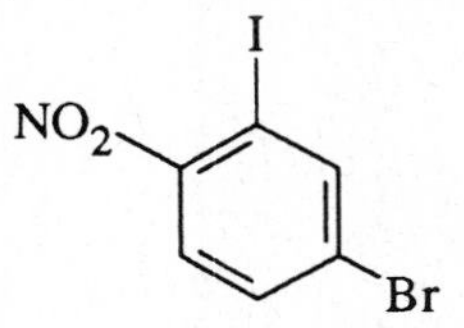 and

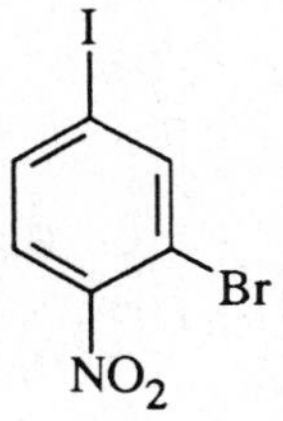

In (a), there is only one ring position at which mesitylene can brominate. In (b), both the bromo group and the methyl group are *ortho, para* directors, and there are two ring positions that satisfy both of these directing effects; hence, two products are formed. In (c), the first nitro group enters either *ortho* or *para* to the methyl group; entry of the second nitro group so as to satisfy the directing effects of both the first nitro group and the methyl group gives the product shown, 2,4-dinitrotoluene. In (d), there are two ring positions that satisfy the *ortho, para*-directing effects of both halogens. In both (b) and (d), there is a third product possible, the 1,2,3-trisubstituted material; however, this is likely to be minor in each case, since the transition state for its formation should be very congested.

27. *m*-xylene < benzene < *p*-dichlorobenzene. *m*-Xylene contains two activating groups, and a sulfonate group can enter so as to satisfy the directing effects of both. *p*-Dichlorobenzene contains two deactivating groups, and, furthermore, the sulfonate group cannot enter the ring at a position that satisfies the directing effects of both chlorines simultaneously.

28. In planning a synthesis using electrophilic aromatic substitution, we have to be concerned with the activating and directing effects of each successive group. If we nitrate first, subsequent Friedel–Crafts acylation, if it occurred, would take place at the *meta* position, as desired; but this reaction in fact will not occur, because the nitro group is too deactivating to permit a Friedel–Crafts reaction to take place (see text page 671). Hence, the acyl group must be introduced first:

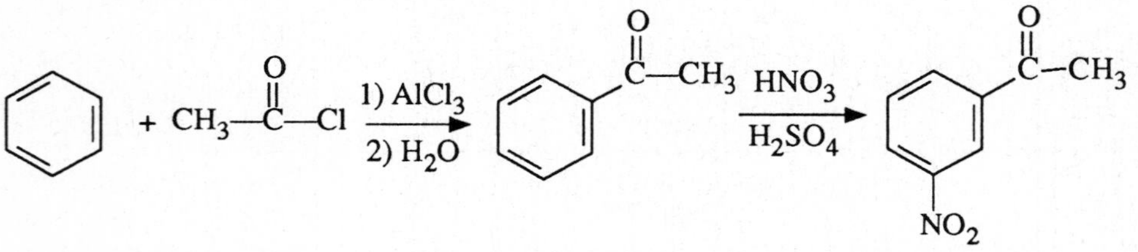

29. Preparation of the cyclohexane derivative is by hydrogenation of *t*-butylbenzene:

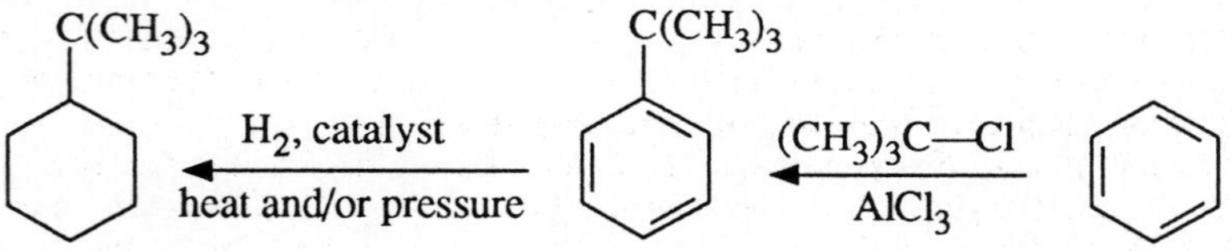

Solutions to Additional Problems

30. (a) No reaction.

(b) [structures: 4-nitrotoluene (CH_3 ... NO_2) + 2-nitrotoluene (CH_3, NO_2)]

(c) [structures: 4-methylbenzenesulfonic acid (CH_3 ... SO_3H) + 2-methylbenzenesulfonic acid (CH_3, SO_3H)]

(d) [structures: 4-propanoyltoluene (CH_3 ... $\overset{O}{\underset{}{C}}-C_2H_5$) + 2-propanoyltoluene ($CH_3$, $C(=O)-C_2H_5$)]

(e) [structures: 1,4-dimethylbenzene (CH_3 ... CH_3) + 1,2-dimethylbenzene (CH_3, CH_3)]

(f) [structures: 4-bromotoluene (CH_3 ... Br) + 2-bromotoluene (CH_3, Br)]

31. (a) Styrene, an alkene, will decolorize a solution of bromine in CCl_4.
    (b) Phenylacetylene, an alkyne, will liberate a gas when treated with C_2H_5MgBr, and will give a precipitate when treated with CuCl or $PbCl_2$.
    (c) Ethylbenzene, because it contains two more carbons, will have a boiling point that is 40–60° higher than that of benzene. Benzene will boil on a steam bath; ethylbenzene will not.

32. A compound that contains a benzene ring must have at least six carbons and four degrees of unsaturation. Compound (a) cannot contain a benzene ring because it has too few degrees of unsaturation; compound (c) cannot contain a benzene ring because it has too few carbons.

33. (a) *p*-dichlorobenzene < *m*-dichlorobenzene < *o*-dichlorobenzene. This follows from the relative orientations and vector additions of the C—Cl bond dipoles.
    (b) The order of boiling points is the same. The greater the dipole moment, the greater the attraction between molecules; and the greater the attraction between molecules, the greater the boiling point. (This principle was first discussed on text pages 282–283.)

34. (a) The order follows from the relative activating effects of the substituents: nitrobenzene < chlorobenzene < benzene.
    (b) In mesitylene, the three methyl groups all direct nitration to the same position; that is, they activate the same position of the ring. In 1,2,4-trimethylbenzene, only two of the three methyl groups activate the same ring position. Hence, the order is: toluene < 1,2,4-trimethylbenzene < mesitylene.
    (c) In *p*-chloroanisole, the chlorine and methoxy group direct to different positions; that is, the chlorine strongly deactivates the position that the methoxy group activates, and the methoxy group deactivates the positions that are least deactivated by the chlorine. In the *meta* isomer, the directing effects of the two substituents do not conflict. In anisole, the deactivating chloro group is absent altogether. The order is: *p*-chloroanisole < *m*-chloroanisole < anisole.
    (d) *p*-bromoacetophenone < acetophenone < *p*-methoxyacetophenone.

35. The unsaturation number of compounds *A* and *B* is 5; hence, both compounds could be aromatic. Because compound *C* is a hydrocarbon, reaction of *A* and *B* with sulfuric acid has effected the loss of oxygen. Dehydration of an alcohol would give these results. Indeed, compound *C* undergoes catalytic hydrogenation; hence, it is an alkene. If compounds *A* and *B* are alcohols, their —OH groups must be on adjacent carbons in order for them to dehydrate to the same alkene. Compound *D*, the hydrogenation product, has an unsaturation number of 5; nitration confirms that it and, by deduction, the other compounds, are aromatic. Since compound *D* can contain no ordinary double bonds (they would have hydrogenated), it must contain a ring *in addition to* the aromatic ring. The structures of the compounds that meet all these criteria are:

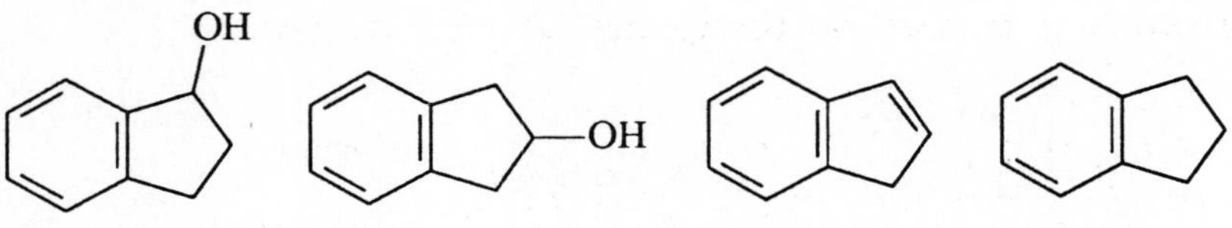

Notice that nitration of compound D can give only two products; what are they?

36. (a) We repeat the sequence in the problem below with each step numbered for reference:

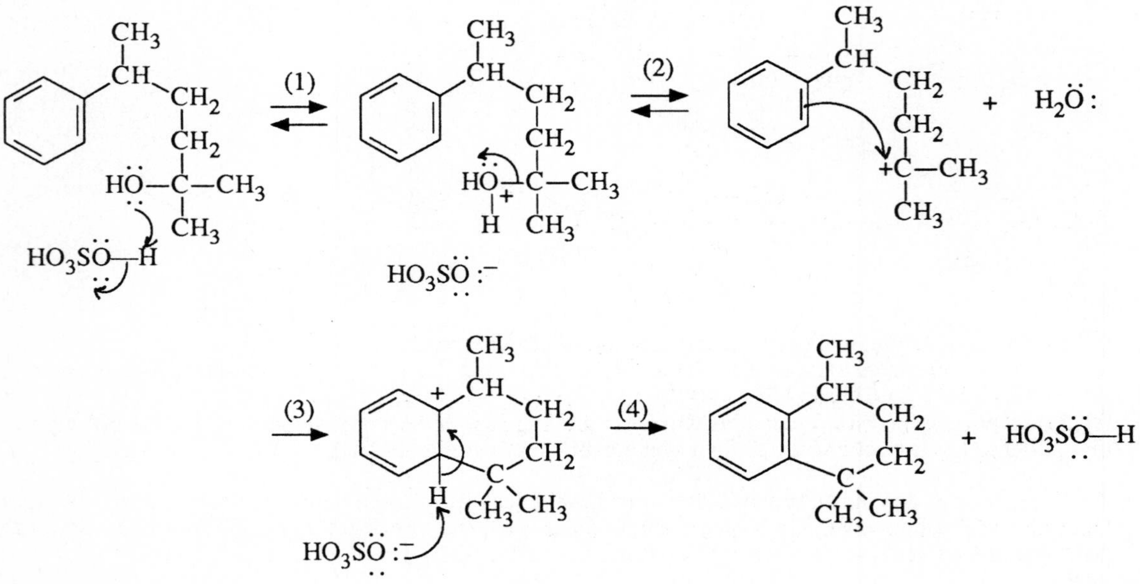

The electrophile, a carbocation, is generated by protonation of the —OH group and loss of water in steps (1) and (2); in step (3), the electrophile is attacked by the benzene π-electrons; and in step (4), a proton is removed to form the substituted aromatic ring.
(b) The curved arrows are shown in the scheme above.
(c) We shall outline the mechanism by showing the intermediates; if you have not already done so, provide the details of the curved-arrow formalism.

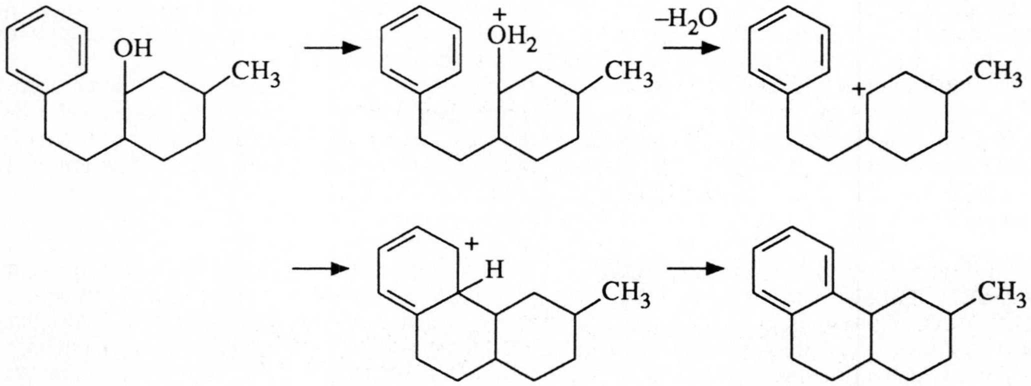

37. Following our usual practice, we'll begin with the target compound and work backward.

(a)

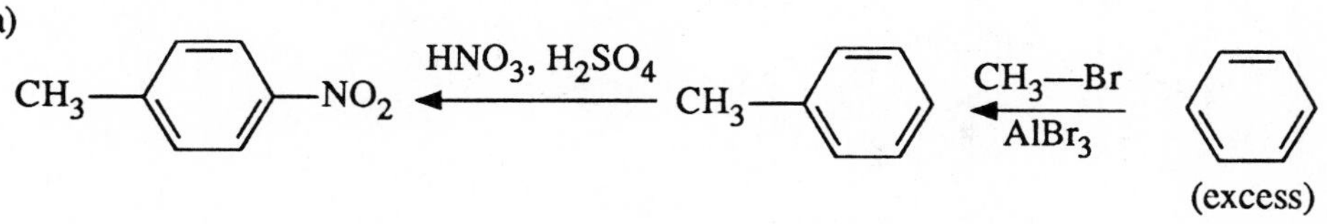

Following the nitration, *p*-nitrotoluene would have to be separated from *o*-nitrotoluene.

(b)

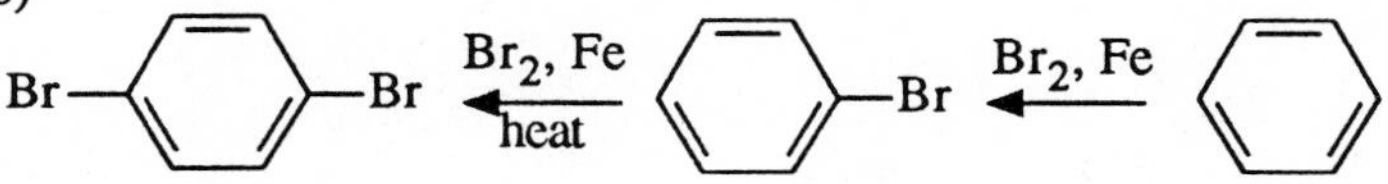

(c)

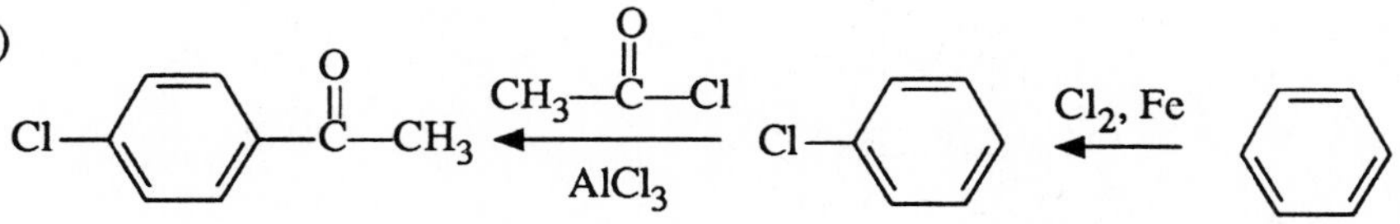

(d)

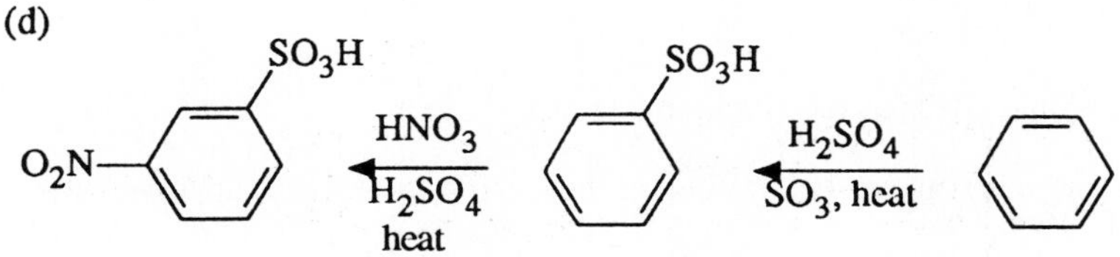

The order of these two steps could in principle be reversed.

(e)

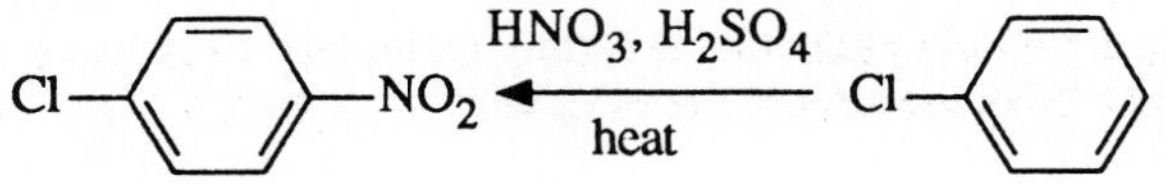

[prepared in part (c)]

(f) 1,3,5-Trinitrobenzene is prepared by three successive nitrations of benzene in a manner exactly analogous to that used for nitration of toluene in Eq. 16.42a–c, text page 671.

(g)

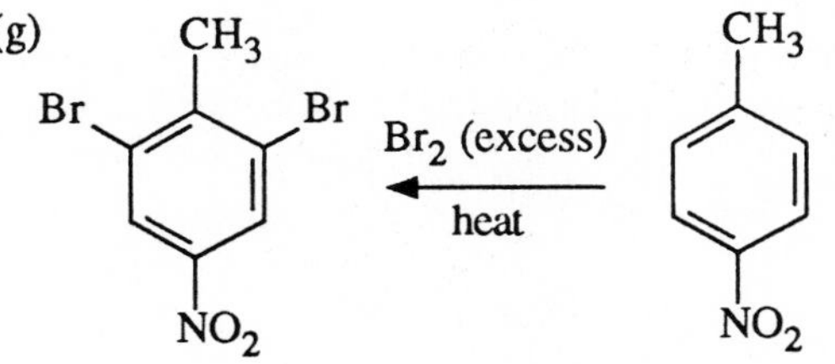

[prepared in part (a)]

(h)

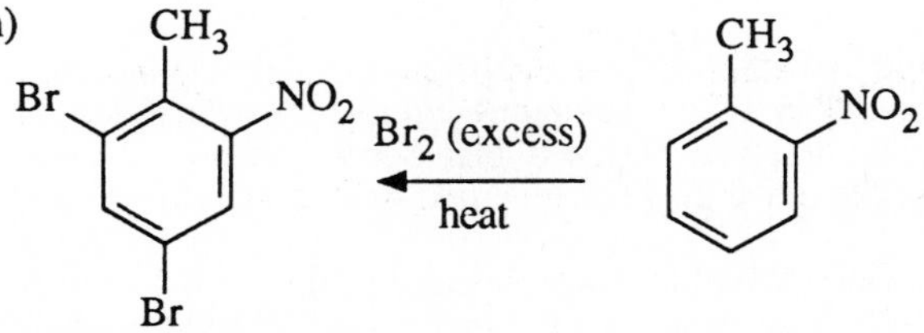

[as a by-product of the synthesis in part (a)]

(i)

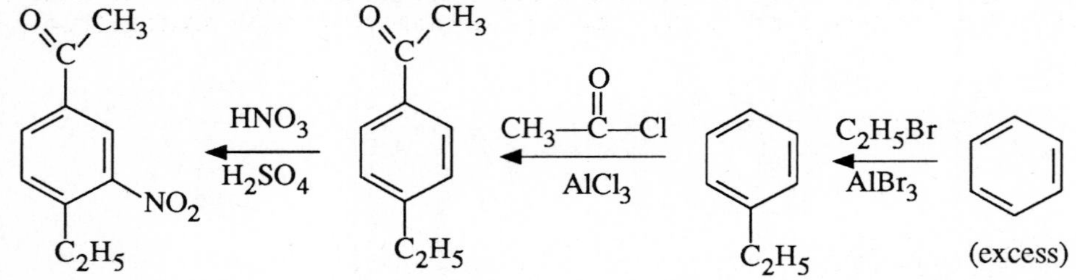

(j)

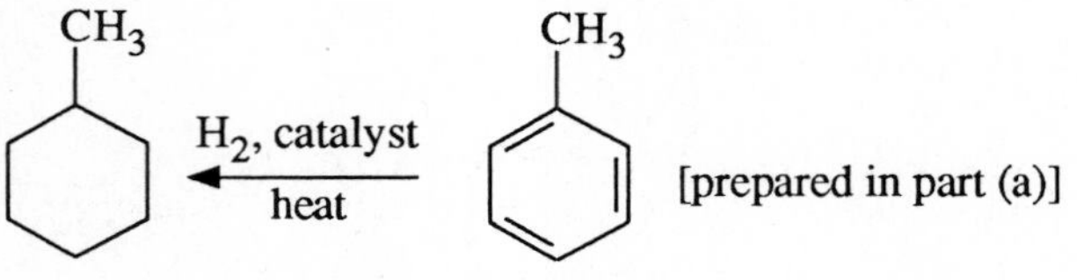

[prepared in part (a)]

(k)

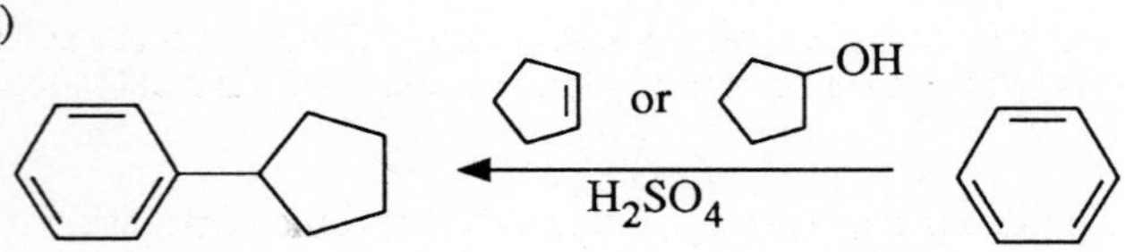

We could also use chlorocyclopentane and $AlCl_3$ as the alkylating agent.

38. The methyl groups in compounds (a) and (c) appear as one singlet; those in compound (b) appear as two singlets, because they are not chemically equivalent. Compounds (a) and (c) are differentiated by the relative integral of the aromatic protons, or by the presence of the resonance for the —CH_2— protons in (c) at about δ 4.5.

39. Compound *A* shows typical aromatic resonances for a *para*-substituted benzene ring, along with the telltale ethyl resonances; the ethyl quartet is in the benzylic region. Hence, we have a benzene ring substituted in its *para* positions with an ethyl group and a bromine. From the molecular formula, there is no unsaturation other than the benzene ring. What else can the compound be but *p*-bromoethylbenzene?

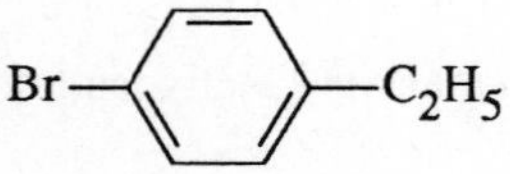

Compound *B* shows a five-proton aromatic resonance, a three-proton doublet, and a one-proton quartet. From the chemical shift of the quartet, this proton must be on a carbon that is adjacent to both the bromine and the benzene ring. The compound is (1-bromoethyl)benzene:

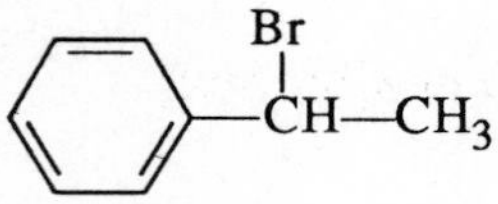

40. (a) The boron on benzeneboronic acid has an empty *p* orbital, and is not capable of stabilizing a carbocation by resonance. It would be difficult to introduce electron deficiency into a compound that is already electron deficient; hence, this compound undergoes substitution much more slowly than benzene itself. Since all deactivating groups other than the halogens are *meta* directors, the principal mononitration product will be *m*-nitrobenzeneboronic acid.

(b) The substituent has no unshared electrons with which to stabilize a carbocation, and its positive charge makes formation of a carbocation particularly difficult. The substituent is a *meta* director, and the product formed should be the *meta*-substitution product.

(c) One benzene ring is capable of stabilizing by resonance the carbocation formed during substitution into the other at an *ortho* or *para* position. Hence, the benzene ring is activating, and *ortho, para* directing:

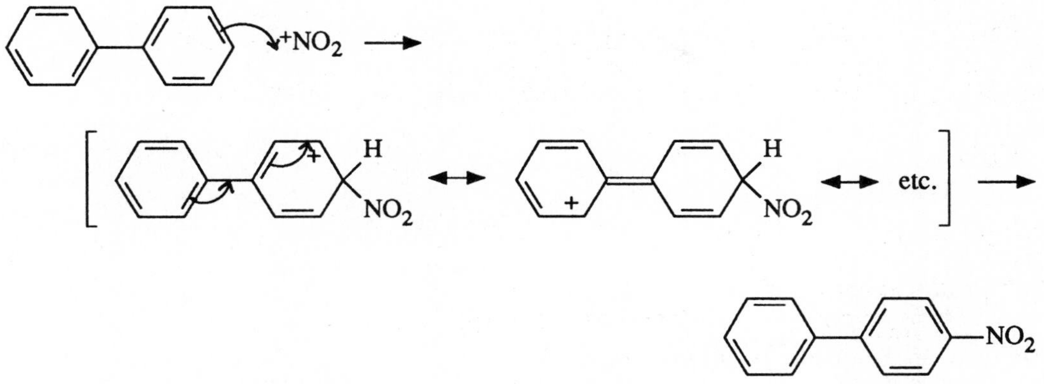

(You should draw the other resonance structures for the carbocation intermediate.) Substitution at the *ortho* position leads to analogous structures, but *meta* substitution does not. Hence, *ortho* and *para* substitution are observed.

(d) Both the methoxy and phenyl groups are *ortho, para* directors [see part (b)], and therefore direct substitution to the same positions of the benzene ring. The major products are:

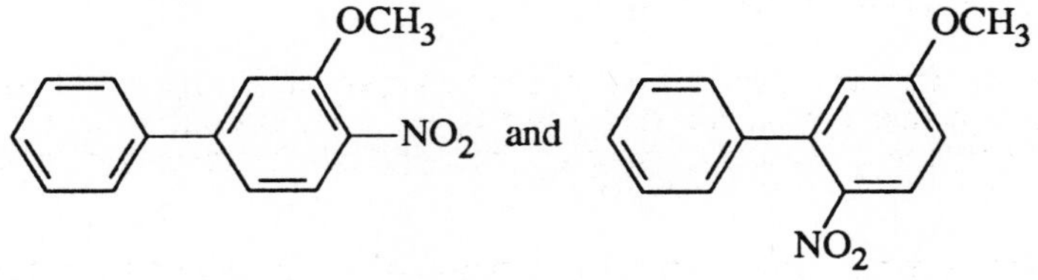

A third substitution product consistent with both directing effects is possible, but it should be relatively minor because the nitro group would be *ortho* to both substituents.

41. (a) The electrophile is "D$^+$" of D$_2$SO$_4$; this is introduced into the *ortho* and *para* positions:

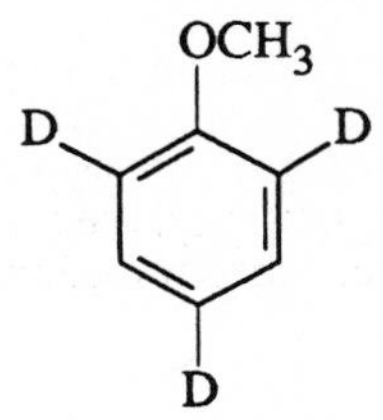

(b) Both alkyl halide groups can react in separate Friedel–Crafts alkylation reactions of benzene:

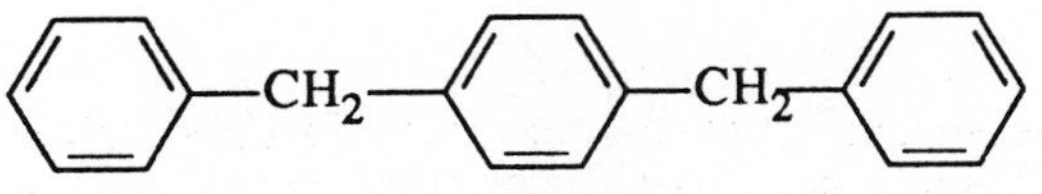

(c) The cyclohexyl ring is merely a large alkyl substituent that directs substitution to the *ortho* and *para* positions of the benzene ring:

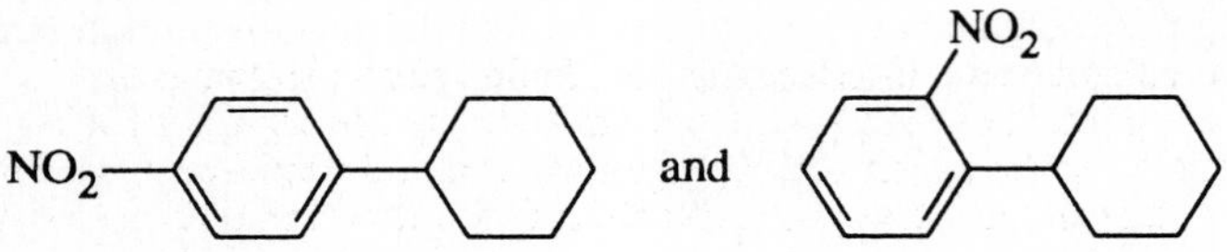

NO$_2$— (cyclohexyl-substituted nitrobenzene)   and   (ortho nitro cyclohexylbenzene)

(d) Ferrocene, like other aromatic compounds, undergoes Friedel–Crafts acylation reactions:

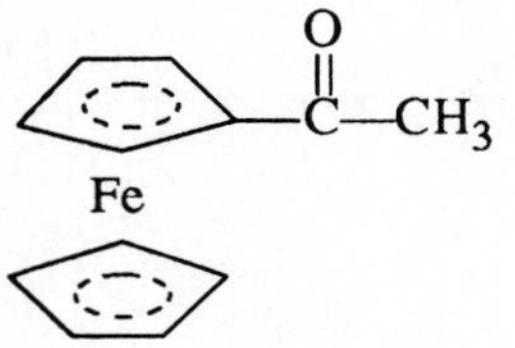

(e) The nitro group is introduced *ortho* to the methoxy substituent and *meta* to the sulfonic acid substituent; the bromine is introduced *ortho* to the methoxy group, the only position that simultaneously satisfies the directing effects of all substituents:

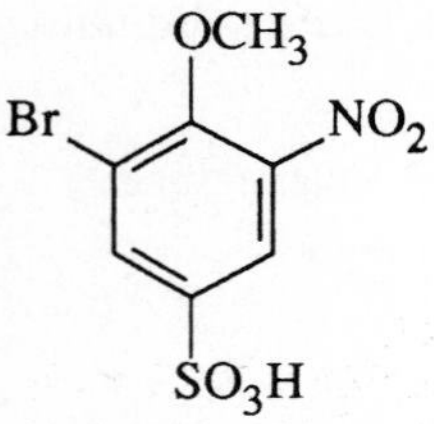

(f) The hint suggests that the reaction is intramolecular. Since the conditions suggest a Friedel–Crafts reaction, it is reasonable that the product results from a Friedel–Crafts cyclization:

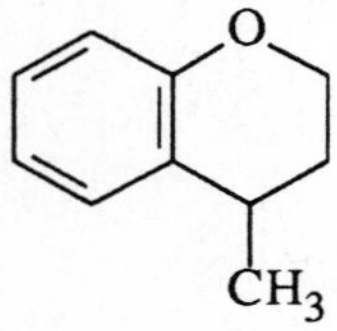

(g) Naphthalene has ten carbons, and the product has fifteen; hence, one equivalent of the acylating reagent is introduced. Since there is no chlorine in the product, the reaction must involve a double acylation by both ends of the naphthalene ring by the acid chloride. The only way that this can occur with the formation of rings of reasonable size is for the acylation to occur across *ortho* positions of the naphthalene ring, or across the *peri* positions, the two positions on either side of the ring junction. These three possibilities account for the three products:

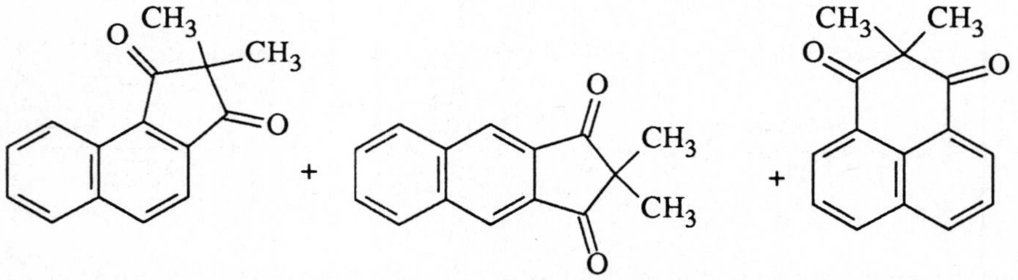

|——— products of *ortho* diacylation ———| product of *peri* acylation

In each case, the two acylation reactions occur as consecutive reactions — that is, one after the other, rather than at the same time.

42. Reaction of a halogen-containing compound with sodium ethoxide to give a hydrocarbon suggests an E2 reaction to give an alkene. Indeed, the NMR spectrum of the product contains alkene absorption as well as aromatic absorption. On the assumption that the reaction with sodium ethoxide is an elimination, it would bring about the loss of the elements of HBr from the starting material; the molecular formula of the alkene (compound B) would then be C_9H_{10}. The unsaturation number of this compound is 5, which accounts for the aromatic ring and an additional double bond. The correct structures for the unknowns are:

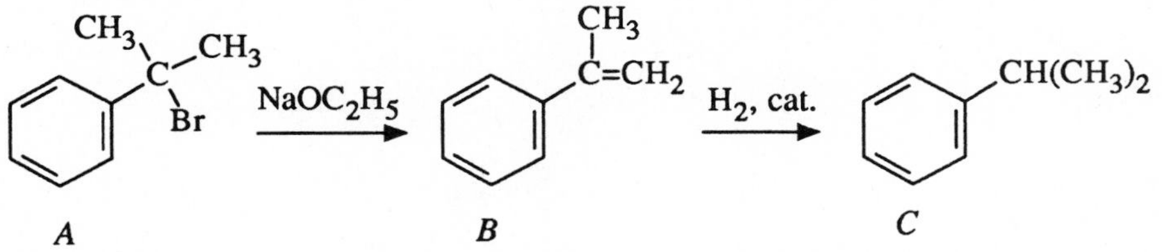

Notice in the NMR spectrum of compound B that the methyl group is a broad singlet. The following structure for compound B is ruled out by the absence of splitting in the —CH_3 signal:

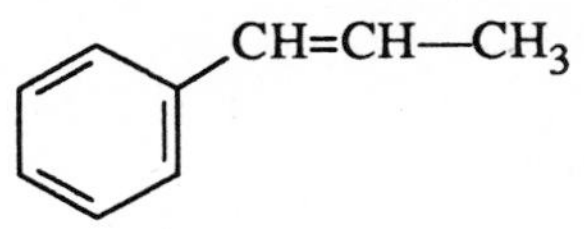

43. (a) The required $\Delta H°$ is the sum of the $\Delta H°$ values in Eqs. 16.45a–c: –49.0 kcal/mol.
(b) The $\Delta H°$ for hydrogenation of three cyclohexenes is $3 \times (-28.3) = -84.9$ kcal/mol.
(c) The discrepancy between these two quantities is 35.9 kcal/mol; that is, about 36 kcal/mol less heat is liberated when benzene is hydrogenated than we would expect from the hydrogenation of three alkenes. This number is remarkably close to the empirical resonance energy of benzene calculated by comparison of its heat of formation with that of cyclooctatetraene (COT) on text page 620.

44. (a) One of the best ways to introduce a hydrogen or deuterium is to treat a Grignard reagent with water or deuterium oxide:

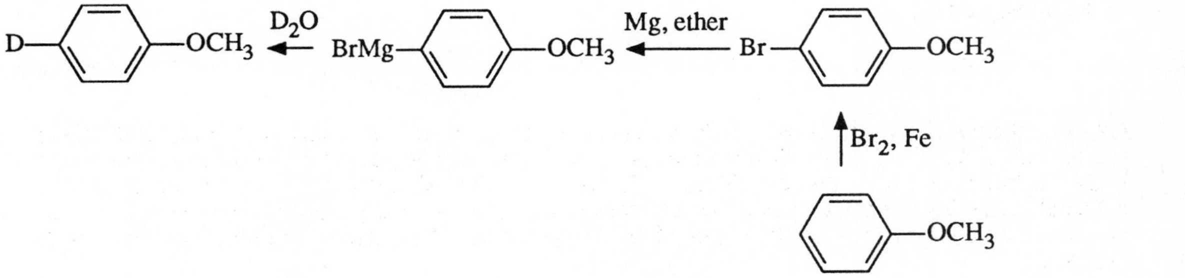

(b)

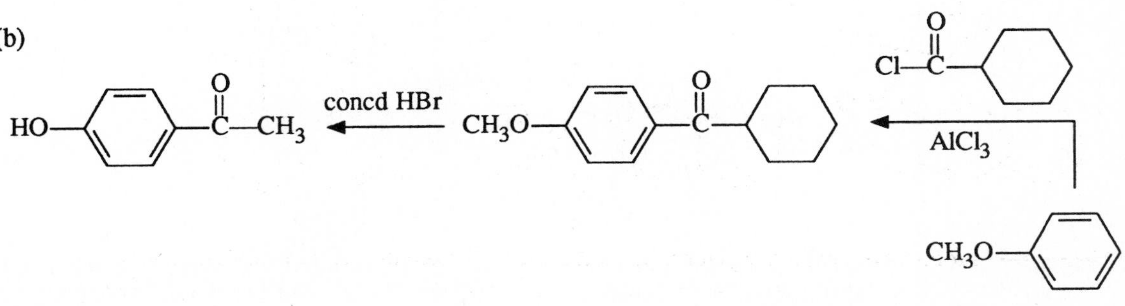

45. (a) *p*-Dibromobenzene can give only one mononitro derivative; hence, it must be compound *A*. *o*-Dibromobenzene can give two mononitro derivatives, and is therefore compound *B*. *m*-Dibromobenzene is compound *C*.

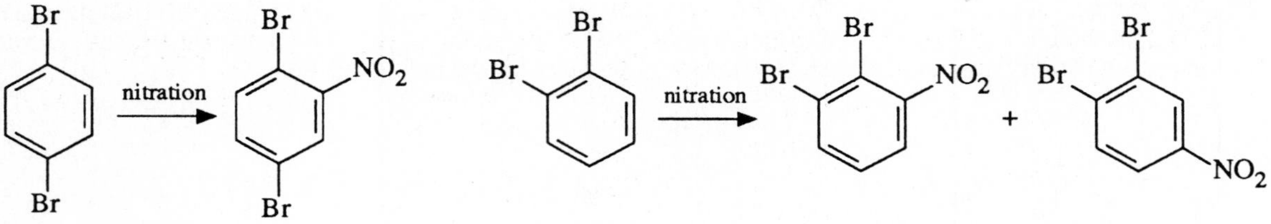

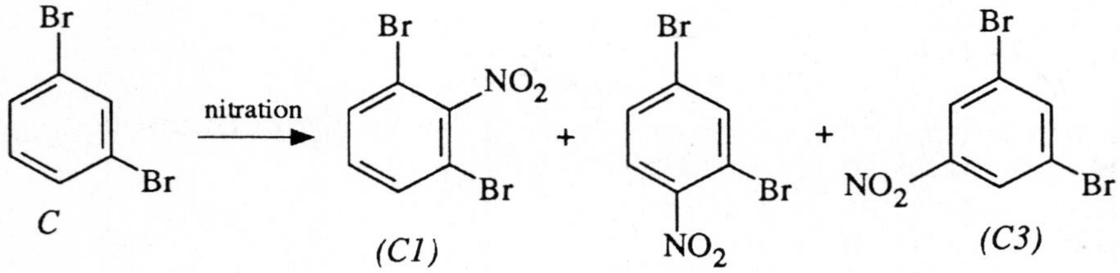

(b)

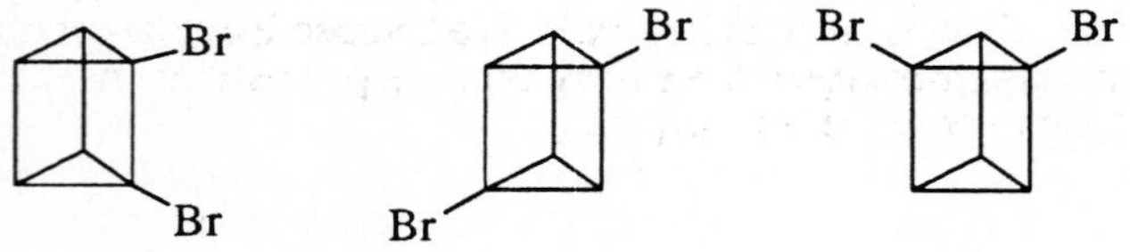

(We leave it to you to draw the mononitro derivatives of each compound.)

(c) Compounds *C1* and *C3* were probably formed in smallest amount. The transition state for formation of compound *C1* is sterically crowded; the formation of compound *C3* satisfies the directing effect of neither bromine substituent.

46. (a) The resonance structures of this anion show that all of its CH groups are equivalent. (These resonance structures are drawn out in the solution to Problem 45b in Chapter 15.)
(b) This compound is aromatic (ten π-electrons); hence, there is a significant ring current present when this compound is situated in a magnetic field. The methyl group is in the *shielding* part of this ring current, and therefore it takes a large magnetic field to bring the methyl hydrogens into resonance. (See the solution to Problem 4b in this chapter for a similar effect.)
(c) The electron density of the unshared pairs on the methoxy group is delocalized to the *ortho* and *para* positions of the ring, but not to the *meta* position:

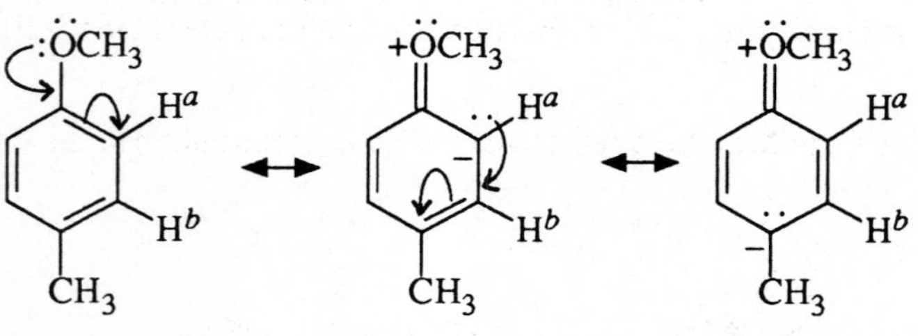

Because H^a is at an *ortho* position, there is more electron density at this proton than there is at proton H^b. Since greater electron density brings about greater shielding (Sec. 13.2D, text page 501), the chemical shift of proton H^a is smaller.

47. When 1,3,5-trimethoxybenzene protonates on a carbon of the ring, the resulting carbocation is stabilized by resonance interaction with each of the methoxy groups:

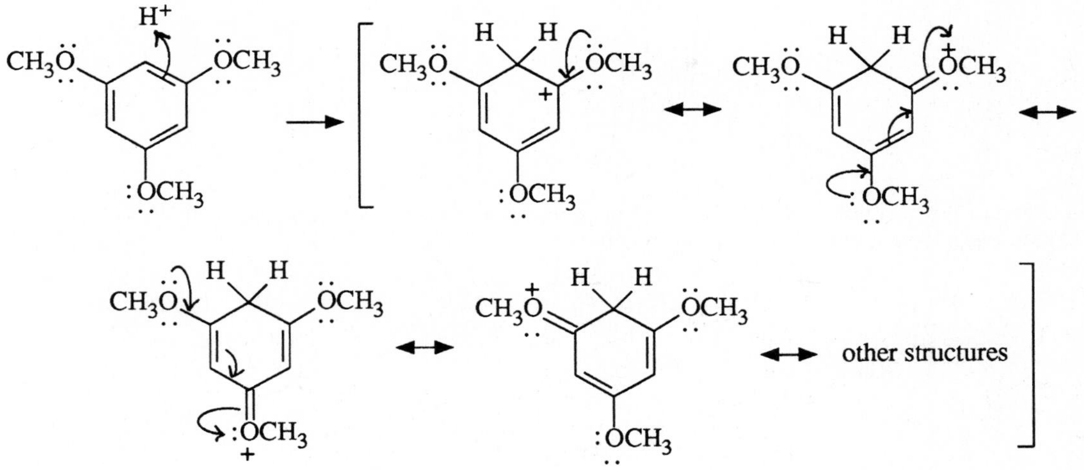

When 1,3,5-trimethoxybenzene protonates on the ether oxygen, there is no resonance stabilization of the resulting carbocation. In the case of anisole (methoxybenzene) itself, the same considerations apply; however, the resonance stabilization of the ring-protonated carbocation is less extensive because it involves only one methoxy group. The data suggest that the intrinsic basicity of the ether oxygen is greater than that of an aromatic double bond. Hence, anisole protonates on the ether oxygen:

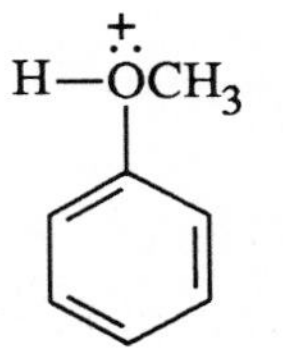

protonated anisole

It takes the enhanced resonance stabilization of all three methoxy groups of 1,3,5-trimethoxybenzene to tilt the balance from oxygen protonation to carbon protonation.

48. The reactivity order is (b) < (a) < (d) < (c). Compound (c) is most reactive because the substituent has an unshared electron pair that can be used to stabilize the intermediate carbocation by resonance. Compounds (a) and (d) are alkyl substituents, which stabilize carbocations; however, the alkyl group of compound (a) contains a positively charged group that would interact unfavorably with a carbocation, offsetting the stabilizing effect of the alkyl carbon. Compound (b) has a positively charged, electronegative substituent attached directly to the ring that would interact most unfavorably with the carbocation. Compounds (c) and (d) will undergo substitution in the *ortho* and *para* positions; compound (b) would undergo substitution in the *meta* position; and the position of substitution in compound (a) would depend on the balance of the stabilizing effect of the alkyl group and the destabilizing effect of the positive charge. (In fact, this compound brominates in the *ortho* and *para* positions.)

49. In order for diphenylsulfone to form, a molecule of benzene must have attacked an electrophile in the following manner:

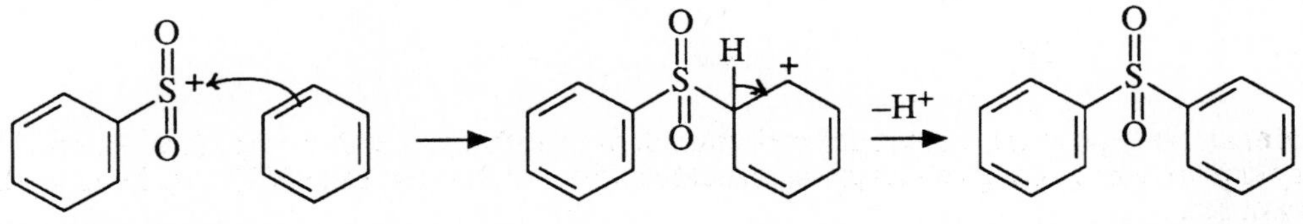

electrophile

The electrophile, in turn, is generated by protonation of benzenesulfonic acid and loss of water:

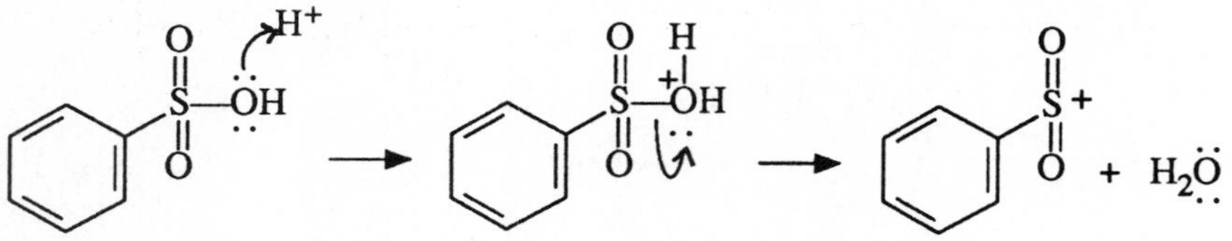

50. (a) Reaction of the nitronium ion (the electrophile in nitration) at the 1-position of naphthalene gives a carbocation intermediate with seven resonance structures:

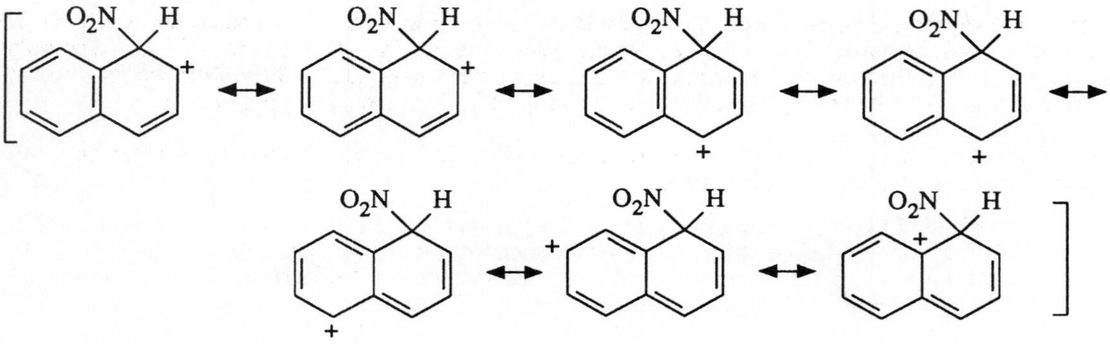

Reaction of the nitronium ion at the 2-position gives a carbocation intermediate with fewer resonance structures (draw these!). The ion with more resonance structures is more stable; by Hammond's postulate, the more stable ion is formed more rapidly.

(b) The answer depends on whether the unshared electron pairs on the oxygen of the methoxy group can be used to delocalize the positive charge in the carbocation intermediate. In fact, this delocalization is possible:

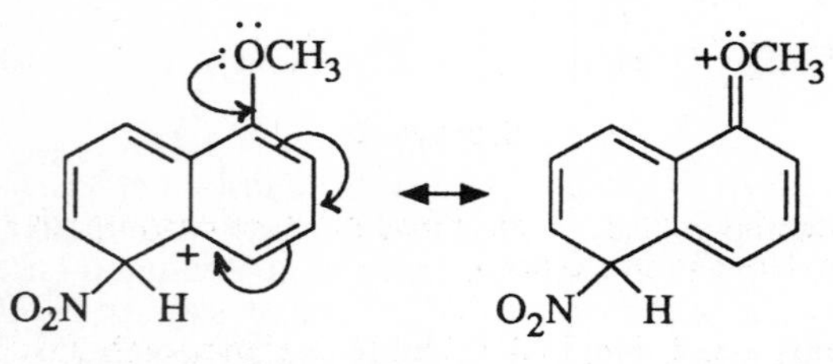

Thus, a methoxy substituent at carbon-1 accelerates nitration at carbon-5 because it stabilizes the intermediate carbocation and, by Hammond's postulate, the transition state for its formation.

51. Parts (a) and (b) are electrophilic aromatic substitution reactions. The essence of the problem in each case is how the electrophile is generated.

(a) From the structure of the product, the electrophile must be the following carbocation:

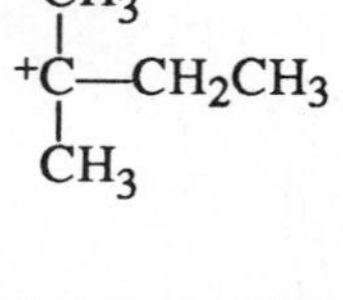

$$\overset{\displaystyle CH_3}{\underset{\displaystyle CH_3}{\overset{|}{\underset{|}{^+C}}}}-CH_2CH_3$$

This is formed by reaction of the alcohol with the Lewis acid BF_3, loss of the leaving group $HO{-}\overset{-}{B}F_3$, and rearrangement of the resulting carbocation:

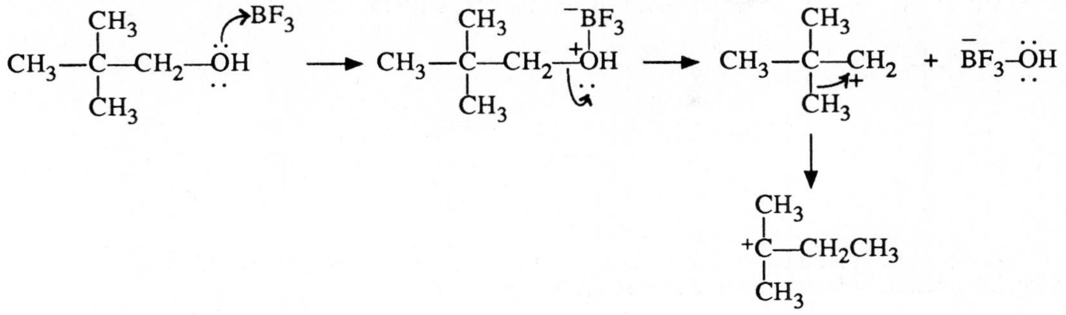

(Recall that we can treat Lewis acids as "fat protons"; that is, for mechanistic purposes, we handle them just as we would handle protons. Were the BF_3 a proton instead, the leaving group would be H_2O.) The carbocation is then attacked by the benzene π-electrons in the usual mechanism of electrophilic aromatic substitution. (We leave it to you to complete the mechanism. If you have difficulty, re-read text page 650.)

(b) The electrophile in this case is formed by protonation of the hydroxy group, loss of water, and rearrangement of the resulting carbocation:

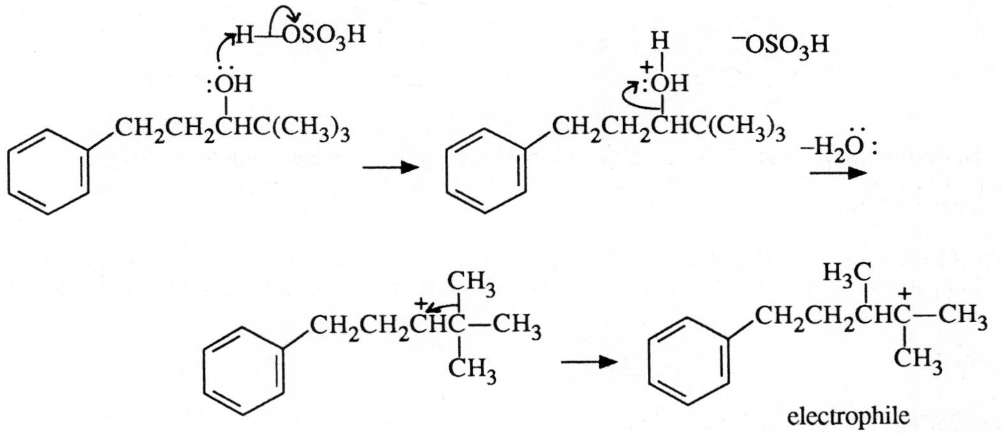

The electron-deficient carbon is then attacked by the benzene π-electrons in an *intramolecular* electrophilic aromatic substitution reaction. (We leave it to you to complete the mechanism.)

(c) In most electrophilic aromatic substitution reactions, a proton is lost in the final step of the mechanism to generate a substituted benzene derivative. In this case, however, a *t*-butyl cation is lost. This carbocation then loses a β-proton to give the by-product isobutylene:

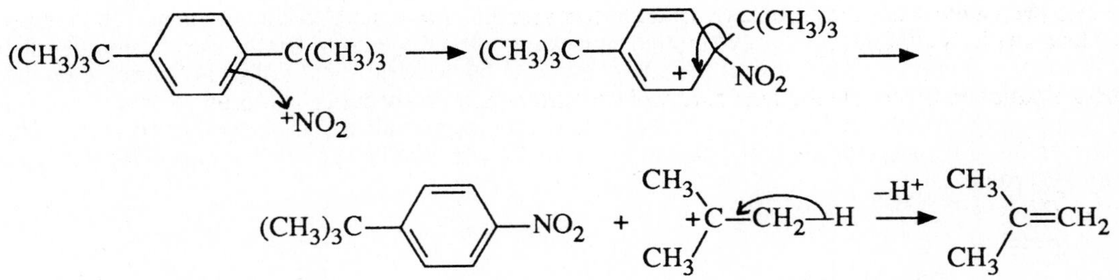

(d) The first step of this transformation is a Diels–Alder reaction to give the bicyclic ether A:

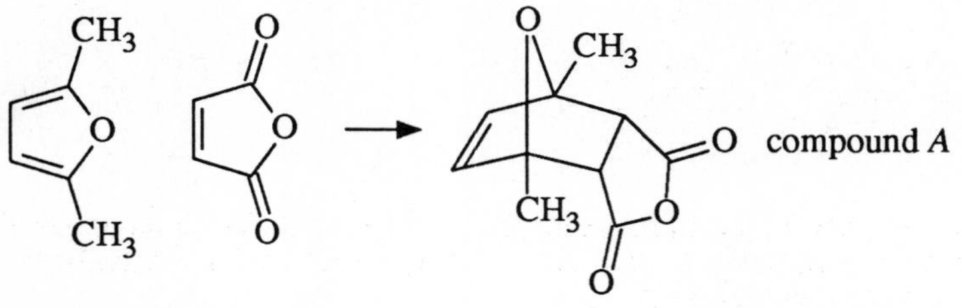

Protonation of compound A and loss of water give the aromatic product:

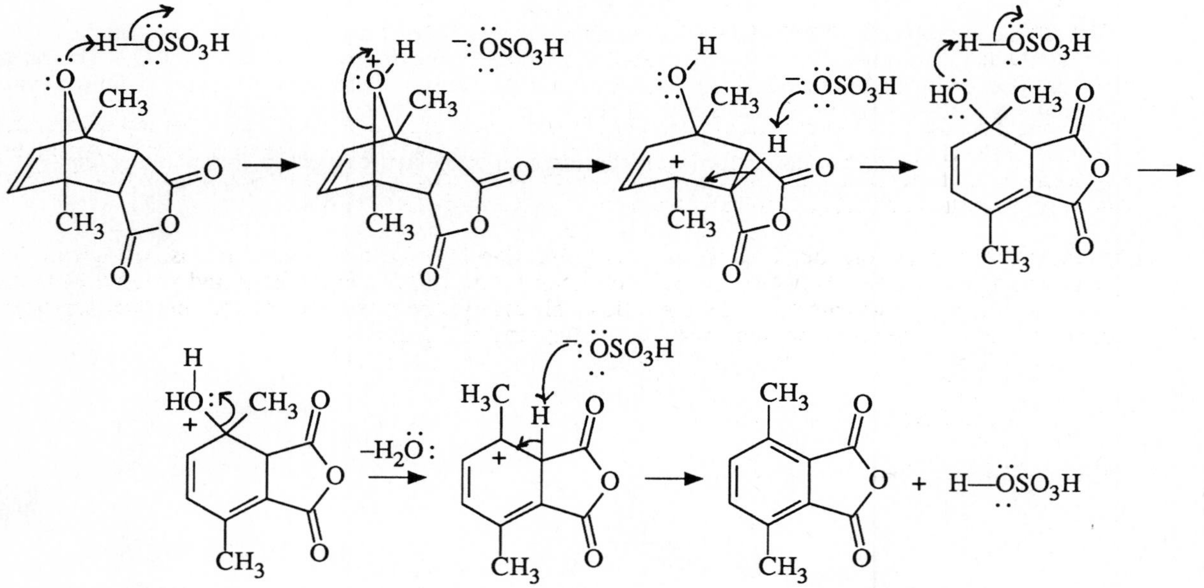

52. (a) The $p + 2$ peak in the mass spectrum suggests the presence of one chlorine; the singlet at $\delta\,3.72$ suggests a methoxy group; and the aromatic signals suggest a *para*-substituted benzene ring. Compound A is *p*-chloroanisole:

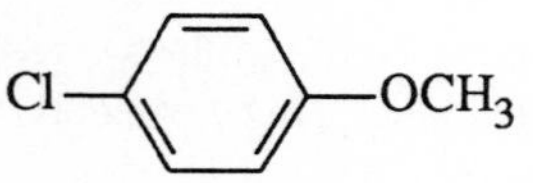

(b) The IR spectrum indicates the presence of an alkene double bond; the NMR shows aromatic protons as well as alkene protons; and the UV spectrum indicates extensive conjugation. On the assumption that the peak at $\delta\,3.7$ is due to a methoxy group, we can take its integral to be three protons. If this is correct, then the apparent aromatic doublet of doublets at $\delta\,6.6$–7.4 integrates for four protons. This, as well as the splitting pattern, suggests a *para*-substituted aromatic ring. The remaining signals integrate for three protons, and are in the alkene region. The —CH=CH$_2$ is the alkene functional group that has three alkene protons. Compound B is *p*-methoxystyrene:

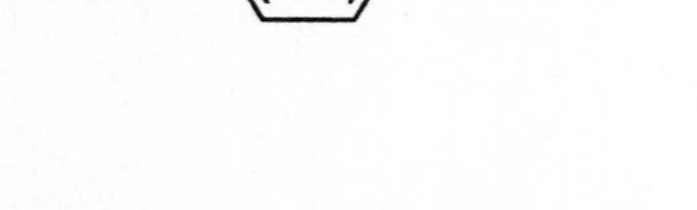

53. In *p*-nitroanisole, there is a strong resonance interaction between the methoxy group and the nitro group:

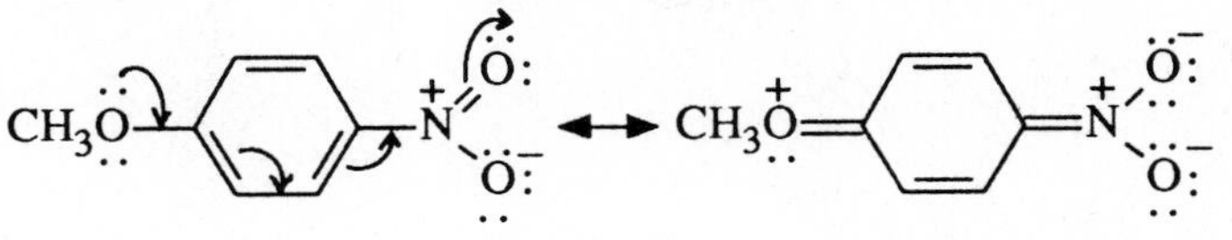

The second structure is relatively important; hence, there is considerable charge separation in the molecule, and a rather large dipole moment. In *p*-chloronitrobenzene, there is an analogous structure that results from resonance interaction of the chlorine lone pairs with the ring:

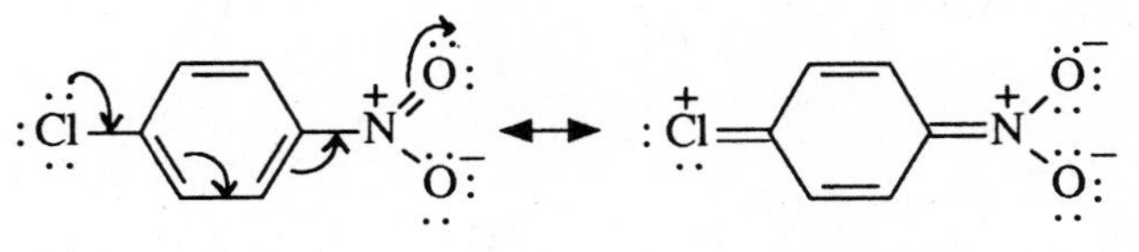

However, because the chlorine electrons are in orbitals of quantum number = 3, their overlap with the carbon orbitals of the ring is much less effective. (See Figure 16.10 and the associated discussion.) Hence, this structure is relatively less important. As a result, there is less charge separation in *p*-chloronitrobenzene than there is in *p*-nitroanisole, and the dipole moment of *p*-chloronitrobenzene is smaller.

54. At the higher temperature, the two *ortho* methyl groups (labeled *a*) are equivalent because rotation of the isopropyl group is rapid. However, at the lower temperature, rotation of the isopropyl group is slow, and the two *ortho* methyl groups are no longer equivalent. Evidently, one is wedged between the two isopropyl methyls, and the other is in the same plane as the isopropyl CH group:

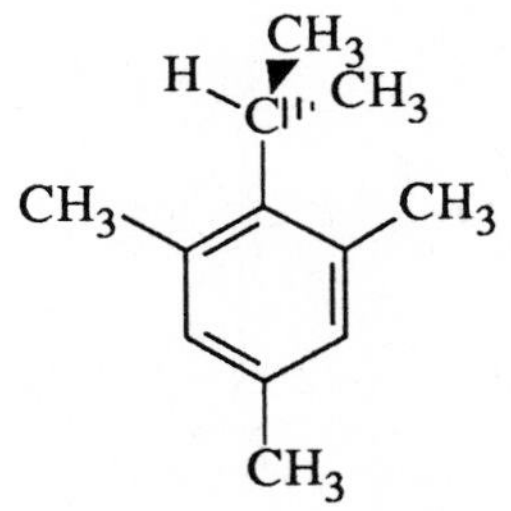

(Notice that if the isopropyl group were turned so that its CH bond is perpendicular to the plane of the benzene ring, the two *ortho* methyl groups would be equivalent. The observed nonequivalence rules out such a conformation.) Because the two *ortho* methyl groups are in different chemical environments, their chemical shifts are different. Hence, there is a distinct resonance for each *ortho* methyl group, and a third signal for the *para* methyl group.

Chapter 17 / Allylic and Benzylic Reactivity

CHAPTER 17 TERMS

allylic group .... Introduction
allylic radical 17.2
benzylic group .... Introduction
benzylic radical 17.2
biosynthesis 17.6B
diterpene 17.6A
essential oil 17.6A

isoprene rule 17.6A
isoprenoid 17.6A
monoterpene 17.6A
pyrophosphate group 17.6B
sesquiterpene 17.6A
terpene 17.6A

CHAPTER 17 CONCEPTS

I. Allylic and Benzylic Species:

A. Introduction:
1. An **allylic group** is a group on a carbon adjacent to a double bond.
2. A **benzylic group** is a group on a carbon adjacent to a benzene ring.
3. In many situations allylic and benzylic groups are unusually reactive.

B. Allylic and Benzylic Cations—S_N1 Reactions:
1. Allylic and benzylic carbocations are resonance stabilized.
a) In an allylic cation, charge is shared between two carbons; *two* products are formed when a nucleophile attacks such a cation, because there are two electron-deficient carbons.

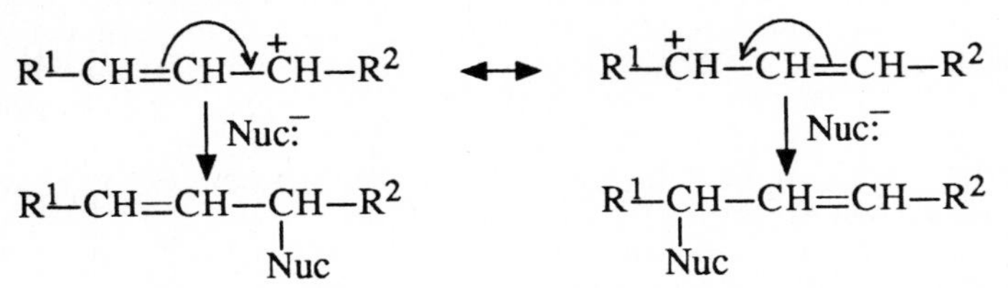

b) The charge on a benzylic carbocation is shared not only by the benzylic carbon, but also by alternate carbons of the ring. When a nucleophile attacks a benzylic cation, *one* product is formed, because the products formed by attack of the nucleophile at the other electron-deficient carbons are not aromatic, and thus lack the stability associated with the aromatic ring.

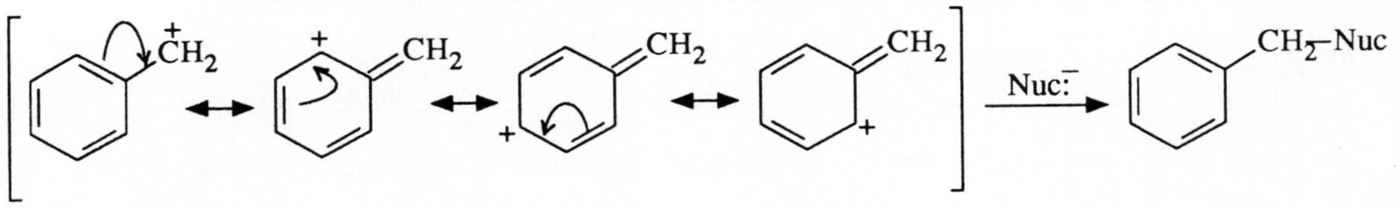

2. Allylic and benzylic alkyl halides are considerably more reactive in S_N1 reactions than their comparably substituted nonallylic or nonbenzylic counterparts.
   a) The greater reactivity of allylic and benzylic halides is due to resonance stabilization of the carbocation intermediates that are formed when they react.
   b) *Ortho* and *para* substituent groups on the benzene ring that activate electrophilic aromatic substitution accelerate S_N1 reactions at the benzylic position even further.
   c) Other reactions that involve carbocation intermediates are also accelerated when the carbocations are allylic or benzylic.

C. Allylic and Benzylic Radicals—Allylic and Benzylic Bromination:
   1. **Allylic** and **benzylic radicals** are readily formed as reactive intermediates.
      a) Allylic radicals:
         (1) Have an unpaired electron at an allylic position.
         (2) Are resonance stabilized.
         (3) Are more stable than comparably substituted nonallylic radicals.

$$CH_2=CH-CH_2-H \xrightarrow[-HX]{X\cdot} \left[CH_2=CH-\dot{C}H_2 \longleftrightarrow \dot{C}H_2-CH=CH_2 \right]$$

      b) Benzylic radicals:
         (1) Have an unpaired electron at a benzylic position.
         (2) Are resonance stabilized.
         (3) Are more stable than comparably substituted nonbenzylic radicals.

   2. The addition of halogen to the alkene double bond is a competing reaction in the case of allylic bromination that is *not* observed with benzylic bromination.
      a) Only addition occurs when an alkene reacts with bromine in the dark at room temperature.
      b) The substitution reaction occurs in the presence of light and heat at very low bromine concentrations.
         (1) *N*-Bromosuccinimide (**NBS**) effectively produces bromine in very low concentrations.
         (2) NBS can be used to effect allylic and benzylic bromination.

D. Allylic and Benzylic Grignard Reagents:
   1. Allylic and benzylic Grignard reagents form easily.
      a) An important side reaction occurs during their formation that does not occur with other Grignard reagents.
      b) The Grignard reagent attacks the alkyl halide from which it is formed to give a coupling product.
         (1) The coupling reaction can be avoided if formation of the Grignard reagent is carried out in relatively dilute solution.
         (2) The rates of the two competing reactions—formation of the Grignard reagent and coupling—respond differently to changes in the alkyl halide concentration.
   2. Allylic and benzylic Grignard reagents resemble **allylic** and **benzylic carbanions**, respectively.
      a) Allylic and benzylic anions are resonance stabilized.
      b) The carbon–magnesium bonds of allylic and benzylic Grignard reagents have more ionic character than the carbon–magnesium bonds of other Grignard reagents.
   3. If the Grignard reagent is unsymmetrical, an allylic Grignard reagent is actually a rapid equilibrating mixture of *two different* reagents.

$$CH_3-CH=CH-CH_2-Br \xrightarrow[ether]{Mg} CH_3-CH=CH-CH_2-MgBr \rightleftarrows \underset{\textstyle CH_3-\overset{\textstyle |}{\underset{\textstyle}{C}H}-CH=CH_2}{\overset{\textstyle MgBr}{}}$$

E. Allylic and Benzylic S_N2 Reactions:
   1. Allylic and benzylic S_N2 reactions are accelerated—the energies of their transition states are reduced by *p*-orbital overlap.
      a) In the transition state of the S_N2 reaction, the carbon at which substitution occurs is sp^2 hybridized.

b) The incoming nucleophile and the departing leaving group are partially bonded to a *p* orbital on this carbon.

c) Overlap of this *p* orbital with the *p* orbitals of an adjacent double bond or phenyl ring provides additional bonding in the transition state that lowers its energy and accelerates the reaction.

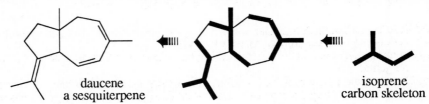

II. The Isoprene Rule—Biosynthesis of Terpenes:

A. <u>Essential Oils and Terpenes</u>:

1. Volatile, pleasant-smelling substances obtained from plants are called **essential oils**.

2. **Terpenes** (also called **isoprenoids**) are a class of natural products with similar atomic composition; many of these compounds are familiar natural flavorings or fragrances.

3. The basis of the terpene classification is the connectivity of the carbon skeleton.

a) All terpenes consist of repeating units that have the same carbon skeleton as the five-carbon diene **isoprene** (the isoprene rule); in many (but not all) terpenes, the isoprene units are connected in a "head-to-tail" arrangement.

b) Their carbon skeletons contain multiples of five carbon atoms (10, 15, 20, ... 5*n*).

(1) **Monoterpenes** have ten carbon atoms in their carbon chains.

(2) **Sesquiterpenes** have fifteen carbon atoms in their carbon chains.

(3) **Diterpenes** have twenty carbon atoms in their carbon chains.

c) Some compounds, such as steroids, are derived from terpenes by skeletal rearrangements.

d) Different terpenes may have the same carbon skeleton functionalized in different ways.

4. Criteria for terpene classification are:

a) A multiple of five carbon atoms in the main carbon chain.

b) The formal carbon connectivity of the isoprene carbon skeleton within each five-carbon unit.

daucene
a sesquiterpene

isoprene
carbon skeleton

B. <u>Biosynthesis of Terpenes</u>:

1. **Biosynthesis** is the synthesis of chemical compounds by living organisms.

2. The repetitive isoprene units in all terpenes have a common origin in two simple five-carbon compounds (structures on text page 702, Eq. 17.34):

a) Isopentenyl pyrophosphate (**IPP**).

b) *γ,γ*-Dimethylallyl pyrophosphate (**DMAP**).

c) Alkyl pyrophosphates are esters of the inorganic acid pyrophosphoric acid.

(1) Pyrophosphate and phosphate are "nature's leaving groups."

(2) IPP and DMAP are readily interconverted in living systems catalytically by an enzyme.

3. Introduction of oxygen substituents into terpene skeletons can occur by:

a) Attack of water on carbocation intermediates.

b) Displacement of pyrophosphates by water.

c) Oxidation reactions in which hydrogen atoms are replaced by oxygen-containing groups.

CHAPTER 17 REACTIONS

I. Allylic and Benzylic Substitution Reactions:

A. <u>Bromination with NBS</u>:
   1. Mechanism of allylic bromination with NBS:
      a) Formation of a bromine atom by the dissociation of the N—Br bond in NBS is the first step.

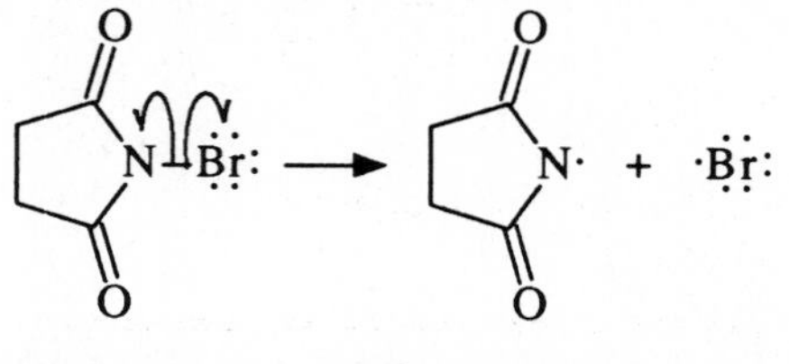

   b) The ensuing substitution reaction has three propagation steps:
      (1) The bromine atom abstracts an allylic hydrogen from the alkene molecule.

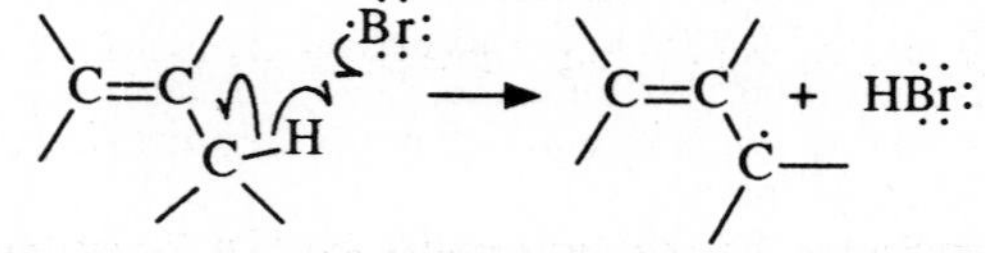

      (2) The HBr thus formed reacts with the NBS in the second propagation step to produce a Br_2 molecule.

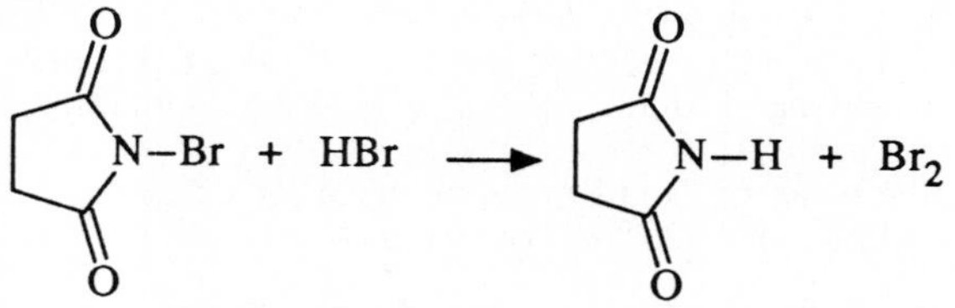

      (3) The last propagation step is the reaction of this bromine molecule with the radical formed in the first propagation step.

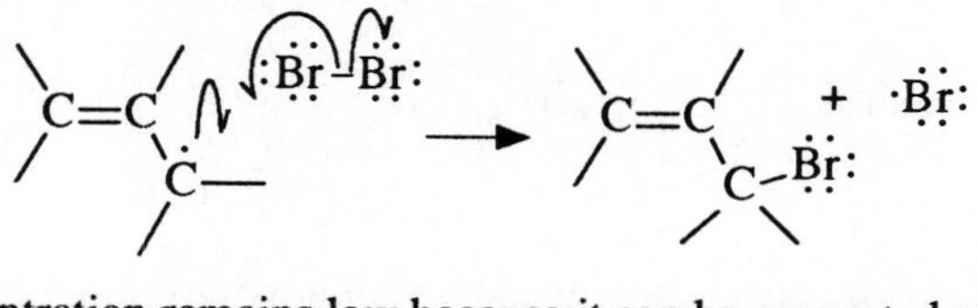

   c) The Br_2 concentration remains low because it can be generated no faster than HBr and an allylic radical are generated.
   d) The low solubility of NBS in CCl_4 is crucial to the success of allylic bromination with NBS.
   2. Because the unpaired electron of an allylic radical is shared between carbons, more than one product is obtained in some allylic brominations; this is not a problem in benzylic bromination reactions.

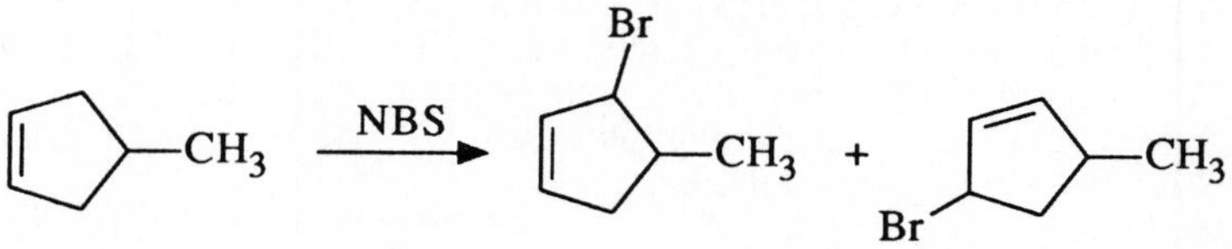

II. Benzylic Oxidation Reactions:

A. Side-Chain Oxidation of Alkylbenzenes:
1. Treatment of alkylbenzene derivatives with strong oxidizing agents under *vigorous* conditions converts alkyl side chains into carboxylic acid groups.
   a) An akyl side chain, regardless of length, is converted to a single carboxylic acid group.
   b) The conditions for this side-chain oxidation are generally vigorous: heat, high concentrations of oxidant, or long reaction times.
2. This oxidation requires the presence of at least *one* benzylic hydrogen.

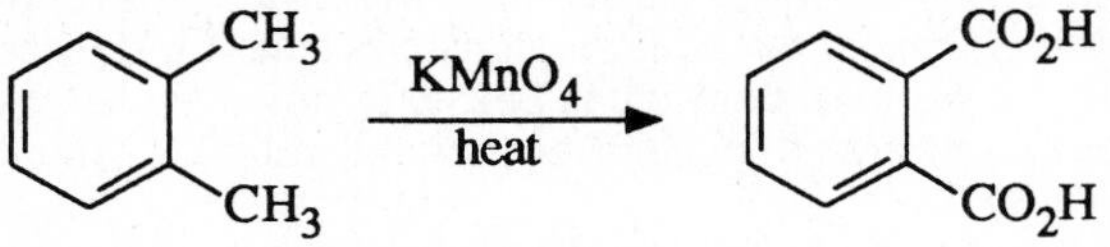

3. *t*-Butylbenzene is resistant to side-chain oxidation.

CHAPTER 17 RULES

Isoprene rule: All terpenes consist of repeating units that have the same carbon skeleton as the five-carbon diene isoprene.

CHAPTER 17 SOLUTIONS

Solutions to In-Text Problems

1. The carbocation formed when trityl chloride ionizes, the *trityl cation* (Ph_3C^+) is stabilized by delocalization of positive charge into *three* phenyl rings. Because the transition state for this ionization resembles the carbocation (Hammond's postulate), the transition state also has unusually low free energy. As a result, the ionization of trityl chloride (the rate-determining step in its S_N1 reactions) is relatively rapid.

2. Hammond's postulate says that we can assess the relative S_N1 reactivities of these compounds by looking at the relative stabilities of the carbocation intermediates formed in their S_N1 reactions. The chloro group destabilizes carbocations by its inductive effect; hence, the S_N1 reactivity of the first compound is greater than that of the other two. The compound with the *p*-chloro substituent, however, is more reactive than the *m*-chloro analog because positive charge in the carbocation intermediate can be delocalized onto a chlorine in the *para* position:

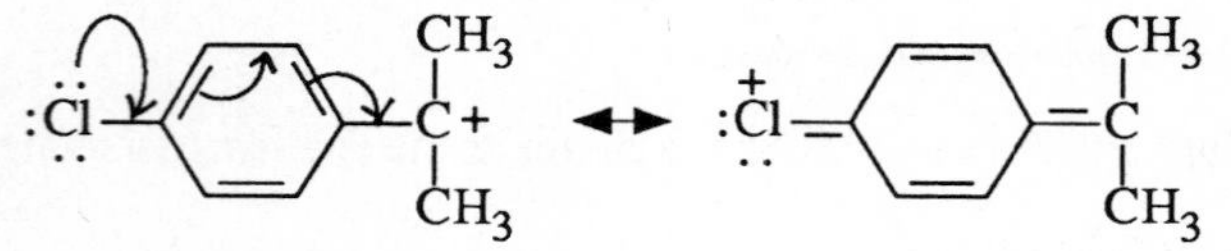

> ➤ Notice that the balance of resonance and inductive effects in benzylic S_N1 reactions is much like it is in electrophilic aromatic substitution (see text pages 664–668). And why not? The same type of intermediate — a carbocation — is involved.

3. 3-Chloro-3-methyl-1-butene would give the same two products, because it gives the same carbocation intermediate. That this intermediate and the one in Eq. 17.7 are identical follows from their resonance structures:

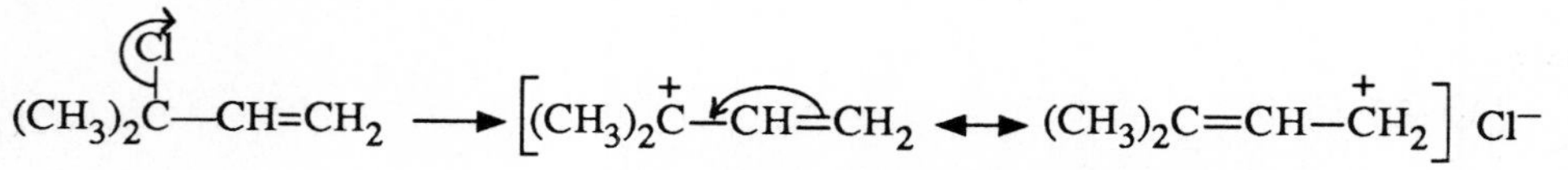

same carbocation as in Eq. 17.7;
gives the same products

4. The allylic radical formed by hydrogen abstraction has two resonance structures; these structures show that the unpaired electron is delocalized to two different carbons. A different product is formed by reaction with bromine at each of the radical sites:

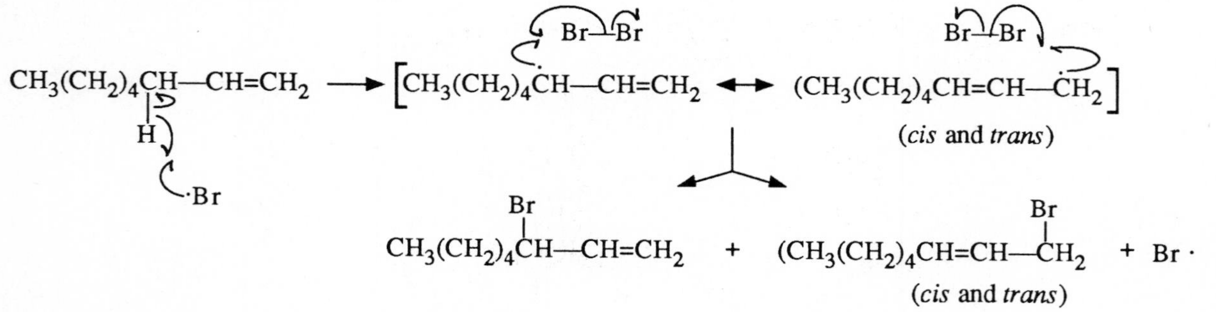

> ➤ When predicting products derived from a resonance-stabilized species, we can treat each resonance structure as if it were a separate compound. We then carry each resonance structure through the reaction. In this example, there are three resonance structures (two being *cis–trans* isomers); hence, there are three products.

5.   (a) There are two allylic radicals possible; one has two resonance structures, but the two structures for the other are identical (draw these radicals and their resonance structures). Hence, there are three products:

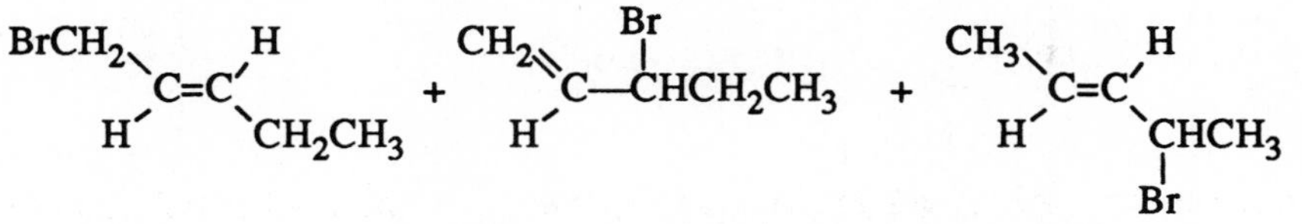

The first and last product could be formed as both *cis* and *trans* isomers.

(b) The allylic radical derived from 3,3-dimethyl-1-cyclohexene has two resonance forms (draw these!); each form leads to one product:

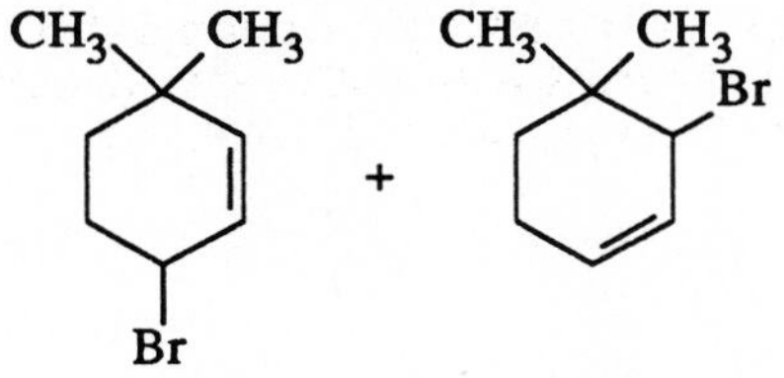

(c) There are two possible benzylic radicals that could be formed:

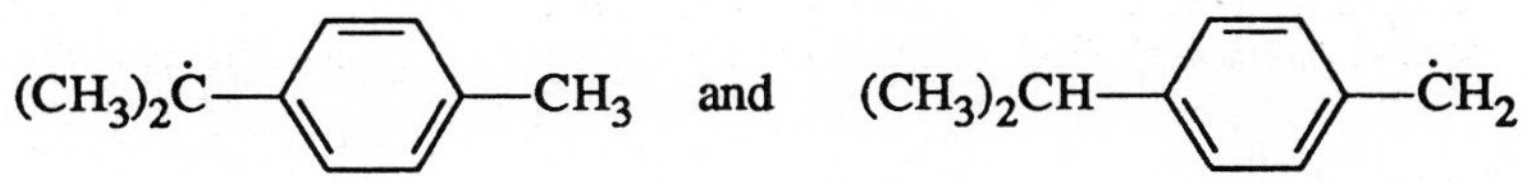

However, the first of these radicals is considerably more stable than the second (why?); hence, the observed product is derived from the first radical:

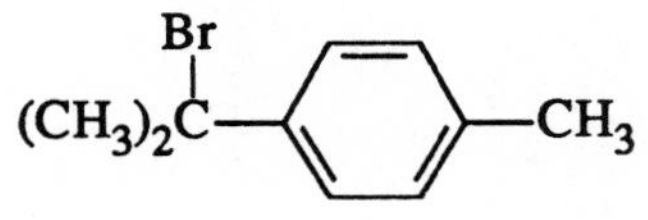

6.   The Grignard reagent undergoes rapid allylic rearrangement. A different product is formed from each isomer of the Grignard reagent:

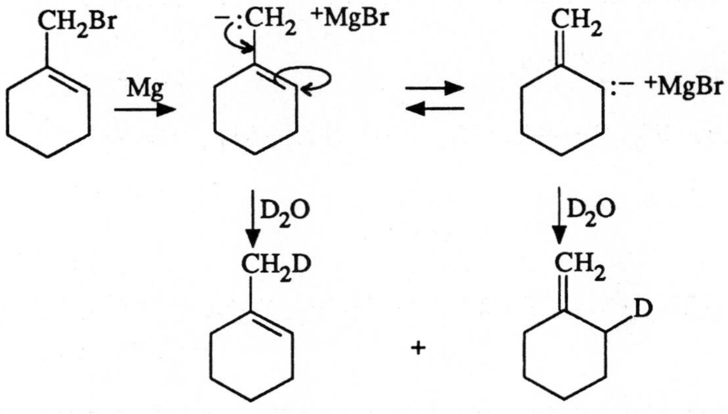

7. Reaction (a) is an S_N1 reaction; because the intermediate carbocation has two resonance structures, we can expect two products:

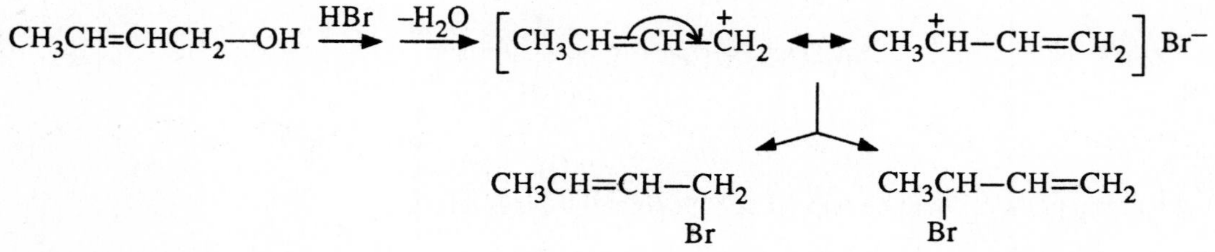

$$CH_3CH=CHCH_2—OH \xrightarrow{HBr} \xrightarrow{-H_2O} \left[CH_3CH=CH\overset{+}{C}H_2 \longleftrightarrow CH_3\overset{+}{C}H—CH=CH_2 \right] Br^-$$

$$CH_3CH=CH—\underset{\underset{Br}{|}}{C}H_2 \qquad CH_3\underset{\underset{Br}{|}}{C}H—CH=CH_2$$

Reaction (b) is an S_N2 reaction. Because there is no intermediate, there is no allylic rearrangement. Only the product $CH_3CH=CH—CH_2—Br$ is observed.

8. (a)   (b)

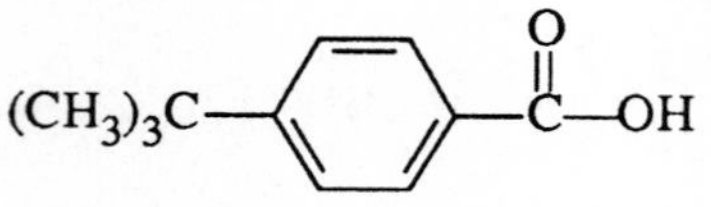

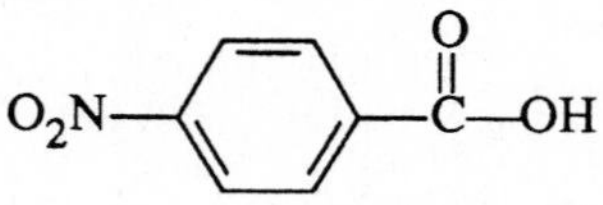

9. The data tell us that compound A is a dialkylbenzene. From the formula, each alkyl group can have only one carbon; hence, the alkyl groups must be methyl groups. Hence compound A is o-xylene. Compound B is a monoalkylbenzene and therefore is ethylbenzene:

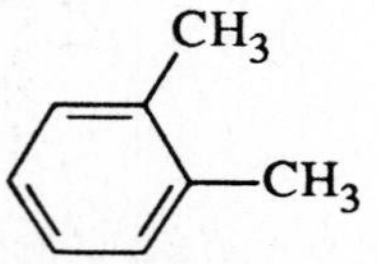

A 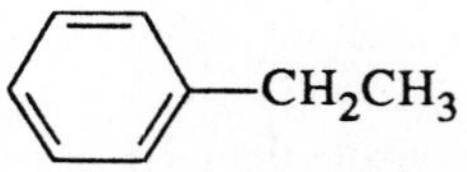 B

10. The isoprene units are shown in dark lines:

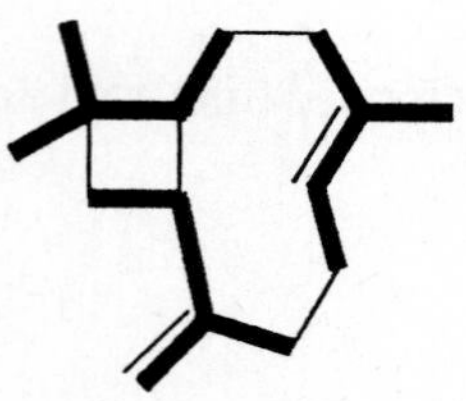

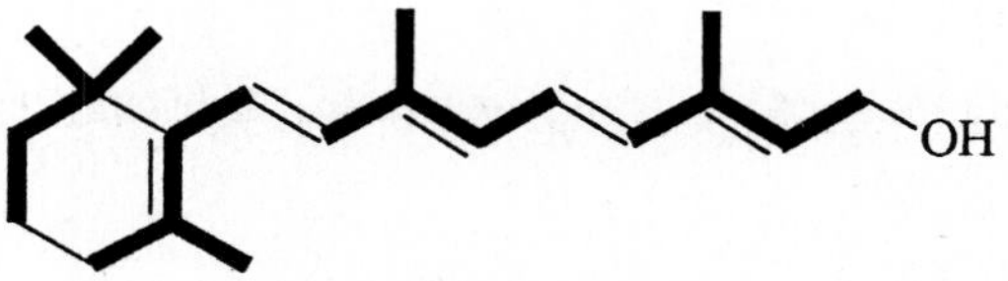

vitamin A

caryophyllene

11. We follow the mechanistic pattern established in Eq. 17.36:

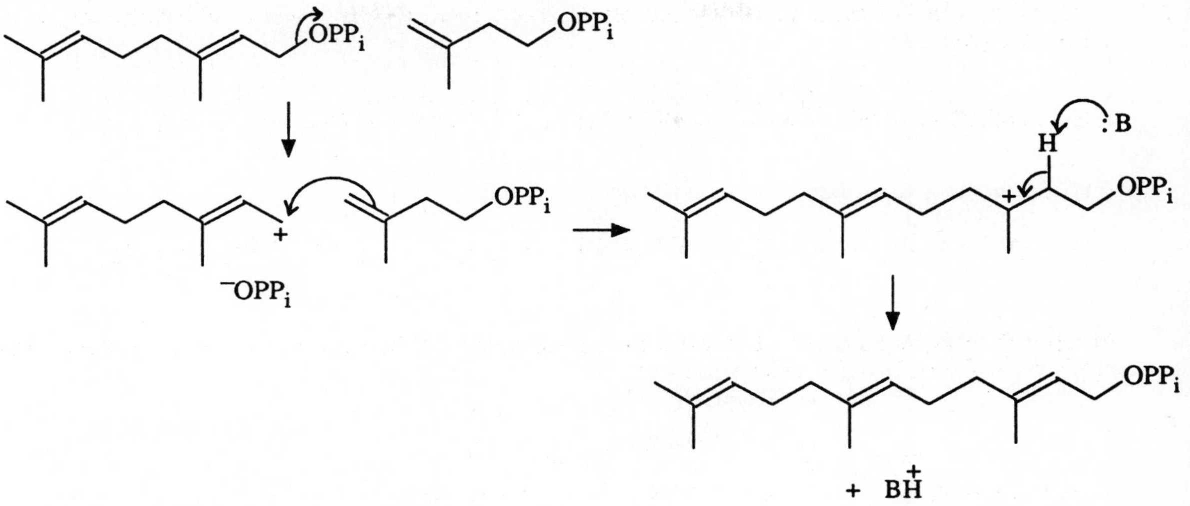

12. (a) Farnesol is formed by hydrolysis of farnesyl pyrophosphate:

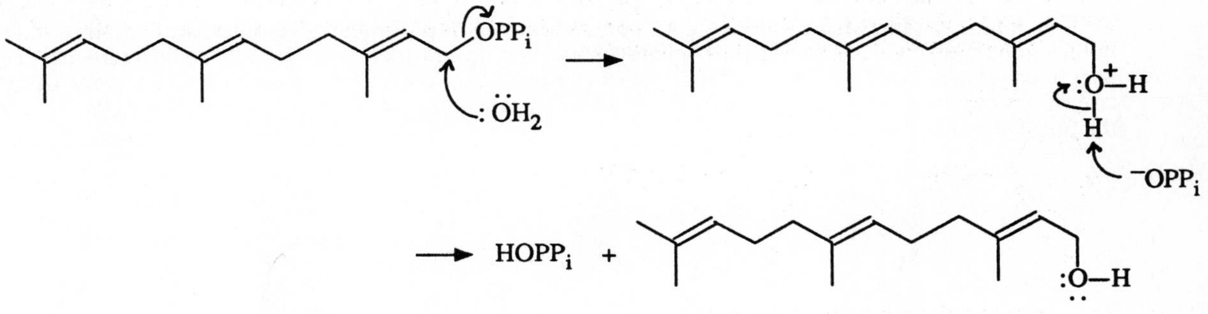

➤ This hydrolysis may take place by attack of water at the phosphorus of pyrophosphate; however, the outcome would be the same.

(b) We can use the carbocation shown as the last structure in Eq. 17.39b:

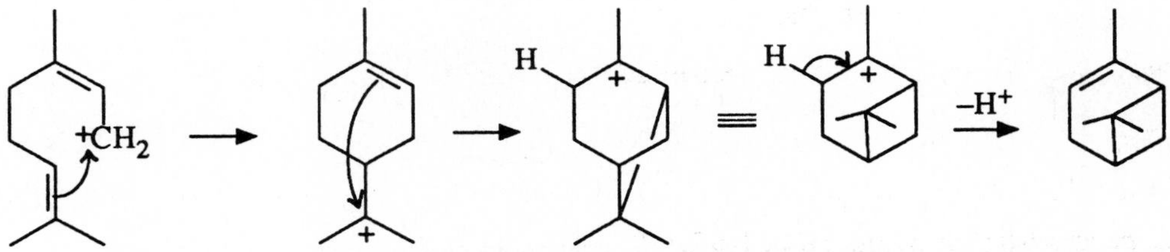

Solutions to Additional Problems

13. (a)   (b)

CH_3—$CHBr$—$CHBr$—CH_3 (*meso*) $BrCH_2$—CH=CH—CH_3 + CH_2=CH—CH—CH_3
                                                         (*cis* and *trans*) |
                                                                                                                 Br

(c) Both would give a mixture of the same two compounds:

$HOCH_2CH$=$CHCH_3$ + CH_2=$CHCHCH_3$
                                                        |
                                                       OH

(d) Both would give a mixture of the same two compounds:

$BrMg$–CH_2CH=$CHCH_3$ + CH_2=$CHCHCH_3$
                                                              |
                                                            MgBr

(e) D—CH_2CH=$CHCH_3$ + CH_2=$CHCHCH_3$
                                                               |
                                                               D

14. Compound (a) has the wrong number of carbons. Compound (b) has the right number of carbons, but does not have the proper carbon skeleton. (Actually, some people consider compound (b) to be a terpene, because it is derived from another terpene by rearrangement. However, we would not classify it as a terpene using the criteria given in the text.) Compounds (c)–(f) are all terpenes; the isoprene units are shown as heavy lines in the following structures:

(c)   (d)   (e)   (f)

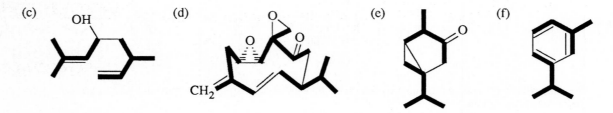

15. (a) Compound B is 1-bromo-2-butene, the product of allylic rearrangement. This compound is formed by ionization of compound A to an allylic cation, and attack of bromide at the other site of positive charge:

CH_3CHCH=CH_2 $\rightleftharpoons$ $\left[CH_3\overset{+}{C}H-CH=CH_2 \leftrightarrow CH_3CH=CH-\overset{+}{C}H_2 \right]$ $\rightleftharpoons$ CH_3CH=$CHCH_2Br$
           |
           Br   Br⁻ B

A

(b) Compound B is favored at equilibrium because it has the more highly substituted double bond.
(c) The ratio of B to A at equilibrium is $[B]/[A]$ = 87/13 = 6.69; this is therefore the equilibrium constant K_{eq} for the reaction. The free-energy difference between B and A is related to the equilibrium constant in the usual way:

$$\Delta G° = -2.3RT \log K_{eq} = (-1.364)(\log 6.69) = -1.13 \text{ kcal/mol}$$

Thus, compound B is more stable than compound A by 1.13 kcal/mol at 25 °C.

16. Let us balance the half-reactions involved. First, the organic half-reaction:

$$Ph—CH_3 + 2H_2O \rightarrow Ph—CO_2H + 6H^+ + 6e^-$$

This is a six-electron oxidation. Now we balance the inorganic half-reaction:

$$MnO_4^- + 4H^+ + 3e^- \rightarrow MnO_2 + 2H_2O$$

This is a three-electron reduction. Comparing the two half-reactions, we see that we can make the number of electrons lost equal the number of electrons gained if two equivalents of permanganate are used to oxidize each equivalent of toluene. The weight of toluene (10 g) corresponds to 0.109 mole; hence, we need 2(0.109) = 0.218 mole of $KMnO_4$ to carry out the oxidation. The molecular weight of $KMnO_4$ is 158.04; hence, (0.218)(158.04) = 34.31 g of $KMnO_4$ are required for the oxidation.

17. As usual, we write each synthesis in reverse, beginning with the target compound.

(a)

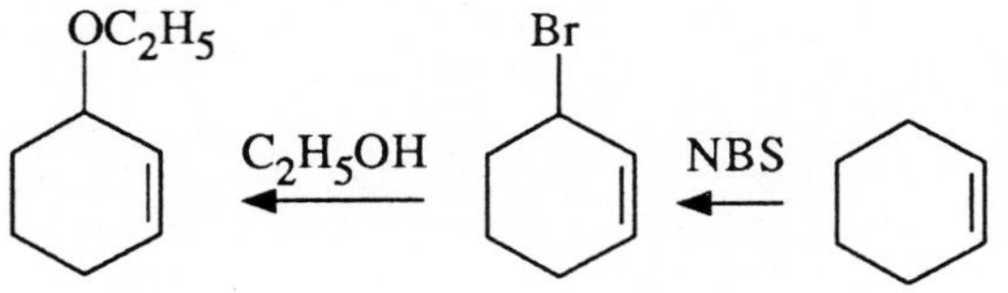

In this synthesis, and in others in this chapter, NBS stands for *N*-bromosuccinimide. The last reaction is an S_N1 solvolysis reaction. Although the carbocation intermediate has two resonance forms (draw them!), they are equivalent; hence, only one product is obtained.

(b)

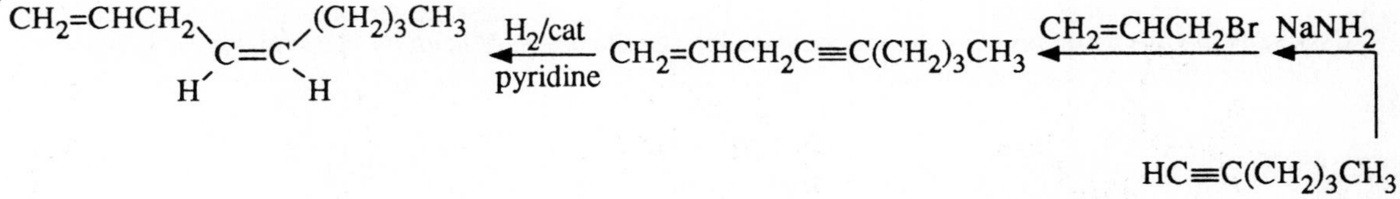

(c)

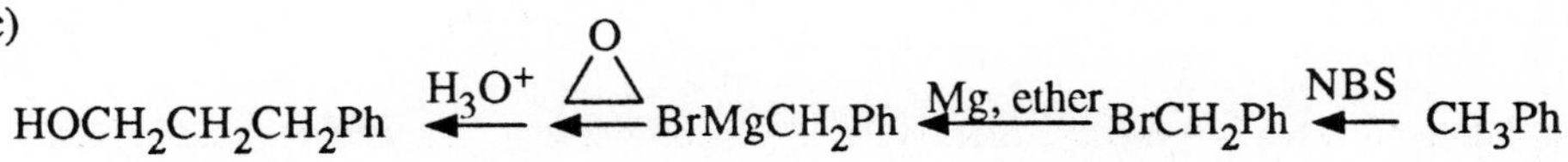

(d)

$$CH_3O—CH_2Ph \xleftarrow[CH_3OH]{CH_3O^-} Br—CH_2Ph \quad \text{[from part (c)]}$$

(e)

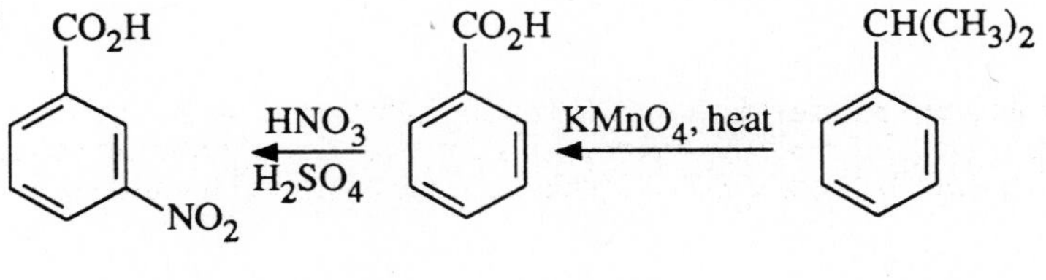

(f)

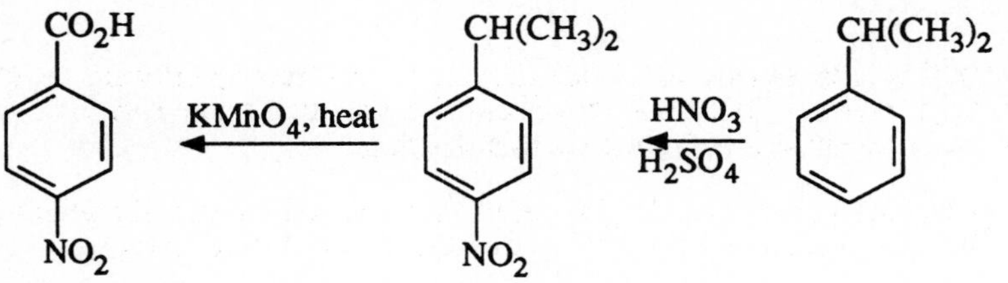

(g)

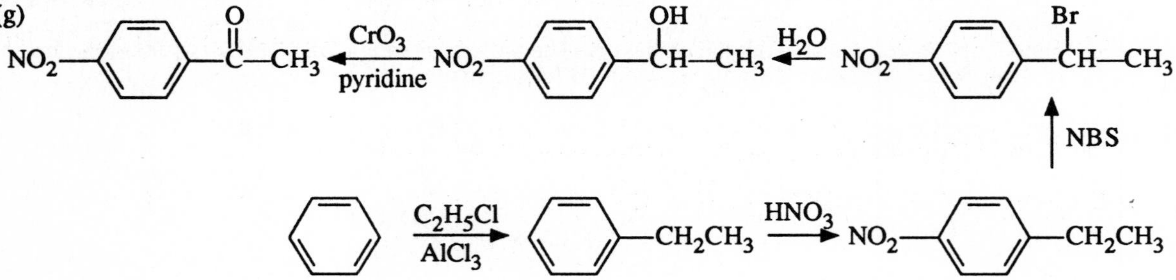

(h)

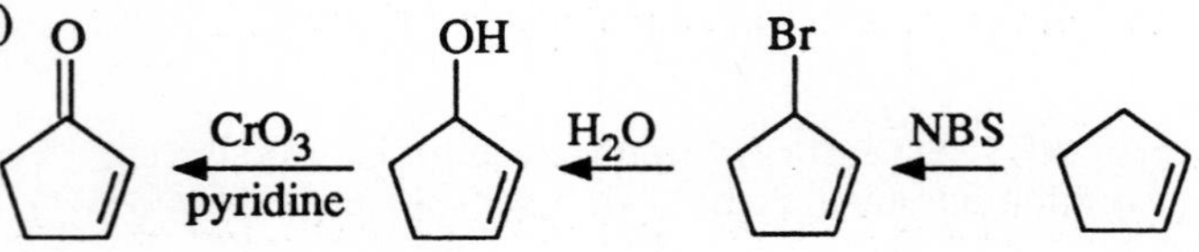

18. The compounds that give the most stable carbocation intermediates are the ones that undergo the most rapid solvolysis. In compound (b), the carbocation intermediate is stabilized by delocalization of charge to the oxygen of the methoxy substituent:

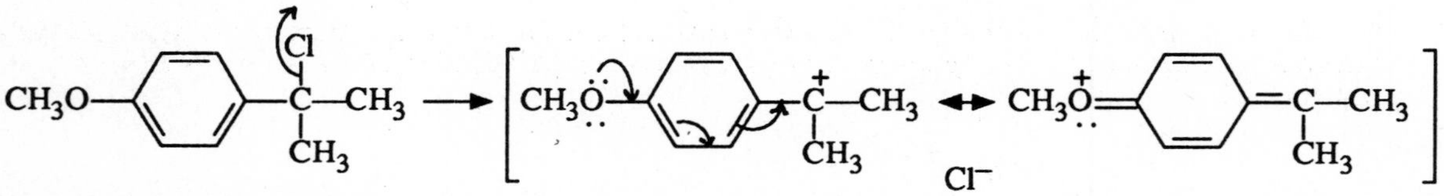

p-methoxy-*t*-cumyl chloride

In (c), a similar delocalization can occur, but fluoro has a greater electron-withdrawing inductive effect than methoxy; hence, the carbocation in this case is less stable and forms less rapidly. In (a) and (d), there is no delocalization of charge in the carbocation intermediate onto the substituent. Furthermore, the inductive effect of the substituent destabilizes positive charge. This destabilization is more severe in (d) because positive charge is delocalized within the ring to a carbon adjacent to the substituent:

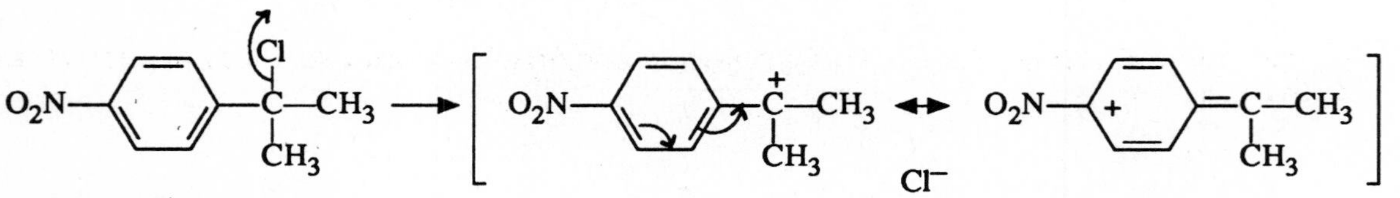

p-nitro-*t*-cumyl chloride

In (a), the positive charge is delocalized to the *adjacent* carbons, and is thus farther away from the nitro group. (Draw these structures.) In summary, the reactivity order is:

(d) < (a) < (c) << (b)

➤ The arguments here are very similar to those used to explain activating and directing effects in electrophilic aromatic substitution. (See text pages 660 and 662.) And they should be similar: the same types of intermediates are involved. (See also the answer to Problem 2, this chapter.)

19. (a) The product is derived from attack of the Grignard reagent on ethylene oxide in the usual manner (Sec. 11.4B). However, because the Grignard reagent is allylic, it is a mixture of two different reagents:

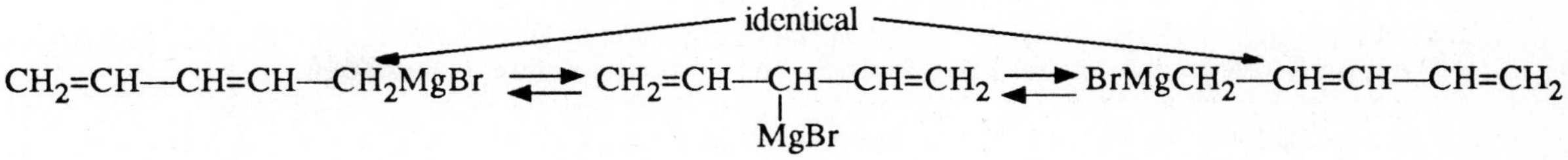

$$\text{CH}_2\text{=CH—CH=CH—CH}_2\text{MgBr} \;\rightleftharpoons\; \text{CH}_2\text{=CH—} \underset{\underset{\text{MgBr}}{|}}{\text{CH}}\text{—CH=CH}_2 \;\rightleftharpoons\; \text{BrMgCH}_2\text{—CH=CH—CH=CH}_2$$

(identical)

The products are therefore derived from attack of each reagent on the epoxide:

$$\text{CH}_2\text{=CHCH=CHCH}_2\text{CH}_2\text{CH}_2\text{—OH} \;+\; \text{CH}_2\text{=CHCHCH=CH}_2$$
$$\underset{\text{CH}_2\text{CH}_2\text{—OH}}{|}$$

(b) In the presence of a good nucleophile, an S_N2 reaction occurs. Since there is no carbocation intermediate, allylic rearrangement is not observed, and the product results from direct displacement:

$$\text{CH}_3\text{CH}_2\text{O—CH}_2\text{CH=CHCH(CH}_3)_2$$

(c) In the absence of a strongly basic nucleophile, the S_N2 reaction cannot occur. Hence, an S_N1 mechanism prevails. Because an allylic carbocation intermediate is formed, two products (corresponding to the two sites of positive charge in the intermediate) are also formed:

$$\text{CH}_3\text{CH}_2\text{O—CH}_2\text{CH=CHCH(CH}_3)_2 \;+\; \text{CH}_2\text{=CHCHCH(CH}_3)_2$$
$$\underset{\text{OCH}_2\text{CH}_3}{|}$$

(d) The carbocation intermediate in this Markovnikov addition has resonance structures in which charge is shared on two carbons of the side-chain; the two products are derived from attack of Br$^-$ at these two positions:

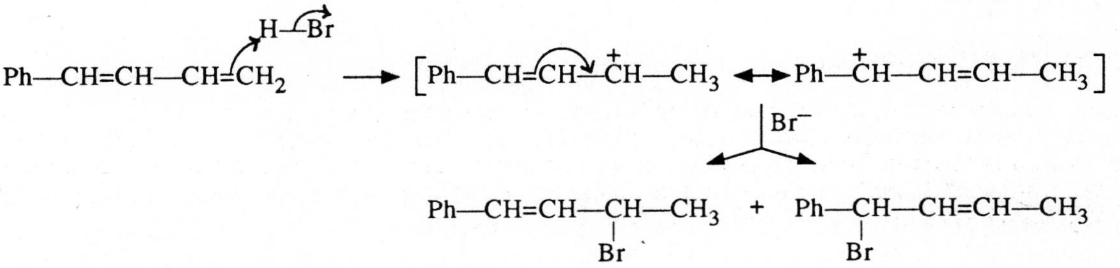

(e) An allylic radical intermediate forms that has two distinguishable resonance structures; the products are derived accordingly:

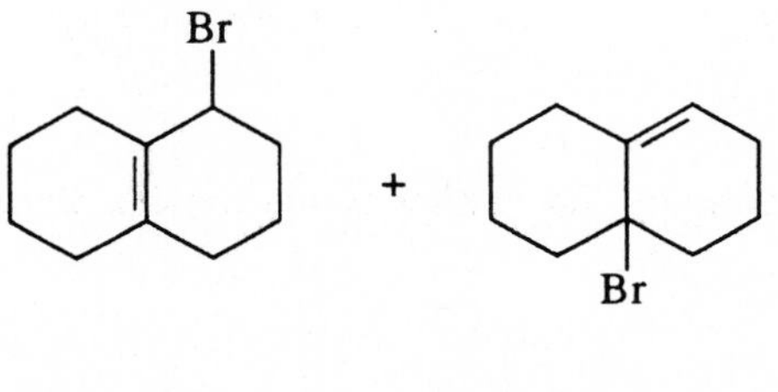

(f) This is a pinacol rearrangement (Sec. 10.1B). The product is derived from formation of the more stable carbocation intermediate. The mechanism is outlined below; fill in the details if necessary.

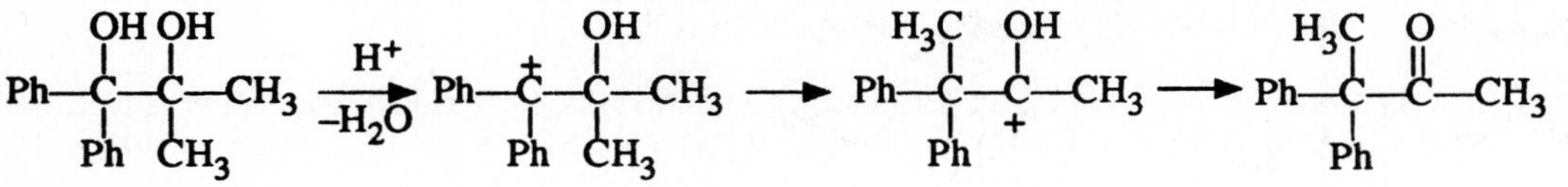

Loss of the other —OH group would give a tertiary carbocation. However, loss of the —OH group shown above is preferred because the resulting carbocation is not only tertiary, but also benzylic.

(g) The —CH₂— groups of the saturated ring are alkyl groups and are oxidized along with the methyl group:

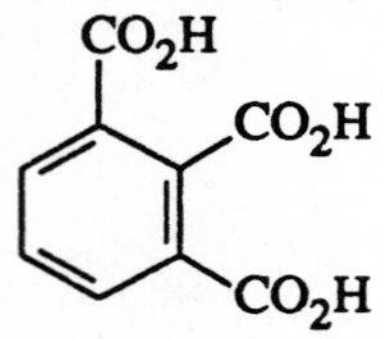

20. The compound that gives the most stable carbocation intermediate dehydrates most rapidly. In each case, a resonance-stabilized carbocation intermediate is formed. In (b) and (c), positive charge can be delocalized onto the oxygen of the methoxy group. In (a), however, the nitro substituent destabilizes positive charge. In (b), the carbocation intermediate is further stabilized because it is tertiary, whereas it is secondary in both (a) and (c). The relative rates, therefore, are in the order

(a) < (c) < (b)

(The arguments here are much like those used in the solutions to Problems 2 and 18.)

21. The reaction involves an intermediate in which the two terminal carbon atoms become equivalent. An S_N1 reaction involving an allylic carbocation intermediate would fill the bill:

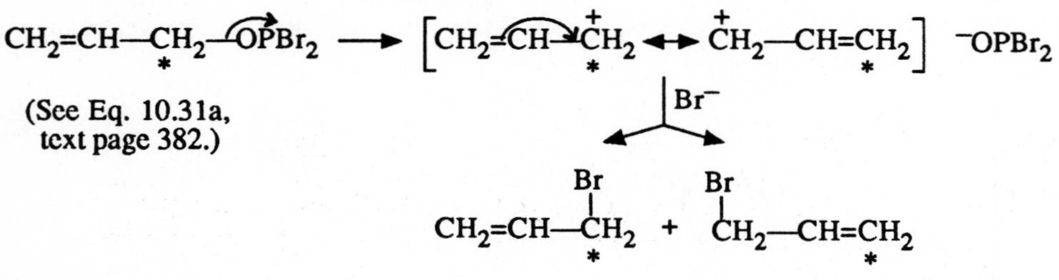

22. Of the ten carbons in limonene, five are allylic. Hence, one molecule of limonene could react at least five times with an allylic chlorinating reagent. These reactions would be particularly rapid because relatively stable allylic radicals would be involved as intermediates. These facts suggest that limonene should be an exceptionally efficient scavenger for free-radical halogenation reagents.

23. Let us first analyze the two compounds in terms of their isoprene units:

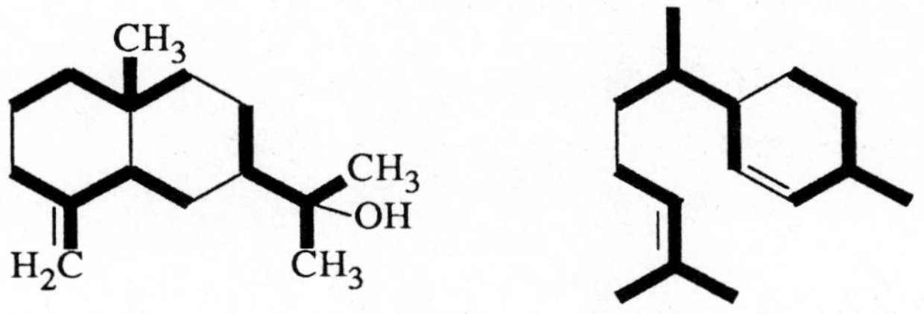

This shows the starting IPP or DMAP units that we shall use to begin the biosynthesis. To save space, we'll write the ionization of the pyrophosphate group, attack of the double bond, and loss of a proton — steps analogous to those in Eqs. 17.35 and 17.36 — as one step. First, the biosynthesis of compound A:

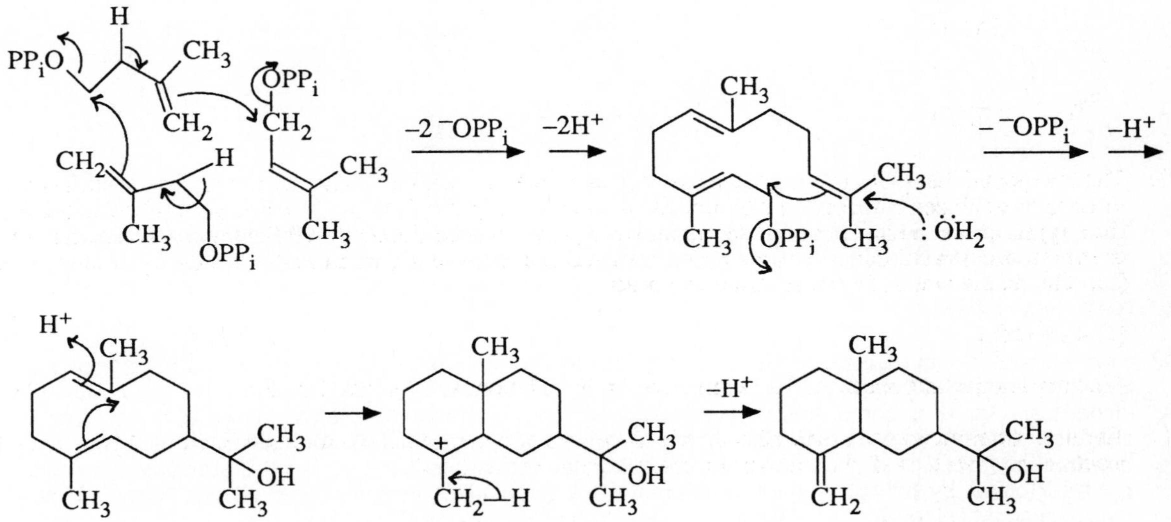

And the biosynthesis of compound B:

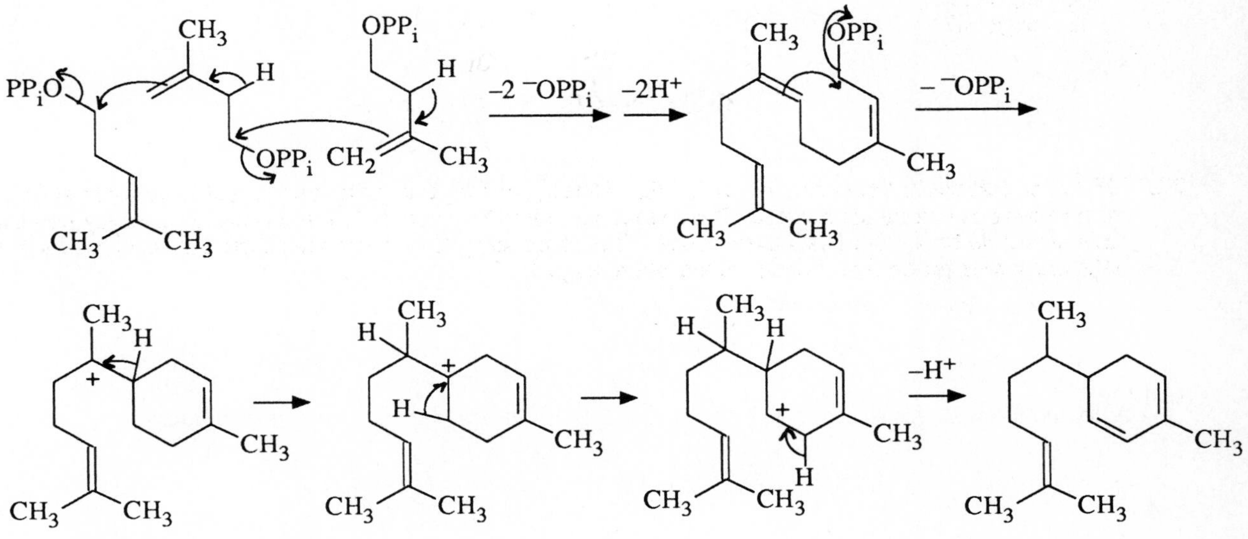

24. The mechanism proposed for prenyl transferase is shown in Eqs. 17.35 and 17.36. The mechanism involves formation of a resonance-stabilized allylic carbocation:

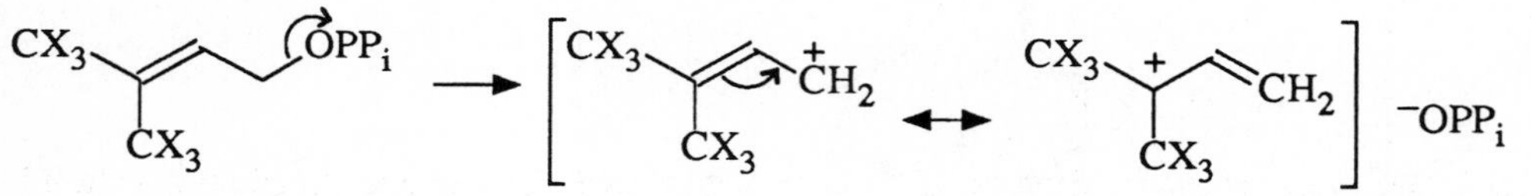

(X = H or F.) When X = F, this carbocation should be destabilized by the inductive effect of the fluorines, and should therefore be formed more slowly, as observed. Demonstrating that the same results are obtained from substitution of fluorine in the two stereochemically different methyl groups provides a strong argument that the effect observed is electronic rather than steric in origin.

25. Compound A forms a resonance-stabilized carbocation when it ionizes:

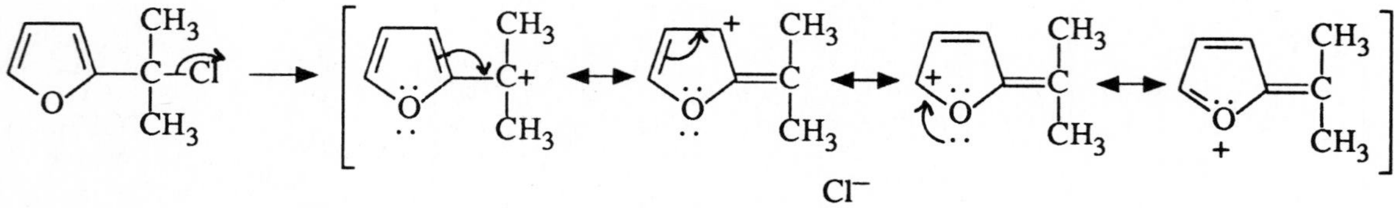

The cation formed by ionization of compound B is not resonance-stabilized. By Hammond's postulate, the transition state structurally resembles the carbocation intermediate. Hence, because the carbocation derived from compound A is more stable relative to starting halide than that derived from compound B, compound A reacts more rapidly.

26. Compound A has an unsaturation number of 5. Because it ultimately affords phthalic acid, it is aromatic; a benzene ring thus accounts for four of the five degrees of unsaturation. Compound C is a chiral secondary alcohol, and the α-carbon of this alcohol is the asymmetric carbon, because conversion to a ketone destroys its chirality. Compound C, in turn, arises from solvolysis of B, a product of either allylic or benzylic bromination. Because A contains an aromatic ring, the formation of compound B is probably a benzylic bromination. A by-product of the formation of C is compound D, presumably an alkene, because it can be hydrogenated back to A. Partial structures for B and C are:

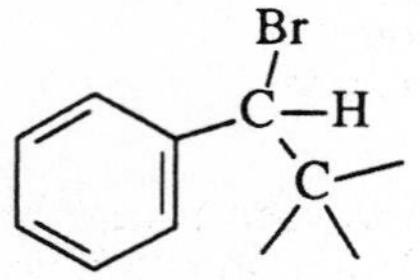

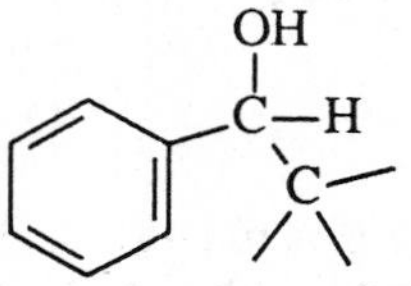

From the structure of B, a partial structure for compound A has to be:

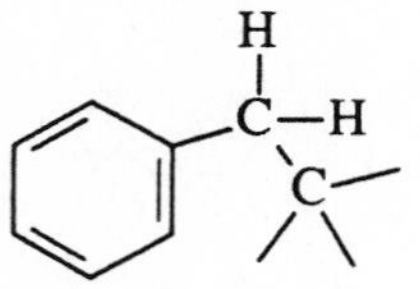

compound A

A compound with this structure and the formula C_9H_{10} can only be one of two possibilities:

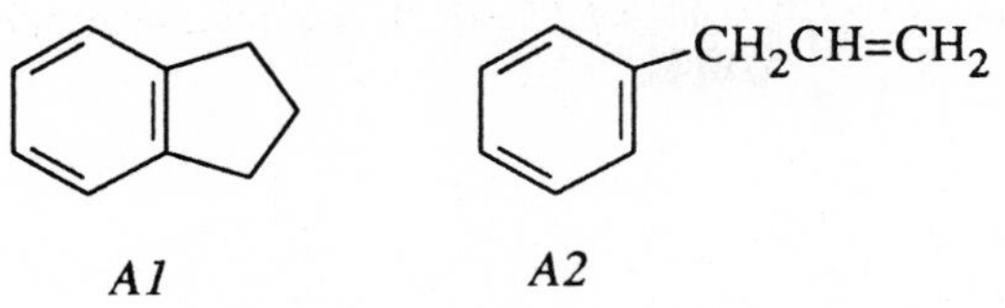
$CH_2CH{=}CH_2$
A1
A2

Bromination, solvolysis, and hydrogenation of *A2* would not give back *A2*, since its double bond would be hydrogenated. Hence, *A1* is the correct structure for compound *A*. The other structures are as follows:

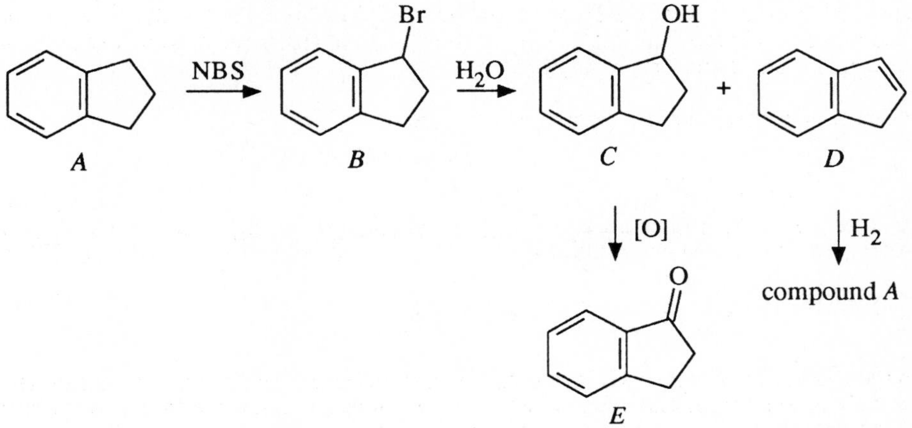
Br
OH
NBS
H_2O
+
A
B
C
D
[O]
H_2
O
compound A
E

27. The observations are accounted for by protonation of benzyl alcohol and ionization to a carbocation:

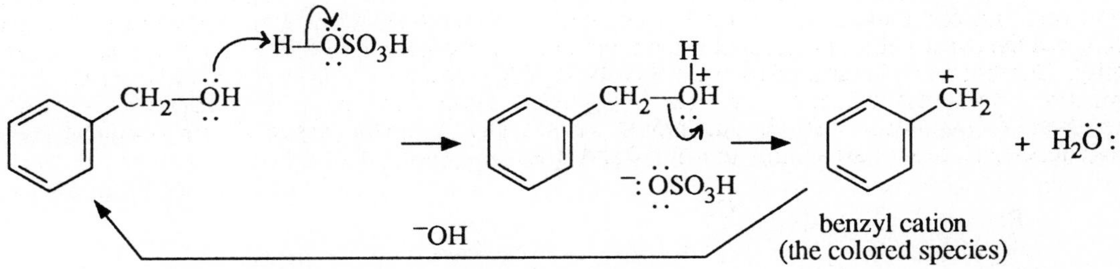
H—$\ddot{O}SO_3H$
CH_2—$\ddot{O}H$
H
CH_2—$\overset{+}{O}H$
$^-$:$\ddot{O}SO_3H$
$\overset{+}{C}H_2$
+ $H_2\ddot{O}$:
^-OH
benzyl cation
(the colored species)

Reaction of the benzyl cation with hydroxide ion gives back benzyl alcohol. The colored species can't be protonated benzyl alcohol because it has no more conjugation than benzyl alcohol itself, and should have a nearly identical UV spectrum.

28. (a) The Grignard reagent is propargylic (that is, allylic to a triple bond). Like an allylic Grignard reagent, this reagent is an equilibrium mixture of two different reagents, each of which is protonated to give a different compound:

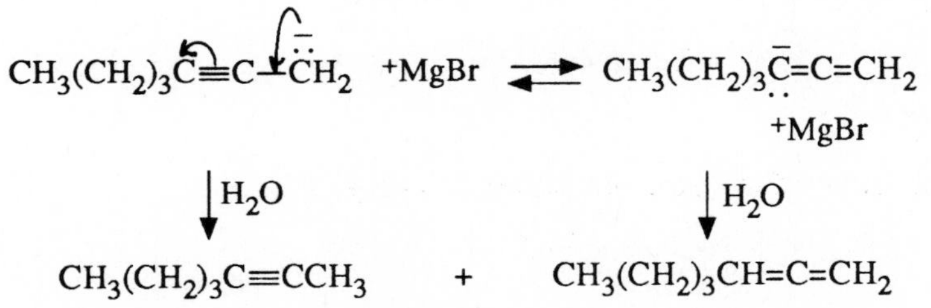
$CH_3(CH_2)_3C{\equiv}C{-}\ddot{C}H_2$ ^+MgBr
$CH_3(CH_2)_3\ddot{C}{=}C{=}CH_2$
^+MgBr
H_2O
H_2O
$CH_3(CH_2)_3C{\equiv}CCH_3$
+
$CH_3(CH_2)_3CH{=}C{=}CH_2$

(b) This is an S_N1 reaction accompanied by rearrangement:

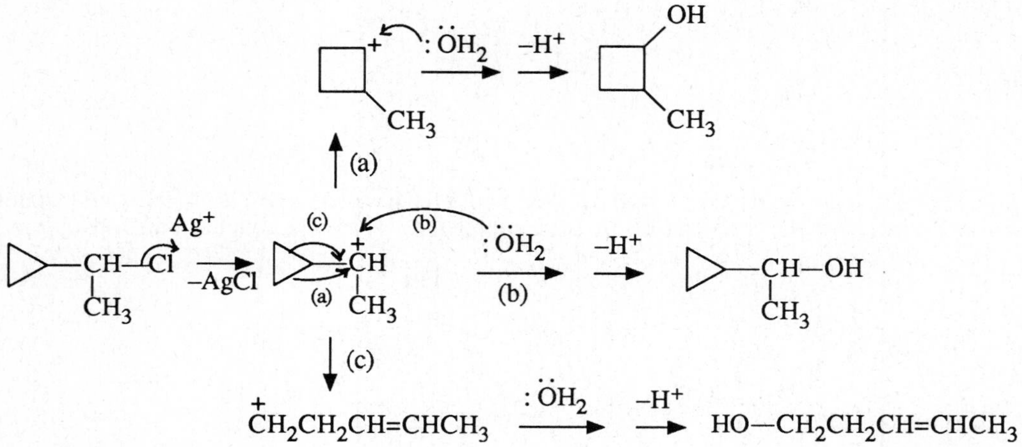

(c) One hydrogen is especially acidic because it is both allylic and propargylic, and the anion formed by removal of this proton is therefore resonance-stabilized. This anion reacts with allyl bromide:

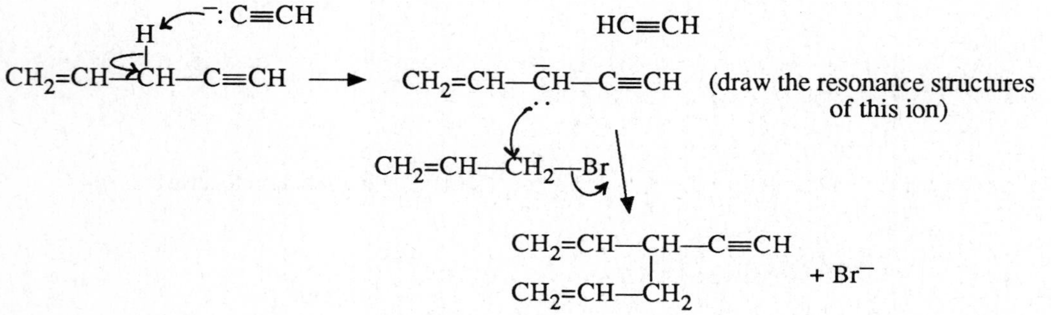

(d) The carbocation formed by protonation of the —OH group and loss of water adds to a neighboring double bond to give a new carbocation; this carbocation adds to a neighboring double bond to give yet another carbocation; and so on, until the product is formed by attack of water on the last carbocation formed:

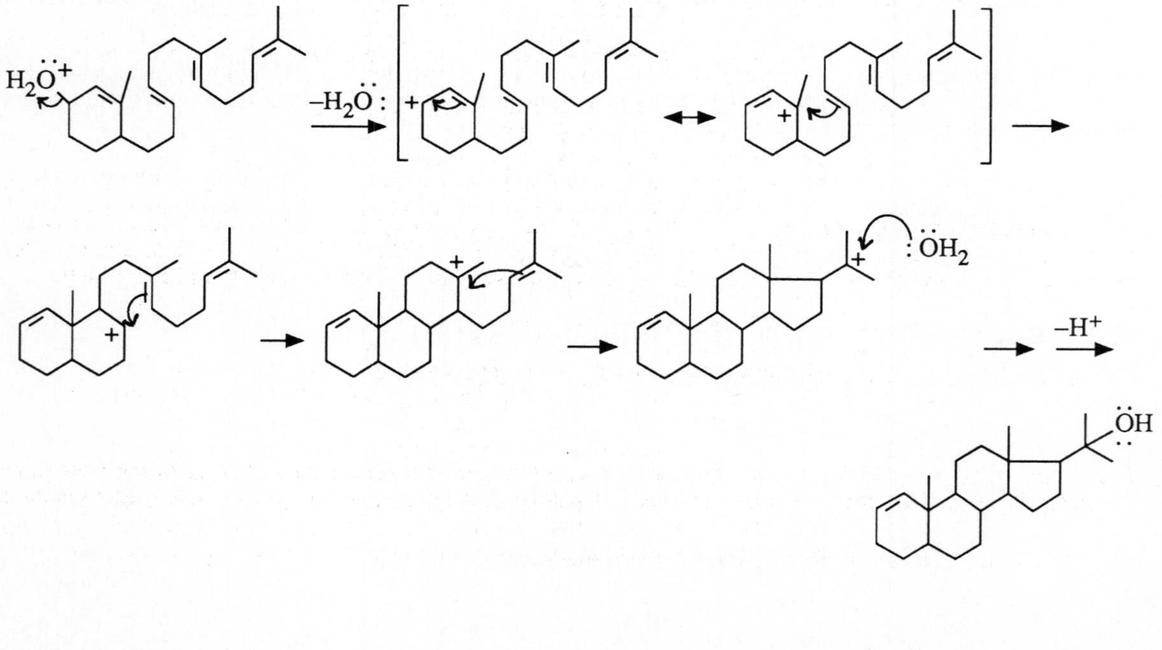

(e) The formation of a cyclopropane suggests (Sec. 9.7) the involvement of the following carbene:

$(CH_3)_2C{=}C{=}C\,:$

This species is formed by loss of chloride ion from the acetylenic anion:

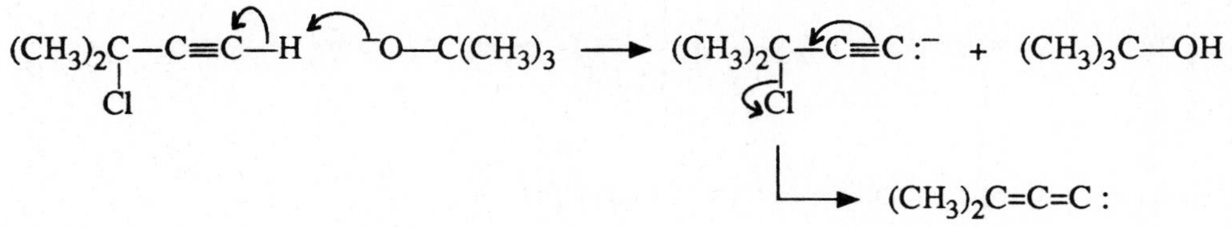

Addition of the carbene to cyclohexene affords the cyclopropane derivative:

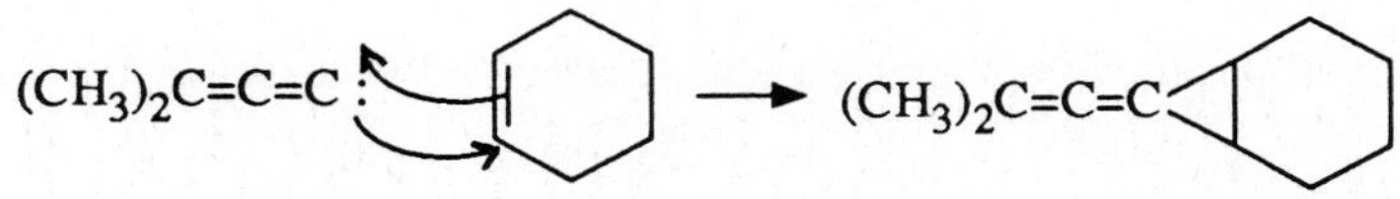

(f) Protonation of the hydroxy group and loss of water give a resonance-stabilized carbocation, which is attacked by ethanol at both sites of positive charge:

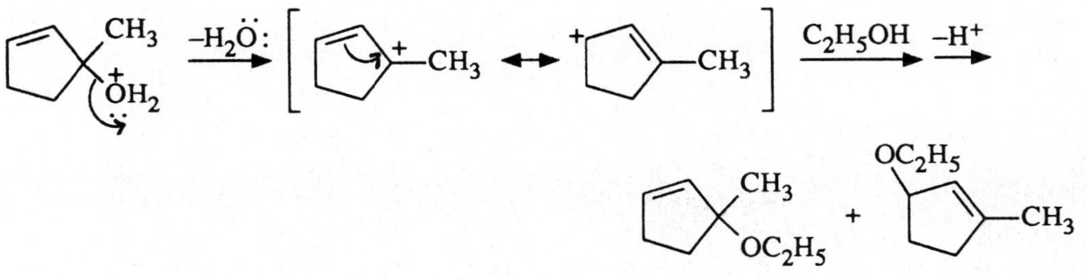

29. There are two possible reaction pathways 1-buten-3-yne could take: protonation of the triple bond or protonation of the double bond. Protonation of the triple bond would give the following 1,2- and 1,4-addition products:

$$CH_2{=}CH{-}C{\equiv}CH \xrightarrow{HCl} CH_3{-}CH(Cl){-}C{\equiv}CH + CH_3{-}CH{=}C{=}CHCl$$

(1) (2)

Neither of these would give a Diels–Alder reaction (neither is a conjugated diene); and product (1) should liberate a gas (CH_4) when treated with CH_3MgBr. Hence, these products do not fit the data. Protonation of the triple bond, however, gives products that are consistent with the information given in the problem:

$$CH_2{=}CH{-}C{\equiv}CH \xrightarrow{HCl} Cl{-}CH_2{-}CH{=}C{=}CH_2 + CH_2{=}CH{-}C(Cl){=}CH_2$$

A *B*

Compound *A*, as an allylic halide, would give a silver nitrate test, because it can ionize to a relatively stable, resonance-stabilized carbocation; and compound *B*, a conjugated diene, would give a Diels–Alder reaction.

30. (a) The trityl radical is particularly stable because it is resonance-stabilized by delocalization of the unpaired electron into all three benzene rings:

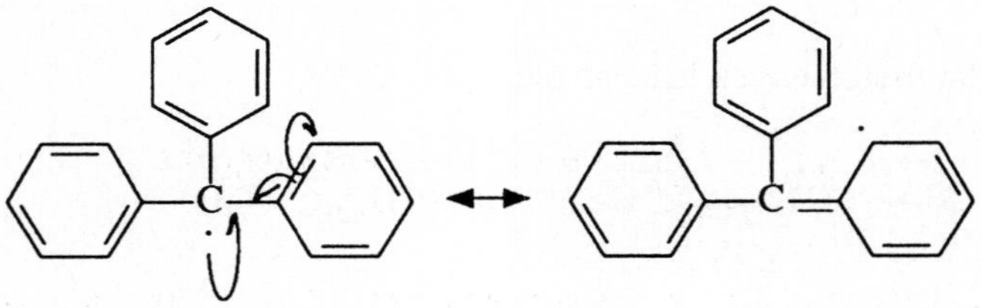

                                 ⟷   ⟷   many other structures

(b) Two trityl radicals could simply combine to form hexaphenylethane:

$Ph_3C\cdot$ $\cdot CPh_3$ ⟶ $Ph_3C\!-\!CPh_3$ hexaphenylethane

(c) One resonance structure of the trityl radical is the following, in which the unpaired electron is delocalized to the *para* position of one ring:

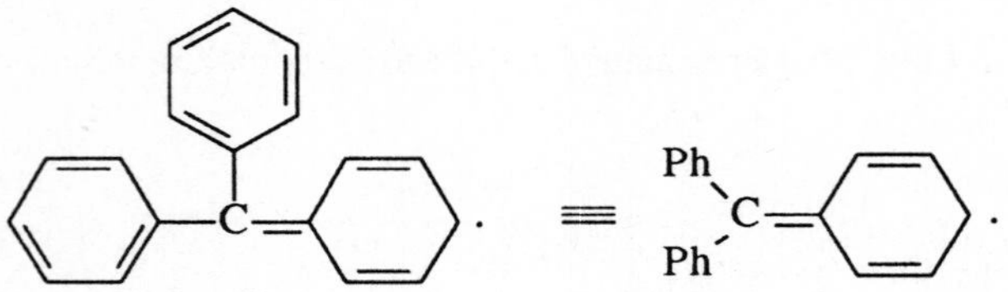

Combination of this radical with the central carbon of another trityl radical gives the observed dimer:

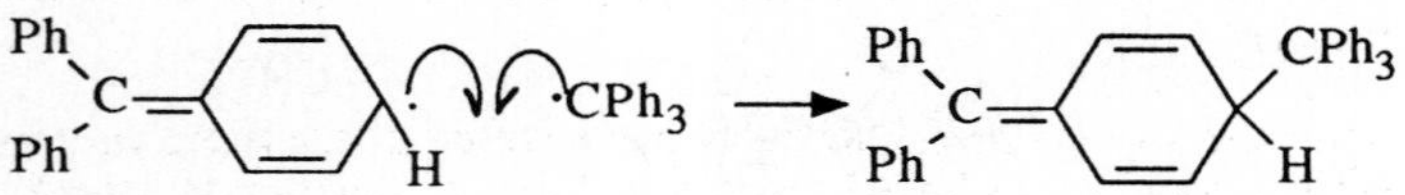

Hexaphenylethane is unstable because each benzene ring is *gauche* to two other benzene rings:

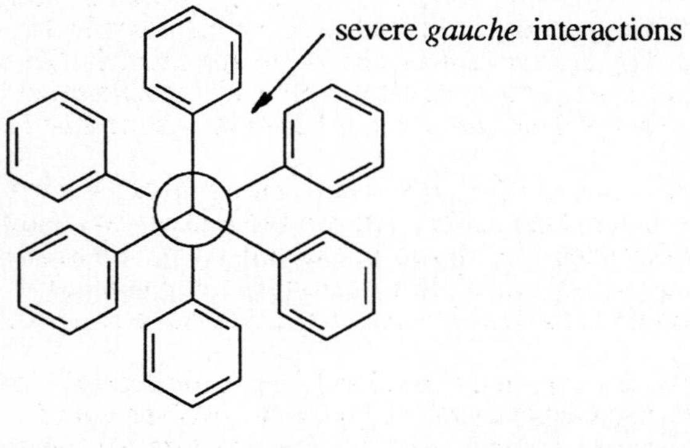

                 severe *gauche* interactions

This large number of unfavorable *gauche* interactions make hexaphenylethane too unstable to exist.

31. (a) The anion is stabilized by delocalization of the unshared pair into all three benzene rings:

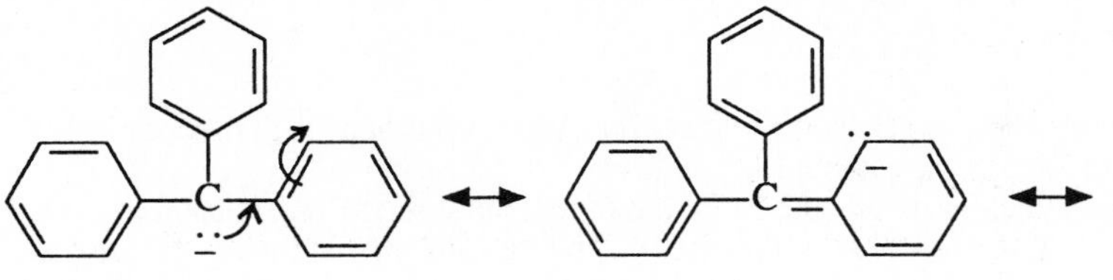

Stabilization of the anion lowers the energy required to form it, and hence lowers the pK_a of its conjugate acid.

(b) The resonance interaction shown in part (a) is optimized if the three rings are coplanar; when the rings are coplanar, there is optimum overlap of the p orbitals of the central carbon and the rings. However, if we make a model of a carbon and three attached coplanar benzene rings, we find that a severe steric interaction prevents the rings from achieving the desired coplanarity:

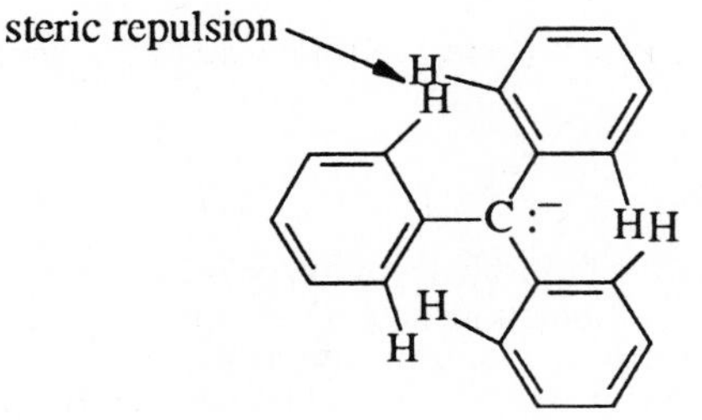

Hence, the rings in the triphenylmethyl anion are turned significantly away from coplanarity, with a resulting cost in orbital overlap. In fluoradene, the unfavorable steric interactions between *ortho* hydrogens are replaced by bonds that constrain the rings into a planar arrangement. The resulting increase in orbital overlap brings about a concomitant increase in stabilization of the anion. As a result, the pK_a of the conjugate acid is lowered significantly relative to that of triphenylmethane.

32. In Section 7.10C, we learned that *anti* stereochemistry is one of the major pieces of evidence that a bromonium ion is involved in alkene bromination. (Similar conclusions have been reached for chlorination reactions.) We also showed (Eq. 7.33a,b, text page 259) that a mechanism involving carbocation intermediates predicts mixed *syn* and *anti* addition. In the present problem, we are dealing with the competition between the two mechanisms: one involving a cyclic *chloronium ion* intermediate and the other involving a carbocation intermediate. When the carbocation intermediate is resonance-stabilized (last two entries in the table), it is stable enough to compete energetically with the chloronium ion as a reaction intermediate. When R = *p*-methoxyphenyl, a carbocation intermediate is further resonance-stabilized by the *para* substituent. (See, for example, the solution to Problem 18.) In this case, the carbocation mechanism competes most effectively with the chloronium-ion mechanism. The loss of stereospecificity is evidence for involvement of the carbocation intermediate.

33. Fact (a) indicates that the transition state involves a molecule of $(C_2H_5)_2NH$ and a molecule of alkyl halide. Fact (b) indicates that the indicated starting materials undergo the reaction shown; had this not been established, one could have postulated that one of the starting alkyl halides is converted into the other by the reaction conditions, and that the observed product originates from only one of the two starting compounds. Fact (c) establishes that the observed product is the actual product of the reaction, and is not derived from a secondary reaction of its allylic isomer.

       Now to the mechanisms of the reactions. We see that, in the reaction of the second alkyl chloride, an allylic rearrangement has occurred. Such allylic rearrangements generally suggest the involvement of carbocation intermediates, which have two resonance forms, and can be attacked at two different carbons. However, the observation of second-order kinetics rules out an S_N1 reaction. Hence, the reaction is evidently a direct displacement at the *allylic carbon*, thus:

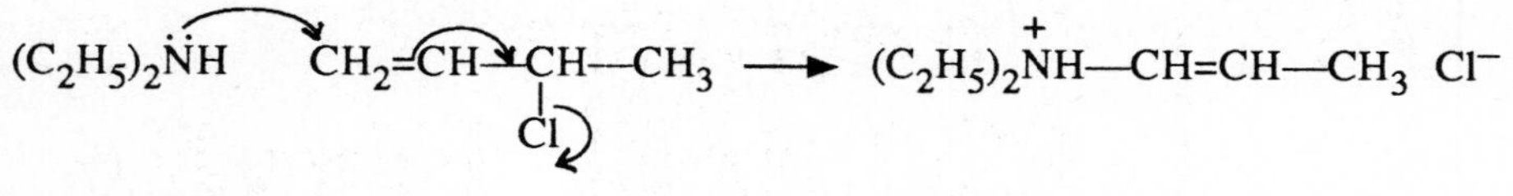

This is the so-called S_N2' mechanism. The other isomer reacts by the conventional S_N2 mechanism, in which the nucleophile attacks at the carbon bearing the halide.

Why does the nucleophile attack at the α-carbon in one case, and at the allylic carbon in the other? The nucleophile is large, and attacks at the least hindered carbon. In one case, this is the allylic carbon; in the other, it is the α-carbon.

34. The reaction is *syn* with respect to the plane of the alkene. For example, the major product comes from attack of the nucleophile and loss of the chloride from one face:

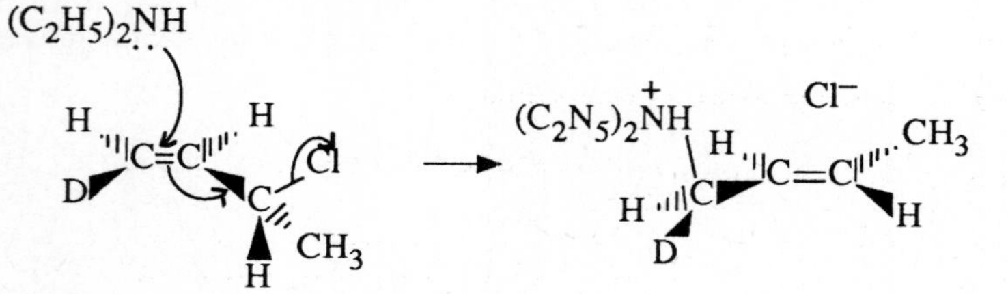

The minor product comes from attack of the nucleophile and loss of the chloride from the opposite face. (You should draw this process.) The major product is preferred because the transition state leading to it resembles a *trans*-alkene; the transition state leading to the minor product resembles a *cis*-alkene, and is thus more strained. The *syn* stereochemistry of this reaction stands in contrast to the *anti* (inversion) stereochemistry of the S_N2 reaction.

➤ The observation of stereospecificity in this reaction is another reason why a carbocation mechanism is not reasonable. (See solution to the previous problem.) A carbocation mechanism predicts a mixture of *syn* and *anti* stereochemistry.

35. Compound *A* is a benzylic bromination product, and it appears that meperidine and compound *B* are S_N1 products, each derived respectively from reaction of one of the nucleophiles present with a carbocation intermediate derived from *A*. We know that S_N1 reactions are generally accompanied by E1 reactions; hence, it is reasonable to suppose that MPTP is such a product — namely, an alkene. Indeed, the elemental analysis of MPTP translates to a molecular formula of $C_{6.927}H_{8.661}N_{0.578}$, or $C_{12}H_{15}N$. This has an unsaturation number of 6. With five unsaturations accounted for by the two rings in the starting material, we conclude that MPTP has an additional ring or double bond:

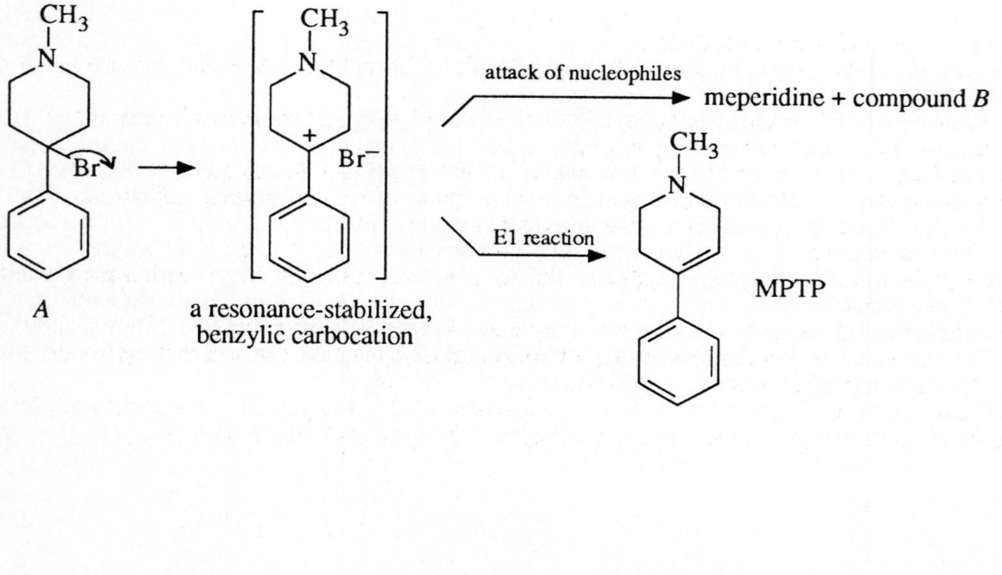

Chapter 18 / Chemistry of Aryl Halides, Vinylic Halides, and Phenols

CHAPTER 18 TERMS

aryl cation 18.3
aryl halide .... Introduction
autoxidation 18.8
benzyne 18.4B
cine substitution 18.4B
diradical 18.8
hemiacetal 18.8
Meisenheimer complex 18.4A

nucleophilic aromatic substitution 18.4A
ortho-quinone 18.7A
para-quinone 18.7A
phenol .... Introduction
phenolate (phenoxide) ion 18.5A
quinone 18.7A
semiquinone 18.7A
vicinal dihalide .... Introduction

CHAPTER 18 CONCEPTS

I. Reactivity of Vinylic and Aryl Halides in Reactions of Ordinary Alkyl Halides:

A. Introduction:
1. **Aryl halides** are compounds in which a halogen is bound to the carbon of a benzene ring (or other aromatic ring)—**benzylic groups** are on the carbon *adjacent* to an aromatic ring.
2. **Vinylic halides** are compounds in which a halogen is bound directly to a carbon of a double bond— **allylic groups** are on the carbon *adjacent* to the double bond.
3. The reactivity of aryl and vinylic halides is quite different from that of ordinary alkyl halides.

B. Lack of Reactivity in S_N1 and E1 Reactions:
1. Vinylic and aryl halides are virtually inert to the conditions that promote the S_N1 or E1 reactions of alkyl halides.
2. To undergo S_N1 or E1 reactions, vinylic halides must ionize to vinylic cations; this ionization is energetically unfavorable because:
   a) Vinylic carbon–halogen bonds are stronger than alkyl carbon–halogen bonds.
   b) Solvolysis of vinylic halides changes the hybridization of one of the carbons from sp^2 in the vinylic halide to sp in the carbocation intermediate.
   c) Vinyl cations are among the most unstable carbocations because of their sp hybridization.
3. To undergo S_N1 or E1 reactions, aryl halides must ionize to aryl cations; this ionization is energetically unfavorable because:
   a) Aryl carbon–halogen bonds are stronger than alkyl carbon–halogen bonds.
   b) Solvolysis of aryl halides changes the hybridization of one of the carbons from sp^2 in the aryl halide to sp in the carbocation intermediate.
   c) The electron-deficient carbon in an aryl cation is bonded to two groups and therefore prefers a linear geometry; this introduces a great deal of strain in a six-membered ring.

C. Lack of Reactivity in S$_N$2 Reactions:
  1. Vinylic and aryl halides are inert under S$_N$2 conditions.
  2. The attacking nucleophile (Nuc:$^-$) must approach the vinylic halide at the backside of the halogen-bearing carbon *and* in the plane of the alkene.
      a) Repulsions in the transition state occur between the leaving group and the substituent on the carbon bearing the leaving group.
      b) The carbon at which substitution occurs is *sp* hybridized in the transition state; *sp* hybridization is the least favorable hybridization state of carbon.
  3. S$_N$2 reactions of aryl halides have additional problems:
      a) Backside attack requires that the attacking nucleophile would have to approach on a path that goes through the plane of the benzene ring.
      b) Since the carbon at the site of attack undergoes an inversion of configuration, an S$_N$2 reaction would yield a highly strained benzene derivative containing a formal *trans*-double bond.

II. Nucleophilic Substitution Reactions of Aryl Halides:

A. Nucleophilic Aromatic Substitution:
  1. Aryl halides that have one or more strongly electronegative groups (especially nitro groups) *ortho* or *para* to the halogen undergo **nucleophilic aromatic substitution reactions**—a type of substitution that occurs by special mechanism.
      a) Nucleophilic aromatic substitution reactions involve nucleophiles and leaving groups.
      b) Nucleophilic aromatic substitution reactions have second-order kinetics.
      c) The reaction goes faster when there are more nitro groups *ortho* and *para* to the halogen leaving group.
  2. The nucleophilic aromatic substitution mechanism involves:
      a) Attack of a nucleophile (Lewis base) on the ring π-electrons to give a resonance-stabilized carbanion intermediate (**Meisenheimer complex**).

Meisenheimer complex

      (1) Formation of this anion is the rate-determining step in many nucleophilic aromatic substitution reactions.
      (2) The negative charge is delocalized throughout the π-electron system of the ring.
      (3) The negative charge in this complex is also delocalized into an *ortho* or *para* nitro group if present.

  b) The Meisenheimer complex breaks down to products by loss of the halide ion.

  3. *Ortho* and *para* nitro groups accelerate the reaction because both their electronegativities and their electron-withdrawing resonance effects stabilize the transition state, which resembles the Meisenheimer complex.

4. Because the halide does not act as a leaving group in the rate-determining step of the reaction, the basicity of the halide is not important in determining the reaction rate; the halide leaving group order of reaction rates is:

$$F^- \gg Cl^- \approx Br^- \approx I^-$$

5. Nucleophilic aromatic substitution reactions involve overall frontside displacement—they require no inversion of configuration.

B. Substitution by Elimination–Addition—Benzyne:
1. β-Elimination of an aryl halide gives an "alkyne" called **benzyne**.
   a) One of the two π-bonds in the triple bond of benzyne is perpendicular to the π-electron system of the aromatic ring.
   b) Benzyne is highly strained and very unstable.

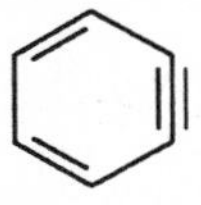

benzyne

2. The mechanism of this reaction is:
   a) Formation of an anion at the *ortho* position; this step requires a strong base because benzene derivatives are only weakly acidic.
   b) Expulsion of a halide ion completes the β-elimination reaction and gives benzyne.

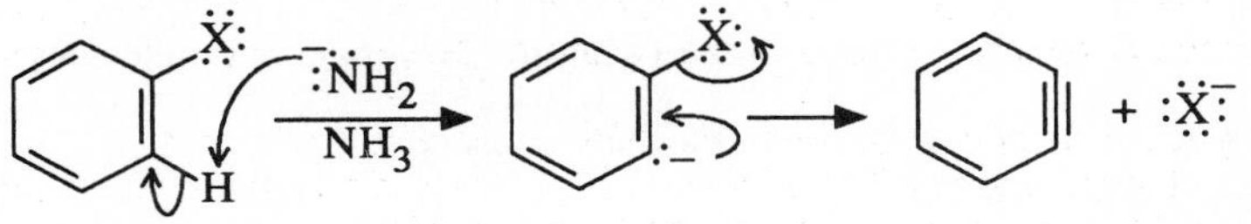

   c) Attack by amide ion gives a new anion.
   d) Protonation of this anion by the solvent completes the reaction.

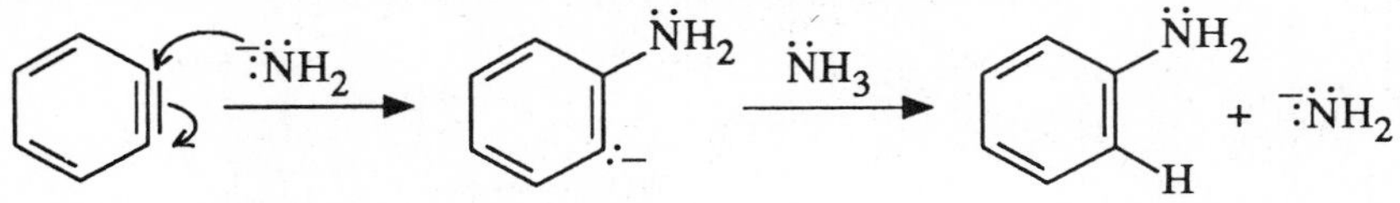

   e) The overall displacement shown is really an elimination-addition process.
3. Because either of the two triply-bonded carbons can be attacked by the base, some of the product results from attack of the nucleophile at the carbon adjacent to the one that bears the halide in the starting material.
   a) This type of substitution is called a *cine* **substitution**.
   b) The benzyne mechanism predicts a mixture of direct and *cine*-substitution products.

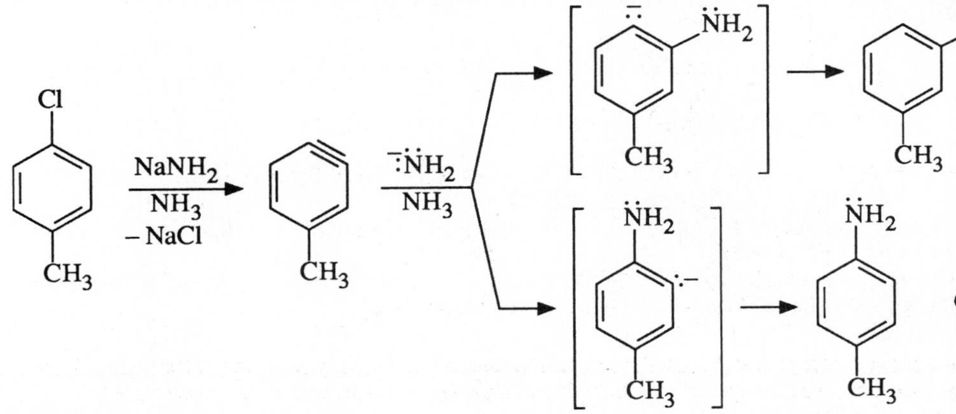

cine-substitution product

direct-substitution product

III. Phenols:

A. Introduction:
1. **Phenols** are compounds in which a hydroxy (—OH) group is bound to an aromatic ring.

2. Phenols, like alcohols, can ionize.
   a) Free energy of ionization is proportional to pK_a; phenols have much lower pK_a values than alcohols, and are thus more acidic than alcohols.
   b) The conjugate base of a phenol is named as a **phenoxide ion** (common nomenclature) or as a **phenolate ion** (systematic nomenclature).
3. Phenols are *completely* converted into their conjugate-base anions by NaOH solution.
   a) Alkali metal salts of phenols have considerable solubility in water because they are ionic compounds.
   b) Phenoxides are converted back into phenols by protonation.
   c) Solubility in 5% NaOH solution is an important qualitative test for phenols.
4. The acidity of phenols can sometimes be used to separate them from mixtures with other organic compounds.

B. Resonance Effect on Acidity:
   1. The enhanced acidity of phenol is due largely to stabilization of its conjugate-base anion by resonance.

   2. Substituent groups can affect the acidity of phenols by inductive effects and some also by resonance effects.

C. Oxidation of Phenols to Quinones:
   1. **Quinones** are compounds having two oxygens doubly bonded to a cyclohexadiene.
      a) *Ortho*-quinones have oxygens with a 1,2 (*ortho*) relationship.
      b) *Para*-quinones have oxygens with a 1,4 (*para*) relationship.

a *para*-quinone   an *ortho*-quinone

      c) *Ortho*-quinones are considerably less stable than the isomeric *para*-quinones. In *ortho*-quinones, the C=O bond dipoles are nearly aligned, and therefore have a repulsive, destabilizing interaction.
   2. Hydroquinone and other phenols can be used as inhibitors of free-radical chain reactions.
      a) Many free radicals abstract a hydrogen from hydroquinone to form a very stable radical called a **semiquinone.**
      b) A second free radical can react with the semiquinone to complete its oxidation to quinone.
      c) Hydroquinone terminates free-radical chain reactions by intercepting free radical intermediates R· and reducing them to R—H.
   3. Oxidation of phenols is a key element in the operation of some food preservatives and photographic developers.

D. Lack of Reactivity of the Phenolic Carbon–Oxygen Bond:
   1. Phenols do not react under conditions used for S_N2 reactions of alcohols and their derivatives for the same reasons that aryl halides do not react (see Sec. 18.1).
   2. Phenols also do not react under conditions used for $S_N1/E1$ reactions of alcohols and their derivatives for the same reasons that aryl halides do not react (see Sec. 18.3).

CHAPTER 18 REACTIONS

I. Reactions of Aryl and Vinyl Halides:

A. Elimination Reactions of Vicinal Halides:
   1. Base-promoted β-elimination reactions of vinyl halides do occur and can be useful in the synthesis of alkynes.
   2. The vinylic proton is more acidic than an alkyl proton, and is therefore more easily removed by a base than an alkyl proton.
   3. The conditions for E2 reactions of vinylic halides are more severe than those for the analogous reactions of ordinary alkyl halides.

$$CH_3-CH{=}\overset{\overset{\displaystyle Br}{|}}{C}-CH_3 \xrightarrow[\text{(CH}_3)_3\text{COH}]{\text{(CH}_3)_3\text{CO}^-\text{ K}^+} CH_3-C{\equiv}C-CH_3 \;+\; KBr$$

B. Aryl and Vinylic Grignard Reagents:
   1. Preparation of Grignard and organolithium reagents from aryl and vicinal halides is analogous to the corresponding reactions of alkyl halides.
   2. Arylmagnesium bromides or iodides can be prepared from the corresponding bromo- or iodobenzenes in either tetrahydrofuran (THF) or diethyl ether solvent; formation of arylmagnesium chlorides from chlorobenzenes *requires* the use of THF.
   3. The preparation of vinylic Grignard reagents also requires THF as a solvent.

C. Substitution Reactions of Aryl Halides:
   1. Aryl halides undergo *electrophilic* aromatic substitution—the substitution of a *proton* of the aryl halide, not the halogen.

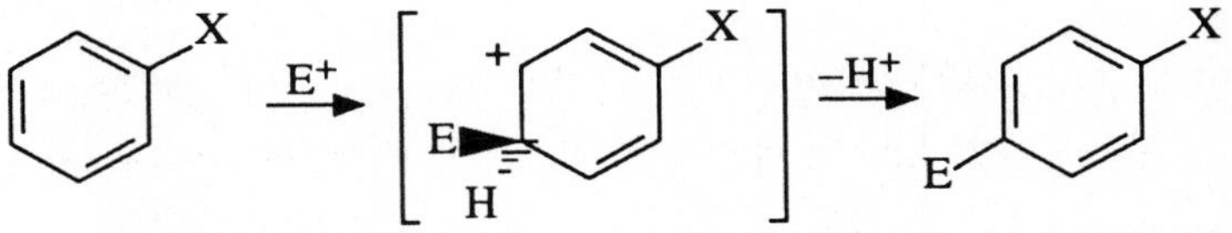

   2. Aryl halides substituted with *ortho-* or *para*-nitro groups (or other conjugated, electron-withdrawing groups) react with Lewis bases in *nucleophilic* aromatic substitution reactions; these involve:
      a) Nucleophilic attack on the aromatic π-electron system to give a resonance-stabilized anionic intermediate (Meisenheimer complex).
      b) Loss of the halide from the Meisenheimer complex.

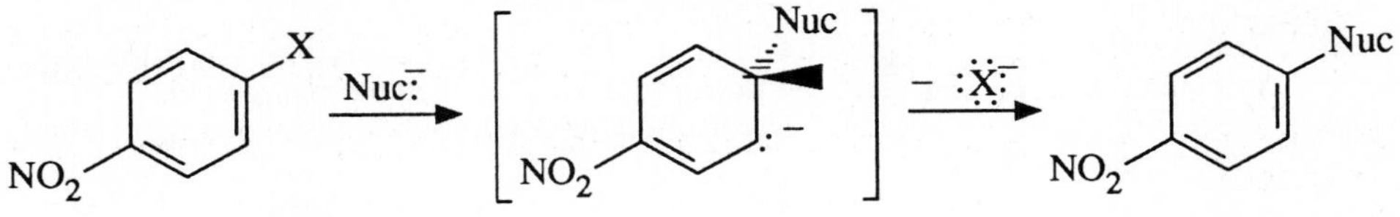

   3. Ordinary aryl halides undergo substitution by the *benzyne* mechanism *only* in the presence of a very strong base such as an alkali metal amide or organolithium reagent; this reaction involves:
      a) β-elimination of the halide to form benzyne.
      b) Addition of the nucleophile to benzyne.

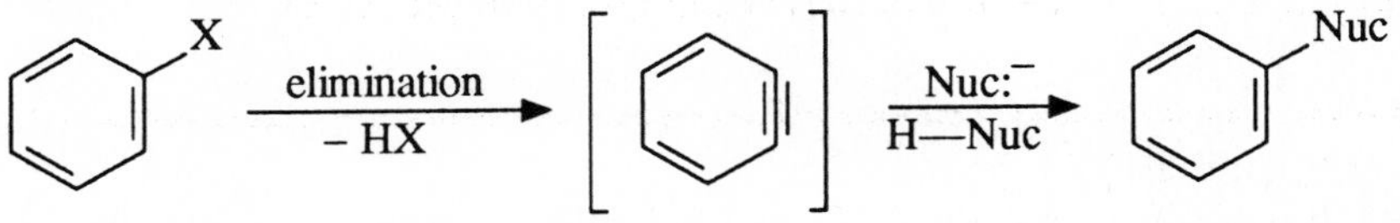

II. Reactions of Phenols and Phenolates:

A. Use of Phenoxides as Nucleophiles:
1. Phenoxides can be used as nucleophiles.
2. Aryl ethers can be prepared by the reaction of a phenoxide anion and an alkyl halide—another example of the Williamson ether synthesis.

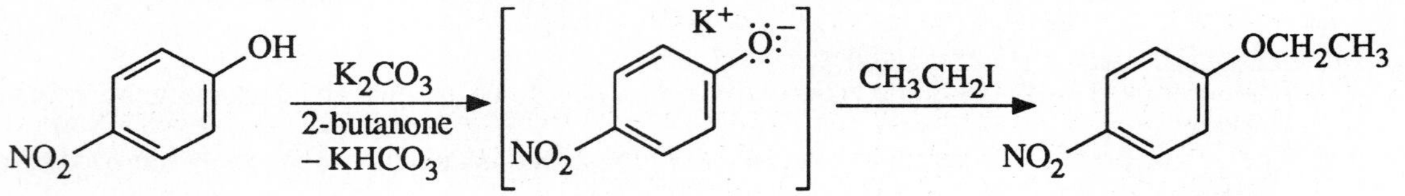

B. Electrophilic Aromatic Substitution Reactions of Phenols:
1. Phenols undergo electrophilic aromatic substitution reactions.
2. Phenols react rapidly with bromine.
   a) Because the —OH group is a strongly activating substituent, the phenol may be halogenated once under mild conditions that do not affect benzene itself.

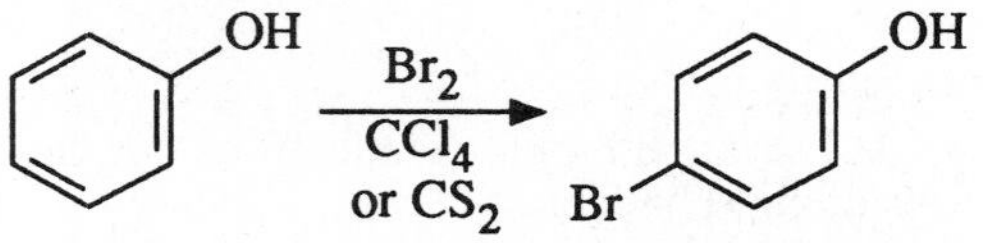

   b) Phenol reacts with aqueous bromine (**bromine water**) to give tribromophenol.
      (1) Bromine reacts with water to give protonated **hypobromous acid**, a more potent electrophile than bromine itself.
      (2) In aqueous solutions near neutrality, phenol partially ionizes to its conjugate-base phenoxide anion; this is very reactive because the bromination intermediate is not a carbocation, but a relatively stable neutral molecule.

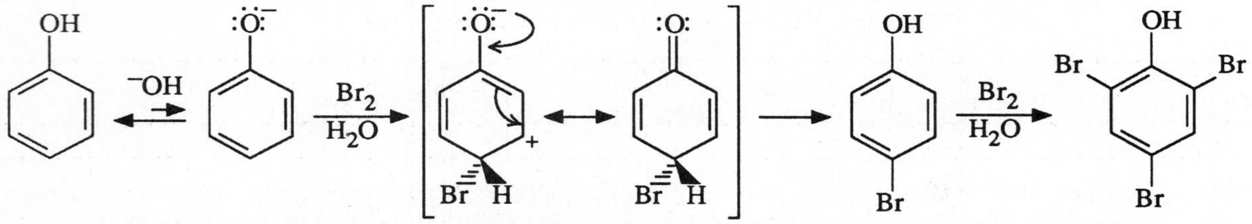

   c) In strongly acidic solution, in which formation of the phenolate anion is suppressed, bromination can be stopped at the 2,4-dibromophenol stage.
3. Phenol is very reactive in other electrophilic substitution reactions.
   a) Phenol can be nitrated *once* under mild condition.
   b) Direct nitration is *not* the preferred method for synthesis of di- and trinitrophenol, because the concentrated HNO3 required for multiple nitrations is an *oxidizing* agent.
   c) The great reactivity of phenol in electrophilic aromatic substitution does not extend to the Friedel–Crafts acylation reaction.
      (1) Friedel–Crafts acylation of phenol occurs slowly, but may be carried out successfully at elevated temperatures.
      (2) Phenols are less reactive because they react rapidly with the AlCl3 catalyst.

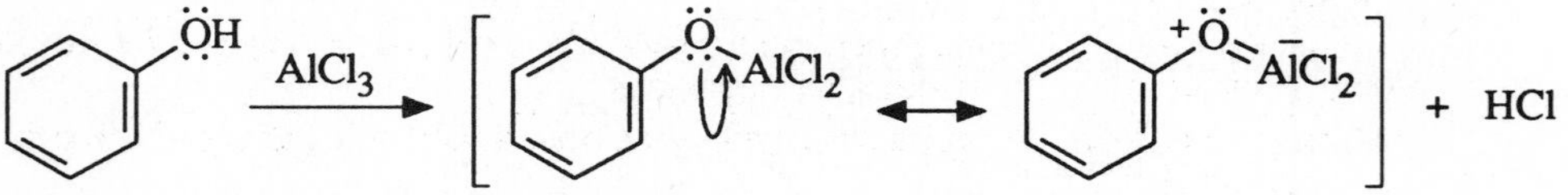

C. Oxidation of Phenols to Quinones:
1. *p*-Hydroxyphenols (hydroquinones), *o*-hydroxyphenols (catechols), and phenols with an unsubstituted position *para* to the hydroxy group are oxidized to quinones.

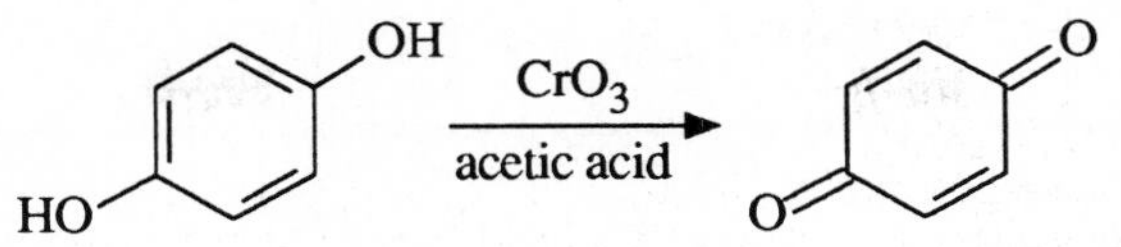

2. The oxidation of hydroquinone and its derivatives to the corresponding *p*-benzoquinone can also be carried out reversibly in an electrochemical cell.

D. Industrial Preparation and Use of Phenol:
1. Phenol and acetone are prepared in the same process from **cumene**, which in turn comes from benzene and propylene, two compounds obtained from petroleum.
2. The production of phenol and acetone is a two-step process.
   a) Cumene undergoes **autoxidation** with molecular oxygen—a free-radical chain reaction that gives **cumene hydroperoxide**.

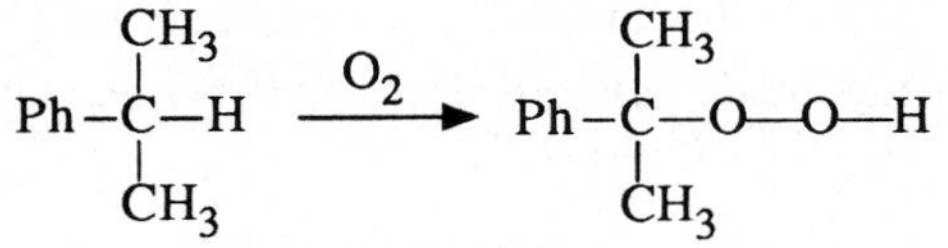

   cumene hydroperoxide

   b) The cumene hydroperoxide rearranges to acetone and phenol under acidic conditions:

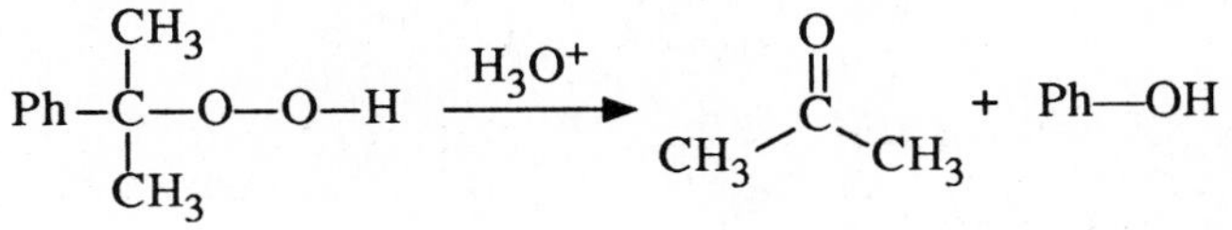

ORGANOHALIDE SUMMARY

Type of Organohalide	Reaction Mechanism	Comments
methyl	S_N2	
primary	S_N2	inversion of configuration
	E2	observed with stong, hindered bases only
secondary	S_N1 and S_N2	
	E1 and E2	Saytzeff products observed except in E2 reactions with hindered bases
tertiary	S_N1	predominant racemization
	E1 and E2	Saytzeff products observed except in E2 reaction with hindered bases
allylic	S_N1 and S_N2	products of allylic rearrangement observed in S_N1 reactions
benzylic	S_N1 and S_N2	
vinylic	no S_N1 or S_N2	
	β-elimination	requires strong base
aromatic	no S_N1 or S_N2	
	nucleophilic aromatic substitution	requires electron-withdrawing groups, typically nitro groups, in *ortho* and/or *para* positions
	elimination–addition (benzyne)	requires strong base; both direct and *cine* substitution occur
	electrophilic aromatic substitution	*proton* is substituted by electrophile

CHAPTER 18 SOLUTIONS

Solutions to In-Text Problems

1.   The benzylic alkyl halide (a) reacts most rapidly (Sec. 17.4); the alkyl halide (b) reacts more slowly; and the aryl halide *p*-bromotoluene is virtually unreactive. Thus, the order of reactivity is:

   (c) < (b) < (a)

2.   We assume that E2 reactions of *vinylic* halides follow the same rules as E2 reactions of *alkyl* halides. Therefore, because *anti* elimination is preferred to *syn* elimination, (b) is faster than (a); and because bromide is a better leaving group than chloride, (a) is faster than (c). Hence, the desired order is:

   (c) < (a) < (b)

3.   In the following mechanism, we let Ph = phenyl.

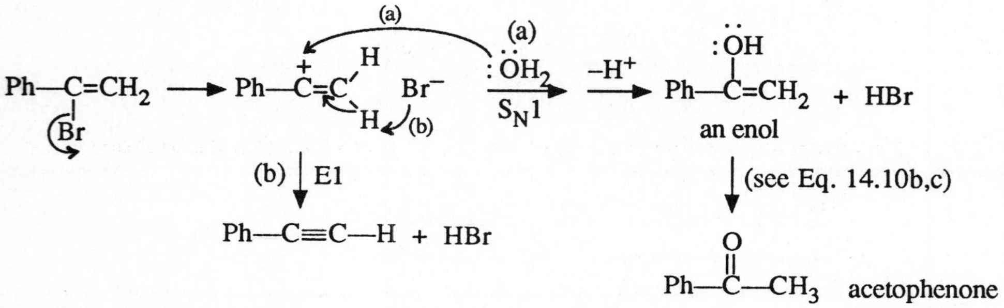

   Notice that solvolysis takes place under extreme conditions (heat), and that attack of water on the vinylic cation gives an *enol*, which, by Eq. 14.10b–c, is immediately transformed into acetophenone.

4.   (a)   (b)

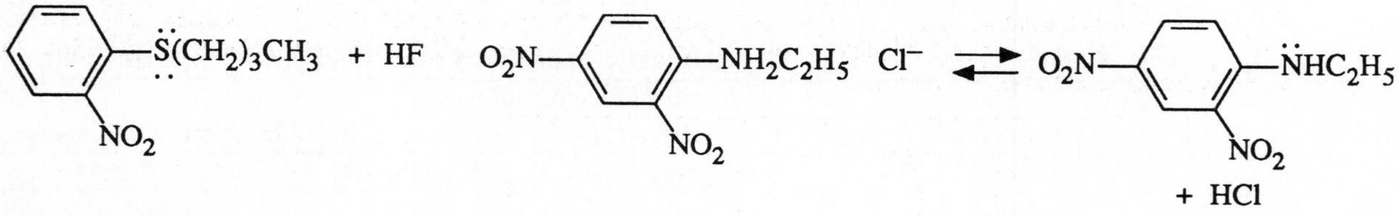

   In (b), the product is deprotonated under the reaction conditions; however, since we have not yet studied the basicity of amines, either answer can be considered correct.

   (c) No reaction. There is no group on the ring that can stabilize the anionic intermediate by resonance.

5.   (a) The compound on the left reacts more rapidly, because the anionic Meisenheimer complex is stabilized by the *para* substituent.

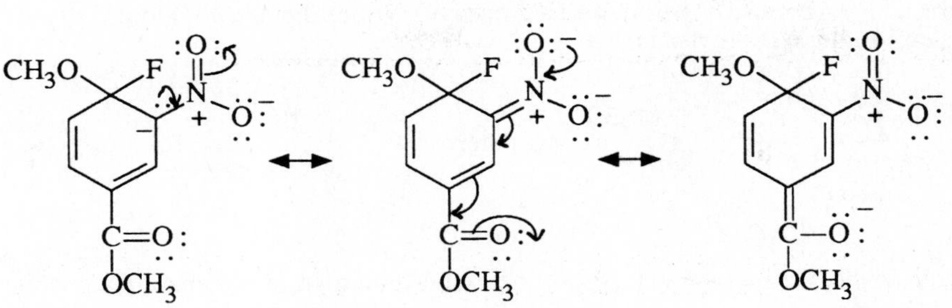

(b) The second compound reacts more rapidly because only in this compound is the nitro group positioned so that the anionic intermediate can be stabilized by resonance.

6.   The two carbons of the benzyne triple bond are nonequivalent; attack of the amide ion at one carbon gives the *meta* isomer; attack at the other carbon gives the *ortho* isomer:

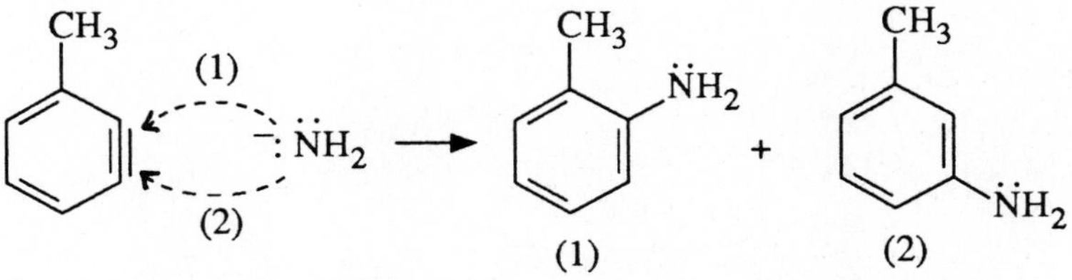

7.   (a) There is one benzyne intermediate possible; it can give the two products (see solution to Problem 6):

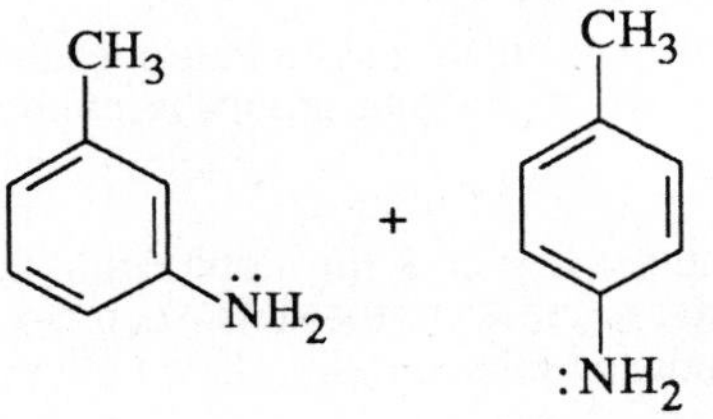

(b) Because there is no β-proton, no benzyne can form; there is no reaction.

(c) Because there are two nonequivalent β-protons, two benzynes can form, each of which can give rise to two products; however, one product is common to both intermediates. Hence, three products are possible; these are the compounds inside the box:

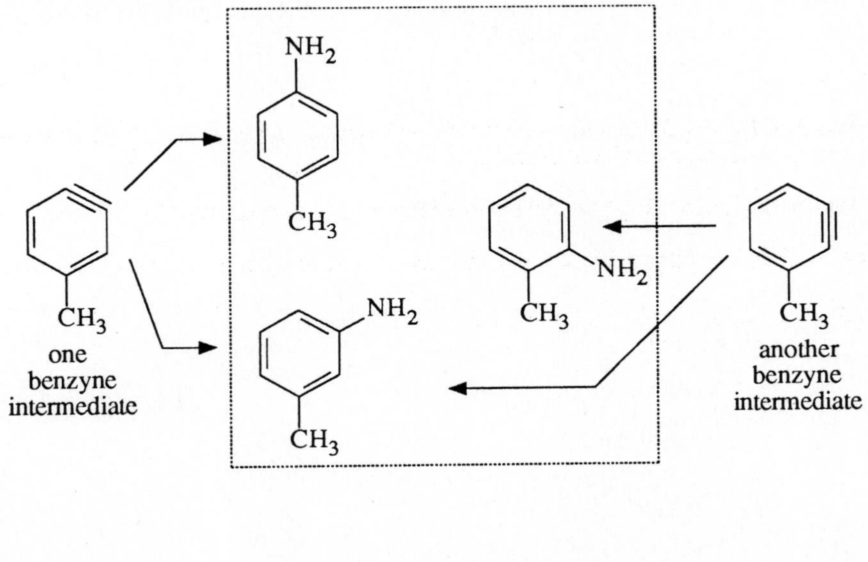

8. According to our usual practice, we construct the synthesis in reverse. Notice that the addition of a two-carbon unit dictates use of a Grignard addition to ethylene oxide:

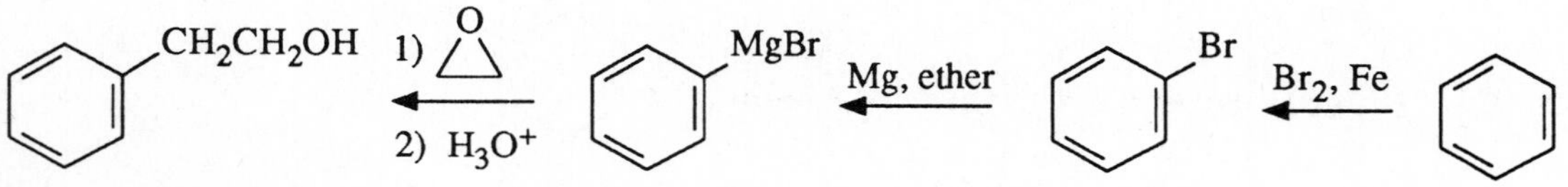

9. (a) *m*-Chlorophenol is more acidic, because the inductive effect of the chloro group stabilizes the conjugate-base anion of *m*-chlorophenol.
    (b) Only in 2,4-dinitrophenol are *both* nitro groups positioned so that they can stabilize the conjugate-base anion by resonance.
    (c) The first compound is more acidic, because the *para*-formyl (—CH=O) group can stabilize the conjugate-base anion by resonance:

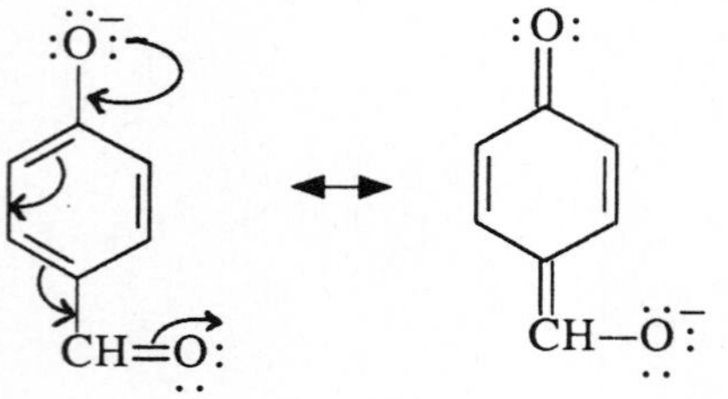

Analogous resonance stabilization is not possible in the *meta*-substituted compound. (Be sure you see why this is so!)
    (d) The cationic nitrogen exerts a strong inductive effect that stabilizes the conjugate-base anion in each case. Recall that inductive effects are strongest when the distance between the two interacting groups is smallest. Hence, the first compound is more acidic.

10. No, because the scheme discussed in the text is predicated on the assumption that both the alcohol and the phenol are insoluble in water. Because both ethanol and phenol are water-soluble compounds, such a scheme would not work. However, the boiling points of these two compounds differ substantially. Ethanol could be removed from phenol simply by boiling it away on a steam bath.

11. The discussion preceding the problem applies to *neutral* phenols that give *ionic* conjugate bases. In this rather unusual case, the phenol is *ionic* (cationic, but ionic nevertheless), and, like many ionic compounds, is *soluble* in water; since this is the form present in acidic solution, the phenol is acid-soluble. The conjugate base of the phenol has both a cationic group and an anionic group within the same molecule, and is therefore neutral. Like many neutral organic compounds, such a compound is not soluble in water. Since this is the form present in basic solution, this species is insoluble in aqueous base:

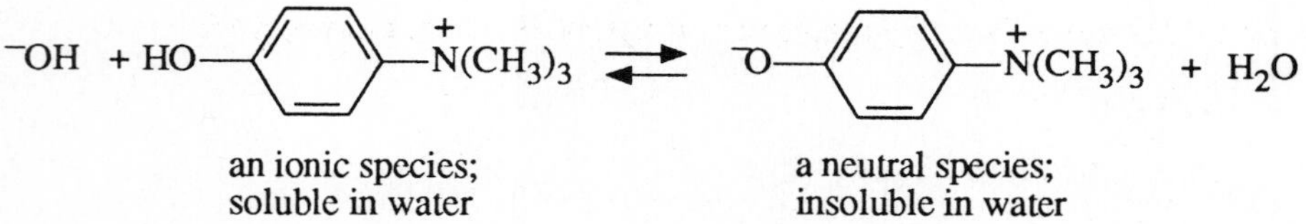

12. As in Problem 8, we notice that a —CH_2CH_2— unit must be added. This is provided by the reaction of
     phenolate ion, formed from phenol in base, with ethylene oxide:

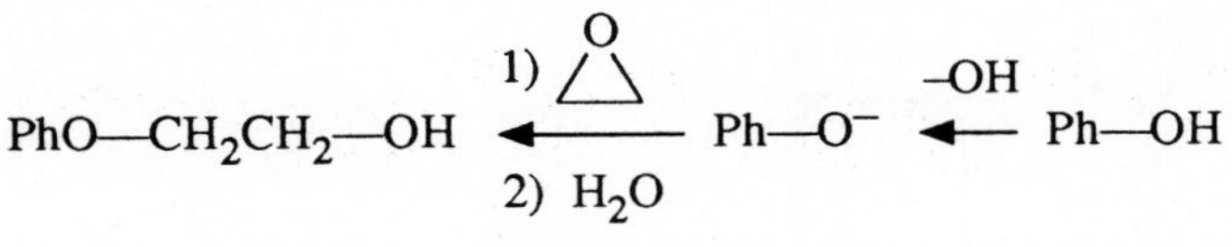

13. It is an *ortho*-quinone, because the two C=O groups are in adjacent positions.

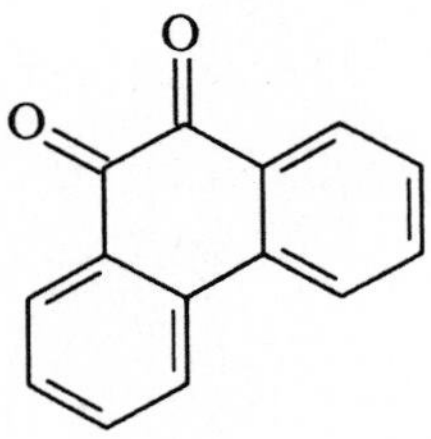

an *o*-quinone

14. (a)   (b)

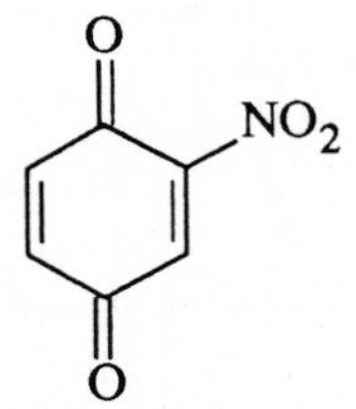

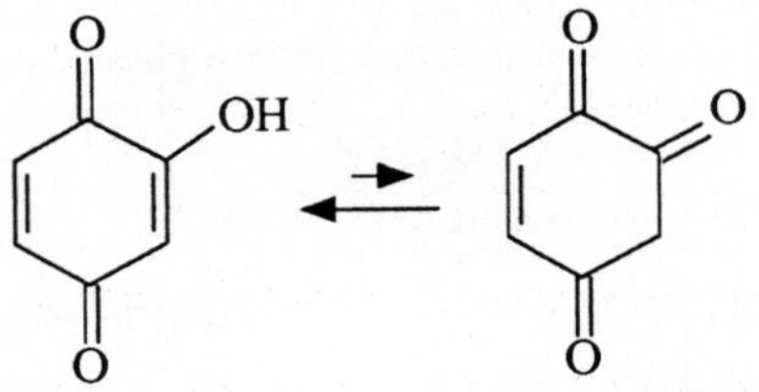

     Notice in (b) that the third —OH group in the starting material, once the *para*-hydroxy groups have been
     oxidized, is no longer a phenol group, but an *enol*; like other enols (text pages 557–559), it is transformed into
     a ketone and is not oxidized further. (Actually, it remains mostly in the enol form, for reasons that we can't
     consider here; but it indeed is not oxidized further.)

15. (a)   (b) 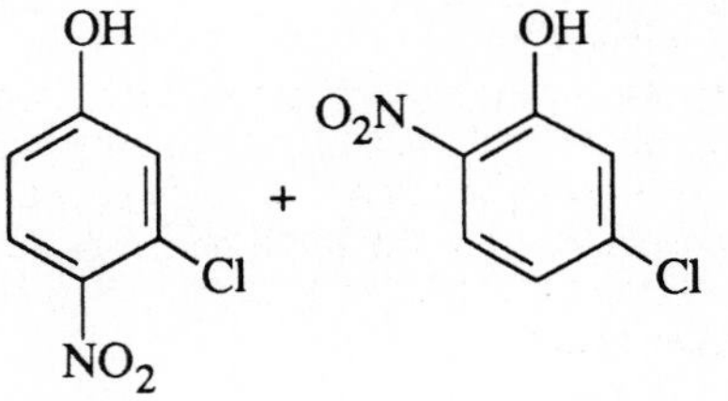   (c) 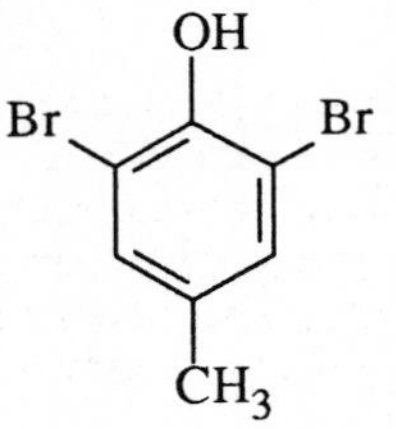   (d)

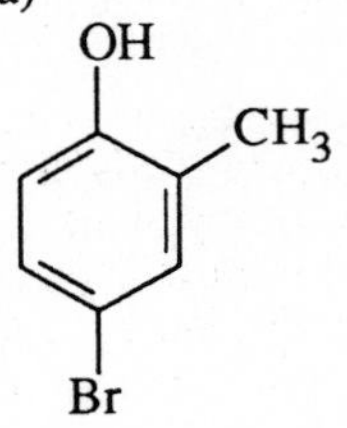

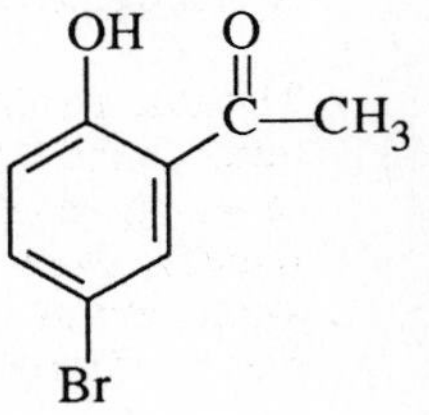

16. It undergoes sulfonation to give the *ortho* and *para* isomers of hydroxybenzenesulfonic acid:

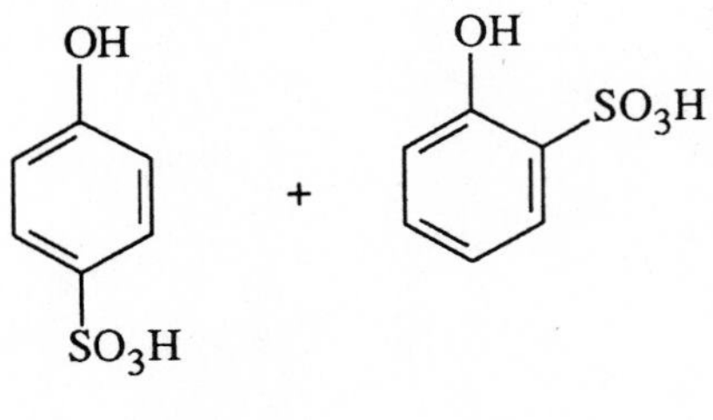

17. (a) The O—O bond of cumene hydroperoxide, like that of all peroxides, is weak, and readily undergoes homolysis. A free-radical chain reaction of one of the radicals resulting from this homolysis leads to product *A*:

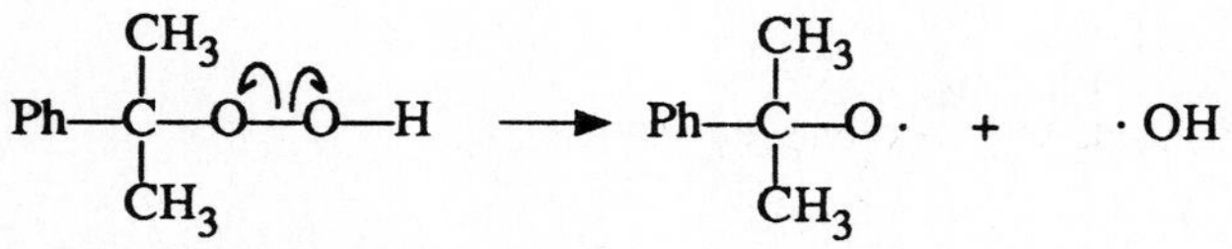

cumene hydroperoxide
(Eq. 18.49a)

A

can enter propagation steps at Eq. 18.50b

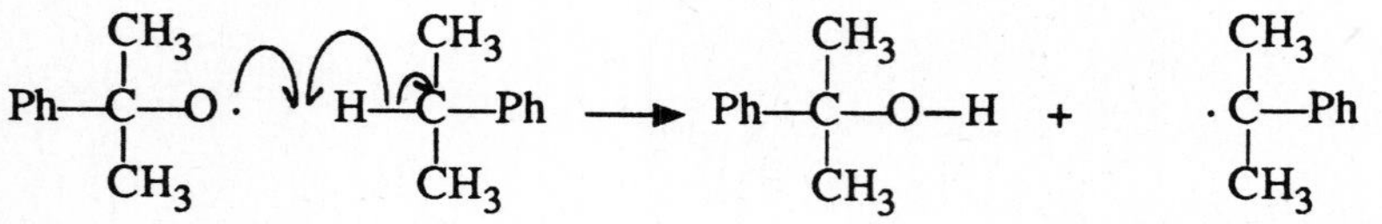

(b) Compound *A*, formed by the side reaction discussed in the previous part of the problem, undergoes acid-catalyzed loss of water to give the relatively stable tertiary benzylic carbocation, which then acts as an electrophile in an electrophilic aromatic substitution reaction on phenol to give compound *B*:

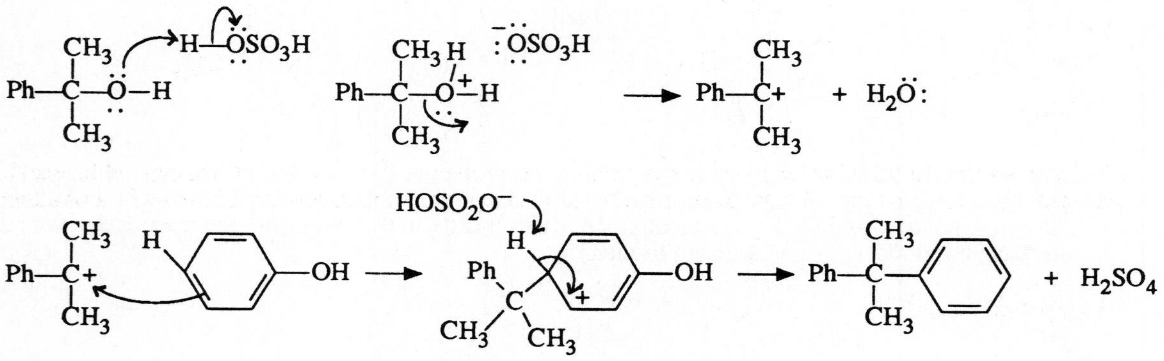

Solutions to Additional Problems

18. (a) No reaction. An ordinary aryl halide such as *p*-iodotoluene does not undergo solvolysis under mild conditions.

    (b) No reaction. An ordinary aryl halide does not undergo S_N2 reactions.

    (c)   (d)   (e)   (f)

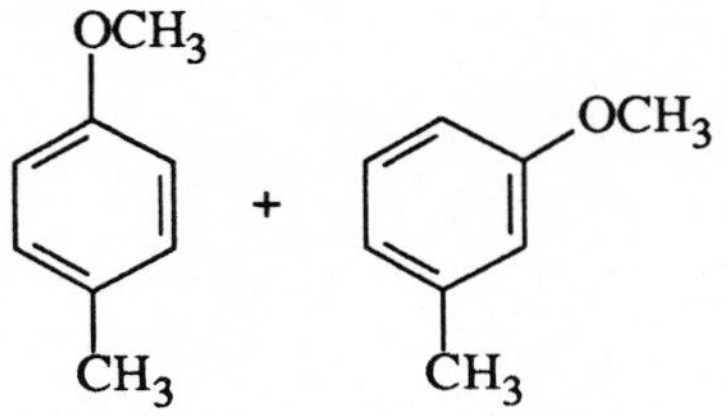

    (from a benzyne intermediate)

19. (a) 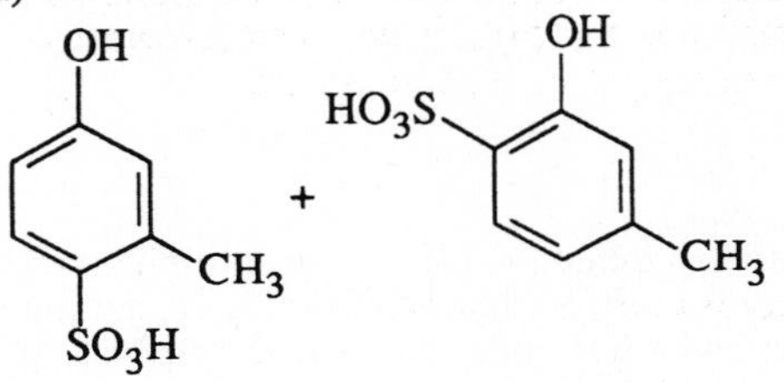   (b)

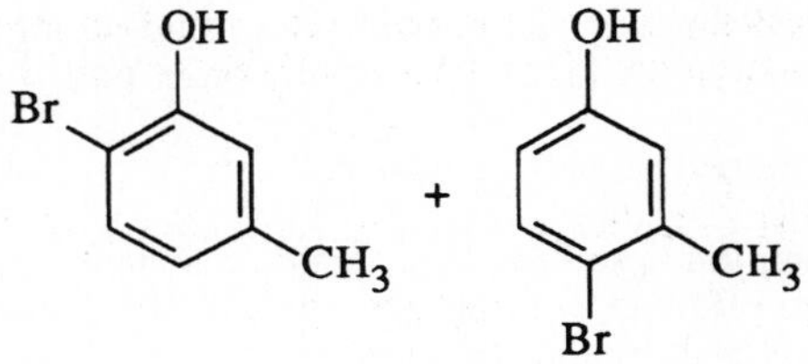

    (c) There are two kinds of answers we could write to this problem. The first is that free-radical bromination of the methyl group will occur. Under these conditions, the ring bromination observed in (b) will also take place:

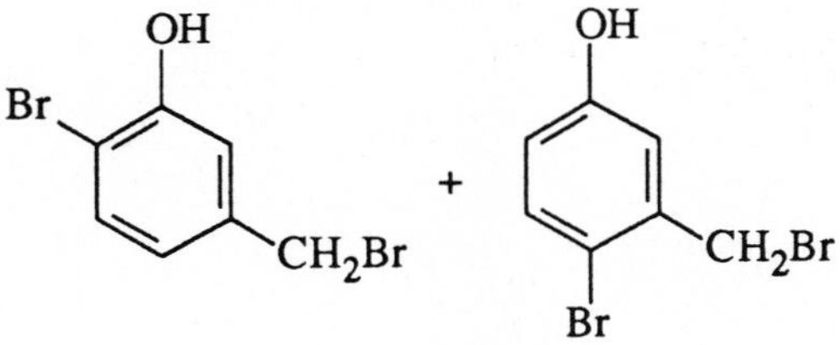

    However, we should remember that phenols are free-radical inhibitors (text pages 160, 737–738). A certain percentage of the phenol present will act to scavenge free-radical chains and prevent side-chain bromination. In this case, the products will be the same as in part (b).

    (d) No reaction.

    (e) In aqueous sodium hydroxide solution, phenols are completely converted into their conjugate-base anions:

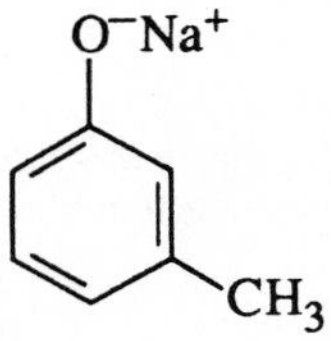

(f)

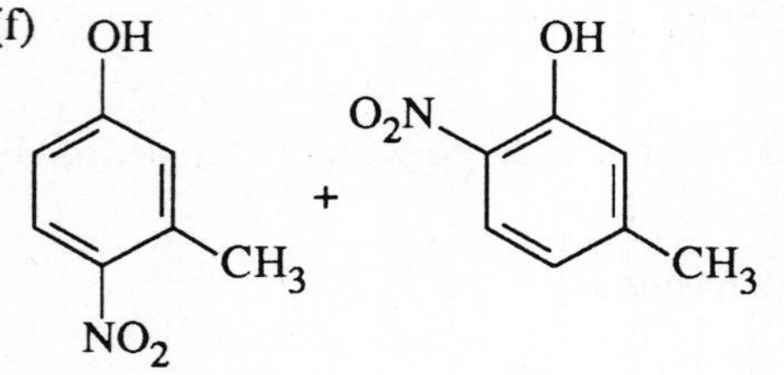

(g)

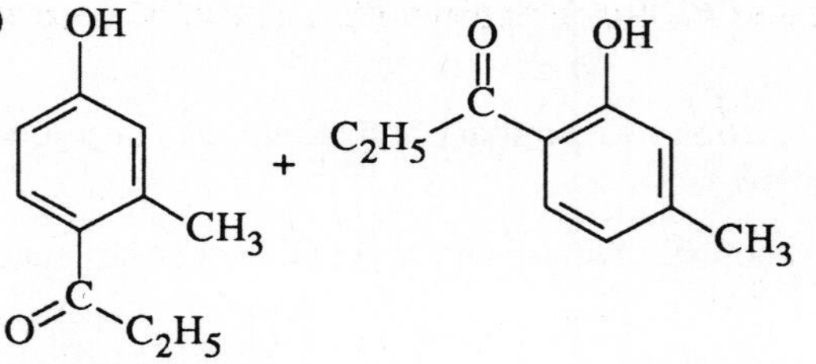

(h)

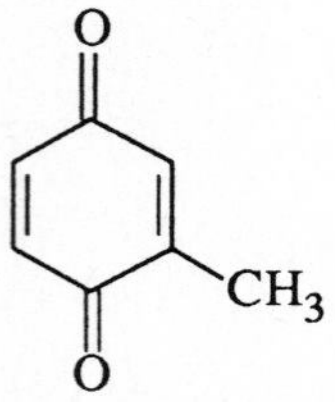

20. (a) Phenols are more acidic than alcohols; and a primary alcohol (benzyl alcohol) is more acidic than a secondary alcohol (cyclohexanol) because of the chain-branching effect (Sec. 8.6C). (In addition, the phenyl group has a significant electron-withdrawing, acid-strengthening inductive effect, although this was not discussed explicitly in the text.) The acidity order is:

cyclohexanol < benzyl alcohol < phenol.

(b) The phenolate ion is stabilized both by a resonance effect and an inductive effect in *p*-nitrophenol, and by only an inductive effect in *p*-chlorophenol. The third compound is nitric acid, a strong acid. Its conjugate-base anion is stabilized both by the inductive effect of the nitro group, which is much closer to the anionic oxygen than it is in the conjugate base of *p*-nitrophenol, and by a resonance effect:

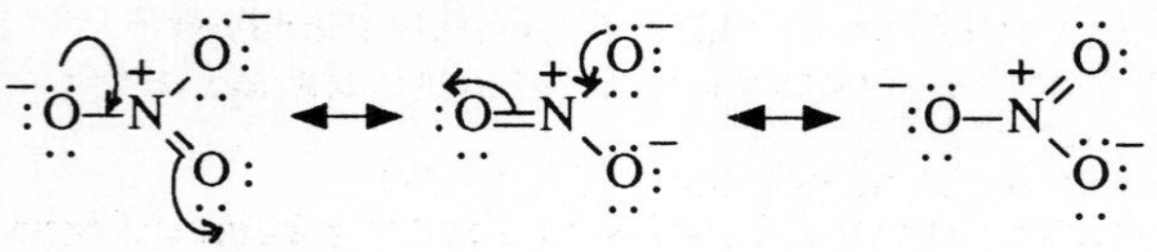

The acidity order is:

p-chlorophenol < *p*-nitrophenol << nitric acid

(c) Mercaptans are more acidic than phenols; and aryl mercaptans (thiophenols) are more acidic than alkyl mercaptans, for the same reason that phenols are more acidic than alcohols. The desired acidity order is:

cyclohexanol < cyclohexyl mercaptan < benzenethiol

(d) The conjugate-base anions of *p*-nitrobenzenethiol and *p*-nitrophenol are stabilized by resonance interaction with their *p*-nitro groups; and aryl thiols are more acidic than "aryl alcohols" (phenols). The acidity order is:

phenol < *p*-nitrophenol < *p*-nitrobenzenethiol

(e) All compounds have *ortho* substituents that interfere with solvation of their conjugate-base anions; this effect is most pronounced with 2,6-di-*t*-butylphenol, which has two large *t*-butyl groups in the *ortho* positions. However, the conjugate base of 2,6-dichlorophenol is stabilized by a compensating, acid-strengthening inductive effect of the two chlorines. The acidity order is:

2,6-di-*t*-butylphenol < 2,4,6-trimethylphenol < 2,6-dichlorophenol

➤ The conjugate base of 2,6-di-*t*-butylphenol is actually a very strong base!

21. (a) We deduce that compound *A* is a phenol because of its solubility in base.

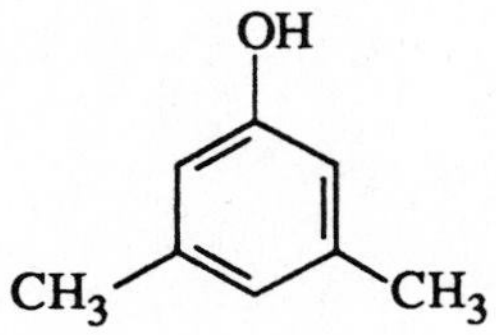

A

(b) Compound *B* is an alcohol, because it is insoluble in base and undergoes a typical alcohol reaction:

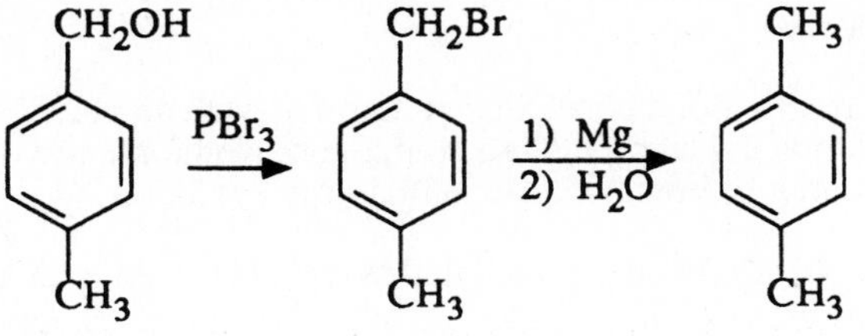

B

22. (a) Phenol is ionized completely to its conjugate-base anion; cyclohexanol is largely unaffected.
     (b) Both compounds form tosylate derivatives:

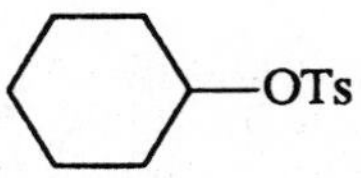

cyclohexyl tosylate 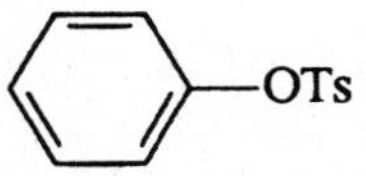   phenyl tosylate

(c) Both compounds are converted completely to their sodium salts and hydrogen gas is evolved.
(d) Cyclohexanol is converted into bromocyclohexane; phenol does not react, because cleavage of the ring—oxygen bond generally does not occur (text page 742).
(e) Cyclohexanol does not react; phenol is brominated in the *para* position (Eq. 18.39).
(f) Cyclohexanol is oxidized to a ketone, cyclohexanone, whereas phenol is oxidized to *p*-benzoquinone:

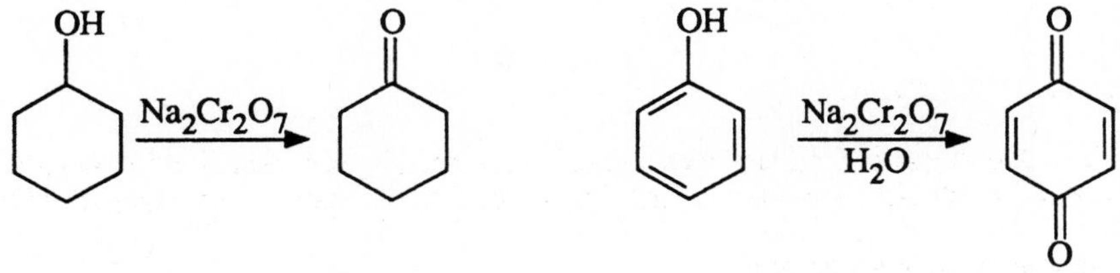

(g) Cyclohexanol is dehydrated to give cyclohexene; phenol is sulfonated:

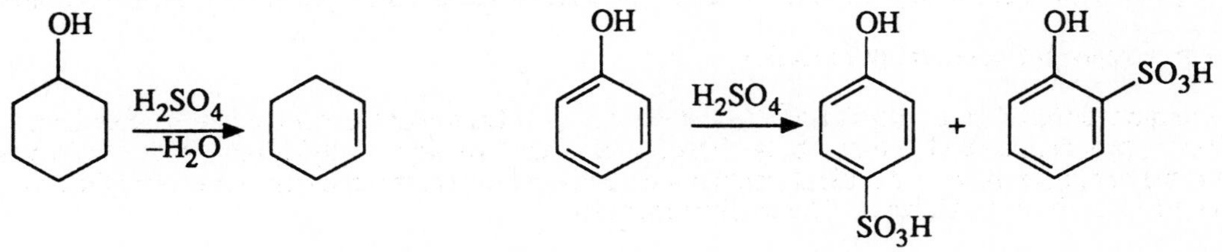

23. (a) The second compound reacts by a nucleophilic aromatic substitution mechanism to give the corresponding phenol with the displacement of fluoride ion:

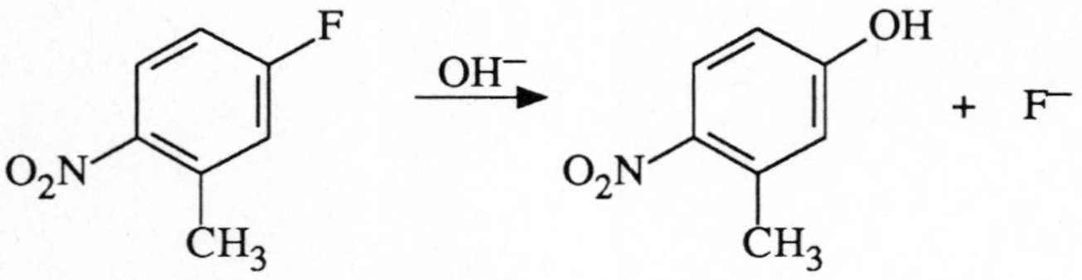

In the first compound, the nitro group is not attached directly to the ring, and therefore cannot exert a resonance effect to stabilize the intermediate Meisenheimer complex.

(b) The Williamson ether synthesis involves an S_N2 reaction of a phenoxide or alkoxide with an alkyl halide; aryl halides do not undergo S_N2 reactions. Because diphenyl ether, the last compound, would require one of the reactants to be bromobenzene, an aryl halide, it cannot be prepared by a Williamson synthesis.

(c) Only the first compound undergoes an S_N1 reaction; aryl halides do not undergo S_N1 reactions. A by-product of the S_N1 solvolysis of an alkyl bromide is HBr:

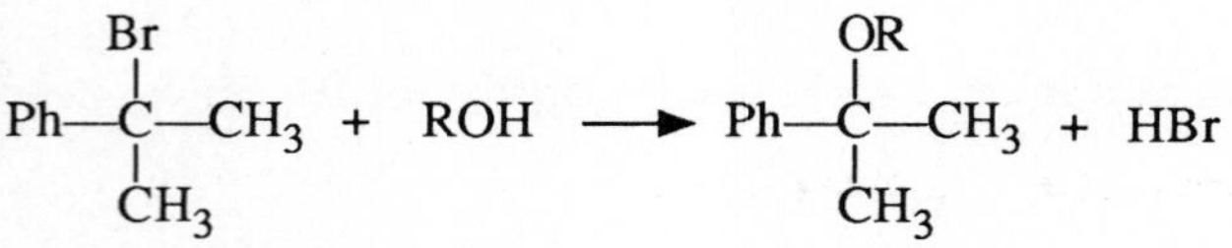

(d) Aryl chlorides do not form Grignard reagents in ether; THF is required (text pages 728–729). Hence, benzyl chloride, an *alkyl* chloride, is the compound that reacts to give benzylmagnesium chloride, Ph—CH$_2$—MgCl.

(e) Ether cleavage in concentrated HI involves either S_N1 or S_N2 mechanisms; neither of these mechanisms are accessible to diphenyl ether. Hence, phenyl cyclohexyl ether is the reactive compound.

(f) The last compound has no β-hydrogens, and therefore cannot form benzyne. The benzyne intermediate from the first compound gives only one product:

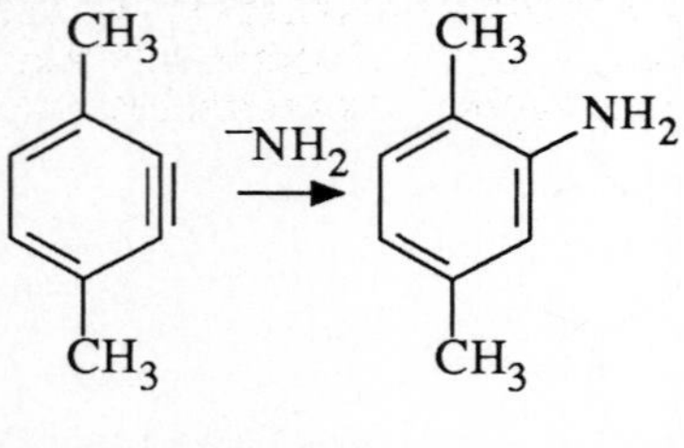

The compound that reacts to give two products is the second compound. This compound can form two benzyne intermediates; however, only two products can be formed, because *A* and *B* below are identical:

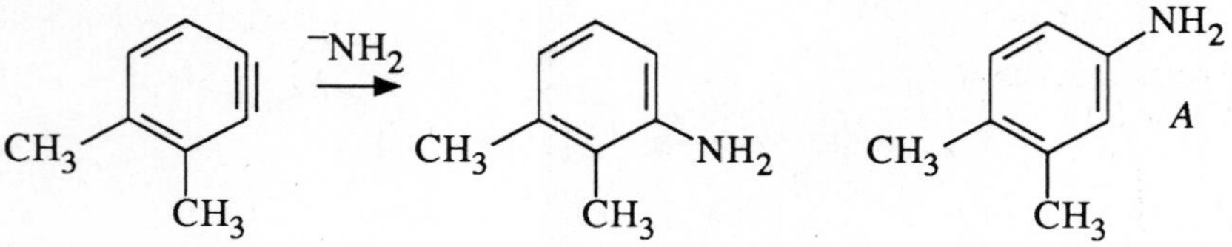

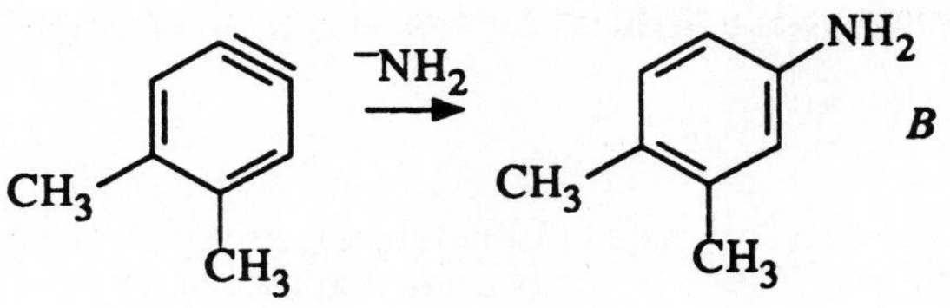

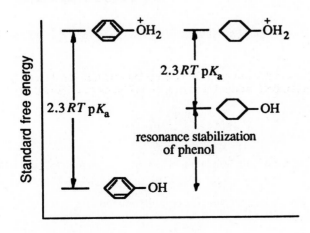

24. (a) Phenol can be protonated on its oxygen:

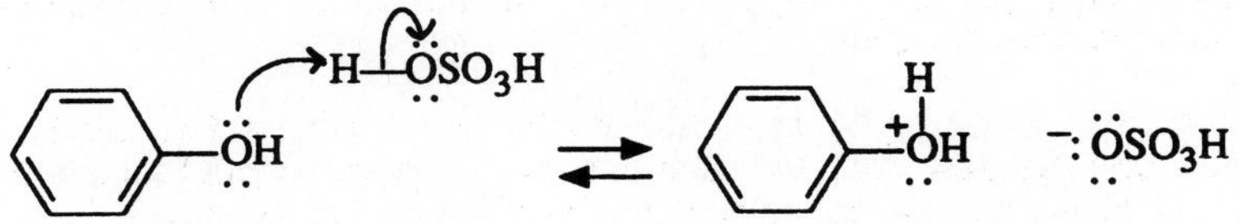

(b) The basicity of phenol is weakened because the unshared electron pairs of the phenol oxygen are delocalized into the aromatic ring; this delocalization is virtually nonexistent in the conjugate acid of phenol, and completely nonexistent in cyclohexanol:

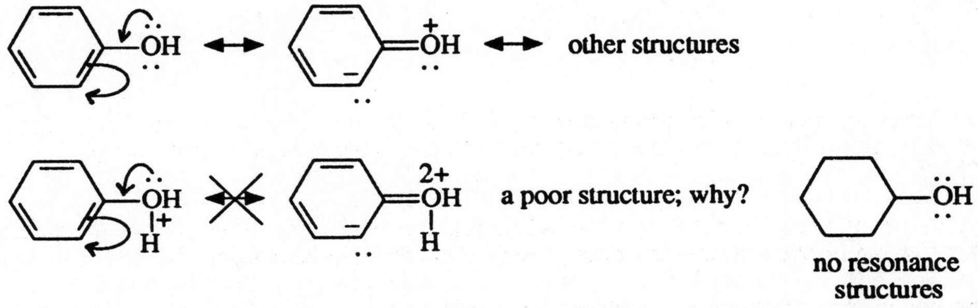

That is, if we place the conjugate acids of phenol and cyclohexanol at the same free energy, phenol has a lower free energy than cyclohexanol because of its resonance stabilization. As a result, more energy is required to protonate phenol than to protonate cyclohexanol, and phenol is therefore less basic. (Another, less precise, way to say the same thing is to say that the electron pair in phenol is "less available" to a proton because it is delocalized into the ring.)

25. The reaction evidently desired by the authors of this passage was a Williamson synthesis:

$$PhS^- \ + \ (CH_3)_3C—Br \ \longrightarrow \ PhS—C(CH_3)_3$$

What they got, however, was a competing elimination of t-butyl bromide to isobutylene; tertiary alkyl halides give E2 reactions, not S_N2 reactions, under basic conditions. The base, the benzenethiolate ion, abstracts a β-proton from t-butyl bromide to give benzenethiol:

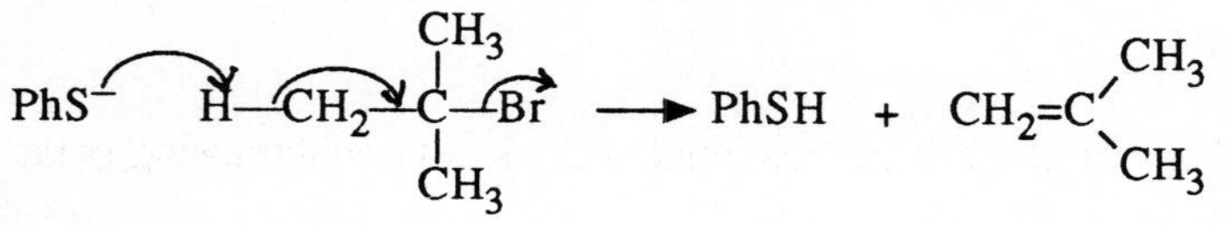

26. (a) This question is most easily answered by considering the mass-action law expression for ionization of a general acid HA to a proton, H_3O^+, and the conjugate base A^-.

$$K_a = \frac{[A^-][H_3O^+]}{[HA]} \ \text{ or } \ \frac{K_a}{[H_3O^+]} = \frac{[A^-]}{[HA]}$$

Taking logarithms,

$$\log K_a - \log [H_3O^+] = \log \frac{[A^-]}{[HA]}$$

or

$$pH - pK_a = \log \frac{[A^-]}{[HA]}$$

From this equation, we see that in order for the ratio $[A^-]/[HA]$ to be large (that is, $\gg 1$), the pH must be greater than the pK_a of the acid. Since $[A^-]$, the conjugate base of the phenol, is the water-soluble form, this is precisely the condition we desire for water solubility. Hence the answer is (3): the pH must be much greater than the pK_a of the phenol. (In other words, phenols dissolve in base — something we have already learned.)

(b) We want one compound to dissolve in water, and the other to remain insoluble. If the pH is adjusted so that it is *above* the pK_a of one phenol, and *below* that of the other, the solution will dissolve the more acidic of the two phenols according to the results of part (a). The less acidic phenol will remain in its neutral, un-ionized form (that is, $[A^-]/[HA] \ll 1$), and it will stay in the ether layer. A pH = 7 buffer meets the required conditions.

27. Since sodium hydroxide converts phenols into their conjugate-base anions, it follows that trace B is that of the p-nitrophenolate ion:

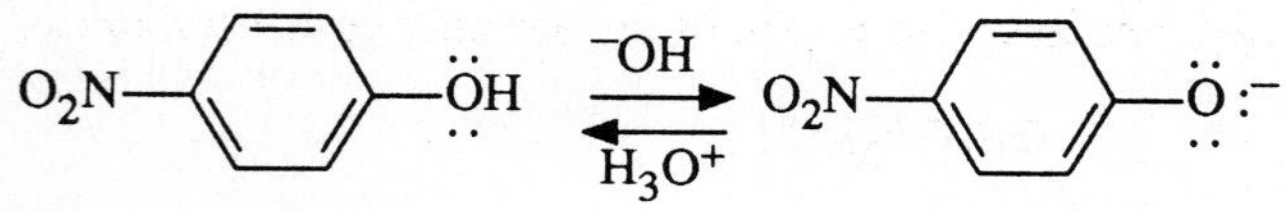

gives trace A gives trace B

In fact, trace B lies far enough into the visible that the p-nitrophenolate ion is colored; because it absorbs blue light, it gives a yellow solution.

28. Attack of electrophilic bromine (Eq. 18.41) at the 4-position of 2,4,6-tribromophenol and loss of a proton from the —OH proton gives the compound shown:

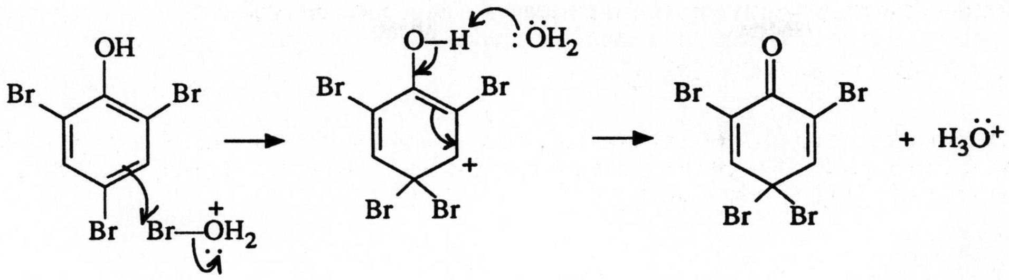

29. (a) The product results from a nucleophilic aromatic substitution; there is an electron-withdrawing group in the *para* position.

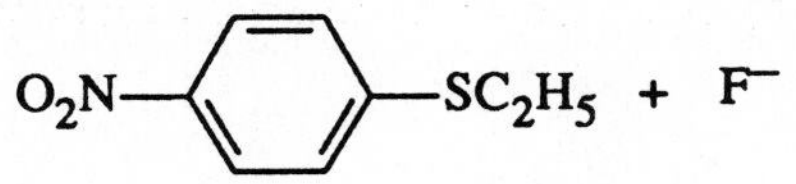

$$O_2N-\!\!\!\bigcirc\!\!\!-SC_2H_5 \;+\; F^-$$

(b) No reaction. There are no electron-withdrawing groups to activate the ring toward nucleophilic aromatic substitution, and the base is not strong enough to form benzyne. (Notice that the base is an *amine*, $R\ddot{N}H_2$, not an *amide ion*, $R\overline{\ddot{N}}H$.)

(c) The products are derived from a benzyne intermediate:

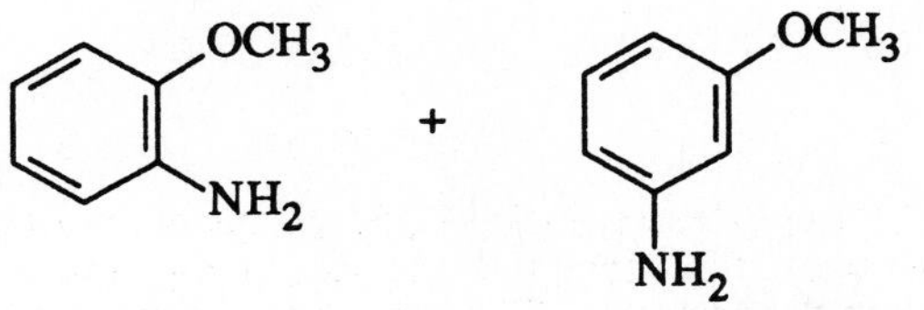

(d) The ring brominates in a position that is *ortho* to one hydroxy group and *para* to the other:

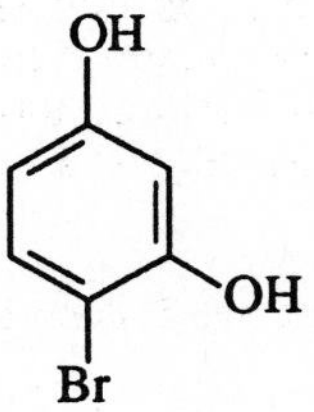

(e) The products are derived from a benzyne intermediate. (Notice the harsh, strongly basic conditions.)

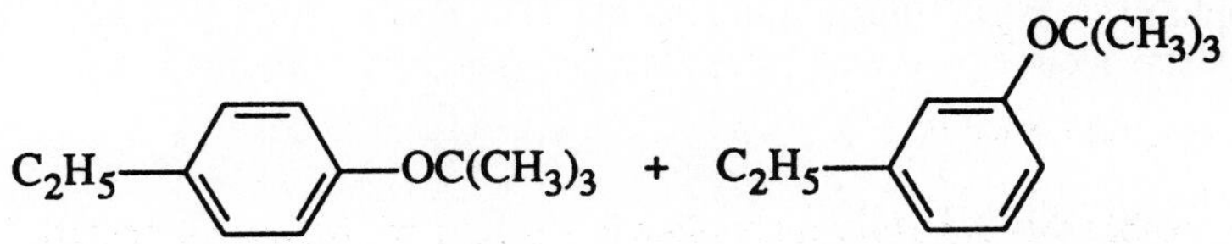

(f) With so many nitro groups, how can we avoid a nucleophilic aromatic substitution? The strongly acidic phenol product, called *picric acid*, ionizes under the basic conditions, and is reprotonated by H_3O^+.

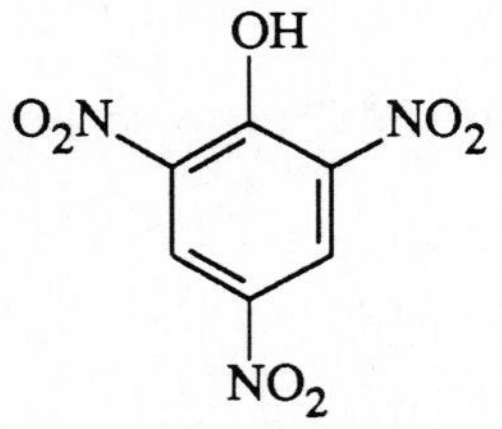

(g) Since this is a phenol, oxidation gives a quinone:

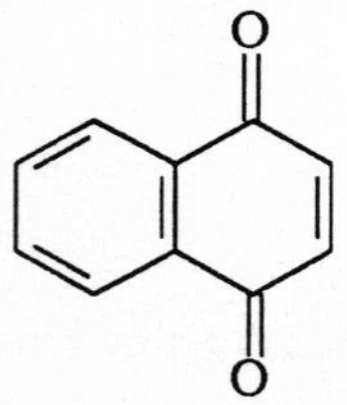

(h) The first reaction forms the mesylate. Since mesylates behave much like halides, the second reaction is the same one that would occur if the intermediate were 1-chloro-2,4-dinitrobenzene: a nucleophilic aromatic substitution.

mesylate (OMs) anion

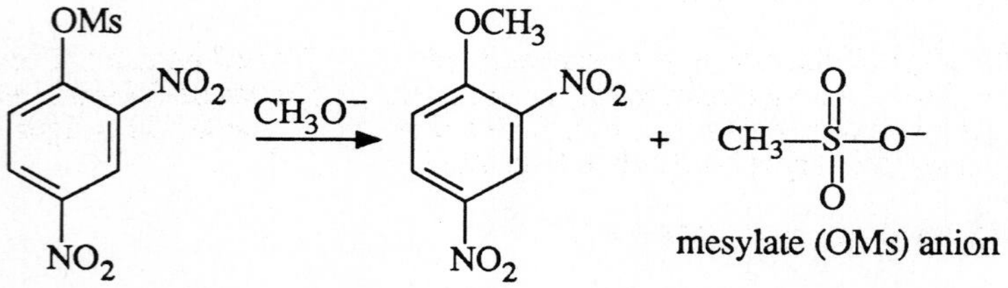

(i) Phenols are oxidized to quinones:

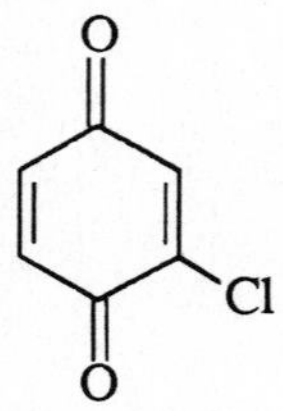

(j) The product results from a nucleophilic aromatic substitution reaction. The cyano group ($—C\equiv N:$), like a nitro group, can stabilize the anionic Meisenheimer complex by resonance. (Show this intermediate and its resonance structures!)

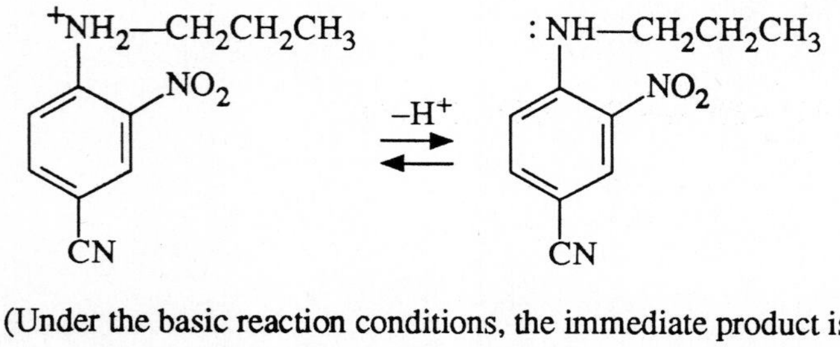

(Under the basic reaction conditions, the immediate product is deprotonated. Either form of the product is an acceptable answer.)

(k) The ring is brominated at a position that is *ortho* to one hydroxy group and *para* to another. That is, the directing effects of two of the three hydroxy groups are satisfied:

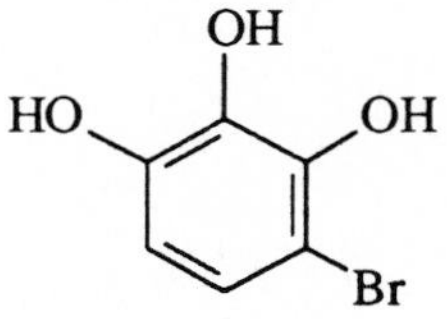

(l) The bromine that bears an *ortho, para* relationship to the nitro groups is activated toward nucleophilic aromatic substitution:

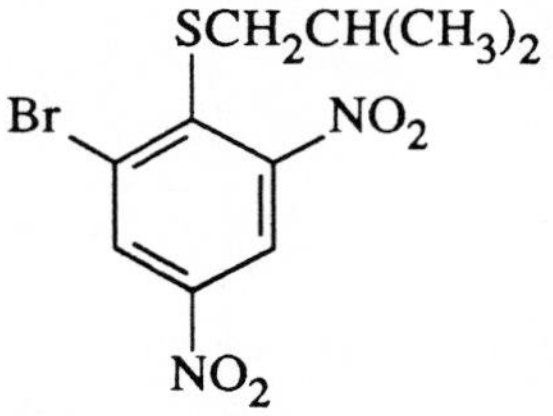

30. (a) The $\Delta H°$ of hydrogenation of 2-butyne is (–1.7 – 35.0) = –36.7 kcal/mol. The $\Delta H°$ of hydrogenation of 2-pentyne is (–6.7 – 30.8) = –37.5 kcal/mol. From these numbers we conclude that hydrogenation of a typical alkyne to a *cis*-alkene liberates about 37 kcal/mol of energy.

(b) In contrast, hydrogenation of the "alkyne" benzyne to the corresponding "*cis*-alkene," benzene, liberates 98.2 kcal/mol (19.8 – 118.0 = –98.2). The difference between this figure and the typical $\Delta H°$ for alkyne hydrogenation, –37 kcal/mol, can be attributed to the amount by which benzyne is unstable. This figure is 61.5 kcal/mol. Benzyne is less stable than a typical alkyne by nearly 62 kcal/mol!

31. As usual, we start with the target compound and work backwards:

(a)

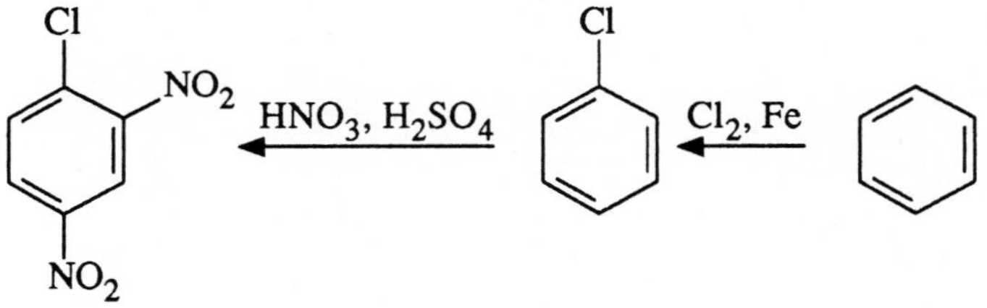

(b)

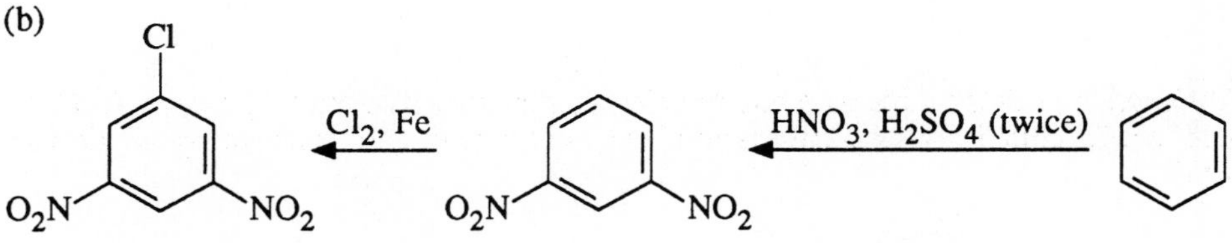

(c)

$$PhC{\equiv}CPh \xleftarrow{Na^+\ C_2H_5O^-} Ph{-}CHBr{-}CHBr{-}Ph \xleftarrow{Br_2} Ph{-}CH{=}CH{-}Ph$$

(d)

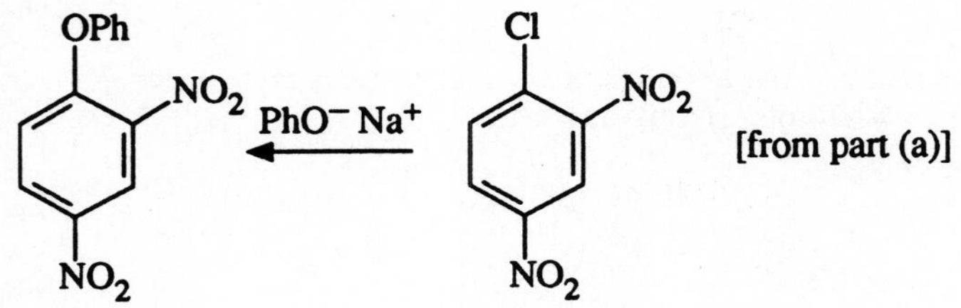

(e)

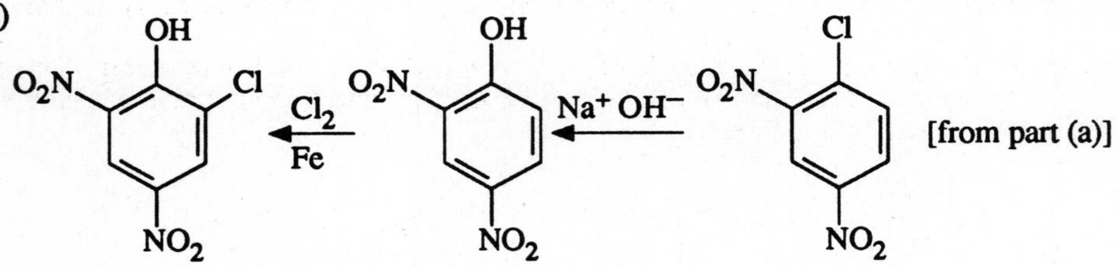

(f)

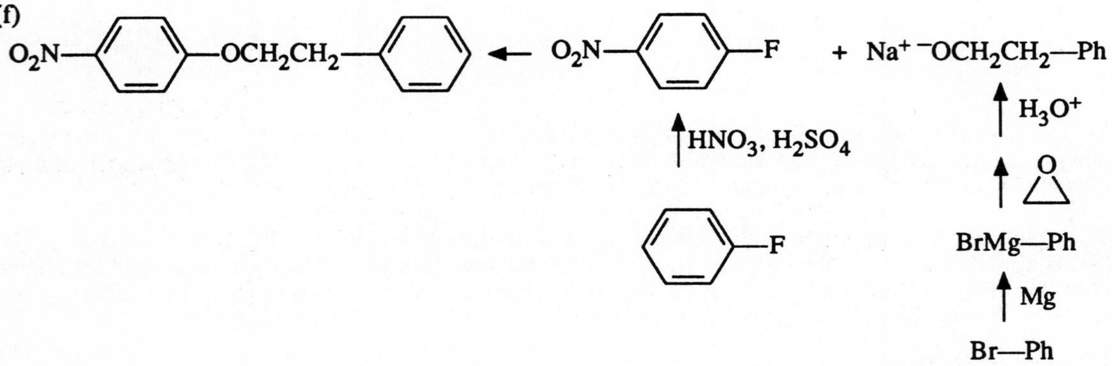

(g)

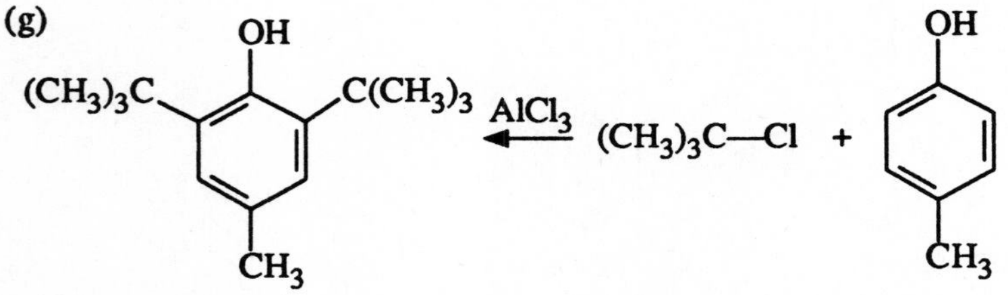

(h)

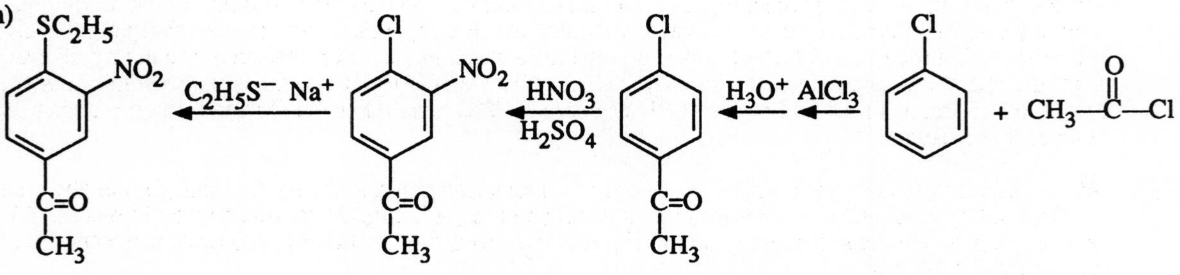

(i)

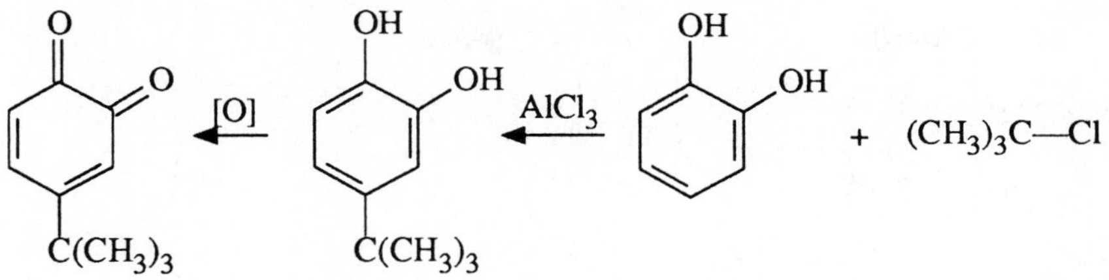

In this synthesis, the term [O] means oxidation by any of the usual methods: chromic acid, Ag_2O, etc.

(j) In this problem, we see that we must add a straight chain of two carbons to the benzene ring. This suggests the addition of a Grignard reagent to ethylene oxide. Once this is accomplished, the remaining task is to convert the —CH_2CH_2OH group into an alkyne.

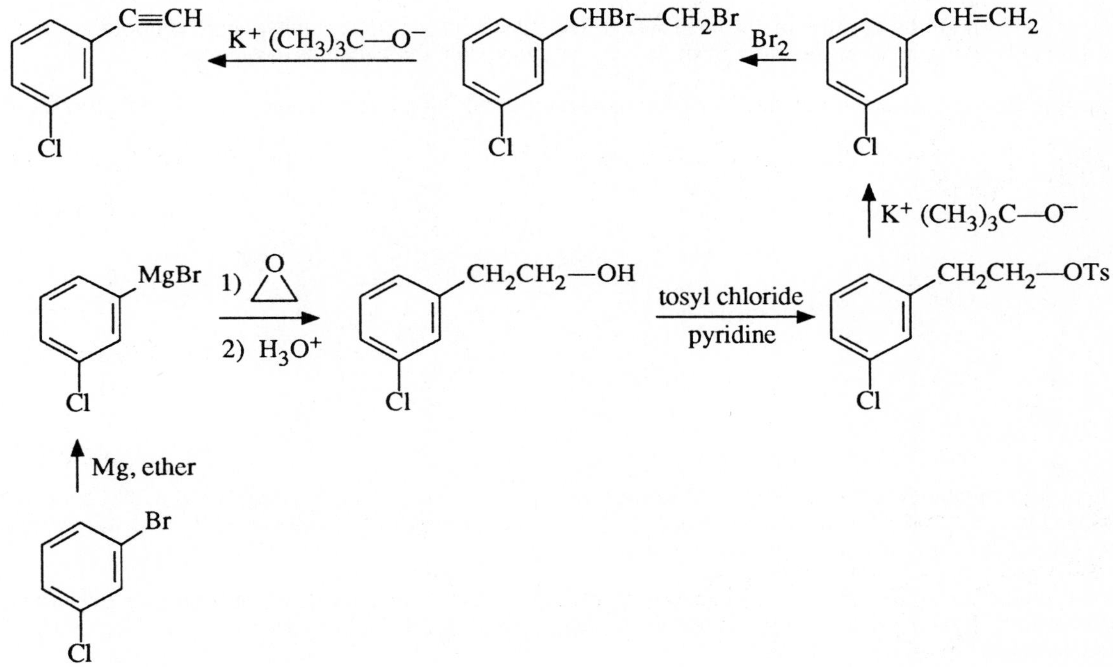

32. The basic principle needed to understand the results is that elimination is most rapid when it occurs with *anti* stereochemistry. In the first reaction, *anti* elimination leads to the observed product. In the second reaction, formation of the alkyne requires a slower *syn* elimination; hence, another process can compete, namely, elimination of a methyl hydrogen and the bromine to form the allene. Elimination of the methyl hydrogen to form the allene is a slower process for two reasons. First, the methyl hydrogen is not as acidic as a vinylic hydrogen. Second, allenes are not so stable as alkynes. The transition state for elimination is destabilized by both of these factors.

33. We are asked to arrange the compounds in order of increasing acidity. In (a), (b), and (d), the phenolate anion is stabilized by resonance interactions with both rings; in (d), it is further stabilized by an inductive effect of the *meta*-nitro group in the second ring; and in (b), it is stabilized even further by resonance interaction with the *para*-nitro group, thus:

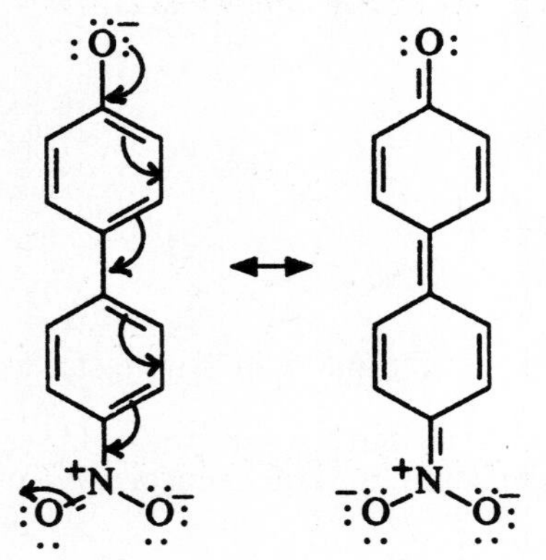

Hence, the required pK_a order is (c) > (a) > (d) > (b). The acidity difference between compounds (a) and (c) might not be great because the nitro group is very far away from the phenolate oxygen.

34. The spectrum is consistent with the formation of an anionic addition intermediate — a Meisenheimer complex:

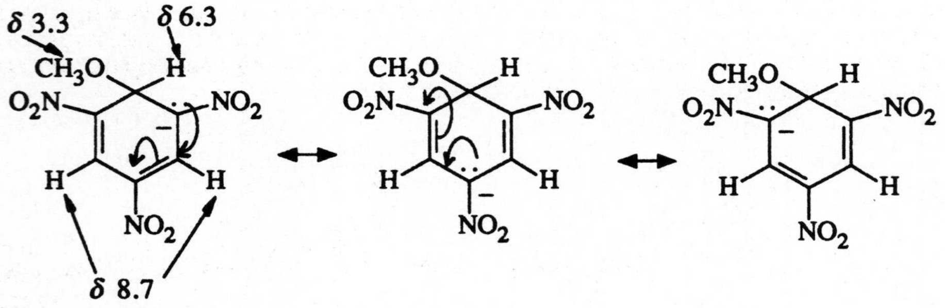

This complex cannot break down (except to starting materials) because the leaving group would have to be hydride ion, H $:^-$, which is simply too basic to be a good leaving group. Since the Meisenheimer complex can't break down, it can be observed by NMR spectroscopy.

35. (a) There are two possibilities. The mechanism could be a nucleophilic aromatic substitution, even though there are no electron-withdrawing groups on the ring, because the conditions are so harsh. More likely, however, is a benzyne mechanism:

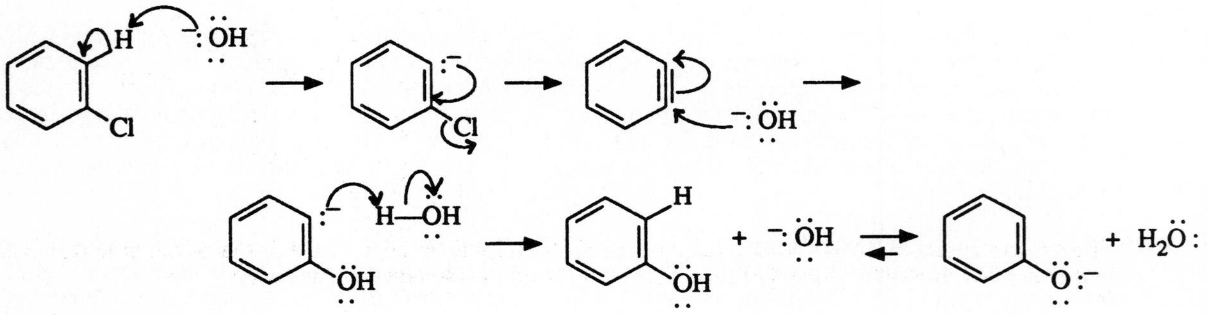

(What experiment could distinguish between the two mechanisms?)

(b) Phenol, formed under the basic conditions of the reaction, ionizes to a phenolate ion; when this ion captures the benzyne intermediate, diphenyl ether is formed.

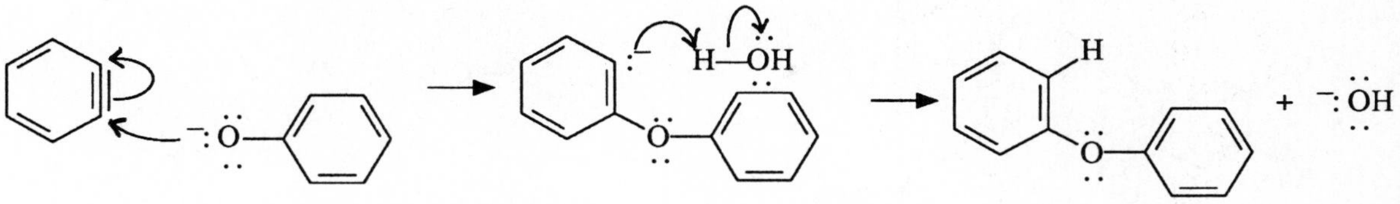

36. The enol (compound *A*) would be more acidic, because its conjugate-base anion, like that of phenol, is resonance-stabilized:

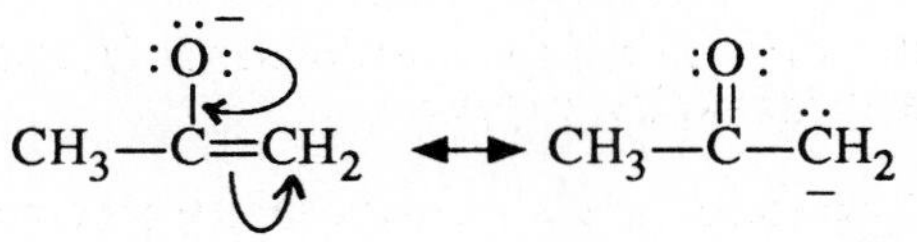

conjugate-base anion of *A*

37. We know that vinylic halides do not undergo S_N2 reactions; hence, this reaction must take place by a special mechanism. The key is to recognize that the leaving-group effect, as well as the effect of a *p*-nitro group, is much like that in nucleophilic aromatic substitution. The mechanism is analogous to a nucleophilic aromatic substitution, except that it occurs at a vinylic, rather than an aromatic, carbon:

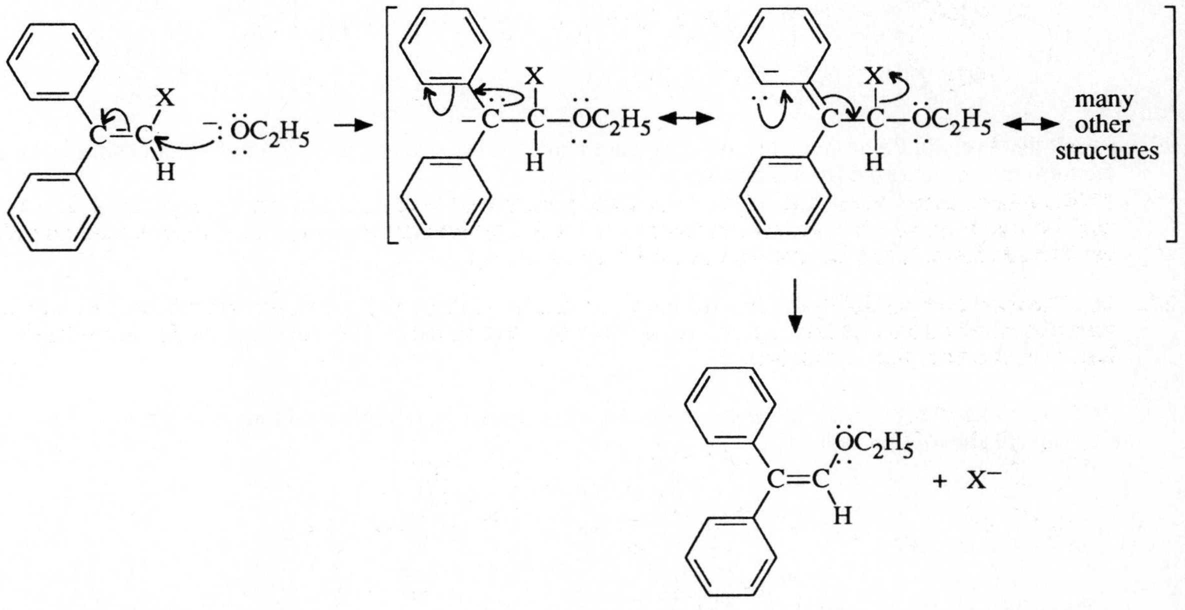

The anionic intermediate is strongly resonance-stabilized by interaction of the unshared electron pair with both rings. A *para*-nitro group in either ring would exert further resonance stabilization.

38. Attack of the phenolate anion on chloroacetic acid in an S_N2 reaction accounts in a straightforward way for the formation of 2,4,5-T:

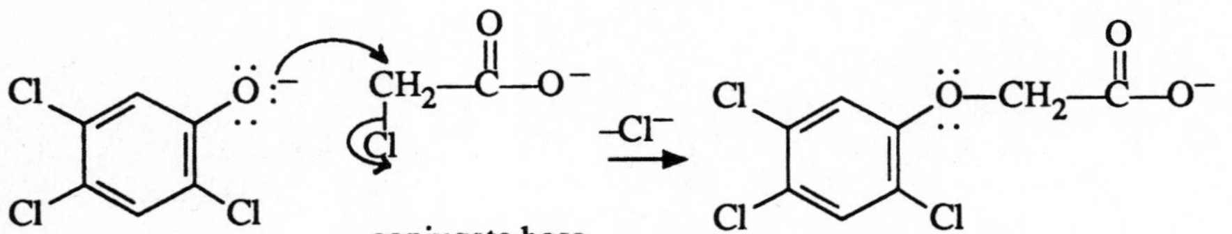

conjugate base
of chloroacetic
acid

gives 2,4,5-T after
protonation

The formation of dioxin is accounted for by a benzyne mechanism similar to that in the solution to Problem 35, except that in this case there are two consecutive benzyne reactions, the second of which is intramolecular. An outline of the mechanism is as follows; fill in the arrow formalism if you have not already done so.

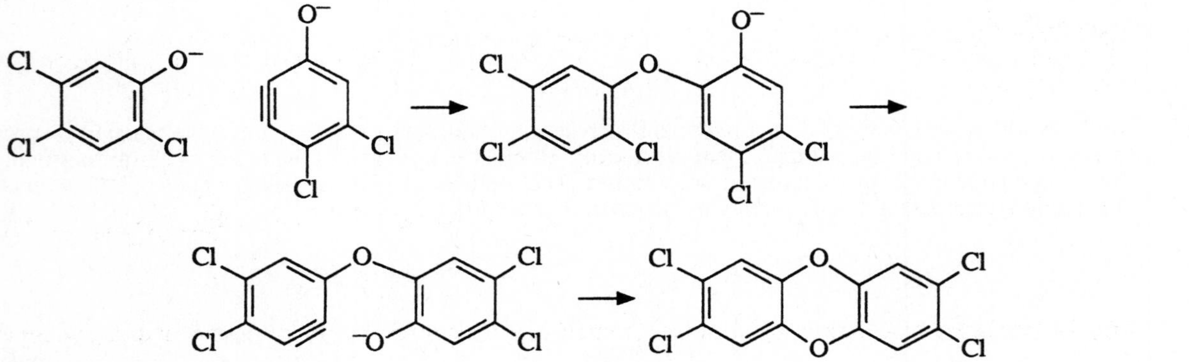

39. Recall that organolithium reagents, like Grignard reagents, are strong bases. Phenyllithium can act as a base in the formation of benzyne from bromobenzene:

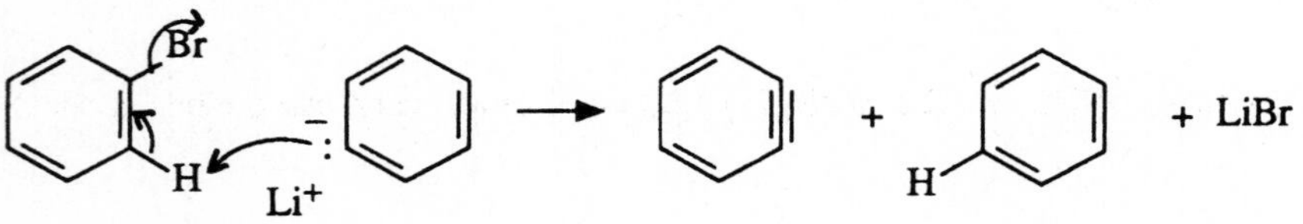

(We show formation of benzyne as one step to save space.) Phenyllithium, acting as a "phenyl anion," then attacks benzyne to form biphenyl:

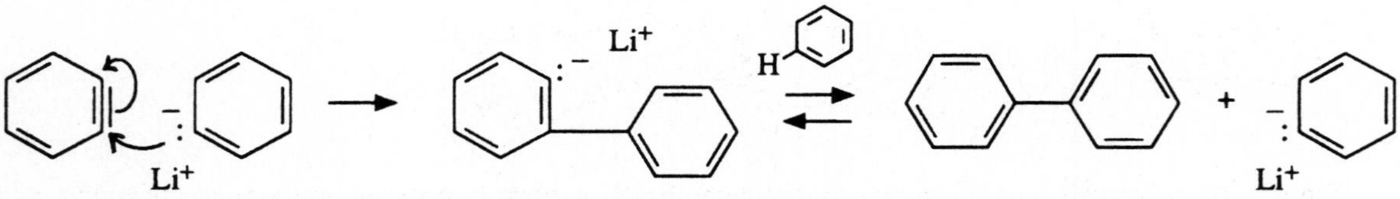

40. (a) This is a nucleophilic aromatic substitution reaction; the anionic intermediate is stabilized by resonance.

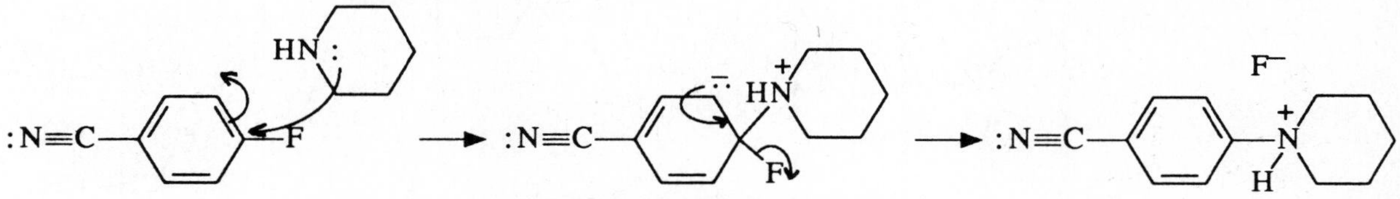

resonance-stabilized anion
(draw the resonance structures)

(b) Benzofuran is an aromatic hetercyclic compound; formation of "benzofuryne," an analog of benzyne, accounts for the products:

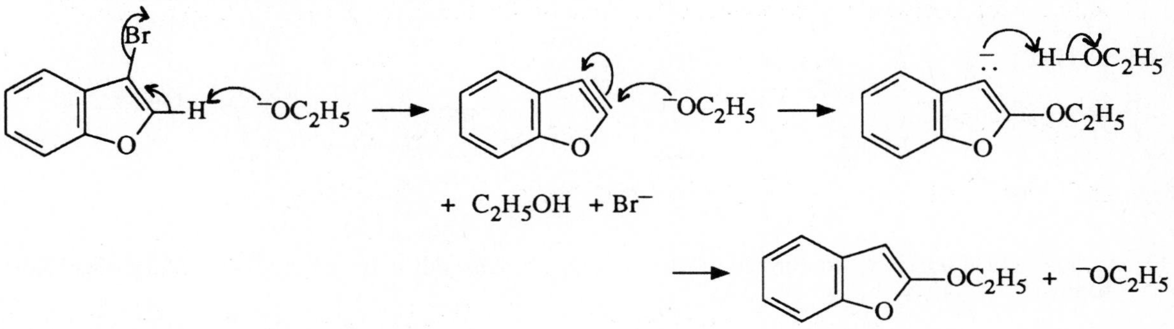

$+ C_2H_5OH + Br^-$

(c) The first step is formation of an α-fluoro Grignard reagent and elimination of fluoride ion to give benzyne:

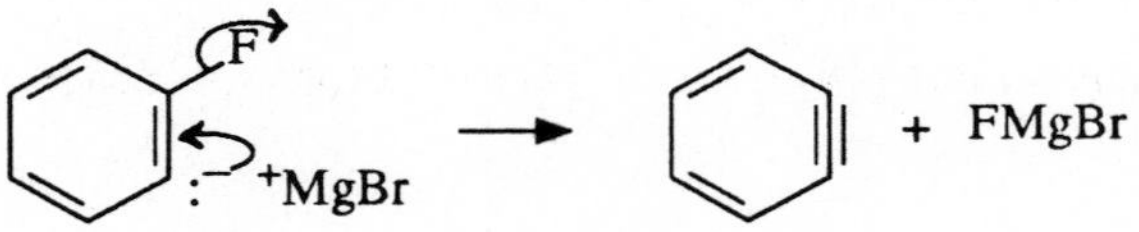

$+ FMgBr$

A Diels–Alder reaction of the benzyne intermediate with phenanthrene (the aromatic compound) gives triptycene:

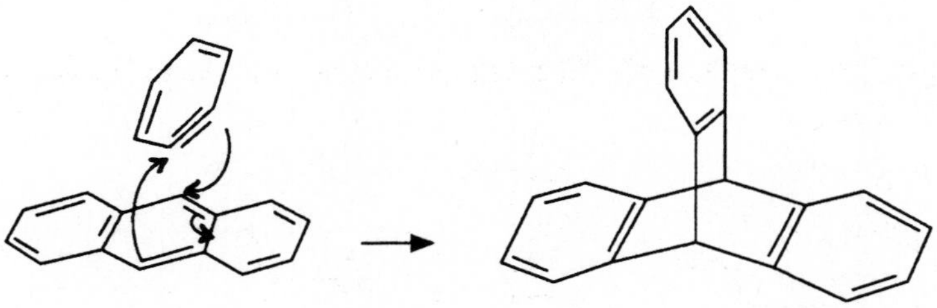

41. The formation of chloride ion indicates that an intermediate is formed prior to the formation of Mephenesin. Since there is base present (the *p*-methylphenoxide ion) along with a chlorohydrin, it is reasonable to postulate that the intermediate is an epoxide, which then reacts with the phenoxide to give Mephenesin:

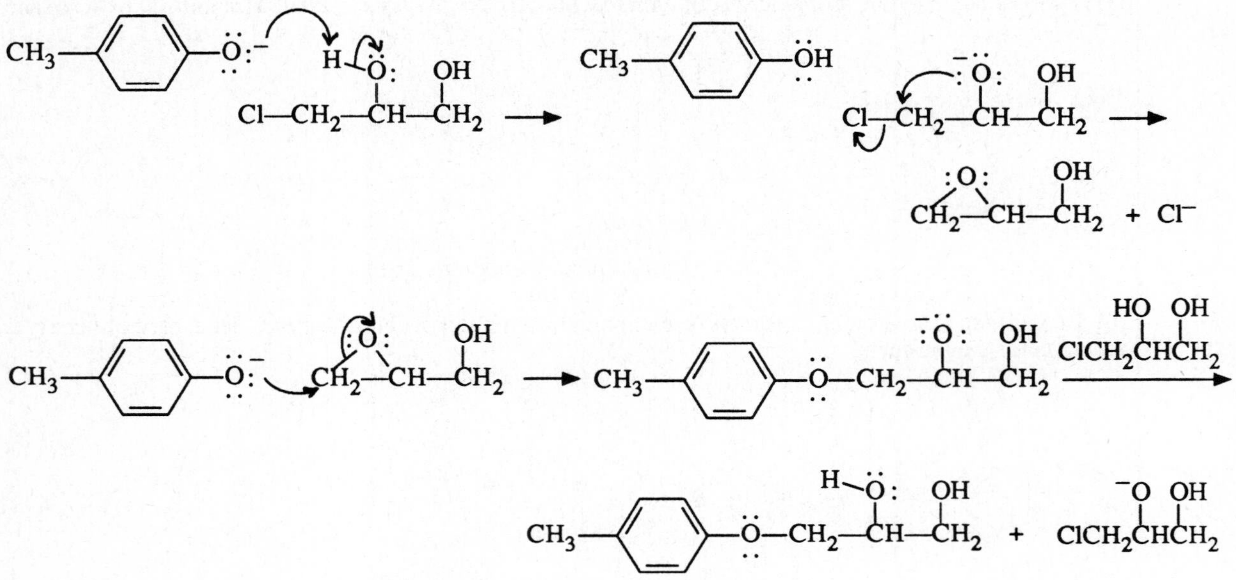

42. A free-radical intermediate, formed as shown in Eq. 18.50b, adds to the *para* position of the phenol BHT as follows:

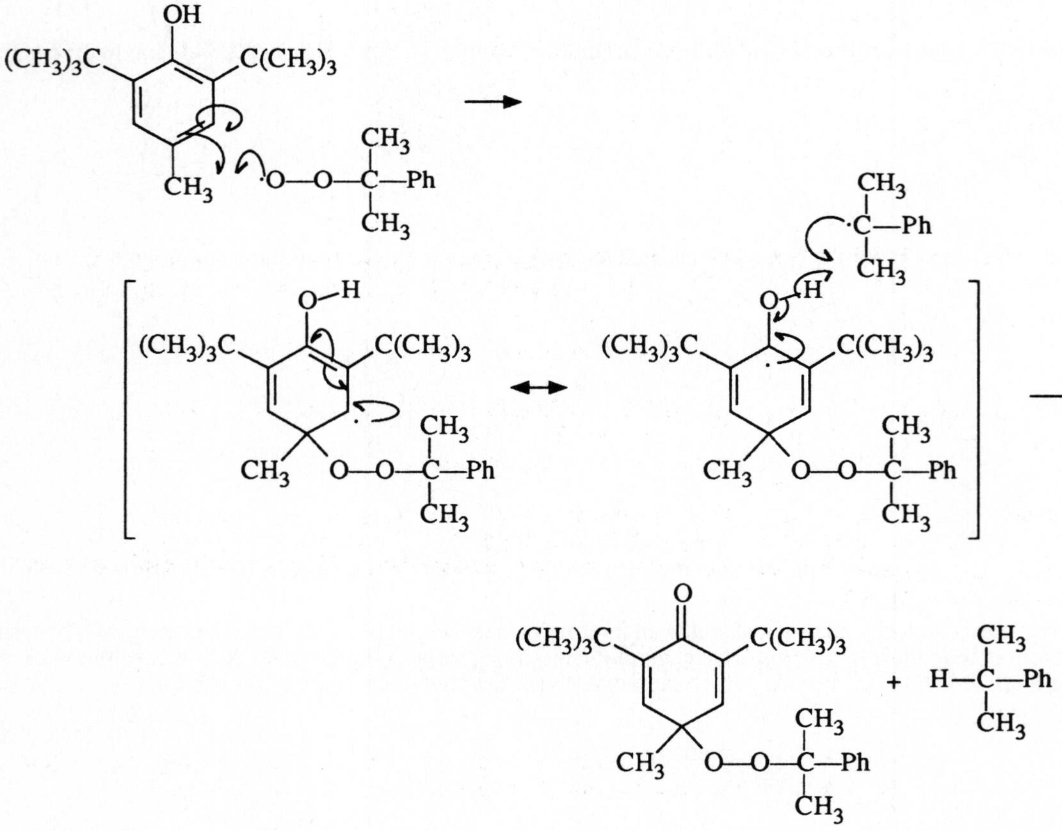

43. (a) In the elimination, a proton would be lost from either β-carbon with equal probability:

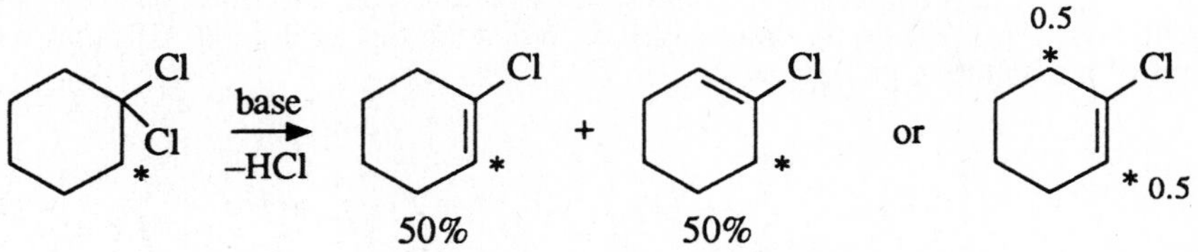

50%   50%

(b) The radiolabeling data are consistent with the formation of a *cyclohexyne* intermediate. The two vinylic chlorides above, each present as 50% of the starting material, react to give the cyclic alkynes, *each of which* can react at either alkyne carbon to give two different products. Four products are formed, each comprising 25% of the product mixture:

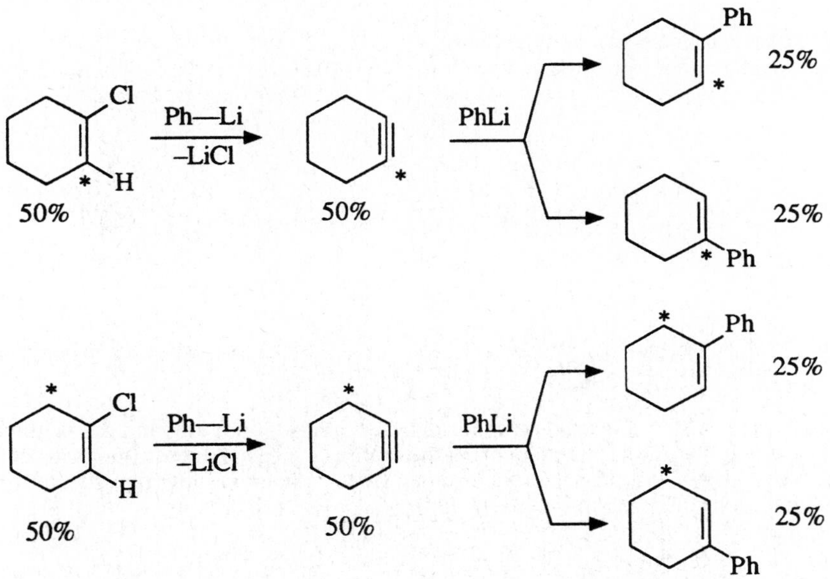

The purpose of this investigation was to gain evidence for or against a cyclic *allene* intermediate, 1,2-cyclohexadiene:

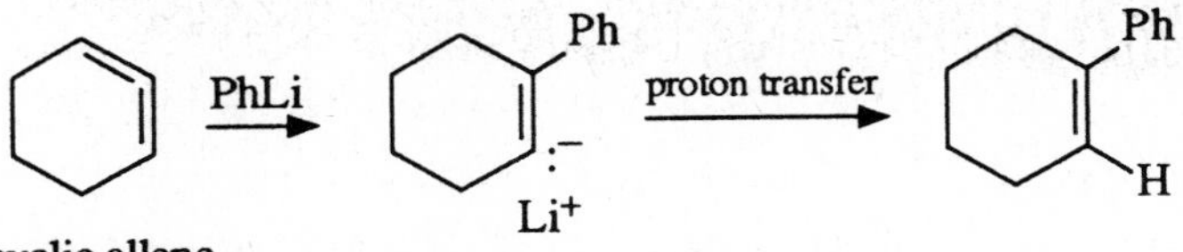

a cyclic allene

The labeling results *clearly exclude* this intermediate. Can you see why? What labeling results are predicted if this intermediate is formed?

44. This is an intramolecular Friedel–Crafts acylation. In the presence of *one equivalent* of Lewis acid AlBr₃, the methoxy-containing ring is acylated. In the presence of *three equivalents* of catalyst, the other ring is acylated. We must explain this difference. The first equivalent of catalyst in each case is used to form the electrophile, an acylium ion (see text page 654, Eq. 16.15) from the acid chloride. When there is additional AlBr₃ present, it complexes with the oxygens of the methoxy groups:

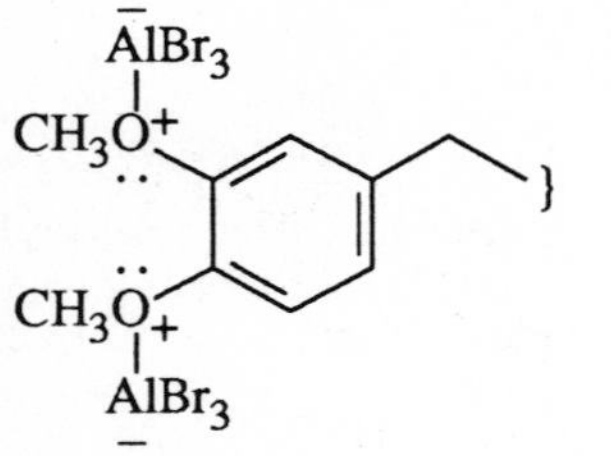

This complexation "ties up" the unshared electrons of the methoxy groups; as a result, they cannot stabilize by resonance the carbocation intermediate that forms when the acylium ion attacks the methoxy-containing ring. Hence, the reactivity of this ring is reduced, and the acylium ion attacks the other ring instead:

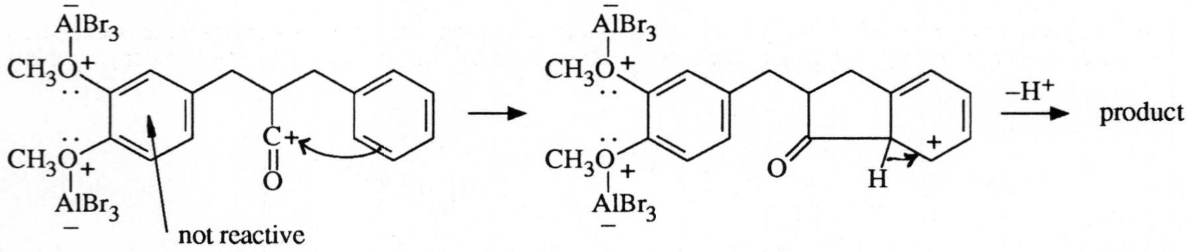

When there is only one equivalent of AlBr₃, it is used up in formation of the acylium ion, and the methoxy groups are free. When the acylium ion attacks the ring bearing the methoxy groups, the resulting carbocation intermediate is resonance-stabilized by one of the methoxy groups. Hence, attack on this ring is faster than attack on the other ring, in which such stabilization is not available:

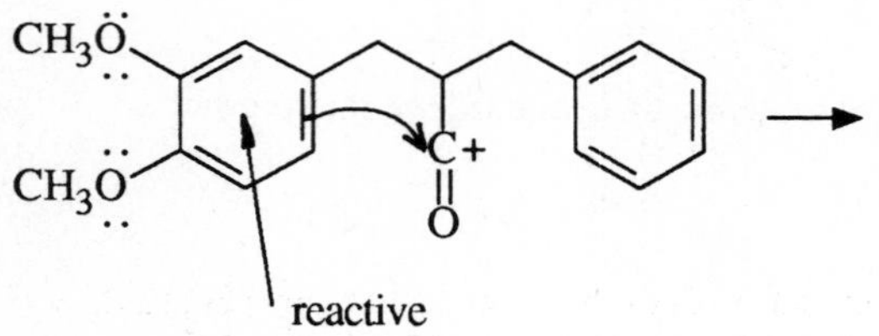

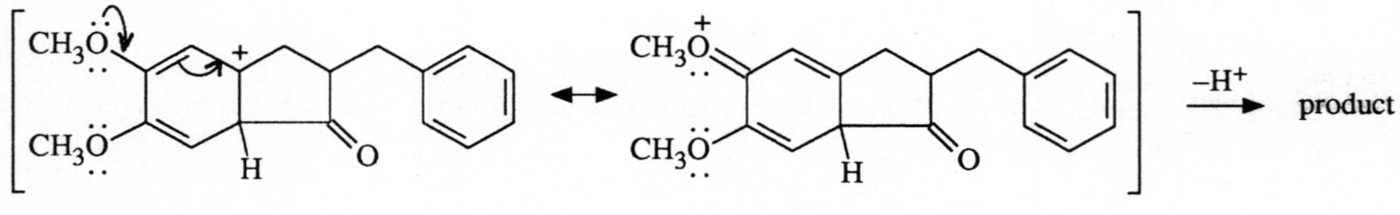

45. (a) In this reaction the epoxide opens to give a resonance-stabilized carbocation *A*, which then rearranges by deuterium migration to give another resonance-stabilized carbocation *B*. (This carbocation is resonance-stabilized not only by interaction with the double bonds in the ring, but also by interaction with the oxygen.) Loss of hydrogen from carbocation *B* gives the major product; loss of deuterium gives the minor product:

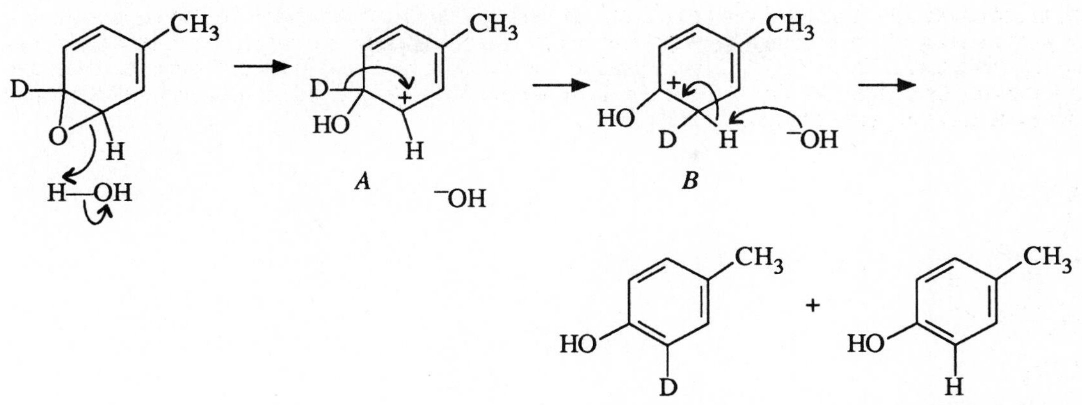

from loss of H   from loss of D

It is reasonable that hydrogen is lost more often than deuterium, because there should be a *primary deuterium isotope effect* on any reaction in which a hydrogen is transferred (Sec. 9.4B, text page 334). Indeed, it appears from the product data that the k_H/k_D for this step is about 3.0!

(b) The position of the methyl group relative to the phenol is determined by how the epoxide opens initially. In the observed mode of ring opening, a more stable carbocation is formed than in the mode of ring opening that is not observed:

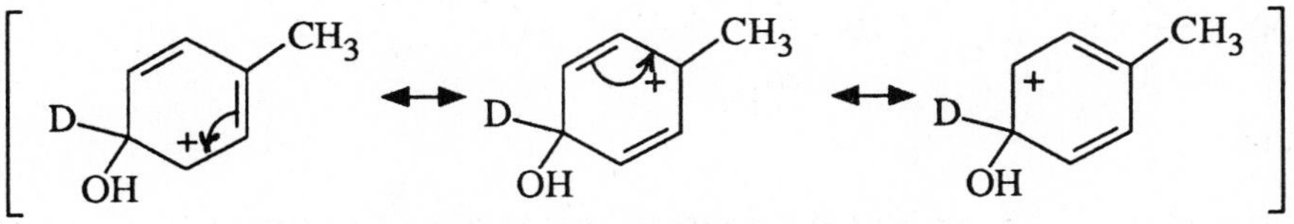

more stable carbocation

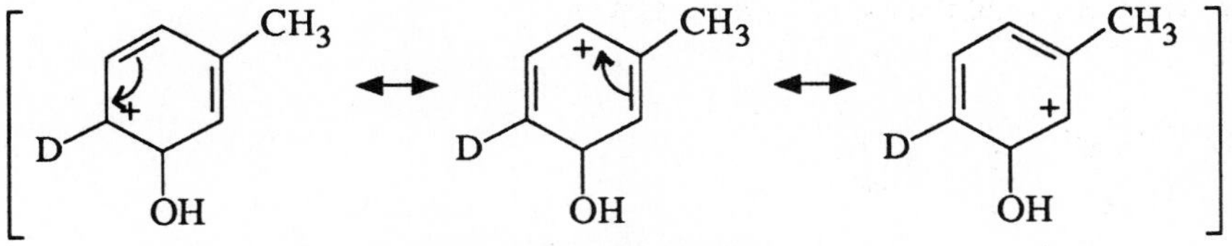

less stable carbocation

We leave it to you to explain why one carbocation is more stable than the other. It has *nothing* to do with the deuterium. (*Hint*: Look at the position of the methyl group with respect to the positive charge!)

Chapter 19 / Chemistry of Aldehydes and Ketones. Carbonyl-Addition Reactions

---

CHAPTER 19 TERMS

α-alkoxy carbocation 19.6
acetal 19.10A
acetal hydrolysis 19.10A
acyl group 19.1A
aldehyde .... Introduction
aldehyde ammonia 19.11A
aldehyde hydrate 19.7
azeotrope 19.10A
benzoyl group 19.1A
carbinolamine 19.11A
carbonyl compound .... Introduction
carbonyl group .... Introduction
Clemmensen reduction 19.12
cyanohydrin 19.7
2,4-dinitrophenylhydrazine (2,4-DNP) 19.11A
2,4-DNP derivative 19.11A
enamine 19.11B
gem-diol 19.7
hemiacetal 19.10A
hydrazine 19.11A
hydrazone 19.11A
hydride ion, H:⁻ 19.8
hydride reduction 19.8
hydroxylamine 19.11A
imine 19.11A
ketal 19.10A
ketene 19.3A

ketone .... Introduction
ketone hydrate 19.7
McLafferty rearrangement 19.3D
methylene group 19.12
miscible 19.2
n-electron 19.3C
$n{\rightarrow}\pi^*$ absorption 19.3C
nitrile 19.7
nucleophilic addition 19.7A
oxaphosphetane 19.13
oxime 19.11A
phenol–formaldehyde resin 19.15
phenylhydrazine 19.11A
phenylhydrazone 19.11A
phosphonium salt 19.13
primary amine 19.11A
protecting group 19.10B
Schiff base 19.11A
secondary amine 19.11B
semicarbazide 19.11A
semicarbazone 19.11A
tertiary amine 19.11B
Tollens' test 19.14
Wittig reaction 19.13
Wolff–Kishner reduction 19.12
ylid 19.13
zinc amalgam (Zn/Hg) 19.12

CHAPTER 19 CONCEPTS

I. Introduction to Ketones and Aldehydes:

A. <u>General</u>:
1. **Carbonyl compounds** contain the **carbonyl group** (C=O) and include:
   a) Aldehydes.
   b) Ketones.
   c) Carboxylic acids.
   d) Most carboxylic acid derivatives.
      (1) Esters.
      (2) Amides.
      (3) Anhydrides.
      (4) Acid chlorides.
2. In a **ketone**, the groups bound to the carbonyl carbon are alkyl or aryl groups.
3. In an **aldehyde**, at least one of the groups at the carbonyl carbon atom is a hydrogen, and the other may be alkyl, aryl, or a second hydrogen.

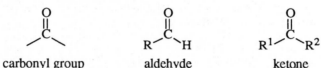

carbonyl group   aldehyde   ketone

4. The carbonyl carbon of a typical aldehyde or ketone is sp^2 hybridized with bond angles approximating 120°.
5. A carbon–oxygen double bond:
   a) Consists of a σ-bond and a π-bond.
   b) Is shorter than a carbon–carbon double bond.

B. <u>Common Nomenclature</u>:
1. In the common nomenclature of aldehydes, the suffix *aldehyde* is added to a prefix that indicates the chain length.

form-	H—	isobutyr-	$(CH_3)_2CH_2$—
acet-	CH_3—	valer-	$CH_3CH_2CH_2CH_2$—
propion-	CH_3CH_2—	isovaler-	$(CH_3)_2CHCH_2$—
butyr-	$CH_3CH_2CH_2$—	benz-	Ph—

   a) Common names are almost always used for the simplest aldehydes.
   b) Benzaldehyde is the simplest aromatic aldehyde.

$$CH_3\text{–}\overset{\overset{\displaystyle CH_3}{|}}{CH}\text{—}CH_2\text{-}\overset{\overset{\displaystyle O}{||}}{C}\text{—H}$$

isovaleraldehyde   benzaldehyde

2. It is occasionally convenient to construct the common name of a ketone by citing the two groups on the carbonyl carbon followed by the word *ketone*.
   a) Acetone is the only nonaromatic ketone for which we shall use a common name.
   b) Certain aromatic ketones are named by attaching the suffix *ophenone* to the appropriate prefix.

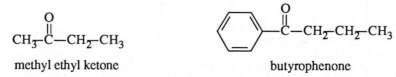

methyl ethyl ketone   butyrophenone

3. Simple substituted aldehydes and ketones can be named in the common system by designating the position of substituents with Greek letters, beginning at the position adjacent to the carbonyl group.

$$\underset{\gamma\text{-chlorovaleraldehyde}}{\text{CH}_3-\overset{\text{Cl}}{\underset{|}{\text{CH}}}-\text{CH}_2-\text{CH}_2-\overset{\text{O}}{\overset{||}{\text{C}}}-\text{H}}$$

4. Many common carbonyl-containing substituent groups are named by adding *yl* to the appropriate prefix (*oyl* in the case of benzene).

$$\underset{\text{acetylacetone}}{\text{CH}_3-\overset{\text{O}}{\overset{||}{\text{C}}}-\text{CH}_2-\overset{\text{O}}{\overset{||}{\text{C}}}-\text{CH}_3} \qquad \underset{\text{benzoylacetone}}{\text{Ph}-\overset{\text{O}}{\overset{||}{\text{C}}}-\text{CH}_2-\overset{\text{O}}{\overset{||}{\text{C}}}-\text{CH}_3}$$

    a) Such groups are called in general **acyl groups**.
    b) To be named as an acyl group, a substituent group must be connected to the remainder of the molecule at its carbonyl carbon.

C. Systematic Nomenclature:
    1. The systematic name of an aldehyde is derived from the hydrocarbon name of the longest carbon chain containing the carbonyl group, dropping the final *e*, and adding the suffix *al*.
        a) The final *e* is not dropped when there is more than one aldehyde group in the carbon chain.
        b) The carbonyl carbon receives the number one in numbering the carbon chain of an aldehyde.
        c) When an aldehyde group is attached to a ring, the suffix *carbaldehyde* is appended to the name of the ring. In aldehydes of this type, carbon-1 is not the carbonyl carbon, but rather the ring carbon attached to the carbonyl group.

$$\underset{\text{propanedial}}{\text{H}-\overset{\text{O}}{\overset{||}{\text{C}}}-\text{CH}_2-\overset{\text{O}}{\overset{||}{\text{C}}}-\text{H}} \qquad \underset{\text{3-methylbutanal}}{^4\text{CH}_3-\overset{\text{CH}_3}{\underset{|}{\overset{3}{\text{CH}}}}-{}^2\text{CH}_2-\overset{\text{O}}{\overset{||}{\overset{1}{\text{C}}}}-\text{H}}$$

3-methylcyclopentanecarbaldehyde

        d) The name benzaldehyde is used both in common and systematic nomenclature.
    2. A ketone is named by giving the hydrocarbon name of the longest carbon chain containing the carbonyl group, dropping the final *e*, and adding the suffix *one*.
        a) The final *e* of the hydrocarbon name is not dropped in the nomenclature of diones, triones, etc.
        b) The position of the carbonyl group is given the lowest possible number.
        c) When a ketone carbonyl group is treated as a substituent, its position is designated by the term *oxo*.

1,3-cyclobutanedione   3-(1-oxoethyl)benzaldehyde

    3. Aldehyde and ketone carbonyl groups receive higher priority for citation as principal groups than —OH or —SH groups. (A complete list of group priorities is given in Appendix I, text page A-1.)

$$-\text{CH}=\text{O} \text{ (aldehyde)} \, > \, \overset{}{\underset{}{\diagup}}\text{C}=\text{O} \text{ (ketone)} \, > \, -\text{OH} \, > \, -\text{SH}$$

$$\underset{\text{6-mercapto-4,4-dimethyl-5-oxo-2-hexynal}}{\text{HS}-{}^6\text{CH}_2-{}^5\overset{\text{O}}{\overset{||}{\text{C}}}-{}^4\overset{\text{CH}_3}{\underset{\underset{\text{CH}_3}{|}}{\overset{|}{\text{C}}}}-{}^3\text{C}\equiv{}^2\text{C}-{}^1\overset{\text{O}}{\overset{||}{\text{C}}}-\text{H}}$$

D. Physical Properties of Aldehydes and Ketones:
    1. Most simple aldehydes and ketones are liquids.
        a) Formaldehyde is a gas.
        b) Acetaldehyde has a boiling point near room temperature.
        c) Aldehydes and ketones have higher boiling points than alkenes or alkanes with similar molecular weights and shapes because of their polarity, which is caused by the C=O bond dipole.

d) Aldehydes and ketones are not hydrogen-bond donors and thus have boiling points that are considerably lower than those of the corresponding alcohols.
2. Aldehydes and ketones with four or fewer carbons have considerable solubility in water because they can accept hydrogen bonds from water at the carbonyl oxygen.
    a) Acetaldehyde and acetone are **miscible** with water (soluble in all proportions).
    b) The water solubility of aldehydes and ketones along a homologous series diminishes rapidly as molecular weight increases.
    c) Acetone and 2-butanone are especially valued as solvents because they are soluble not only in water, but also in a wide variety of organic compounds.

II. Spectroscopy of Aldehydes and Ketones:

A. IR Spectroscopy:
    1. The principal infrared absorption of aldehydes and ketones is the C=O stretching absorption, a strong absorption that occurs in the vicinity of 1700 cm^{-1}.
    2. The position of the C=O stretching absorption varies predictably for different types of carbonyl compounds.
        a) 1710–1715 cm^{-1} for simple ketones.
        b) 1720–1725 cm^{-1} for simple aldehydes.
    3. The stretching absorption of the carbonyl–hydrogen bond of aldehydes near 2710 cm^{-1} is another characteristic absorption.
    4. Compounds in which the carbonyl group is conjugated with aromatic rings, double bonds, or triple bonds have lower carbonyl stretching frequencies than unconjugated carbonyl compounds.
    5. In cyclic ketones with rings containing fewer than six carbons, the carbonyl absorption frequency increases significantly as the ring size decreases.

B. NMR Spectroscopy:
    1. The characteristic NMR absorption common to both aldehydes and ketones is that of the protons on the carbons adjacent to the carbonyl group (α-protons), which occurs in the δ 2.0–2.5 region of the spectrum.
    2. The absorption of the aldehyde proton is quite distinctive, occurring in the δ 9–10 region of the NMR spectrum; the carbonyl group has a greater deshielding effect than the carbon–carbon double bond because of the electronegativity of the carbonyl oxygen.

C. UV Spectroscopy:
    1. The $\pi \rightarrow \pi^*$ absorptions of unconjugated aldehydes and ketones occur at about 150 nm (below the wavelength range of common UV spectrometers).
    2. A much weaker absorption occurs in the 260–290 nm region.
        a) This absorption is caused by excitation of the unshared electrons (sometimes called the **n-electrons**) on oxygen.
        b) This high-wavelength absorption is usually referred to as an **n$\rightarrow\pi^*$ absorption**.
        c) The $n\rightarrow\pi^*$ absorptions arise from promotion of one of the n (unshared) electrons on the carbonyl oxygen to a π^* molecular orbital.
            (1) $n\rightarrow\pi^*$ absorptions are weak.
            (2) These bands are theoretically forbidden and thus have very low intensity.
    3. Compounds whose carbonyl groups are conjugated with double or triple bonds have strong UV absorptions (high extinction coefficients).
        a) The $\pi\rightarrow\pi^*$ absorptions of conjugated carbonyl compounds arise from the promotion of a π-electron from a bonding to an antibonding (π^*) molecular orbital.
        b) The λ_{max} of a conjugated aldehyde or ketone is governed by the same variables that affect the λ_{max} of conjugated dienes.
            (1) The number of conjugated double bonds.
            (2) Substitution on the double bond.
        c) When an aromatic ring is conjugated with a carbonyl group, the typical aromatic absorptions are more intense and occur at higher wavelength than those of benzene.

D. Mass Spectrometry:
    1. Important fragmentations of aldehydes and ketones are:
        a) Cleavage of the parent ion at the bond between the carbonyl group and the adjacent carbon.

(1) In *inductive cleavage*, the alkyl fragment carries the charge and carbonyl fragment carries the unpaired electron.

(2) In *α-cleavage*, the carbonyl fragment carries the charge and the alkyl fragment carries the unpaired electron.

b) Cleavage at the carbon–hydrogen bond accounts for the fact that many aldehydes show a strong $p - 1$ peak.

c) Cleavage at a β-carbon through a **McLafferty rearrangement** is a common mechanism for the production of odd-electron fragment ions in the mass spectrometry of carbonyl compounds.

hydrogen transfer   α-cleavage

III. Synthesis and Reactivity of Aldehydes and Ketones:

A. Review of Ketone and Aldehyde Synthetic Methods:

1. The three most important preparations of aldehydes and ketones already discussed are:

a) Oxidation of alcohols (Sec. 10.6, text page 383).

(1) Primary alcohols can be oxidized to aldehydes.

(2) Secondary alcohols can be oxidized to ketones.

b) Hydration and hydroboration of alkynes (Sec. 14.5, text page 557).

c) Friedel–Crafts acylation (Sec. 16.4E, text page 653).

2. Less important synthetic methods that have already been discussed are:

a) Ozonolysis of alkenes (Sec. 5.5, text page 148).

b) Pinacol rearrangement of glycols (Sec. 10.1B, text page 372).

c) Periodate cleavage of glycols (Sec. 10.6D, text page 392).

B. Introduction to Aldehyde and Ketone Reactions:

1. The reactions of aldehydes and ketones can be conveniently grouped into two categories:

a) Reactions of the carbonyl group.

b) Reactions involving the α-carbon.

2. There are three types of important carbonyl-group reactions of aldehydes and ketones:

a) The most important carbonyl-group reaction is addition to the C=O double bond.

b) The carbonyl oxygen is weakly basic and thus reacts with Lewis and Brønsted acids; carbonyl basicity is important because it plays a role in several other carbonyl-group reactions.

c) Aldehydes can be oxidized to carboxylic acids.

C. Reversible Addition Reactions of Aldehydes and Ketones:

1. One of the most typical reactions of aldehydes and ketones is *addition* to the carbon–oxygen double bond; two such reactions are:

a) Hydration (addition of water) to give a **hydrate** or *gem*-**diol**.

b) Addition of HCN.

(1) The product of HCN addition is termed a **cyanohydrin**—a special class of **nitrile** (organic cyanide).

(2) The preparation of cyanohydrins is another method of forming carbon–carbon bonds.

2. All carbonyl-addition reactions show a complementarity between the polarity of the addition reagent and the polarity of the carbonyl group.

a) The electropositive end of the addition reagent (the proton) adds to the electronegative end of the carbonyl (the oxygen).

b) The electronegative end of the reagent (—OH or —CN) adds to the electropositive end of the carbonyl group (the carbonyl carbon).

D. <u>Basicity of Aldehydes and Ketones</u>:
   1. Aldehydes and ketones are weakly basic and react at the carbonyl oxygen with protons or Lewis acids.
     a) The protonated form of an aldehyde or ketone is resonance stabilized.

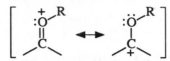

an α-hydroxy carbocation

     b) Closely related to protonated aldehydes and ketones are **α-alkoxy carbocations** (cations in which the acidic proton is replaced by an alkyl group).

an α-alkoxy carbocation

     c) Such ions are considerably more stable than ordinary alkyl cations and owe their stabilities to resonance interaction of the electron-deficient carbon with the neighboring oxygen.
     d) This resonance effect far outweighs the electron-attracting inductive effect of the oxygen which, by itself, would destabilize these carbocations.
   2. Aldehydes and ketones in solution are considerably less basic than alcohols; their conjugate acids are more acidic than those of alcohols.
     a) The relative acidity of protonated alcohols and carbonyl compounds is yet another example of a solvent effect.
     b) One reason for the greater basicity of alcohols in solution is that protonated alcohols have more O—H protons to participate in hydrogen bonding to solvent than do protonated aldehydes or ketones.

E. <u>Equilibrium in Carbonyl-Addition Reactions</u>:
   1. Hydration and cyanohydrin formation are reversible.
     a) Cyanohydrin formation favors the product in the case of aldehydes and methyl ketones, but not aromatic ketones.
     b) Hydration occurs more extensively with aldehydes than with ketones.
   2. Trends in addition reaction to aldehydes and ketones are:
     a) Addition is more favorable for aldehydes than for ketones.
     b) Electronegative groups near the carbonyl carbon make carbonyl addition more favorable.
     c) Addition is less favorable when groups are present that donate electrons by resonance to the carbonyl carbon.
   3. Compounds with the most favorable addition equilibria tend to react most rapidly in addition reactions. Thus aldehydes are generally more reactive than ketones in addition reactions; formaldehyde is more reactive than other aldehydes.

F. <u>Protecting Groups</u>:
   1. Carbonyl groups react with a number of reagents used with other functional groups but can be rendered inert to these reagents by the use of **protecting groups**.
   2. **Acetals** are commonly used to protect the carbonyl groups of aldehydes and ketones from basic, nucleophilic reagents.
     a) Once the protection is no longer needed, the protecting group is easily removed and the carbonyl group re-exposed by treatment with dilute aqueous acid.
     b) Because acetals are hydrolyzed in acid, they *do not* protect carbonyl groups under acidic conditions.

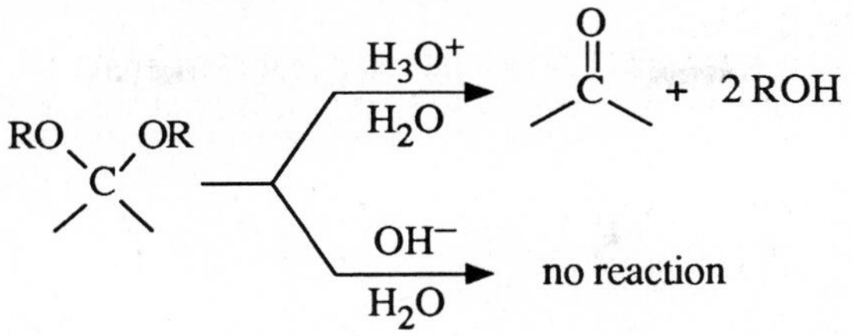

$$RO \underset{}{\overset{}{\underset{C}{\diagdown}}} OR \quad \overset{H_3O^+}{\underset{H_2O}{\longrightarrow}} \quad \overset{O}{\overset{\|}{C}} + 2\,ROH$$

$$\overset{OH^-}{\underset{H_2O}{\longrightarrow}} \quad \text{no reaction}$$

G. Manufacture and Use of Aldehydes and Ketones:
1. Formaldehyde is manufactured by the oxidation of methanol over a silver catalyst.
2. Formaldehyde is used in the synthesis of a class of polymers known as **phenol–formaldehyde resins**.
   a) A **resin** is a polymer with a rigid three-dimensional network of repeating units.
   b) Phenol–formaldehyde resins are produced by heating phenol and formaldehyde with acidic or basic catalysts.
   c) The phenol–formaldehyde resin, Bakelite, was the first useful synthetic polymer.
3. The simplest ketone, acetone, is co-produced with phenol by the autoxidation–rearrangement of cumene (Sec. 18.8, text page 743).

IV. Introduction to Amines:

A. General:
1. A **primary amine** (general structure RNH_2) is an organic derivative of ammonia in which *only one* ammonia hydrogen is replaced by an alkyl or aryl group.
2. A **secondary amine** (general structure R_2NH) is an organic derivative of ammonia in which *two* ammonia hydrogens are replaced by alkyl or aryl groups—the nitrogen may be part of a ring.
3. A **tertiary amine** (general structure R_3N) is an organic derivative of ammonia in which *all three* ammonia hydrogens are replaced by alkyl or aryl groups—the nitrogen may be part of a ring.

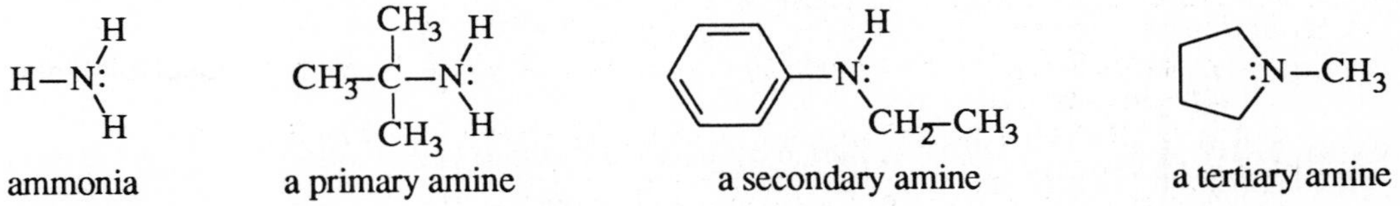

CHAPTER 19 REACTIONS

I. Carbonyl-Addition Reactions:

  A. <u>Mechanisms of Carbonyl-Addition Reactions</u>:
    1. Carbonyl-addition reactions occur by two general types of mechanisms:
      a) The **nucleophilic addition** mechanism occurs under *basic* conditions.
        (1) A nucleophile attacks the carbonyl group at the carbonyl carbon; the carbonyl oxygen becomes negatively charged.
        (2) The negatively charged oxygen is a relatively strong base and is protonated by water (or HCN in the case of cyanohydrin formation) to complete the addition.

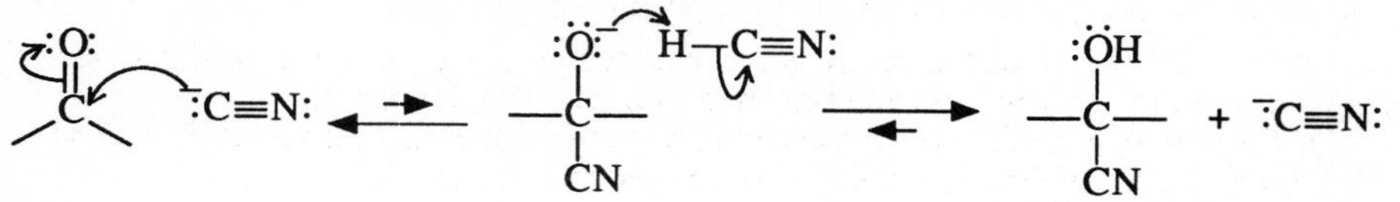

a cyanohydrin

      (*a*) This pathway occurs with aldehydes and ketones because the negative charge is placed on oxygen, an electronegative atom, in the transition state.
      (*b*) Attack of the nucleophile occurs on the carbon of the carbonyl group rather than the oxygen for the same reason—the negative charge is placed on oxygen, the more electronegative atom.
      (*c*) When a nucleophile attacks a carbonyl group, it attacks the π-bond from above or below the plane of the molecule, pushing an electron pair onto the carbonyl oxygen.

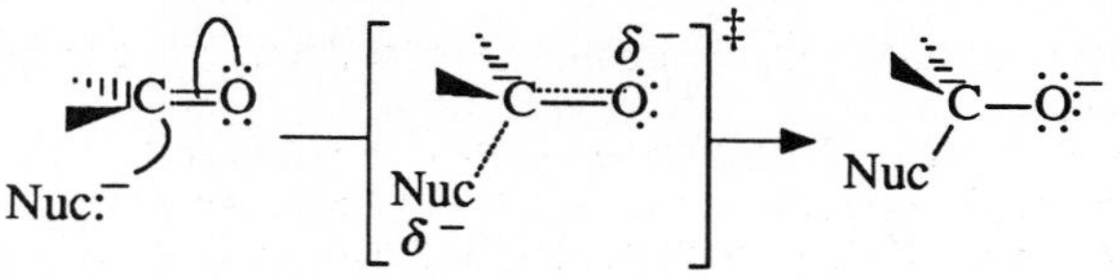

      b) The second mechanism occurs under *acidic conditions* and is closely analogous to electrophilic addition to alkenes.
        (1) The carbonyl group is first protonated by an acid in solution; the protonated carbonyl compound has carbocation character.
        (2) The electron-deficient carbon is attacked by a nucleophile, which then loses a proton completing the addition.
        (3) Acid-catalyzed hydration of carbonyl compounds is an example of this mechanism.

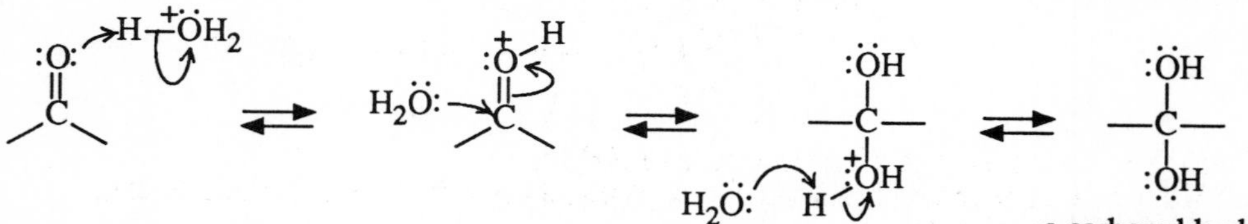

a carbonyl hydrate

    2. Under basic conditions:
      a) The nucleophile is usually a fairly strong base.
      b) The acid that protonates the negative oxygen is usually the conjugate acid of the nucleophile (a weak acid).
    3. Under acidic conditions:
      a) The carbonyl is protonated by a relatively strong acid.
      b) The nucleophile is usually a fairly weak base.

  B. <u>Reduction of Aldehydes and Ketones to Alcohols</u>:
    1. Aldehydes and ketones are reduced to alcohols with either lithium aluminum hydride (LiAlH$_4$) or sodium borohydride (NaBH$_4$), which serve as sources of hydride ion (H:$^-$), a good nucleophile.

a) These reactions result in the net *addition* of the elements of H_2 across the C=O bond and are *not* reversible.
b) Reduction of an aldehyde gives a primary alcohol.
c) Reduction of a ketone gives a secondary alcohol.

an aldehyde $\quad$ $\quad\xrightarrow{\text{hydride reduction}}\quad$ R—CH—H $\quad$ a primary alcohol

a ketone $\quad$ $\quad\xrightarrow{\text{hydride reduction}}\quad$ R—CH—R $\quad$ a secondary alcohol

2. $LiAlH_4$ and $NaBH_4$ reductions are generally referred to as **hydride reductions** and are examples of nucleophilic addition.
3. The reaction of $LiAlH_4$ with aldehydes and ketones involves the nucleophilic attack of hydride on the carbonyl carbon; all four hydride equivalents of $LiAlH_4$ are active.
   a) A lithium ion coordinated to the carbonyl oxygen acts as a Lewis-acid catalyst.
   b) Hydride attacks the carbonyl carbon to give an alkoxide salt.
   c) The alkoxide salt is converted by protonation into the alcohol product; the proton source is water (or an aqueous solution of a weak acid such as ammonium chloride), which is added in a *separate* step to the reaction mixture.

   d) $LiAlH_4$ reacts violently with water and therefore must be used in dry solvents such as anhydrous ether or THF.
4. The reaction of $NaBH_4$ with aldehydes and ketones involves the nucleophilic attack of hydride on the carbonyl carbon; all four hydride equivalents of $NaBH_4$ are active.
   a) The sodium ion of $NaBH_4$ does not coordinate to the carbonyl group as well as the lithium ion does.
   b) $NaBH_4$ reductions are carried out in protic solvents, such as alcohols; hydrogen bonding between the protic solvent and the carbonyl group serves as a weak acid catalysis that activates the carbonyl group.
   c) $NaBH_4$ reacts only slowly with alcohols, and can even be used in water if the solution is not acidic.

5. $LiAlH_4$ is a much more reactive reagent than $NaBH_4$.
   a) There are a number of functional groups that react with $LiAlH_4$ but not $NaBH_4$:
      (1) Alkyl halides.
      (2) Alkyl tosylates.
      (3) Nitro groups.
   b) The greater selectivity and safety of $NaBH_4$ make it the preferred reagent in many applications.
6. Aldehydes and ketones can also be reduced to alcohols by catalytic hydrogenation.
   a) This reaction is analogous to the hydrogenation of an alkene.

b) It is usually possible to use catalytic hydrogenation for the selective reduction of an alkene double bond in the presence of a carbonyl group; palladium catalysts are particularly effective in this reduction.

$$\text{Ph-CH=CH-CH=O} \xrightarrow[\text{5\% Pd/C}]{H_2} \text{Ph-CH}_2\text{-CH}_2\text{-CH=O}$$

C. <u>Reactions of Aldehydes and Ketones with Grignard Reagents</u>:

1. The most important single application of Grignard reagents in organic chemistry is their addition to aldehydes and ketones in an ether solvent, followed by protonolysis, to give alcohols. (See Appendix IV, text page A-7, for a review of other syntheses of alcohols.)
   a) The magnesium of the Grignard reagent, a Lewis acid, coordinates with the carbonyl oxygen.
   b) The carbon group of the Grignard reagent attacks the carbonyl carbon to form a magnesium alkoxide.
   c) Addition of dilute acid in a separate step to the reaction mixture gives the alcohol.

   d) The Grignard synthesis of tertiary and some secondary alcohols can also be turned into an alkene synthesis by dehydration of the alcohol with acid during the hydrolysis step.

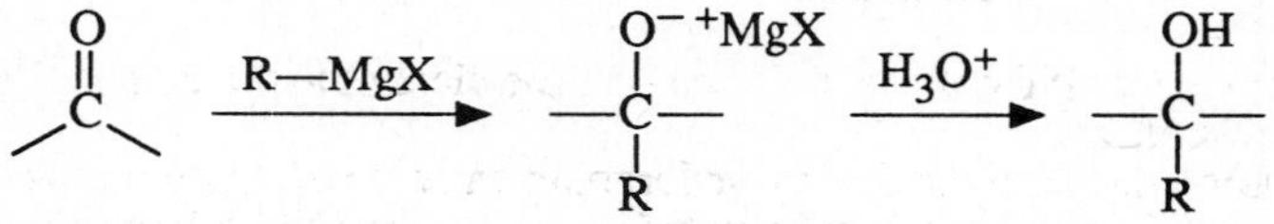

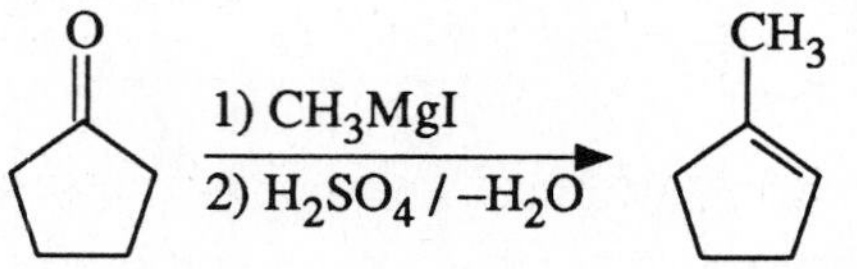

2. The reaction of organolithium and sodium acetylide reagents with aldehydes and ketones are fundamentally similar to the Grignard reaction.
3. The net effect of the Grignard reaction, followed by hydrolysis, is addition of R—H (R = an alkyl or aryl group) across the C=O double bond; this addition is *not* reversible.
   a) Primary alcohols are synthesized by the addition of Grignard reagents to formaldehyde.
   b) Secondary alcohols are synthesized by the addition of Grignard reagents to aldehydes other than formaldehyde.
   c) Tertiary alcohols are synthesized by the addition of Grignard reagents to ketones.

formaldehyde

primary alcohol

aldehyde

secondary alcohol

ketone

tertiary alcohol

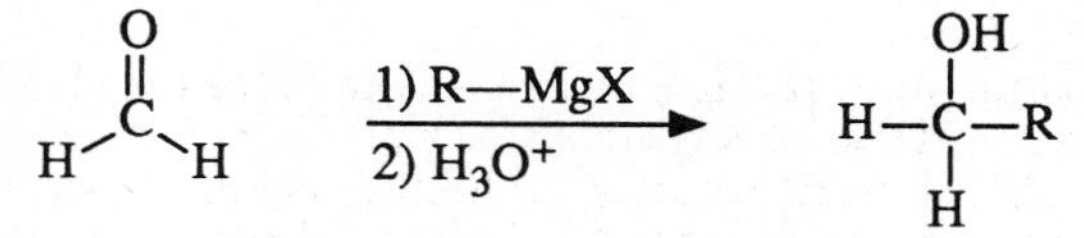

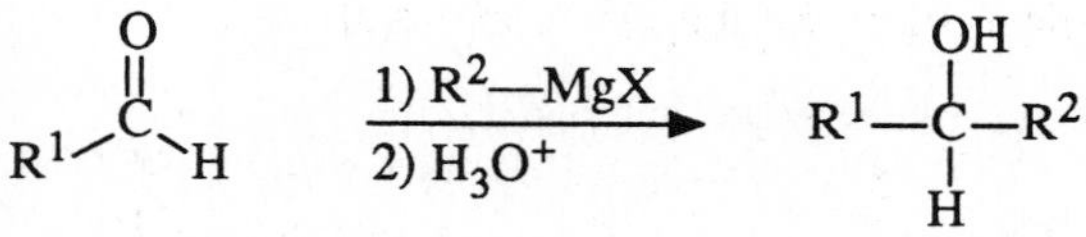

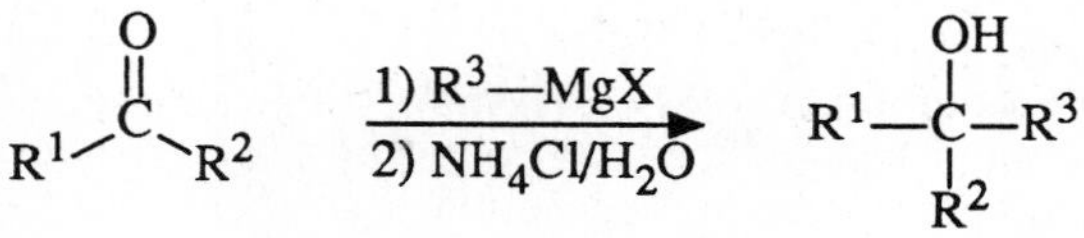

4. The Grignard reaction is an excellent method of carbon–carbon bond formation. (See Appendix V, text page A-10, for a review of other reactions used to form carbon–carbon bonds.)

D. Preparation and Hydrolysis of Acetals:
   1. When an aldehyde or ketone reacts with a large excess of an alcohol in the presence of a trace of mineral acid, an acetal is formed. An **acetal** is a diether in which both ether oxygens are bound to the same carbon. (Acetals are ethers of hydrates or *gem*-diols.)

$$2\ R-OH\ +\ \underset{}{C}(=O) \underset{}{\overset{H_3O^+}{\rightleftharpoons}}\ \underset{RO\ \ OR}{C}\ +\ H_2O$$

   2. Two moles of alcohol are required in the formation of acetals, but one mole of a 1,2- or 1,3-diol reacts to form a cyclic acetal, in which the acetal group is part of a five- or six-membered ring, respectively.

$$HO\frown OH\ +\ \underset{}{C}(=O) \underset{}{\overset{H_3O^+}{\rightleftharpoons}}\ \underset{}{O\frown O\ C}\ +\ H_2O$$

   3. Acetal formation is reversible and involves an acid-catalyzed carbonyl addition followed by a substitution:
     a) The first step is acid-catalyzed addition of the alcohol to the carbonyl group; the product is called **a hemiacetal**.
     b) The hemiacetal reacts further by undergoing an acid-catalyzed S_N1 reaction in which the —OH group of the hemiacetal is substituted by —OR from the solvent alcohol.

$$\underset{}{C}(=O) \overset{ROH}{\underset{addition}{\longrightarrow}} \underset{a\ hemiacetal}{\overset{RO\ \ OH}{C}} \overset{ROH,\ H^+}{\underset{\substack{substitution\\ (S_N1\ mechanism)}}{\longrightarrow}} \underset{an\ acetal}{\overset{RO\ \ OR}{C}}$$

   4. The reaction is driven to the right by applying LeChatelier's principle in one or both of the following ways:
     a) The use of excess alcohol as the solvent.
     b) The removal of the water by-product (usually by **azeotropic** distillation).
   5. Acetals in the presence of acid and excess water are transformed rapidly back into their corresponding carbonyl compounds.
     a) This process is called **acetal hydrolysis**.
     b) By the principle of microscopic reversibility, the mechanism of acetal hydrolysis is the reverse of the mechanism of acetal formation.
   6. Acetals are *stable* in base because protonation of the acetal is required in order to form the carbocation intermediate in the hydrolysis reaction.
   7. Hemiacetals in most cases cannot be isolated because they react further to yield acetals or decompose to aldehydes or ketones (in water).
     a) Simple aldehydes form appreciable amounts of hemiacetals in alcohol solution, just as they form appreciable amounts of hydrates in water.
     b) Five- and six-membered cyclic hemiacetals form spontaneously from the corresponding hydroxy aldehydes, and most are stable, isolable compounds; the five- and six-carbon sugars are important biological examples of cyclic hemiacetals.

II. Oxidation of Aldehydes and Ketones:

A. Oxidation of Aldehydes:
   1. Common oxidants, such as Cr(VI) reagents, $KMnO_4$, or nitric acid, can be used in the oxidation of aldehydes to carboxylic acids; these oxidizing agents are the same ones used for oxidizing alcohols.

2. Some aldehyde oxidations begin as addition reactions.
  a) In the oxidation of aldehydes by Cr(VI) reagents, the *hydrate*, not the aldehyde, is actually the species oxidized.
  b) For this reason, some water should be present in solution for aldehyde oxidations with Cr(VI) to occur at a reasonable rate.

3. In the laboratory, aldehydes can be conveniently oxidized to carboxylic acids with Ag(I).
  a) If the silver ion is solubilized as its ammonia complex, $^+Ag(NH_3)_2$, oxidation of the aldehyde is accompanied by the deposition of a metallic silver mirror on the walls of the reaction vessel.
  b) This observation can be used as a convenient test for aldehydes, known as **Tollens' test**.

ammonium salt of a carboxylic acid

4. Many aldehydes are oxidized by the oxygen in air upon standing for long periods of time; this process is called **autoxidation**.

B. Oxidation of Ketones:
  1. Ketones cannot be oxidized without breaking carbon–carbon bonds.
  2. Ketones are resistant to mild oxidation with Cr(VI) reagents.

III. Reactions of Aldehydes and Ketones with Amines:

A. Imine Formation with Primary Amines:
  1. An **imine** (sometimes called a **Schiff base**) is a nitrogen analog of an aldehyde or ketone in which the C=O group is replaced by a C=N—R group.
    a) Imines are prepared by the reaction of aldehydes or ketones with primary amines.
    b) Formation of imines is reversible and generally takes place with acid or base catalysis, or with heat.

an imine

  c) Imine formation is typically driven to completion in one or both of the following ways:
      (1) Precipitation of the imine.
      (2) Removal of water.
  2. Mechanistically, imine formation is a *carbonyl-addition reaction* followed by *elimination* of water.
    a) In the first step of the mechanism, the nucleophile (the amine) reacts with the aldehyde or ketone to give an unstable addition compound called a **carbinolamine**.
    b) Like other alcohols, carbinolamines undergo acid-catalyzed dehydration.

a carbinolamine   an imine

  3. Certain types of imine adducts sometimes find use as derivatives of aldehydes and ketones because they are almost always solids with well-defined melting points (see Table 19.3, text page 794, for the corresponding structures).

> a) **Hydroxylamine** ⇒ **oximes.**
> b) **Hydrazine** ⇒ **hydrazones.**
> c) **Phenylhydrazine** ⇒ **phenylhydrazones.**
> d) **2,4-Dinitrophenylhydrazine** ⇒ **2,4-dinitrophenylhydrazone (2,4-DNP derivatives).**
> e) **Semicarbazide** ⇒ **semicarbazones.**
>
> 4. As a rule, imines derived from the reaction of aldehydes or ketones with ammonia are *not* stable, although they are believed to be intermediates in certain reactions.

B. Enamine Formation with Secondary Amines:

1. An **enamine** is analog of an enol in which the —OH group is replaced by an —NR_2 group.

2. When an aldehyde or ketone with α-hydrogens reacts with a secondary amine, an enamine is formed.
   a) Just as most aldehydes and ketones are more stable than their corresponding enols, most imines are more stable than their corresponding enamines.
   b) Since secondary amines *cannot* form imines, they form enamines instead.
3. Like imine formation, enamine formation is reversible, and must be driven to completion by the removal of one of the reaction products (usually water).
   a) The mechanism of enamine formation begins like the mechanism of imine formation, as a nucleophilic addition to give a carbinolamine intermediate.
   b) Dehydration of the carbinolamine involves proton loss from the adjacent carbon.

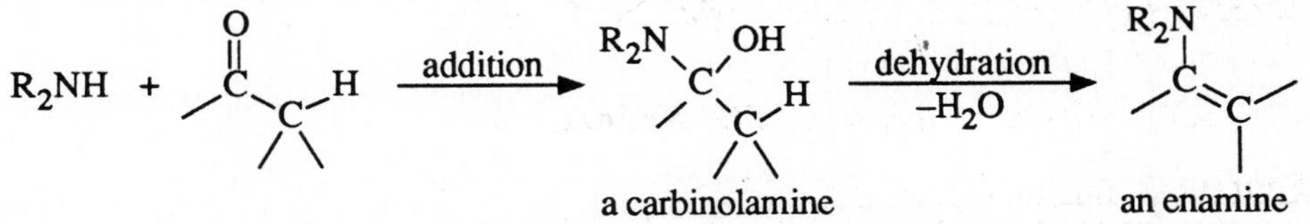

4. Enamines, like imines, are converted back into their corresponding carbonyl compounds and amines in aqueous acid.

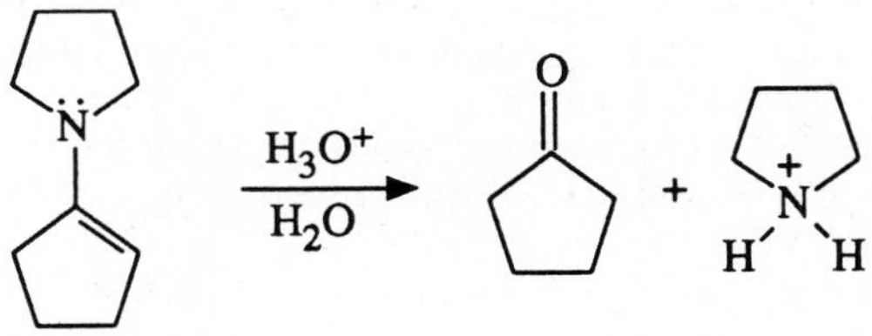

C. Tertiary Amines:

1. Tertiary amines *do not* react with aldehydes and ketones to form stable derivatives.

IV. Conversion of Ketones and Aldehydes into Alkanes and Alkenes:

A. Reduction of Carbonyl Groups to Methylene Groups—the Wolff–Kishner Reduction:

1. A carbonyl group of an aldehyde or ketone can be reduced completely to a **methylene group** (—CH_2—).
2. One procedure for effecting this transformation involves heating the aldehyde or ketone with **hydrazine** (NH_2—NH_2) and *strong* base.

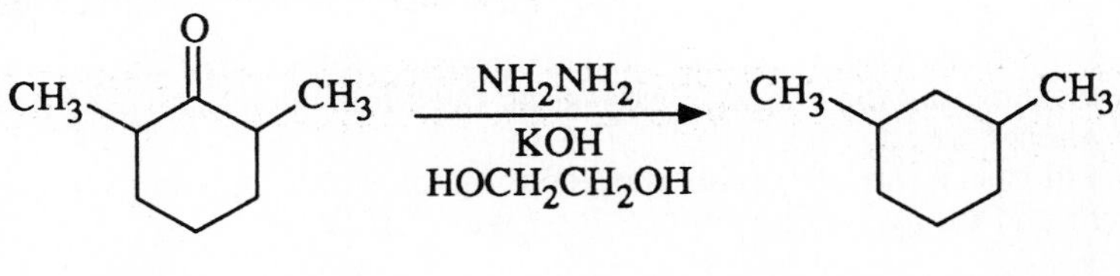

a) This reaction, called the **Wolff–Kishner reduction**, typically utilizes ethylene glycol or similar compounds as co-solvents.
b) The high boiling points of these solvents allow the reaction mixtures to reach the high temperatures required for the reduction to take place at a reasonable rate.
3. The Wolff–Kishner reduction is an extension of imine formation—an intermediate in the reduction is a hydrazone (the imine of hydrazine).
4. A series of acid–base reactions leads to the expulsion of nitrogen and formation of a carbanion, which is instantaneously protonated by water to yield the product.

5. The same overall transformation can be achieved under *acidic* conditions by a reaction called the **Clemmensen reduction**, which involves reduction of an aldehyde or ketone with **zinc amalgam** (a solution of zinc metal in mercury) in the presence of HCl.

6. The Wolff–Kishner and Clemmensen reactions are particularly useful for the introduction of alkyl groups into a benzene ring by:
a) Friedel–Crafts acylation to give an aryl ketone.
b) Wolff–Kishner or Clemmensen reduction to yield the corresponding alkyl group.

B. Conversion of Aldehydes and Ketones into Alkenes: The Wittig Alkene Synthesis:
1. Another addition–elimination reaction, called the **Wittig reaction**, is an important method for preparing alkenes from aldehydes and ketones.
2. The nucleophile in the Wittig reaction is a type of **ylid**.
a) An ylid is any compound with opposite charges on adjacent covalently bound atoms, each of which has an electronic octet.
b) Because phosphorus can accommodate more than eight valence electrons, a phosphorus ylid has an uncharged resonance structure.
c) Although the structures of phosphorus ylids are sometimes written with phosphorus–carbon double bonds, the charged structures, in which each atom has an octet of electrons, are very important contributors.

3. Phosphorus ylids are prepared by:
a) The reaction of an alkyl halide with triphenylphosphine (Ph3P) to give a **phosphonium salt**; this is a typical S_N2 reaction and is therefore limited for the most part to primary alkyl halides.
b) The phosphonium salt can be converted into its conjugate base, the ylid, by reaction with a strong base such as an organolithium reagent.

4. The mechanism of the Wittig reaction involves:
a) Attack of a nucleophile (the anionic carbon of the ylid) on the carbonyl carbon and formation of an **oxaphosphetane** intermediate—a saturated four-membered ring containing both oxygen and phosphorus as ring atoms.
b) Under the usual reaction conditions, the oxaphosphetane spontaneously breaks down to the alkene and the by-product triphenylphosphine oxide.

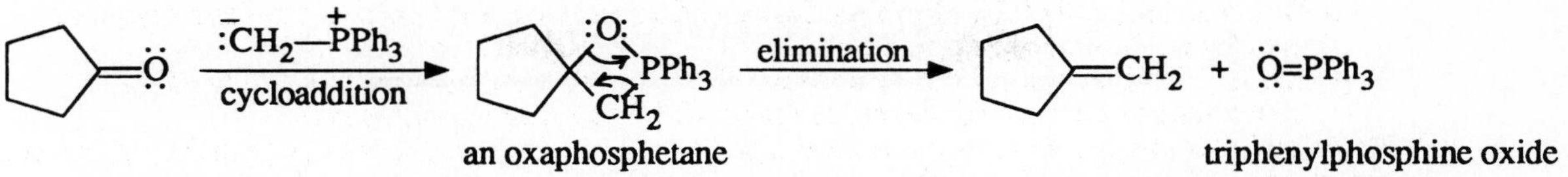

an oxaphosphetane   triphenylphosphine oxide

5. The Wittig reaction is important because it gives alkenes in which there is no ambiguity about the position of the alkene double bond.
   a) The reaction is thus a completely *regioselective* reaction.
   b) The reaction is particularly useful for the synthesis of alkenes that are hard to obtain by other means.
6. To plan the synthesis of an alkene by the Wittig reaction, consider the origin of each part of the product, and then reason back to starting materials.
   a) One carbon of the alkene double bond originates from the alkyl halide used to prepare the ylid; the other is the carbonyl carbon of the aldehyde or ketone.
   b) In principle, two Wittig syntheses are possible for any given alkene.
   c) Most Wittig syntheses are planned so that a primary alkyl halide can be used as one of the starting materials. [See 3a) above.]

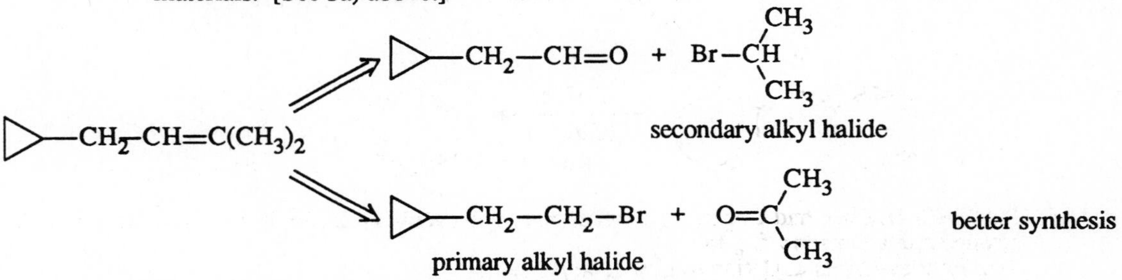

d) The Wittig reaction in many cases gives mixtures of *E* and *Z* isomers.

CHAPTER 19 SOLUTIONS

Solutions to In-Text Problems

1. (a)

$(CH_3)_2CHCH=O$

(b)

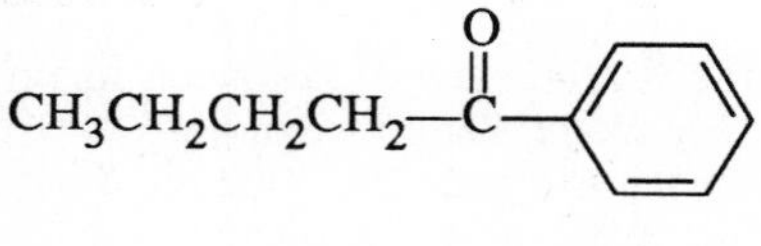

$CH_3CH_2CH_2CH_2$—$\overset{\displaystyle O}{\overset{\|}{C}}$—Ph

(c)

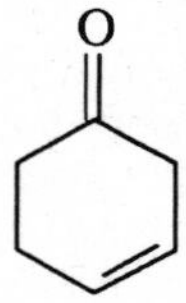

(d)

$ClCH_2CH_2CH_2CH=O$

(e)

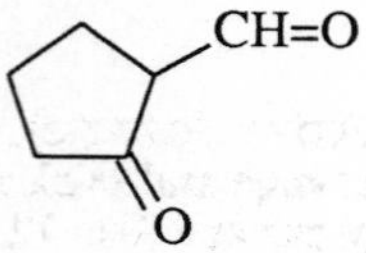

—CH=O

(f)

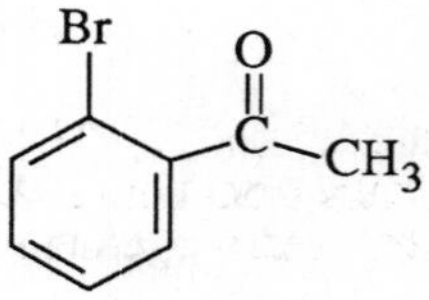

Br   —$\overset{\displaystyle O}{\overset{\|}{C}}$—$CH_3$

(g)

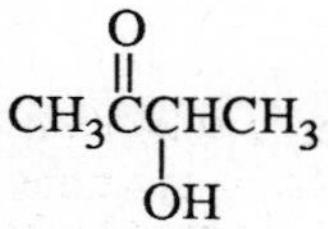

$CH_3\overset{\displaystyle O}{\overset{\|}{C}}CHCH_3$
           $\underset{\displaystyle OH}{}$

(h)

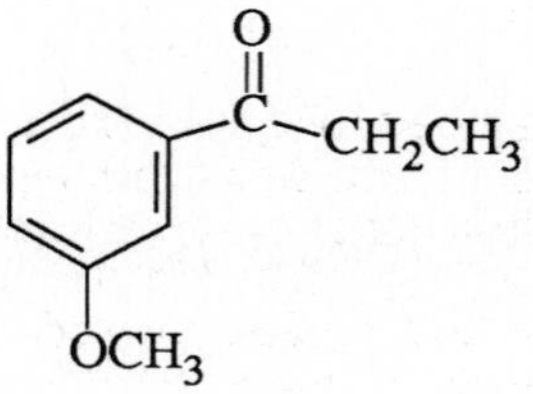

—$\overset{\displaystyle O}{\overset{\|}{C}}$—$CH_2CH_3$

OCH_3

(i)

$CH_3CH_2\overset{}{\underset{\displaystyle Cl}{C}H}\overset{\displaystyle O}{\overset{\|}{C}}$—⟨ ⟩—CH=O

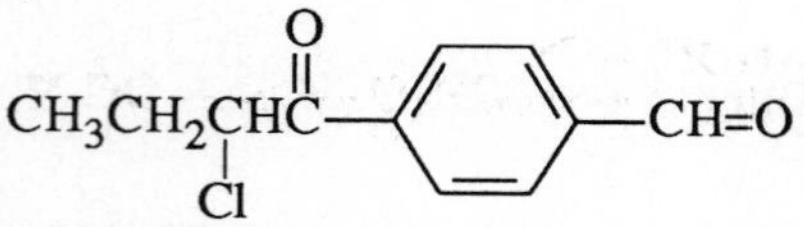

2. (a) 2,4-dimethyl-3-pentanone   (b) 2-propanone   (c) 3-allyl-2,4-pentanedione
    (d) (E)-3-ethoxy-2-propenal   (e) 3-methylcyclobutanecarbaldehyde
    (f) 4,4-dimethyl-2,5-cyclohexadien-1-one

3. (a) The aldehyde C=O stretching absorption occurs at about 10 cm^{-1} higher frequency than the ketone C=O stretching absorption.
    (b) Because 2-cyclohexen-1-one is conjugated, the carbonyl stretching frequency of this compound should occur at considerably lower frequency.
    (c) 2-Butanone should have a C=O stretching absorption and no O—H stretching absorption; 3-buten-2-ol should have an O—H stretching absorption, —CH=CH$_2$ alkene absorption (1640, 910, and 990 cm^{-1}), and no carbonyl stretching absorption.

4. (a)   (b)   (c)

$(CH_3)_2CHCH=O$ $CH_3CH_2\overset{\displaystyle O}{\overset{\|}{C}}CH_3$ C_2H_5O—⟨ ⟩—$\overset{\displaystyle O}{\overset{\|}{C}}$—$CH_3$

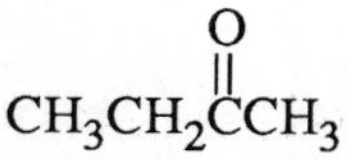

isobutyraldehyde   2-butanone

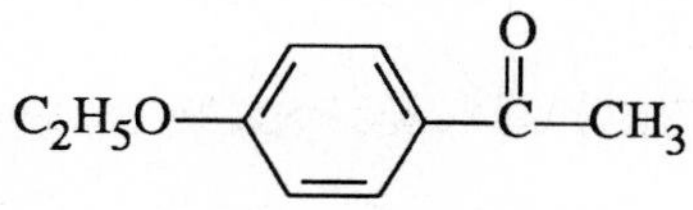

p-ethoxyacetophenone

5. (a) 2-Cyclohexen-1-one should have UV absorption at the higher wavelength because it is conjugated.
    (b) In p-methylacetophenone, the phenyl ring is conjugated with the carbonyl group; in 1-phenyl-2-propanone, the phenyl ring is not conjugated with the carbonyl. Hence, p-methylacetophenone should have UV absorption at the higher wavelength.
    (c) Because the first compound has more double bonds in conjugation, it has UV absorption at the higher wavelength.

6. In the conjugate-base anion of *p*-hydroxyacetophenone, the negative charge is delocalized throughout the conjugated π-electron system.

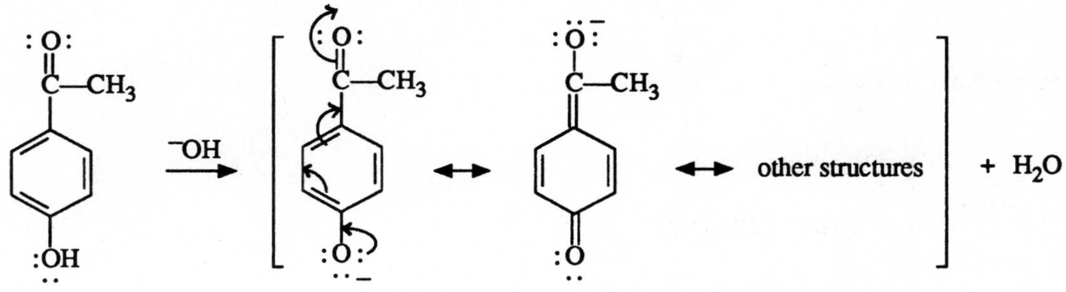

Since ionization creates a conjugated species (the anion), it is reasonable that there should be some effect of ionization on the UV spectrum. Since *p*-methoxyacetophenone cannot ionize, its UV spectrum is unaffected by base.

7. In 2-heptanone, we expect major peaks at $m/e = 43$ (from α-cleavage), 71 (from inductive cleavage), and 58 (from McLafferty rearrangement). In 3-heptanone, the peaks from both inductive cleavage and α-cleavage should occur at $m/e = 57$; and the ion formed by McLafferty rearrangement should occur at $m/e = 72$.

8. The first reaction proceeds by an S_N2 mechanism because the alkyl halide is primary. The second reaction, however, involves an S_N1 mechanism because the intermediate α-alkoxy carbocation is particularly stable:

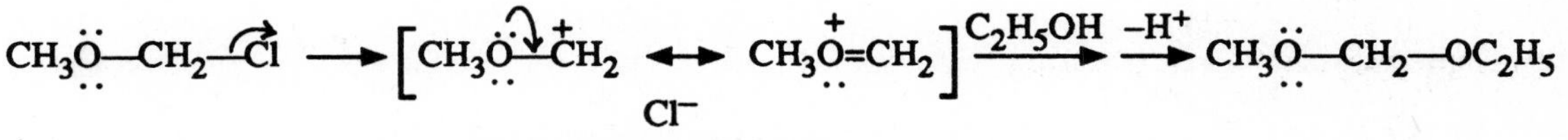

an α-alkoxy carbocation

The stability of this intermediate is reflected in a low energy for the transition state of the reaction, and thus a greater rate. If the second reaction were an S_N2 process, little difference in the rates of the two reactions would be expected.

9. The conjugate acid of 3-buten-2-one is stabilized by resonance interaction with the carbon–carbon double bond:

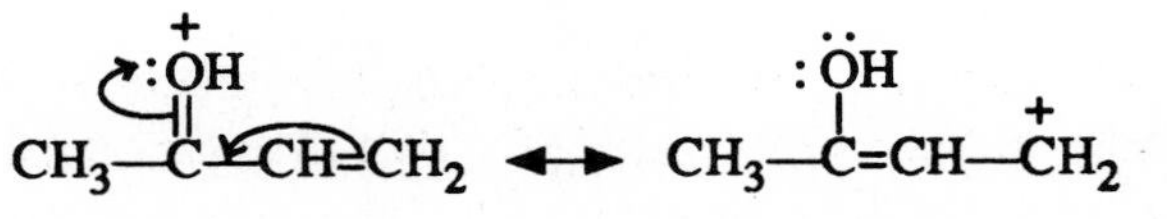

Because 2-butanone has no carbon–carbon double bond, its conjugate acid is not stabilized by similar resonance.

10. In base-catalyzed hydration, $^-$OH acts as the nucleophile, and H—OH as the acid:

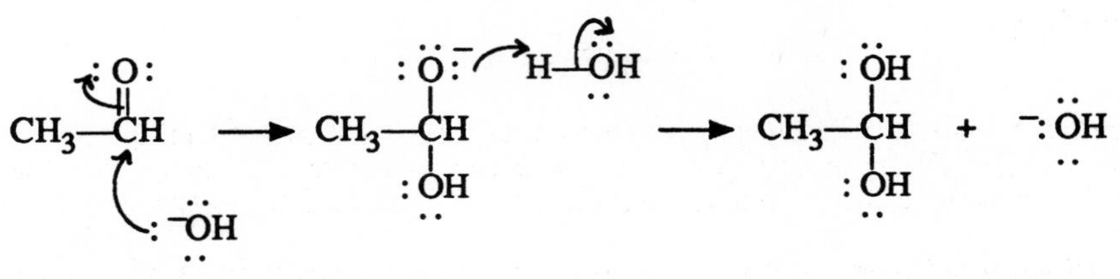

11. Methanol (R—OH, R = CH$_3$) reacts exactly like water (R—OH, R = H); see Eq. 19.17a and b.

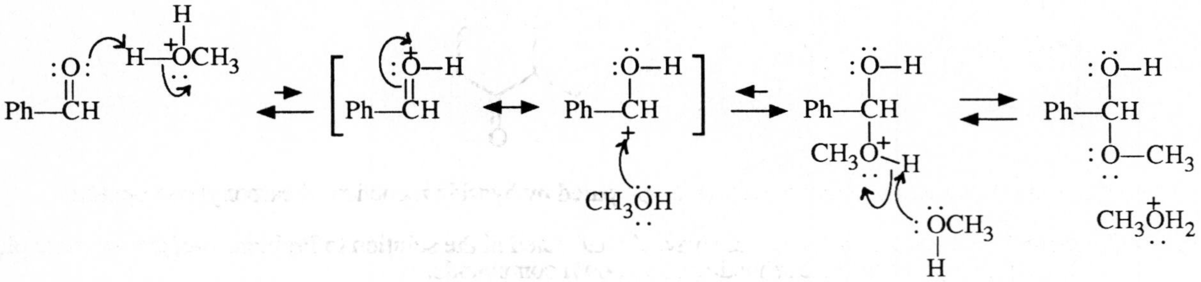

12. The middle carbonyl group is hydrated. The carbon of a carbonyl group bears a partial positive charge. The central carbonyl group is bonded to two partially positive carbonyl carbons, each of which destabilizes the partial positive charge on the carbon of the central carbonyl group. On the other hand, the other two carbonyl groups are conjugated with the benzene ring. Adjacent electronegative groups promote carbonyl-addition reactions, and conjugation makes carbonyl-addition reactions more difficult. It follows that the central carbonyl group is more susceptible to hydration. The structure of the hydrate is as follows:

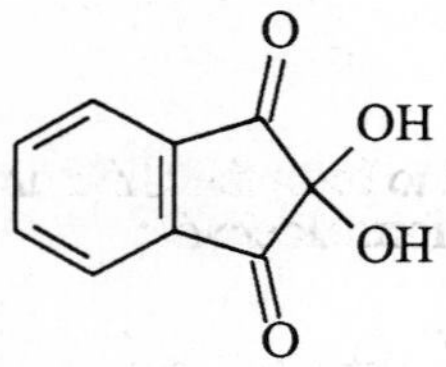

13. (a) The second compound, 1-bromo-2-propanone, is more reactive because the electronegative bromine atom is closer to the carbonyl group.
(b) The first compound, 2,3-butanedione, is more reactive, because the partial positive charge on one carbonyl destabilizes the partial positive charge on the other. (See the solution to Problem 12 for a similar situation.)
(c) The first compound, *p*-nitrobenzaldehyde, is more reactive, because the *p*-nitro group destabilizes the positive charge on the carbonyl carbon by its inductive effect. In contrast, the *p*-methoxy group in the second compound stabilizes the positive charge on the carbonyl carbon by a resonance effect:

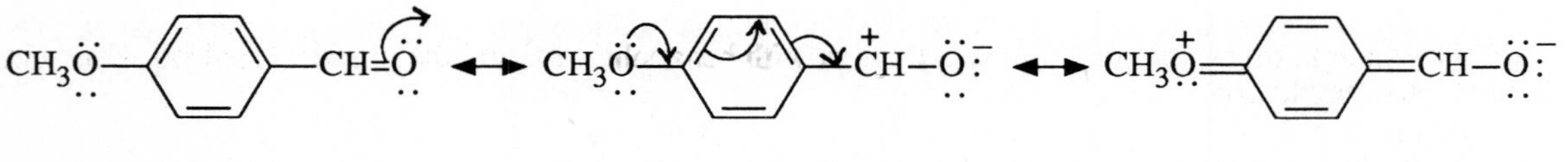

(d) The second compound, cyclopropanone, is more reactive. In the carbonyl form, the bond angles at the carbonyl group want to be 120°, but they are constrained by the three-membered ring to be 60°. As a result, there is a lot of strain in the carbonyl form. In the hydrate, the bond angle is approximately tetrahedral (109.5°). Because this angle is closer to the 60° bond angle enforced by the ring, there is less strain in the hydrate. Hence, formation of the hydrate relieves the strain in cyclopropanone. There is little or no strain in cyclopentanone.

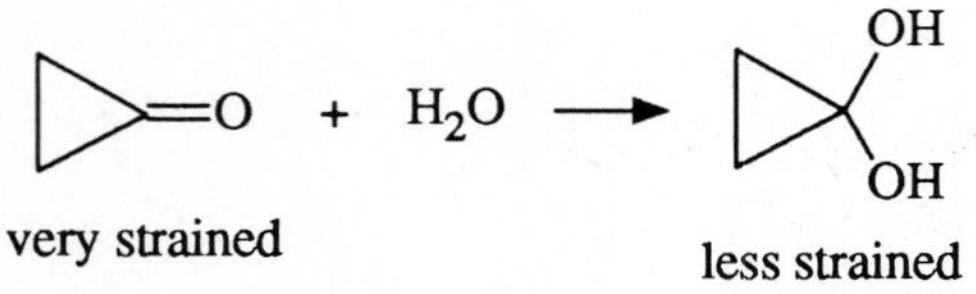

very strained   less strained

14. (a)   (b) 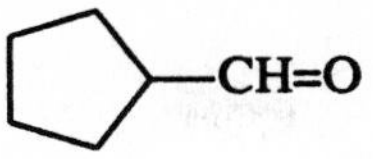   (c)

CH$_3$CCH$_2$CH$_3$ ⬠—CH=O   [bicyclic structure with OH at ring junction and C=O at bottom]

with O above the first carbonyl carbon

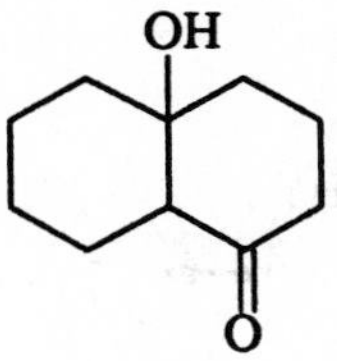

Notice in (c) that tertiary alcohols cannot be prepared by hydride reduction of carbonyl compounds.

15.   Compound (c) cannot be prepared this way. As indicated in the solution to Problem 14c, tertiary alcohols cannot be prepared by hydride reduction of carbonyl compounds.

16.   Ethyl bromide is used to prepare ethylmagnesium bromide, C$_2$H$_5$MgBr. This Grignard reagent is then allowed to react respectively with each compound given below, followed by protonolysis.

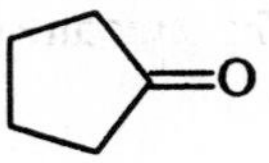

(a) 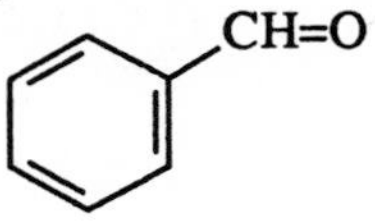   (b)   (c)   (d)

[benzaldehyde, CH=O]   CH$_3$CH$_2$—C—CH$_3$ [cyclopentanone, =O]   CH$_2$=O

with O above the carbonyl

(e) 1-Propanol from part (d) is converted into 1-bromopropane, which is then used to form the Grignard reagent propylmagnesium bromide. This Grignard reagent is allowed to react with formaldehyde:

$$CH_3CH_2CH_2OH \xrightarrow{HBr} CH_3CH_2CH_2Br \xrightarrow[ether]{Mg} CH_3CH_2CH_2MgBr \xrightarrow{CH_2=O \quad H_3O^+} CH_3CH_2CH_2CH_2OH$$

(Alternatively, the reaction of ethylmagnesium bromide and ethylene oxide, followed by protonolysis, will also give 1-butanol.)

(f) 1-Propanol from part (d) is oxidized to propanal:

$$CH_3CH_2CH_2OH \xrightarrow{CrO_3/pyridine} CH_3CH_2CH=O$$

(g) Ethylmagnesium bromide is allowed to react with benzophenone, and the product is subjected to acid-catalyzed dehydration:

$$Ph_2C=O \xrightarrow{CH_3CH_2MgBr \quad H_3O^+} Ph_2\overset{OH}{\underset{}{C}}-CH_2CH_3 \xrightarrow[-H_2O]{H_2SO_4} Ph_2C=CHCH_3$$

17.   (a) Either isopropylmagnesium bromide can be added to acetaldehyde, or methylmagnesium iodide can be added to isobutyraldehyde:

$$(CH_3)_2CHMgBr + CH_3CH=O$$

or

$$CH_3MgI + (CH_3)_2CHCH=O$$

$$\xrightarrow{H_3O^+} CH_3)_2CH-\overset{OH}{\underset{}{CH}}-CH_3$$

(b) Either methyl magnesium iodide can be added to 1-phenyl-2-propanone, or benzylmagnesium chloride can be added to acetone:

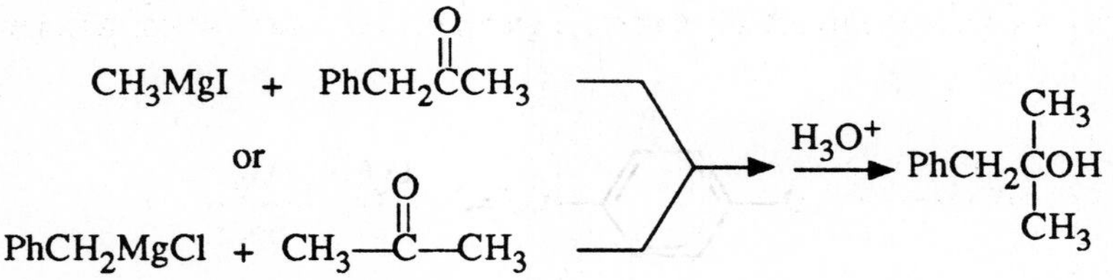

$$CH_3MgI \;+\; PhCH_2\overset{\displaystyle O}{\overset{\|}{C}}CH_3$$

or

$$PhCH_2MgCl \;+\; CH_3-\overset{\displaystyle O}{\overset{\|}{C}}-CH_3$$

$$\xrightarrow{\;H_3O^+\;} PhCH_2\overset{\displaystyle CH_3}{\underset{\displaystyle CH_3}{\overset{|}{\underset{|}{C}}}}OH$$

18. The mechanism follows the pattern used in the solution to Problem 11.

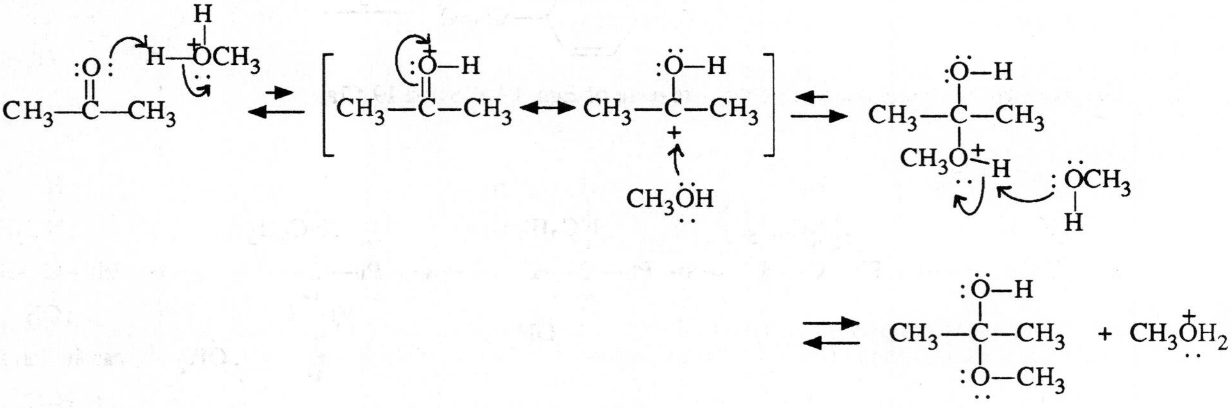

19. (a)   (b)   (c)

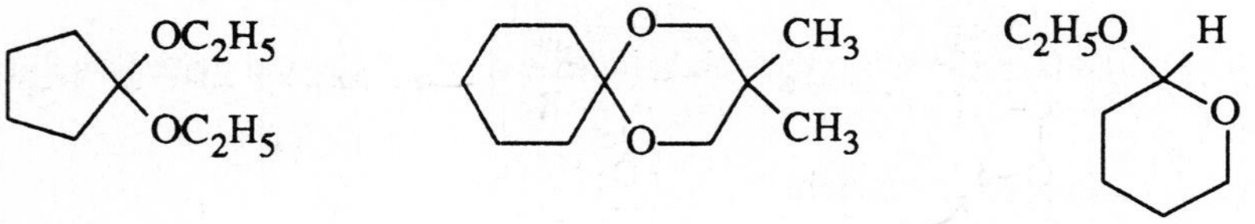

Reaction (a) involves simple acetal formation; reaction (b) involves formation of a *cyclic* acetal; and reaction (c) involves formation of a mixed acetal (an acetal derived from two different alcohols) from a cyclichemiacetal. In part (c), the formula tells us that only two carbons are introduced; hence only one molecule of ethanol reacts.

20. The compounds formed are two structurally isomeric sets of two diastereomers.

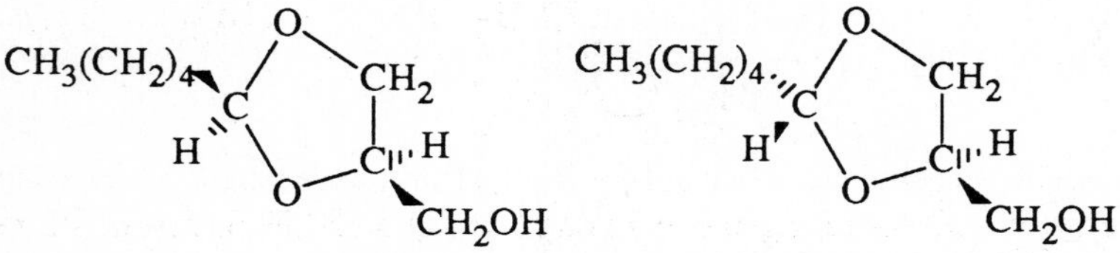

(There are two enantiomers of each.)

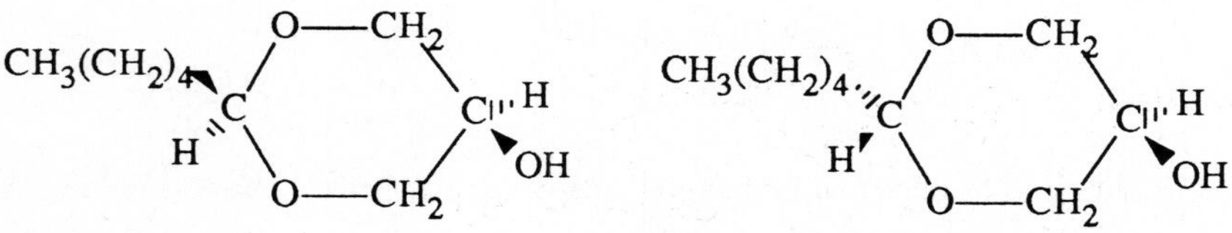

meso compounds; both are achiral

21. The best way to introduce deuterium regiospecifically (that is, in a specific place) is by protonolysis of a Grignard reagent in D_2O. However, we have to protect any carbonyl group present when we use a Grignard reagent.

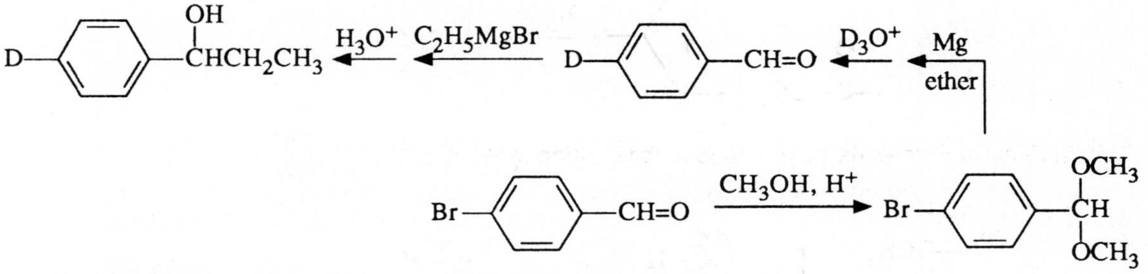

22. The required mechanism is in effect the reverse of Eqs. 19.57b and 19.57a.

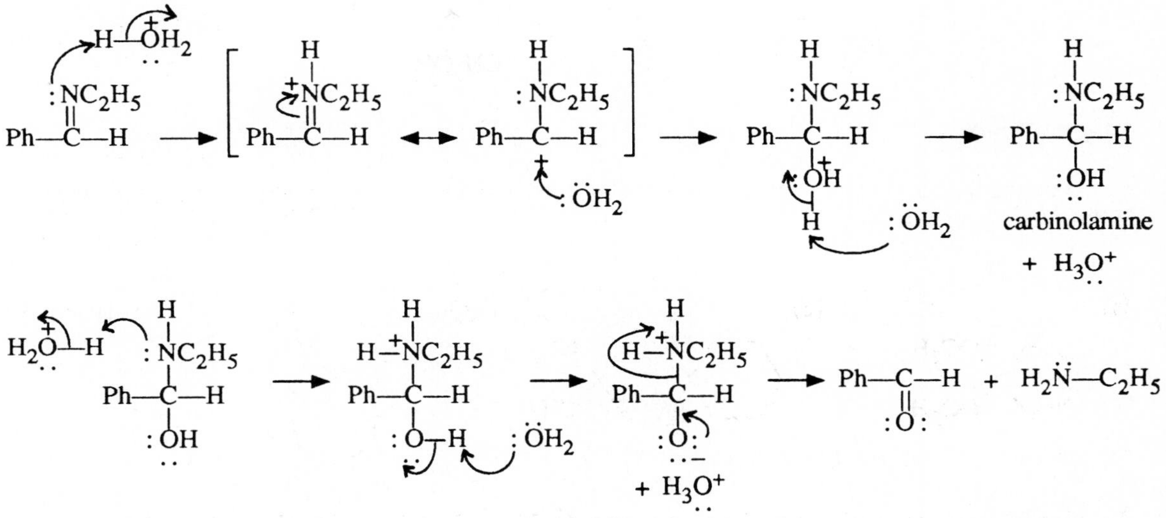

23. (a) 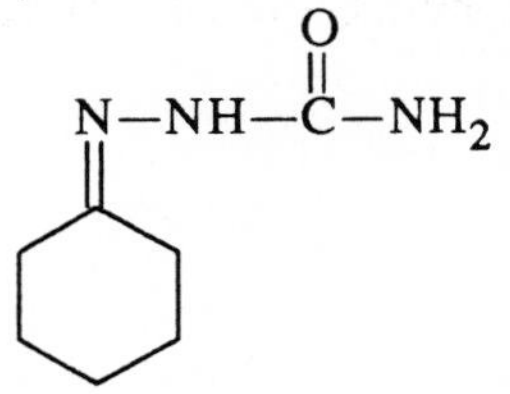   (b) 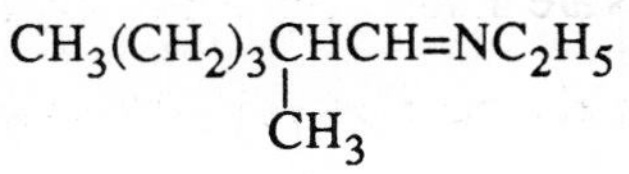   (c)

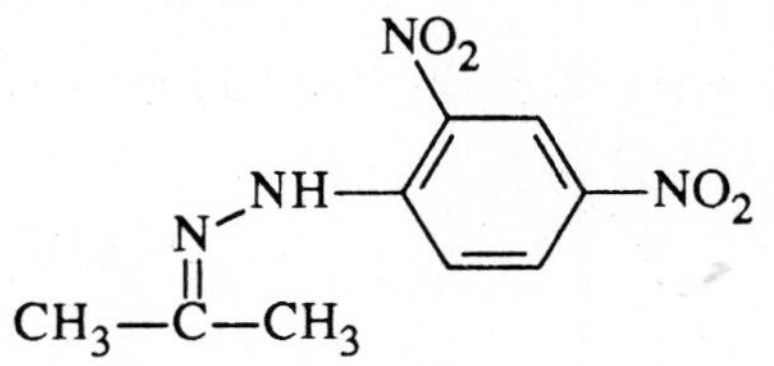

24. *Cis–trans* (or *E,Z*) isomerization about the carbon–nitrogen double bond accounts for the formation of the two DNP derivatives. (Nitrogen inversion in imines is very slow.)

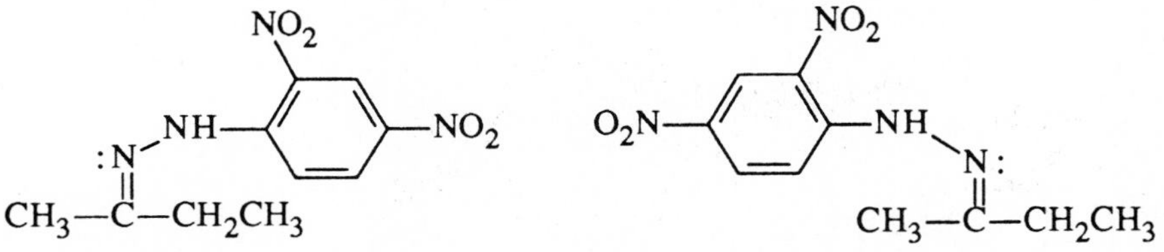

25. The —NH_2 group adjacent to the carbonyl group is not nucleophilic because its unshared electron pair is delocalized into the carbonyl group:

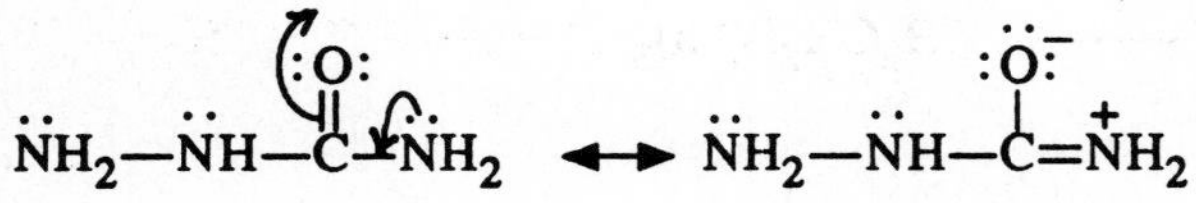

This delocalization stabilizes the molecule toward any reaction of this nitrogen in which the electron pair is involved as a base (or nucleophile). That is, the stabilizing effect of this resonance interaction is lost in the tetrahedral addition intermediate. The unshared pair on the other —NH_2 group is not delocalized, and therefore this nitrogen is more reactive as a nucleophile. (Less precisely, but more descriptively, we can say that the delocalized electron pair is "less available" for nucleophilic reactions.)

26. (a)   (b)

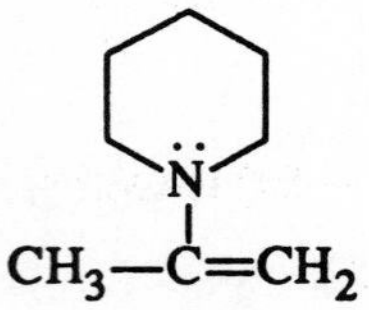

$$PhCH=CH—\ddot{N}(CH_3)_2$$

27. Any compound with a carbonyl group on any of the alkyl carbons could in principle react to give the product shown.

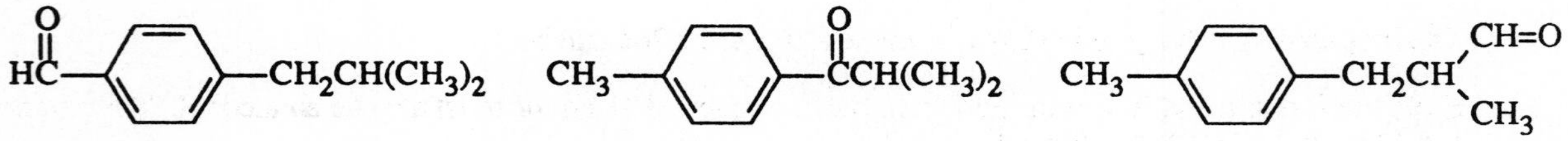

(These are the structures containing only one carbonyl group.)

28. As usual, we construct the synthesis in reverse:

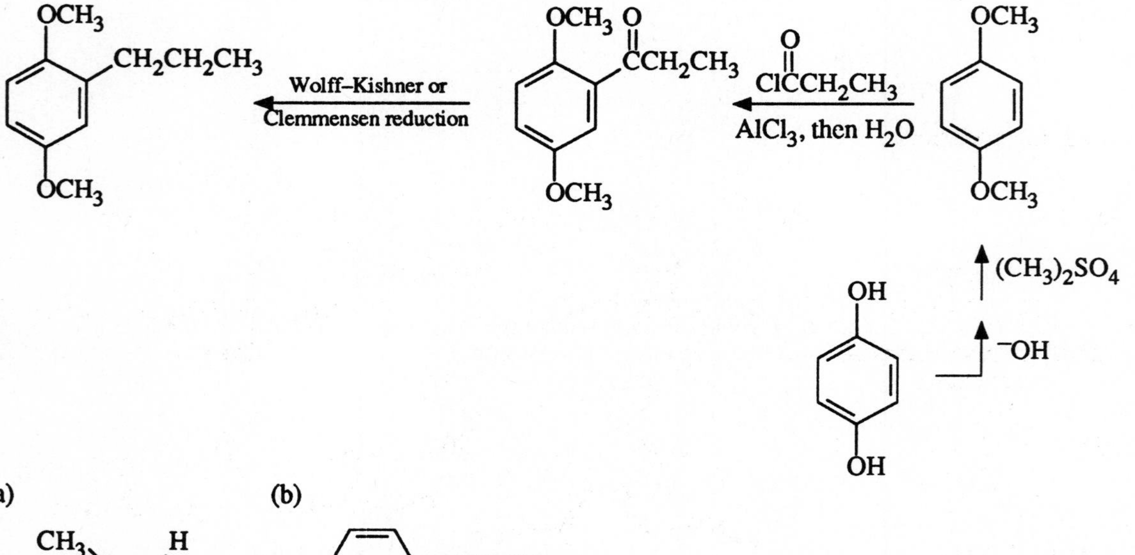

29. (a)   (b)

30. (a)

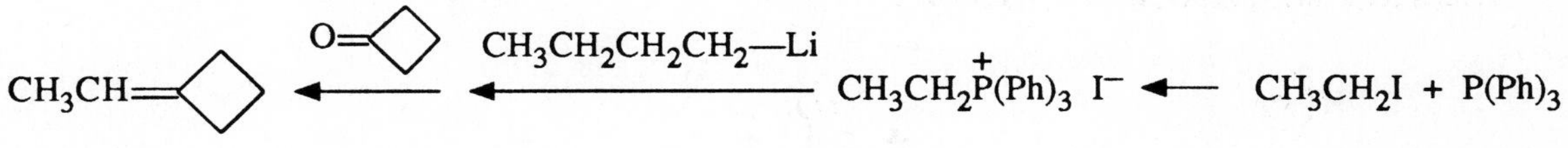

(b)

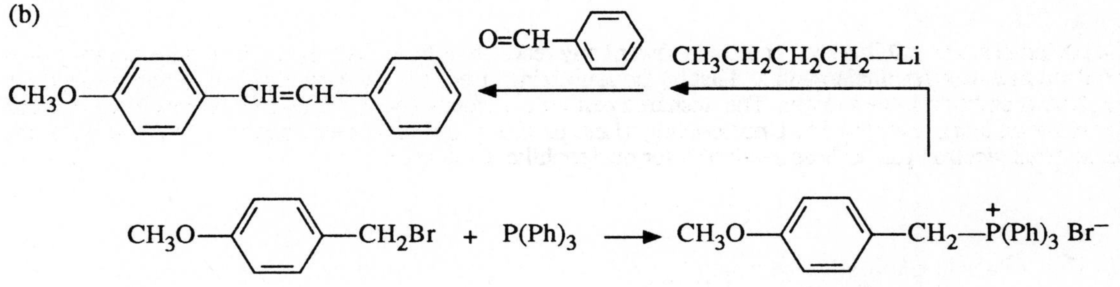

The second synthesis is carried out the same way, except that benzyl bromide (Ph—CH2—Br) is used as the alkyl halide, and *p*-methoxybenzaldehyde as the aldehyde.

(c)

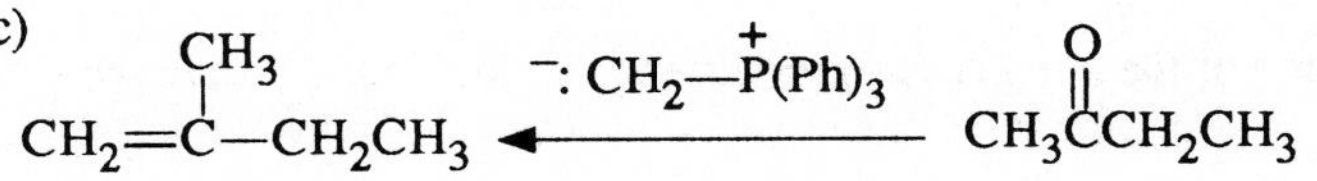

The preparation of the ylid is shown in the text in Eq. 19.76a and b.

31. From the formula and its unsaturation number, the required aldehyde must also be an alcohol. The compound is 4-(hydroxymethyl)benzaldehyde:

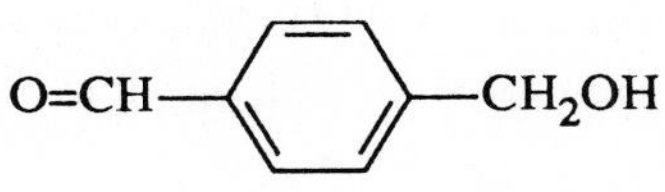

Solutions to Additional Problems

32. (a)

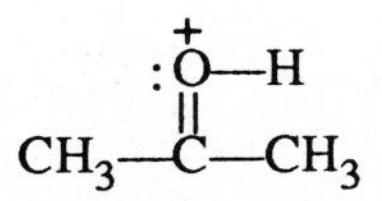

(small amount; otherwise no reaction)

(b)

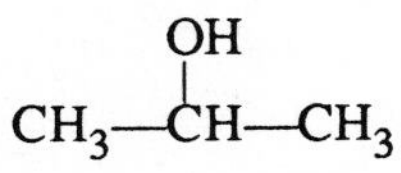

(c) no reaction

(d)

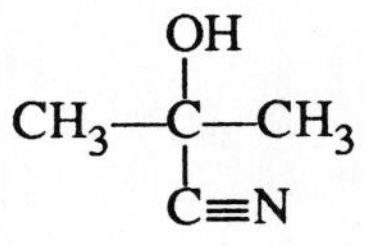

(e)

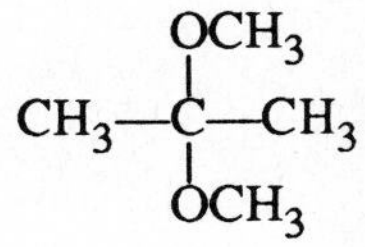

(f)

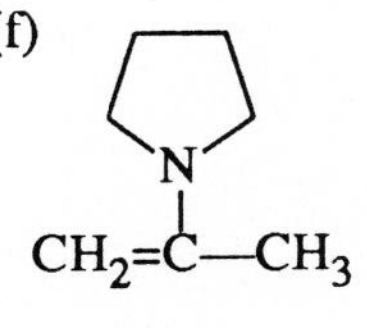

(g)

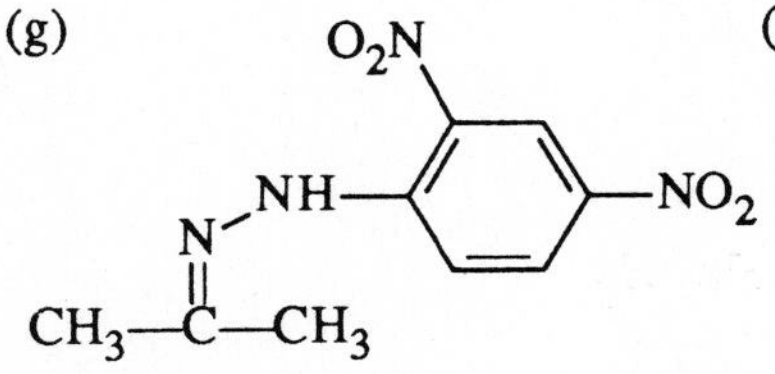

(h)

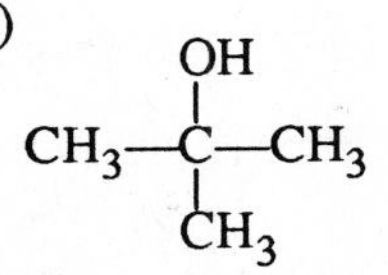

(i)

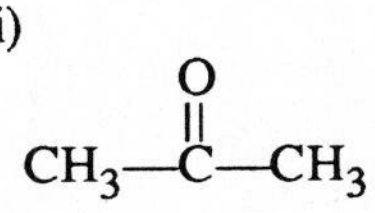

(j) $(CH_3)_2C{=}CH_2$ (k) same as (b) (l) same as (j) (m) $CH_3CH_2CH_3$

33. In the following answers, R— = $CH_3CH_2CH_2$— .

(a) 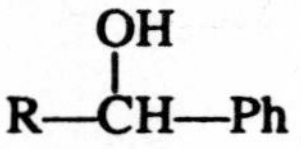   (b) R—CH_2OH (c) 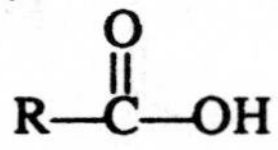   (d) same as (c)

$$\underset{\text{R}-\overset{\displaystyle OH}{\underset{|}{CH}}-\text{Ph}}{}$$

$$\underset{\text{R}-\overset{\displaystyle O}{\overset{\|}{C}}-\text{OH}}{}$$

(e) R—CH=N—OH   (f) same as (c)

34. The compound is *p*-methylbenzaldehyde:

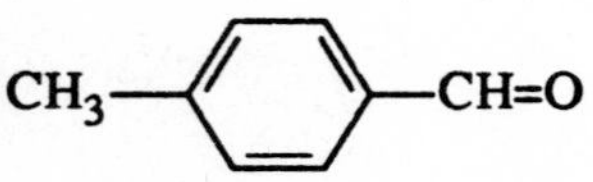

$$CH_3-\!\!\!\left\langle\!\!\!\bigcirc\!\!\!\right\rangle\!\!\!-CH{=}O$$

35. (a) This is a nucleophilic addition reaction in which the sulfur of bisulfite acts as the nucleophile:

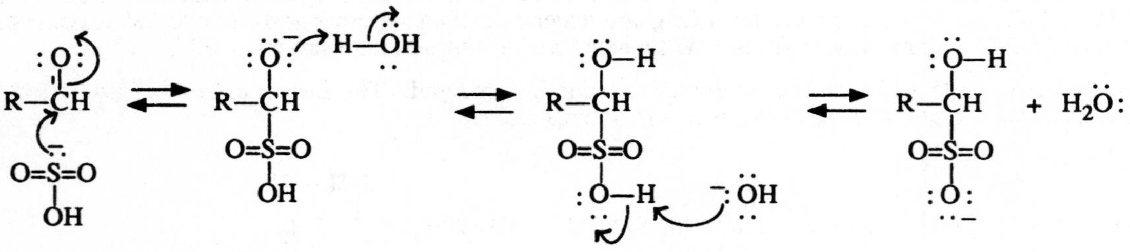

(b) Acid reacts with HSO_3^- to give H_2SO_3, which, in turn, decomposes to SO_2 and H_2O. The formation of a gas makes this reaction irreversible and pulls the equilibria above back toward starting materials. In other words, formation of the bisulfite addition product is reversed. Similarly, ⁻OH reacts with HSO_3^- to give sulfite ion, SO_3^{2-}. This reaction also pulls the equilibria above back toward starting materials with the result that the bisulfite addition product decomposes.

36. In each case stereoisomers are formed.

(a)

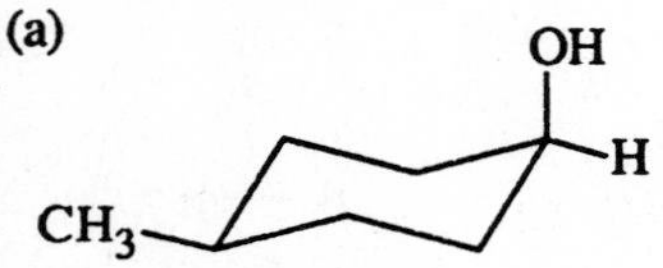

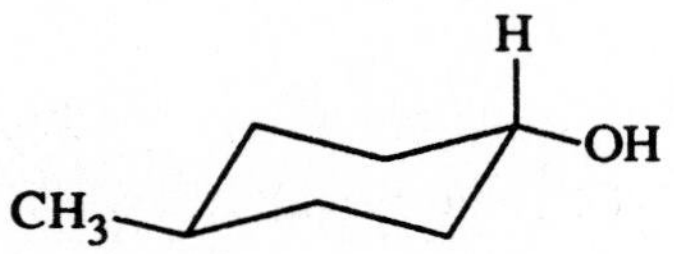

(b)

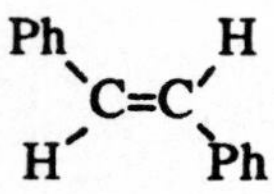

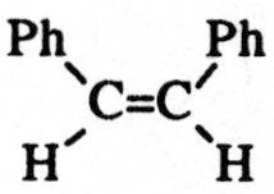

(c)

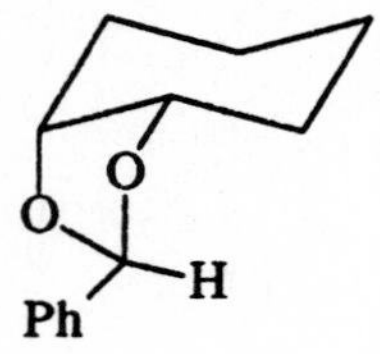

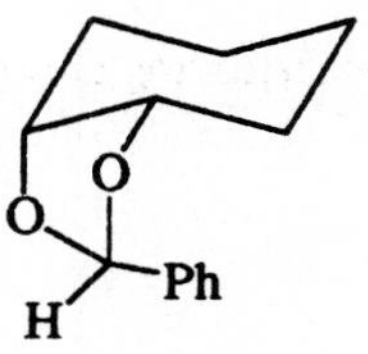

37. (a)   (b) 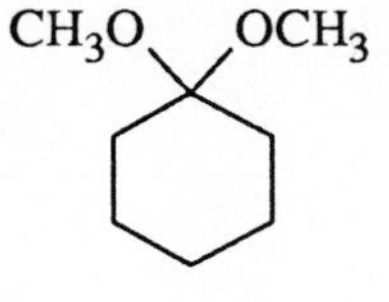   (c) 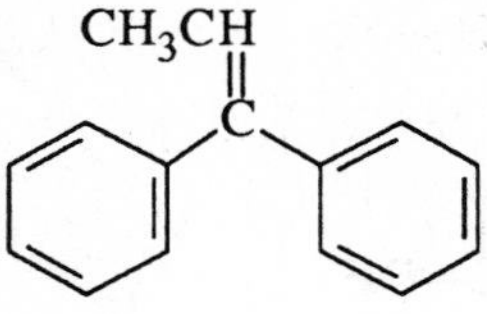   (d) 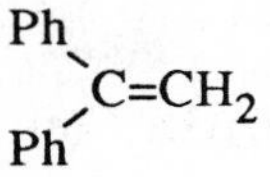   (e)

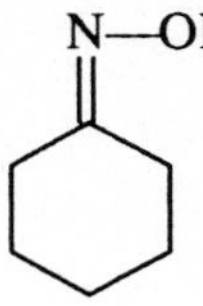

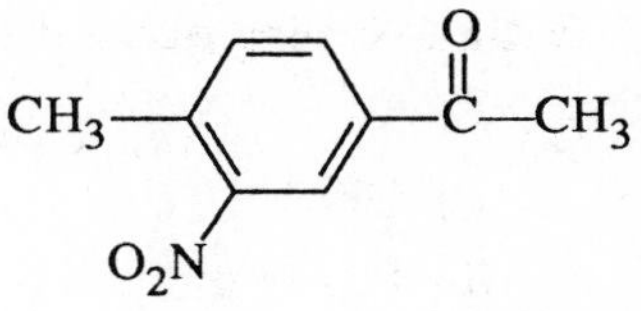

(f) 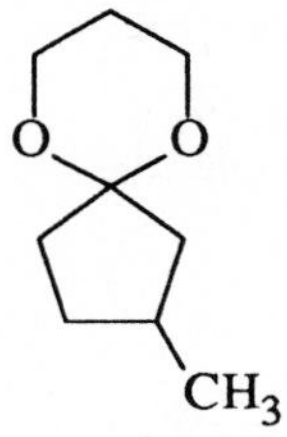   (g) 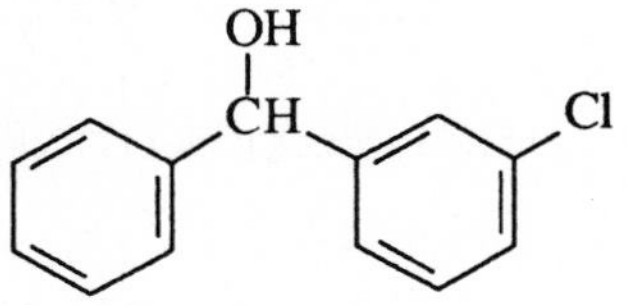   (h) 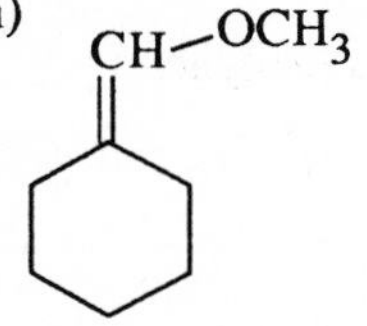   (i)

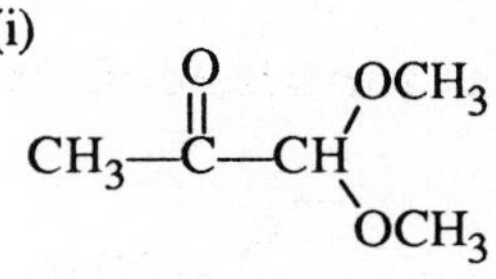

Product (c) results from dehydration of the tertiary alcohol formed in the Grignard reaction. The answer to (g) relies on the fact that aryl bromides form Grignard reagents in ether, whereas aryl chlorides do not (text page 729, Eq. 18.25). The reaction in (h) is a Wittig reaction; the phosphonium salt involved is

CH_3O—CH_2—$\overset{+}{P}(Ph)_3$ Cl^-, and butyllithium is used to form the ylid. The answer to (i) relies on the fact that aldehydes are more reactive than ketones in addition reactions.

(j)   (k) 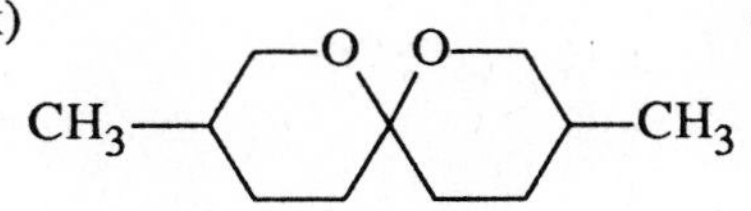   (l)

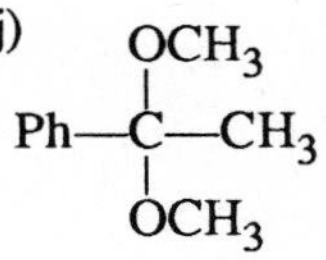

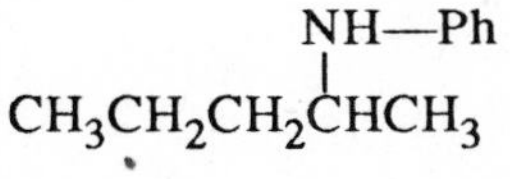

Reaction (j) is the result of two successive acid-catalyzed Markovnikov additions. Reaction (k) involves intramolecular acetal formation; since a carbonyl and two alcohol groups are within the same molecule, everything needed for acetal formation is present. In reaction (l), an imine formed in the reaction mixture is reduced by $NaBH_4$, as the hint suggests.

(m) The carbonyl group is reduced to an alcohol, which is then ionized by NaH. The resulting species is essentially a Wittig-reaction intermediate, as the hint suggests; this intermediate breaks down to an alkene:

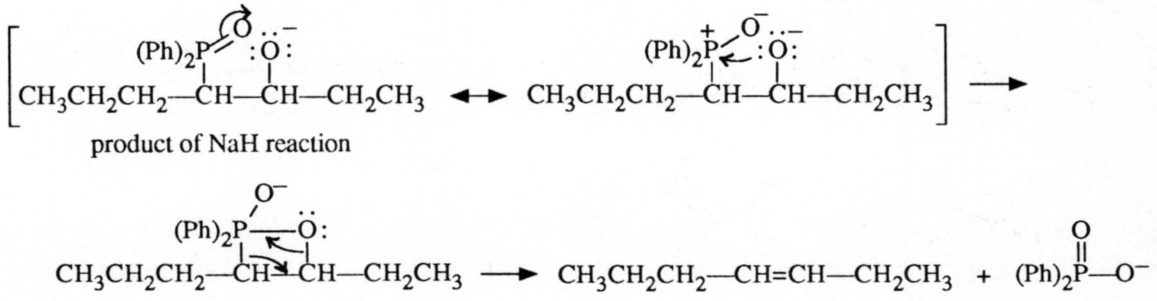

product of NaH reaction

(n) This reaction is a double Wittig reaction involving the following double ylid:

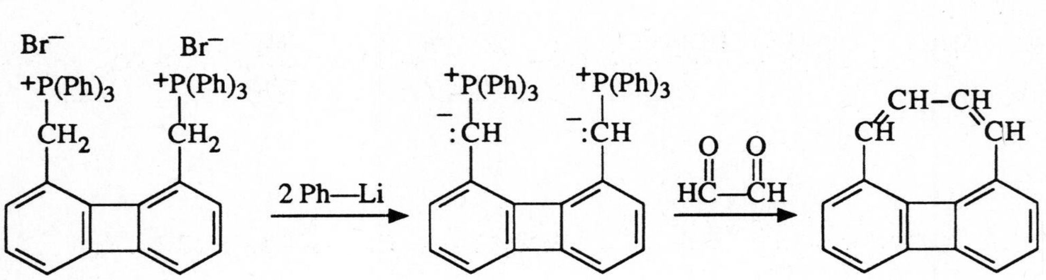

38. According to our usual convention, these syntheses are written from products to starting materials.

(a)

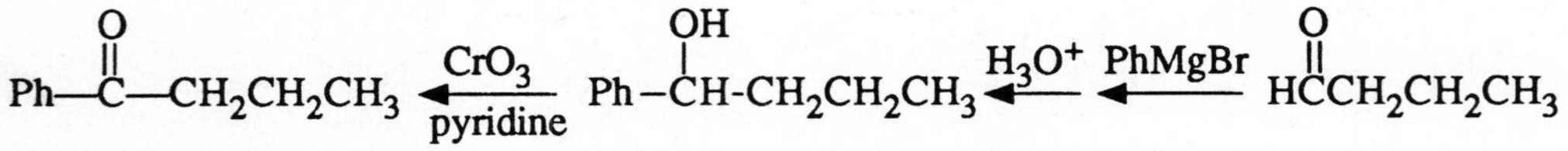

(b)

$$CH_2{=}CHCH(CH_3)_2 \xleftarrow{(Ph)_3\overset{+}{P}-\overset{-}{C}H_2} O{=}CHCH(CH_3)_2$$

The preparation of the ylid is given in Eq. 19.76a and b, text page 802.

(c)

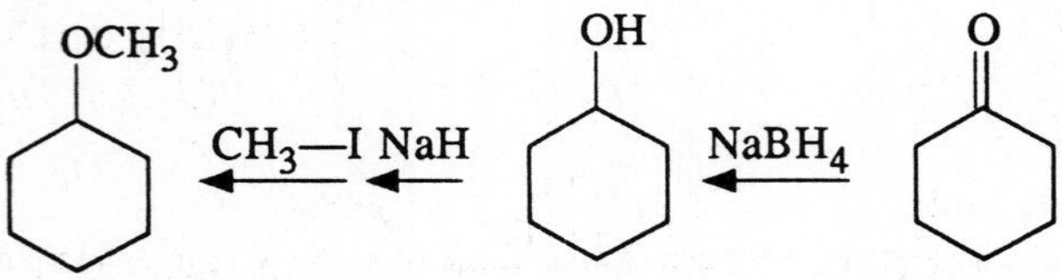

(d)

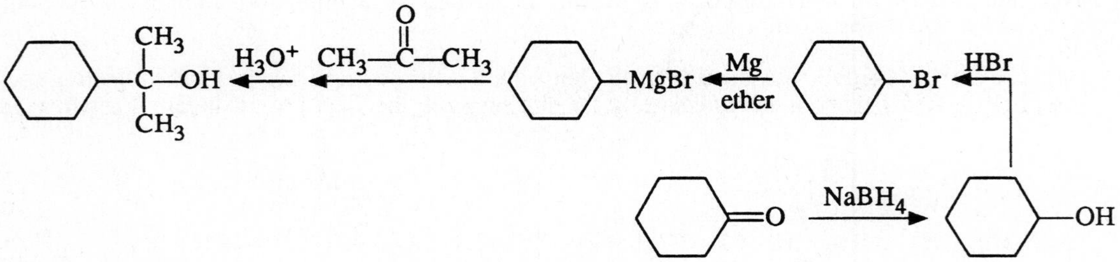

(e)

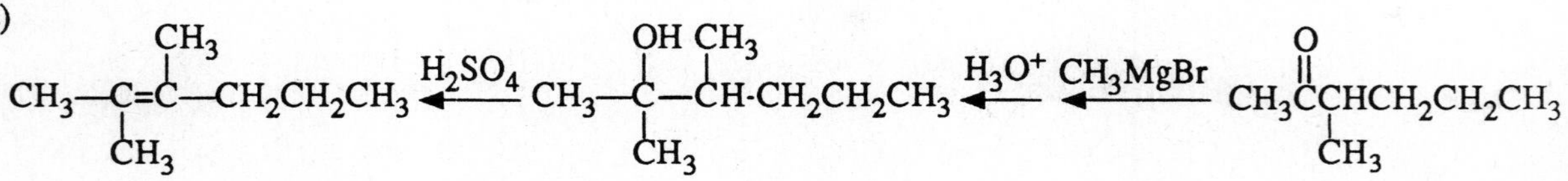

(f)

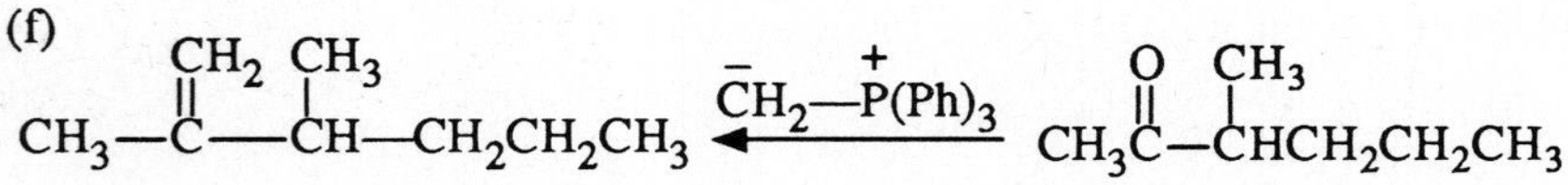

The preparation of the ylid is given in Eq. 19.76a and b, text page 802.

(g)

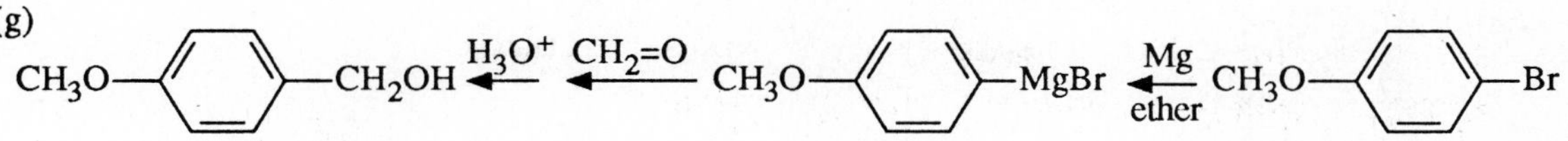

CH_3O—⟨benzene ring⟩—CH_2OH $\xleftarrow[\ ]{H_3O^+ \ \ CH_2=O}$ CH_3O—⟨benzene ring⟩—$MgBr$ $\xleftarrow[ether]{Mg}$ CH_3O—⟨benzene ring⟩—Br

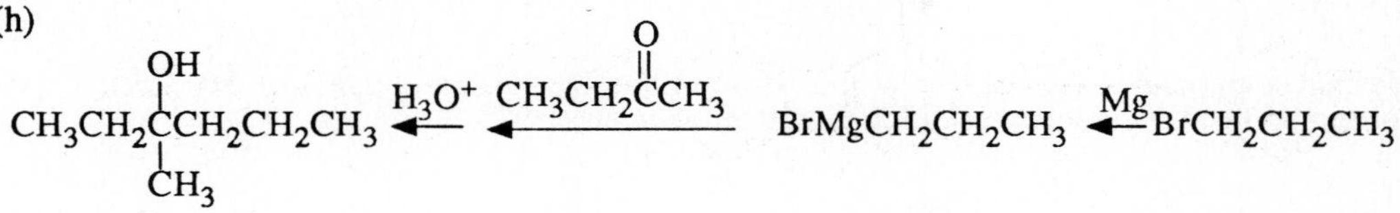

(h)

$$\underset{\overset{|}{CH_3}}{CH_3CH_2\overset{\overset{OH}{|}}{C}CH_2CH_2CH_3} \xleftarrow[\ ]{H_3O^+ \ \ CH_3CH_2\overset{O}{\overset{||}{C}}CH_3} BrMgCH_2CH_2CH_3 \xleftarrow[\ ]{Mg} BrCH_2CH_2CH_3$$

(i)

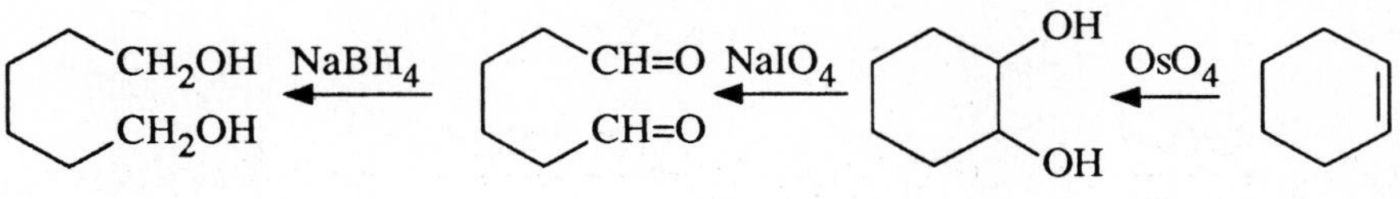

$$\underset{CH_2OH}{\overset{CH_2OH}{\text{⟨ring⟩}}} \xleftarrow[\ ]{NaBH_4} \underset{CH=O}{\overset{CH=O}{\text{⟨ring⟩}}} \xleftarrow[\ ]{NaIO_4} \underset{OH}{\overset{OH}{\text{⟨ring⟩}}} \xleftarrow[\ ]{OsO_4} \text{⟨cyclohexene⟩}$$

(j)

$CH_3(CH_2)_3$—⟨benzene ring⟩—$CH_2CH_2CH_3$ $\xleftarrow[\overset{-}{OH},\ heat]{H_2N-NH_2}$ $CH_3CH_2CH_2\overset{O}{\overset{||}{C}}$—⟨benzene ring⟩—$CH_2CH_2CH_3$

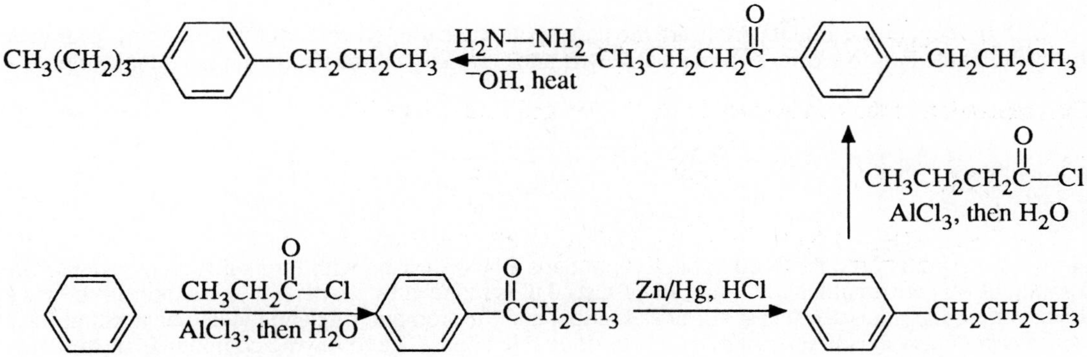

$\uparrow$ $\begin{array}{c} CH_3CH_2CH_2\overset{O}{\overset{||}{C}}\text{—Cl} \\ AlCl_3,\ then\ H_2O \end{array}$

⟨benzene⟩ $\xrightarrow[AlCl_3,\ then\ H_2O]{CH_3CH_2\overset{O}{\overset{||}{C}}\text{—Cl}}$ ⟨benzene ring⟩—$\overset{O}{\overset{||}{C}}CH_2CH_3$ $\xrightarrow{Zn/Hg,\ HCl}$ ⟨benzene ring⟩—$CH_2CH_2CH_3$

(k)

$PhCH_2\overset{O}{\overset{||}{C}}Ph$ $\xleftarrow[\ ]{H_2Cr_2O_4}$ $PhCH_2\overset{\overset{OH}{|}}{C}HPh$ $\xleftarrow[2)\ H_3O^+]{1)\ PhCH=O}$ $PhCH_2MgBr$ $\xleftarrow[\ ]{Mg}$ $PhCH_2Br$ $\xleftarrow[\ ]{HBr}$ $PhCH_2OH$

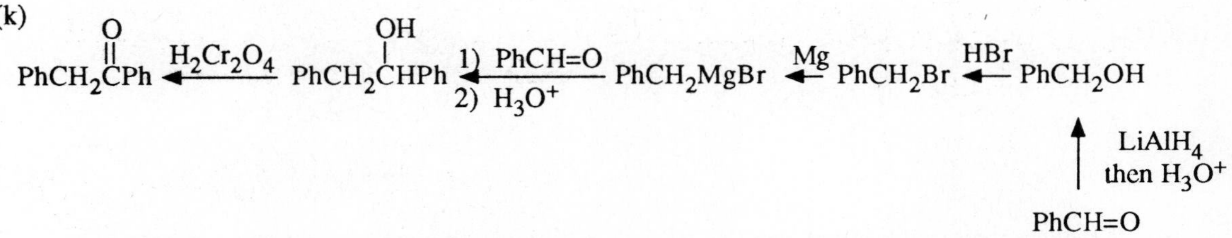

$\uparrow$ $\begin{array}{c} LiAlH_4 \\ then\ H_3O^+ \end{array}$

$PhCH=O$

(l)

$CH_3\overset{O}{\overset{||}{C}}$—⟨benzene ring⟩—$D$ $\xleftarrow[\ ]{D_3O^+ \ \ Mg}$ $\underset{\overset{|}{CH_3O}}{CH_3\overset{\overset{CH_3O}{|}}{C}}$—⟨benzene ring⟩—$Br$ $\xleftarrow[\ ]{CH_3OH,\ H^+}$ $CH_3\overset{O}{\overset{||}{C}}$—⟨benzene ring⟩—$Br$

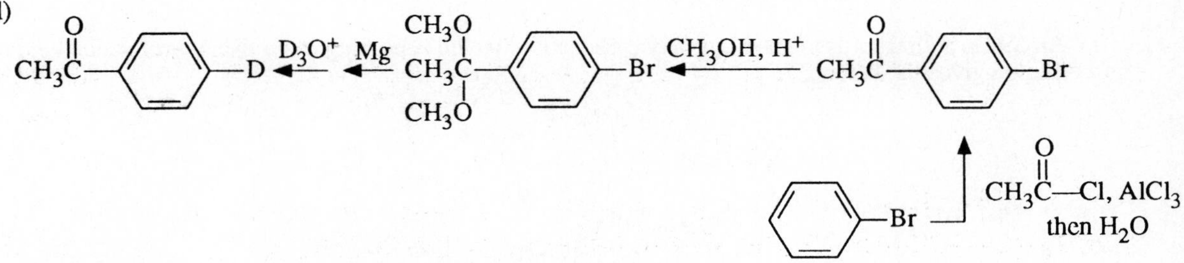

$\uparrow$ $\begin{array}{c} CH_3\overset{O}{\overset{||}{C}}\text{—Cl, AlCl}_3 \\ then\ H_2O \end{array}$

⟨benzene ring⟩—Br

(m)

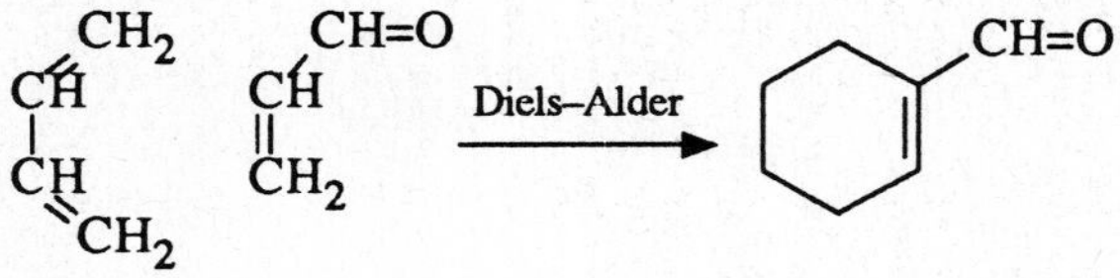

(n) The desired compound is a cyclic hemiacetal. If we synthesize the appropriate hydroxy aldehyde, the hemiacetal should form spontaneously. (See Eq. 19.50, text page 790.)

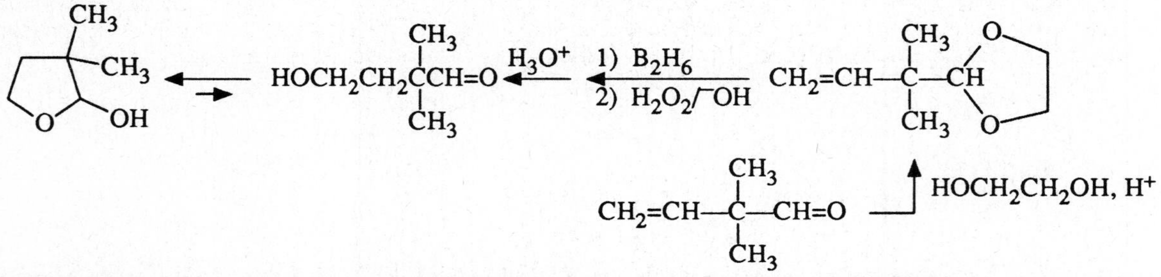

39. For each imine, the starting materials are the corresponding carbonyl compounds and primary amines. In (b), the cyclic imine must be formed from an aldehyde and a primary amine within the same molecule.

(a)

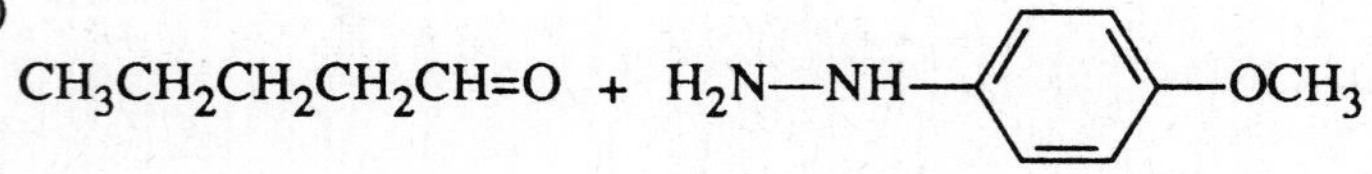

$$CH_3CH_2CH_2CH_2CH=O \ + \ H_2N-NH-\!\!\!\!\!\bigcirc\!\!\!\!\!-OCH_3$$

(b)

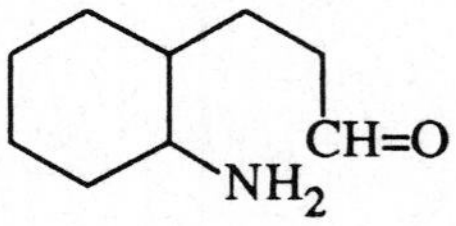

40. From the oxidation product D, compound A contains a benzene ring with four substituent groups. Since compound A is not an aldehyde (no Tollens' test), but is reduced by $LiAlH_4$, it would appear to be a ketone. Since compound A has six degrees of unsaturation, and the aromatic ring and the ketone account for five, it would appear also to contain a ring or additional double bond. The following compounds fit the data:

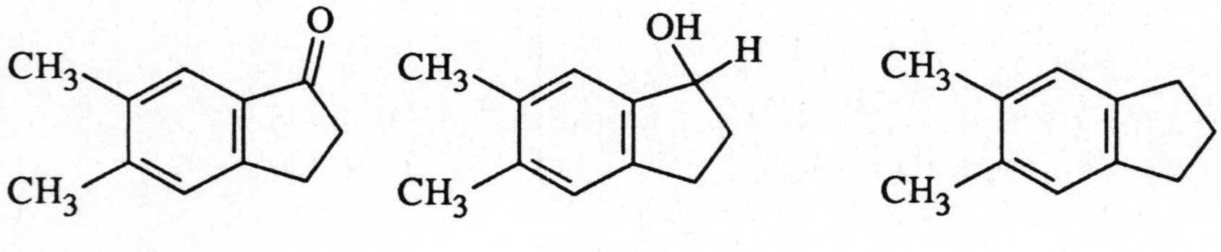

A	B	C

Notice that compound B is chiral, and would oxidize back to compound A, and that compound C would oxidize to the acid D given in the problem.

41. (a) An S_N1 reaction leads to an α-hydroxy carbocation, which is nothing more than a protonated ketone. Loss of a proton gives the ketone.

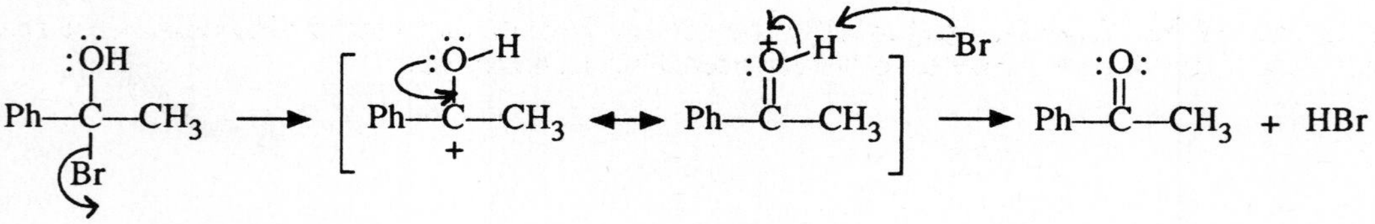

(b) The glycol resulting from this sequence has an —OH and a —Br on the same carbon; this results in the formation of an aldehyde by a mechanism analogous to that shown in (a):

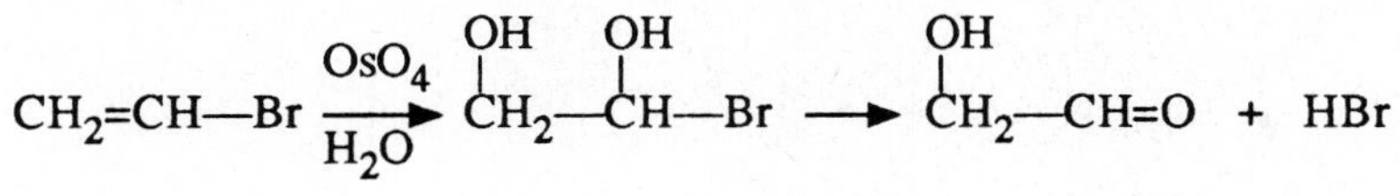

42. (a) We can see that carbon-4 of two phenol molecules becomes attached to the carbonyl carbon of the cyclohexanone. We shall outline the mechanism; at this point you should be able to provide the curved-arrow formalism, if you have not already done so. Protonation of the carbonyl oxygen gives a protonated ketone, which is also an α-hydroxy carbocation (see text pages 771–772). The electron-deficient carbon of this species acts as an electrophile in electrophilic aromatic substitution. The product is an alcohol A.

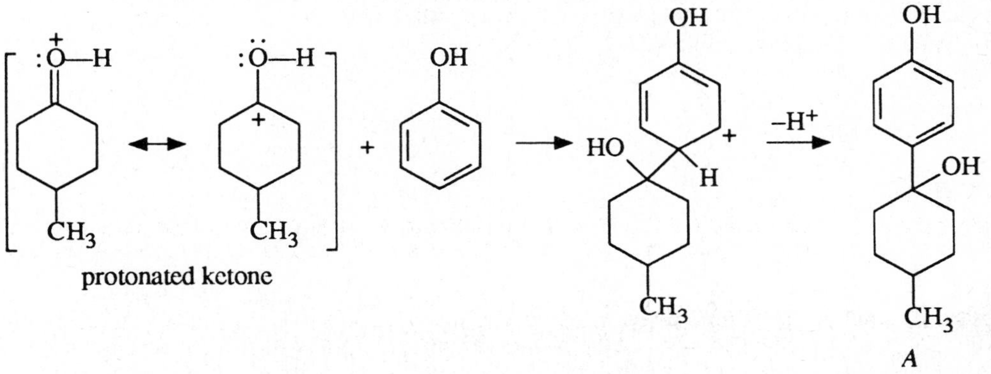

Protonation of alcohol A and loss of water give a relatively stable carbocation B. (Why is it stable?) This carbocation acts as the electrophile in an electrophilic aromatic substitution on a second equivalent of phenol.

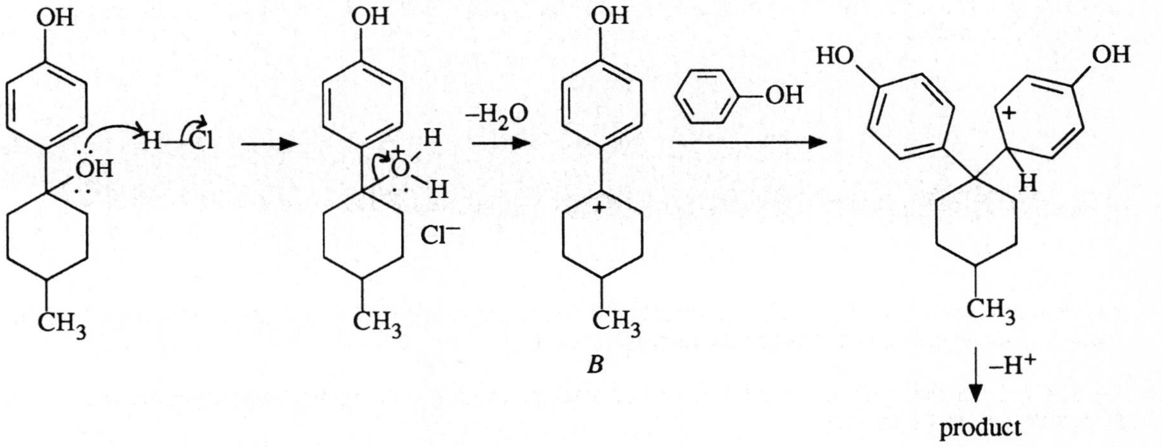

43. We have learned to think of $LiAlH_4$ as a source of hydride ion, $H:^-$. In each case, hydride attacks the epoxide and opens it to give an alkoxide, which is then protonated when acid is added:

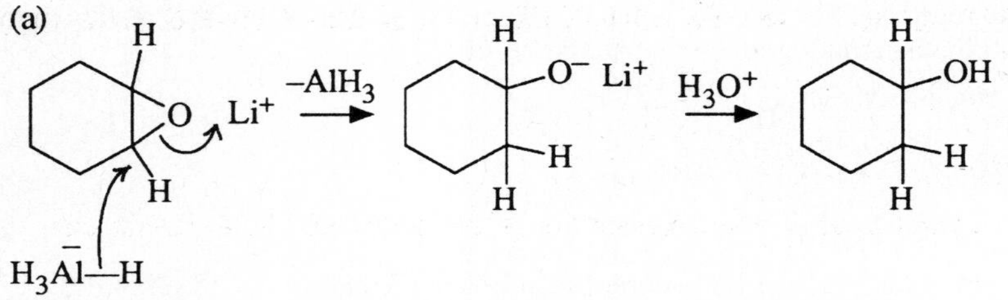

(a)

Although the reaction occurs by a backside-attack mechanism, the stereochemistry of the reaction is of no consequence to the identity of the product.

(b) In this example, the same type of process occurs. Because the epoxide has asymmetric carbons, the stereochemistry of the product depends on the stereochemistry of the reaction. Backside attack of hydride gives inversion of configuration at the point of attack:

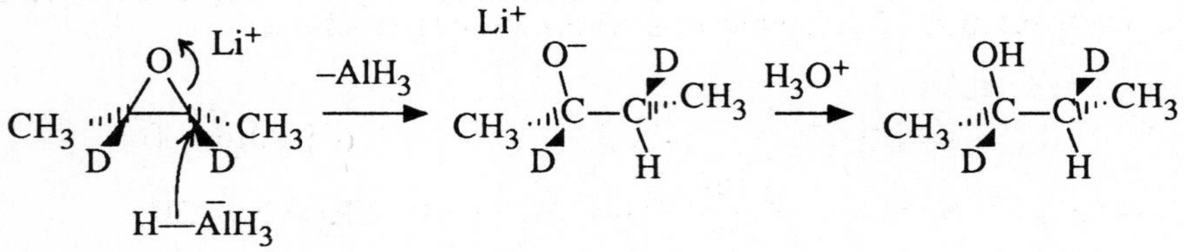

Because the starting materials are achiral — the epoxide is a *meso* compound — it follows that the product must be racemic (Sec. 7.8A). You should verify that the *enantiomer* of the product shown above is obtained if attack of hydride occurs at the other carbon of the epoxide. Since the two carbons are identically substituted, and differ only in their stereochemical configurations, the achiral $^-AlH_4$ anion cannot distinguish between them. As a result, attack at either carbon is equally likely.

44.   (a) This reaction involves addition of water to the double bond, followed by loss of H_2S.

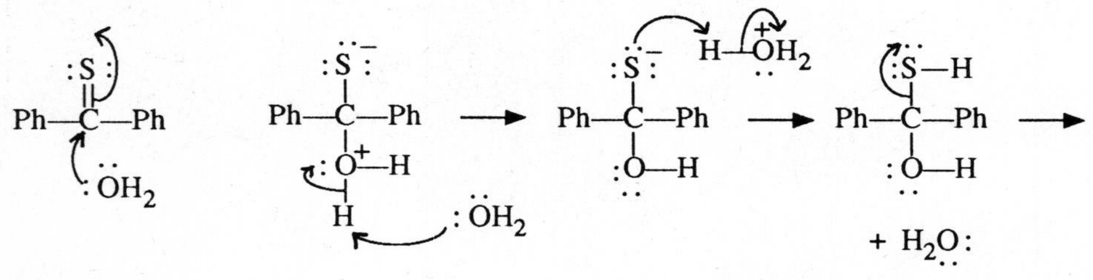

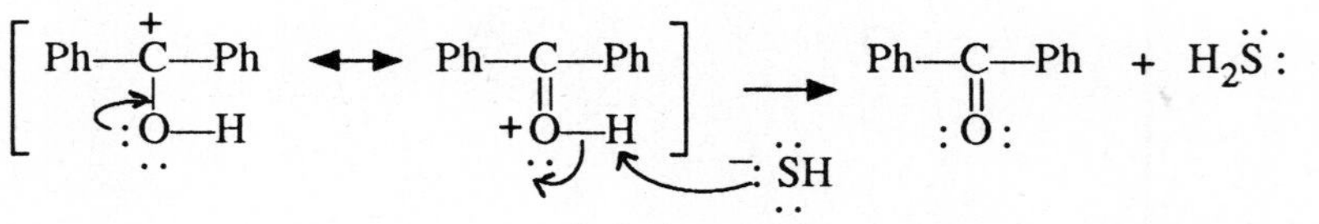

(b) S_N1 ionization of the chloride gives a relatively stable α-alkoxy carbocation (see text page 772), which is attacked by water to furnish a hemiacetal:

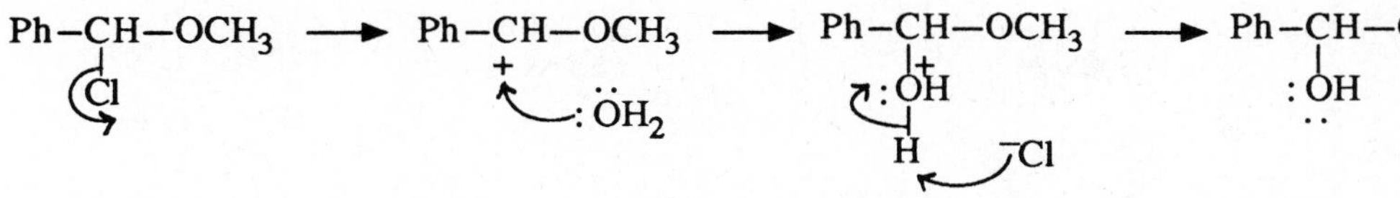

$$Ph-CH-OCH_3 \longrightarrow Ph-CH-OCH_3 \longrightarrow Ph-CH-OCH_3 \longrightarrow Ph-CH-OCH_3 + HCl$$

The hemiacetal is converted into benzaldehyde by a mechanism that is the reverse of that for hemiacetal formation:

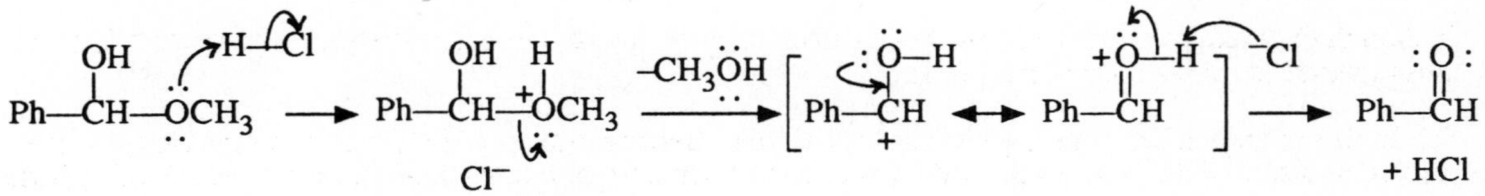

(c) Triphenylphosphine, a nucleophile, reacts with the epoxide to give the same type of intermediate that is produced in a conventional Wittig reaction. This intermediate breaks down to an alkene.

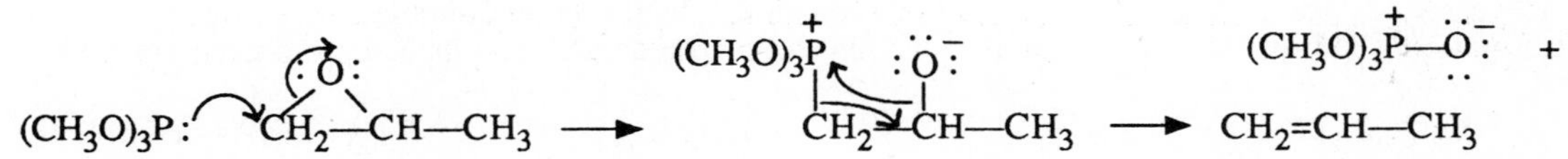

(d) The alcohol is oxidized to an aldehyde. Under the acidic conditions, the aldehyde is protonated; the carbonyl carbon, which has carbocation character, adds to the double bond to give another carbocation. Loss of a proton yields the final product.

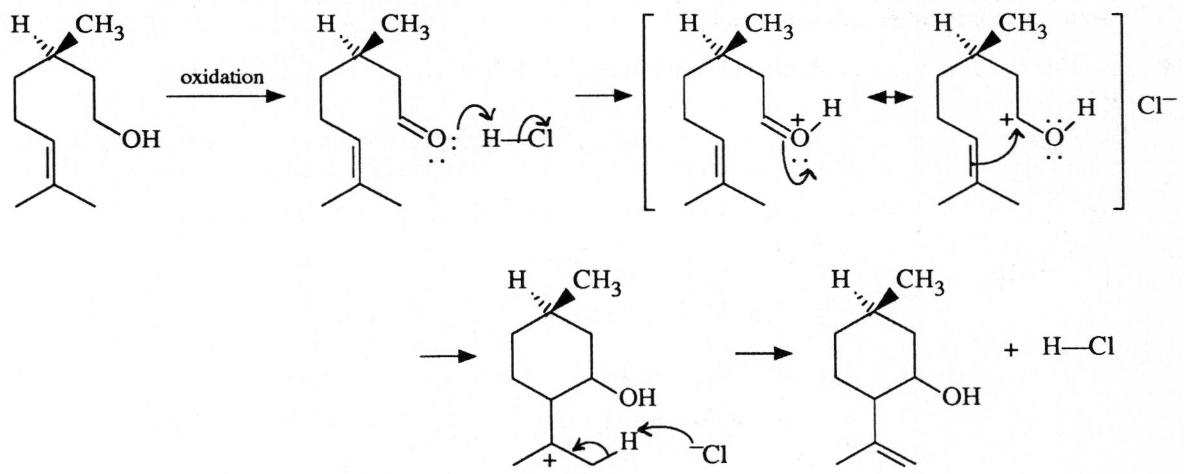

(e) Enamine formation with one aldehyde group is followed by enamine formation with the second. (Undoubtedly an imine is formed with the first aldehyde, but it is in equilibrium with an enamine.) The mechanism of imine formation follows that in Sec. 19.11A and B. We begin our mechanism with the first imine:

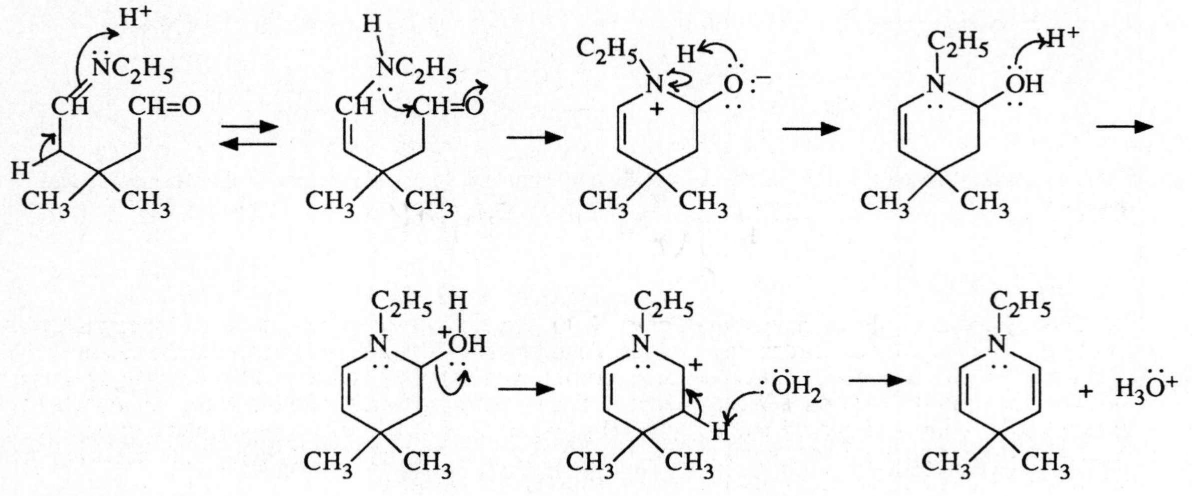

(f) The epoxide, after protonation, opens to a carbocation, which is an intermediate in the pinacol rearrangement (Sec. 10.1B). Completion of the pinacol rearrangement results in a protonated aldehyde.

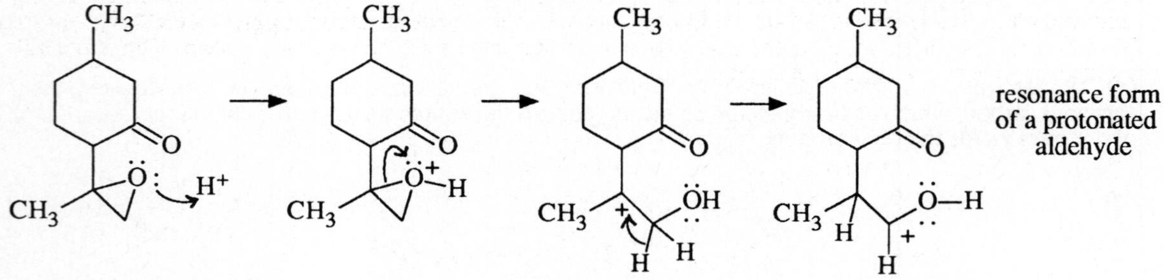

The oxygen of the second carbonyl group attacks the α-hydroxy carbocation. Loss of protons and water complete the formation of the furan ring. Notice that furan is an aromatic heterocycle (Sec. 15.7; Problem 29, text page 623).

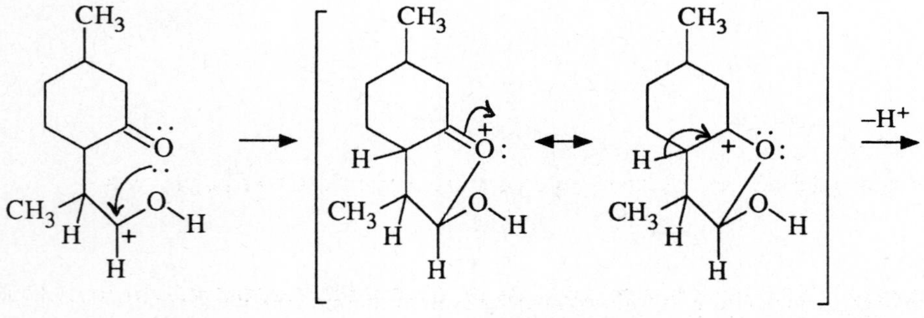

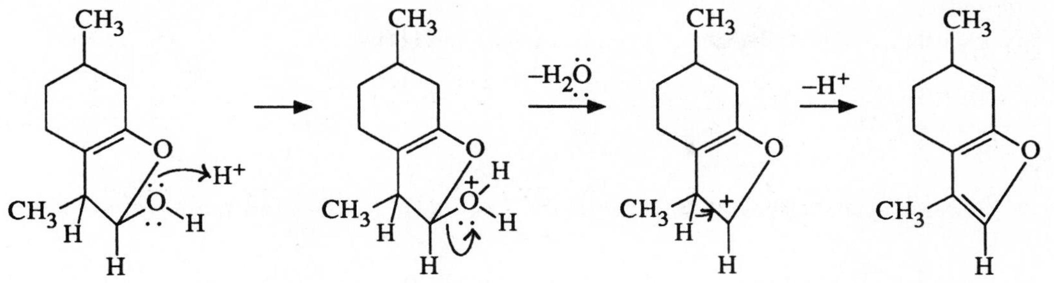

45. (a) Thumbs wants to add a Grignard reagent to a ketone in the presence of an aldehyde. Since aldehydes are more reactive than ketones in addition reactions, Thumbs can expect addition to occur to the aldehyde instead. It is also likely that Thumbs might expect some product resulting from addition to both carbonyl groups.
    (b) Thumbs wants to carry out a Wittig reaction. There is nothing wrong with his Wittig reaction, but he can expect trouble with the preparation of the ylid. His first step is attack of triphenylphosphine on neopentyl bromide. As we learned in Chapter 9 (see text pages 329–330, Table 9.2, and Figure 9.2), neopentyl halides are not reactive in S_N2 reactions because of their substantial branching.

46. The mass spectrum indicates the presence of one bromine atom; the NMR spectrum indicates a *para*-substituted benzene ring, and the IR spectrum suggests the presence of a conjugated carbonyl group. On the assumption that the aromatic signal in the NMR spectrum integrates for four protons (a *para*-substituted benzene ring has four protons), the singlet integrates for three protons. A three-proton singlet suggests a methyl group, and its chemical shift suggests that it is adjacent to either the benzene ring or the carbonyl group. The structural elements we have accounted for are these:

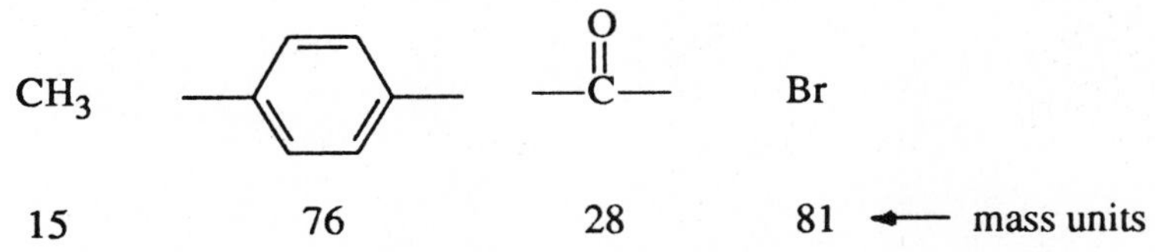

    These groups account for all of the 200 mass units. All we have to do is put them together. The peaks in the mass spectrum at m/e = 155 and 157 have the proper mass for a bromophenyl cation. Hence, the compound is *p*-bromoacetophenone:

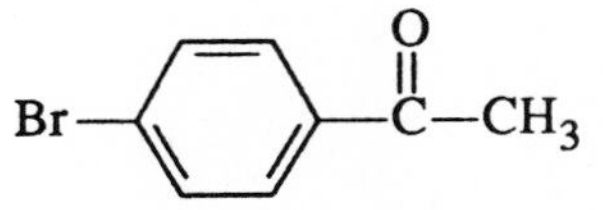

47. (a) The δ 9.8 signal indicates an aldehyde, and the nine-proton δ 1.1 singlet indicates a *t*-butyl group.

    $(CH_3)_3C—CH=O$

    (b) The NMR spectrum indicates a high degree of symmetry, and the IR spectrum suggests an aromatic ketone in which the carbonyl group and the aromatic ring are conjugated:

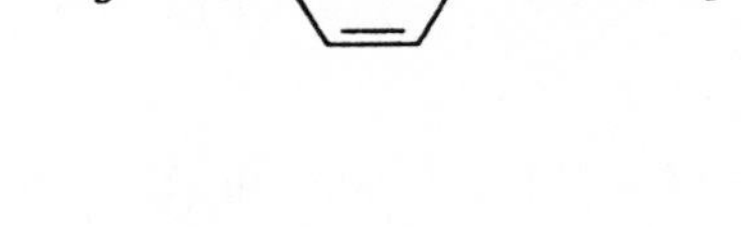

(c) The data indicate a conjugated aldehyde with an *E*-double bond.

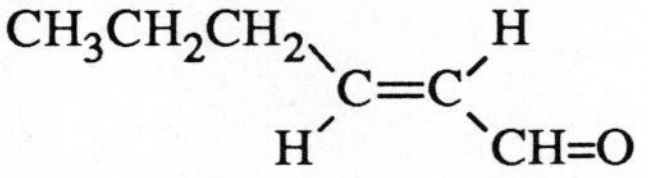

48. There are a number of syntheses possible; all involve the same last step. The shortest synthesis is as follows:

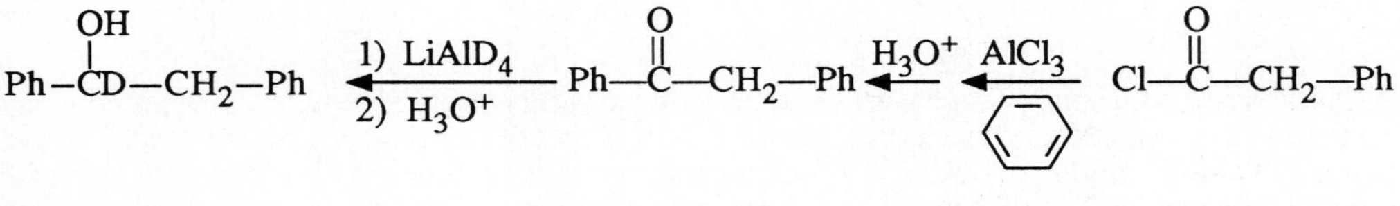

49. (a) In 1,2-cyclopentanedione, the C—O bond dipoles are virtually aligned. This creates a large net dipole moment for the molecule:

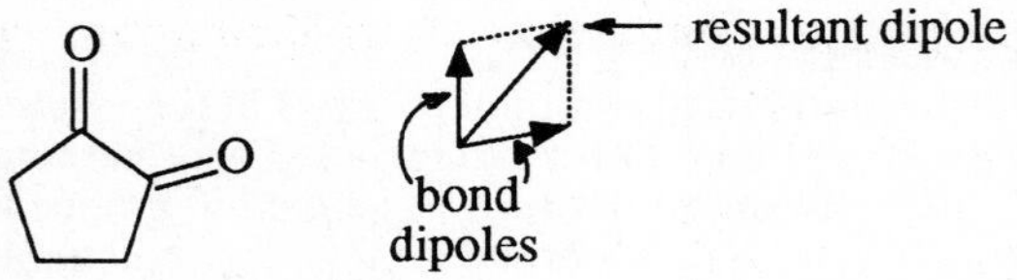

The alignment of bond dipoles is a **destabilizing** effect. Biacetyl can avoid this alignment by rotation about the single bond between the carbonyl **groups:**

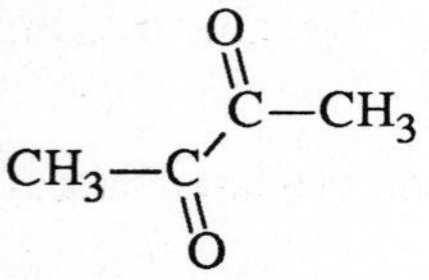

It should be clear that the dipole moment of biacetyl would be zero if the carbonyl groups were aligned as shown in this structure. Evidently, the alignment is somewhere between 0° and 180° — more like that shown in the following Newman projection:

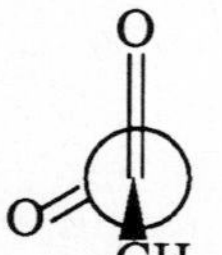

Biacetyl avoids the 180° conformation because, in this conformation (as well as in the 0° conformation), there is overlap between the carbonyl π-electron systems. This overlap, symbolized by the resonance structures below, creates a very unfavorable charge distribution.

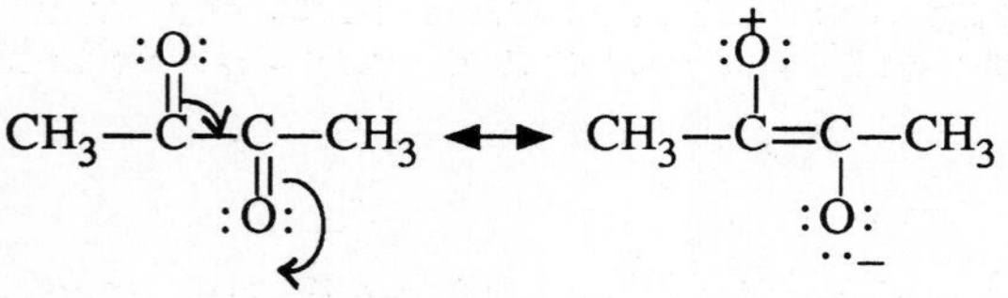

In summary, biacetyl avoids the 0° conformation because of dipole-dipole repulsion; it avoids the 180° **conformation because** of the unfavorable overlap.

(b) The $n \rightarrow \pi^*$ absorption disappears because a reaction occurs in which the carbonyl group is converted into another group that does not have this absorption. This reaction is addition of ethanethiol to give the thiol analog of a hemiacetal:

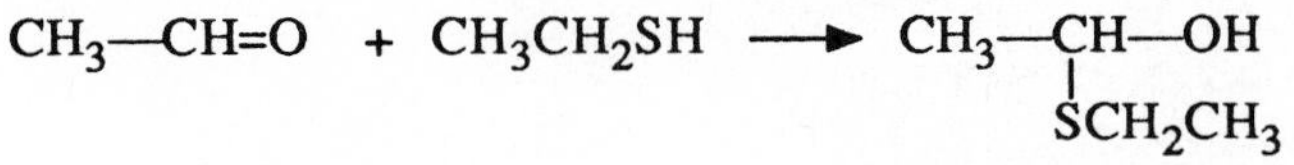

$$CH_3-CH{=}O \ + \ CH_3CH_2SH \ \longrightarrow \ CH_3-\underset{\underset{SCH_2CH_3}{|}}{CH}-OH$$

(c) This compound exists largely as a cyclic hemiacetal:

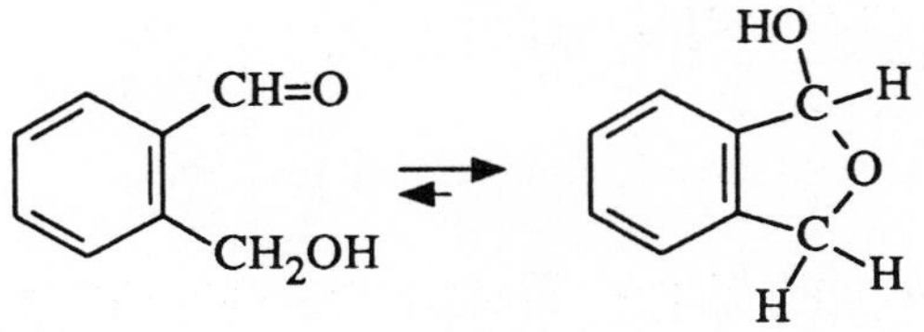

If we make the reasonable assumption that the rate of the Tollens' test is proportional to the concentration of the aldehyde, then we expect the Tollens' test to develop slowly because the hemiacetal equilibrium removes a significant fraction of the aldehyde.

50. (a)

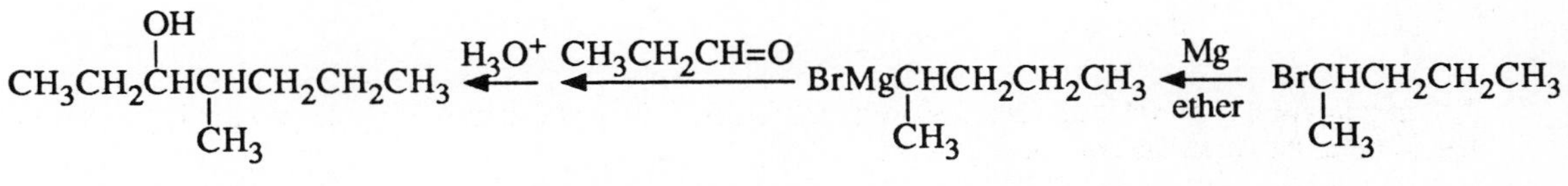

(b) The product has two asymmetric carbons and can exist as a pair of diastereomers. Two diastereomers would be formed even if the starting alkyl halide were optically pure.

51. We'll present two syntheses. The first is based on the hint: Hydration of acetophenone in a large excess of isotopically labeled water will eventually "wash out" the ^{16}O.

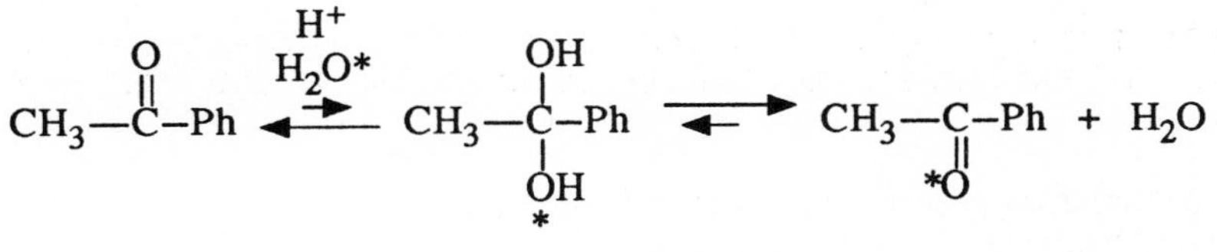

The resulting labeled ketone is then reduced with $NaBH_4$ or $LiAlH_4$.

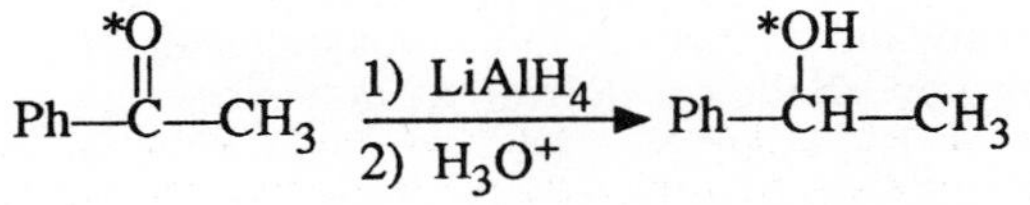

This method is simple, but it requires a large excess of isotopically labeled water to label the ketone. Another way would be to reduce acetophenone to 1-phenyl-1-ethanol, convert it into 1-chloro-1-phenylethane, and then carry out an S_N1 reaction in isotopic water containing enough THF or other inert solvent to dissolve the alkyl halide:

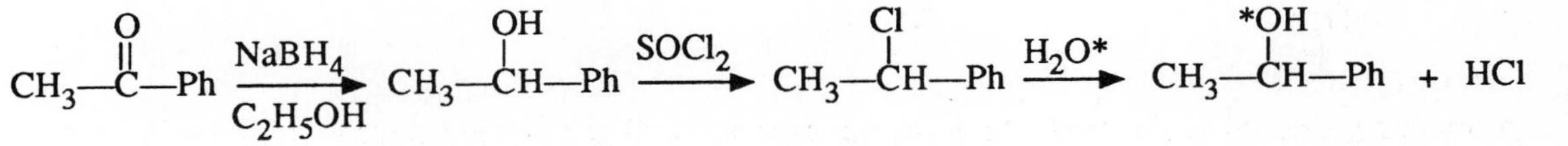

52. (a) This cyclic trimer exists in a chair form. Two stereoisomers of this form are possible: an all-*cis* form, and a form in which one of the trichloromethyl groups is *trans* to the other two:

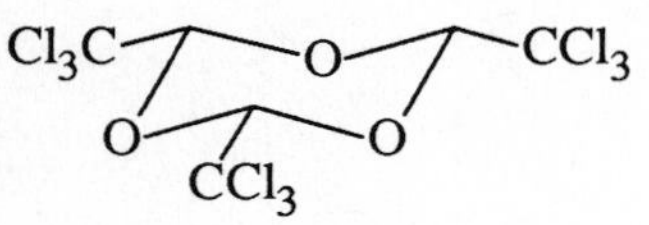

and

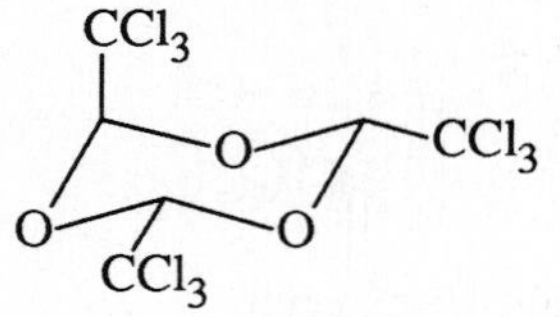

We cannot, of course, tell which form is which from the melting and boiling points. (It turns out that the left structure is the *β*-form, and the right structure the *α*-form.)

(b) Proton NMR would show one singlet for the compound with the left structure, and two singlets in a 2 : 1 integral ratio for the compound with the right structure.

53. The IR spectrum suggests a ketone conjugated with an alkene double bond. A C=O accounts for 28 mass units, leaving 54 mass units unaccounted for. In the NMR spectrum there are vinylic protons and either allylic protons or protons α to a carbonyl, or both. The ratio of vinylic protons to other protons is 14 : 28, or 1 : 2. If there are two vinylic protons and four other protons, we have accounted for six more mass units, leaving 48 mass units, or four carbons, unaccounted for. A —CH=CH— group, a ketone C=O group, and two —CH$_2$— groups are indicated; the following structure, 2-cyclopenten-1-one, is consistent with the spectra:

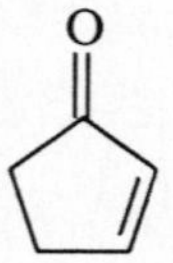

54. (a) Cyclic acetals can be formed from the hydroxy groups that are in a 1,2-relationship (compound *A*), or from the hydroxy groups that are in a 1,3-relationship (compound *B*):

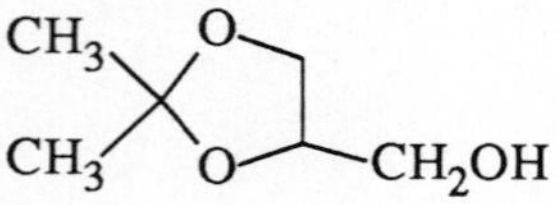

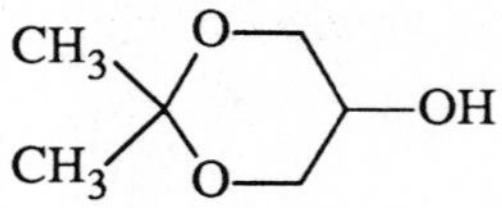

(b) Compound *A* is chiral and can therefore exist as enantiomers. Compound *B* is a *meso* compound and therefore cannot be resolved into enantiomers.

55. Compound *A* is a hydroxy aldehyde, by the following reasoning. It gives a Tollens' test; hence, the compound is an aldehyde. The remaining oxygen must be part of either a hydroxy group or ether group, because the molecule has an unsaturation number of 1. Because the compound oxidizes to a dicarboxylic acid, the remaining oxygen must be part of a hydroxy group. Let us draw all the *chiral* hydroxy aldehydes that would oxidize to *achiral* dicarboxylic acids:

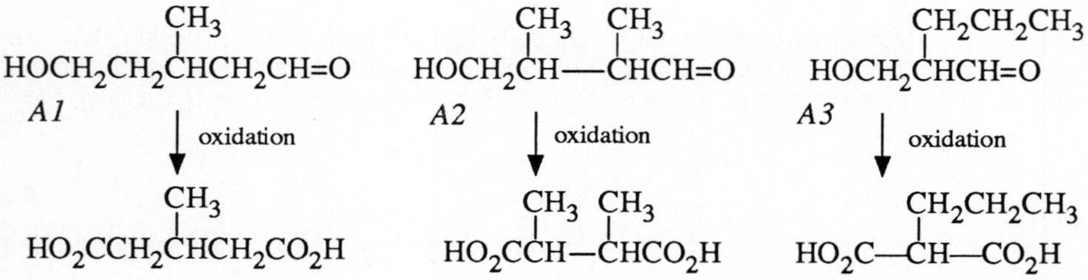

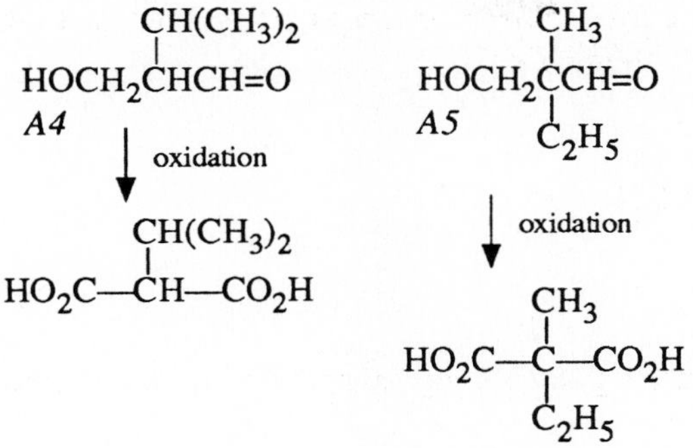

$$\underset{A4}{\underset{\text{HOCH}_2\overset{\displaystyle \overset{\text{CH(CH}_3)_2}{|}}{\text{CH}}\text{CH=O}}}$$

$$\underset{A5}{\underset{\text{HOCH}_2\overset{\displaystyle \overset{\text{CH}_3}{|}}{\underset{\overset{\displaystyle |}{\text{C}_2\text{H}_5}}{\text{C}}}\text{CH=O}}}$$

oxidation ↓

oxidation ↓

$$\text{HO}_2\text{C—}\overset{\displaystyle \overset{\text{CH(CH}_3)_2}{|}}{\text{CH}}\text{—CO}_2\text{H}$$

$$\text{HO}_2\text{C—}\overset{\displaystyle \overset{\text{CH}_3}{|}}{\underset{\overset{\displaystyle |}{\text{C}_2\text{H}_5}}{\text{C}}}\text{—CO}_2\text{H}$$

The slow oxidation by Tollens' reagent suggests that compound *A* has an aldehyde carbonyl group that for some reason resists oxidation. Indeed, compounds *A1* and *A2* can form cyclic acetals, which would not be oxidized by Tollens' reagent. The small amount of free hydroxy aldehyde in samples of these compounds would undergo the Tollens' test, but the Tollens' reaction would be slow because of the low concentration of reactive species. (See the solution to Problem 49c for a similar situation.)

cyclic hemiacetal form of *A1*

cyclic hemiacetal form of *A2*

The (2*R*,3*R*) and (2*S*,3*S*) forms of compound *A2* would oxidize to an optically active carboxylic acid. Hence, only the (2*R*,3*S*) or (2*S*,3*R*) forms remain candidate structures, since these would oxidize to a *meso* dicarboxylic acid. Only these forms of compound *A2* and either enantiomer of *A1* are candidate structures. The data in the problem do not permit a decision between these.

Compound *B* is the hydroxy acid resulting from oxidation of either *A1* or *A2*:

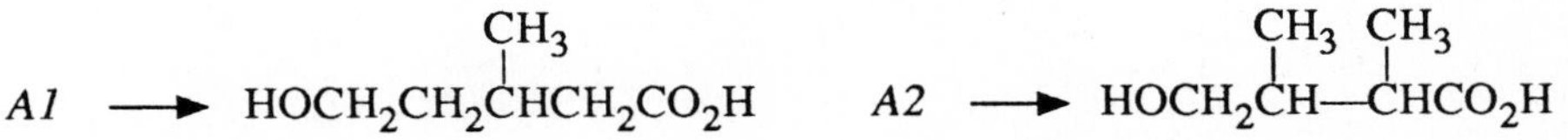

$$A1 \longrightarrow \underset{B1}{\text{HOCH}_2\text{CH}_2\overset{\displaystyle \overset{\text{CH}_3}{|}}{\text{CH}}\text{CH}_2\text{CO}_2\text{H}}$$

$$A2 \longrightarrow \underset{B2}{\text{HOCH}_2\overset{\displaystyle \overset{\text{CH}_3}{|}}{\text{CH}}\text{—}\overset{\displaystyle \overset{\text{CH}_3}{|}}{\text{CH}}\text{CO}_2\text{H}}$$

Finally, the NaBH$_4$ reduction reduces the aldehyde in either structure to a —CH$_2$OH group to give an achiral diol.

Chapter 20 / Chemistry of Carboxylic Acids

CHAPTER 20 TERMS

acid chloride 20.9A
acid-catalyzed esterification 20.8A
acyloxy group 20.9B
adipic acid 20.1A
anhydride 20.9B
anionic surfactant 20.5
carbonic acid 20.1A
carboxylate ion 20.4A
carboxylate oxygen 20.7
carboxylic acid .... Introduction
cationic surfactant 20.5
chlorosulfonic acid 20.9A
cyclic anhydride 20.9B
decarboxylation 20.11
dicarboxylic acid 20.1A
ester 20.8A
fatty acid 20.5
Fischer esterification 20.8A

glutaric acid 20.1A
β-keto acid 20.11
malonic acid 20.1A
malonic acid derivative 20.11
micelle 20.5
oxalic acid 20.1A
phospholipid 20.5
phthalic acid 20.1A
pimelic acid 20.1A
salicylic acid 20.1A
saponification 20.5
soap 20.5
succinic acid 20.1A
sulfonic acid .... Introduction
sulfonyl chloride 20.9A
surfactant 20.5
synthetic detergent 20.5
tetrahedral addition intermediate 20.8A

CHAPTER 20 CONCEPTS

I. Introduction to Carboxylic Acids:

A. <u>Common Nomenclature of Carboxylic Acids</u>:
1. The characteristic functional group in a **carboxylic acid** is the **carboxy group,** $—CO_2H$.
2. Common nomenclature is widely used for the simpler carboxylic acids, some of which owe their origin to the natural source of the acid.
3. In common nomenclature, carboxylic acids are named by adding the suffix *ic acid* to the prefix for the appropriate group.

form-	H—	isobutyr-	$(CH_3)_2CH—$
acet-	$CH_3—$	valer-	$CH_3CH_2CH_2CH_2—$
propion-	$CH_3CH_2—$	isovaler-	$(CH_3)_2CHCH_2—$
butyr-	$CH_3CH_2CH_2—$	benzo-	Ph—

4. Substitution in the common system is denoted with Greek letters rather than numbers; the position adjacent to the carboxy group is designated as α.

$$Cl—\overset{\delta}{C}H_2-\overset{\gamma}{C}H_2-\overset{\beta}{C}H_2-\overset{\alpha}{C}H_2-\overset{\overset{\textstyle O}{\|}}{C}—OH$$

carboxy group

δ-chlorovaleric acid

5. Carboxylic acids with two carboxy groups are called **dicarboxylic acids**; the unbranched dicarboxylic acids are particularly important and are invariably known by their common names:

oxalic acid	HO_2CCO_2H	glutaric acid	$HO_2C(CH_2)_3CO_2H$
malonic acid	$HO_2CCH_2CO_2H$	adipic acid	$HO_2C(CH_2)_4CO_2H$
succinic acid	$HO_2C(CH_2)_2CO_2H$	pimelic acid	$HO_2C(CH_2)_5CO_2H$

   a) Phthalic acid is an important aromatic dicarboxylic acid.
   b) Carbonic acid has two —OH groups that share a single carbonyl group.

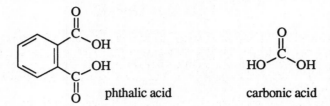

phthalic acid   carbonic acid

6. Many carboxylic acids were known long before any system of nomenclature existed, and their time-honored traditional names are widely used.

B. Systematic Nomenclature of Carboxylic Acids:
   1. A carboxylic acid is named systematically by dropping the final *e* from the name of the hydrocarbon with the same number of carbon atoms and adding the suffix *oic acid* (the final *e* is not dropped in the name of dicarboxylic acids).
   2. When the carboxylic acid is derived from a cyclic hydrocarbon, the suffix *carboxylic acid* is added to the name of the hydrocarbon. One exception to this nomenclature is benzoic acid, for which the IUPAC recognizes the common name.
   3. The numbering of the principal chain in substituted carboxylic acids assigns the carbonyl carbon the number one (in carboxylic acids derived from cyclic hydrocarbons, numbering begins at the ring carbon bearing the carboxy group).

3,3-dimethylbutanoic acid   3-ethylcyclopentanecarboxylic acid

   4. When carboxylic acids contain other functional groups, the carboxy groups receive priority over aldehyde and ketone carbonyl groups, hydroxy groups, and mercapto groups:

$$—CO_2H \,\rangle\, —CH{=}O \,\rangle\, {\gt}C{=}O \,\rangle\, —OH \,\rangle\, —SH$$

6-hydroxy-2,5-dimethyl-3-oxo-4-hexenoic acid

   (A complete list of nomenclature priorities for all the functional groups covered in the text is given in Appendix I, text page A-1.)

C. Structure and Physical Properties of Carboxylic Acids:
   1. Carbonyl groups in carboxylic acids have about the same bond lengths as carbonyl groups in aldehydes and ketones.
   2. The C—O single-bond lengths of carboxylic acids are considerably smaller than those in alcohols or ethers.
      a) The C—O bond in an acid is an sp^2-sp^2 single bond, whereas the C—O bond in an alcohol or ether is an sp^3-sp^3 single bond.
      b) Carboxylic acids have a resonance structure in which this bond has some double bond character.
   3. The carboxylic acids of lower molecular weight have acrid, piercing odors and considerably higher boiling points than many other organic compounds of about the same molecular weight and shape.

a) The high boiling points of carboxylic acids can be attributed not only to their polarity, but also to the fact that they form very strong hydrogen bonds.

b) In the solid state, and under some conditions in both the gas phase and solution, carboxylic acids exist as hydrogen-bonded dimers.

4. Many aromatic and dicarboxylic acids are solids.

5. The simpler carboxylic acids have substantial solubilities in water.

II. Spectroscopy of Carboxylic Acids:

A. IR Spectroscopy:

1. There are two important bands in the infrared spectrum of a typical carboxylic acid.

a) A strong C=O stretching absorption occurs near 1710 cm^{-1} (due to carboxylic acid dimers).

b) The O—H stretching absorption of carboxylic acids is much broader than the O—H stretching absorption of alcohols or phenols and covers a very wide region of the spectrum—typically 2400–3600 cm^{-1}.

c) The strong carbonyl band and the broad O—H stretching band are the hallmarks of a carboxylic acid.

2. A conjugated carbon–carbon double bond affects the position of the carbonyl absorption much less in acids than it does in aldehydes and ketones; a substantial shift in the carbonyl absorption is observed, however, for acids in which the carboxy group is on an aromatic ring.

B. NMR Spectroscopy:

1. The α-protons of carboxylic acids show NMR absorptions in the δ 2–2.5 chemical shift region.

2. The carboxylic acid O–H proton signal is found far downfield, in the δ 9–13 region, and in many cases is broad.

a) The O–H proton resonances of carboxylic acids occur at positions that depend on the acidity of the acid and its concentration.

b) The O—H proton resonance of a carboxylic acid is readily distinguished from the resonance of an aldehydic proton because only the acid proton rapidly exchanges with D_2O.

III. Acidity and Basicity of Carboxylic Acids:

A. Acidity of Carboxylic and Sulfonic Acids:

1. The O–H proton of a carboxylic acid is acidic.

a) Carboxylic acids are among the most acidic organic compounds—more acidic than alcohols or phenols.

b) The conjugate bases of carboxylic acids are called generally **carboxylate ions**; carboxylate salts are named by replacing the *ic* in the name of the acid with the suffix *ate*.

2. The acidity of carboxylic acids is due to resonance stabilization of their conjugate-base carboxylate ions.

a) Resonance stabilization of carboxylate anions is more important than resonance stabilization of phenoxide anions.

b) In a carboxylate anion, charge is delocalized onto another oxygen, an electronegative atom.

carboxylate ion

3. The acidity of carboxylic acids is enhanced by the presence of electronegative groups near the carboxy group (an inductive effect); electronegative groups farther removed from the carboxy group have less effect on acidity.

4. Sulfonic acids are much stronger than comparably substituted carboxylic acids (almost as strong as mineral acids) and are useful as acid catalysts in organic solvents because they are more soluble than most mineral acids.

a) The sulfur atom in a sulfonic acid has a high oxidation state.

b) The octet structure for a sulfonate anion shows that sulfur has considerable positive charge, which stabilizes the negative charge on the oxygens.

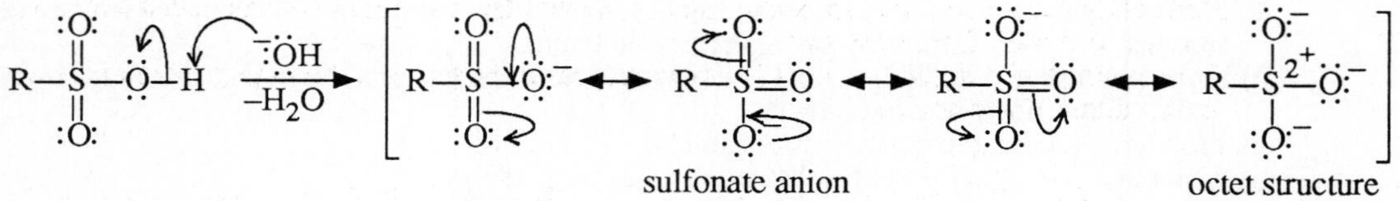

sulfonate anion   octet structure

5. Many carboxylic acids of moderate molecular weight are not soluble in water; their alkali metal salts, however, are ionic compounds and in many cases are much more soluble in water.
   a) Many water-insoluble carboxylic acids dissolve in solutions of alkali metal hydroxides (NaOH, KOH), carbonates (Na_2CO_3), or bicarbonates ($NaHCO_3$) because the insoluble acids are converted completely into their soluble salts.
     (1) A typical carboxylic acid can be separated from mixtures with other water-insoluble, non-acidic substances by extraction with NaOH, Na_2CO_3, or $NaHCO_3$ solution.
     (2) After separating the basic aqueous solution, it can be acidified with mineral acid to yield the carboxylic acid, which may be isolated by filtration or extraction with organic solvents.
   b) Carboxylic acids may also be separated from phenols by extraction with 5% aqueous $NaHCO_3$ solution if the phenol is not one that is unusually acidic.

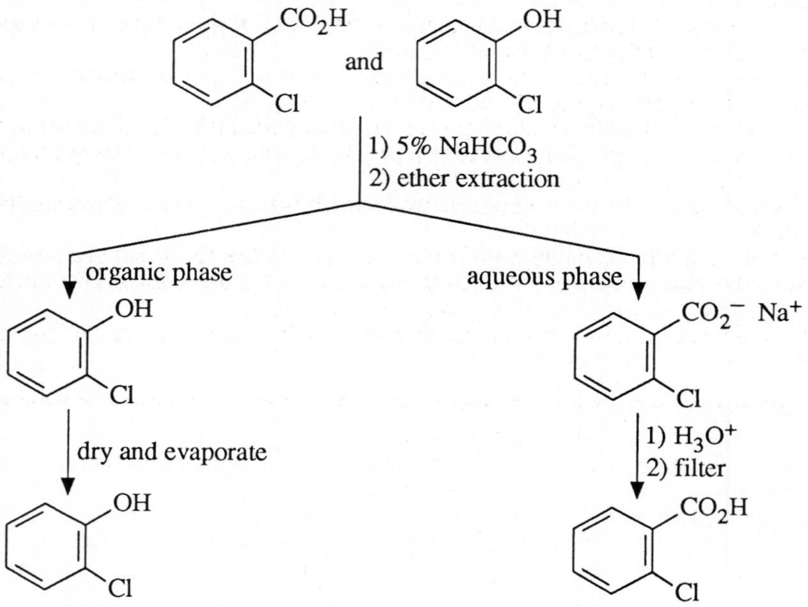

B. <u>Basicity of Carboxylic Acids</u>:
   1. The carbonyl oxygen of a carboxylic acid is weakly basic.
     a) Protonation of the carbonyl oxygen occurs because a resonance-stabilized cation is formed.

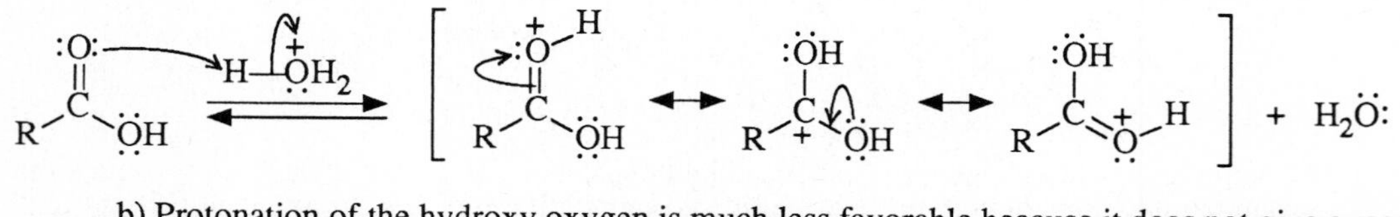

     b) Protonation of the hydroxy oxygen is much less favorable because it does not give a resonance-stabilized cation.
   2. The basicity of carboxylic acids plays a very important role in many of their reactions.

C. <u>Fatty Acids, Soaps, and Detergents</u>:
   1. Carboxylic acids with long, unbranched carbon chains are called **fatty acids**.
     a) Fatty acids are liberated from fats and oils by a hydrolytic process called **saponification**.

b) Some fatty acids contain carbon–carbon double bonds; *cis* double bonds occur widely in nature, but *trans* double bonds are rare.

c) The sodium and potassium salts of fatty acids, called **soaps**, are the major ingredients of commercial soaps.

$$CH_3CH_2CH_2CH_2CH_2CH_2CH_2CH_2CH_2CH_2CH_2CH_2CH_2CH_2CH_2\overset{O}{\overset{\|}{C}}-O^-\ Na^+ \quad or \quad n\text{-}C_{15}H_{31}\overset{O}{\overset{\|}{C}}-O^-\ Na^+$$

a soap   sodium palmatate (sodium hexadecanoate)

        (1) Hard-water scum is a precipitate of the calcium or magnesium salts of fatty acids.

        (2) Some **synthetic detergents** are the salts of sulfonic acids.

        (3) Many soaps and detergents have not only cleansing properties, but also germicidal characteristics.

2. Soaps and detergents are two examples of a larger class of molecules known as **surfactants**—molecules with two structural parts that interact with water in opposing ways:

    a) They have a polar head group, which energetically prefers to be solvated by water.

    b) They have a hydrocarbon tail, which is not well solvated by water.

    c) In a soap, the polar head group is the carboxylate anion, and the hydrocarbon tail is the carbon chain.

3. Soaps and detergents are examples of **anionic surfactants**—surfactants with an anionic polar head group; **cationic surfactants** are also known.

    a) Surfactants in aqueous solution spontaneously form **micelles**, which are approximately spherical aggregates of 50–150 surfactant molecules.

    b) The micellar structure satisfies the solvation requirements of both the polar head groups, which are close to water (on the *outside* of the sphere), and the nonpolar groups, which associate with each other (on the *inside* of the micelle).

4. The antiseptic action of some surfactants owes its success to a phenomenon similar to micelle formation.

    a) A cell membrane is made up of molecules called **phospholipids** that are also surfactants.

    b) When the bacterial cell is exposed to a solution containing a surfactant, the cell-membrane phospholipids tend to associate with the surfactant.

    c) In some cases this disrupts the membrane enough that the cell can no longer function, and it dies.

CHAPTER 20 REACTIONS

I. Synthesis and Reactivity of Carboxylic Acids:

A: Synthesis of Carboxylic Acids—Review:
  1. Methods for preparing carboxylic acids introduced in previous chapters:
      a) Ozonolysis of alkenes, followed by oxidative workup with H_2O_2 (Sec. 5.5).
      b) Oxidation of primary alcohols (Sec. 10.6).
      c) Side-chain oxidation of alkylbenzenes (Sec. 17.5).
      d) Oxidation of aldehydes (Sec. 19.14).

B. Synthesis of Carboxylic Acids with Grignard Reagents:
  1. Addition of a Grignard reagent to carbon dioxide followed by protonolysis gives a carboxylic acid.
      a) Addition of the Grignard reagent to carbon dioxide gives the halomagnesium salt of a carboxylic acid.
      b) When aqueous acid is added to the reaction mixture in a *separate* reaction step, the free carboxylic acid is formed.

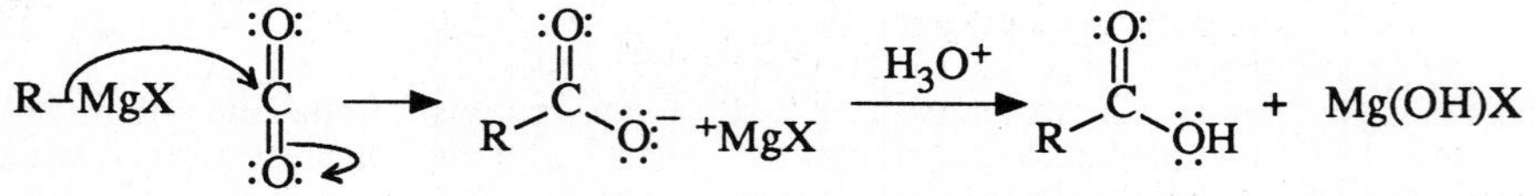

  2. The reaction of Grignard reagents with CO_2 is another method for the formation of carbon–carbon bonds (for a review of other carbon–carbon bond formation reactions, see Appendix V, text page A-10).

C. Introduction to Carboxylic Acid Reactions:
  1. Reactions of carboxylic acids can be categorized into four types:
      a) Carbonyl-group reactions—the most typical carbonyl-group reaction of carboxylic acids and their derivatives is substitution at the carbonyl group.
      b) Reactions at the oxygen of the —OH group (**carboxylate oxygen**).
      c) Decarboxylation—loss of the carboxy group as CO_2.
      d) Reactions involving the α-carbon.
  2. The mechanism of carbonyl-substitution reactions is an extension of the mechanism of carbonyl addition and is a sequence of two processes:
      a) Addition to the carbonyl group: A nucleophile attacks the carbonyl carbon of a carboxylic acid derivative in exactly the same way that it attacks an aldehyde or ketone, and a tetrahedral intermediate addition compound is formed.
      b) Elimination to generate the carbonyl group: A group from the original acid derivative is expelled as a leaving group from the addition intermediate to give a new carboxylic acid derivative.

II. Reaction of Carboxylic Acids at the Carbonyl Group:

A. Acid-catalyzed Esterification of Carboxylic Acids:
  1. Esters are carboxylic acid derivatives with the general structure R^1COR^2.
  2. When a carboxylic acid is treated with a large excess of an alcohol in the presence of a strong acid catalyst, an ester is formed; this reaction is called **acid-catalyzed esterification (Fischer esterification)**.

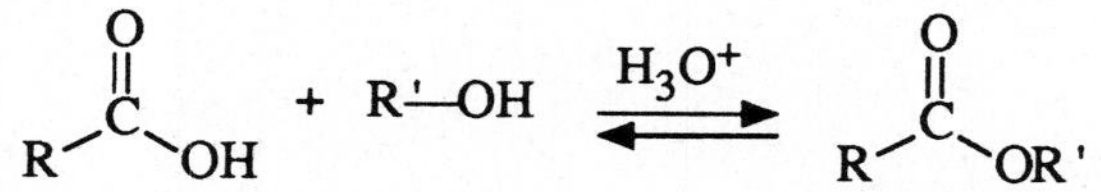

      a) Acid-catalyzed esterification is a substitution of —OH at the carbonyl group of the acid by the alcohol; the —OH group leaves as water.
      b) The equilibrium constants for esterification with most primary alcohols are near unity.

(1) The equilibrium is driven toward the ester by using a large excess of solvent (application of LeChatelier's principle) and by using sulfuric acid as the catalyst.

(2) Besides its catalytic effect, sulfuric acid has strong dehydration properties that help remove the by-product water.

    c) Acid-catalyzed esterification *cannot* be applied to the synthesis of esters from phenols or tertiary alcohols.

3. The mechanism of acid-catalyzed esterification serves as a model for the mechanisms of other acid-catalyzed reactions of carboxylic acids and their derivatives.

    a) The carboxylic acid is first protonated; the protonated intermediate has carbocation character.

    b) Alcohol attacks this carbocation to form, after loss of a proton, a **tetrahedral addition intermediate**.

    c) The tetrahedral addition intermediate reacts further by protonation, loss of water, and deprotonation to give the ester product.

       (1) The tetrahedral intermediates in esterification reactions are in most cases too unstable to isolate and observe directly.

       (2) Esterification is one of many substitution reactions of carboxylic acids and their derivatives that involve tetrahedral addition intermediates.

B. Synthesis of Acid Chlorides:

1. **Acid chlorides** are carboxylic acid derivatives in which the —OH group has been replaced by —Cl.

    a) Acid chlorides are invariably prepared from carboxylic acids.

    b) Two reagents used for this purpose are thionyl chloride ($SOCl_2$) and phosphorus pentachloride (PCl_5).

2. Acid chloride synthesis fits the general pattern of substitution reactions at a carbonyl group—substitution of —OH by —Cl.

3. Acid chlorides are very reactive toward nucleophiles and serve as useful reagents:

    a) For the synthesis of other carboxylic acid derivatives.

    b) As acylating reagents in Friedel–Crafts acylation.

4. **Sulfonyl chlorides** are the acid chlorides of sulfonic acids.

    a) Sulfonyl chlorides can be prepared by treating sulfonic acids with PCl_5.

    b) Aromatic sulfonyl chlorides can be prepared directly by the reaction of aromatic compounds with chlorosulfonic acid ($ClSO_3H$).

       (1) This reaction is a variation of aromatic sulfonation, an electrophilic aromatic substitution reaction.

       (2) Chlorosulfonic acid acts as an electrophile in this reaction.

       (3) The sulfonic acid produced in the reaction is converted into the sulfonyl chloride by reaction with another equivalent of chlorosulfonic acid.

C. Synthesis of Anhydrides:

1. **Carboxylic acid anhydrides** have the general structure RC—O—CR.

    a) Anhydrides are prepared by treatment of carboxylic acids with strong dehydrating agents (usually P_2O_5).

b) In this reaction, the —OH of one carboxylic acid molecule is substituted by the **acyloxy group** of another.

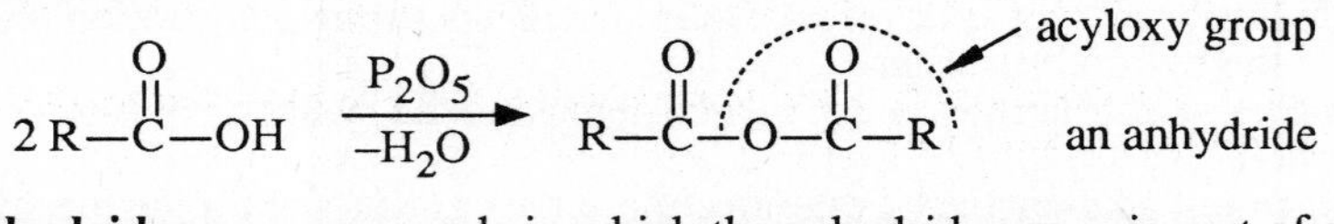

2. **Cyclic anhydrides** are compounds in which the anhydride group is part of a ring.
   a) Cyclic anhydrides containing five- and six-membered rings are readily prepared from their corresponding dicarboxylic acids.
   b) Formation of cyclic anhydrides with five- or six-membered rings is so facile that in some cases it occurs on heating the dicarboxylic acid.

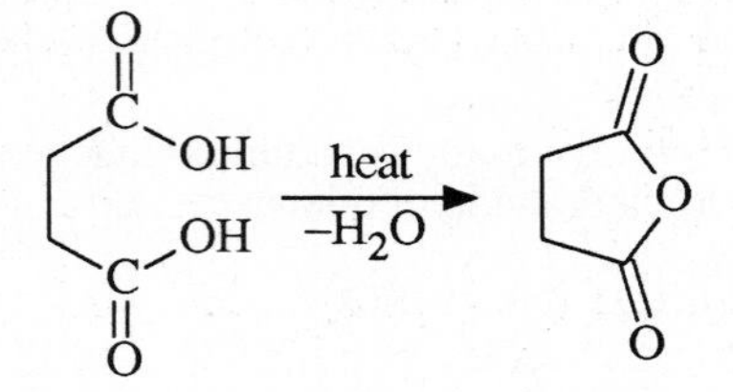

3. Most anhydrides may themselves be used to form other anhydrides.
4. Anhydrides, like acid chlorides, are used in the synthesis of other carboxylic acid derivatives.

D. Reduction of Carboxylic Acids to Alcohols:
   1. When a carboxylic acid is treated with LiAlH$_4$, followed by dilute acid, it is reduced to a primary alcohol.
      a) The reduction involves an aldehyde intermediate.
      b) The aldehyde is further reduced by LiAlH$_4$ to give the alkoxide of the primary alcohol.
      c) Addition of dilute acid in a separate step affords the alcohol.

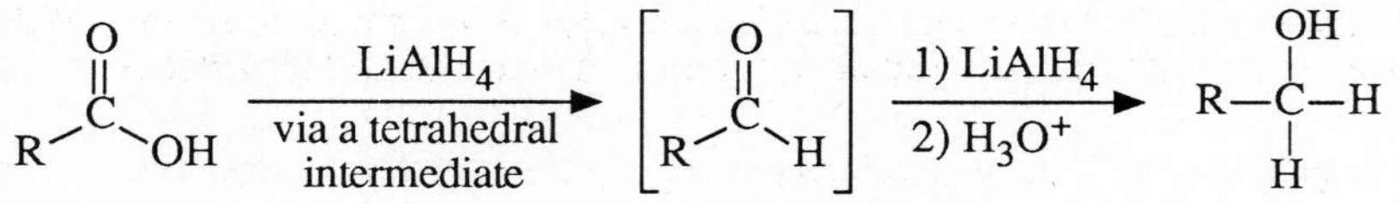

   2. The LiAlH$_4$ reduction of acids incorporates two different types of carbonyl reactions:
      a) A net substitution reaction at the carbonyl group to give an aldehyde intermediate.
      b) An addition to the aldehyde thus formed.
   3. Sodium borohydride (NaBH$_4$) *does not* reduce carboxylic acids.

III. Reaction of Carboxylic Acids at the Oxygen of the —OH Group:

A. Esterification by Alkylation:
   1. When carboxylic acids are treated with **diazomethane** in ether solution, they are rapidly converted into their methyl esters.
      a) Protonation of diazomethane by the carboxylic acid gives the **methyldiazonium ion**; this ion has one of the best leaving groups, molecular nitrogen.
      b) An S$_N$2 reaction of the methyldiazonium ion with the carboxylate oxygen results in the displacement of N$_2$ and formation of the ester.

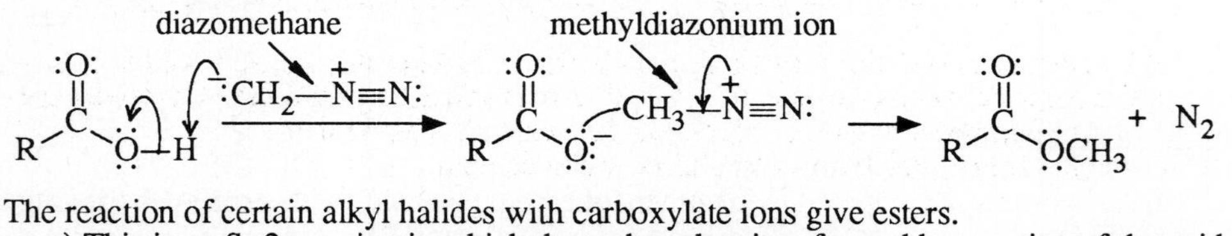

   2. The reaction of certain alkyl halides with carboxylate ions give esters.
      a) This is an S$_N$2 reaction in which the carboxylate ion, formed by reaction of the acid and a base (such as K$_2$CO$_3$), acts as the nucleophile that attacks the alkyl halide.

$$R-\overset{\overset{\displaystyle O}{\|}}{C}-OH \xrightarrow[-KHCO_3]{K_2CO_3} R-\overset{\overset{\displaystyle O}{\|}}{C}-O^- \ K^+ \xrightarrow[-KBr]{PhCH_2Br} R-\overset{\overset{\displaystyle O}{\|}}{C}-OCH_2Ph$$

b) This reaction works best on alkyl halides that are *especially* reactive in the S_N2 reaction, such as methyl iodide and benzylic or allylic halides.

IV. Decarboxylation of Carboxylic Acids:

A. <u>Decarboxylation of Carboxylic Acids</u>:
1. The loss of carbon dioxide from a carboxylic acid is called **decarboxylation**.
2. Certain types of carboxylic acids are readily decarboxylated; among these are:
   a) **β-Keto acids** (carboxylic acids with a keto group in the β-position).
   b) **Malonic acid** derivatives.
   c) Derivatives of **carbonic acid**.

a β-keto acid

a malonic acid derivative

a carbonic acid derivative

3. β-Keto acids readily decarboxylate at room temperature in acidic solution.
   a) Decarboxylation of a β-keto acid involves an enol intermediate that is formed by an internal proton transfer from the carboxylic acid group to the carbonyl oxygen of the ketone.
   b) Enols are transformed spontaneously into their corresponding ketones.

enol intermediate

4. The acid form of the β-keto acid decarboxylates more readily than the conjugate-base carboxylate form because the latter has no acidic proton that can be donated to the β-carbonyl oxygen.
5. Malonic acid and its derivatives readily decarboxylate upon heating in acid solution. This reaction, which *does not* occur in base, bears a close resemblance to the decarboxylation of β-keto acids, because both types of acids have a carbonyl group β to the carboxy group.
6. Carbonic acid is unstable and decarboxylates spontaneously in acid solution to CO_2 and water.
   a) Any carbonic acid derivative with a free carboxylic acid group will also decarboxylate under acidic conditions.

$$R-\overset{..}{N}H-\overset{\overset{\displaystyle O}{\|}}{C}-OH \xrightarrow{H_3O^+} CO_2 + R-\overset{..}{N}H_2 \xrightleftharpoons{H_3O^+} R-\overset{+}{N}H_3$$

b) Under basic conditions, carbonic acid is converted into its salts and does not decarboxylate.
c) Carbonic acid derivatives in which both carboxylic acid groups are derivatized are stable:
   (1) **Carbonate esters**, which are diesters of carbonic acid.
   (2) **Ureas**, which are diamides of carbonic acid.

CHAPTER 20 SOLUTIONS

Solutions to In-Text Problems

1.   (a)   (b)   (c)

$$CH_3CH_2\underset{\underset{CH_3}{|}}{CH}CH_2CH_2\overset{\overset{O}{\|}}{C}-OH \qquad HOCH_2CH_2CH_2\overset{\overset{O}{\|}}{C}-OH \qquad Cl_2CHCH_2\overset{\overset{O}{\|}}{C}-OH$$

(d)   (e)   (f)

$$CH_3CH_2CH_2-\!\!\!\left\langle\ \right\rangle\!\!\!-\overset{\overset{O}{\|}}{C}-OH \qquad CH_3CH_2CH=CHCH_2\overset{\overset{O}{\|}}{C}-OH \qquad HO-\overset{\overset{O}{\|}}{C}-\!\!\!\left\langle\ \right\rangle\!\!\!-\overset{\overset{O}{\|}}{C}-OH$$

(g)   (h)   (i)

$$HO-\overset{\overset{O}{\|}}{C}-\underset{\underset{Cl}{|}}{\overset{\overset{Cl}{|}}{C}}-CH_2CH_2CH_2\overset{\overset{O}{\|}}{C}-OH \qquad\qquad HO-\overset{\overset{O}{\|}}{C}-\overset{\overset{O}{\|}}{C}-OH$$

(h) structure: $O\!\!=\!\!C\!\!-\!\!OH$ on a benzene ring with OCH_3 at the para position.

2.   (a) 9-methyldecanoic acid, or ω-methylcapric acid (The term ω [omega] means "on the last carbon of a chain."
     (b) 2,4-dichlorobenzoic acid   (c) 3-hydroxy-4-oxo-1-cyclohexanecarboxylic acid
     (d) 2,2-dimethylbutanoic acid, or β,β-dimethylbutyric acid (e) cyclopropanecarboxylic acid
     (f) α-methylmalonic acid, or 2-methylpropanedioic acid

3.   The concentration of dimer would be greater in CCl_4. In water, the solvent can hydrogen bond to an acetic acid molecule; there is less energetic advantage to formation of hydrogen-bonded dimers. In CCl_4, however, the only hydrogen bonding available to an acetic acid molecule is from another acetic acid molecule.

4.   The compound is isobutyric acid, $(CH_3)_2CH-CO_2H$.

5.   (a) The first and second ionizations of malonic acid:

$pK_a = 2.86$ $pK_a = 5.70$

$$HO_2C-CH_2-CO_2H \rightleftharpoons HO_2C-CH_2-CO_2^- \rightleftharpoons {}^-O_2C-CH_2-CO_2^-$$
$$+\ H_3O^+ \qquad\qquad\qquad +\ H_3O^+$$

(b) A carboxy substituent is electron-withdrawing (electronegative) groups because of the partial positive charge on its carbonyl carbon. Hence, one carboxy group in malonic acid enhances the ionization of the other. As a result, malonic acid itself is more acidic than acetic acid, which lacks the carboxy substituent. However, after the first carboxy group ionizes, it bears a negative charge. Ionization of the second carboxy group forms a second negative charge, which interacts repulsively with the first, thus raising the energy of the doubly charged, dianionic species. As a result, the pK_a of the second ionization is raised relative to that of acetic acid.
(c) As the lengths of the carbon chains increase, the carboxy substituents are separated by greater distances. Since inductive effects decrease with increasing distance, the effect of one carboxy group on the ionization of another also decreases.

➤ Actually, the two pK_a values never become *exactly* the same; even for very long carbon chains, they differ by log 4 (0.6) units. The reason for this is statistical. A dicarboxylic acid is at least four times as acidic as its singly ionized form because the neutral form has twice as many protons, and is thus twice as likely to ionize once; and the dianion has twice as many carboxylate ions as the monoanion, and is thus twice as likely to be protonated. Notice that the first and second pK_a values of adipic acid approach this limit of 0.6 units (they differ by 0.67 units).

6. Extract an ether solution of the two compounds with $NaHCO_3$ or NaOH solution. The acid will ionize and dissolve as its anion in the water layer. *p*-Bromotoluene, however, will remain in the ether layer. Remove the water layer and acidify it with HCl to precipitate *p*-bromobenzoic acid.

7. The synthesis of cyclopentanecarboxylic acid:

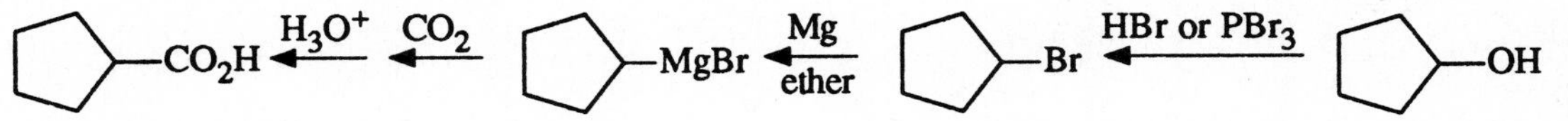

8. Both carboxy groups are esterified; the product is dipropyl adipate:

$$CH_3CH_2CH_2O\overset{O}{\underset{\|}{C}}(CH_2)_4\overset{O}{\underset{\|}{C}}OCH_2CH_2CH_3 \qquad \text{dipropyl adipate}$$

9. (a) The mechanism is the exact reverse of Eq. 20.19a–d, with R— = Ph—. We'll outline it, and you provide the arrow formalism, if you have not already done so:

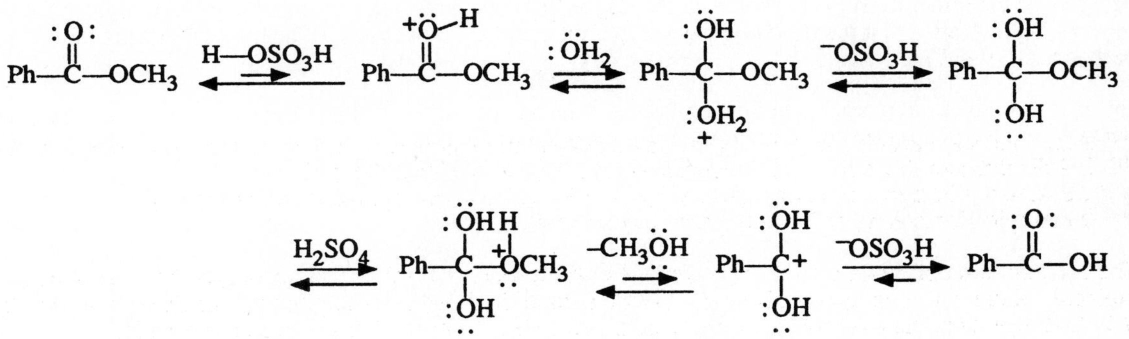

(b) We would use water as the solvent.
(c) In a solution of NaOH, ⁻OH ion is the nucleophile:

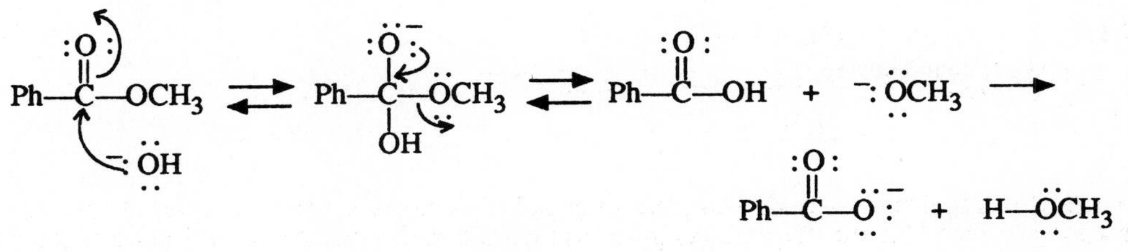

(d) As shown in the last step of the previous equation, the acid ($pK_a = 4$) reacts with sodium methoxide to give the carboxylate ion and methanol ($pK_a = 15$). This reaction is essentially irreversible ($K_{eq} = 10^{11}$).

10. (a)

$$(CH_3)_2CHC{-}OCH_3$$

methyl isobutyrate

(b)

$$(CH_3)_2CHC{-}OCH_2CH_2CH_2CH_3$$

butyl isobutyrate

(c)

$$(CH_3)_2CHC{-}OCH_2Ph$$

benzyl isobutyrate

11. (a) This reaction is essentially a Markovnikov addition of acetic acid to the alkene:

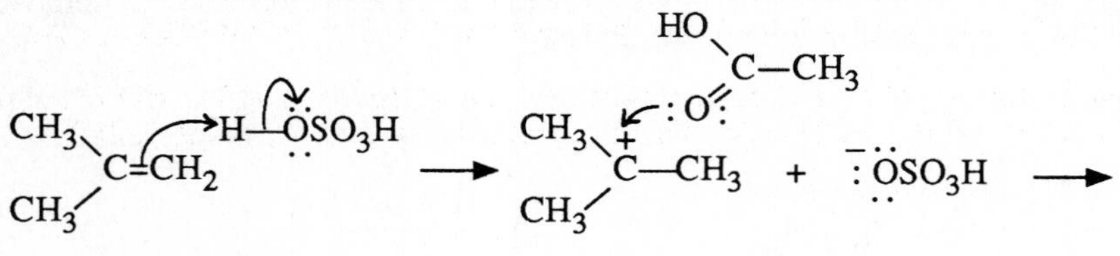

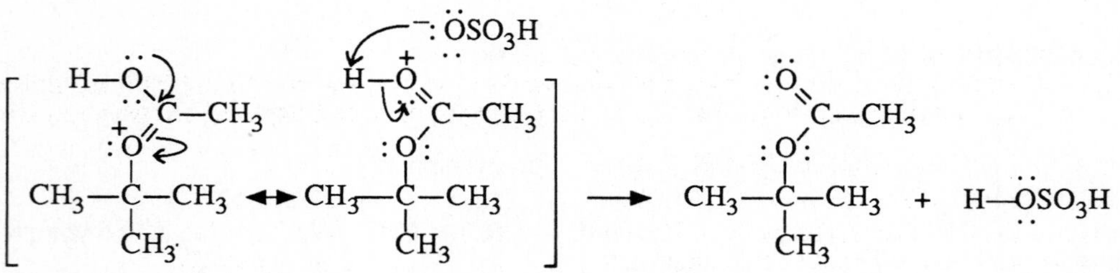

The role of the mineral acid is to protonate the **alkene**. (Acetic acid is not strong enough to protonate the alkene appreciably.) Notice that the *carbonyl oxygen*, not the carboxylate oxygen, of acetic acid attacks the carbocation (why?).

(b) It is more like the reactions in Section 20.8B, because the carboxy group is acting as a nucleophile. In Section 20.8B, the *ionized* carboxy group is the nucleophile; in this reaction, the *un-ionized* carboxy group is the nucleophile. In conventional acid-catalyzed esterification, the alcohol is the nucleophile.

12. A Friedel–Crafts acylation is the key step in this synthesis:

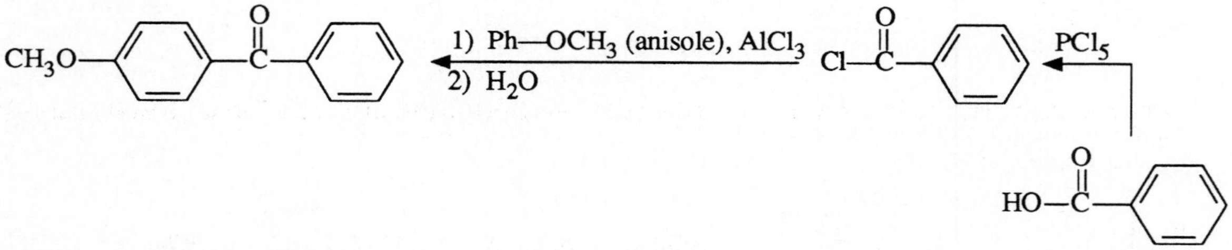

13. Maleic acid forms the cyclic anhydride.

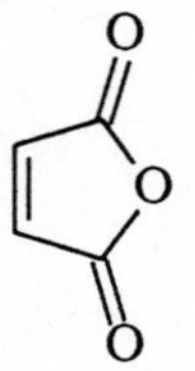

maleic anhydride

(We ran into maleic anhydride as a dienophile in the Diels–Alder reaction; Sec. 15.3, Eq. 15.9, text page 595.) A cyclic fumaric anhydride would contain a *trans* double bond in a five-membered ring, and would be too strained to exist.

14. (a)   (b)   (c)

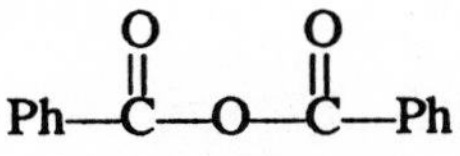

benzoic anhydride   malonyl dichloride

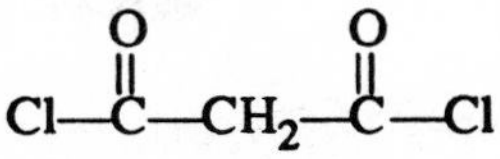

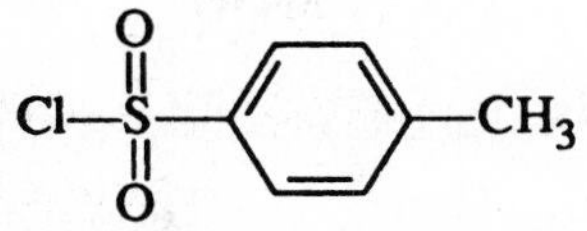

p-toluenesulfonyl chloride

Remember p-toluenesulfonyl chloride, or tosyl chloride? It is used to make tosylate derivatives of alcohols; see Eq. 10.21, text page 378. Part (c) of this problem shows how this important reagent is prepared.

15. The compound has an unsaturation number of 6. Hence, there are two double bonds in addition to the phenyl ring. The following compound, p-formylbenzoic acid, would be reduced by LiAlH$_4$ to the given diol.

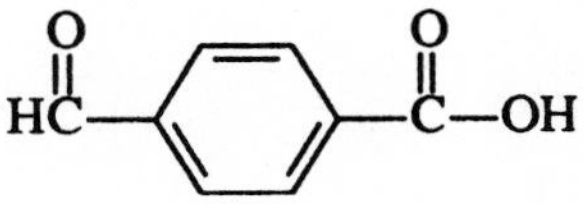

16. Compound (a) is a β-keto acid, compound (b) is a malonic acid derivative, and compound (c) is the sodium salt of a carbamic acid very similar to the one in Eq. 20.48. Each compound decarboxylates; the products are as follows:

(a)   (b) 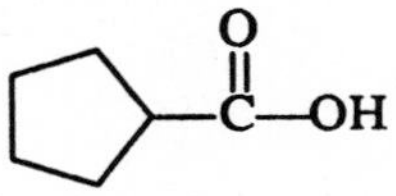   (c)

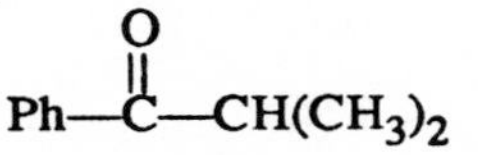

$$C_2H_5NH_2 + H^+ \rightleftharpoons C_2H_5\overset{+}{N}H_3$$

17. This β-keto acid does not decarboxylate because the enol that would form violates Bredt's rule; it has a bridgehead double bond:

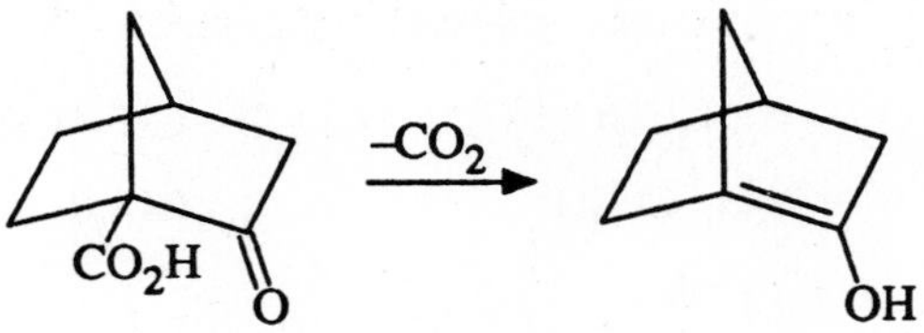

violates Bredt's rule

18. To answer the question, we start with the product and "add back" a carboxylic acid group at every possible β-position:

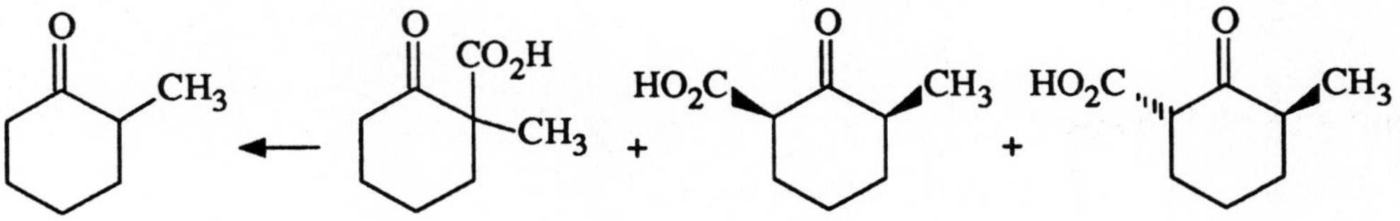

Solutions to Additional Problems

19. For convenience, we shall abbreviate the propyl group ($CH_3CH_2CH_2$—) as Pr—.

(a)   (b)   (c) $CH_3CH_2CH_2CH_2OH$ (d) no reaction

$$Pr-\overset{\overset{O}{\|}}{C}-OC_2H_5 \qquad Pr-\overset{\overset{O}{\|}}{C}-O^- Na^+$$

(e)   (f)   (g)   (h)   (i)

$$Pr-\overset{\overset{O}{\|}}{C}-Cl \qquad Pr-\overset{\overset{O}{\|}}{C}-OCH_3 \qquad CH_3CH\overset{OCH_2CH_2CH_2CH_3}{\underset{OCH_2CH_2CH_2CH_3}{<}} \qquad Ph-\overset{\overset{O}{\|}}{C}-Pr \qquad Ph-CH_2CH_2CH_2CH_3$$

20. (a)   (b)   (c)   (d)

$$Ph-\overset{\overset{O}{\|}}{C}-OCH_3$$

$$\overset{CO_2H}{\underset{NO_2}{\text{(benzene ring)}}}$$

$$Ph-\overset{\overset{O}{\|}}{C}-Cl \qquad Ph-\overset{\overset{O}{\|}}{C}-O-\overset{\overset{O}{\|}}{C}-Ph$$

(e)

$$Ph-\overset{\overset{O}{\|}}{C}-O^- {}^+MgBr \ + \ CH_4$$

In problems such as part (b), we must not lose sight of the fact that there are two functional groups in the benzoic acid molecule: the carboxy group and the aromatic ring. Nitration is a reaction of the ring. In (d), we must recall that a Grignard reagent reacts as a base with any acid.

21. A dicarboxylic acid with the formula $C_6H_{10}O_4$ has no unsaturation except for its carboxy groups.

$$\underset{(1)}{HO_2C-(CH_2)_4-CO_2H} \quad \underset{\underset{CO_2H}{|}}{HO_2C-CH_2CH_2CHCH_3} \quad \underset{\underset{CO_2H}{|}}{HO_2C-CH_2CHCH_2CH_3} \quad \underset{\underset{CO_2H}{|}}{HO_2C-CH-CH_2CH_2CH_3}$$

$$\underset{(2)}{} \qquad \underset{(3)}{} \qquad \underset{(4)}{}$$

$$\underset{(5)}{HO_2C-\overset{\overset{CH_3}{|}}{CH}-CH_2CH_2-CO_2H} \qquad \underset{(6)}{HO_2C-CH_2\overset{\overset{CH_3}{|}}{CH}CH_2-CO_2H} \qquad \underset{(7)}{HO_2C-\overset{\overset{CH_3}{|}}{CH}-\overset{\overset{CH_3}{|}}{CH}-CO_2H}$$

$$\underset{(8)}{HO_2C-\overset{\overset{CH_3}{|}}{\underset{\underset{CO_2H}{|}}{C}}-CH_2CH_3} \qquad \underset{(9)}{HO_2C-\overset{\overset{C_2H_5}{|}}{CH}-CH_2-CO_2H}$$

The dicarboxylic acids that form cyclic anhydrides on heating are those in which the anhydride is part of a five- or six-membered ring: compounds (2), (3), (5), (6), (7), and (9). The dicarboxylic acids that decarboxylate are the malonic acid derivatives — those that have two carboxy groups on the same carbon: compounds (4), (5), and (8). The chiral dicarboxylic acids are compounds (2), (3), (5), (7), and (9). Compound (7) can also exist as a *meso* stereoisomer, which, like all *meso* compounds, is not chiral.

22. (a) It takes one mole of NaOH to neutralize one mole of hexanoic acid (or any other monocarboxylic acid). Hence, the problem reduces to finding out how many moles of hexanoic acid there are in 100 mg, then finding the number of milliliters corresponding to that number of moles of 0.1 N NaOH solution. Hexanoic acid ($C_6H_{12}O_2$) has a molecular weight of 116.16. The number of moles in 100 mg is $(100 \times 10^{-3}$ g$)/(116.16$ g/mol$) = 8.61 \times 10^{-4}$ mol. The number of mL of NaOH required is

$$\frac{8.61 \times 10^{-4} \text{ mol}}{(0.1 \text{ mol/L})(10^{-3} \text{ L/mL})} = 8.61 \text{ mL}$$

(b) *Two* moles of NaOH are required to neutralize each mole of succinic acid because there are two carboxy groups in each molecule. The molecular weight of succinic acid is 118.1, and there is 8.47×10^{-4} mol of succinic acid in 100 mg. Hence, $2 \times 8.47 \times 10^{-4}$ mol, or 16.94×10^{-4} mol of NaOH, or 8.47 mL, is required.

We can use the neutralization of a carboxylic acid to determine its molecular weight by simply determining how many moles of NaOH are required to neutralize a given weight of the acid. If the acid has a single carboxy group, the moles of NaOH required are equal to the moles of acid used. Dividing the weight of the acid used by the moles of NaOH used gives the molecular weight of the acid. As indicated above, we have to know how many carboxy groups are present. In general, the moles of acid present are the moles of NaOH used divided by the number of carboxy groups.

23. When we say that there is 50% of the label on each oxygen, what we really mean is that the acid is a mixture of the following two compounds:

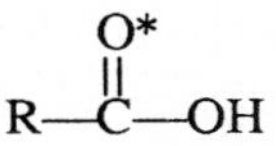

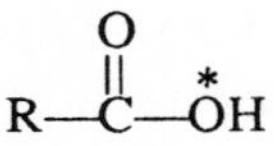

The mixture is formed by movement of the proton back and forth between the two oxygens. One mechanism is for one carboxylic acid molecule to protonate another, and then for the process to reverse:

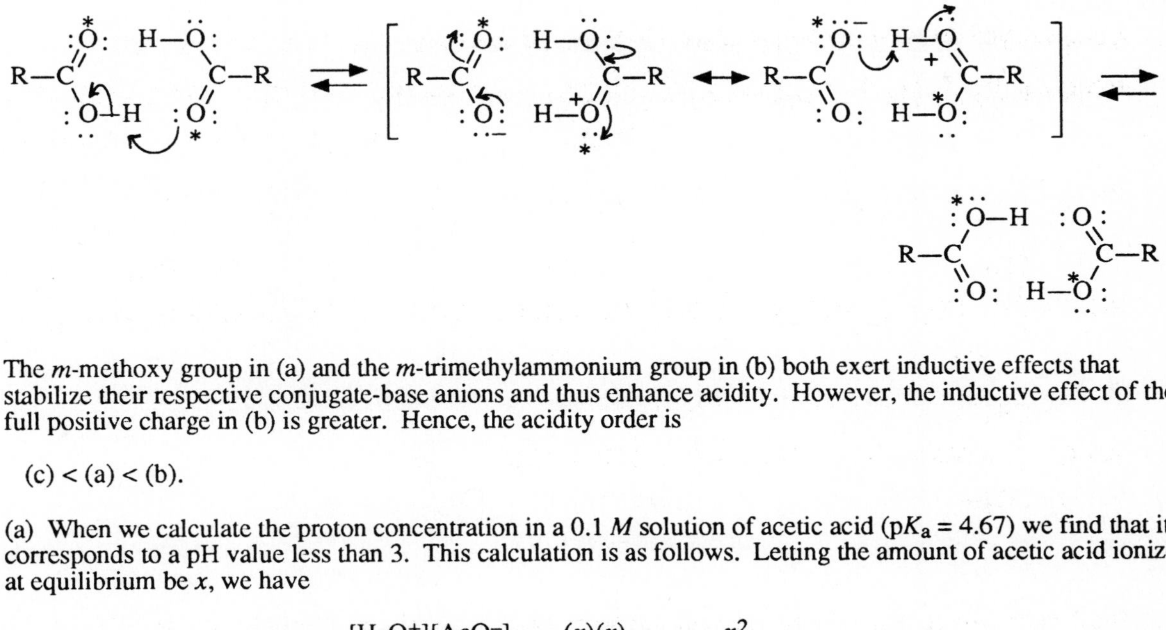

24. The *m*-methoxy group in (a) and the *m*-trimethylammonium group in (b) both exert inductive effects that stabilize their respective conjugate-base anions and thus enhance acidity. However, the inductive effect of the full positive charge in (b) is greater. Hence, the acidity order is

(c) < (a) < (b).

25. (a) When we calculate the proton concentration in a 0.1 M solution of acetic acid ($pK_a = 4.67$) we find that it corresponds to a pH value less than 3. This calculation is as follows. Letting the amount of acetic acid ionized at equilibrium be x, we have

$$K_a = 10^{-4.76} = 1.74 \times 10^{-5} = \frac{[H_3O^+][AcO^-]}{[HOAc]} = \frac{(x)(x)}{(0.1 - x)} = \frac{x^2}{0.1 - x}$$

Making the approximation that x is small relative to the amount of acetic acid present, we have

$$\frac{x^2}{0.1} = 1.74 \times 10^{-5}$$

or $x = [H_3O^+] = 1.32 \times 10^{-3}$

$-\log x = pH = 2.88$

Thus, the pH is less than 3, and acetic acid will turn litmus paper red.

An analogous calculation for phenol using $K_a = 10^{-10}$ gives for the pH 5.5. Since this is greater than 3, a 0.1 M aqueous solution of phenol does not turn litmus paper red.

(b) The mass-action law for acid dissociation, when rearranged, gives

$$[H_3O^+] = K_a \frac{[HOAc]}{[^-OAc]}$$

Letting the ratio [HOAc]/[$^-$OAc] = r,

$$[H_3O^+] = 1.74 \times 10^{-5} \times r$$

When $r = 1/3$, $[H_3O^+] = 5.74 \times 10^{-6}$ M, or pH = 5.24.
When $r = 3$, $[H_3O^+] = 5.22 \times 10^{-5}$ M, or pH = 4.28.
When $r = 1$, $[H_3O^+] = 1.74 \times 10^{-5}$ M, or pH = 4.76 (that is, the pH of the solution equals the pK_a of the acid).

26. (a) This is simply esterification of isobutyric acid.

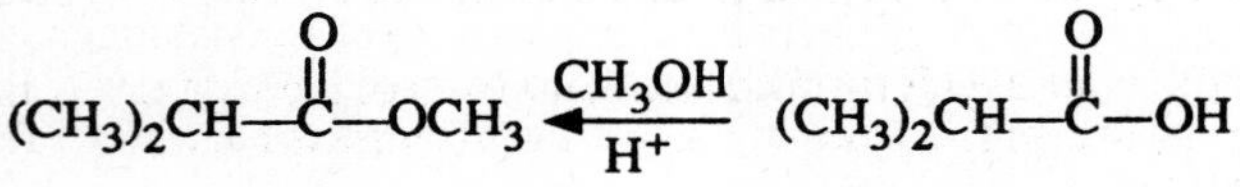

(Diazomethane or CH$_3$I/K$_2$CO$_3$ could also be used to prepare the methyl ester.)

(b) In this synthesis we have to add a carbon atom to isobutyric acid:

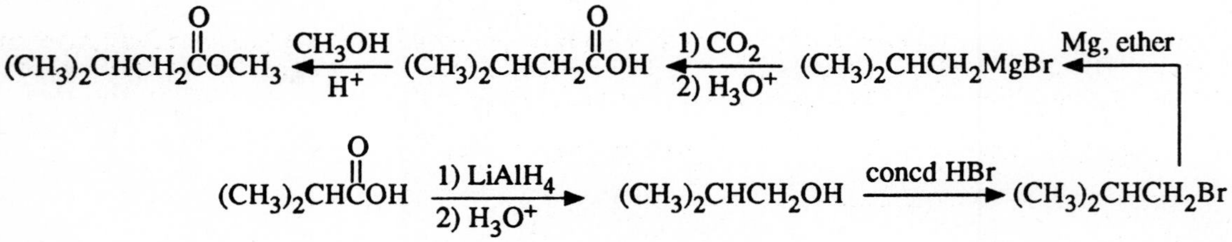

(c) Here we must use an alcohol derived from isobutyric acid to esterify acetic acid:

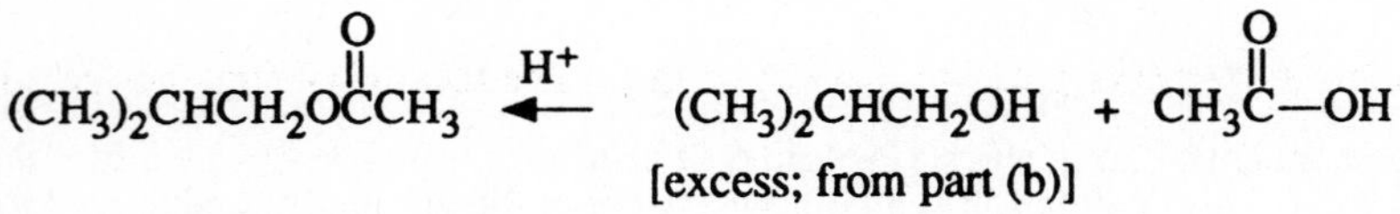

[excess; from part (b)]

(d) The acid chloride derived from isobutyric acid is used in a Friedel–Crafts acylation reaction:

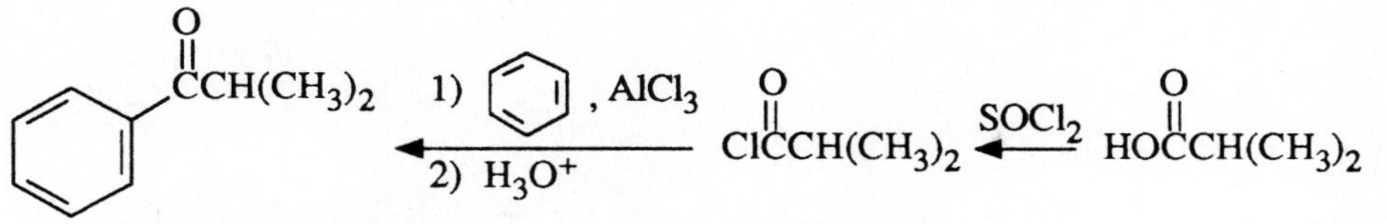

$$\text{(structure: phenyl-}\overset{O}{\overset{\|}{C}}CH(CH_3)_2) \quad \xleftarrow[\text{2) } H_3O^+]{\text{1) benzene , AlCl}_3} \quad \overset{O}{\overset{\|}{Cl}C}CH(CH_3)_2 \quad \xleftarrow{SOCl_2} \quad HO\overset{O}{\overset{\|}{C}}CH(CH_3)_2$$

(e)

$$CH_3\overset{O}{\overset{\|}{C}}CH(CH_3)_2 \xleftarrow[\text{pyridine}]{CrO_3} CH_3\overset{OH}{\overset{|}{C}}HCH(CH_3)_2 \xleftarrow[\text{2) } H_3O^+]{\text{1) } CH_3MgBr} H\overset{O}{\overset{\|}{C}}CH(CH_3)_2 \xleftarrow[\text{pyridine}]{CrO_3} HOCH_2CH(CH_3)_2$$

$$\text{[from part (b)]}$$

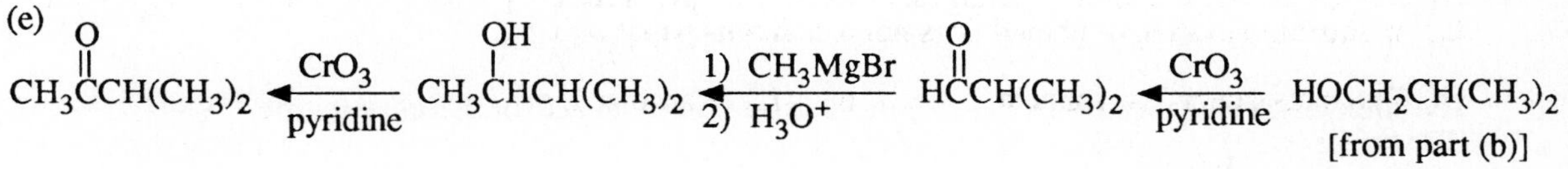

27. This reaction requires addition of a carbon atom to the carbon chain. What better way than with addition of a Grignard reagent to CO_2?

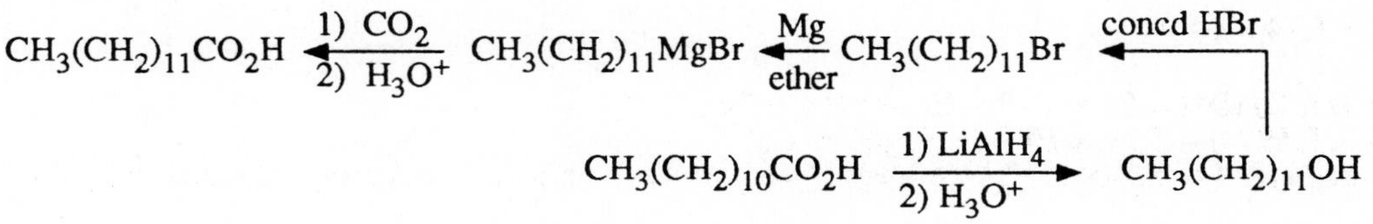

$$CH_3(CH_2)_{11}CO_2H \xleftarrow[\text{2) } H_3O^+]{\text{1) } CO_2} CH_3(CH_2)_{11}MgBr \xleftarrow[\text{ether}]{Mg} CH_3(CH_2)_{11}Br \xleftarrow{\text{concd HBr}}$$

$$CH_3(CH_2)_{10}CO_2H \xrightarrow[\text{2) } H_3O^+]{\text{1) } LiAlH_4} CH_3(CH_2)_{11}OH$$

➤ This sequence exemplifies a fairly general strategy for one-carbon chain extension of a carboxylic acid.

28. The enantiomers of 4-methylhexanoic acid are of *known* absolute configuration. Hence, the student Kane should convert each one into 3-methylhexane by a process that does not affect the asymmetric carbon. The overall transformation desired, then, is the following:

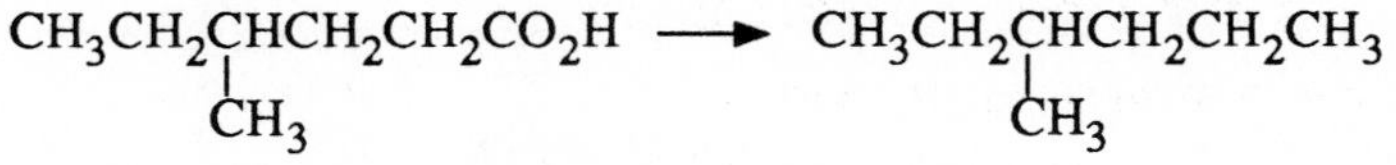

$$CH_3CH_2\overset{|}{\underset{CH_3}{C}}HCH_2CH_2CO_2H \longrightarrow CH_3CH_2\overset{|}{\underset{CH_3}{C}}HCH_2CH_2CH_3$$

Suppose, for example, that (*S*)-4-methylhexanoic acid gives (–)-3-methylhexane (that is, a 3-methylhexane sample with negative optical rotation). Then the two molecules should have corresponding configurations, and the configuration of (–)-3-methylhexane would thus be shown to be *S*:

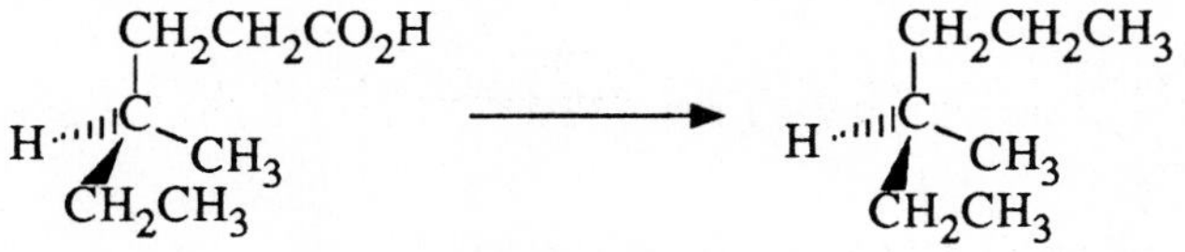

$$\begin{array}{c} CH_2CH_2CO_2H \\ H\cdots C \\ \diagup \quad \diagdown CH_3 \\ CH_2CH_3 \\ S \end{array} \longrightarrow \begin{array}{c} CH_2CH_2CH_3 \\ H\cdots C \\ \diagup \quad \diagdown CH_3 \\ CH_2CH_3 \\ S \end{array}$$

The problem now is the conversion of a carboxy group to a methyl group. The following sequence should work:

$$CH_3CH_2CHCH_2CH_2CH_3 \xleftarrow{H_3O^+} CH_3CH_2CHCH_2CH_2CH_2MgBr \xleftarrow[ether]{Mg} CH_3CH_2CHCH_2CH_2CH_2Br$$
$$\hphantom{CH_3CH_2C}|\hphantom{CH_2CH_2CH_3 \xleftarrow{H_3O^+} CH_3CH_2C}|\hphantom{CH_2CH_2CH_2MgBr \xleftarrow[ether]{Mg} CH_3CH_2C}|$$
$$\hphantom{CH_3CH_2C}CH_3 \hphantom{CH_2CH_2CH_3 \xleftarrow{H_3O^+} CH_3CH_2C}CH_3 \hphantom{CH_2CH_2CH_2MgBr \xleftarrow[ether]{Mg} CH_3CH_2C}CH_3$$

$\uparrow$ PBr$_3$ or HBr

$$CH_3CH_2CHCH_2CH_2CO_2H \xrightarrow[\text{2) }H_3O^+]{\text{1) LiAlH}_4} CH_3CH_2CHCH_2CH_2CH_2OH$$
$$\hphantom{CH_3CH_2C}|\hphantom{CH_2CH_2CO_2H \xrightarrow[\text{2) }H_3O^+]{\text{1) LiAlH}_4} CH_3CH_2C}|$$
$$\hphantom{CH_3CH_2C}CH_3 \hphantom{CH_2CH_2CO_2H \xrightarrow[\text{2) }H_3O^+]{\text{1) LiAlH}_4} CH_3CH_2C}CH_3$$

Notice that the asymmetric carbon is unaffected by this transformation.

29. The strongest acid that can exist in any solvent is the conjugate acid of the solvent itself. Why is this so? Either HBr (in this case) is a weaker acid than the *protonated* solvent (that is, Br$^-$ is a stronger base than the solvent), or else HBr is a stronger acid than the protonated solvent, in which case it will protonate the solvent. But then the protonated solvent becomes the effective acid. In aqueous solution, HBr is completely ionized. That is, it protonates the solvent water completely to give H$_3$O$^+$, because H$_3$O$^+$ is a weaker acid than HBr. In acetic acid, the strongest acid that can exist is a protonated acetic acid molecule:

$$CH_3-\overset{\displaystyle :\overset{\displaystyle +}{O}-H}{\underset{\displaystyle |}{C}}-OH$$

pK$_a$ = –6

Since protonated acetic acid, with a pK$_a$ of about –6, is a much stronger acid than protonated water, with a pK$_a$ of –1.7, HBr is a stronger acid in acetic acid solvent than in aqueous solution.

30. (a) The systematic name of valproic acid is 2-propylpentanoic acid.
    (b) A common name of valproic acid is α-propylvaleric acid.
    (c) There are several possible syntheses; we shall describe two. In these syntheses, Pr— is an abbreviation for the propyl group, CH$_3$CH$_2$CH$_2$— . The first synthesis:

$$\underset{Pr}{\overset{Pr}{>}}CH-CO_2H \xleftarrow[\text{3) }H_3O^+]{\substack{\text{1) Mg, ether} \\ \text{2) CO}_2}} \underset{Pr}{\overset{Pr}{>}}CH-Br \xleftarrow{PBr_3} \underset{Pr}{\overset{Pr}{>}}CH-OH \xleftarrow[\text{2) }H_3O^+]{\text{1) PrMgBr}} Pr-CH=O$$

And the second synthesis:

$$\underset{Pr}{\overset{Pr}{>}}CH-CO_2H \xleftarrow{HNO_3} \underset{Pr}{\overset{Pr}{>}}CH-CH_2OH \xleftarrow[\text{2) }H_2O_2/\ ^-OH]{\text{1) B}_2H_6} \underset{Pr}{\overset{Pr}{>}}CH=CH_2 \xleftarrow{^-CH_2-\overset{+}{P}(Ph)_3}$$

$$\underset{\substack{\text{from the} \\ \text{previous synthesis}}}{\longrightarrow} \underset{Pr}{\overset{Pr}{>}}CH-OH \xrightarrow{CrO_3,\ pyridine} \underset{Pr}{\overset{Pr}{>}}C=O$$

The first synthesis is preferable because it is shorter.

31. We should use a method that does not involve loss of one of the oxygens of the carboxylic acid. Thus, acid-catalyzed esterification is not the optimum method, because this method involves cleavage of the bond between the carbonyl carbon and the carboxylate oxygen (text page 834; Eq. 20.18). Esterification with either diazomethane, or with CH$_3$I and K$_2$CO$_3$ would be the preferred method (Sec. 20.8B).

32. The data indicate that nonanedioic acid (or its ester) is derived from the carboxy end of the fatty acid, malonic acid from the middle, and hexanoic acid from the other end. The structure of *A* is:

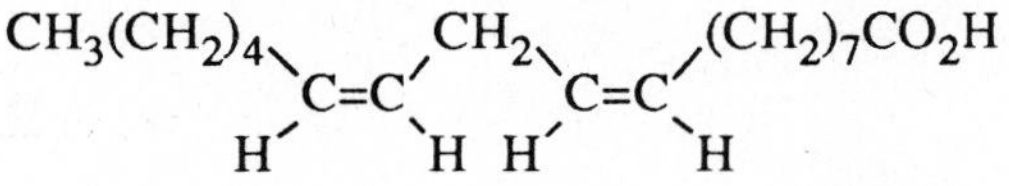

➤ The stereochemistry about the double bonds is not determined by the data. However, it turns out that most common fatty acids have *cis* double bonds.

33. (a) The even mass suggests an even-electron ion. McLafferty rearrangement is a common cleavage mechanism by which even-electron ions are formed:

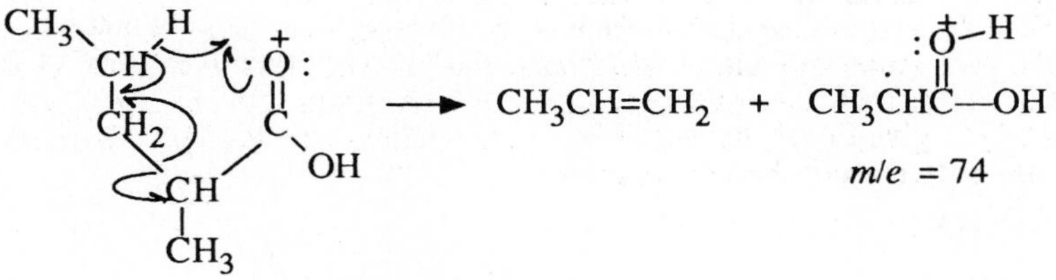

(b) Benzoic acid has a molecular weight of 122. A fragment at $m/e = 105$ corresponds to loss of 17 mass units, or loss of the —OH group by an α-cleavage mechanism:

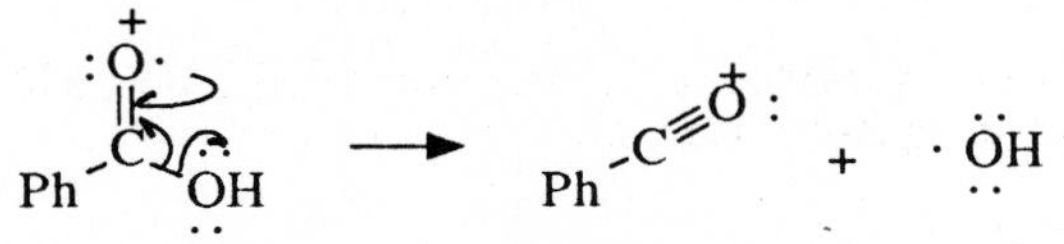

molecular ion

acylium ion
$m/e = 105$

A fragment at $m/e = 77$ is the phenyl cation, formed by inductive cleavage:

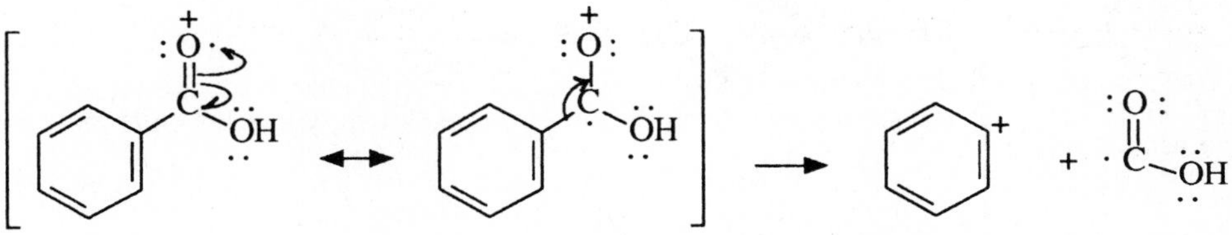

$m/e = 77$

34. Dissolve the mixture in a suitable solvent; since the company specializes in chlorinated organic compounds, methylene chloride might be readily available for the purpose. Extract with 5% $NaHCO_3$ solution. *p*-Chlorobenzoic acid is removed as its conjugate-base anion into the aqueous layer. Acidification of the aqueous layer affords *p*-chlorobenzoic acid. Then extract the methylene chloride solution with 5% aqueous NaOH solution. *p*-Chlorophenol is extracted as its conjugate-base anion into the aqueous layer, from which it is subsequently recovered by acidification. Evaporation of the solvent affords a mixture of 4-chlorocyclohexanol and chlorocyclohexane. Fractional distillation removes the lower-boiling chlorocyclohexane. Only 4-chlorocyclohexanol remains.

➤ If you know about steam distillation, this would be an even better way to remove the chlorocyclohexane, since 4-chlorocyclohexanol would probably not steam distill.

35. The IR spectra indicate that each compound is a carboxylic acid (hardly surprising, in view of the subject of this chapter!). In addition, compound (c) has a *trans* double bond. The structures are:

(a)

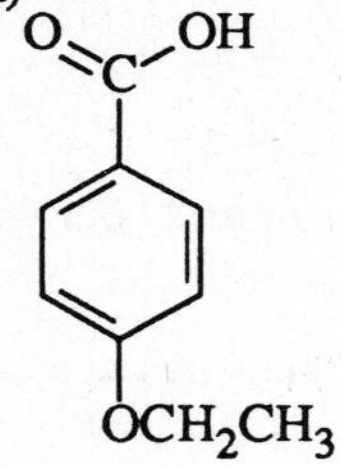
OH
O
C
OCH$_2$CH$_3$

(b)

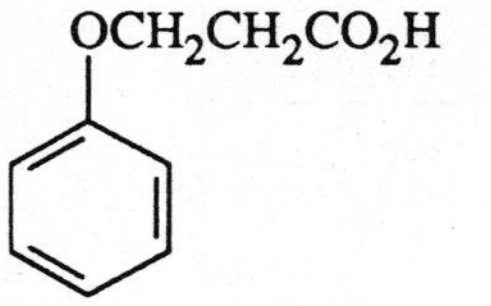
OCH$_2$CH$_2$CO$_2$H

(c)

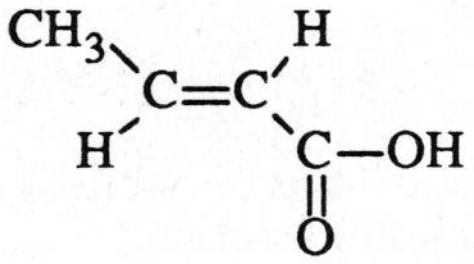
CH$_3$
H
C=C
H
C—OH
O

36. To confirm the labeling pattern, oxidize the compound vigorously with $KMnO_4$ or other reagent that will degrade the side chain to give benzoic acid. If the labeling is as desired, all radioactivity will be gone in the product benzoic acid:

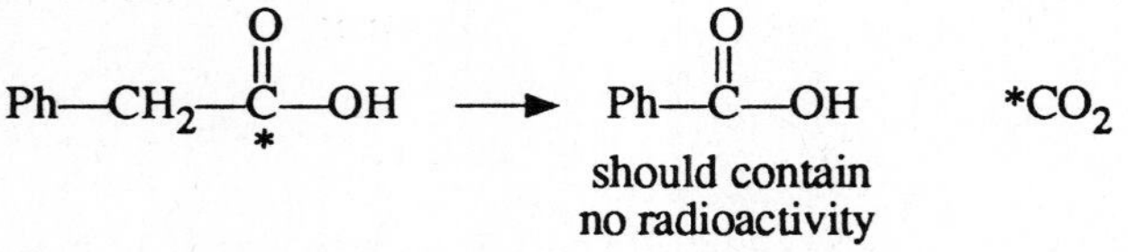
Ph—CH$_2$—C—OH
Ph—C—OH
*CO$_2$
should contain
no radioactivity

37. The compounds that can form cyclic anhydrides are those for which anhydride formation results in unstrained five- or six-membered rings. We must consider each cyclohexane derivative not only as drawn, but in the form in which the chair cyclohexane is flipped. The compounds that can form cyclic anhydrides are (b), (c), (d), and (e). The structures of these anhydrides are as follows:

(b)

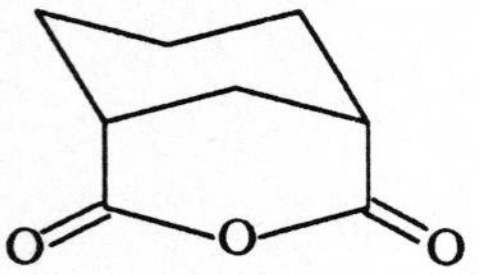

(c)

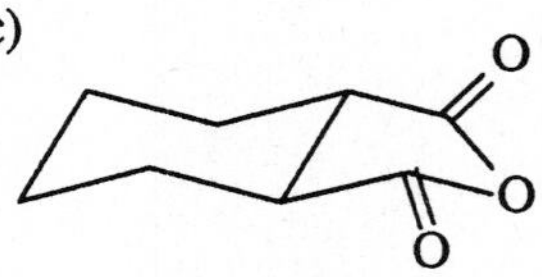

(d)

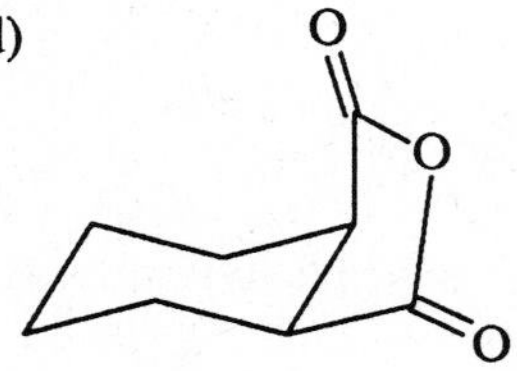

(e)

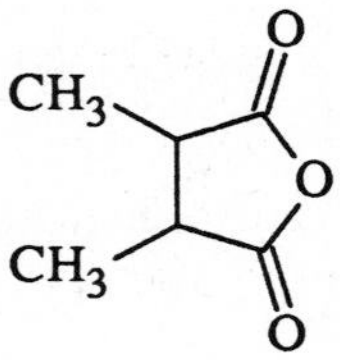
CH$_3$
CH$_3$

Compound (a), however, *cannot* form a cyclic anhydride, because the carboxy groups are too far apart to form an unstrained ring. If these points are not apparent from the structures as drawn, you *must* build and examine a model of each.

38. (a)

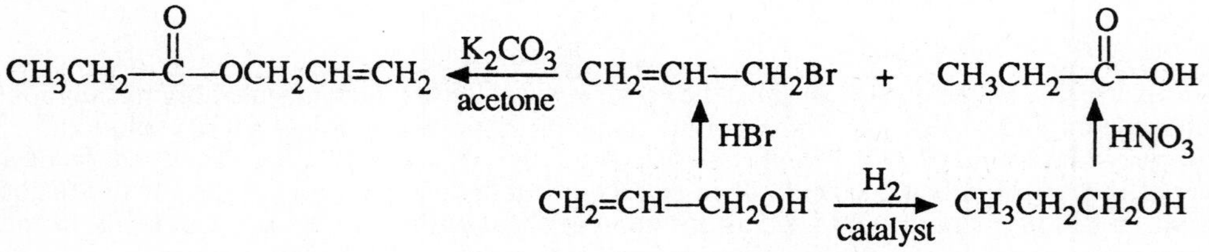
CH$_3$CH$_2$—C—OCH$_2$CH=CH$_2$
K$_2$CO$_3$
acetone
CH$_2$=CH—CH$_2$Br
+
CH$_3$CH$_2$—C—OH
HBr
HNO$_3$
CH$_2$=CH—CH$_2$OH
H$_2$
catalyst
CH$_3$CH$_2$CH$_2$OH

(b)

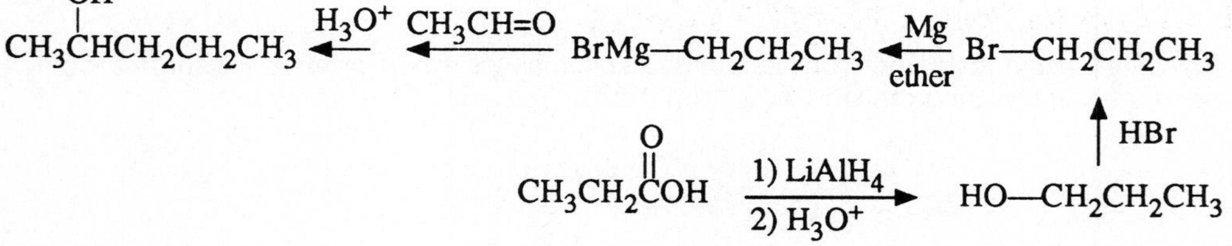
OH
CH$_3$CHCH$_2$CH$_2$CH$_3$
H$_3$O$^+$
CH$_3$CH=O
BrMg—CH$_2$CH$_2$CH$_3$
Mg
ether
Br—CH$_2$CH$_2$CH$_3$
HBr
CH$_3$CH$_2$COH
1) LiAlH$_4$
2) H$_3$O$^+$
HO—CH$_2$CH$_2$CH$_3$

(c)

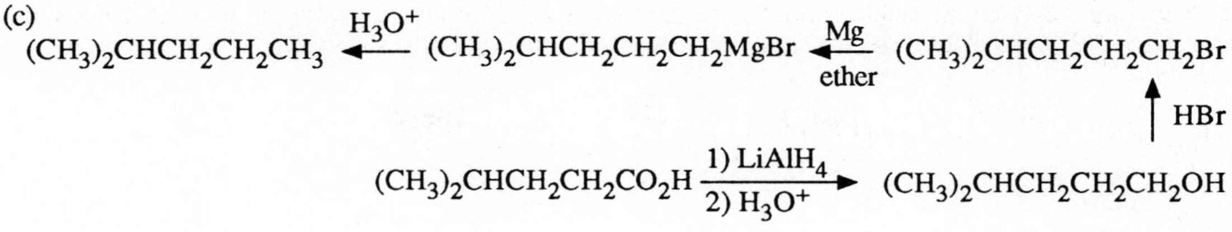

$(CH_3)_2CHCH_2CH_2CH_3 \xleftarrow{H_3O^+} (CH_3)_2CHCH_2CH_2CH_2MgBr \xleftarrow[\text{ether}]{Mg} (CH_3)_2CHCH_2CH_2CH_2Br$

$\uparrow$ HBr

$(CH_3)_2CHCH_2CH_2CO_2H \xrightarrow[\text{2) } H_3O^+]{\text{1) LiAlH}_4} (CH_3)_2CHCH_2CH_2CH_2OH$

(d)

$(CH_3)_2CH(CH_2)_4CH_3 \xleftarrow[\text{ether}]{H_3O^+ \quad Mg} \overset{Br}{(CH_3)_2\overset{|}{C}(CH_2)_4CH_3} \xleftarrow{HBr} \overset{OH}{(CH_3)_2\overset{|}{C}(CH_2)_4CH_3} \longleftarrow$

1) $(CH_3)_2C{=}O$

2) H_3O^+

$CH_3(CH_2)_3CO_2H \xrightarrow[\text{2) } H_3O^+]{\text{1) LiAlH}_4} HO(CH_2)_4CH_3 \xrightarrow{\text{concd HBr}} Br(CH_2)_4CH_3 \xrightarrow[\text{ether}]{Mg} BrMg(CH_2)_4CH_3$

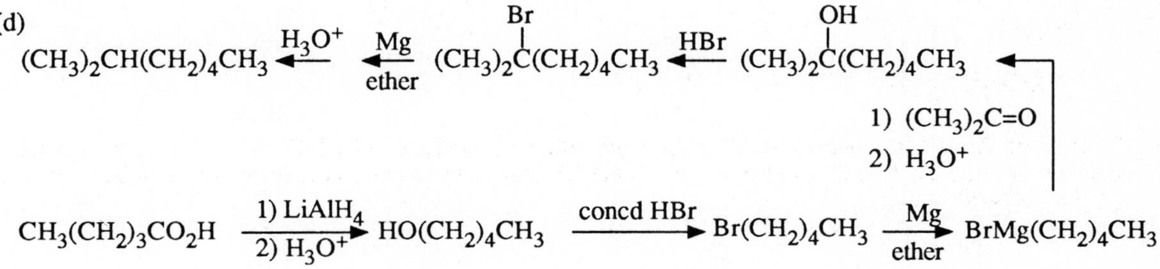

(e)

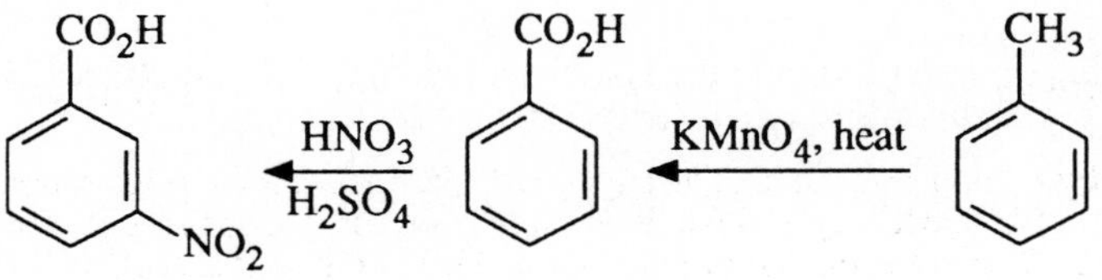

(f)

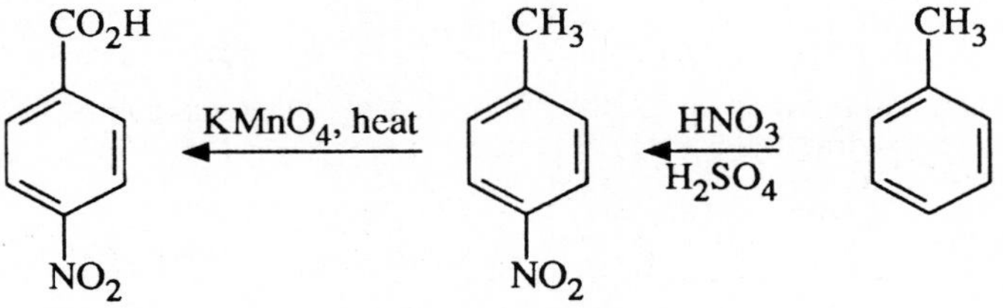

p-Nitrotoluene must be separated from its *ortho* isomer in this synthesis.

(g)

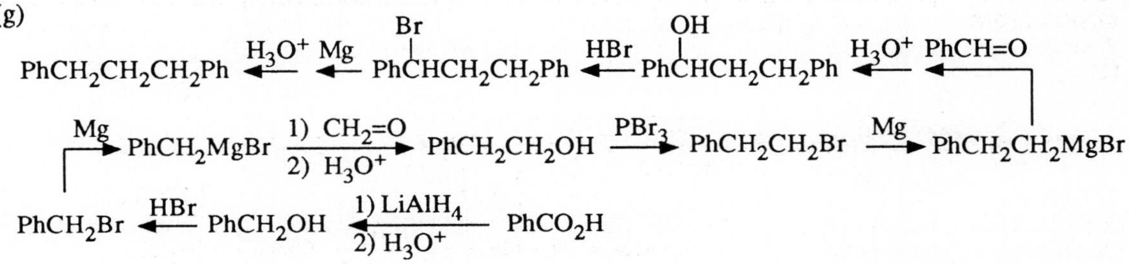

$PhCH_2CH_2CH_2Ph \xleftarrow{H_3O^+ \ Mg} \overset{Br}{Ph\overset{|}{C}HCH_2CH_2Ph} \xleftarrow{HBr} \overset{OH}{Ph\overset{|}{C}HCH_2CH_2Ph} \xleftarrow{H_3O^+ \ PhCH{=}O} $

$\xrightarrow{Mg} PhCH_2MgBr \xrightarrow[\text{2) } H_3O^+]{\text{1) } CH_2{=}O} PhCH_2CH_2OH \xrightarrow{PBr_3} PhCH_2CH_2Br \xrightarrow{Mg} PhCH_2CH_2MgBr$

$PhCH_2Br \xleftarrow{HBr} PhCH_2OH \xleftarrow[\text{2) } H_3O^+]{\text{1) LiAlH}_4} PhCO_2H$

Benzaldehyde can be prepared by the oxidation of benzyl alcohol, which, in turn, is prepared in the first step of the synthesis. All Grignard reagents are formed in ether solvents (diethyl ether or THF). There are a number of other satisfactory routes for preparation of this compound.

(h)

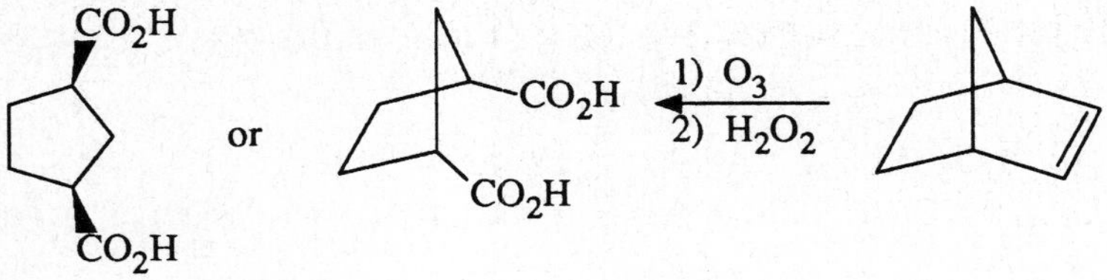

(i)

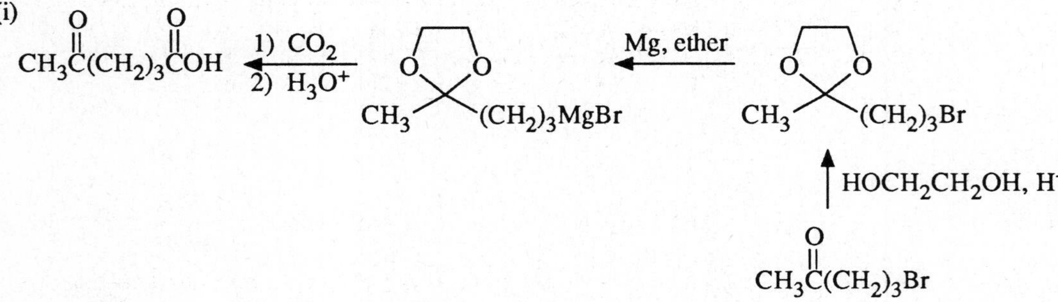

Notice that we must use a protecting group in order to shield the ketone carbonyl group from the action of the Grignard reagent. The choice of a cyclic acetal is arbitrary; any acetal could have been used.

39. (a) This is an esterification by the alkylation mechanism (Sec. 20.8B).

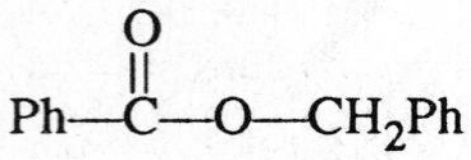

(b) This is esterification by a diazomethane derivative in which the hydrogens of diazomethane are formally substituted by phenyl groups. Hence, a diphenylmethyl ester is obtained:

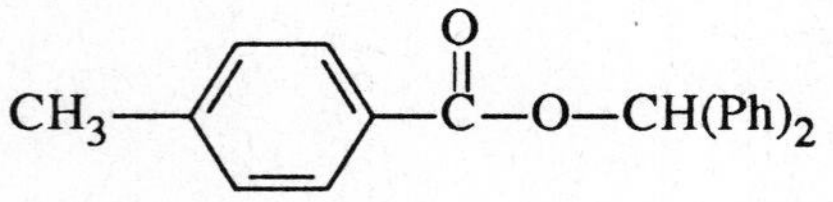

(c) This is formally a disubstituted malonic acid in which the two alkyl substituents are "tied back" into a ring. Loss of one carboxy group by decarboxylation gives one diastereomer; loss of the other carboxy group gives the other stereoisomer:

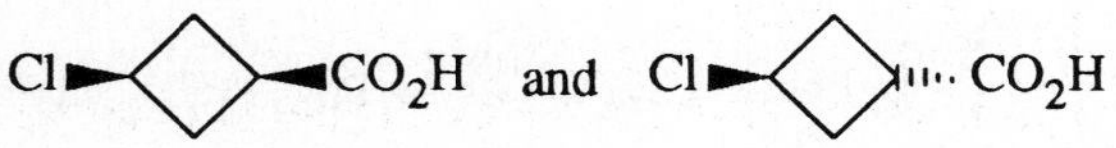

(d) This is the reaction of a carboxylate salt with an alkyl halide (Sec. 20.8B); in this case, the reaction is intramolecular, and an intramolecular ester (that is, a lactone) is formed:

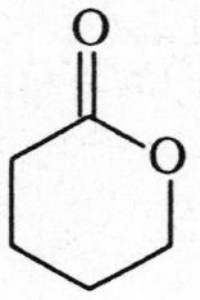

(e) Each "end" of the ethylene glycol molecule is esterified to an "end" of a phthalic acid molecule, and vice versa. Where will it all end? The result is the polymer Dacron:

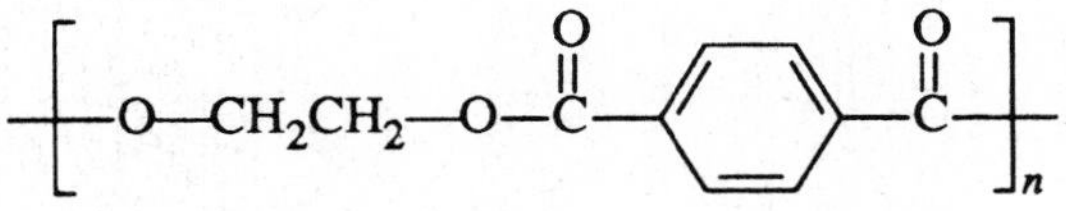

(f) This is essentially an oxymercuration reaction in which the solvent acetic acid attacks the intermediate mercurinium ion. (Compare Secs. 5.3B and 11.1B.)

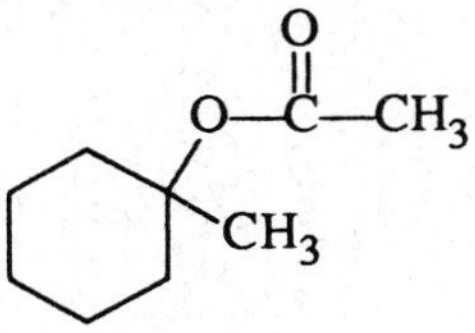

(g) The propionate anion, formed by the reaction of propionic acid with NaOH, reacts as a nucleophile with the epoxide:

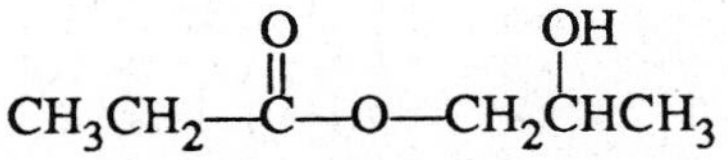

➤ We might ask why the NaOH does not react with the epoxide. In general, ionization reactions in which protons are removed by bases are *much* faster than reactions of the bases as nucleophiles at a carbon atom.

(h) The phenol groups and the carboxylic acid groups are ionized in turn and alkylated by dimethyl sulfate to give a dimethyl ether ester derivative.

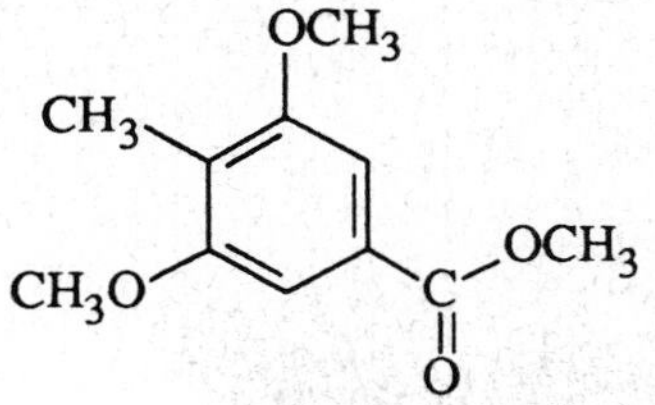

40. The most acidic group in penicillin is the carboxylic acid group, which should have a pK_a in the range 3–4. This group would be ionized in blood at pH = 7.4, but not in the stomach at pH 2. Since the molecule should be more water-soluble in its ionic form, it should be more soluble in blood.

41. (a) This hydrolysis is closely analogous to acetal hydrolysis, which, in turn, is the exact reverse of acetal formation; see Eq. 19.47, text pages 788–789. We'll draw the structures; you provide the curved arrows if you have not already done so.

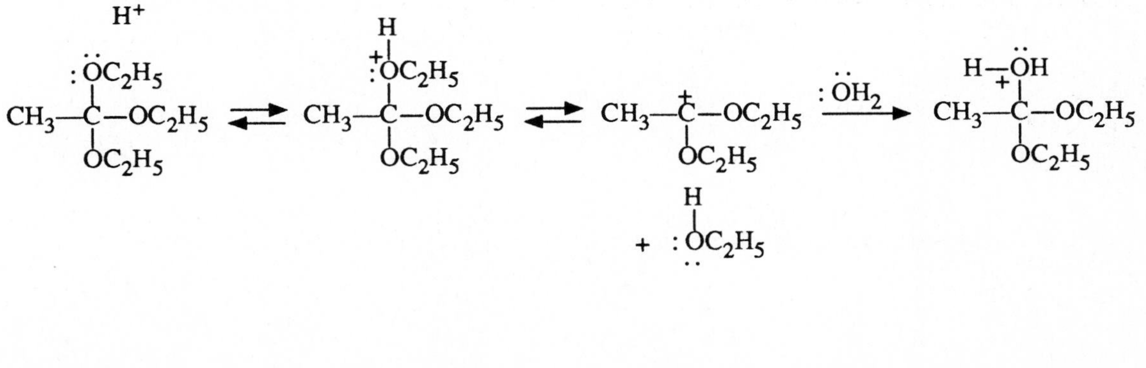

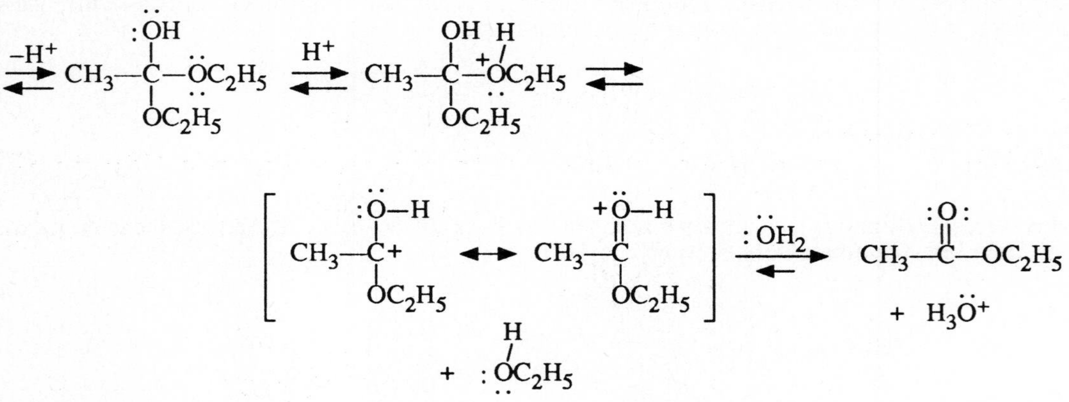

$$\xrightarrow{-H^+} CH_3\overset{\displaystyle :\overset{..}{O}H}{\underset{\displaystyle \overset{|}{O}C_2H_5}{\overset{|}{C}}}\overset{..}{O}C_2H_5 \xrightarrow{H^+} CH_3\overset{\displaystyle OH\ H}{\underset{\displaystyle \overset{|}{O}C_2H_5}{\overset{|}{C}}}\overset{+/}{\underset{..}{O}}C_2H_5 \rightleftharpoons$$

$$\left[CH_3-\overset{\displaystyle :\overset{..}{O}-H}{\underset{\displaystyle \overset{|}{O}C_2H_5}{C}}+ \longleftrightarrow CH_3-\overset{\displaystyle +\overset{..}{O}-H}{\underset{\displaystyle \overset{|}{O}C_2H_5}{C}} \right] \xrightarrow[\longleftarrow]{:\overset{..}{O}H_2} CH_3-\overset{\displaystyle :O:}{C}-OC_2H_5$$

$$+ \underset{\displaystyle :\overset{\overset{\displaystyle H}{|}}{\overset{..}{O}}C_2H_5}{} \qquad + H_3\overset{..}{O}^+$$

(b) The protonated carboxylic acid is attacked by the carbonyl oxygen of the ketone. This produces carbocation character at the carbonyl carbon of the ketone, which is attacked by methanol. Again we leave it to you to provide the curved arrows.

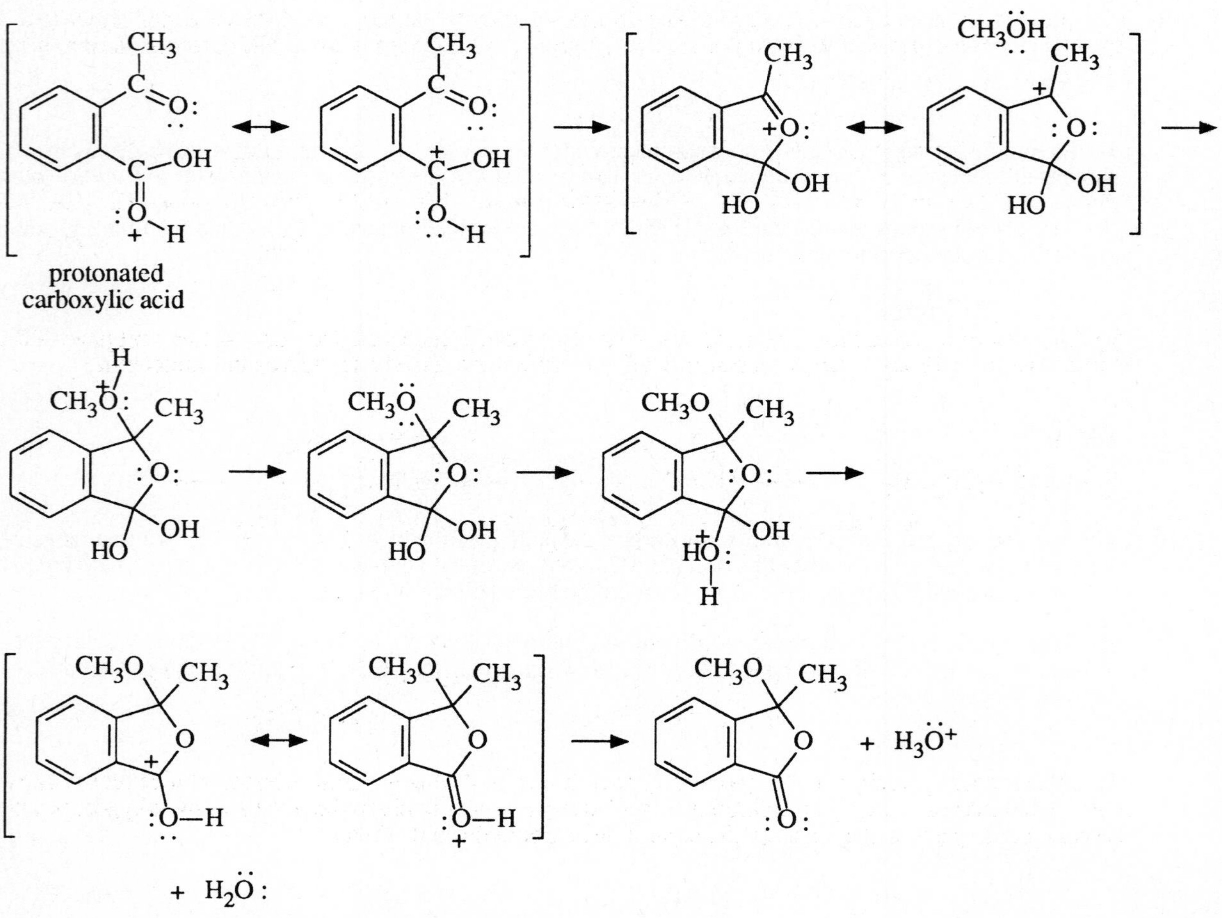

protonated
carboxylic acid

+ H_2\overset{..}{O}:

(c) Protonation of the carbon–carbon double bond of isobutylene gives a carbocation, which is attacked by the carbon of carbon monoxide. Addition of water to the resulting acylium ion gives the product:

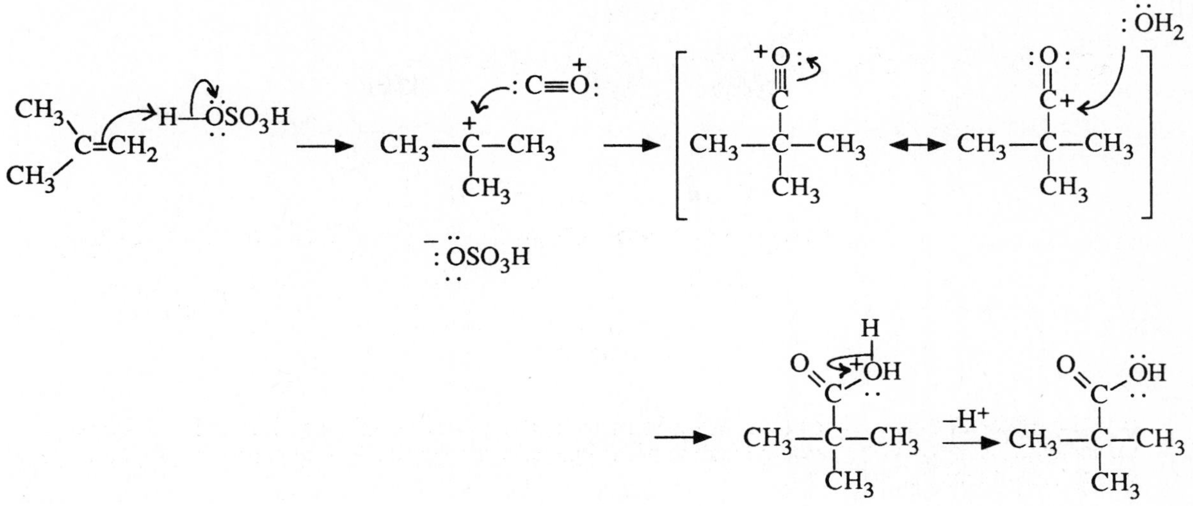

(d) The carboxylic acid can catalyze its own decarboxylation by protonation of the epoxide. (If we think of an epoxide as a three-membered analog of a carbonyl group, this reaction is similar to decarboxylation of a β-keto acid.)

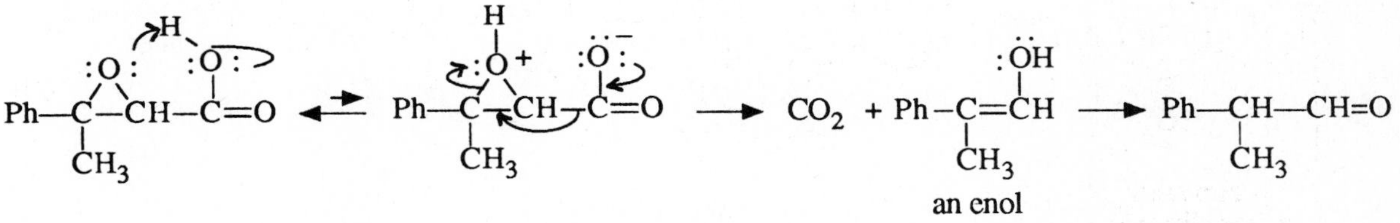

an enol

(e) This reaction is analogous to mercuric-ion catalyzed acetylene hydration (Eq. 14.14b, text page 560), except that the carboxylic acid group within the molecule rather than water acts as the nucleophile.

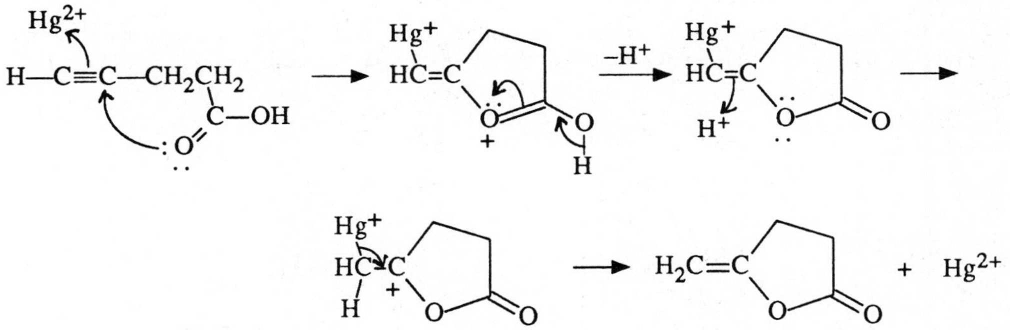

(f) This reaction is a Markovnikov addition of acetic acid to the alkene double bond. Notice that in this and other reactions above in which a carboxylic acid group acts as a nucleophile, the carbonyl oxygen, not the carboxylate oxygen, is the nucleophilic atom in the carboxylic acid. (Why?)

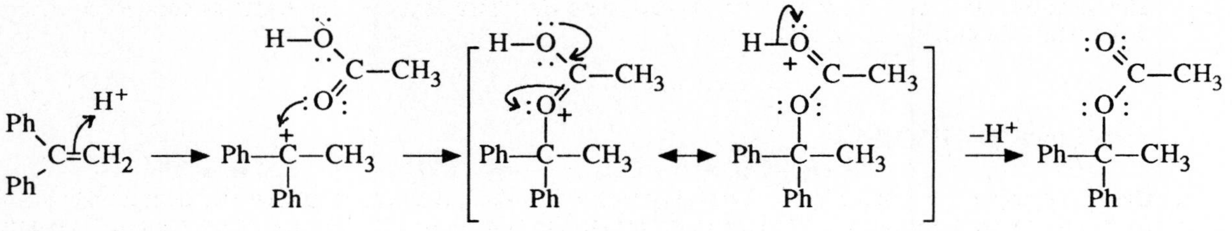

42. Compound A is 3-(4-hydroxyphenyl)propionic acid:

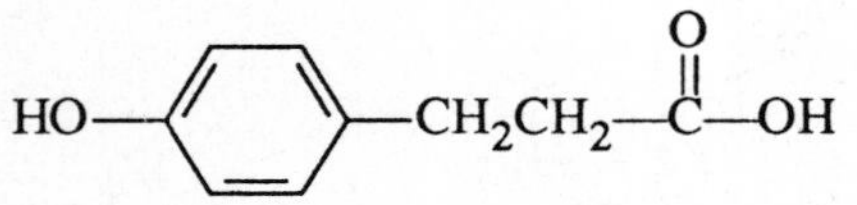

The parent ion has $m/e = 166$. The titration data suggests a phenol and a carboxylic acid. The base shift in the UV spectrum confirms a phenol. The NMR spectrum suggests a *para*-substituted benzene ring and four alkyl hydrogens. With so much hydroxy-containing functionality, the solubility in hot water is understandable.

43. The analytical data dictate an empirical formula of C_3H_5, or a minimal molecular formula of C_6H_{10}. A hydrocarbon cannot have an odd mass; hence, the peak in the mass spectrum at $m/e = 67$ cannot be the parent ion. Given that the ozonolysis product is a dicarboxylic acid, we deduce that the hydrocarbon A contains a double bond *within a ring*. From the neutralization data, we calculate a molecular weight of the dicarboxylic acid B to be 146. (See the solution to Problem 22 for the molecular weight calculation from neutralization data.) From the following transformation in ozonolysis, we deduce that the molecular weight of the alkene must be 82:

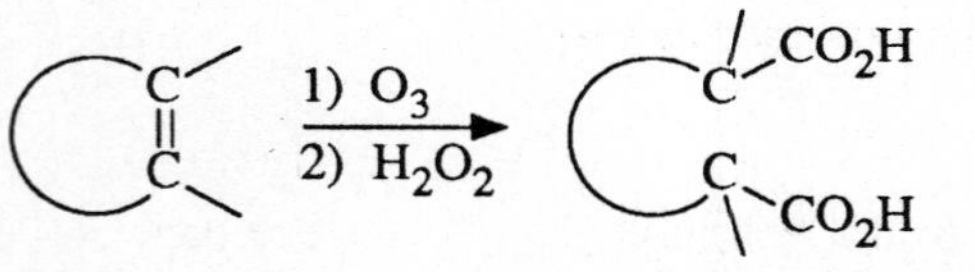

$$146 - 64 = 82$$

A peak at $m/e = 67$ corresponds to loss of 15 mass units, or a methyl group. Evidently, the ring is substituted with a methyl group in such a way that the dicarboxylic acid B is chiral. The compound is 3-methyl-1-cyclopentene.

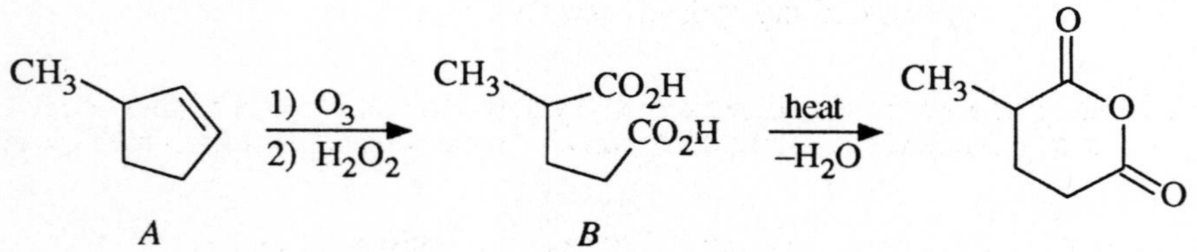

(Notice that 4-methyl-1-cyclopentene would not give a chiral dicarboxylic acid on ozonolysis.)

44. The unsaturation number of A is 3. Heating causes loss of CO_2; hence, compound A has the partial structure

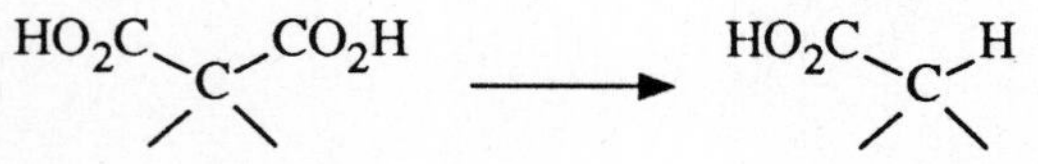

The transformation of B, C, and E with LiAlH$_4$, then HBr, then Mg, then H$_2$O, effects conversion of a carboxylic acid group into a methyl group:

$$\overset{\overset{\displaystyle O}{\parallel}}{-C}-OH \longrightarrow -CH_3$$

Because compounds C and E give the same compound by this treatment, it follows that compounds A and D, from which C and E originate, have the same carbon skeleton — that is, they are stereoisomers. The only compounds that fit *all* the data along with the conversions involved are as follows:

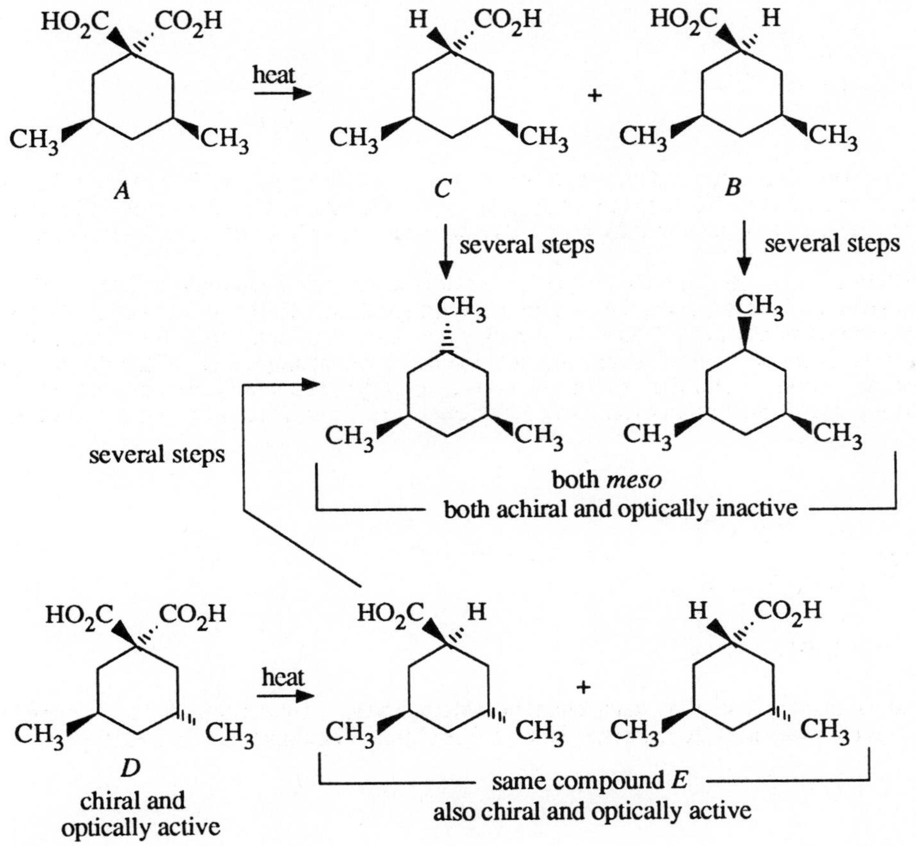

> The data in this problem take advantage of the unique symmetry of the trimethylcyclohexanes derived from the correct compounds, a symmetry that is absent in the analogous hydrocarbons derived from other candidates such as the following:

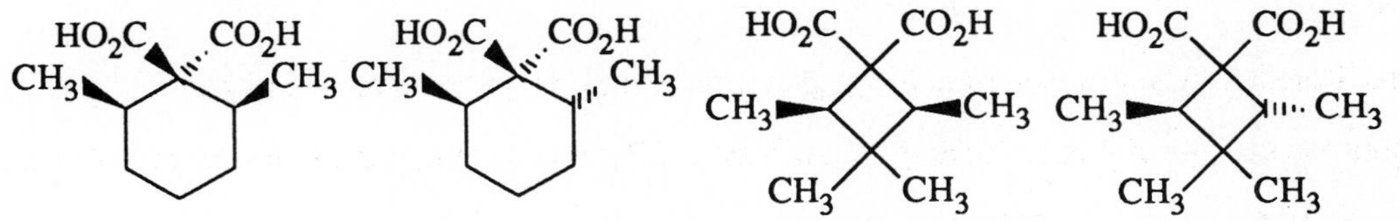

Chapter 21 / Chemistry of Carboxylic Acid Derivatives

CHAPTER 21 TERMS

acetamido group 21.1
acetoxy group 21.1
acid halide 21.1
acylammonium salt 21.8A
addition polymer 21.12A
amide 21.1
anhydride 21.1
carbamic acid 21.1G
carbamoyl group 21.1
carboxy group 21.1
carboxylic acid derivative .... Introduction
carboxymethyl group 21.1
chloroformyl group 21.1
condensation polymer 21.12A
cyano group .... Introduction
dimethyl carbonate 21.1G
ester 21.1
ethoxycarbonyl group 21.1
fat 21.12B
hydroxamate test 21.8C
hydroxamic acid 21.8C
imide 21.1E
imidic acid 21.7D

lactam 21.1E
lactone 21.1A
lipid bilayer 21.12B
lithium dialkylcuprate 21.10B
methoxycarbonyl group 21.1
methyl carbamate 21.1G
mixed anhydride 21.1C
nitrile 21.1
nylon 21.12A
phosgene 21.1G
phospholipid 21.12B
polyester 21.12A
primary amide 21.1E
Rosenmund reduction 21.9D
saponification 21.7A
Schotten–Baumann reaction 21.8A
secondary amide 21.1E
sulfonate ester 21.8A
tertiary amide 21.1E
transesterification 21.8C
urea 21.1G
wax 21.12B

CHAPTER 21 CONCEPTS

I. Nomenclature and Classification of Carboxylic Acid Derivatives:

A. Introduction to Carboxylic Acid Derivatives:
1. **Carboxylic acid derivatives** are compounds that can be hydrolyzed under acidic or basic conditions to give the corresponding carboxylic acid.
2. There is a structural and chemical similarity among carboxylic acids and their derivatives.
   a) With the exception of nitriles, all carboxylic acid derivatives contain a carbonyl group.
   b) Many important reactions of these compounds occur at the carbonyl group.
   c) The cyano group (—C≡N) of nitriles has reactivity that resembles that of a carbonyl group.

B. Esters and Lactones:
1. Esters are named, in both common and systematic nomenclature, as derivatives of their parent carboxylic acids by applying a variation of the system used in naming carboxylate salts.
   a) The group attached to the carboxylate oxygen is named first as a simple alkyl or aryl group.

b) This name is followed by the name of the parent carboxylate constructed by dropping the final *ic acid* from the name of the acid and adding the suffix *ate*.
   (1) In common nomenclature:
       (*a*) The alkyl or aryl group is numbered, using Greek letters, from the point of attachment.
       (*b*) Substitution is indicated by numbering the acid portion of the ester as in acid nomenclature, beginning with the carbon adjacent to the carbonyl group as the *α*-position.
   (2) In systematic nomenclature:
       (*a*) The alkyl or aryl group is numbered from the point of attachment.
       (*b*) Substitution is indicated by numbering the acid portion of the ester as in acid nomenclature, beginning with the carbonyl as carbon-1.
2. Cyclic esters are called **lactones.**
   a) The common name of a simple lactone is derived from the acid with the same number of carbons in its principal chain.
   b) The ring size is denoted by a Greek letter corresponding to the point of attachment of the lactone ring oxygen to the carbon chain.

common name: phenyl *β*-chloroisovalerate
systematic name: phenyl 3-chloro-3-methylbutanoate

δ-valerolactone

C. Acid Halides:
   1. Acid halides are named in any system of nomenclature by replacing the *ic acid* ending of the acid with the suffix *yl*, followed by the name of the halide.
   2. When the acid halide group is attached to a ring, the compound is named as an alkanecarbonyl halide.

$$Cl-CH_2-CH_2-\underset{\underset{CH_3}{|}}{\overset{\overset{CH_3}{|}}{C}}-CH_2-\overset{\overset{O}{\|}}{C}-Cl$$

common name: *δ*-chloro-*β,β*-dimethylvaleryl chloride
systematic name: 5-chloro-3,3-dimethylpentanoyl chloride

3-methoxy-1-cyclopentanecarbonyl bromide

D. Anhydrides:
   1. To name an anhydride, the word *acid* in the name of the parent acid is replaced with *anhydride*.
   2. **Mixed anhydrides,** derived from *two different* acids, are named by citing the two parent acids in alphabetical order.

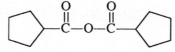

cyclopentanecarboxylic anhydride

$$Ph-\overset{\overset{O}{\|}}{C}-O-\overset{\overset{O}{\|}}{C}-CH_3$$
acetic benzoic anhydride
(a mixed anhydride)

E. Nitriles:
   1. In the common system, nitriles are named by dropping the *ic* or *oic acid* from the name of the acid with the same number of carbon atoms (counting the nitrile carbon) and adding the suffix *onitrile* (the name of the three-carbon nitrile is shortened in common nomenclature to propionitrile).
   2. In systematic nomenclature, the suffix *nitrile* is added to the name of the hydrocarbon with the same number of carbon atoms.
   3. When the nitrile group is attached to a ring, a special *carbonitrile* nomenclature is used.

I—CH$_2$—CH$_2$—C≡N:

common name: β-iodopropionitrile
systematic name: 3-iodopropanenitrile

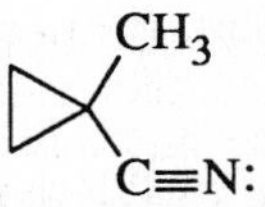

1-methyl-1-cyclopropanecarbonitrile

F. Amides, Lactams, and Imides:
1. Simple amides are named in any system by replacing the *ic* or *oic acid* suffix of the acid name with the suffix *amide*.
2. When the amide functional group is attached to a ring, the suffix *carboxamide* is used.
3. Amides are classified by the number of hydrogens attached to the amide nitrogen:
   a) Primary—*two* hydrogens attached.
   b) Secondary—*one* hydrogen attached.
   c) Tertiary—*no* hydrogens attached.
4. Substitution on nitrogen in secondary and tertiary amides is designated with the letter *N* (italicized or underlined).

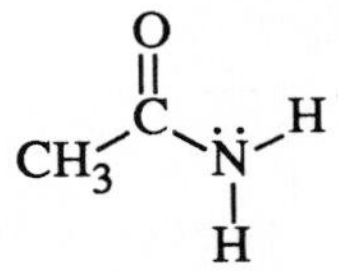

acetamide
(a primary amide)

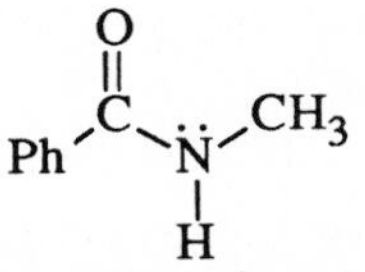

N-methylbenzamide
(a secondary amide)

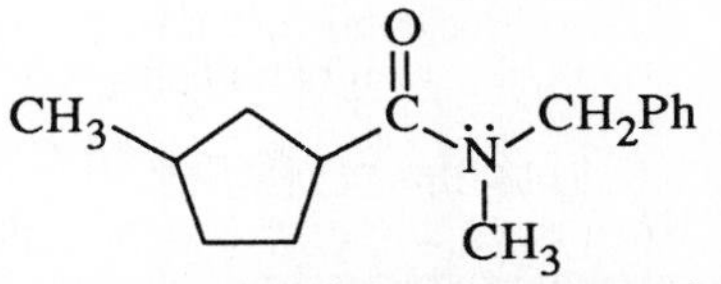

N-benzyl-*N*,3-dimethylcyclopentanecarboxamide
(a tertiary amide)

5. Cyclic amides are called **lactams** and are classified by ring size with Greek letters:
   a) γ-Lactam —5-membered ring.
   b) β-Lactam —4-membered ring.
6. **Imides** are formally the nitrogen analogs of anhydrides (cyclic imides are of greater importance than open-chain imides).

glutarimide
(an imide)

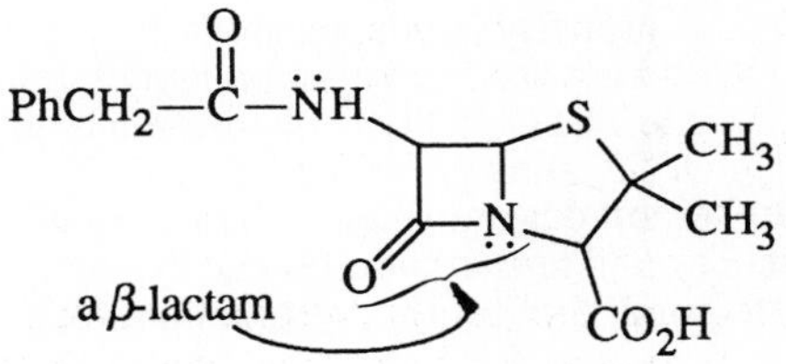

a β-lactam   Penicillin G

G. Nomenclature of Substituent Groups:
1. The priorities for citing principal groups in a carboxylic acid derivative are as follows (a complete list of functional group priorities is given in Appendix I, text page A-1):

acid › anhydride › ester › acid halide › amide › nitrile

2. The names used for citing these groups as substituents are listed in Table 21.2, text page 862.

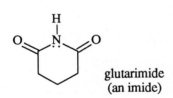

2-cyano-*N*-methyl-*N*-propylacetamide

H. Carbonic Acid Derivatives:
1. Esters of carbonic acid are named like other esters.
2. Other important carbonic acid derivatives have special names that must be learned:

phosgene

urea

carbamic acid

II. Basicity and Physical Properties of Carboxylic Acid Derivatives:

A. Basicity of Carboxylic Acid Derivatives:
 1. Carboxylic acid derivatives are weakly basic at the carbonyl oxygen.
  a) The basicity of an ester is about the same as that of the corresponding carboxylic acid.
  b) Amides are considerably more basic than other acid derivatives.
 2. Nitriles are very weak bases.
  a) The basicity of nitriles is poor because the electron pair on the nitrogen is in an *sp* orbital.
  b) Nitriles are the least basic of the nitrogen analogs.

B. Physical Properties of Esters:
 1. Esters are polar molecules, but they lack the capability of acids to donate hydrogen bonds.
 2. Lower esters are typically volatile, water-insoluble fragrant liquids with lower density than water.

C. Physical Properties of Anhydrides and Acid Chlorides:
 1. Most of the lower anhydrides and acid chlorides are dense, water-insoluble liquids with acrid, piercing odors.
 2. The boiling points are not very different from those of other polar molecules of about the same molecular weight and shape.

D. Physical Properties of Nitriles:
 1. Nitriles are among the most polar organic compounds; their polarity is reflected in their boiling points, which are rather high, despite the absence of hydrogen bonding.
 2. The nitrile C≡N bond length is significantly less than the acetylene C≡C bond length.
 3. Acetonitrile is miscible with water and propionitrile has a moderate solubility in water, whereas higher nitriles are insoluble in water.

E. Physical Properties of Amides:
 1. Primary and secondary amides, like carboxylic acids, tend to associate into hydrogen-bonded dimers or higher aggregates in the solid state, pure liquid state, or in solvents that do not form hydrogen bonds.
  a) This property is of substantial biological importance.
  b) With increased substitution at nitrogen:
   (1) The capacity for hydrogen bonding is reduced.
   (2) Boiling points decrease (in spite of the increase in molecular weight).
 2. The lower amides are water-soluble, polar molecules with high boiling points.
 3. Secondary and tertiary amides can exist in both *E* and *Z* conformations about the carbonyl–nitrogen single bond; the Z-form predominates in most cases for steric reasons.

 4. Amides have an important resonance structure in which the carbonyl–nitrogen bond has substantial double-bond character.

III. Spectroscopy of Carboxylic Acid Derivatives:

A. IR Spectroscopy:
 1. The most important feature in the IR spectra of most carboxylic acid derivatives is the C=O stretching absorption or for nitriles, the C≡N stretching absorption.
 2. Some noteworthy IR absorption trends of carboxylic acid derivatives are as follows (see Table 21.3, text page 867, for a complete listing):
  a) Esters are readily differentiated from carboxylic acids, aldehydes, or ketones by the unique ester carbonyl absorption at 1735 cm^{-1}.

b) Lactones, lactams, and cyclic anhydrides, like cyclic ketones, have carbonyl absorption frequencies that increase dramatically as the ring size decreases.

c) Anhydrides and some acid chlorides have two carbonyl absorptions; the two carbonyl absorptions of anhydrides are due to the symmetrical and unsymmetrical stretching vibrations of the carbonyl group.

d) The carbonyl absorption of amides occurs at much lower frequency than that of other carbonyl compounds.

e) The C≡N stretching absorption of nitriles generally occurs in the triple-bond region of the spectrum; this absorption is stronger, and occurs at a somewhat higher frequency, than the C≡C absorption of an acetylene.

f) Primary and secondary amides show N—H absorptions in the 3200–3400 cm^{-1} and 1640 cm^{-1} regions of the spectrum.

    (1) Many primary amides show a double N—H stretching absorption.

    (2) Secondary amides show a single strong N—H stretching absorption.

    (3) Strong N—H bending absorption occurs in the vicinity of 1640 cm^{-1}.

    (4) Tertiary amides lack both of these N—H vibrations.

B. NMR Spectroscopy:

    1. The α-proton resonances of all carboxylic acid derivatives are observed in the δ 1.9–3 region of the NMR spectrum.

    2. In esters, the chemical shifts of protons on the carbon adjacent to oxygen occur at about 0.6 ppm lower field than the analogous protons in alcohol and ethers; this shift is attributed to the electronegativity of the carbonyl group.

    3. The N-alkyl protons of amides have chemical shifts in the δ 2.6–3 ppm chemical shift region.

       a) The N—H proton resonances of primary and secondary amides are broad and are observed in the δ 7.5–8.5 region.

       b) The signals for these protons are caused by a slow chemical exchange with the protons of other protic substances and by unresolved splitting with ^{14}N, which has a nuclear spin.

    4. Amide N—H resonances can be washed out by exchange with D_2O.

C. Solving Structural Problems Involving Nitrogen-Containing Compounds:

    1. Compounds containing an odd number of nitrogen atoms have odd molecular weight.

    2. There is a special formula for calculating the unsaturation number of a compound containing nitrogen.

$$U = \frac{2C + 2 + N - (H + X)}{2}$$

    3. An odd-electron ion or even-electron ion in the mass spectrum of a compound containing nitrogen cannot be deduced simply by its mass, since the number of nitrogens present determines whether the mass is odd or even.

IV. Occurrence and Use of Carboxylic Acids and Their Derivatives:

A. Nylon and Polyesters:

    1. Two of the most important polymers produced on an industrial scale are **nylon** and **polyesters**.

       a) Nylon is the general name given to a group of polymeric amides.

       b) Nylon is an example of a **condensation polymer**, a polymer formed in a reaction that liberates a small molecule, in this case water.

       c) Polyesters are condensation polymers derived from the reaction of diols and diacids.

       d) An **addition polymer** (for example polyethylene) is formed *without* liberation of a small molecule.

B. Waxes, Fats, and Phospholipids:

    1. Waxes, fats, and phospholipids are all important naturally occurring ester derivatives of fatty acids.

    2. A **wax** is an ester of a fatty acid and a fatty alcohol (an alcohol with a long unbranched carbon chain).

$CH_3CH_2CH_2CH_2CH_2CH_2CH_2CH_2CH_2CH_2CH_2CH_2CH_2CH_2CH_2$—C=O

                                                                           a wax

$CH_3CH_2CH_2CH_2CH_2CH_2CH_2CH_2CH_2CH_2CH_2CH_2CH_2CH_2CH_2$—O

3. A **fat** is an ester derived from a molecule of glycerol and three molecules of fatty acid.
   a) The three acyl groups in a fat may be the same or different.
   b) Treatment of a fat with NaOH yields glycerol and the sodium salts of the fatty acids (soaps).

$$CH_3CH_2CH_2CH_2CH_2CH_2CH_2CH_2CH_2CH_2CH_2CH_2CH_2{\overset{\overset{\textstyle O}{\|}}{C}}{-}O{\diagdown}$$

$$CH_3CH_2CH_2CH_2CH_2CH_2CH_2CH_2CH_2CH_2CH_2CH_2CH_2{\overset{\overset{\textstyle O}{\|}}{C}}{-}O{-}CH \qquad \text{a fat}$$

$$CH_3CH_2CH_2CH_2CH_2CH_2CH_2CH_2CH_2CH_2CH_2CH_2CH_2{\overset{\overset{\textstyle O}{\|}}{C}}{-}O{\diagup}$$

4. **Phospholipids** are closely related to fats, since they too are esters of glycerol.
   a) Phospholipids differ from fats in that one of the terminal oxygens of glycerol in a phospholipid is esterified to a special type of organic phosphate derivative, forming a polar head group in the molecule.
   b) The remaining two oxygens of glycerol are esterified to fatty acids.

$$CH_3CH_2CH_2CH_2CH_2CH_2CH_2CH_2CH_2CH_2CH_2CH_2CH_2{\overset{\overset{\textstyle O}{\|}}{C}}{-}O{\diagdown} \qquad \text{a phospholipid}$$

$$CH_3CH_2CH_2CH_2CH_2CH_2CH_2CH_2CH_2CH_2CH_2CH_2CH_2{\overset{\overset{\textstyle O}{\|}}{C}}{-}O{-}CH$$

$$CH_2{-}O{-}\overset{\overset{\textstyle O}{\|}}{\underset{\underset{\textstyle O^-}{|}}{P}}{-}O{-}CH_2CH_2\overset{+}{N}(CH_3)_3$$

V. Reactivity of Carboxylic Acid Derivatives:

A. <u>General</u>:
1. The reactions of carboxylic acid derivatives can be categorized as follows:
   a) Carbonyl-group reactions—the most common being reaction with nucleophiles, which include:
      (1) Water (hydrolysis) or hydroxide ion (saponification).
      (2) Alcohols or alkoxides (alcoholysis, or transesterfication [in the case of esters]).
      (3) Amines (aminolysis).
      (4) Hydrides (reduction).
      (5) Organometallic reagents.
   b) Addition to nitriles.
   c) Reactions involving the α-carbon.
   d) Reactions at the nitrogen of amides.
2. One carbonyl-group reaction of acid derivatives is the reaction of the carbonyl oxygen (or the nitrile nitrogen) as a base.
3. The major carbonyl-group reaction of carboxylic acid derivatives is substitution at the carbonyl group.
4. The C≡N bond behaves chemically much like a carbonyl group.

B. <u>Relative Carbonyl Reactivity of Carboxylic Acid Derivatives</u>:
1. Relative reactivity is determined by the stability of each type of compound relative to its transition state for addition or substitution; the more a compound is stabilized, the less reactive it is.
2. The trend in carbonyl reactivity of carboxylic acid derivatives parallels the trend in leaving group effectiveness:

acid chlorides › anhydrides » esters, acids › amides › nitriles

Cl^- › CO_2^- » RO^-, HO^- › R_2N^-

3. Anything that stabilizes a carboxylic acid derivative relative to its addition intermediate (or transition state) will:
   a) Increase its free energy of activation.
   b) Decrease its reactivity.
4. Substituent groups affect the stability of carbonyl compounds through the operation of the same two types of electronic effects that have been considered before:
   a) Inductive effects

(1) Consider the polarity of the C=O bond and approximate the carbonyl carbon as a carbocation; electronegative groups attached to the carbonyl carbon destabilize its positive charge.

(2) The tetrahedral addition intermediate (or transition state) has less positive charge.

(3) The inductive effect of an electron-withdrawing group raises the energy of a carbonyl compound more than ·it raises the energy of the transition state; thus, the free energy of activation decreases and the reactivity increases.

    (a) The electron-withdrawing inductive effects of substituent groups are in the same order as the relative reactivities of the corresponding carboxylic acid derivatives.

    (b) This order is also reflected in relative acid strengths of the corresponding acids:

$$HCl \; \rangle \; RCO_2H \; \rangle \; ROH \; \rangle \; R_2NH$$

b) Resonance effects

    (1) Resonance effects stabilize carboxylic acid derivatives.

    (2) Resonance stabilization does not exist in the tetrahedral intermediate:

        (a) Resonance lowers the energy of a carbonyl compound relative to that of its transition state.

        (b) The free energy of activation is increased and the reactivity is reduced.

    (3) The resonance effect of oxygen stabilizes esters and anhydrides more than the resonance effect of chlorine stabilizes acid chlorides.

    (4) Resonance interaction of chlorine with a carbonyl group requires overlap of chlorine $3p$ orbitals with carbon $2p$ orbitals; this overlap is less effective than the overlap of p orbitals with the same quantum number.

    (5) The resonance stabilization of an amide is more important than that in an ester because nitrogen is less electronegative than oxygen and accepts positive charge more readily.

5. Acid chlorides are the most reactive carboxylic acid derivatives because the destabilizing inductive effect of chlorine is more important than its stabilizing resonance effect.

6. Esters and amides are less reactive because of strong resonance effects in these compounds, which override the inductive effects of oxygen and nitrogen.

7. Anhydrides are much more reactive than esters, but less reactive than acid chlorides because of a balance of these effects.

8. Reactions of nitriles in base are slower than those of other acid derivatives.

    a) The nitrogen is less electronegative than oxygen, and therefore accepts negative charge less readily.

    b) The protonated form of a nitrile is what reacts with nucleophiles in acid solution, but there is little of this form present .

C. Mechanism of Substitution at the Carbonyl Group:

    1. Substitution reactions at the carbonyl group occur by two types of mechanisms.

        a) Under basic conditions:

            (1) A nucleophile (⁻:Nuc) attacks the carbonyl carbon to give a tetrahedral addition intermediate in which the carbonyl oxygen assumes a negative charge.

            (2) The leaving group (X:⁻)is then expelled from the tetrahedral intermediate.

        b) Under acidic conditions:

            (1) The carbonyl is first protonated; this protonation imparts cationic character to the carbonyl carbon.

            (2) This carbon is then attacked by a relatively weak base (N̈uc—H) to form a tetrahedral addition intermediate.

            (3) After proton transfer to the leaving group —X, it is expelled as H—X.

CHAPTER 21 REACTIONS

I. Hydrolysis of Carboxylic Acid Derivatives:

A. Hydrolysis of Acid Chlorides and Anhydrides:
  1. Acid chlorides and anhydrides react rapidly with water, even in the absence of acids or bases.
  2. The hydrolysis reactions of acid chlorides and anhydrides are almost never used for the preparation of acids, because these derivatives are themselves usually prepared from acids.

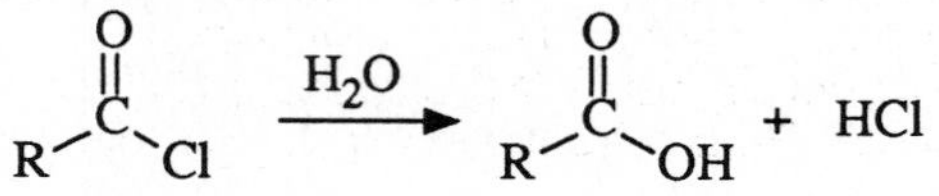

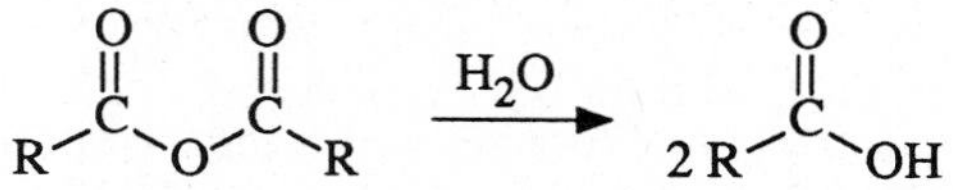

B. Basic Hydrolysis (Saponification) of Esters and Lactones:
  1. Ester hydrolysis in aqueous hydroxide is called **saponification**; the term saponification is sometimes used to refer to hydrolysis in base of any acid derivative.
  2. The mechanism of ester saponification involves:
      a) Attack by the nucleophilic hydroxide anion to give a tetrahedral addition intermediate from which an alkoxide ion is expelled.
      b) The alkoxide ion thus formed reacts with the carboxylic acid to give the carboxylate salt and the alcohol.

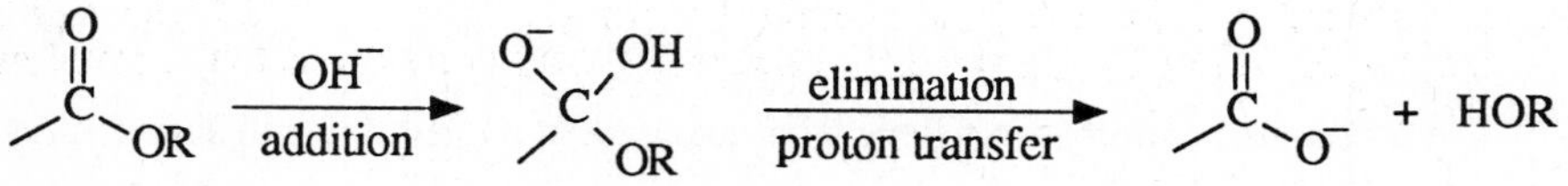

  3. The equilibrium in this reaction lies far to the right because the carboxylic acid is a much stronger acid than alcohol by-product; saponification is effectively irreversible.
  4. Many esters can be saponified with just *one equivalent* of ⁻OH.
  5. Saponification converts a lactone completely into the salt of the corresponding hydroxy acid; upon acidification, the hydroxy acid forms.

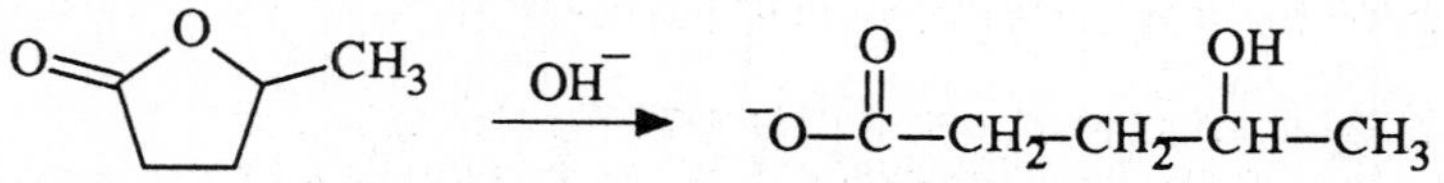

      a) If a hydroxy acid is allowed to stand in acidic solution, it comes to equilibrium with the corresponding lactone—an acid-catalyzed, intramolecular esterification.
      b) Lactones containing five- and six-membered rings are favored at equilibrium over their corresponding hydroxy acids; those with ring sizes smaller than five or larger than six are less stable than their corresponding hydroxy acids.

C. Acid-Catalyzed Hydrolysis of Esters:
  1. Esters can be hydrolyzed to carboxylic acids in aqueous mineral acid, and in most cases this reaction is slow and must be carried out with an excess of water.
  2. By the principle of microscopic reversibility, the mechanism of acid-catalyzed hydrolysis is the exact reverse of acid-catalyzed esterification.

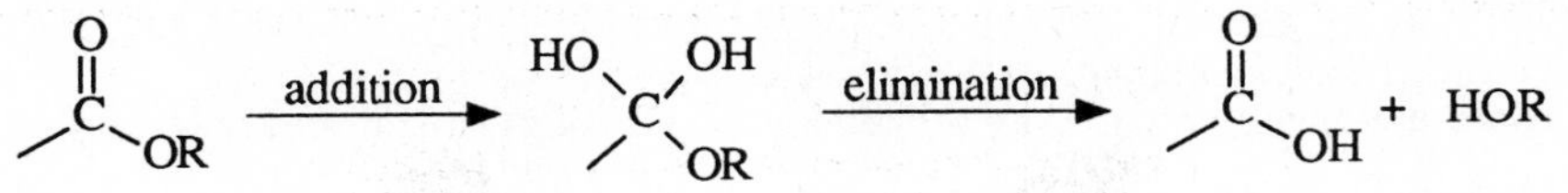

3. Saponification, followed by acidification, is a much more convenient method for hydrolysis of most esters because:
   a) It is faster.
   b) It is irreversible.
   c) It can be carried out not only in water but also in a variety of solvents, even alcohols.

D. Acidic Cleavage of Tertiary Esters:
   1. Esters derived from tertiary alcohols, such as *t*-butyl esters, are converted rapidly by acid into carboxylic acids, but by a different mechanism that does not require water.
      a) The first step is protonation of the ester carbonyl oxygen.
      b) The protonated ester undergoes an S_N1 reaction to give the carboxylic acid and a relatively stable tertiary carbocation. The mechanism is like the S_N1 mechanism for substitution in a tertiary alcohol.
      c) This cation undergoes the usual carbocation reactions.

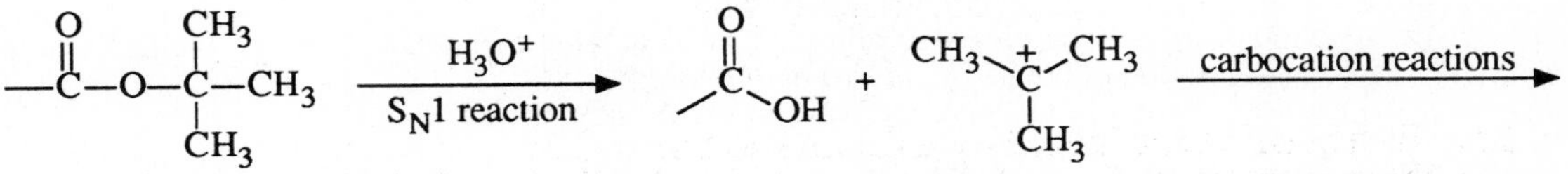

   2. Cleavage of tertiary esters by this mechanism involves breaking the *alkyl–oxygen* bond, whereas acid-catalyzed ester hydrolysis by the carbonyl-substitution mechanism involves breaking the *carbonyl–oxygen* bond.

E. Hydrolysis of Amides:
   1. Amides can be hydrolyzed to carboxylic acids and ammonia or amines by heating them in acidic or basic solution.
   2. In acid, protonation of the ammonia or amine by-product drives the hydrolysis equilibrium to completion; the amine can be isolated, if desired, by addition of base to the reaction mixture following hydrolysis.

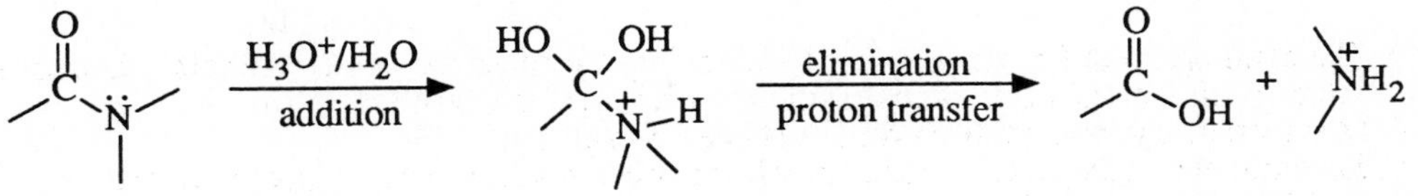

   3. Hydrolysis of amides in base is analogous to saponification of esters; the reaction is driven to completion by formation of the carboxylic acid salt.

F. Hydrolysis Reactions of Carboxylic Acid Derivatives—Summary:
   1. Hydrolysis of amides and nitriles require heat as well as acid or base.
   2. Hydrolysis of esters requires acid or base, but requires heating only briefly, if at all.
   3. Hydrolysis of acid chlorides and anhydrides occurs rapidly at room temperature even in the absence of acid or base.

II. Reactions of Carboxylic Acid Derivatives with Alcohols:

A. Reaction of Acid Chlorides with Alcohols and Phenols:
   1. Esters are formed rapidly when acid chlorides react with alcohols or phenols in the presence of pyridine or a related base.

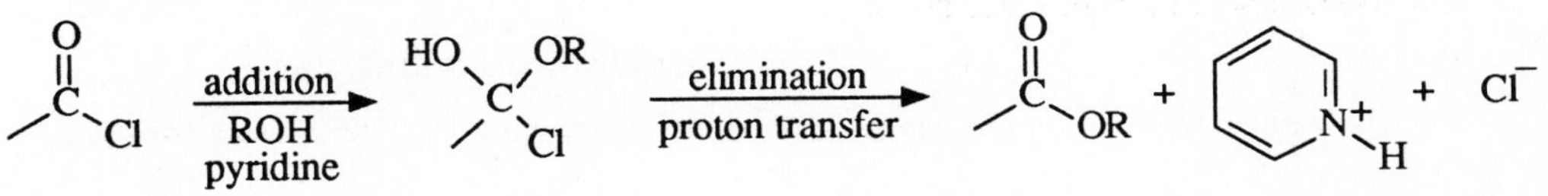

2. Esters of tertiary alcohols and phenols, which cannot be prepared by acid-catalyzed esterification, can be prepared by this method.
3 **Sulfonate esters** are prepared by the analogous reactions of sulfonyl chlorides with alcohols.

B. Reaction of Esters with Alcohols:
  1. When an ester reacts with an alcohol under acidic conditions, or with an alkoxide under basic conditions, a new ester is formed.

  2. This type of reaction, called **transesterification**, typically has an equilibrium constant near unity.
  3. The reaction is driven to completion by the use of an excess of the displacing alcohol or by removal of a relatively volatile alcohol by-product as it is formed.

III. Reactions of Carboxylic Acid Derivatives with Amines:

A. Reaction of Acid Chlorides with Ammonia and Amines:
  1. The reaction of an acid chloride with ammonia or its organic derivatives (amines) yields an amide.
    a) Reaction with ammonia yields a **primary amide**.
    b) Reaction with a primary amine yields a **secondary amide**.
    c) Reaction with a secondary amine yields a **tertiary amide**.
  2. The amine attacks the carbonyl group to form a tetrahedral intermediate, which expels chloride ion; a proton-transfer step yields the amide.
    a) An important aspect of amide formation is the proton transfer in the last step of the mechanism.
    b) Unless another base is added to the reaction mixture, the starting amine acts as the base in this step; if the only base present is the amine nucleophile, then at least *two* equivalents must be used:
      (1) One equivalent as the nucleophile.
      (2) One equivalent as the base in the final proton-transfer step.

  3. In the **Schotten–Baumann** technique for amide formation, the reaction is run with a water-insoluble acid chloride and an amine in a separate layer over an aqueous solution of NaOH.
  4. The presence of a tertiary amine does not interfere with amide formation by another amine because a tertiary amine itself cannot form an amide.

B. Reaction of Esters with Amines:
  1. The reaction of esters with ammonia or amines yields amides.

  2. The reaction of esters with hydroxylamine ($:NH_2OH$) gives *N*-hydroxyamides; these compounds are known as **hydroxamic acids**.

a hydroxamic acid

    a) This chemistry forms the basis for the **hydroxamate test**, used mostly for esters.

b) The hydroxamic acid products are easily recognized because they form highly colored complexes with ferric ion.

IV. Reactions of Carboxylic Acid Derivatives with Hydrides:

A. Reduction of Acid Chlorides to Aldehydes:
   1. Acid chlorides can be reduced to aldehydes by either of two procedures:
      a) Hydrogenation over a catalyst that has been deactivated, or poisoned, with an amine, such as quinoline, that has been heated with sulfur.

      (1) This reaction is called the **Rosenmund reduction**.
      (2) The poisoning of the catalyst prevents further reduction of the aldehyde product.
   b) Reaction at low temperature with lithium tri(t-butoxy)aluminum hydride.

      (1) The hydride reagent used in this reduction is derived by the replacement of three hydrogens of $LiAlH_4$ by t-butoxy groups.
      (2) The preparation of $LiAlH[OC(CH_3)_3]_3$ owes its success to the poor reactivity of its hydride; the one remaining hydride reduces only the most reactive functional groups.
      (3) Because acid chlorides are more reactive than aldehydes toward nucleophiles, the reagent reacts preferentially with the acid chloride reactant rather than with the product aldehyde.
      (4) $LiAlH_4$ is so reactive that it fails to discriminate to a useful degree between the aldehyde and acid chloride groups, and reduces acid chlorides to primary alcohols—$LiAlH_4$ reduces carboxylic acids and all carboxylic acid derivatives.

B. Reduction of Esters to Primary Alcohols:
   1. The reduction of esters to alcohols involves a carbonyl-substitution reaction followed by a carbonyl-addition reaction.
      a) The active nucleophile in $LiAlH_4$ reductions is the hydride ion, $H:^-$, which replaces alkoxide at the carbonyl group of the ester to give an aldehyde.
      b) The aldehyde reacts rapidly with $LiAlH_4$ to give, after protonolysis, the alcohol.

   2. Sodium borohydride reacts very sluggishly or not at all with most esters.

C. Reduction of Amides to Amines:
   1. Amides are reduced to amines with $LiAlH_4$ and can be used to prepare:
      a) Primary amines from primary amides.
      b) Secondary amines from secondary amides.
      c) Tertiary amines from tertiary amides.
   2. The mechanism of the reaction of a secondary amide with lithium aluminum hydride involves:
      a) Formation of an imine intermediate in a series of mechanistic steps.
      b) Reduction of the imine and protonolysis in a separate step to yield the product amine.

3. The reductions of primary and tertiary amides involve somewhat different mechanisms, but they too involve loss of oxygen rather than nitrogen as a leaving group.

V. Reactions of Carboxylic Acid Derivatives with Organometallic Reagents:

A. Reaction of Acid Chlorides with Lithium Dialkylcuprates:
1. The reaction of an acid chloride with a Grignard reagent can in principle be stopped at the ketone; however, both Grignard reagents and acid chlorides are so reactive that this transformation is difficult to achieve in practice without careful control of the reaction conditions.
2. The reaction of **lithium dialkylcuprates** with acid chlorides gives ketones in excellent yield; lithium dialkylcuprates typically react with acid chlorides and aldehydes, very slowly with ketones, and not at all with esters.

3. Lithium dialkylcuprates react much like Grignard or lithium reagents, but are less reactive; a lithium dialkylcuprate can be considered conceptually as an alkyl anion complexed with copper.
   a) Lithium dialkylcuprate reagents are prepared by the reaction of two equivalents of an organolithium reagent with one equivalent of cuprous chloride, CuCl.
   b) The first equivalent forms an alkylcopper compound; the driving force for this reaction is the preference of lithium, the more electronegative metal, to exist as an ionic compound (LiCl).
   c) The copper of an alkylcopper reagent is a Lewis acid and reacts accordingly with alkyl anion from an second equivalent of the organolithium reagent; the product of this reaction is a lithium dialkylcuprate.

$$RLi + CuI \longrightarrow LiI + CuR \xrightarrow{RLi} LiCuR_2$$

B. Reaction of Esters with Grignard Reagents:
1. Most carboxylic acid derivatives react with Grignard or organolithium reagents; one of the most important reactions of this type is the reaction of esters with Grignard reagents.
2. In this reaction, tertiary alcohols are formed after protonolysis (secondary alcohols are formed from esters of formic acid after protonolysis); two equivalents of organometallic reagent react per mole of ester.
   a) This reaction is a substitution followed by an addition.
   b) A ketone is formed in the substitution step.
   c) The ketone intermediate is not isolated because ketones are more reactive than esters toward nucleophilic reagents.
   d) The ketone reacts with a second equivalent of the Grignard reagent to form a magnesium alkoxide, which, after hydrolysis, gives the alcohol.

3. This reaction is a very important method for the synthesis of alcohols in which at least two of the groups on the α-carbon of the alcohol product are identical.

VI. Reactions of Carboxylic Acid Derivatives with Other Nucleophiles:

A. Reaction of Acid Chlorides with Carboxylate Salts:
   1. Even though carboxylate salts are weak nucleophiles, acid chlorides are reactive enough to be attacked by carboxylate salts and afford anhydrides.
   2. The reaction of acid chlorides with carboxylate salts can be used to prepare mixed anhydrides.

B. Reaction of Acid Chlorides with Aromatic Rings—Friedel–Crafts Acylation:
   1. Friedel–Crafts acylation is a reaction of aromatic hydrocarbons with acid chlorides; the nucleophilic electrons are the π-electrons of the aromatic ring.
   2. A strong Lewis acid such as $AlCl_3$ is required to activate the acid chloride by forming an acylium ion (Sec. 16.4E, text page 653).

C. Reactions of Anhydrides with Nucleophiles:
   1. Anhydrides react with nucleophiles in much the same way as acid chlorides.
   2. Because most anhydrides are prepared from the corresponding carboxylic acids, the use of an anhydride to prepare an ester or amide wastes one equivalent of the parent acid as a leaving group.
      a) This reaction is used only with inexpensive and readily available anhydrides, such as acetic anhydride.
      b) One exception to this generalization is the formation of half-esters and amides from cyclic anhydrides.
   3. Half-amides of dicarboxylic acids are produced in analogous reactions of amines and cyclic anhydrides; these compounds can be cyclized to imides by treatment with dehydrating agents, or in some cases, just by heating.

VII. Addition Reactions of Nitriles:

A. Hydrolysis of Nitriles:
   1. Nitriles behave mechanistically much like carbonyl compounds, and thus are hydrolyzed to carboxylic acids and ammonia by heating them in acidic or basic solution.
   2. The mechanism of nitrile hydrolysis in acid begins as an addition to the $C\equiv N$ bond.
      a) The addition product, an **imidic acid**, is unstable and is converted under the reaction conditions to an amide.
      b) The amide thus formed does not survive under the vigorous conditions of nitrile hydrolysis, and is hydrolyzed to a carboxylic acid and ammonium ion.

   3. In the hydrolysis of nitriles in base, the nitrile group (like a carbonyl group) is attacked by basic nucleophiles and, as a result, the electronegative nitrogen assumes a negative charge.
      a) Proton transfer gives an imidic acid.
      b) The imidic acid reacts further to give the corresponding amide which, in turn, hydrolyzes under the reaction conditions to the carboxylate salt of the corresponding carboxylic acid.

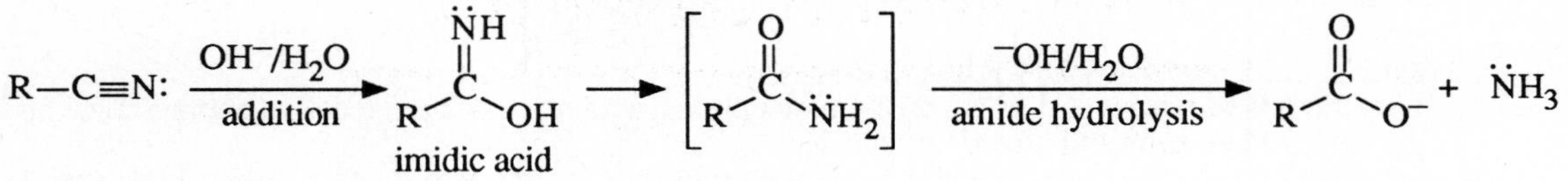

$$R—C\equiv N: \xrightarrow[\text{addition}]{OH^-/H_2O} \underset{\text{imidic acid}}{R—\overset{\overset{\ddot N H}{\|}}{C}—OH} \longrightarrow \left[\underset{}{R—\overset{\overset{O}{\|}}{C}—\ddot N H_2}\right] \xrightarrow[\text{amide hydrolysis}]{^-OH/H_2O} R—\overset{\overset{O}{\|}}{C}—O^- + \ddot N H_3$$

4. The hydrolysis of nitriles is a useful way to prepare carboxylic acids because nitriles, unlike many other carboxylic acid derivatives, are generally synthesized from compounds other than the acids themselves.

$$R—CH_2—Br \xrightarrow{\ ^-:C\equiv N: \ } R—CH_2—C\equiv N: \xrightarrow{\text{hydrolysis}} R—CH_2—CO_2H$$

B. Reduction of Nitriles to Primary Amines:

1. Nitriles are reduced to primary amines by reaction with $LiAlH_4$, followed by the usual protonolysis step.
2. This reaction probably occurs as two successive nucleophilic additions; an amine is formed when water is added to the reaction mixture.

$$R—C\equiv N: \xrightarrow[\text{addition}]{LiAlH_4} \left[R—CH=\ddot N:^- \ Li^+\right] \xrightarrow[\text{2) } H_3O^+/H_2O]{\text{1) } LiAlH_4} R—CH_2—\overset{+}{N}H_3$$

3. Nitriles are also reduced to primary amines by catalytic hydrogenation; an imine is an intermediate in the reaction. The imine is not isolated, but is hydrogenated to the amine product.

$$R—C\equiv N: \xrightarrow[\text{catalyst}]{H_2} \left[\underset{\text{imine}}{R—CH=\ddot N H}\right] \longrightarrow R—CH_2—\ddot N H_2$$

4. Any synthesis of a carboxylic acid can be used as part of an amine synthesis, provided that the amine has a —CH_2— group adjacent to the amine nitrogen; the carbonyl or $C\equiv N$ carbon of the carboxylic acid derivative ends up as the —CH_2— group adjacent to the amine nitrogen.

VIII. Synthesis of Carboxylic Acid Derivatives—Review:

A. Synthesis of Acid Chlorides:
1. Reaction of carboxylic acids with $SOCl_2$ or PCl_5 (Sec. 20.9A, text page 839).

B. Synthesis of Anhydrides:
1. Reaction of carboxylic acids with dehydrating agents (Sec. 20.9B, text page 841).
2. Reaction of acid chlorides with carboxylate salts (Sec. 21.8A, text page 884).

C. Synthesis of Esters:
1. Acid-catalyzed esterification of carboxylic acids (Sec. 20.8A, text page 833).
2. Alkylation of carboxylic acids or carboxylates (Sec. 20.8B, text page 837).
3. Reaction of acid chlorides and anhydrides with alcohols or phenols (Sec. 21.8, text page 884).
4. Transesterification of other esters (Sec. 21.8C, text page 889).

D. Synthesis of Amides:
1. Reaction of acid chlorides or anhydrides with amines (Sec. 21.8, text page 884).

E. Synthesis of Nitriles:
1. S_N2 reaction of cyanide ion with alkyl halides or sulfonate esters—primary or unbranched secondary alkyl halides or sulfonate esters are required (Sec. 9.3, text page 323).
2. Cyanohydrin formation (Sec. 19.7, text page 773).

CHAPTER 21 SOLUTIONS

Solutions to In-Text Problems

1. (a)

$$N{\equiv}CCH_2CH_2CH_2CH_2CO_2H$$

(b)

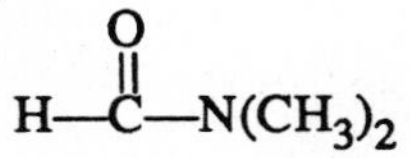

$$H{-}\overset{O}{\overset{\|}{C}}{-}N(CH_3)_2$$

(c)

$$CH_3CH_2CH_2CH_2\overset{O}{\overset{\|}{C}}{-}O{-}CH(CH_3)_2$$

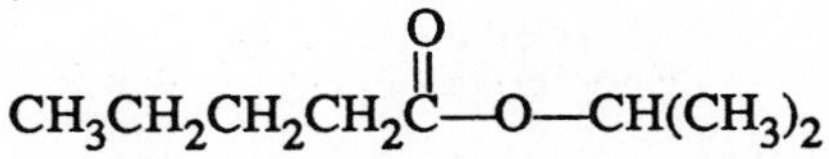

(d)

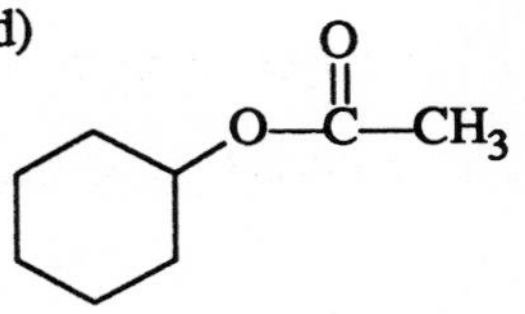

$$\overset{O}{\underset{\|}{O{-}C{-}CH_3}}$$

(e)

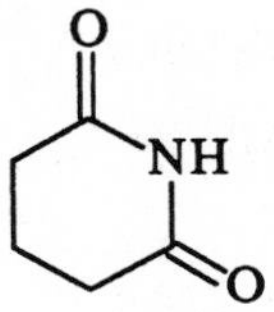

(f)

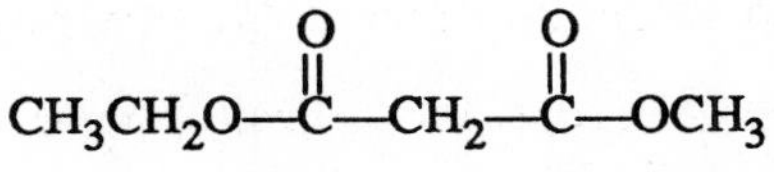

$$CH_3CH_2O{-}\overset{O}{\overset{\|}{C}}{-}CH_2{-}\overset{O}{\overset{\|}{C}}{-}OCH_3$$

(g)

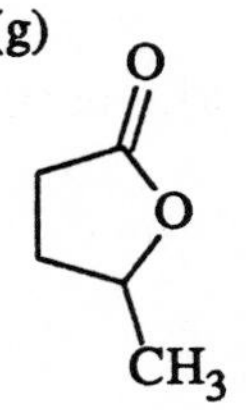

(h)

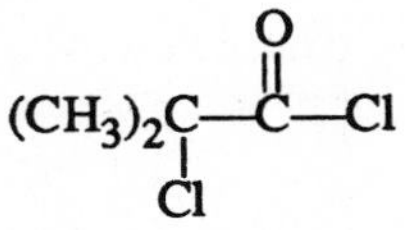

$$(CH_3)_2\underset{\underset{Cl}{|}}{C}{-}\overset{O}{\overset{\|}{C}}{-}Cl$$

(i)

$$HO{-}\overset{O}{\overset{\|}{C}}{-}CH_2CH_2CHCH_2{-}\overset{O}{\overset{\|}{C}}{-}OH$$

$$\underset{O{=}\underset{OCH_2CH_3}{\overset{C}{\diagdown}}}{}$$

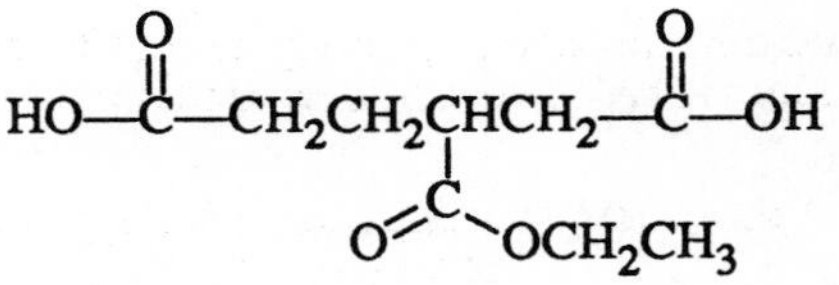

2. (a) butyronitrile or butanenitrile   (b) cyclopropanecarbonyl chloride   (c) maleic anhydride
    (d) isoamyl isovalerate or 3-methylbutyl 3-methylbutanoate   (e) *N,N*-dimethylbenzamide
    (f) ethyl 3-oxopentanoate   (g) 1-methyl-3-butenyl propanoate

3. One way to force certain functional groups into otherwise unstable conformations is to constrain them within rings. Thus, a small- or medium-ring lactam must have the *E* configuration:

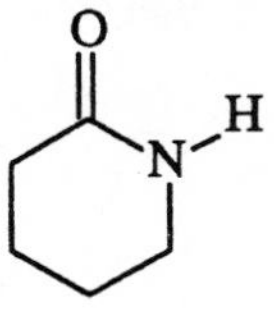

4. The dipole moment data suggest that esters, like amides, prefer the *Z* configuration about the carbonyl–oxygen single bond. In this configuration, the methyl–oxygen bond dipole in methyl acetate tends to subtract from the C=O bond dipole. In the dipole moment of 2-butanone, on the other hand, nothing dilutes the contribution of the C=O bond dipole.

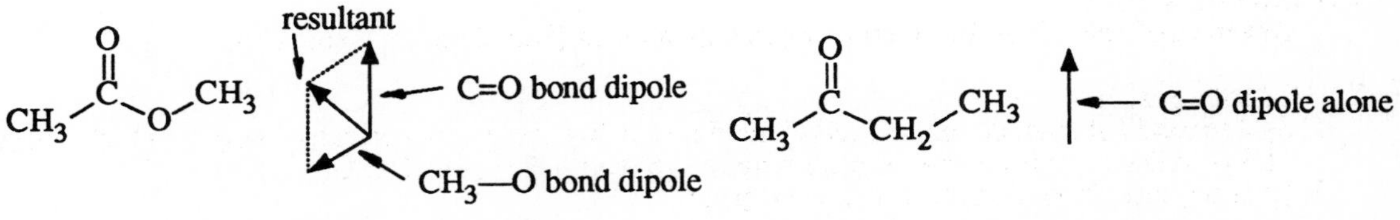

resultant ← C=O bond dipole
CH₃—O bond dipole

C=O dipole alone

5. (a) The carboxylic acid has strong, broad O—H absorption; the ester does not. Furthermore, the ester carbonyl absorption is at higher frequency.
    (b) Ethyl butyrate, an ester, has carbonyl absorption; the ether does not.
    (c) The nitrile has characteristic C≡N absorption, but no carbonyl absorption. The amide has carbonyl

absorption but no C≡N absorption.

(d) Both have methyl singlets and the triplet-quartet pattern characteristic of ethyl groups. However, the methyl singlet in methyl propionate is further downfield than the methyl singlet in ethyl acetate; and the —CH₂— signal of the ethyl quartet is further downfield in ethyl acetate than the —CH₂— signal in methyl propionate.

6.   The compound is *N*-ethylacetamide:

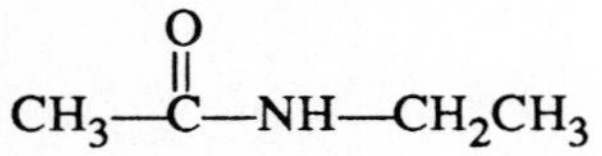

$$
\begin{array}{c}
\text{O} \\
\|\\
\text{CH}_3\text{—C—NH—CH}_2\text{CH}_3
\end{array}
$$

7.   (a) The first compound should have the greater basicity, because its conjugate acid is resonance-stabilized by interaction with the double bond:

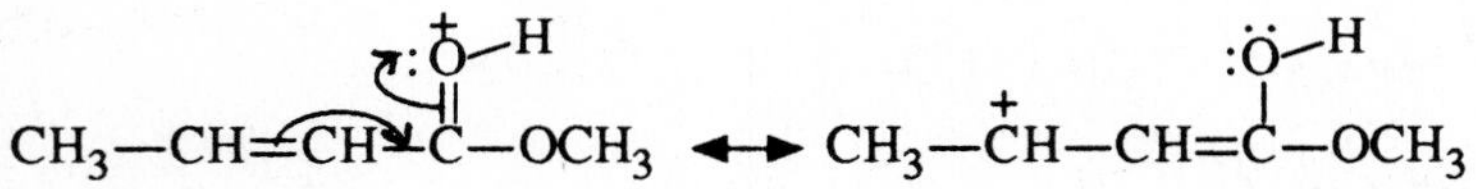

$$
\text{CH}_3\text{—CH=CH—C(—O—H)—OCH}_3 \;\longleftrightarrow\; \text{CH}_3\text{—CH—CH=C(—O—H)—OCH}_3
$$

(b) The first compound is more basic because the conjugate acid is stabilized by resonance interaction with the methoxy group:

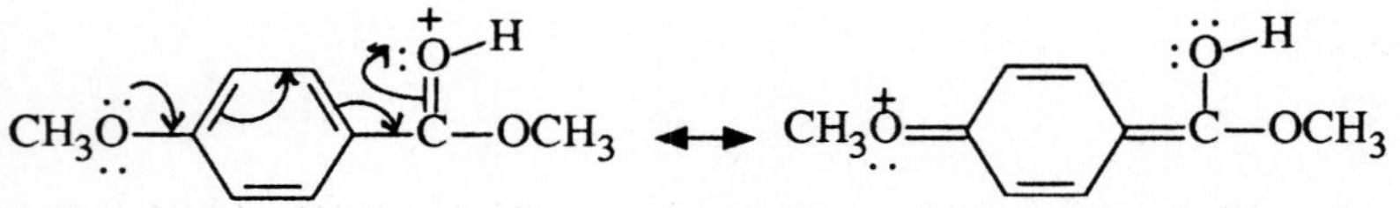

$$
\text{CH}_3\ddot{\text{O}}\text{—(ring)—C(—O—H)—OCH}_3 \;\longleftrightarrow\; \text{CH}_3\overset{+}{\text{O}}\text{=(ring)=C(—O—H)—OCH}_3
$$

8.   (a) From the mechanism in Eq. 21.11a–c we see that the oxygen of water is incorporated into the product acid. The products are:

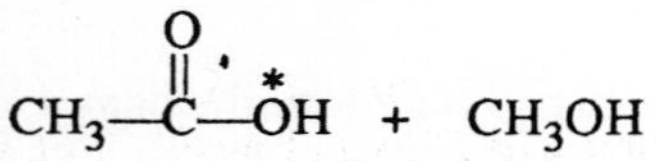

$$
\begin{array}{c}
\text{O} \\
\|\\
\text{CH}_3\text{—C—O*H}
\end{array}
\;+\; \text{CH}_3\text{OH}
$$

(The labeled oxygen is distributed between the two oxygens of the acid; see the solution to Problem 23 in Chapter 20.)

(b) In this case, cleavage of the bond to the *t*-butyl group occurs. (See the mechanism in Eq. 21.14a–b.) Water attacks the *t*-butyl cation to give labeled *t*-butyl alcohol as one of the products.

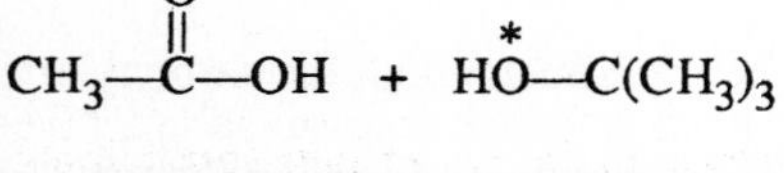

$$
\begin{array}{c}
\text{O} \\
\|\\
\text{CH}_3\text{—C—OH}
\end{array}
\;+\; \text{H}\overset{*}{\text{O}}\text{—C(CH}_3\text{)}_3
$$

9.   (a) The mechanism of *N*-methylbenzamide hydrolysis in acid:

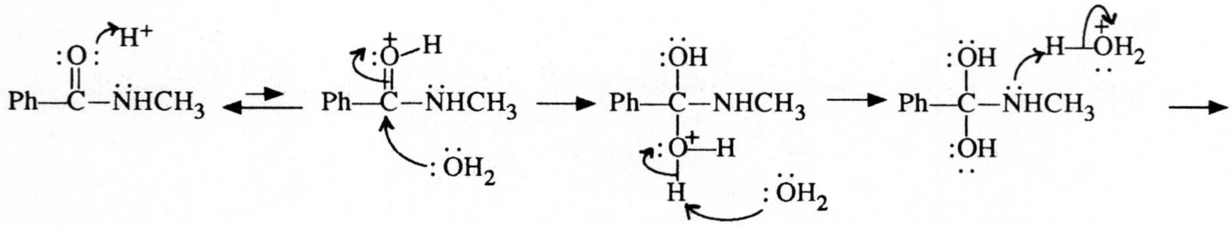

$$
\text{Ph—C(=O:)—NHCH}_3 \;\underset{}{\overset{H^+}{\rightleftharpoons}}\; \text{Ph—C(—}\overset{+}{\text{O}}\text{—H)—NHCH}_3 \;\xrightarrow{:\ddot{O}H_2}\; \text{Ph—C(—}\overset{..}{\text{O}}\text{H)(—}\overset{+}{\text{O}}\text{—H)—NHCH}_3 \;\xrightarrow{}\; \text{Ph—C(—}\overset{..}{\text{O}}\text{H)(—}\overset{..}{\text{O}}\text{H)—}\overset{+}{\text{N}}\text{HCH}_3 \;\longrightarrow
$$

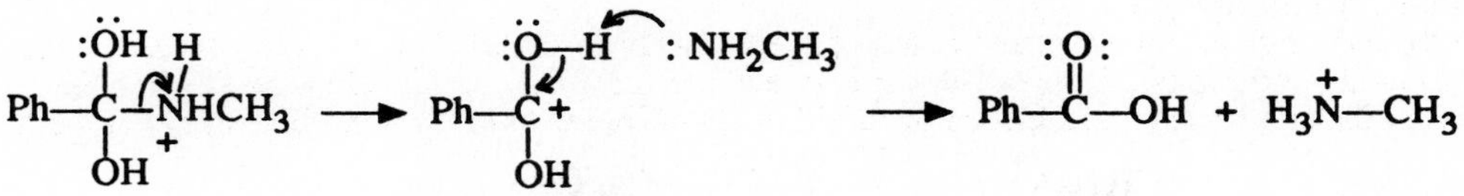

Notice how this mechanism fits the pattern in Eq. 21.20.

(b) The mechanism of hydrolysis in base:

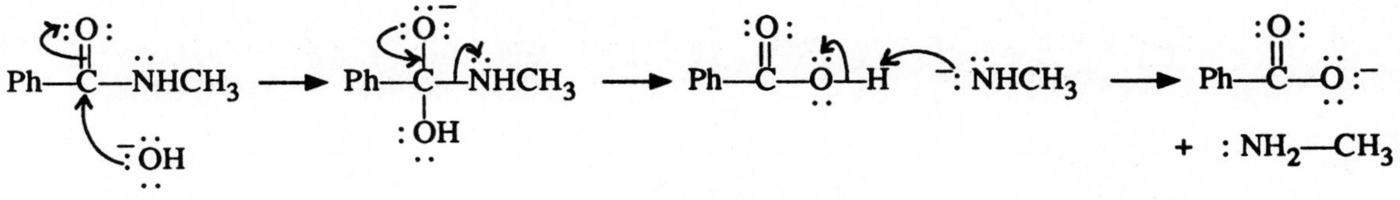

Notice that this mechanism fits the pattern in Eq. 21.19.

10. (a) This is ester saponification followed by protonation of the carboxylate ion:

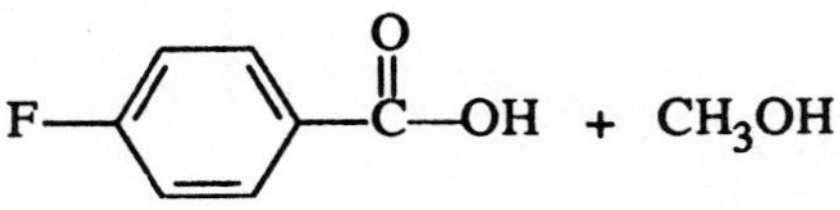

(b) There are two potentially hydrolyzable groups; however, esters are considerably more reactive than nitriles. Only the ester group is saponified.

$$N\equiv C-CH_2-\overset{O}{\overset{\|}{C}}-O^- \; + \; CH_3OH$$

(c) Hydrolysis of both amides gives carbonic acid, which, in turn, breaks down to CO_2 and water. The by-product is two equivalents of ammonium ion, $^+NH_4$.

(d) Lactams are cyclic amides and, like other amides, they hydrolyze:

$$H_3\overset{+}{N}-CH_2CH_2CH_2-\overset{O}{\overset{\|}{C}}-OH$$

(The basic amino group is protonated under the acidic conditions.)

11. In both reactions, we follow the usual pattern of nucleophilic substitution at carbonyl groups: formation of a tetrahedral intermediate followed by loss of the leaving group.

(a)

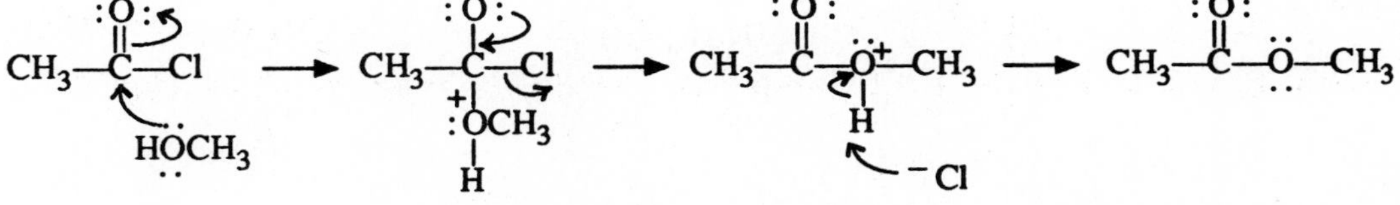

(b)

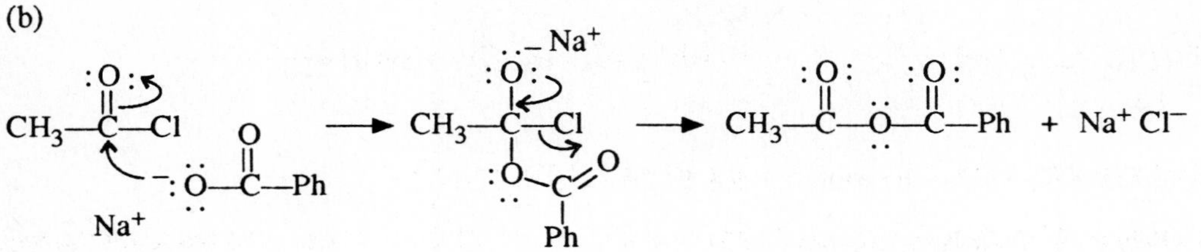

12. (a)

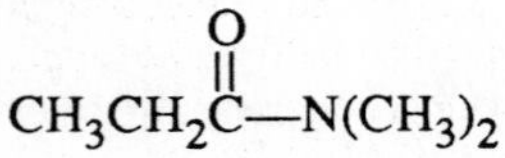

CH$_3$CH$_2$C—N(CH$_3$)$_2$

(b)

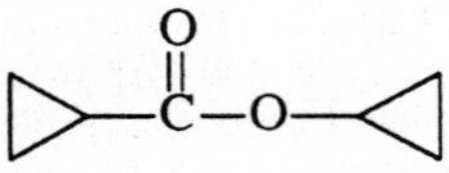

(c)

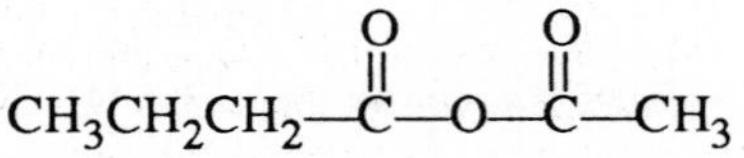

CH$_3$CH$_2$CH$_2$—C—O—C—CH$_3$

(d)

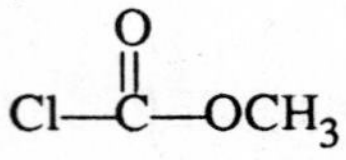

Cl—C—OCH$_3$

(e)

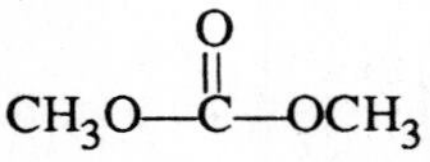

CH$_3$O—C—OCH$_3$

(f)

PhCH$_2$—C—S—C$_2$H$_5$

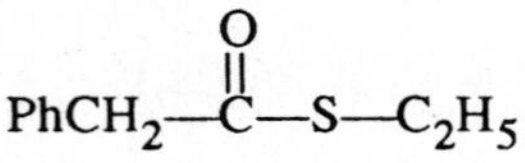

(g)

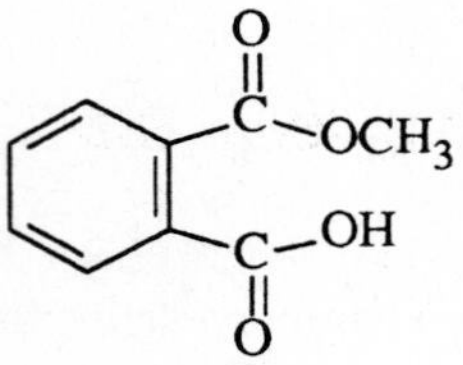

(h)

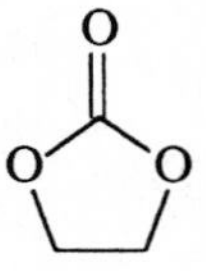

+ 2 CH$_3$CH$_2$OH

13. (a) This compound is a sulfonate ester (Sec. 10.3A). The methanesulfonate group behaves as a leaving group very similar to halide. Hence, this group is displaced from the —CH$_2$— group by the labeled hydroxide in an S$_N$2 reaction:

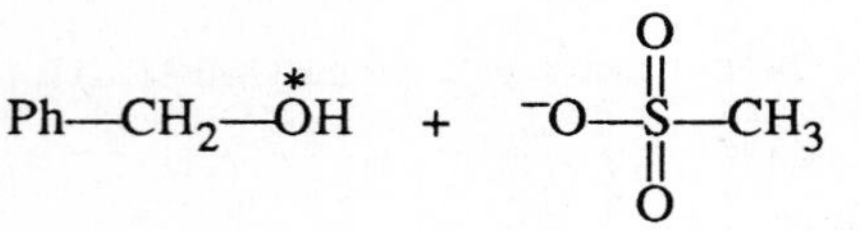

Ph—CH$_2$—$\overset{*}{\text{O}}$H + $^-$O—S—CH$_3$ (* = ^{18}O)

(b) This is a saponification; hydroxide attacks the carbonyl carbon.

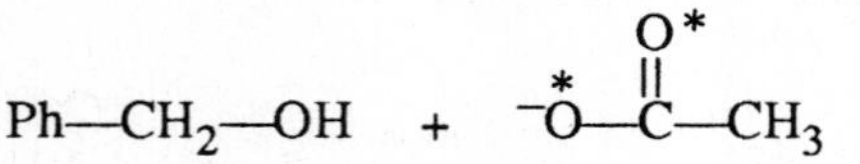

Ph—CH$_2$—OH + $^-\overset{*}{\text{O}}$—C—CH$_3$ (* = ^{18}O)

Half the isotopic label is at each oxygen of the carboxylate ion (why?).

14. (a)

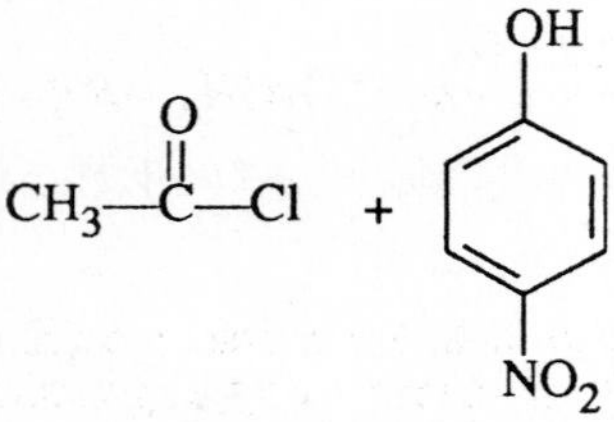

CH$_3$—C—Cl +

(b)

CH$_3$CHOH + Cl—S—⟨ ⟩—CH$_3$
  |
  Ph

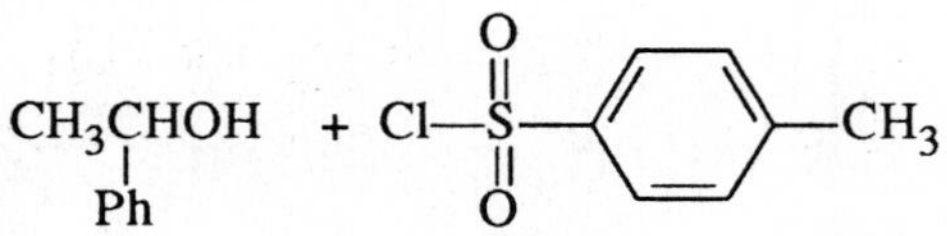

(c)   (d)

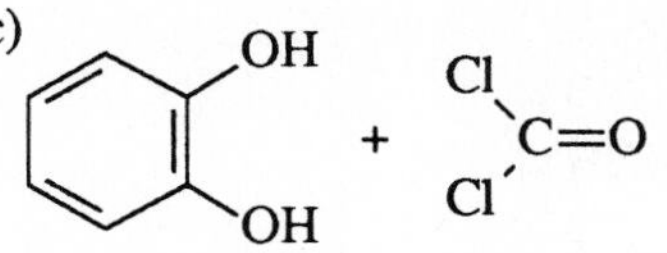

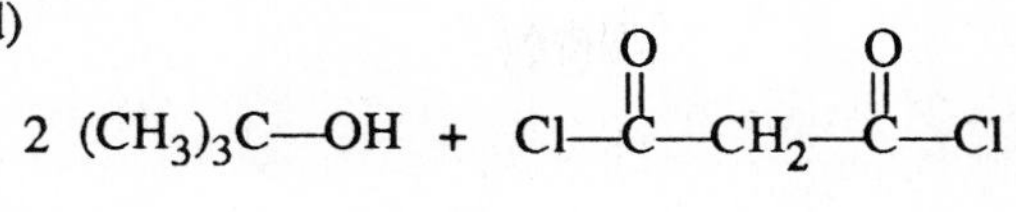

(In some cases we might want to include a basic catalyst such as pyridine.)

15. (a) Reduce the acid chloride either with hydrogen over a poisoned catalyst (Rosenmund reduction) or with lithium tri-*t*-butylaluminum hydride.
(b) We could convert the acid chloride into an ester or carboxylic acid by reaction with an alcohol and water, respectively, and then reduce either product with LiAlH$_4$. However, if we think about the mechanism of the LiAlH$_4$ reduction, we would come to the conclusion that acid chlorides themselves should be reduced to alcohols with this reagent. Hence, we treat the acid chloride with LiAlH$_4$, then H$_3$O$^+$.
(c) Convert the acid chloride to the amide with ammonia, then reduce the amide with LiAlH$_4$.
(d) Convert the acid chloride to a tertiary amide, then reduce this amide:

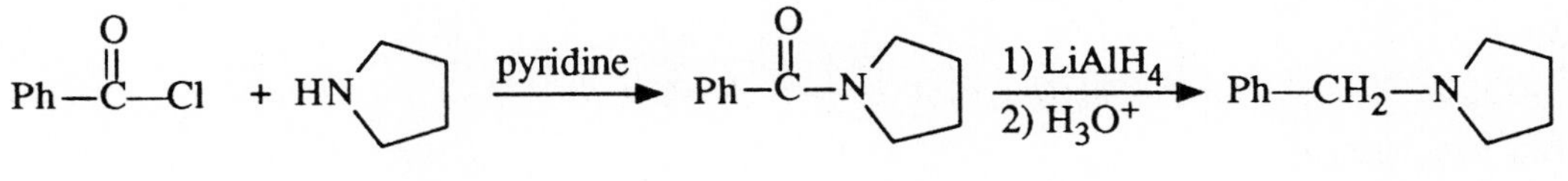

16. (a)   (b)   (c)

PhCH$_2$CH$_2$NH$_2$

HO—CH$_2$—CH$_2$—CH$_2$—NH$_2$

17. Both an amide and the corresponding nitrile would give the same product:

(CH$_3$)$_2$CHCH$_2$CH$_2$C—NH$_2$ and   (CH$_3$)$_2$CHCH$_2$CH$_2$C≡N

18. (a) An imine *A* is formed as an intermediate.

$$R—C≡N \xrightarrow{\text{H}_2/\text{catalyst}} R—CH=NH \xrightarrow{\text{H}_2/\text{catalyst}} R—CH_2—NH_2$$
               imine *A*   amine

A molecule of product *amine* can attack the *imine* intermediate *A* to give an addition intermediate that can expel ammonia, giving a new imine *B*. Hydrogenation of this new imine gives the by-product:

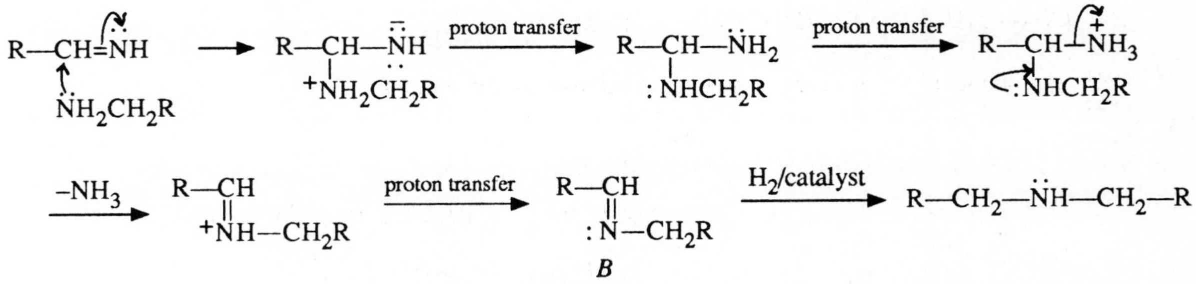

(b) Ammonia prevents this side reaction by reacting with imine *B* (or its protonated precursor) to drive the entire scheme back toward the original imine, from which R—CH$_2$—NH$_2$ is formed by hydrogenation.

19. (a)

$$\text{Ph}-\underset{\underset{\text{Ph}}{|}}{\overset{\overset{\text{OH}}{|}}{\text{C}}}-\text{Ph} \xleftarrow{\text{H}_3\text{O}^+} \underset{\text{(excess)}}{\xleftarrow{\text{PhMgBr}}} \text{Ph}-\overset{\overset{\text{O}}{\|}}{\text{C}}-\text{OCH}_3 \xleftarrow{\text{CH}_3\text{OH, H}^+} \text{Ph}-\overset{\overset{\text{O}}{\|}}{\text{C}}-\text{OH}$$

(b)

$$\text{CH}_3\text{CH}_2\overset{\overset{\text{O}}{\|}}{\text{C}}\text{CH}_2\text{CH}_3 \xleftarrow{\text{H}_3\text{O}^+} \xleftarrow{(\text{C}_2\text{H}_5)_2\text{Cu}^-\text{Li}^+} \text{CH}_3\text{CH}_2\overset{\overset{\text{O}}{\|}}{\text{C}}-\text{Cl} \xleftarrow{\text{SOCl}_2} \text{CH}_3\text{CH}_2\overset{\overset{\text{O}}{\|}}{\text{C}}-\text{OH}$$

(c)

$$\text{CH}_3\text{CH}_2\underset{\underset{\text{CH}_3}{|}}{\overset{\overset{\text{OH}}{|}}{\text{C}}}\text{CH}_2\text{CH}_2\text{CH}_3 \xleftarrow{\text{H}_3\text{O}^+} \xleftarrow{\text{C}_2\text{H}_5\text{MgBr}} \text{CH}_3\overset{\overset{\text{O}}{\|}}{\text{C}}\text{CH}_2\text{CH}_2\text{CH}_3 \xleftarrow{\text{H}_3\text{O}^+} \xleftarrow{(\text{CH}_3)_2\text{Cu}^-\text{Li}}$$

$$\text{HO}-\overset{\overset{\text{O}}{\|}}{\text{C}}-\text{CH}_2\text{CH}_2\text{CH}_3 \xrightarrow{\text{PCl}_5} \text{Cl}-\overset{\overset{\text{O}}{\|}}{\text{C}}-\text{CH}_2\text{CH}_2\text{CH}_3$$

(d) The first synthesis:

$$\text{CH}_3-\underset{\underset{\text{CH}_3}{|}}{\overset{\overset{\text{OH}}{|}}{\text{C}}}-\underset{\underset{\text{CH}_3}{|}}{\text{CH}}-\text{CH}_3 \xleftarrow{\text{H}_3\text{O}^+} \xleftarrow{\text{CH}_3\text{MgI}} \text{CH}_3-\overset{\overset{\text{O}}{\|}}{\text{C}}-\text{CH}(\text{CH}_3)_2 \xleftarrow{\text{H}_3\text{O}^+} \xleftarrow{(\text{CH}_3)_2\text{Cu}^-\text{Li}^+}$$

$$\text{N}\equiv\text{CCH}(\text{CH}_3)_2 \xrightarrow[\text{heat}]{\text{H}_2\text{O, H}^+} \text{HO}-\overset{\overset{\text{O}}{\|}}{\text{C}}-\text{CH}(\text{CH}_3)_2 \xrightarrow{\text{SOCl}_2} \text{Cl}-\overset{\overset{\text{O}}{\|}}{\text{C}}-\text{CH}(\text{CH}_3)_2$$

In the second synthesis, we begin with the acid chloride from the first synthesis and prepare the ester. (Or we could use the acid itself and esterify with methanol.)

$$\text{CH}_3-\underset{\underset{\text{CH}_3}{|}}{\overset{\overset{\text{OH}}{|}}{\text{C}}}-\underset{\underset{\text{CH}_3}{|}}{\text{CH}}-\text{CH}_3 \xleftarrow{\text{H}_3\text{O}^+} \underset{\text{(excess)}}{\xleftarrow{\text{CH}_3\text{MgI}}} \text{CH}_3\text{O}-\overset{\overset{\text{O}}{\|}}{\text{C}}-\text{CH}(\text{CH}_3)_2 \xleftarrow{\text{CH}_3\text{OH}} \text{Cl}-\overset{\overset{\text{O}}{\|}}{\text{C}}-\text{CH}(\text{CH}_3)_2$$

20. This could be prepared by the reaction of two equivalents of ethylmagnesium bromide with ethyl formate:

$$\text{H}-\overset{\overset{\text{O}}{\|}}{\text{C}}-\text{OC}_2\text{H}_5 \xrightarrow[\text{(excess)}]{\text{CH}_3\text{CH}_2\text{MgBr}} \xrightarrow{\text{H}_3\text{O}^+} \text{CH}_3\text{CH}_2\underset{\underset{\text{OH}}{|}}{\text{CH}}\text{CH}_2\text{CH}_3$$

There are other acceptable syntheses that can be used.

21. In each case the lithium dimethylcuprate reagent reacts with the acid chloride group selectively.

(a)

$$\text{N}\equiv\text{C}(\text{CH}_2)_{10}-\overset{\overset{\text{O}}{\|}}{\text{C}}-\text{CH}_3$$

(b)

$$\text{CH}_3(\text{CH}_2)_3\text{O}-\overset{\overset{\text{O}}{\|}}{\text{C}}(\text{CH}_2)_4\overset{\overset{\text{O}}{\|}}{\text{C}}-\text{CH}_3$$

22.   A second synthesis involves the reaction of CO_2 with the Grignard reagent prepared from 1-bromobutane, which is prepared as shown in Eq. 21.74.

$$HO-\overset{\overset{\displaystyle O}{\|}}{C}-(CH_2)_3CH_3 \xleftarrow{H_3O^+} \xleftarrow{CO_2} BrMg(CH_2)_3CH_3 \xleftarrow{Mg,\ ether} Br(CH_2)_3CH_3$$

23.   2-Hydroxypropionic acid can be prepared by hydrolysis of acetaldehyde cyanohydrin:

$$CH_3\overset{\overset{\displaystyle OH}{|}}{C}HCO_2H \xleftarrow{H_3O^+,\ heat} CH_3\overset{\overset{\displaystyle OH}{|}}{C}HCN \xleftarrow{HCN} CH_3CH{=}O$$

➤ Why doesn't the cyanohydrin dehydrate like other alcohols when it is heated in acid? Because the carbocation intermediate in such a dehydration is not very stable. Can you see why?

24.   (a) Nylon should be more resistant, because amides hydrolyze more slowly than esters.
      (b) The polyester would converted into a mixture of the following two alcohols:

$$HOCH_2CH_2OH \quad \text{and} \quad HOCH_2\!-\!\!\left\langle\!\!\bigcirc\!\!\right\rangle\!\!-\!CH_2OH$$

25.   (a) Catalytic hydrogenation at high pressure.
      (b) Treatment with concentrated HCl and $ZnCl_2$.
      (c) Treatment with NaCN or KCN and heat.
      (d) Catalytic hydrogenation or $LiAlH_4$ reduction.
      (e) Hydrolysis in hot aqueous acid.
      (f) Heat; or convert the diacid into a di-acid chloride, and add the amine.

26.   The water hydrolyzes a small amount of the lactam to the ε-amino acid:

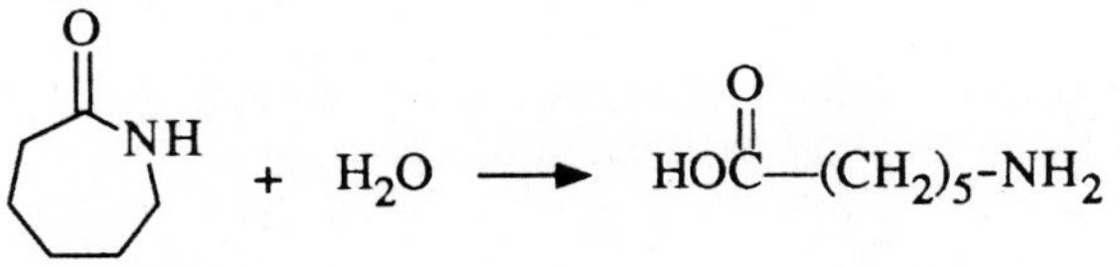

$$\overset{\displaystyle O}{\underset{\text{(ring)}}{\bigcirc}}\!\!NH \;+\; H_2O \longrightarrow HO\overset{\overset{\displaystyle O}{\|}}{C}-(CH_2)_5\text{-}NH_2$$

The amino group of the ε-amino acid, in turn, attacks the carbonyl group of another lactam molecule to open the ring and form a dimer. Then the amino group of the dimer attacks another molecule of lactam to form a trimer; and so on, until a very l-o-n-g molecule is formed.

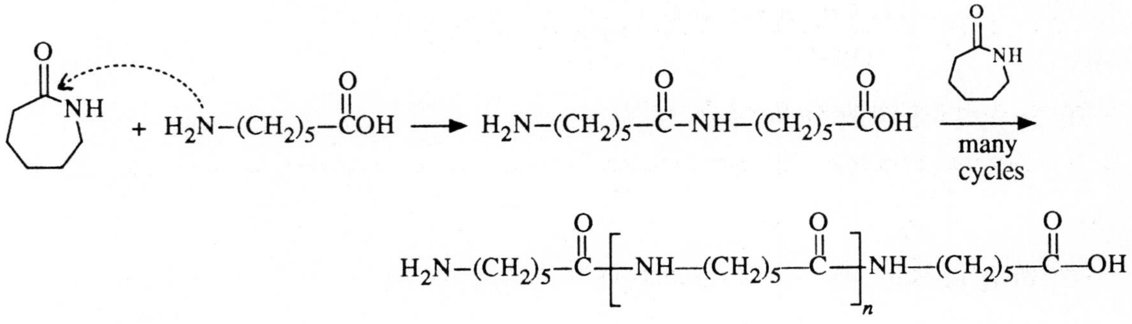

$$H_2N-(CH_2)_5-\overset{\overset{\displaystyle O}{\|}}{C}\!\!\left[\!\!-NH-(CH_2)_5-\overset{\overset{\displaystyle O}{\|}}{C}\!\!-\!\right]_n\!\!NH-(CH_2)_5-\overset{\overset{\displaystyle O}{\|}}{C}-OH$$

Solutions to Additional Problems

27. (a) $C_2H_5-\overset{O}{\overset{\|}{C}}-OH$ (b) $C_2H_5-\overset{O}{\overset{\|}{C}}-S-C_2H_5$ (c) $C_2H_5-\overset{O}{\overset{\|}{C}}-OC(CH_3)_3$ (d) $C_2H_5-\overset{O}{\overset{\|}{C}}-CH_3$ (e) $C_2H_5-\overset{O}{\overset{\|}{C}}-H$

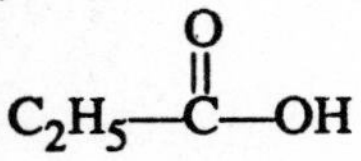

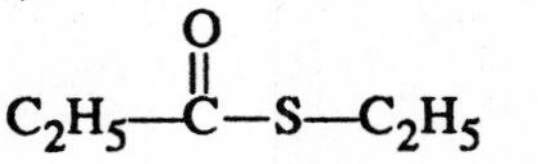

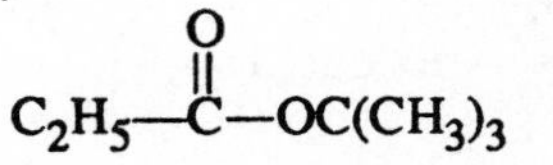

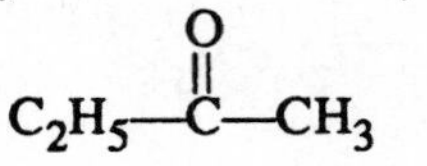

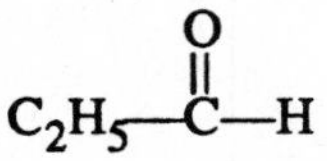

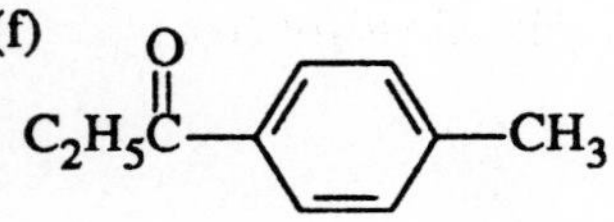

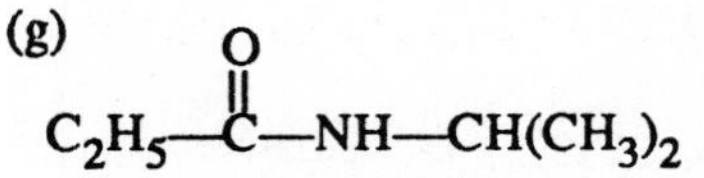

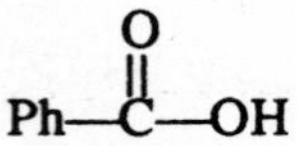

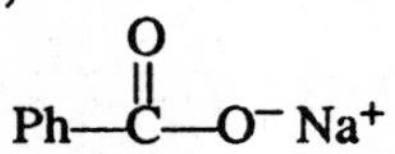

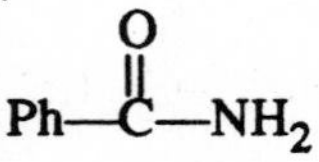

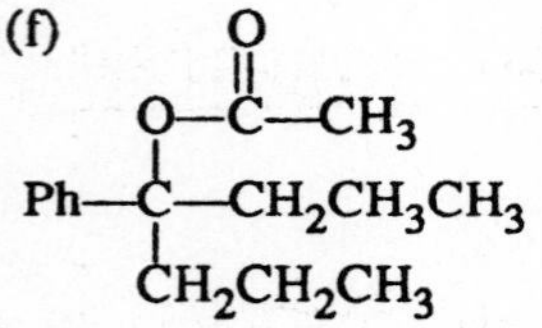

(f) $C_2H_5\overset{O}{\overset{\|}{C}}\!\!-\!\!\langle\text{benzene ring}\rangle\!\!-\!\!CH_3$ (g) $C_2H_5-\overset{O}{\overset{\|}{C}}-NH-CH(CH_3)_2$ (h) $C_2H_5-\overset{O}{\overset{\|}{C}}-O-\overset{O}{\overset{\|}{C}}-Ph$

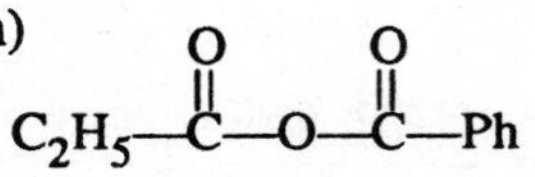

(i) $C_2H_5-\overset{O}{\overset{\|}{C}}-O-\langle\text{benzene ring}\rangle-CH_3$

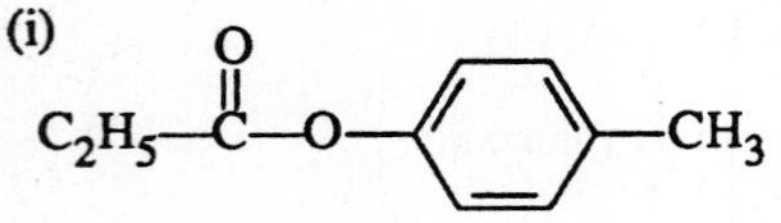

28. (a) $Ph-\overset{O}{\overset{\|}{C}}-OH$ (b) $Ph-\overset{O}{\overset{\|}{C}}-O^-\,Na^+$ (c) $Ph-\overset{O}{\overset{\|}{C}}-NH_2$ (d) $Ph-CH_2-OH$ (e) $Ph-\overset{\overset{\displaystyle OH}{|}}{\underset{\underset{\displaystyle CH_2CH_2CH_3}{|}}{C}}-CH_2CH_3CH_3$

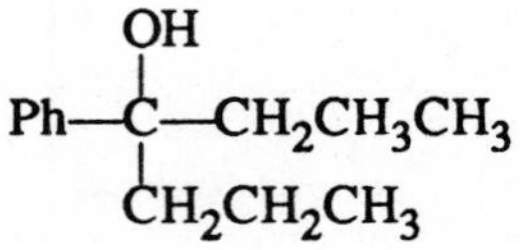

(f) $Ph-\overset{\overset{\displaystyle O-\overset{O}{\overset{\|}{C}}-CH_3}{|}}{\underset{\underset{\displaystyle CH_2CH_2CH_3}{|}}{C}}-CH_2CH_3CH_3$ (g) $Ph-\overset{\overset{\displaystyle O-SO_2Ph}{|}}{\underset{\underset{\displaystyle CH_2CH_2CH_3}{|}}{C}}-CH_2CH_3CH_3$ (h) no reaction

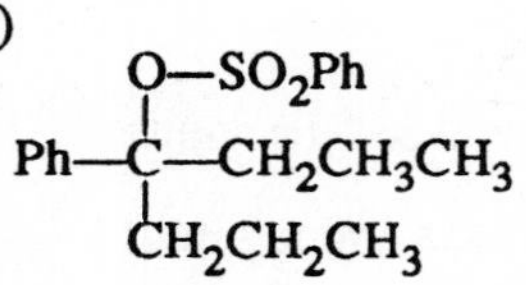

Ethanol is a by-product in reactions (a)–(e). In (h), ethoxide ion does indeed attack the carbonyl group, but it simply displaces the ethoxide that is already there. Thus, there is a reaction, but it is invisible!

29. (a) The compound has to be a primary amide:

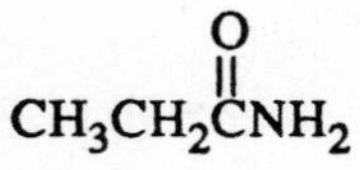

$CH_3CH_2\overset{O}{\overset{\|}{C}}NH_2$

(b) Nitriles liberate ammonia as a by-product of hydrolysis in base: $CH_3CH_2C{\equiv}N$

(c)

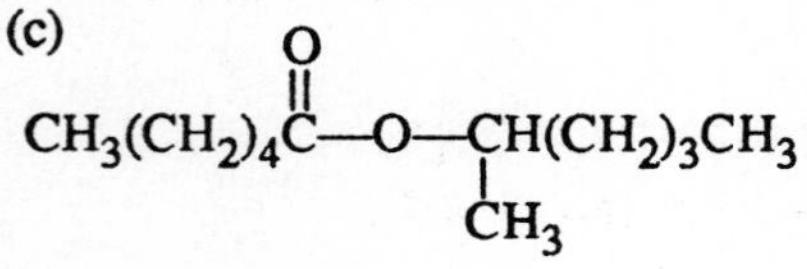

$CH_3(CH_2)_4\overset{O}{\overset{\|}{C}}-O-\underset{\underset{\displaystyle CH_3}{|}}{CH}(CH_2)_3CH_3$

(d)

$CH_3(CH_2)_3O-\overset{O}{\overset{\|}{C}}-CH_3$

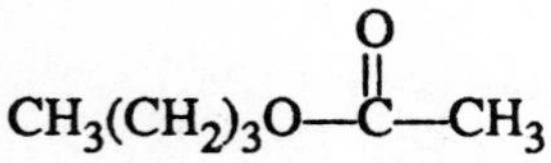

➤ When we think about reactions of carboxylic acid derivatives, we often focus on what happens to the *acyl* portion of the derivative and forget about the leaving group. These problems remind us that there are in many cases two products formed when carboxylic acid derivatives react.

30. The best way to work this problem is to start with the structure and work backward.

$$C_2H_5-\overset{\overset{\displaystyle O}{\|}}{C}-Cl, \ AlCl_3, \ then \ H_2O \qquad Ph-\overset{\overset{\displaystyle O}{\|}}{C}-C_2H_5 \qquad Ph-\overset{\overset{\displaystyle OH}{|}}{CH}-C_2H_5 \qquad Ph-\overset{\overset{\displaystyle Br}{|}}{CH}-C_2H_5 \qquad Ph-CH_2CH_2CH_3$$

$$A \qquad\qquad\qquad\qquad B \qquad\qquad C \qquad\qquad D \qquad\qquad E$$

31. We oxidize the aldehyde to a carboxylic acid and then use reactions of carboxylic acid derivatives.

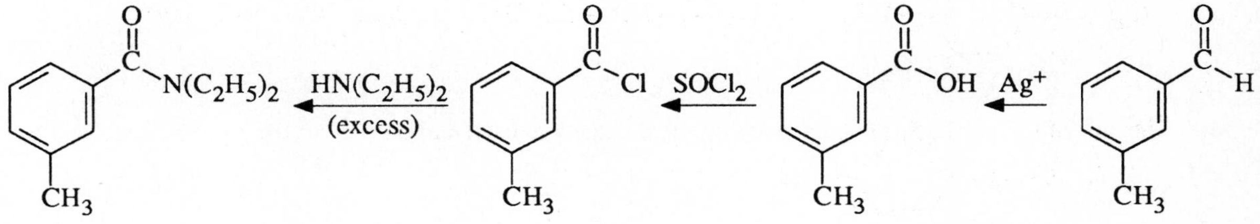

32. (a)

(b)

(c)

(d)

$$CH_3CH_2CH_2CH_2NH_2 \xleftarrow[\text{2) }H_3O^+]{\text{1) LiAlH}_4} CH_3CH_2CH_2\overset{\overset{\displaystyle O}{\|}}{C}NH_2 \xleftarrow{NH_3} CH_3CH_2CH_2\overset{\overset{\displaystyle O}{\|}}{C}Cl$$
$$\text{[from part (b)]}$$

(e)

$$CH_3(CH_2)_4NH_2 \xleftarrow[\text{Raney Ni}]{H_2} CH_3(CH_2)_3C\equiv N \xleftarrow{^-C\equiv N} CH_3(CH_2)_3Br \xleftarrow{HBr} CH_3(CH_2)_3OH$$

$$\Big\uparrow \begin{array}{l} \text{1) LiAlH}_4 \\ \text{2) }H_3O^+ \end{array}$$

$$CH_3CH_2CH_2CO_2H$$

(f)

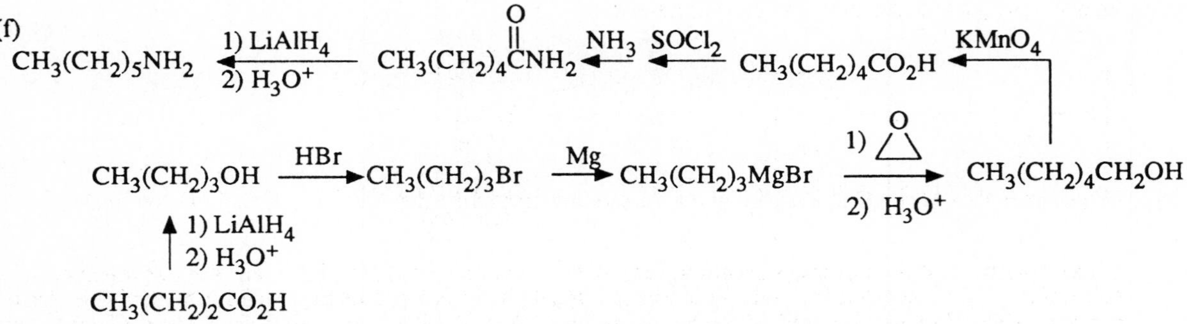

$$CH_3(CH_2)_5NH_2 \xleftarrow[\text{2) } H_3O^+]{\text{1) LiAlH}_4} CH_3(CH_2)_4\overset{\overset{\displaystyle O}{\|}}{C}NH_2 \xleftarrow{NH_3} \xleftarrow{SOCl_2} CH_3(CH_2)_4CO_2H \xleftarrow{KMnO_4}$$

$$CH_3(CH_2)_3OH \xrightarrow{HBr} CH_3(CH_2)_3Br \xrightarrow{Mg} CH_3(CH_2)_3MgBr \xrightarrow[\text{2) } H_3O^+]{\text{1) } \triangle O} CH_3(CH_2)_4CH_2OH$$

$$\Big\uparrow \begin{array}{l}\text{1) LiAlH}_4 \\ \text{2) } H_3O^+\end{array}$$

$$CH_3(CH_2)_2CO_2H$$

33. This mixed anhydride has two carbonyl groups. Attack at each carbonyl gives the respective products:

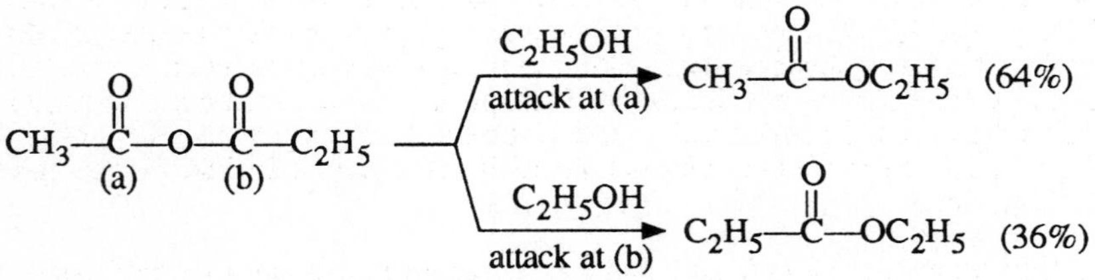

$$CH_3\overset{\overset{\displaystyle O}{\|}}{\underset{(a)}{C}}-O-\overset{\overset{\displaystyle O}{\|}}{\underset{(b)}{C}}-C_2H_5$$

attack at (a), C_2H_5OH: $CH_3-\overset{\overset{\displaystyle O}{\|}}{C}-OC_2H_5$ (64%)

attack at (b), C_2H_5OH: $C_2H_5-\overset{\overset{\displaystyle O}{\|}}{C}-OC_2H_5$ (36%)

The identity of the esters follows from their relative boiling points: the ester of higher molecular weight has the greater boiling point. The reason that attack of ethanol at carbonyl (a) predominates could be that the ethyl group is larger and provides greater steric hindrance. From the relative percentages of the products formed, the difference is not large, however.

34. (a) We can take our cue from the structure of the acetic acid dimer on text page 822.

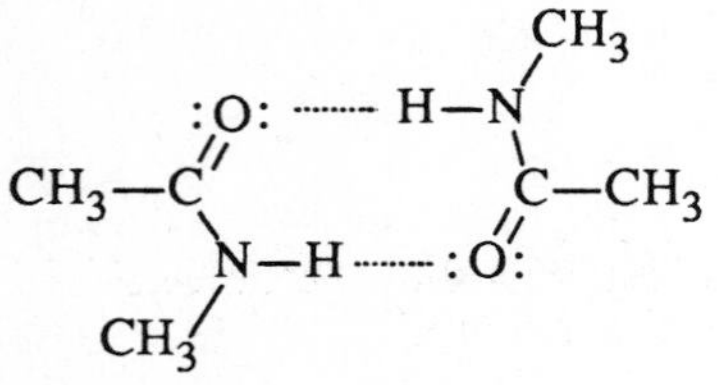

(b) Water competes for the hydrogen bonds of the amide, and thus reduces the energetic advantage (lowers the equilibrium constant) for hydrogen bonding. Carbon tetrachloride cannot hydrogen bond; the only hydrogen bonding available to the amide molecule is with another molecule of itself.

(c) As shown in the structure in part (a), the amide must adopt the *E* configuration about the carbon–nitrogen bond to form a hydrogen-bonded dimer. Yet we know that amides prefer the *Z* configuration. In other words, the energetic advantage of hydrogen bonding is offset by the energetic disadvantage of adopting the *E* configuration. An amide that is "stuck" in the *E* configuration should form dimers more readily. As we showed in the solution to Problem 3, lactams such as γ-butyrolactam have the *E* configuration, and therefore should form hydrogen-bonded dimers more readily.

35. Resonance stabilization of the carboxylate (see Eq. 20.4, text page 825) lowers its energy relative to an addition intermediate, which has no resonance structures:

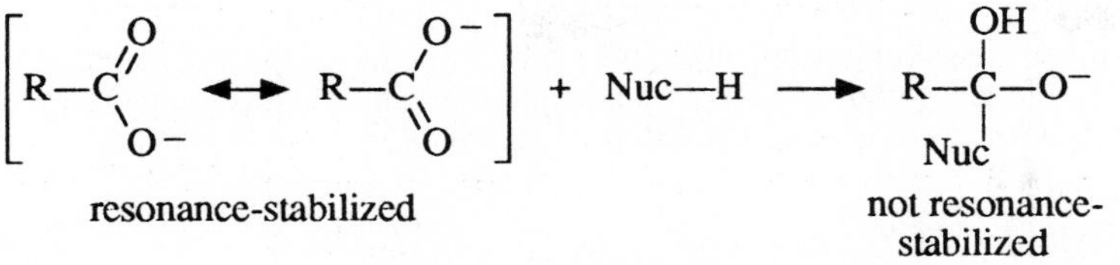

resonance-stabilized   not resonance-
                                                       stabilized

These resonance structures are more important than those of an ester (why?). Loss of this resonance stabilization is an energetic cost that a carboxylate must pay in order to undergo addition reactions. As we showed in Sec. 21.7F, stabilization of a carboxylic acid derivative makes it less reactive in acyl substitution reactions.

36. Thiol esters are (b) less reactive than acid chlorides, but more reactive than esters. Because sulfur orbitals are derived from quantum level 3, they overlap less effectively with the carbonyl π-orbital than the oxygen orbitals in an ester. Hence, thiol esters do not enjoy resonance stabilization to the same extent as an oxygen ester. This weakened resonance suggests increased reactivity of thiol esters. (The principles involved are discussed in Sec. 21.7F.) On the other hand, sulfur is less electronegative than chlorine; the inductive effect of sulfur destabilizes a thiol ester less than the inductive effect of chlorine destabilizes an acid chloride. Hence, thiol esters are less reactive than acid chlorides.

37. Compound A is an anhydride. Compound B has both ester and acid absorption, and is thus a half-ester. The formula and NMR spectrum are consistent with methyl hydrogen succinate as the structure of B; it follows that this compound arises from reaction of methanol with succinic anhydride, which is compound A:

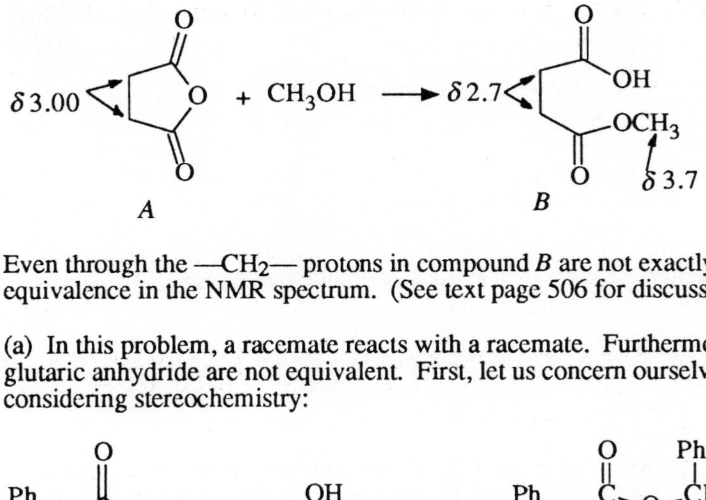

Even through the —CH_2— protons in compound B are not exactly equivalent, they show "accidental" equivalence in the NMR spectrum. (See text page 506 for discussion of a similar case.)

38. (a) In this problem, a racemate reacts with a racemate. Furthermore, the two carbonyl groups of α-phenyl-glutaric anhydride are not equivalent. First, let us concern ourselves with the structures of the products without considering stereochemistry:

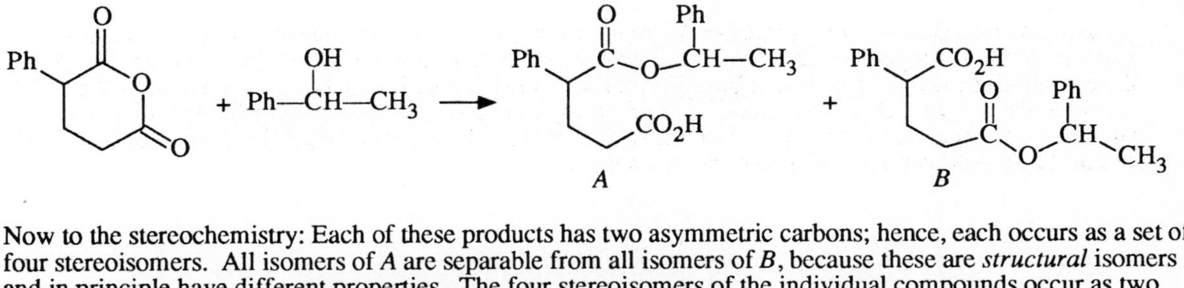

Now to the stereochemistry: Each of these products has two asymmetric carbons; hence, each occurs as a set of four stereoisomers. All isomers of A are separable from all isomers of B, because these are *structural* isomers and in principle have different properties. The four stereoisomers of the individual compounds occur as two diastereomeric sets of two enantiomers. The diastereomers are separable; the enantiomers are not (without optical resolution).

(b) We get the same two structural isomers. As before, each occurs as a pair of diastereomers. However, the enantiomer of each diastereomer is not present because the alcohol of *R* configuration is not present. Hence, all compounds are separable.

➤ Notice that hydrolysis of the separated diastereomers would give optically pure samples of α-phenylglutaric acid. This illustrates one technique of *optical resolution*: React a racemate with an optically pure compound, separate into diastereomers, and then split the individual diastereomers chemically into optically pure compounds.

39. Carbon dioxide is just another carbonyl compound, and its acid-catalyzed hydration follows the pattern for acid-catalyzed hydration of aldehydes and ketones (Eq. 19.17, text page 776): protonation of the carbonyl group and attack of the nucleophile.

40. (a) Klutz is trying to displace an —OH group with a cyano group. In order to act as a leaving group, the —OH group must be protonated. HCN ($pK_a = 9.4$) is not a strong enough acid to bring about this protonation. Because H—CN is such a weak acid, there is also little cyanide present to act as a nucleophile.
(b) What Klutz would get is a mixture of diacid, diester, and monoester. Once some monoester is formed, there is no reason to expect that its remaining carboxy group would not also react under the reaction conditions. Of course, *some* of the desired product would form, but the yield would be poor.
(c) Klutz wants to achieve a "crossed" reaction between the acetic acid and benzoic acid. However, there is also nothing to prevent the reaction of two acetic acid molecules to give acetic anhydride, or two benzoic acid molecules to give benzoic anhydride. Although some of the desired material would form, it would be part of a complex mixture.
(d) Unfortunately for Klutz, methyl salicylate contains a phenolic —OH group which is a strong enough acid to consume completely one equivalent of NaOH; the conjugate-base anion of the phenol —OH group is formed in this reaction. There is then no ⁻OH remaining to effect the saponification. It would take *two* equivalents of NaOH to saponify methyl salicylate: one to titrate the phenol, and the second for the saponification.
(e) Klutz is correct in thinking that amides hydrolyze in base, but, unfortunately, the molecule has two other functional groups more reactive than the amide Klutz wants to hydrolyze. One is the ester group, and the second is the β-lactam group. Esters are more reactive than amides, and, although a β-lactam is an amide, it is strained; hydrolysis opens the four-membered ring, relieving the strain.

41. It is convenient to follow these reactions using Fischer projections, since the asymmetric carbon is unaffected:

42. (a) The preparation of nylon-4,6 requires the following starting materials:

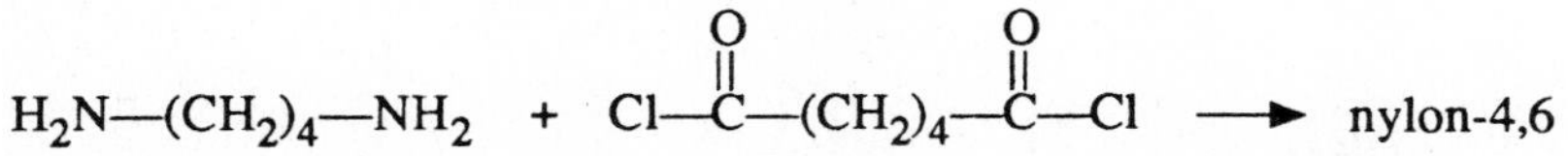

$$H_2N\text{—}(CH_2)_4\text{—}NH_2 \quad + \quad Cl\text{—}\overset{\overset{\displaystyle O}{\|}}{C}\text{—}(CH_2)_4\text{—}\overset{\overset{\displaystyle O}{\|}}{C}\text{—}Cl \quad \longrightarrow \quad nylon\text{-}4,6$$

The acid chloride is prepared from the corresponding diacid, adipic acid:

$$Cl\text{—}\overset{\overset{\displaystyle O}{\|}}{C}\text{—}(CH_2)_4\text{—}\overset{\overset{\displaystyle O}{\|}}{C}\text{—}Cl \quad \xleftarrow{\ SOCl_2\ } \quad HO\text{—}\overset{\overset{\displaystyle O}{\|}}{C}\text{—}(CH_2)_4\text{—}\overset{\overset{\displaystyle O}{\|}}{C}\text{—}OH$$

The amine is prepared from the four-carbon diacid, succinic acid, which is converted into its acid chloride. This in turn is allowed to react with ammonia and the resulting amide is reduced to the diamine:

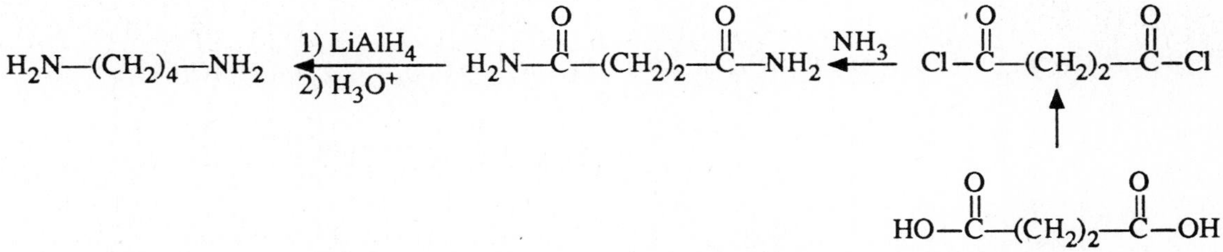

$$H_2N\text{—}(CH_2)_4\text{—}NH_2 \quad \xleftarrow[\ 2)\ H_3O^+\ ]{\ 1)\ LiAlH_4\ } \quad H_2N\text{—}\overset{\overset{\displaystyle O}{\|}}{C}\text{—}(CH_2)_2\text{—}\overset{\overset{\displaystyle O}{\|}}{C}\text{—}NH_2 \quad \xleftarrow{\ NH_3\ } \quad Cl\text{—}\overset{\overset{\displaystyle O}{\|}}{C}\text{—}(CH_2)_2\text{—}\overset{\overset{\displaystyle O}{\|}}{C}\text{—}Cl$$

$$\uparrow$$

$$HO\text{—}\overset{\overset{\displaystyle O}{\|}}{C}\text{—}(CH_2)_2\text{—}\overset{\overset{\displaystyle O}{\|}}{C}\text{—}OH$$

(b) Reduction of succinic acid (see previous part) with $LiAlH_4$ gives 1,4-butanediol, $HO\text{—}(CH_2)_4\text{—}OH$; this is allowed to react with the acid chloride of glutaric acid, $HO_2C\text{—}(CH_2)_3\text{—}CO_2H$.

43. The formula of the product corresponds to two molecules of lactic acid minus two water molecules, and indicates three degrees of unsaturation. Acids react with alcohols to form esters. Evidently, this compound is a cyclic ester, which means that it must be the following dilactone.

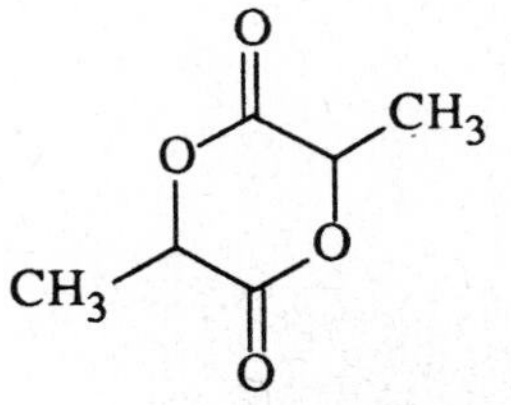

lactic acid dilactone

An ordinary lactone would have a three-membered ring and would be strained.

44. (a) With bromine, the double bond would brominate, and the phenol ring would brominate once (see Eq. 18.39, text page 739):

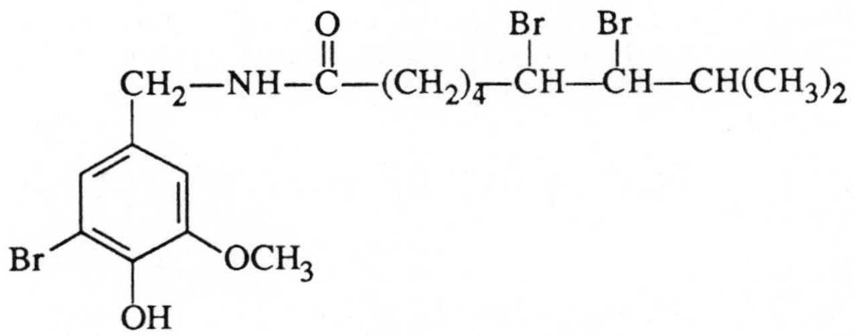

(b) Dilute aqueous NaOH will convert the phenol into its conjugate-base anion.
(c) Dilute HCl will not react, except to protonate the carbonyl oxygen of the amide to a small extent.

(d) Concentrated HCl will bring about hydrolysis of the amide.

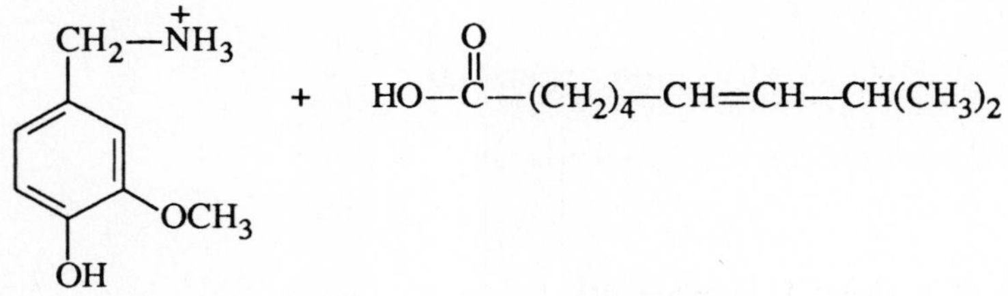

(The amine is protonated under the acidic reaction conditions.) There might also be some cleavage of the aromatic ether. Finally, protonation of the double bond will occur followed by rearrangement of the secondary carbocation to a tertiary carbocation and formation of a tertiary alkyl halide:

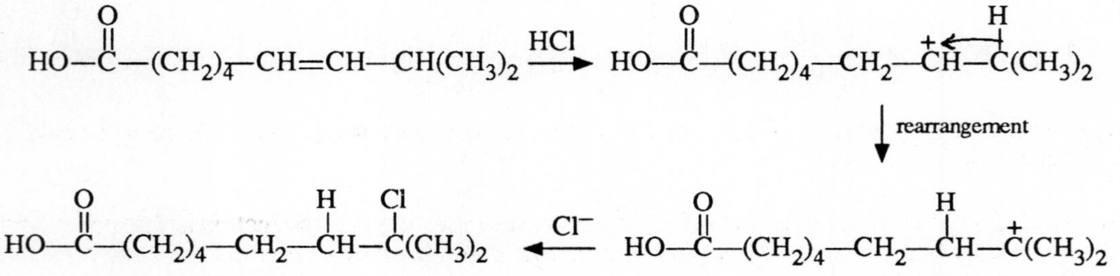

(e) The double bond would be hydrogenated:

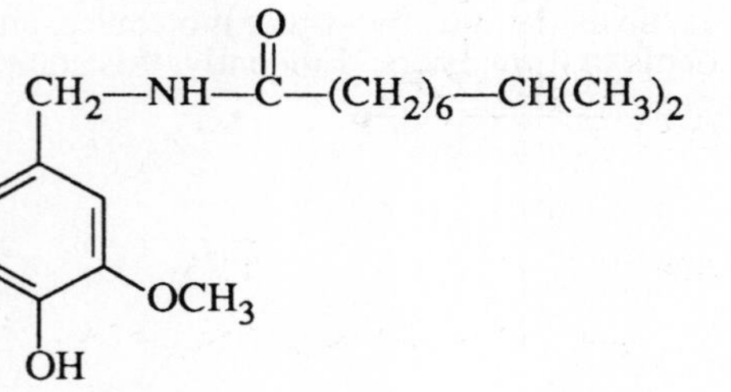

(f) The conjugate-base anion of the phenol group would form a methyl ether:

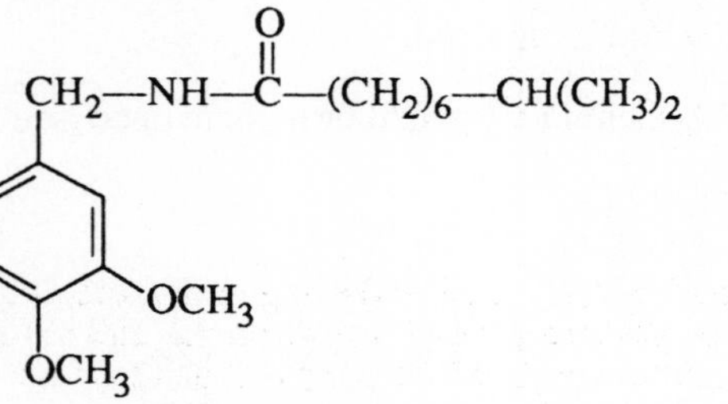

(g) The amide would hydrolyze and the ether would cleave:

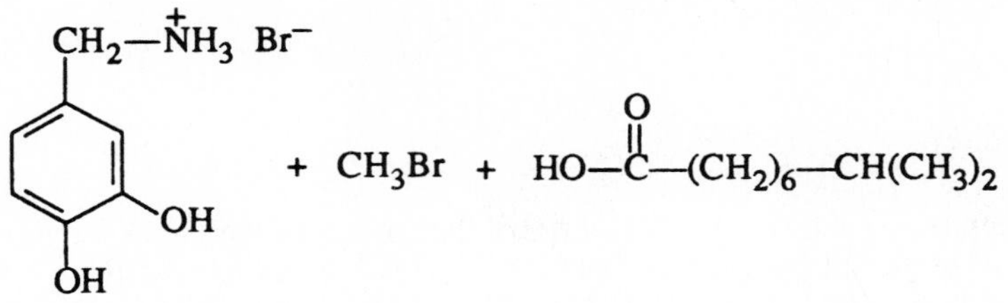

45. Compound *B* is the cyclic anhydride of α,α-dimethylmalonic acid:

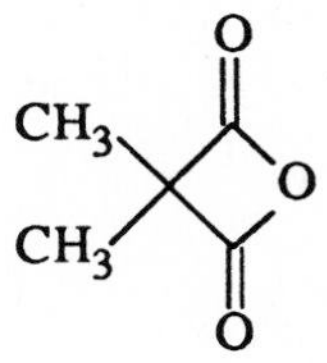

Like all cyclic anhydrides, this compound reacts with water to give the corresponding dicarboxylic acid, and with alcohols to give half-esters.

46. The structure of β-methylglutaric acid provides the carbon skeleton. The key deduction is that compound *A* has two degrees of unsaturation and, from the other information given, must be a lactone. The compounds and their reactions are as follows:

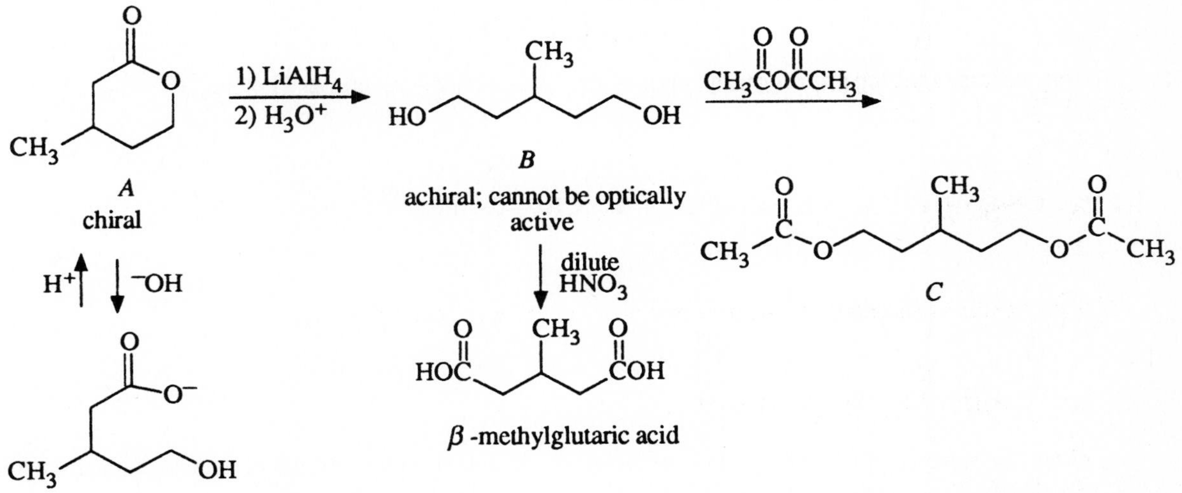

47. The titration data show that (15.00 − 5.30), or 9.70 mL of 1*N* NaOH is used in the saponification. Assuming one ester group per molecule of *A*, then one mole of NaOH is required for saponification per mole of ester. Thus 2 g of ester corresponds to 9.7×10^{-3} moles; the molecular weight of the ester is thus $(2.00/9.7 \times 10^{-3})$ or 206 g/mol. To solve the problem, we now look for a structure, and we find one: an oxidation product of alcohol *C* is acetophenone. This means that alcohol *C* must be 1-phenylethanol:

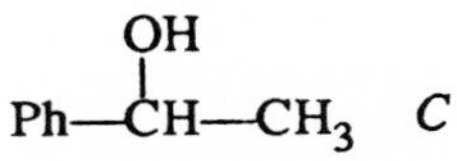

Since this alcohol is optically active, it must be *a particular enantiomer* of 1-phenylethanol rather than the racemate. (We can't tell which enantiomer from the data given.) A partial structure for the ester *A*, then, is:

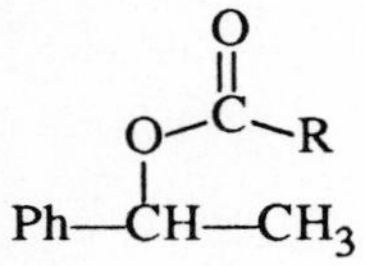

$$
\begin{array}{c}
\overset{\displaystyle O}{\underset{\displaystyle O-\overset{\displaystyle \|}{C}\diagdown R}{}} \\
Ph-\overset{\displaystyle |}{C}H-CH_3 \qquad A \quad \text{(partial structure)}
\end{array}
$$

(The structure of the R— group is yet to be established.) We determine the molecular weight of R simply by subtracting the mass of the known part of the structure above from 206, the total molecular weight of the ester. Doing this, we find that the mass of R is 57. Since R must contain only carbon and hydrogen (why?), it must be some type of butyl group. Since the acid liberated on saponification is optically active, it follows that R must be a *sec*-butyl group, since this is the only type of butyl group that contains an asymmetric carbon. Hence, the structure of *A* is completely established:

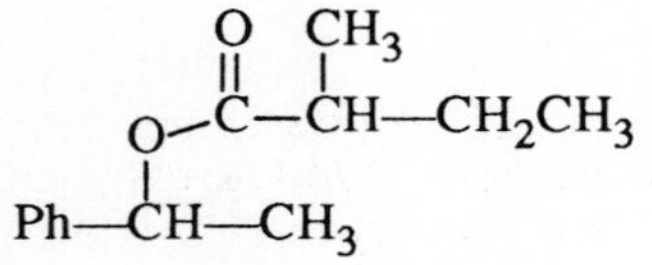

$$
\begin{array}{c}
\overset{\displaystyle O}{} \ \ \overset{\displaystyle CH_3}{} \\
O-\overset{\displaystyle \|}{C}-\overset{\displaystyle |}{C}H-CH_2CH_3 \\
Ph-\overset{\displaystyle |}{C}H-CH_3 \qquad\qquad A
\end{array}
$$

Since acetophenone is achiral, reduction must give *racemic* 1-phenylethanol (compound *D*); this is simply the racemate of alcohol *C*. When the racemic *D* reacts with the optically active acid chloride derived from *B*, two diastereomeric esters are formed: one is identical to *A*, and the other is the diastereomer of *A*:

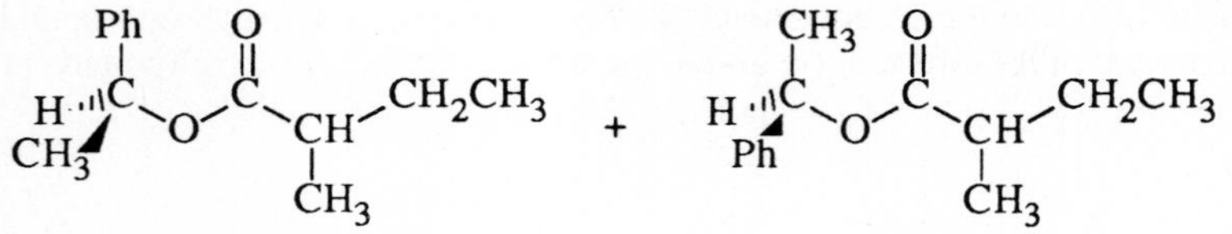

48.   (a) Saponification of the ester forms an enol which spontaneously reverts to a ketone. (See Eq. 14.12, text page 559.)

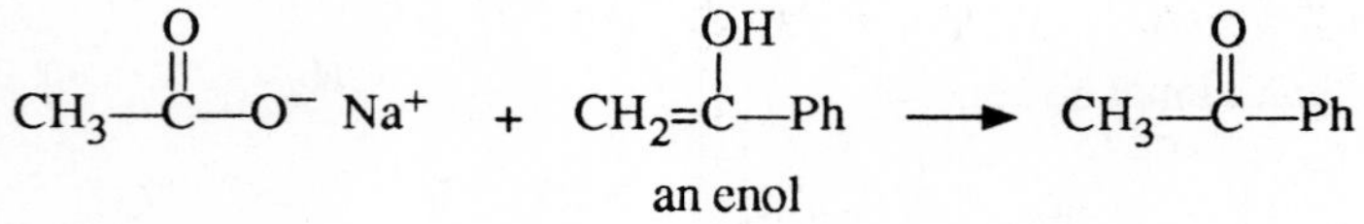

$$
\overset{\displaystyle O}{\underset{}{CH_3-\overset{\|}{C}-O^-}} \ Na^+ \ + \ \overset{\displaystyle OH}{\underset{}{CH_2=\overset{|}{C}-Ph}} \ \longrightarrow \ \overset{\displaystyle O}{\underset{}{CH_3-\overset{\|}{C}-Ph}}
$$
$$
\text{an enol}
$$

(b) This is a simple transesterification reaction:

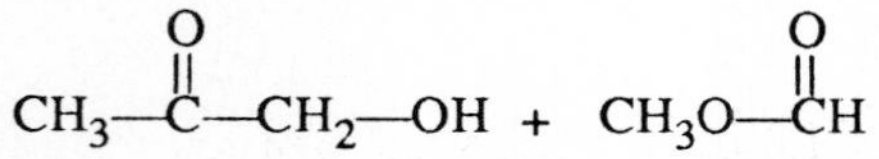

$$
\overset{\displaystyle O}{\underset{}{CH_3-\overset{\|}{C}-CH_2-OH}} \ + \ \overset{\displaystyle O}{\underset{}{CH_3O-\overset{\|}{C}H}}
$$

(c) Since the starting amine contains two amino groups, reaction with an excess of an acid chloride should give a "double amide."

$$
\overset{\displaystyle O}{\underset{}{Ph-\overset{\|}{C}-NH-NH-\overset{\|}{C}-Ph}} \qquad \overset{\displaystyle O}{}
$$

(d) Both the amide and the nitrile functional groups are hydrolyzed: the amide first, then the nitrile.

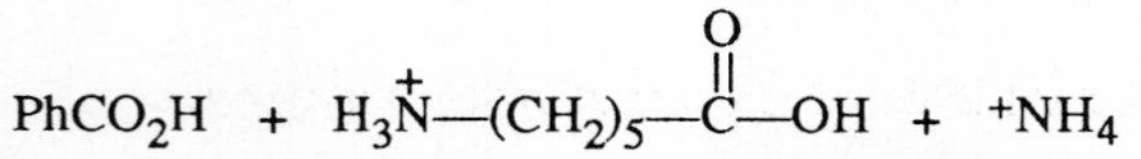

$$
PhCO_2H \ + \ \overset{+}{H_3}N-(CH_2)_5-\overset{\displaystyle O}{\overset{\|}{C}}-OH \ + \ {}^+NH_4
$$

(e) The sulfonyl chloride reacts with the alcohol to give a sulfonate ester *A*. Hydroxide then displaces the sulfonate anion by attack at the methyl group. The labeled oxygen ends up in the sulfonate anion:

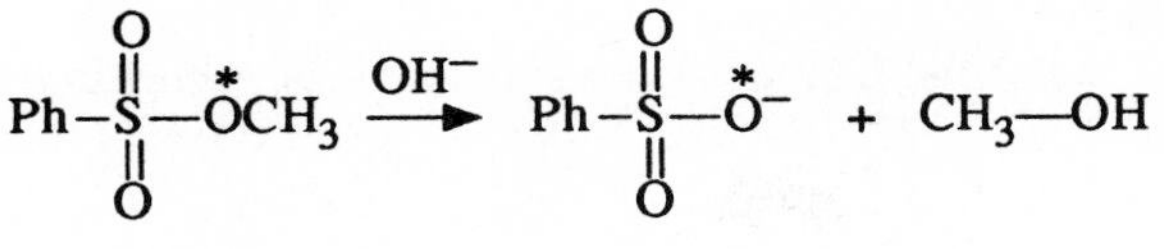

A

(f) When the ester that is formed reacts with hydroxide ion, cleavage at the bond between the labeled oxygen and the carbonyl group occurs. Hence, the labeled oxygen ends up in the alcohol rather than the product carboxylate.

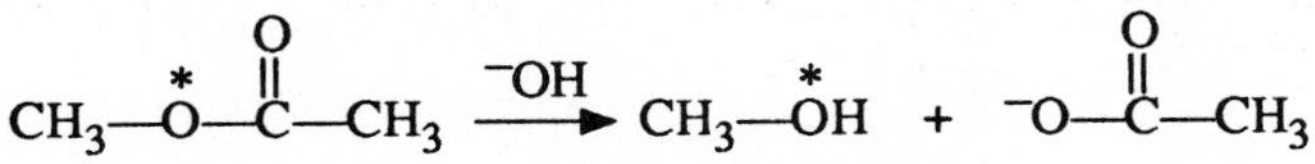

➤ Parts (e) and (f) illustrate a fundamental difference between the reactions of sulfonate esters and carboxylate esters. Sulfonate esters react with nucleophiles by cleavage at the alkyl–oxygen bond. Most simple carboxylate esters react by cleavage at the bond between the carbonyl group and the oxygen.

(g) The compound formed results from attack of both the carboxy group and the amino group on the acid chloride. Called *isatoic anhydride*, the compound is both an amide and a mixed anhydride. (The formula tells us that a ring must be formed.)

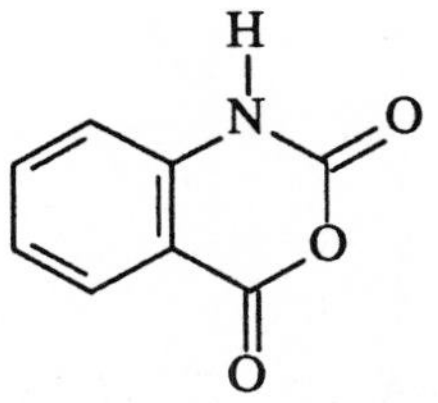

(h) The formula tells us that the reaction is intramolecular; it is an intramolecular aminolysis in which the amino group attacks the carbonyl and displaces the —OCH_3 group as CH_3OH:

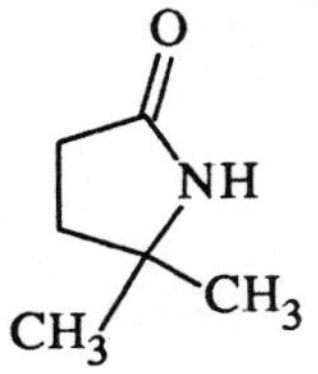

(i) This is a diamide of carbonic acid — that is, a dialkylurea. It hydrolyzes to carbonic acid (H_2CO_3), protonated *t*-butylamine [$(CH_3)_3C$—$\overset{+}{N}H_3$], and ammonium ion ($^+NH_4$). The carbonic acid, in turn, breaks down to CO_2 and H_2O.

(j) This is a transesterification reaction. It is just like a saponification, except that the fatty acids are converted into methyl esters rather than soaps.

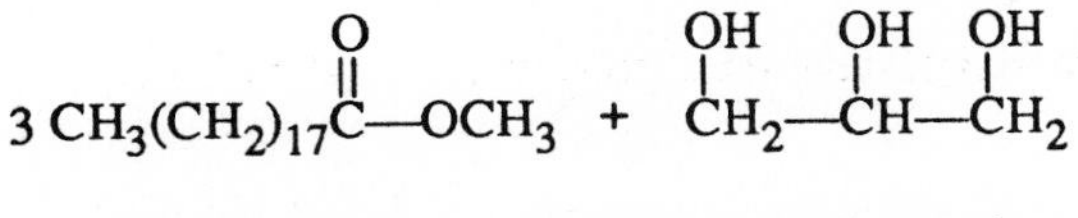

(k) Like all amides, lactams are reduced to amines, but the amines from lactam reduction are cyclic.

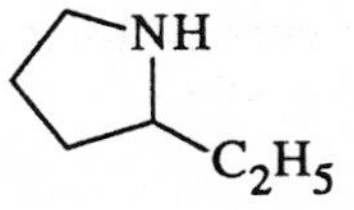

(l) Esters react with Grignard reagents to give tertiary alcohols, The same is true of lactones, except that the by-product alcohol is part of the same molecule.

$$CH_3(CH_2)_3CH_2\overset{\overset{\displaystyle OH}{|}}{C}HCH_2CH_2\underset{\underset{\displaystyle CH_3}{|}}{\overset{\overset{\displaystyle OH}{|}}{C}}{-}CH_3$$

(m) Since aldehydes are much more reactive than esters, and since there is only one equivalent of the Grignard reagent, the aldehyde reacts preferentially. The resulting hydroxy ester then undergoes transesterification with the alcohol within the same molecule. Hence, a lactone is formed:

$$CH_3O{-}\overset{\overset{\displaystyle O}{\|}}{C}{-}(CH_2)_3{-}\overset{\overset{\displaystyle OH}{|}}{C}H{-}Ph \xrightarrow[\text{(transesterification)}]{\text{lactonization}} \quad + \quad CH_3OH$$

(n) The Grignard displaces one $C_2H_5O^-$ group to give the simple ester ethyl propionate, then another, to give a ketone 3-pentanone; this in turn reacts with the Grignard reagent to give a tertiary alcohol, which is the isolated product:

$$C_2H_5O{-}\overset{\overset{\displaystyle O}{\|}}{C}{-}C_2H_5 \xrightarrow{C_2H_5MgBr} C_2H_5{-}\overset{\overset{\displaystyle O}{\|}}{C}{-}C_2H_5 \xrightarrow{C_2H_5MgBr \;\; H_3O^+} C_2H_5{-}\underset{\underset{\displaystyle C_2H_5}{|}}{\overset{\overset{\displaystyle OH}{|}}{C}}{-}C_2H_5$$

product of the first
Grignard reaction

➤ Reaction of a Grignard reagent with diethyl carbonate provides a general synthesis of tertiary alcohols $R_3C{-}OH$ in which all R groups are identical.

(o) LiAlH$_4$ reacts with acid chlorides just as it does with esters. Chloride is lost as a leaving group to give an aldehyde, which is then reduced to a primary alcohol $(CH_3)_3C{-}CH_2{-}OH$.

49. (a)   (b)   (c)

$$N{\equiv}C{-}CH_2{-}\overset{\overset{\displaystyle O}{\|}}{C}{-}OC_2H_5 \qquad CH_3O{-}\hexagon{-}\overset{\overset{\displaystyle O}{\|}}{C}{-}NH_2 \qquad HC{\equiv}C{-}\overset{\overset{\displaystyle O}{\|}}{C}{-}OCH_2CH_3$$

(d) $HO{-}CH_2CH_2{-}C{\equiv}N$ (e) $\underset{Ph}{\overset{H}{\diagdown}}C{=}C\underset{H}{\overset{C{\equiv}N}{\diagup}}$ (f)

$$CH_3{-}\underset{\underset{\displaystyle Br}{|}}{C}H{-}\overset{\overset{\displaystyle O}{\|}}{C}{-}OCH_2CH_3$$

You should show why each compound is consistent with the data, if you have not already done so.

50. The first reaction gives the acetate ester. Saponification gives back the original alcohol, because saponification occurs with cleavage at the bond between the carbonyl and the oxygen; hence, the configuration of the asymmetric carbon is unaffected:

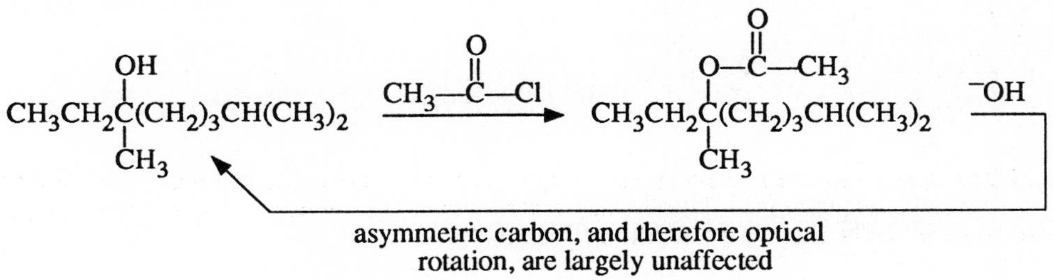

asymmetric carbon, and therefore optical
rotation, are largely unaffected

Because the ester is tertiary, acidic cleavage goes through a carbocation mechanism in which the bond to the asymmetric carbon is broken (see text page 875). The achiral carbocation reacts with water to give the *racemic* alcohol. (There is some inversion, but mostly racemization is observed. The is the same type of result as with tertiary alkyl halides; see text page 353.)

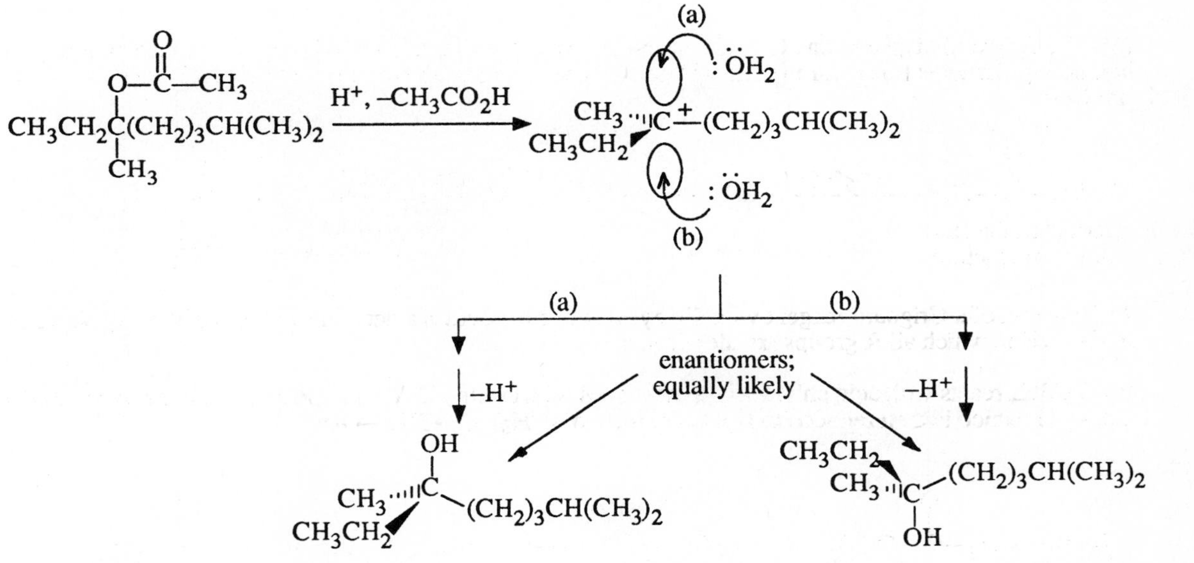

51. (a)

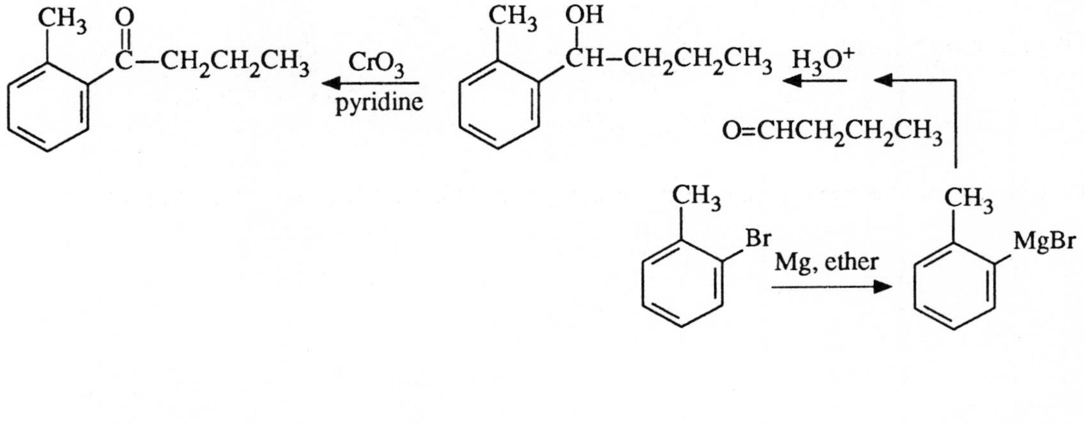

(b)

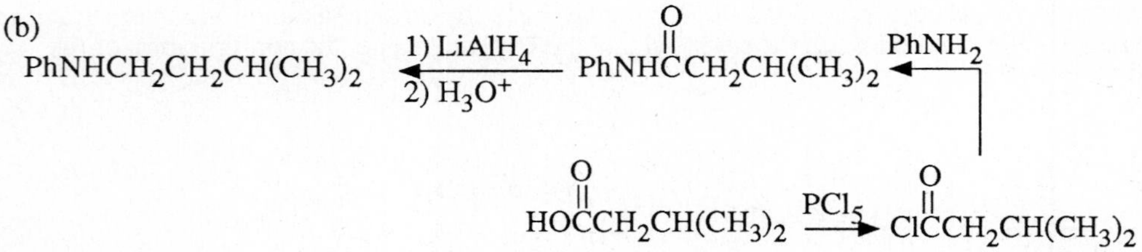

$$PhNHCH_2CH_2CH(CH_3)_2 \xleftarrow[\text{2) H}_3\text{O}^+]{\text{1) LiAlH}_4} \underset{\substack{\| \\ O}}{PhNHCCH_2CH(CH_3)_2} \xleftarrow{PhNH_2}$$

$$\underset{\substack{\| \\ O}}{HOCCH_2CH(CH_3)_2} \xrightarrow{PCl_5} \underset{\substack{\| \\ O}}{ClCCH_2CH(CH_3)_2}$$

(c)

$$\underset{HO}{\overset{*}{}}\overset{*O}{\underset{\|}{C}}-CH_2CH_2-\overset{O*}{\underset{\|}{C}}\overset{*}{-OH} \xleftarrow{H_2O*} Cl-\overset{O}{\underset{\|}{C}}-CH_2CH_2-\overset{O}{\underset{\|}{C}}-Cl \xleftarrow{SOCl_2} HO-\overset{O}{\underset{\|}{C}}-CH_2CH_2-\overset{O}{\underset{\|}{C}}-OH$$

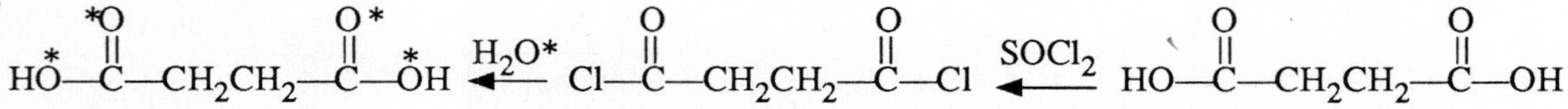

Another way would be to treat succinic anhydride with labeled water; succinic anhydride is prepared by heating succinic acid. However, this would not give as great an amount of isotope incorporation as the method above (why?). Notice that the isotope at any one oxygen in a given carboxy group is automatically scrambled to both positions; see the solution to Problem 23, Chapter 20.

(d)

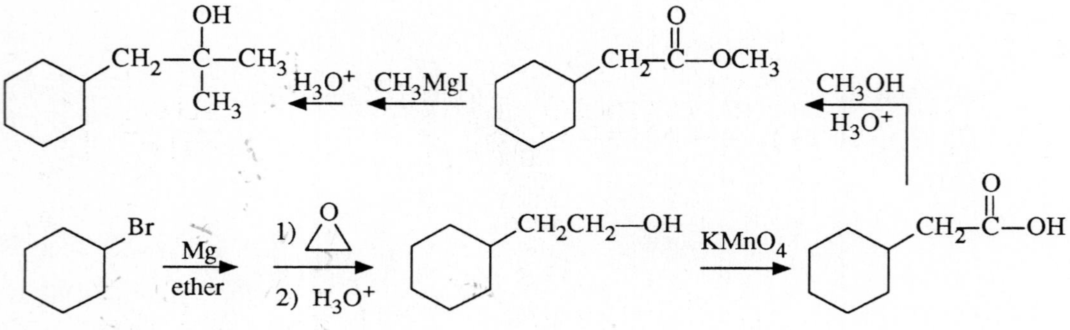

(e)

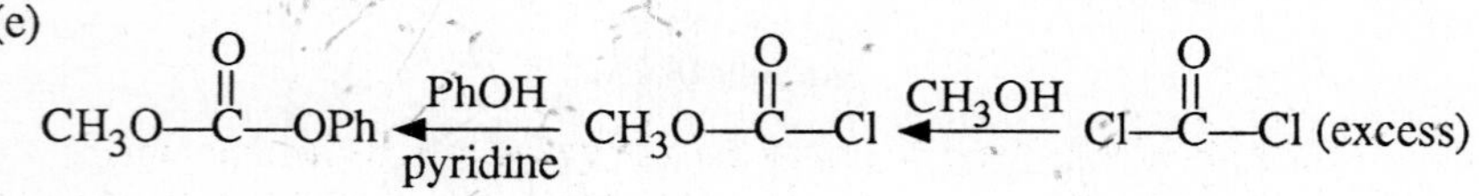

$$\underset{\substack{\| \\ O}}{CH_3O-C-OPh} \xleftarrow[\text{pyridine}]{\text{PhOH}} \underset{\substack{\| \\ O}}{CH_3O-C-Cl} \xleftarrow{CH_3OH} \underset{\substack{\| \\ O}}{Cl-C-Cl} \text{ (excess)}$$

(f)

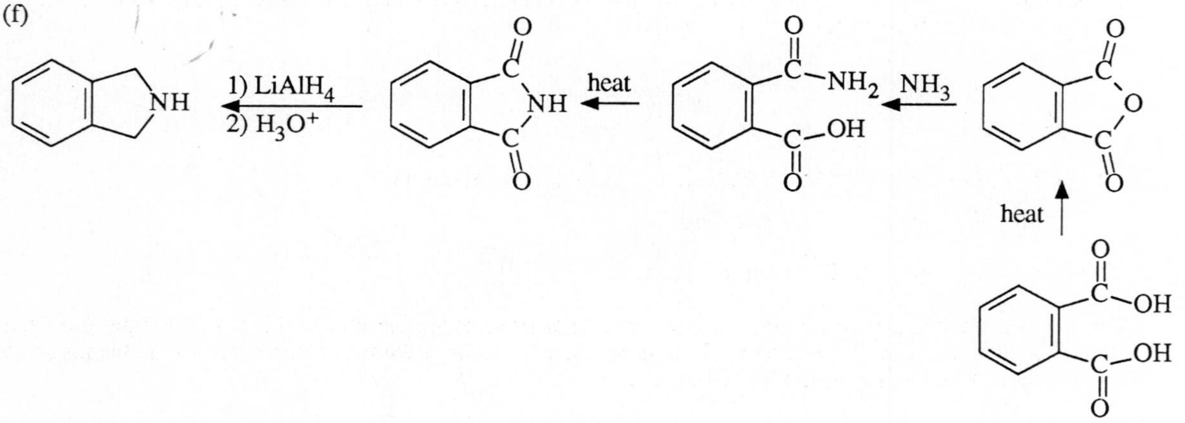

(g)

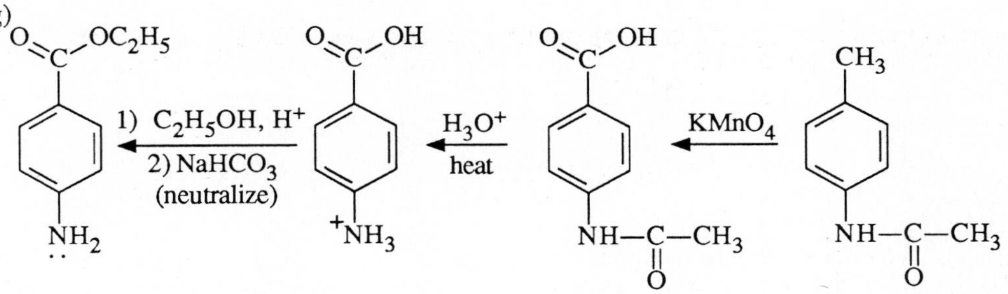

(h)

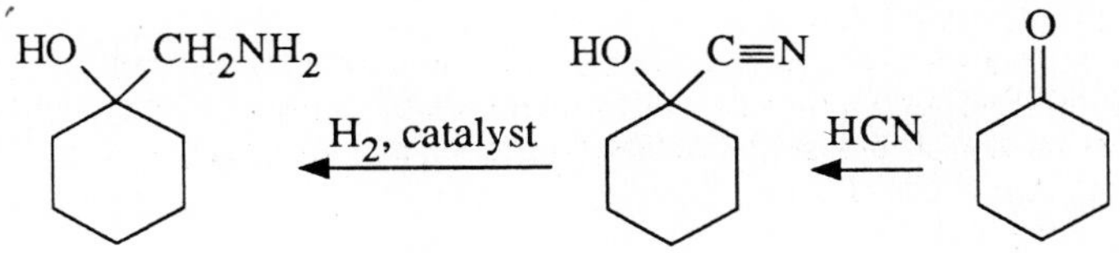

(i)

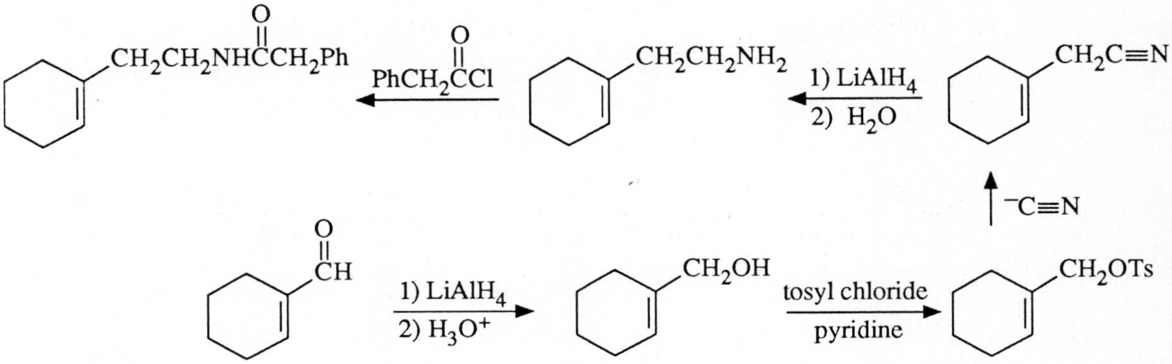

52. (a) The compound that reacts with benzaldehyde is a substituted derivative of hydroxylamine; hence, compound *A* is a substituted oxime (see Table 19.3, text page 794) formed by the usual mechanism of imine formation. Let us abbreviate the 2,4-dinitrophenyl group as Ar—, and the phenyl group, as usual, as Ph—. We begin the mechanism with the structure of *A*.

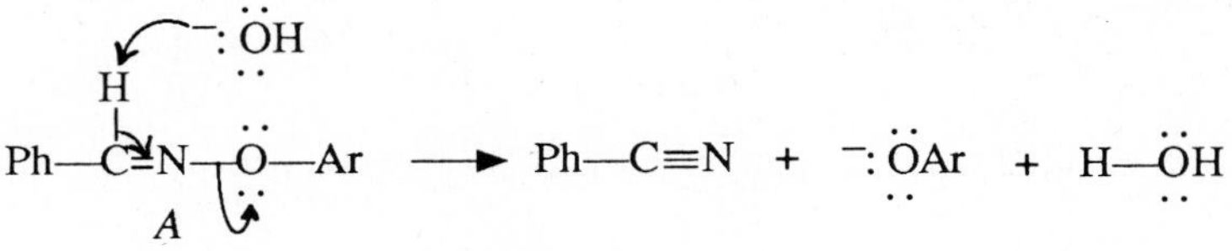

The reaction is simply an E2-like elimination.

(b) The iodine forms an iodonium-ion intermediate analogous to a bromonium ion (see text page 136), and the NaHCO$_3$ ionizes the carboxylic acid. The carboxylate ion attacks the iodonium ion from the back side to give the product. We begin with the iodonium ion:

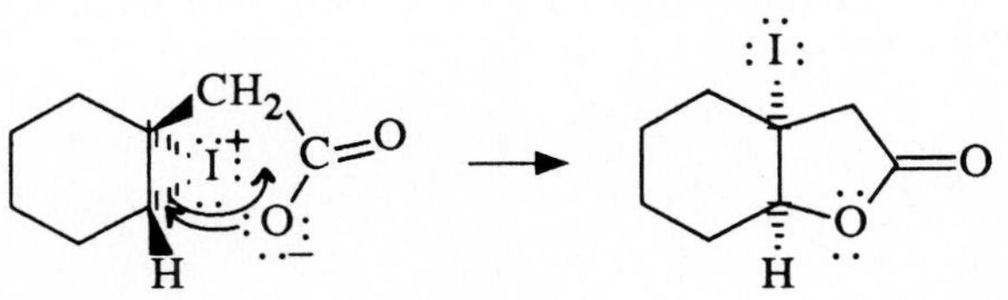

(c) Protonation of the carbonyl oxygen makes the carbonyl group a good leaving group. It departs when the bromide ion attacks in an S_N2 reaction to give the bromoacid. We begin with the protonated lactone.

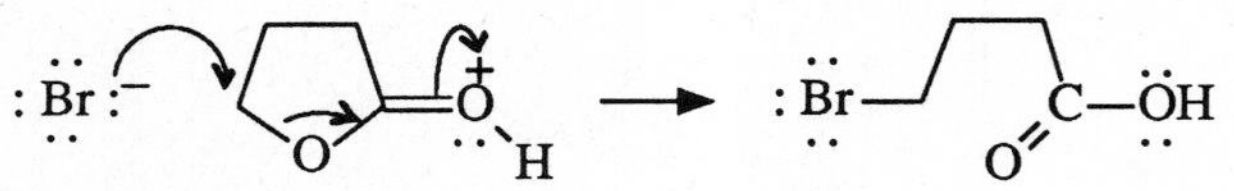

The bromoacid is then esterified by the usual mechanism (Sec. 20.8A). Another mechanism involves transesterification of the lactone to a hydroxy ester, followed by conversion of the hydroxy group to a halide. This mechanism is a reasonable alternative. However, the mechanism above is probably the correct one, since a protonated carbonyl group is such a good leaving group.

(d) This involves hydration of the double bond in the ring to give compound A below by the usual mechanism (Sec. 4.8), followed by acid-catalyzed transesterification to give the lactone:

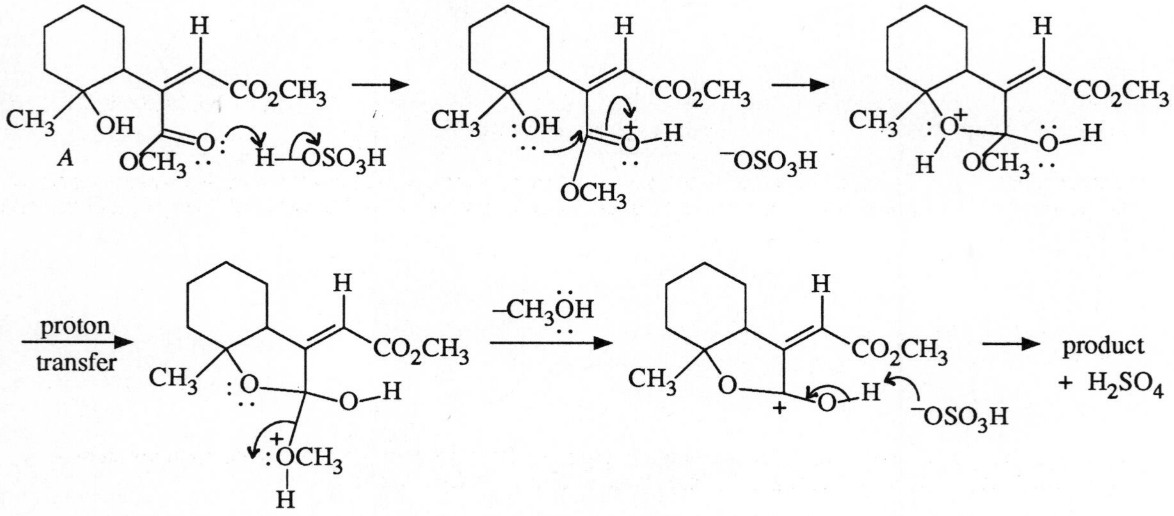

(e) The first step in this transformation is formation of a Grignard reagent. The carbon of the Grignard reagent is anion-like. A simple movement of electron pairs effects elimination of a carboxylate ion, which is protonated when acid is added to give the final product.

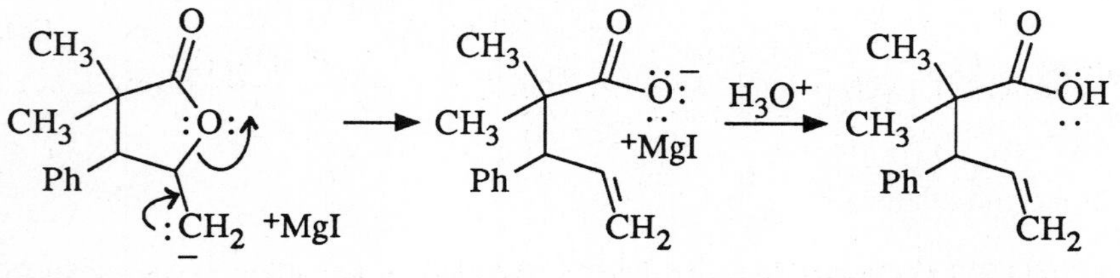

(f) This reaction is a variation of oxymercuration. The mercurinium ion, formed at one double bond, is attacked by the π-electrons of the second double bond. The resulting carbocation is then attacked by the carboxy group. The mercury is removed by $NaBH_4$ treatment. We begin the mechanism with the mercurinium ion; formation of mercurinium ions is discussed in Section 5.3B.

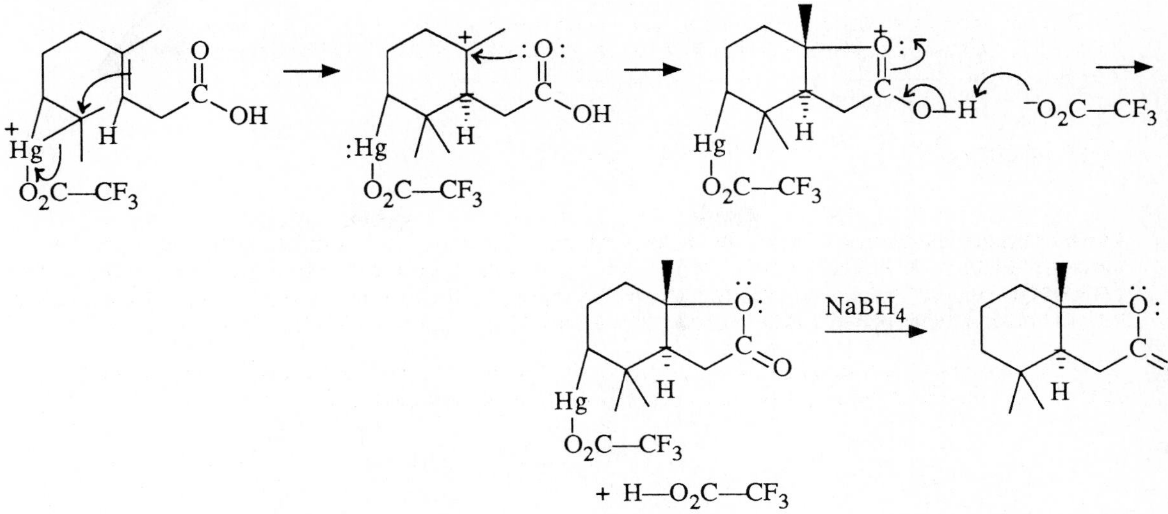

The stereochemistry shown is a consequence of the fact that all bonds are formed by backside attack. (The bond formations shown as separate steps above are probably concerted.)

53. The existence of *three* signals is a consequence of the fact that rotation about the carbonyl–nitrogen bond is slow, and that the two *N*-methyl groups are nonequivalent; one is *cis* to the carbonyl oxygen, and the other is *trans*.

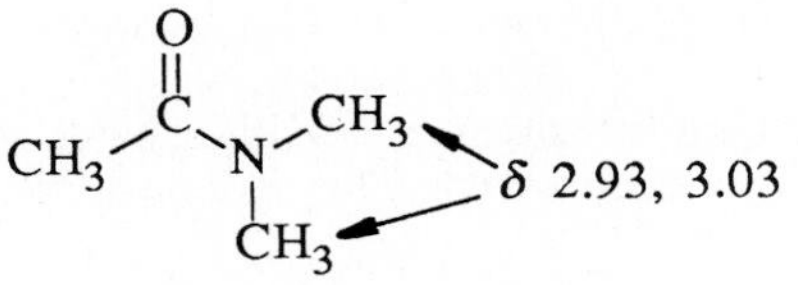

At higher temperature, the rate of rotation is increased to the point that the NMR spectrometer cannot distinguish the two methyl groups. Related phenomena are discussed in Sec. 13.7.

54. (a) The conversion of ester *A* to the tosylate does not affect the asymmetric carbon. The subsequent reaction of the tosylate with KBr is an S_N2 reaction and therefore proceeds with inversion of configuration. Since saponification does not affect the asymmetric carbon, (–)-*C* has inverted configuration relative to the starting ester *A*. To summarize:

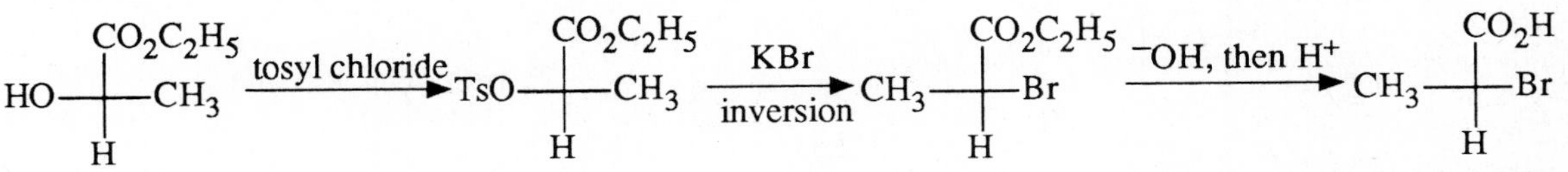

(b) Reaction of (–)-*C* with dilute NaOH followed by esterification (which does not affect the asymmetric carbon) can give (–)-*A* only if the reaction with dilute NaOH occurs with *retention of configuration*. Similarly, reaction of (–)-*C* with concentrated NaOH must proceed with *inversion of configuration*. The results in concentrated base are consistent with an S_N2 reaction of ¯OH at the asymmetric carbon:

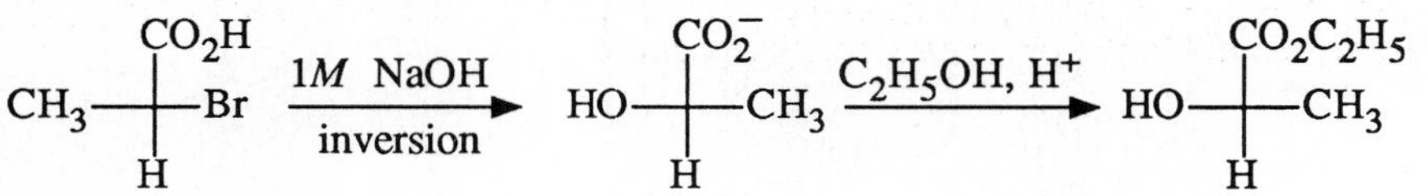

The reaction of (–)-*C* with dilute NaOH occurs (as shown above) with *retention* of configuration. Since we know of no displacement mechanisms that go with retention, the only possibility is that there are two successive inversions taking place. (Two inversions = one retention.) The first inversion occurs when the carboxylate oxygen attacks the α-carbon to give an unusual β-lactone intermediate. This very strained intermediate is then opened with a second inversion by displacement with water or hydroxide.

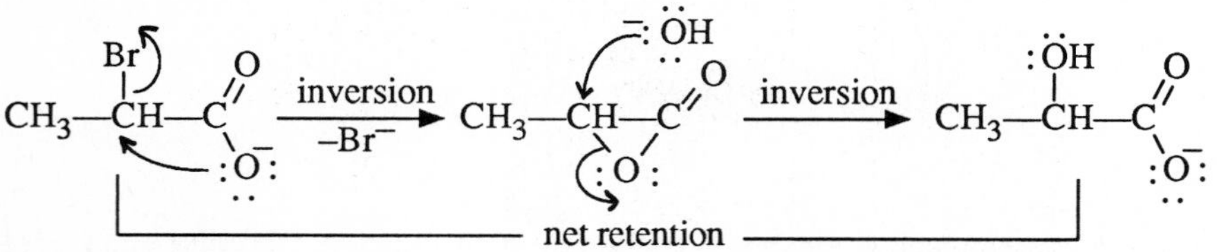

Formation of the β-lactone is an example of *neighboring-group participation* (Sec. 11.6). It is faster than direct attack of hydroxide because the carboxylate ion is present within the same molecule. However, it results in the formation of a strained intermediate, which reacts rapidly with hydroxide. The dilute hydroxide serves to ionize the starting acid and open the β-lactone. The rate of this reaction does not depend on hydroxide concentration, for the rate-determining step is formation of the β-lactone. The direct attack of hydroxide, in contrast, is a conventional S_N2 reaction that proceeds with inversion of configuration. The rate of this reaction depends on the nucleophile ($^-$OH) concentration. In 1*M* NaOH solution, the concentration of NaOH is high enough that the direct S_N2 mechanism is faster than the neighboring-group mechanism. In dilute base, the direct S_N2 mechanism is so slow that the neighboring-group mechanism is observed. This accounts for the differing stereochemical results as a function of base concentration.

55.   (a) Esterification requires attack of the nucleophile (in this case, methanol) on the carbonyl carbon. The two *ortho* methyl groups prevent this attack in the following way. First, the plane of the carbonyl group is turned perpendicular to the plane of the ring to prevent serious steric interactions that would otherwise occur:

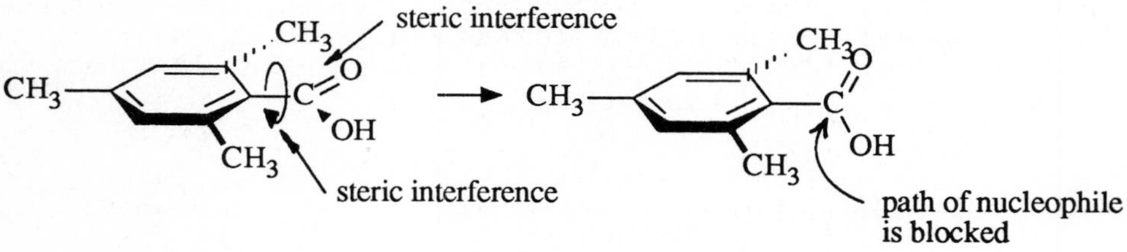

Second, as shown above, the nucleophile must attack the carbonyl carbon perpendicular to the carbonyl plane (see Figure 19.8, text page 775); as shown above, this path is blocked by the methyl groups. Diazomethane, however, does not react at the carbonyl carbon, but at the carboxylate oxygen, which is far enough out from the ring that its reactions are unaffected by steric hindrance.
(b) Once we make the methyl ester with diazomethane, we expect to have trouble hydrolyzing it, because ester hydrolysis involves attack by water at the carbonyl carbon. This process is also blocked by the *ortho* methyl groups. However, the *t*-butyl ester does not cleave by attack of water at the carbonyl carbon, but by a dissociative, S_N1 mechanism (see text page 875). This process takes place at the carboxylate oxygen, which is far enough removed from the ring that steric hindrance does not interfere. In fact, cleavage of the *t*-butyl ester should reduce steric hindrance, and therefore should be particularly rapid for this ester.
(c) Aqueous NaOH cleaves any ester by attack at the carbonyl carbon (saponification). This is hindered for the same reasons that the other nucleophilic reactions above are hindered, and as a result is evidently too slow to be observed.

56. The labeling experiment indicates that the two carbonyl carbon atoms become indistinguishable during the hydrolysis. The results are accounted for by an anhydride intermediate:

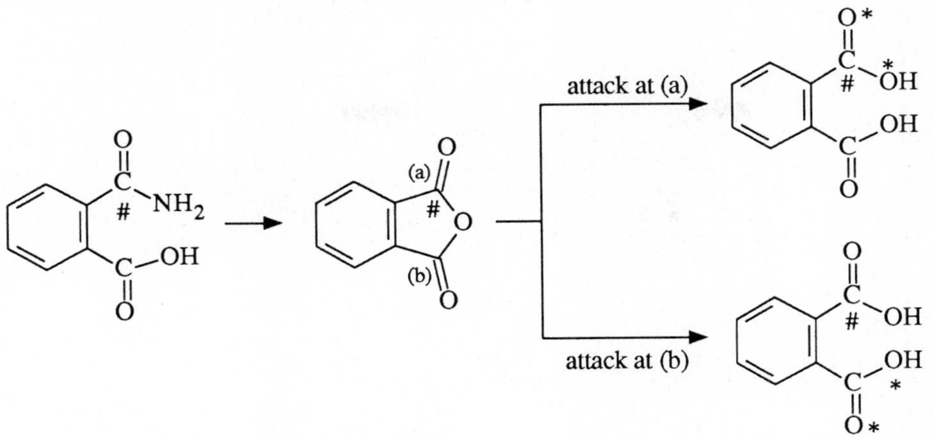

(We leave it to you to show how the anhydride forms.) Because the two carbonyl groups of the anhydride are chemically indistinguishable, equal amounts of label are incorporated at each by attack of labeled water. This is another example of neighboring-group participation, in this case by the neighboring carboxy group.

Chapter 22 / Chemistry of Enols, Enolate Ions, and α,β-Unsaturated Carbonyl Compounds

CHAPTER 22 TERMS

acetoacetic ester synthesis 22.6C
acetyl-CoA 22.7
1,4-addition 22.8A
aldol 22.4A
aldol condensation 22.4A
Claisen condensation 22.5A
Claisen–Schmidt condensation 22.4C
coenzyme A 22.7
conjugate addition 22.8A
crossed aldol condensation 22.4C
crossed Claisen condensation 22.5C
cyanoethylation 22.8A
β-dicarbonyl compound 22.2
Dieckmann condensation 22.5B
enol 22.3
enolate ion 22.1A

F-strain 22.6B
haloform reaction 22.3B
Hell–Volhard–Zelinsky (HVZ) reaction 22.3C
β-hydroxy aldehyde 22.4A
β-hydroxy ketone 22.4A
intramolecular reaction 22.4C
iodoform test 22.3B
β-keto ester 22.5A
malonic ester synthesis 22.6A
Michael addition 22.8A,C
polyketide 22.7B
Robinson annulation 22.8C
sulfonamide 22.1A
tautomer 22.2
α,β-unsaturated carbonyl compound ...... Introduction

CHAPTER 22 CONCEPTS

I. Acidity of Carbonyl Compounds—Enolate Ions:

A. Formation of Enolate Anions:
1. The α-hydrogens of many carbonyl compounds, as well as those of nitriles, are weakly acidic—much more acidic than other types of hydrogens bound to carbon.
2. Ionization of an α-hydrogen gives the conjugate-base anion, called an **enolate ion**.
    a) Enolate ions are resonance stabilized—the orbitals of enolate ions overlap.
    b) The anionic carbon of an enolate ion is sp^2 hybridized.
        (1) This hybridization allows the electron pair of an enolate anion to occupy a p orbital, which overlaps with the π-orbital of a carbonyl group.
        (2) This additional overlap provides additional bonding and hence additional stabilization.
        (3) The negative charge in an enolate ion is delocalized onto oxygen, an electronegative atom.

c) Carbonyl compounds have a lower pK_a (greater acidity) than carbon acids that lack this stabilization.

d) The pK_as of most carbonyl compounds are *lowered* by resonance stabilization of their *conjugate-base enolate ions*.

e) Esters are less acidic than aldehydes or ketones because un-ionized esters are stabilized by resonance within the ester group itself.
   (1) The resonance stabilization of esters accounts for their lower acidity.
   (2) The resonance effect overrides the inductive effect of the carboxylate oxygen, which, in the absence of resonance, would increase the acidity of esters.

3. Amide N—H protons are formally α-protons; the N—H protons are the most acidic protons in primary and secondary amides; carboxylic acid O—H protons are also α-protons.

4. The acidity order of carbonyl compounds corresponds to the reactive electronegativities of the atoms to which the acidic hydrogens are bound:

   reactivities: carboxylic acids > amides > aldehydes, ketones

   electronegativities: oxygen > nitrogen > carbon

5. Amides of sulfonic acids, called sulfonamides, are somewhat stronger acids than carboxylic acid amides, just as sulfonic acids are stronger than carboxylic acids.

B. Introduction to Reactions of Enolate Ions:

1. Enolate ions are key reactive intermediates in many important reactions of carbonyl compounds:
   a) They are Brønsted bases and react with Brønsted acids.
   b) They are not only Brønsted bases, but Lewis bases as well; they react as nucleophiles.
      (1) Enolate ions attack the carbon of carbonyl groups. This attack is the first step of carbonyl addition reactions and carbonyl substitution reactions of enolate ions.
      (2) Enolate ions, like other nucleophiles, also react with alkyl halides and sulfonate esters.

2. The formation of enolate ions and their reactions with Brønsted acids have two simple but important consequences:
   a) In an aldehyde or ketone only the α-hydrogens can be exchanged for deuterium by treating the carbonyl compound with base or acid in D_2O.

   b) If an optically active aldehyde or ketone has an asymmetric α-carbon, and if this carbon bears a hydrogen, the compound will be racemized by base.
      (1) The enolate ion is achiral because of its sp^2 hybridization at the anionic carbon.
      (2) The ionic α-carbon and its attached groups lie in one plane.
      (3) An asymmetric α-carbon in the carbonyl compound is no longer asymmetric in the enolate anion.
      (4) The anion can be reprotonated at either face to give either enantiomer with equal probability.

3. Chemical exchange and racemization occur much more readily on aldehydes and ketones than on esters, because aldehydes and ketones are more acidic.

C. Enolization of Carbonyl Compounds:

1. Carbonyl compounds with α-hydrogens are in equilibrium with vinylic alcohol isomers called **enols**.
   a) Enols and their parent carbonyl compounds are **tautomers** of each other—structural isomers that are formally related only by the shift of a hydrogen and one or more π-bonds.

b) Most carbonyl compounds are considerably more stable than their corresponding enols; the C=O double bond of a carbonyl group is a stronger bond than the C=C of an enol.

c) Phenol is formally an enol, but the enol form of phenol is more stable than its two keto tautomers because phenol is aromatic.

d) The enols of β-dicarbonyl compounds (two carbonyl groups separated by one carbon) are also relatively stable.

(1) These enol forms are conjugated, but their parent carbonyl compounds are not; the π-electron overlap associated with conjugation provides additional bonding that stabilizes the enol.

(2) The intramolecular hydrogen bond present in such enols provides increased bonding and increased stabilization.

3. The interconversions of carbonyl compounds and their enols are catalyzed by both acids and bases.

a) Base-catalyzed enolization involves the intermediacy of the enolate ion, and is thus a consequence of the acidity of the α-hydrogen.

(1) Protonation of the enolate anion by water on the α-carbon gives back the carbonyl compound; protonation on oxygen gives the enol.

(2) The enolate ion is the conjugate base of not only the carbonyl compound, but also the enol.

b) Acid-catalyzed enolization involves the conjugate acid of the carbonyl compound.

(1) Loss of the proton from the α-carbon gives the enol.

(2) An enol and its carbonyl tautomer have the same conjugate acid.

4. Exchange of α-hydrogens for deuterium as well as racemization at the α-carbon are catalyzed not only by bases but also by acids and can be explained by the intermediacy of enols.

a) Formation of a carbonyl compound from an enol reintroduces hydrogen from solution at the α-carbon; this fact accounts for the observed isotope exchange.

b) The α-carbon of an enol, like that of an enolate ion, is not asymmetric.

c) The absence of chirality in the enol accounts for the racemization observed when an aldehyde or ketone with a hydrogen at an asymmetric α-carbon is treated with acid.

II. Approaches to Organic Synthesis:

A. Synthesis with the Aldol Condensation:

1. The Aldol condensation:

a) Is an addition reaction involving two aldehyde or ketone molecules.

b) Can be carried out in acidic or basic solution.

c) Is often used to prepare α,β-unsaturated carbonyl compounds.

2. Given an α,β-unsaturated aldehyde or ketone as a synthetic target, two questions should be asked:

a) What starting materials are required in the aldol condensation?

(1) The starting materials for an aldol condensation can be determined by mentally "splitting" the α,β-unsaturated carbonyl compound at the double bond.

(2) Replace the double bond on the carbonyl side by two hydrogens and on the other side by a carbonyl oxygen (=O).

b) Knowing the required starting materials, is the aldol condensation of these compounds a feasible one?

B. <u>Synthesis with the Claisen Condensation</u>:
   1. The Claisen condensation:
      a) Is a substitution reaction of an enolate ion with an ester group.

$$\underset{}{-\!\!\overset{\overset{O}{\|}}{C}\!-\!OR} \; + \; \overset{\overset{O}{\|}}{\underset{|}{\bar{C}H}\!-\!C\!-} \;\longrightarrow\; \overset{H^+}{\longrightarrow} \; -\!\overset{\overset{O}{\|}}{C}\!-\!\underset{|}{CH}\!-\!\overset{\overset{O}{\|}}{C}\!- \; + \; HOR$$

      b) Requires a full equivalent of base, and does not occur in acid.
   2. Because ionization of the product β-keto ester is crucial to the success of the Claisen condensation, the starting ester must have at least *two* α-hydrogens: one for each of the ionizations.
   3. Think of the Claisen condensation when the synthesis of a β-dicarbonyl compound is desired.
   4. Given a β-dicarbonyl compound, first determine what the required starting materials should be if the compound is to be prepared by a Claisen condensation.
      a) Mentally reverse the Claisen condensation in two ways—add the elements of an alcohol across the carbon–carbon bond at either carbonyl group.

      b) Determine whether the Claisen condensation of the required starting materials is reasonable.
      c) If a crossed Claisen condensation is required, determine whether it is one of those that gives mostly one product, or whether it would be expected to give a difficult-to-separate mixture.

C. <u>Synthesis with the Malonic Ester Reaction</u>:
   1. The malonic ester synthesis involves alkylation of a malonic ester derivative. In many cases the alkylated derivative is saponified and decarboxylated to give a substituted acetic acid derivative.
   2. To determine whether the malonic ester synthesis can be used for the synthesis of a carboxylic acid:
      a) Determine whether the desired carboxylic acid is formally an acetic acid with one or two alkyl groups on its α-carbon.
      b) Mentally reverse the decarboxylation, hydrolysis, and alkylation steps to arrive at the structures of the alkyl halides (or sulfonate esters) that must be used.

      c) If the alkyl halides are among those that will undergo the S_N2 reaction, then the target carboxylic acid can in principle be prepared by the malonic ester synthesis.

D. <u>Synthesis with the Acetoacetic Ester Reaction</u>:
   1. The acetoacetic ester synthesis involves alkylation of a β-keto ester. In many cases the alkylated derivative is saponified and decarboxylated to give a branched ketone.
   2. If a target ketone is to be prepared, mentally reverse the acetoacetic ester synthesis.
      a) Replace an α-hydrogen of the target ketone with a carboethoxy group to unveil the β-keto ester required for the synthesis.
      b) The β-keto ester itself is then analyzed in terms of the alkyl halides required for the alkylation.

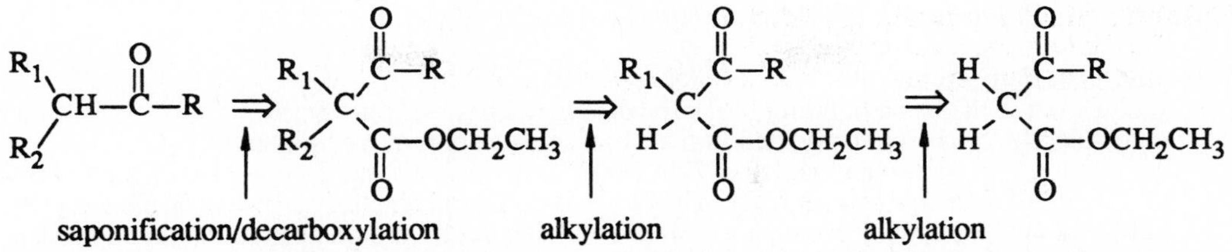

saponification/decarboxylation   alkylation   alkylation

3. Determine whether the β-keto ester is one that can be made by the Claisen condensation.

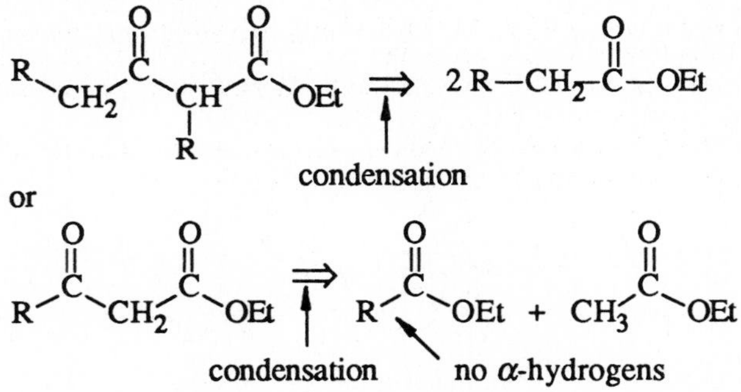

condensation

or

condensation   no α-hydrogens

E. Synthesis with Conjugate-Addition Reactions:
   1. Any group at the β-position of a carbonyl compound can in principle be delivered as a nucleophile in a conjugate addition.
   2. Mentally reverse the conjugate addition by subtracting a nucleophilic group from the β-position of the target molecule, and a positive fragment (usually a proton) from the α-position.

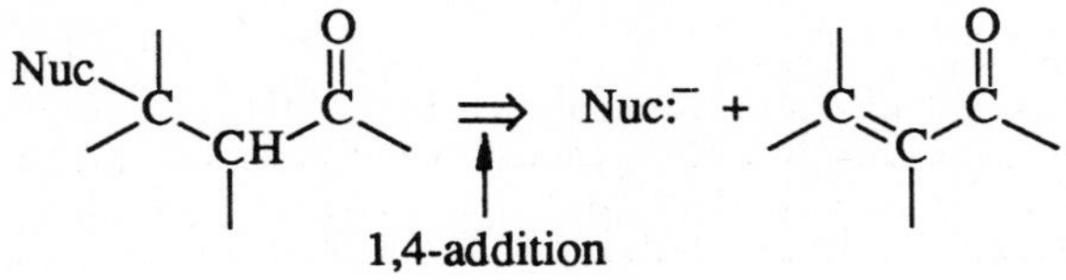

1,4-addition

F. Conjugate-Addition *vs.* Carbonyl-Group Reactions:
   1. Conjugate addition competes with familiar addition to the carbonyl group.
      a) Conjugate addition, in most cases, is irreversible.
      b) Conjugate-addition products are more stable than the carbonyl-addition products.
   2. If carbonyl addition is reversible, then conjugate addition drains the carbonyl compounds from the addition equilibrium, and the conjugate-addition product is formed ultimately—another case of kinetic *vs.* thermodynamic control of a reaction.
      a) The conjugate-addition product is the *thermodynamic* (more stable) product of the reaction.
      b) The conjugate-addition product is more stable than the competing carbonyl-addition product because a C=O bond is stronger than a C=C bond.
   3. Relatively weak bases that give reversible carbonyl-addition reactions with ordinary aldehydes and ketones tend to give conjugate addition with α,β-unsaturated aldehydes and ketones.
   4. In the case of esters, it is also found that relatively weak bases, such as ⁻CN, thiolate anions (⁻SR), and amines (RNH_2 and R_2NH) give conjugate-addition products.
   5. Strong bases give irreversible carbonyl-addition or carbonyl-substitution reactions.
      a) Strong bases that react *irreversibly* at the carbonyl groups of esters give carbonyl-substitution products.
      b) $LiAlH_4$ reduces α,β-unsaturated esters at the carbonyl group, because attack of hydride ion on the carbonyl group is irreversible.

III. Biosynthesis of Compounds Derived from Acetate:

A. Biosynthesis of Fatty Acids:
1. Acetyl-CoA is the basic building block for the biosynthesis of fatty acids.
   a) Acetyl-CoA is first converted into a closely related derivative, malonyl-CoA.
      (1) The acetyl- and malonyl-CoA derivatives are transesterified to give different thiol esters.
      (2) These compounds react in an enzyme-catalyzed reaction to give an acetoacetyl thiol ester.
   b) The nucleophilic electron pair is made available not by proton abstraction, but by loss of CO_2 from malonyl-CoA; the loss of CO_2 also serves to drive the Claisen condensation to completion.
   c) The product then undergoes successively a carbonyl reduction, a dehydration, and a double-bond reduction, each catalyzed by an enzyme; the net result of these three reactions is that the acetyl thiol ester is converted into a thiol ester with two additional carbons.

$$CH_3-\overset{O}{\overset{\|}{C}}-SR \ + \ {}^-O-\overset{O}{\overset{\|}{C}}-CH_2-\overset{O}{\overset{\|}{C}}-SR \ \xrightarrow{\text{condensation}} \ CH_3-\overset{O}{\overset{\|}{C}}-CH_2-\overset{O}{\overset{\|}{C}}-SR \ \xrightarrow{\text{reduction}}$$

$$CH_3-\overset{OH}{\overset{|}{C}H}-CH_2-\overset{O}{\overset{\|}{C}}-SR \ \xrightarrow{\text{elimination}} \ CH_3-CH{=}CH-\overset{O}{\overset{\|}{C}}-SR \ \xrightarrow{\text{reduction}} \ CH_3CH_2CH_2-\overset{O}{\overset{\|}{C}}-SR$$

or

$$CH_3-\overset{O}{\overset{\|}{C}}-SR \ + \ {}^-O-\overset{O}{\overset{\|}{C}}-CH_2-\overset{O}{\overset{\|}{C}}-SR \ \xrightarrow[\substack{\text{2) reduction} \\ \text{3) elimination} \\ \text{4) reduction}}]{\text{1) condensation}} \ CH_3CH_2CH_2-\overset{O}{\overset{\|}{C}}-SR$$

2. This sequence of reactions is then repeated until the proper chain length is obtained.
   a) At each cycle another two carbons are added to the chain.
   b) The fatty acid thiol ester is then transesterified to glycerol to form fats and phospholipids.
3. The common fatty acids have an even number of carbon atoms; those with an odd number of carbon atoms are relatively rare.

B. Biosynthesis of Aromatic Compounds—Polyketides:
1. One of the major pathways for the biosynthesis of aromatic compounds involves ester condensations and aldol condensations.
2. The intermediates in such pathways are **polyketides**—keto esters with carbonyl groups at alternate carbons.

a polyketide (an enol form) $\xrightarrow[\text{reactions}]{\text{condensation}}$

CHAPTER 22 REACTIONS

I. α-Halogenation of Carbonyl Compounds:

A. <u>Acid-Catalyzed α-Hydrogenation of Aldehydes and Ketones</u>:
   1. Halogenation of an aldehyde or ketone in acid solution usually results in the replacement of one α-hydrogen by halogen.
      a) Enols are reactive intermediates in these reactions.
      b) Halogenation of an enol involves a resonance-stabilized carbocation intermediate, which loses a proton to give the α-haloketone.

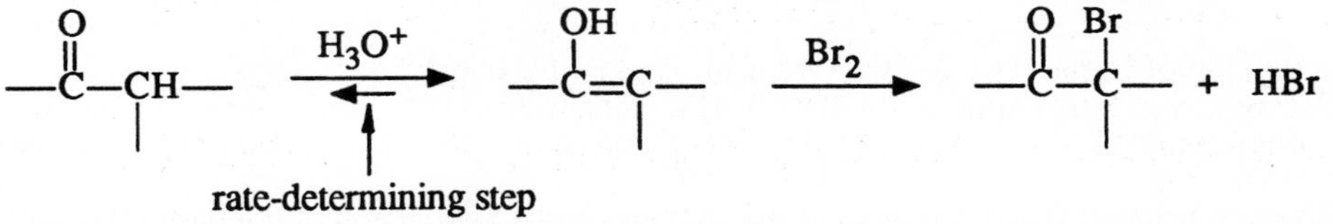

2. The rate law implies that even though the reaction is a halogenation, the rate is independent of the halogen concentration.

$$\text{rate} = k\,[\text{ketone}][\text{H}_3\text{O}^+]$$

   a) Halogens cannot be involved in the transition state for the rate-determining step of the reaction.
   b) Enol formation is the rate-determining step in acid-catalyzed halogenation of aldehydes and ketones.
3. Enolization of a halogenated ketone is much slower than enolization of an unhalogenated ketone; the inductive effect of a halogen at the α-carbon destabilizes the carbocation intermediate in enolization and retards the reaction.

B. <u>Halogenation of Aldehydes and Ketones in Base—the Haloform Reaction</u>:
   1. Halogenation of aldehydes and ketones with α-hydrogens also occurs in base; however, *all* α-protons are substituted by halogen.

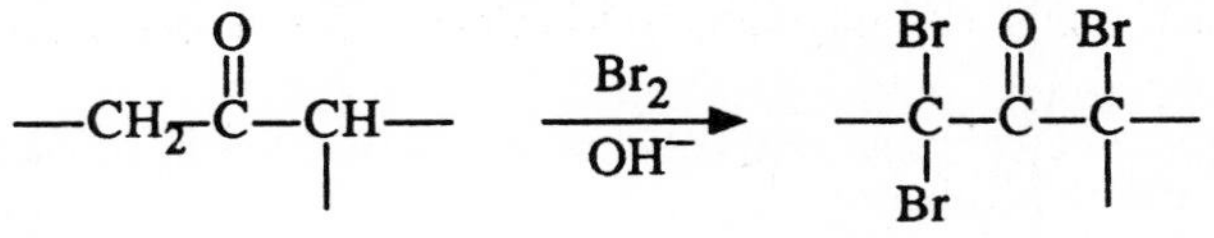

2. When the aldehyde or ketone starting material is either acetaldehyde or a methyl ketone, the trihalo carbonyl compound is not stable under the reaction conditions, and it reacts further to give, after acidification of the reaction mixture, a carboxylic acid and a haloform.
   a) This reaction is called the **haloform reaction**.
   b) A carbon–carbon bond is broken and the carbonyl compound is oxidized.
3. The mechanism of the haloform reaction begins with formation of an enolate ion as a reactive intermediate.
   a) The enolate ion reacts as a nucleophile with halogen to give an α-halo carbonyl compound.
   b) A dihalo and trihalo carbonyl compound are formed more rapidly in successive halogenations.
   c) A carbon–carbon bond is broken when the trihalo carbonyl compound undergoes a substitution reaction at the carbonyl group.
      (1) The leaving group in this reaction is a trihalomethyl anion, which is much less basic than ordinary carbanions.

(2) It reacts almost irreversibly with the carboxylic acid by-product to drive the overall haloform reaction to completion.

(3) The carboxylic acid itself can be isolated by acidifying the reaction mixture.

$$R-\overset{O}{\overset{||}{C}}-CH_3 \xrightarrow[\text{via enolate}]{Br_2/OH^-} R-\overset{O}{\overset{||}{C}}-CH_2-Br \xrightarrow[\text{twice more}]{Br_2/OH^-} R-\overset{O}{\overset{||}{C}}-CBr_3 \xrightarrow[\substack{\text{C-C bond}\\\text{cleavage}}]{Br_2/OH^-} R-\overset{O}{\overset{||}{C}}-O^- + HCBr_3$$

4. The haloform reaction can be used to prepare carboxylic acids from readily available methyl ketones.

5. The haloform reaction is used as a qualitative test for methyl ketones, called the **iodoform test**.

   a) A compound of unknown structure is mixed with alkaline I_2.

   b) A yellow precipitate of iodoform is taken as evidence for a methyl ketone (or acetaldehyde).

   c) α-Substituted ethanol derivatives also give a positive iodoform test because they are oxidized to methyl ketones (or to acetaldehyde, in the case of ethanol) by the basic iodine solution.

C. α-Bromination of Carboxylic Acids—The Hell–Volhard–Zelinsky Reaction:

   1. A bromine is substituted for an α-hydrogen when a carboxylic acid is treated with Br_2 and a catalytic amount of red phosphorus or PBr_3; this reaction is called the **Hell–Volhard–Zelinsky (HVZ) reaction**.

   2. The first stage in the mechanism of this reaction is the conversion of the carboxylic acid into a small amount of acid bromide by the catalyst PBr_3.

      a) The acid bromide enolizes in the presence of acid; this reaction is similar to the acid-catalyzed bromination of ketones.

      b) The enol of the acid bromide then brominates.

$$-\overset{O}{\underset{|}{\overset{||}{CH}}}-\overset{O}{\overset{||}{C}}- \xrightarrow[\text{catalyst}]{PBr_3} -\overset{O}{\underset{|}{\overset{||}{CH}}}-\overset{O}{\overset{||}{C}}-Br \xrightarrow[\text{via enol}]{Br_2} \overset{Br}{\underset{|}{\overset{|}{-C}}}-\overset{O}{\overset{||}{C}}-Br \xrightarrow{RCO_2H} \overset{Br}{\underset{|}{\overset{|}{-C}}}-\overset{O}{\overset{||}{C}}-OH + R-\overset{O}{\overset{||}{C}}-Br$$

      (1) When a *small amount* of PBr_3 catalyst is used, the α-bromo acid bromide sets up an equilibrium with unreacted acid to form more acid bromide, which is then brominated—the reaction product is the α-bromo acid.

      (2) If *one full equivalent* of PBr_3 catalyst is used, the α-bromo acid bromide is the reaction product.

      (3) The reaction mixture can be added to an alcohol to give an α-bromo ester.

D. Reactions of α-Halo Carbonyl Compounds:

   1. Most α-halo carbonyl compounds are very reactive in S_N2 reactions, and can be used to prepare other α-substituted carbonyl compounds.

   2. In the case of α-halo ketones, nucleophiles used in these reactions must not be too basic.

      a) Stronger bases promote enolate-ion formation; and the enolate ions of α-halo ketones undergo other reactions.

      b) More basic nucleophiles can be used with α-halo acids, since acids do not easily form enolate ions; their reactivity is similar to that of allylic alkyl halides in S_N2 reactions

   3. α-Halo carbonyl compounds react so slowly by the S_N1 mechanism that this reaction is not useful; reactions that require the formation of carbocations alpha to carbonyl groups generally do not occur.

II. Condensations Involving Enols and Enolate Ions of Aldehydes and Ketones:

A. Base-Catalyzed Aldol Condensation:

   1. In aqueous base, acetaldehyde undergoes a reaction called the **aldol condensation**.

      a) Two acetaldehyde molecules react to form a β-hydroxy aldehyde called **aldol**.

      b) An enolate ion, formed by reaction of acetaldehyde with aqueous NaOH, adds to a second molecule of acetaldehyde. This is an addition to a carbonyl group with an enolate ion as the nucleophile.

$$CH_3-\overset{O}{\overset{||}{C}}-H \xrightarrow{OH^-} \overset{-}{C}H_2-\overset{O}{\overset{||}{C}}-H \xrightarrow{CH_3CH=O} CH_3-\overset{OH}{\underset{|}{C}}-CH_2-\overset{O}{\overset{||}{C}}-H \quad \text{aldol}$$

    2. The aldol condensation is reversible.
        a) The equilibrium for the aldol condensation is much more favorable for aldehydes than for
           ketones.
        b) Only if the product is removed as it is formed can acetone be used.
    3. In many cases, the conditions of an aldol condensation can be chosen to make the hydroxy aldehyde or
       hydroxy ketone addition product undergo dehydration.

$$2\ R-CH_2-\overset{\overset{\displaystyle O}{\|}}{C}-H \xrightarrow[\substack{\text{condensation} \\ via\ \text{enolate}}]{OH^-} R-CH_2-\underset{\underset{\displaystyle R}{|}}{\overset{\overset{\displaystyle OH}{|}}{CH}}-CH-\overset{\overset{\displaystyle O}{\|}}{C}-H \xrightarrow[\text{dehydration}]{OH^-} R-CH_2-CH=\underset{\underset{\displaystyle R}{|}}{C}-\overset{\overset{\displaystyle O}{\|}}{C}-H$$

        a) Moderately concentrated NaOH catalyzes this dehydration reaction.
        b) β-Hydroxy aldehydes and β-hydroxy ketones undergo base-catalyzed dehydration because:
           (1) The α-hydrogen is relatively acidic.
           (2) The product is conjugated and therefore particularly stable.
    4. The product of an aldol condensation–dehydration sequence is an α,β-unsaturated carbonyl
       compound.
    5. The major use of the aldol condensation is the preparation of α,β-unsaturated aldehydes and ketones.
       Whether addition products or α,β-unsaturated carbonyl compounds are obtained depends on the
       reaction conditions, which must be determined on a case-by-case basis.

  B. <u>Acid-Catalyzed Aldol Condensation</u>:
    1. Aldol condensations are also catalyzed by acid; the reactive intermediates are enols.
    2. Protonation of an aldehyde or ketone gives its conjugate acid, which behaves like a carbocation.
        a) The protonated carbonyl group adds to the double bond of an enol derived from a second
           molecule of ketone starting material.
        b) This addition gives another protonated carbonyl group, which upon loss of a proton gives the
           aldol condensation product.
        c) Under the acidic conditions, the alcohol product dehydrates by the usual mechanism for acid-
           catalyzed alcohol dehydration to give an α,β-unsaturated carbonyl compound.

$$2\ RCH_2-\overset{\overset{\displaystyle O}{\|}}{C}-CH_2R \xrightarrow[\substack{\text{condensation} \\ via\ \text{enol}}]{H_3O^+} RCH_2-\underset{\underset{\displaystyle CH_2R}{|}}{\overset{\overset{\displaystyle HO}{|}}{C}}-CHR-\overset{\overset{\displaystyle O}{\|}}{C}-CH_2R \xrightarrow{\text{dehydration}} RCH_2-C=\underset{\underset{\displaystyle CH_2R}{|}}{CR}-\overset{\overset{\displaystyle O}{\|}}{C}-CH_2R$$

  C. <u>Special Types of Aldol Condensations</u>:
    1. If two different carbonyl compounds are used, a **crossed aldol condensation** occurs, and up to
       four different aldol condensation products can be obtained as a difficult-to-separate mixture.
    2. Under protic conditions (aqueous or alcoholic acid or base), useful crossed aldol condensations as a
       practical matter are limited to situations in which a ketone with α-hydrogens is condensed with an
       aldehyde without α-hydrogens.
    3. An important example of this type of crossed aldol condensation is the Claisen–Schmidt condensation.
        a) A ketone with α-hydrogens is condensed with an aromatic aldehyde that has no α-hydrogens.

$$\underset{Ph}{\overset{\overset{\displaystyle O}{\|}}{C}}{}_{\diagdown H}\ +\ CH\underset{\diagup CH_3}{\overset{\overset{\displaystyle O}{\|}}{C}} \xrightarrow[via\ \text{enol}]{\text{condensation}} \underset{Ph}{\overset{\overset{\displaystyle OH}{|}}{CH}}\diagdown_{CH_2}\underset{\diagup CH_3}{\overset{\overset{\displaystyle O}{\|}}{C}} \xrightarrow{\text{dehydration}} Ph-CH=CH-\overset{\overset{\displaystyle O}{\|}}{C}-CH_3$$

        b) There are three reasons why the Claisen–Schmidt condensation proceeds as it does.
           (1) The aldehyde cannot condense with itself; it has no α-hydrogens.
           (2) Addition of the ketone enolate to an aldehyde is slower than addition to a second molecule
              of ketone; aldehydes are more reactive than ketones.
           (3) If addition to the ketone does occur, it is reversible and has an unfavorable equilibrium
              constant.
        c) The Claisen–Schmidt condensation, like other aldol condensations, is also catalyzed by acid.

4. When a molecule contains more than one aldehyde or ketone group, an **intramolecular reaction** (a reaction within the same molecule) is possible; the resulting formation of a ring is particularly favorable when unstrained five- and six-membered rings can be formed.

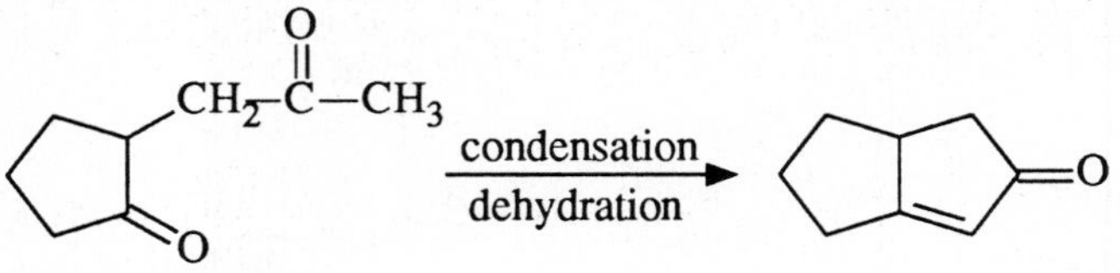

III. Condensation Reactions Involving Ester Enolate Ions:

A. Claisen Condensation:
   1. The **Claisen condensation** is a reaction used for the formation of β-dicarbonyl compounds: compounds with two carbonyl groups in a β-relationship. Such compounds include β-keto esters and β-diketones.
   2. In the simplest type of Claisen condensation, an enolate ion is formed by reaction of an ester with an alkoxide base. This enolate ion then undergoes a carbonyl-substitution reaction with a second molecule of ester.

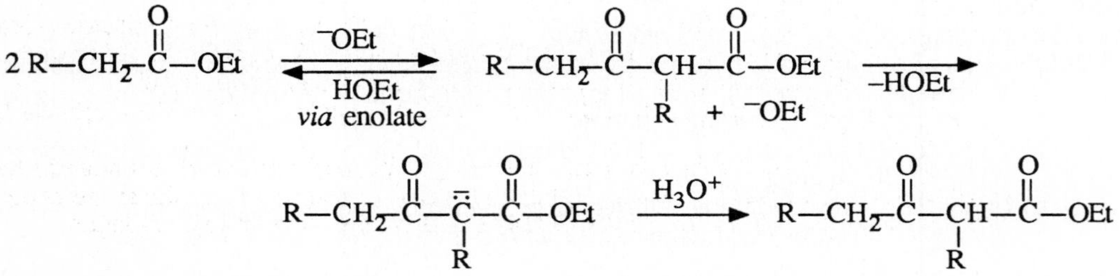

   a) The overall reaction is readily reversible, and the equilibrium favors the starting materials.
   b) The Claisen condensation has to be driven to completion by applying LeChatelier's principle.
      (1) This is usually accomplished by using one equivalent of alkoxide catalyst.
      (2) The hydrogens adjacent to both carbonyl groups in the β-keto ester product are especially acidic; the alkoxide removes one of these hydrogens to form quantitatively the conjugate base of the product.
   c) The un-ionized β-keto ester product is formed after acid is added subsequently to the reaction mixture.
   3. Attempts to react an ester that has only one α-hydrogen give little or no product.
      a) The desired condensation product has no α-protons acidic enough to react completely with the alkoxide.
      b) If the desired product is subjected to the conditions of the Claisen condensation, it readily decomposes back to starting materials because of the reversibility of the Claisen condensation.

B. Dieckmann Condensation:
   1. Intramolecular Claisen condensations take place readily when five- or six-membered rings can be formed.

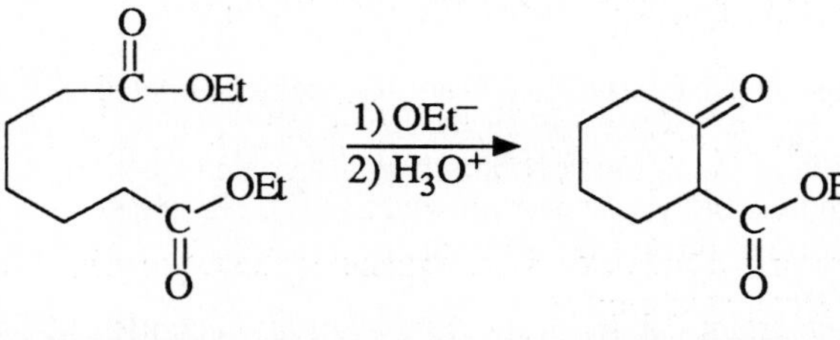

   2. The intramolecular Claisen condensation reaction is called the **Dieckmann condensation**.
   3. The α-proton must be removed from the initially formed product in order for the reaction to be driven to completion.

C. Crossed Claisen Condensation:

1. The Claisen condensation of two *different* esters is called a **crossed Claisen condensation**; the crossed Claisen condensation of two esters that both have α-hydrogens gives a mixture of four compounds that are typically difficult to separate.
2. Crossed Claisen condensations are possible if one ester is especially reactive, or has no α-hydrogens. Formate esters and diethyl carbonate are frequently used in this type of reaction.

no α-hydrogens

$$H-\overset{\overset{\displaystyle O}{\|}}{C}-OEt \;+\; R-CH_2-\overset{\overset{\displaystyle O}{\|}}{C}-OEt \quad \xrightarrow[\text{2) H}_3\text{O}^+]{\text{1) OEt}^-} \quad H-\overset{\overset{\displaystyle O}{\|}}{C}-\underset{\underset{\displaystyle R}{|}}{C}H-\overset{\overset{\displaystyle O}{\|}}{C}-OEt$$

3. Another type of crossed Claisen condensation is the reaction of ketones with esters having no α-hydrogens.

a) In this type of reaction, the enolate ion of a ketone attacks the carbonyl group of an ester.
b) There are four reasons why this type of condensation is successful:
   (1) The aldol condensation of two ketones is reversible, whereas the Claisen condensation is irreversible because one equivalent of base is used to form the enolate ion of the product.
   (2) The ester has no α-hydrogens, and thus cannot condense with itself.
   (3) Because ketones are more acidic than esters, the ketone enolate is the major enolate species in solution.
   (4) The ester is present in excess and is therefore the major carbonyl compound in solution.
c) The product is a β-diketone, which, like a β-keto ester, is especially acidic at the α-position, and ionizes completely under the basic conditions to drive the reaction to completion.

IV. Alkylation of Ester Enolate Ions:

A. Direct Alkylation of Enolate Ions Derived from Simple Monoesters:

1. A family of very strong, hindered nitrogen bases can be used to form stable enolate ions at –78° from esters.
   a) These amide bases are strong enough to convert esters completely into their conjugate-base enolate ions.
      (1) Attack of the amide base on the carbonyl group of the ester is inhibited by the large branched groups on the amide base.
      (2) Such an effect of hindrance in a nucleophile has been aptly termed **F-strain**, or "front-strain."
   b) The ester enolate anions formed with these bases can be alkylated directly with alkyl halides, and esters that are trisubstituted at the α-position can be prepared with this method.
   c) The nitrogen bases themselves are generated from the corresponding amines and butyllithium at –78° in tetrahydrofuran.

$$i\text{-}Pr_2\overset{..}{N}H \quad \xrightarrow[-78°]{\text{MeLi}} \quad i\text{-}Pr_2\overset{..}{N}:^- \;\; Li^+ \;+\; CH_4\uparrow$$

$$-\underset{|}{\overset{|}{C}}H-\overset{\overset{\displaystyle O}{\|}}{C}-OEt \quad \xrightarrow[\text{2) RX}]{\text{1) } i\text{-}Pr_2\overset{..}{N}:^- \text{ Li}^+/-78°} \quad -\underset{|}{\overset{\overset{\displaystyle R}{|}}{C}}-\overset{\overset{\displaystyle O}{\|}}{C}-OEt$$

2. This type of reaction is considerably more expensive than the malonic ester synthesis and requires special inert-atmosphere techniques.

B. <u>Acetoacetic Ester Synthesis</u>:
    1. The preparation of alkylated β-keto esters is called the **acetoacetic ester synthesis.**
        a) β-Keto esters are substantially more acidic than ordinary esters, and are completely ionized by alkoxide bases.
        b) The resulting enolate ions can be alkylated by alkyl halides or sulfonate esters.

$$
\underset{}{-\overset{O}{\overset{\|}{C}}-CH_2-\overset{O}{\overset{\|}{C}}-OEt} \quad \xrightarrow[\text{2) } R_1X]{\text{1) } OEt^-} \quad -\overset{O}{\overset{\|}{C}}-\underset{R_1}{\overset{|}{C}H}-\overset{O}{\overset{\|}{C}}-OEt \quad \xrightarrow[\text{2) } R_2X]{\text{1) } OEt^-} \quad -\overset{O}{\overset{\|}{C}}-\underset{R_1'\ \ R_2}{C}-\overset{O}{\overset{\|}{C}}-OEt
$$

    2. β-Keto esters can be saponified or hydrolyzed, and the resulting β-keto acids can be easily decarboxylated to yield ketones.

$$
-\overset{O}{\overset{\|}{C}}-\underset{R_1'\ \ R_2}{C}-\overset{O}{\overset{\|}{C}}-OEt \quad \xrightarrow[\text{2) } H_3O^+]{\text{1) } OH^-} \quad -\overset{O}{\overset{\|}{C}}-\underset{R_1'\ \ R_2}{C}-\overset{O}{\overset{\|}{C}}-OH \quad \xrightarrow{H_3O^+} \quad -\overset{O}{\overset{\|}{C}}-\underset{R_2}{\overset{R_1}{C}H} + CO_2
$$

        a) The acetoacetic ester synthesis can be extended to a preparation of ketones in the same sense that the malonic ester synthesis can be extended to a preparation of substituted acetic acids.
        b) If the desired β-keto ester is disubstituted at the α-position, alkaline hydrolysis is usually avoided since alkaline conditions promote reversal of the Claisen or Dieckmann condensations of disubstituted β-keto esters.
    3. The use of a *t*-butyl ester permits an ester cleavage under mild acidic conditions.

C. <u>Malonic Ester Synthesis</u>:
    1. The synthesis of alkylated derivatives of malonate esters is called the **malonic ester synthesis.**
    2. Diethyl malonate (**malonic ester**), like many other β-dicarbonyl compounds, has unusually acidic α-protons.
        a) Its conjugate-base enolate ion can be formed quantitatively with alkoxide bases such as sodium ethoxide.
        b) The conjugate-base anion of diethyl malonate is nucleophilic, and it reacts with alkyl halides and sulfonate esters in typical S_N2 reactions.
            (1) This reaction can be used to introduce alkyl groups at the α-position of malonic ester.
            (2) This reaction is limited to alkyl halides and sulfonates that can undergo S_N2 reactions.
        c) A monoalkylated derivative of diethyl malonate can be treated again with ethoxide and alkylated a second time.

$$
EtO-\overset{O}{\overset{\|}{C}}-CH_2-\overset{O}{\overset{\|}{C}}-OEt \quad \xrightarrow[\text{2) } R_1X]{\text{1) } OEt^-} \quad EtO-\overset{O}{\overset{\|}{C}}-\underset{R_1}{\overset{|}{C}H}-\overset{O}{\overset{\|}{C}}-OEt \quad \xrightarrow[\text{2) } R_2X]{\text{1) } OEt^-} \quad EtO-\overset{O}{\overset{\|}{C}}-\underset{R_1'\ \ R_2}{C}-\overset{O}{\overset{\|}{C}}-OEt
$$

    3. The malonic ester synthesis can be extended to the preparation of carboxylic acids.
        a) Saponification and acidification of the diester gives a substituted malonic acid derivative.
        b) Heating any malonic acid derivative causes it to decarboxylate.

$$
EtO-\overset{O}{\overset{\|}{C}}-\underset{R_1'\ \ R_2}{C}-\overset{O}{\overset{\|}{C}}-OEt \quad \xrightarrow[\text{2) } H_3O^+]{\text{1) } OH^-} \quad HO-\overset{O}{\overset{\|}{C}}-\underset{R_1'\ \ R_2}{C}-\overset{O}{\overset{\|}{C}}-OH \quad \xrightarrow[\text{heat}]{H_3O^+} \quad R_1-\underset{R_2}{\overset{|}{C}H}-\overset{O}{\overset{\|}{C}}-OH + CO_2
$$

            (1) The result of alkylation, saponification, and decarboxylation is a carboxylic acid that is formally a disubstituted acetic acid—an acetic acid molecule with two alkyl groups on its α-carbon.
            (2) An ester of malonic acid bearing only one alkyl group at its α-carbon may also be hydrolyzed and decarboxylated to give a "monoalkylated acetic acid."

V. Conjugate-Addition Reactions:

A. Conjugate Addition to α,β-Unsaturated Carbonyl Compounds:
  1. An addition to the double bond of an α,β-unsaturated carbonyl compound is a **conjugate addition** (**1,4-addition**).

1,4-addition   protonation   tautomerization

  a) Consider the initial product in the addition of HBr to an α,β-unsaturated carbonyl compound and see that the H and the Br add in a 1,4-relationship, just as they do in the 1,4-addition to butadiene.

1,4-addition

  b) The 1,4-relationship specifies the number of atoms between the H and the Br after the *initial* addition; it has nothing to do with the numbering of the carbonyl compound for nomenclature purposes.
  2. Nucleophilic addition to the carbon–carbon double bonds of α,β-unsaturated aldehydes, ketones, esters, and nitriles is a rather general reaction that can be observed with a variety of nucleophiles.
  a) The addition of a nucleophile to acrylonitrile is a useful reaction called **cyanoethylation**.
  b) Quinones are α,β-unsaturated carbonyl compounds, and also undergo similar addition reactions.
  c) When cyanide is the nucleophile, a new carbon–carbon bond is formed—the nitrile group can subsequently be converted into a carboxylic acid group by acid hydrolysis.
  3. Addition of a nucleophile to the double bond of an α,β-unsaturated carbonyl compound can occur because it gives a resonance-stabilized enolate ion intermediate.
  a) The overall result of the reaction after protonation is net addition to the double bond.
  b) **Nucleophilic conjugate additions** are sometimes called **Michael additions**.
  4. Acid-catalyzed additions to the carbon–carbon double bonds of α,β-unsaturated carbonyl compounds are also known.
  a) The more basic portion of an α,β-unsaturated carbonyl compound is not the double bond, but rather the carbonyl oxygen.
  b) Protonation on the carbonyl oxygen yields a cation in which some of the positive charge is present on the β-carbon.
  c) Attack of a nucleophile at the β-carbon yields an enol, which rapidly reverts to the observed carbonyl product.

B. Conjugate Addition of Enolate Ions—Michael Addition:
  1. Enolate ions undergo conjugate-addition reactions with α,β-unsaturated carbonyl compounds. This type of reaction is called a **Michael addition**.

  2. The Michael addition goes to completion because a carbon–carbon π-bond in the starting α,β-unsaturated carbonyl compound is replaced by a stronger carbon–carbon σ-bond.
  3. Many Michael addition products can in principle originate from two different pairs of reactants.
  a) The pair of reactants with the less basic enolate ion is chosen.
  b) Stronger bases tend to give carbonyl-group reactions rather than conjugate-addition reactions.

4. In one useful variation of the Michael addition, called the **Robinson annulation,** a Michael addition product can be subjected to an intramolecular aldol condensation reaction to form a ring. (An annulation is a ring-forming reaction.)

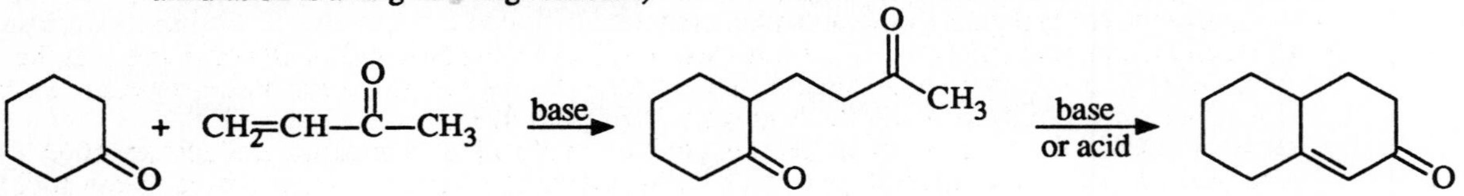

VI. Reactions of α,β-Unsaturated Carbonyl Compounds with Other Nucleophiles:

A. Reduction of α,β-Unsaturated Carbonyl Compounds:
   1. The carbonyl group of an α,β-unsaturated aldehyde or ketone is reduced to an alcohol with lithium aluminum hydride.

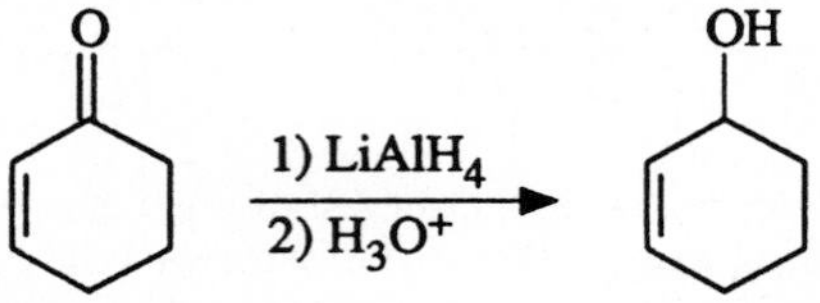

   a) This reaction involves the attack of hydride at the carbonyl carbon, and is therefore a carbonyl addition.
   b) Carbonyl addition is not only faster than conjugate addition, but in this case, also irreversible.
      (1) The hydride is a very poor leaving group.
      (2) Reduction of the carbonyl group with LiAlH$_4$ is a kinetically controlled reaction.
   2. Many α,β-unsaturated carbonyl compounds are reduced by NaBH$_4$ to give mixtures of both carbonyl-addition products and conjugate-addition products.
   3. The carbon–carbon double bond of an α,β-unsaturated carbonyl compound can in most cases be reduced selectively by catalytic hydrogenation.

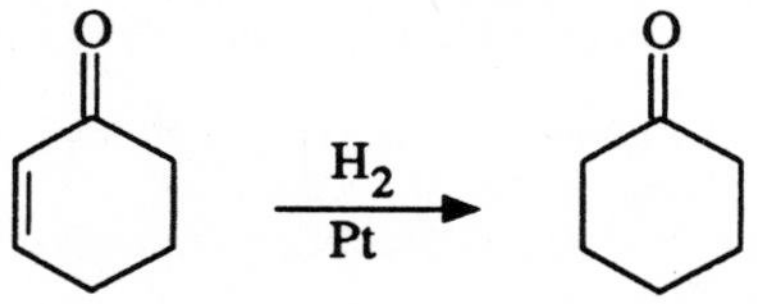

B. Addition of Organolithium Reagents to the Carbonyl Group:
   1. Organolithium reagents react with α,β-unsaturated carbonyl compounds to yield products of carbonyl addition.
   2. The product is the result of kinetic control, since carbonyl addition is rapid and irreversible.

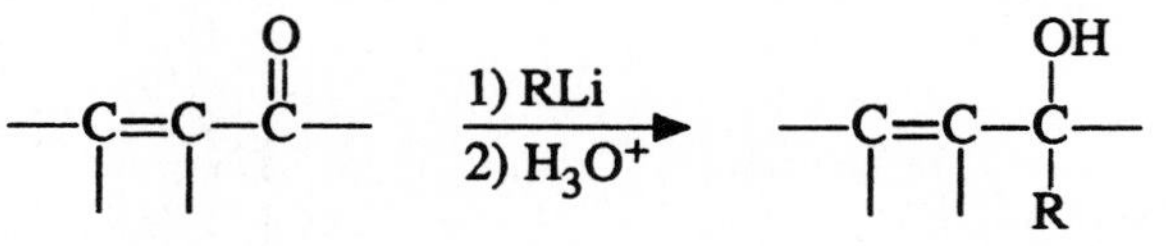

C. Conjugate Addition of Lithium Dialkylcuprate Reagents:
   1. Lithium dialkylcuprate reagents give exclusively products of conjugate addition when they react with α,β-unsaturated esters and ketones.

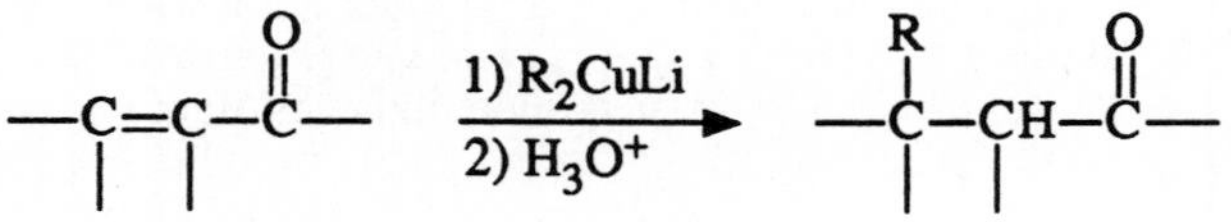

       a) Conjugate addition is also observed with Grignard reagents to which small amounts of CuCl have been added.

       b) Magnesium dialkylcuprate reagents are formed under these circumstances, and these react much like the corresponding lithium dialkyl cuprates.

2. Although the mechanism may be more complex, the reaction can be conceptually envisioned as the attack of an alkyl anion from the dialkylcuprate on the β-carbon to give a resonance-stabilized enolate ion; protonation of this ion gives the conjugate-addition product.

3. It is found that mixtures of carbonyl-addition products and conjugate-addition products are often obtained when Grignard reagents react with α,β-unsaturated carbonyl compounds; to obtain addition with an α,β-unsaturated carbonyl compound and avoid conjugate addition, it is usually best to use an organolithium reagent.

CHAPTER 22 SOLUTIONS

Solutions to In-Text Problems

1. The acidic proton in each case is the one on the carbon *between* the two carbonyl groups. The anions formed when these protons are ionized are stabilized by resonance interaction with *two* carbonyl groups. For example, the resonance structures of the anion formed in the ionization of ethyl acetoacetate are as follows (B:$^-$ = base):

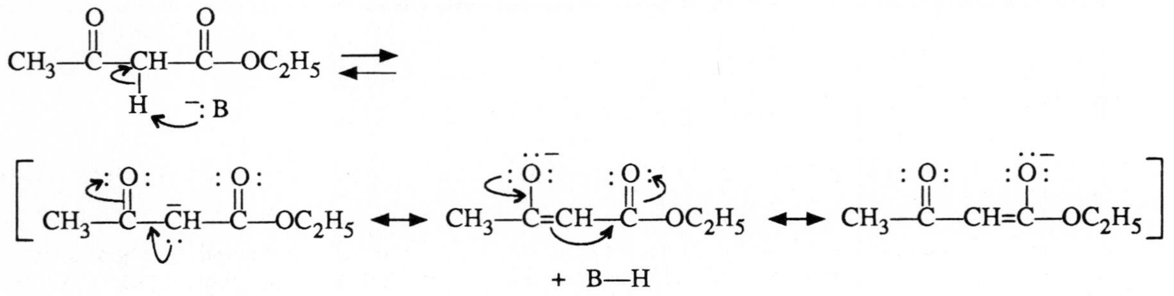

(Recall from text pages 300–301 that stabilization of a conjugate-base anion lowers the pK_a of an acid.) You should draw the resonance structures of the conjugate-base anion of diethyl malonate if you have not already done so.

2. Did you draw the structures before attempting to answer the question? If not, do so now and attempt to answer the question before reading further. Use the index if you need help with the structures. Succinimide is more acidic because its conjugate-base anion is stabilized by resonance interaction with two carbonyl groups. (See previous problem.)

3. The mechanism involves formation of the conjugate-base enolate anion and its reaction with D_2O. This happens repetitively until all the α-hydrogens have been replaced by deuterium.

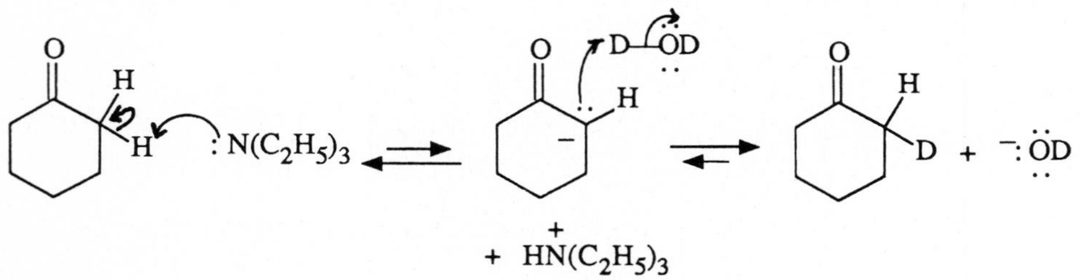

Since D_2O is the solvent, there is a large excess of deuterium in the solvent relative to the hydrogen in the ketone. Hence, once a hydrogen has been removed, the probability that it will return is very small. Only the α-hydrogens are replaced because these are the only hydrogens in the molecule that are acidic enough to be removed.

4. The first part of the problem is to predict the spectrum of 2-butanone *before* it undergoes exchange. The NMR spectrum of 2-butanone is summarized in Problem 4(b), text page 766. The resonances at δ 2.03 and δ 2.38 are those of the α-hydrogens. When the α-hydrogens are replaced by deuteriums, these resonances disappear, as does the splitting associated with them. Hence, when 2-butanone is treated with D_2O in base, the NMR spectrum of 2-butanone becomes a singlet at δ 0.95.

5. As shown in Eq. 15.42, text page 613, the enolate ion has a resonance structure that violates Bredt's rule. Because this resonance structure is strained, it is not important. Since the enolate ion is not resonance-stabilized, it is not formed as easily as ordinary enolate ions. Because exchange depends upon formation of the enolate ion, exchange does not occur.

6. (a)

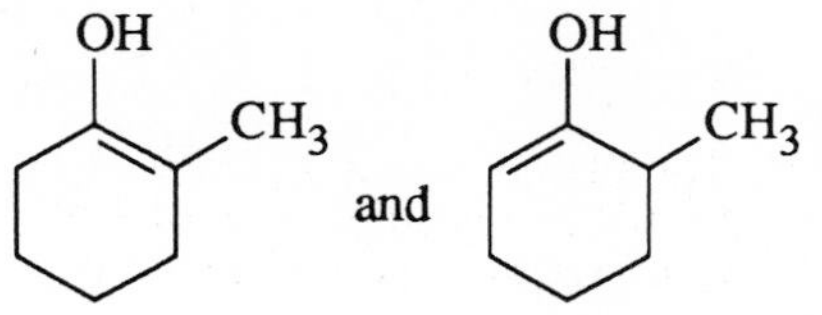

(b) None.

(c) $CH_2{=}C(OH){-}N(CH_3)_2$

(d) $CH_2{=}C(OH){-}CH_2CH_3$ and $CH_3{-}C(OH){=}CHCH_3$ (*E* and *Z*)

(e) $CH_3CH_2CH_2C(CH_3){=}C(OH)_2$

(f) $CH_3CH{=}C{=}NH$

Compound (b), benzaldehyde, has no enol forms because it has no α-hydrogens. In order to form an enol, a compound must have α-hydrogens.

7. (a) One of the reasons enols of β-diketones are stabilized is that they can form internal hydrogen bonds. Such hydrogen bonds are particularly advantageous to the molecule when it cannot form other types of hydrogen bonds. In hexane, for example, the only hydrogen bonding available to 2,4-pentanedione is internal hydrogen bonding. When the solvent can donate and accept hydrogen bonds, the energetic advantage of enol formation due to hydrogen bonding is eliminated. Hence, the amount of enol form in water is reduced. Of course, the advantage due to conjugation is still present; thus, 2,4-pentanedione has much more enol form than ordinary ketones even in water.
(b) The strong UV absorption is due to the $\pi \rightarrow \pi^*$ transition in the enol; this, in turn, is associated with the conjugated π-electron system in the enol. Since the diketone form lacks this conjugation, it also lacks the strong UV absorption. Since there is less of the enol form in water for the reasons given in part (a), there is also a weaker UV absorption.

8. (a) The mechanism of deuterium exchange in acidic solution involves the enol intermediate:

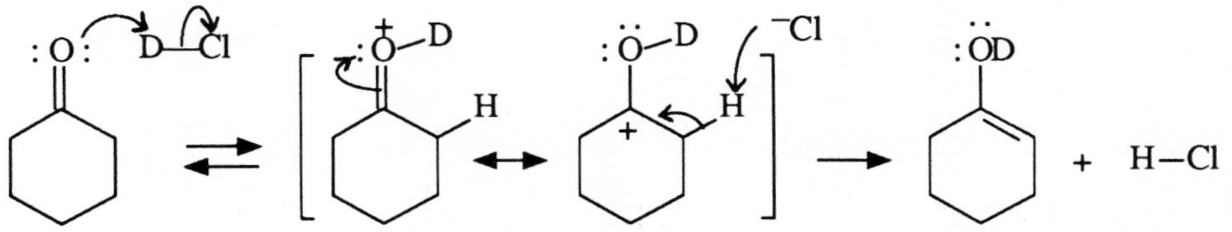

Once the enol is formed, the reverse reaction involving DCl as the acid forms the deuterated species:

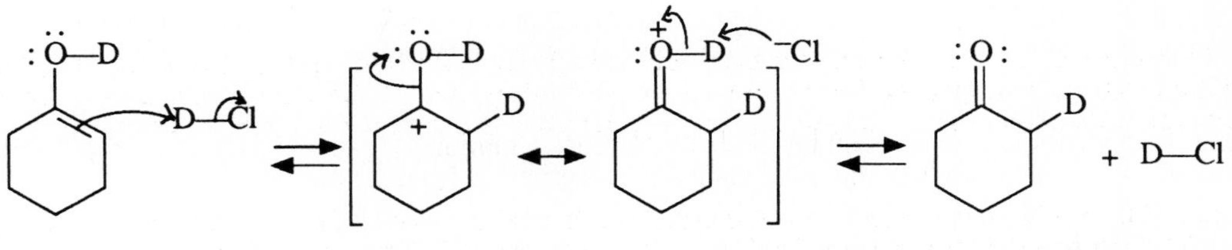

These two reactions continue indefinitely and ultimately bring about the exchange of all α-protons. Because deuterated acid is the solvent and is in excess, it is much more probable for the enol to be protonated by deuterated acid than by the small amount of HCl or H_3PO_4 formed in the reaction.

(b) The racemization occurs because the enol is achiral and can be protonated from either face of the double bond:

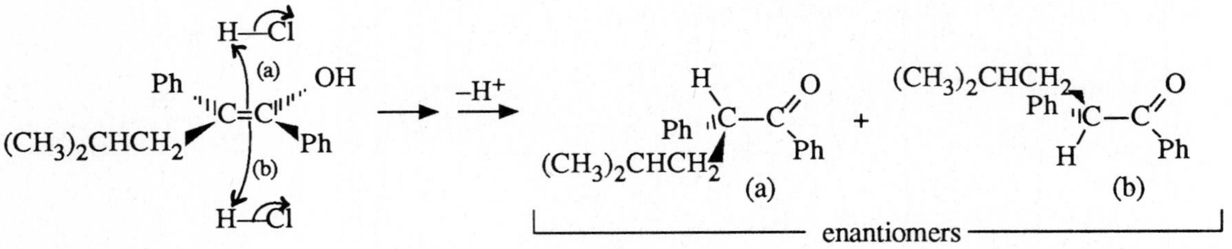

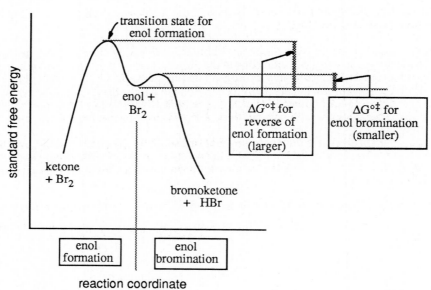

Protonation from opposite faces gives enantiomers. (The mechanisms of formation of the enol, and loss of the proton from the protonated enol, follow from Eq. 22.16a–b.)

9. Since enol formation is rate-determining, the transition state for this reaction has the highest standard free energy:

Bromination of the enol is the faster reaction because, according to the diagram above, it has the lower standard free energy of activation.

10. (a) The rate is the same because the rate-determining step is the same: formation of the enol.
(b) The rate is the same because, as the rate law in Eq. 22.22 shows, the rate is independent of halogen concentration. If the rate is independent of halogen *concentration*, it must be independent of the *type* of halogen.

11. Compound (b) does not react because it has no α-hydrogens. Compound (c) is oxidized to acetophenone, a methyl ketone, which then reacts in the usual manner. The products from (a) and (c) are:

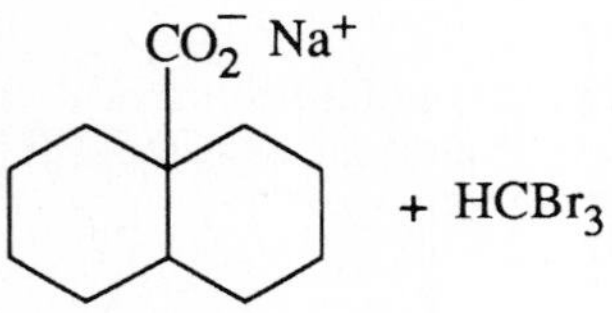

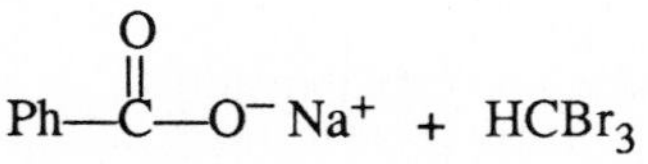

12.   The compound is 2,5-hexanedione:

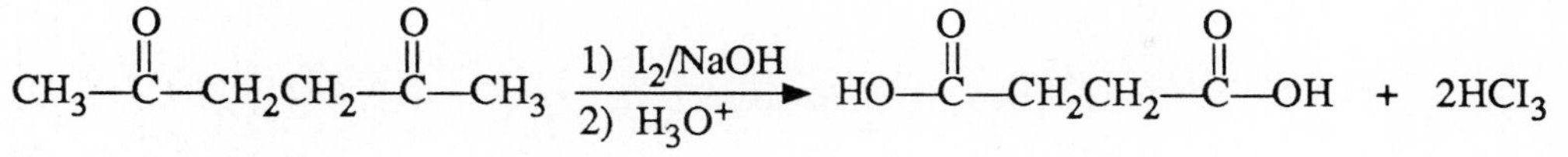

13.   The α-bromo acid bromide is formed from the reaction with PBr_3 and Br_2; this then reacts with ammonia to give the α-amino amide.

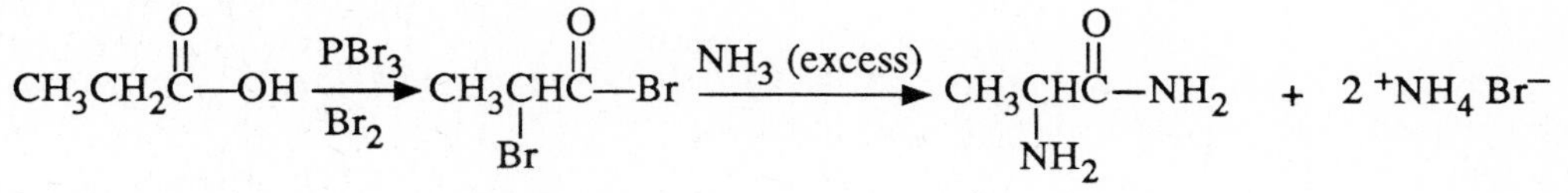

14.   The pyridine displaces bromide ion in an S_N2 reaction:

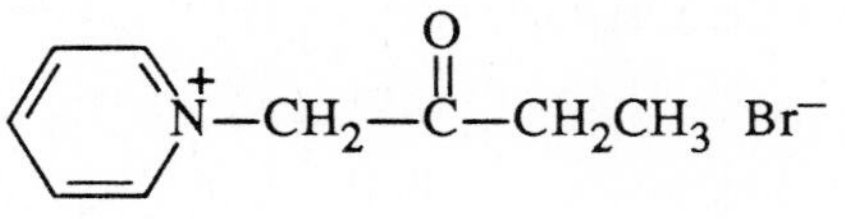

15.   The purpose of the NaOH is to form the conjugate-base anion of 2,4-dichlorophenol. This anion is the nucleophile that reacts with α-chloroacetic acid. (The phenol itself is not nucleophilic enough to act as a nucleophile in an S_N2 reaction.) With this in mind we can write the mechanism:

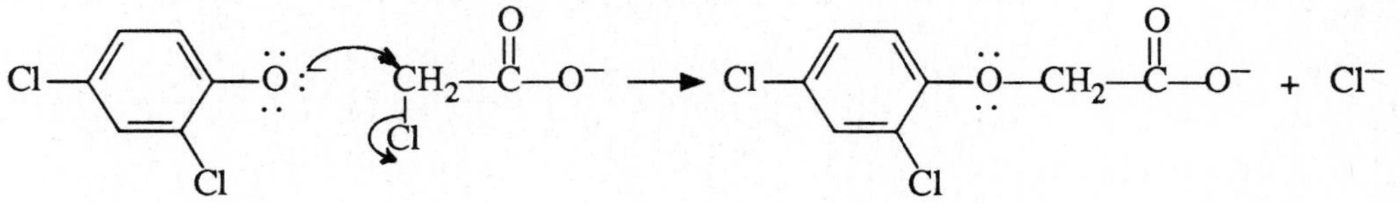

Notice that α-chloroacetic acid is also ionized under the conditions of the reaction. Since the carboxylate ion also can act as a nucleophile, we might expect the following side reaction to give compound *A*:

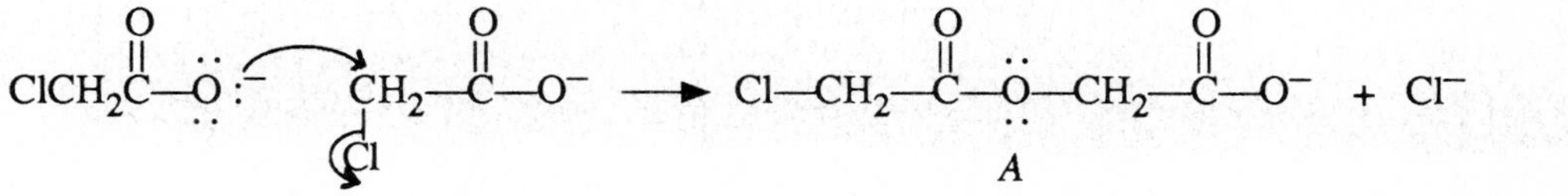

Another side reaction is the attack of ⁻OH on the chloro acid to give compound *B*:

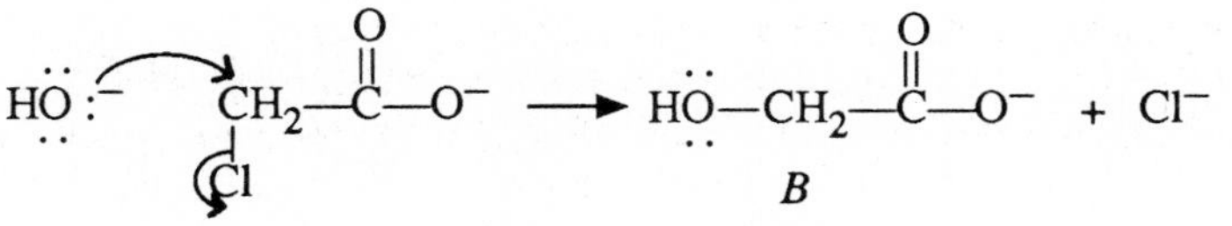

Furthermore, if compound *A* above forms, it would probably react rapidly to give compound *B* by the following mechanism:

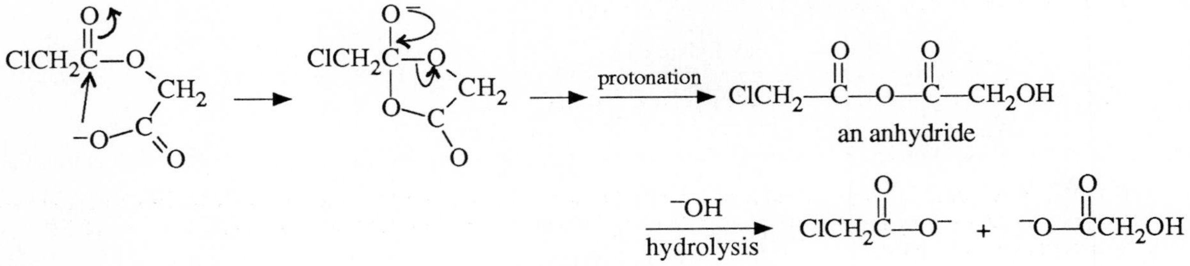

ClCH$_2$C—O—C—CH$_2$OH
an anhydride

$\xrightarrow[\text{hydrolysis}]{^-\text{OH}}$ ClCH$_2$C—O$^-$ + $^-$O—CCH$_2$OH

16. The aldol condensation of propionaldehyde proceeds as follows:

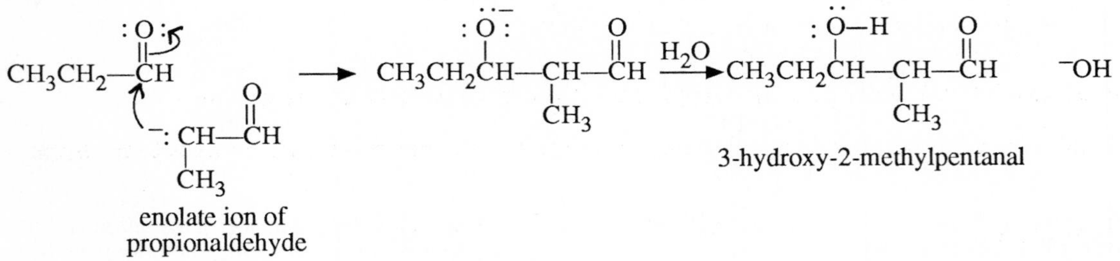

3-hydroxy-2-methylpentanal

enolate ion of
propionaldehyde

17. The four products are as follows:

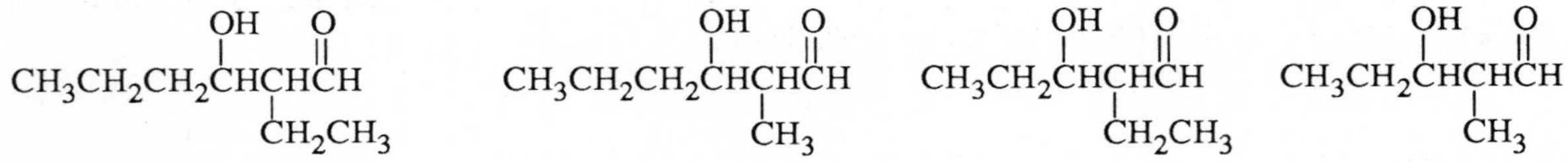

OH O
CH$_3$CH$_2$CH$_2$CHCHCH
CH$_2$CH$_3$

B + B

OH O
CH$_3$CH$_2$CH$_2$CHCHCH
CH$_3$

B + P

OH O
CH$_3$CH$_2$CHCHCH
CH$_2$CH$_3$

P + B

OH O
CH$_3$CH$_2$CHCHCH
CH$_3$

P + P

18. (a) This is a Claisen–Schmidt condensation:

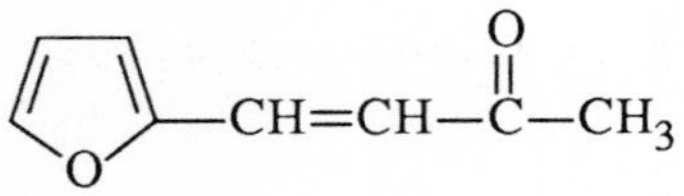

—CH=CH—C—CH$_3$

(b) This is an intramolecular aldol condensation to form a five-membered ring:

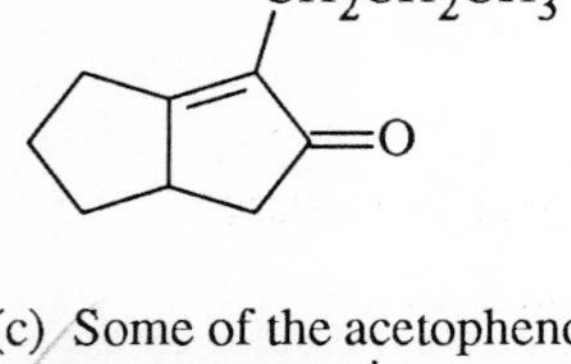

CH$_2$CH$_2$CH$_3$

=O

(c) Some of the acetophenone would condense with the hexanal; but since hexanal is an aldehyde, we can also expect some reaction to occur between two equivalents of hexanal:

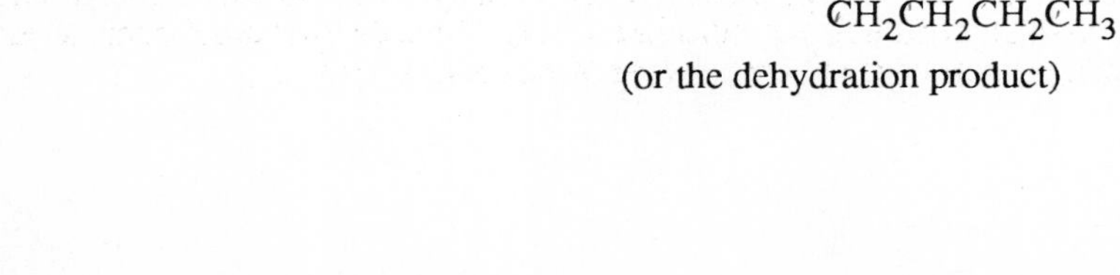

Ph—C—CH=CH(CH$_2$)$_4$CH$_3$ + CH$_3$(CH$_2$)$_4$CHCHCH
CH$_2$CH$_2$CH$_2$CH$_3$

(or the dehydration product)

19. (a) This synthesis requires the following starting materials and is satisfactory, since it represents the reaction of a ketone with an aldehyde that has no α-hydrogens:

$$CH_3O-\text{⟨aryl⟩}-CH{=}O \ + \ CH_3CH_2\overset{O}{\overset{\|}{C}}CH_2CH_3$$

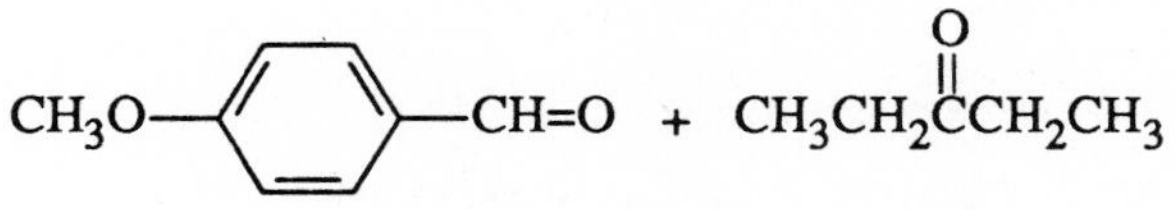

(b) This product also requires the reaction of a ketone with an aldehyde that has no α-hydrogens; however, the ketone has two *nonequivalent* types of α-hydrogens, and therefore could react to give a mixture of the following two products:

$$Ph-CH{=}\underset{\underset{CH_3}{|}}{C}-\overset{O}{\overset{\|}{C}}-CH_2CH_2CH_3 \ + \ CH_3CH_2\overset{O}{\overset{\|}{C}}-\underset{\underset{CHPh}{\|}}{C}-CH_2CH_3$$

Because a mixture is anticipated, the desired product would not be formed in good yield.

(c) This compound would require an *intramolecular* aldol condensation of the following keto aldehyde:

$$CH_3\overset{O}{\overset{\|}{C}}(CH_2)_5\overset{O}{\overset{\|}{C}}H$$

However, since aldehyde carbonyl groups are more prone to addition than ketone carbonyls, and since the various α-hydrogens should have comparable acidity, the desired product would not be the one formed in greatest amount. The major product formed should be:

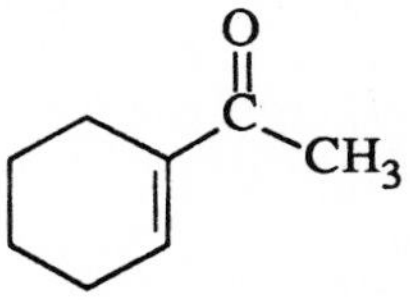

(d) The synthesis requires the following cyclic diketone; the product formed is the only possible aldol condensation product. Hence the reaction is satisfactory.

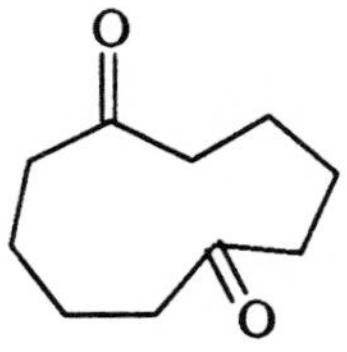

Be sure to convince yourself that all possible enolate ions would react to give the same product.

(e) This is a "double" aldol condensation that requires the following starting materials:

$$PhCH_2\overset{O}{\overset{\|}{C}}CH_2Ph \ + \ Ph\overset{O}{\overset{\|}{C}}-\overset{O}{\overset{\|}{C}}Ph$$

The α-diketone is much more reactive than an ordinary ketone (why?). Since the only possible enolate ion is derived from the other ketone, the resulting reaction is the most likely one. Once the first aldol condensation has occurred, the second takes place rapidly because it forms a ring of reasonable size.

(f) The formation of this product requires an intramolecular aldol condensation of the following compound:

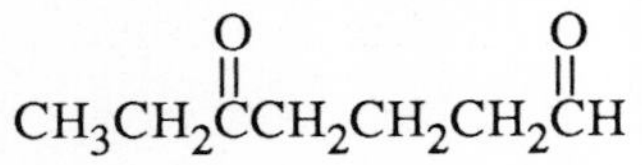

$$CH_3CH_2\overset{\overset{\displaystyle O}{\|}}{C}CH_2CH_2CH_2\overset{\overset{\displaystyle O}{\|}}{C}H$$

Since aldehyde carbonyls are more reactive than ketone carbonyls, and this compound results from the reaction of an enolate with the aldehyde carbonyl, this compound is likely to be formed in good yield.

(g) The required starting materials are $(CH_3)_2C=O$ (acetone) and $CH_3CH=O$ (acetaldehyde). When these two compounds are subjected to basic conditions, acetaldehyde will react with itself. Hence, this compound will not be formed in good yield, if at all.

(h) This compound results from the reactions of two equivalents of $PhCH=O$ (benzaldehyde) with one of $(CH_3)_2C=O$ (acetone); that is, it is a double Claisen–Schmidt reaction. Provided that benzaldehyde is present in large excess, it is a reasonable reaction.

20. Besides the given product, there are three others possible:

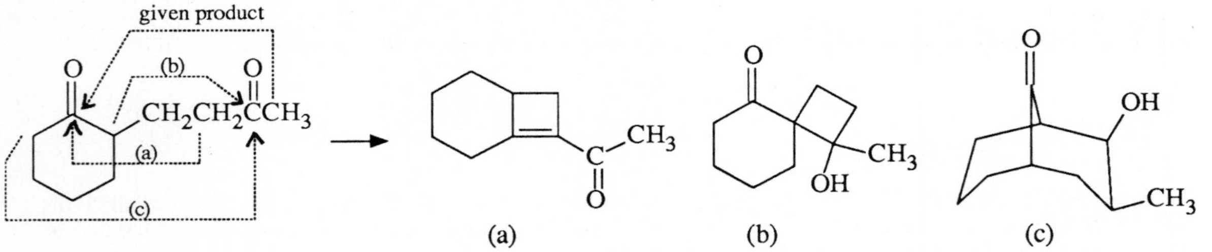

Compounds (a) and (b) are strained. Furthermore, compound (b) cannot dehydrate to give an α,β-unsaturated (conjugated) ketone. Compound (c) is not particularly strained, but if it dehydrates into the bridgehead to give the α,β-unsaturated ketone, it violates Bredt's rule; and if it dehydrates the other way is is not conjugated. Hence, it (and its dehydration products) are not as stable as the product that is formed.

21. (a)   (b)   (c)   (d)

$(CH_3CH_2)_3C{-}OH$

$(CH_3)_2CH{-}$

$(CH_3)_3C{-}O{-}\overset{\overset{\displaystyle O}{\|}}{C}{-}CH_3$

$CH_3CH_2CH_2OH$

(e)   (f)

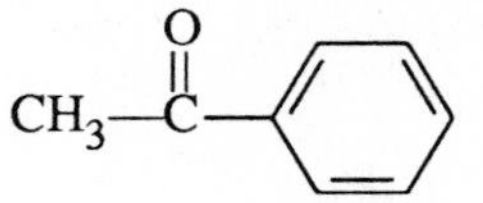

$CH_3\overset{\overset{\displaystyle O}{\|}}{C}{-}O{-}\overset{\overset{\displaystyle O}{\|}}{C}CH_3$

$CH_3{-}\overset{\overset{\displaystyle O}{\|}}{C}{-}$

22.

$$CH_3CH_2CH_2\overset{\overset{\displaystyle O}{\|}}{C}{-}\underset{\underset{\displaystyle CH_2CH_3}{|}}{\overset{\displaystyle ..}{C}}{-}\overset{\overset{\displaystyle O}{\|}}{C}{-}OEt \quad \xrightarrow{H^+} \quad CH_3CH_2CH_2\overset{\overset{\displaystyle O}{\|}}{C}{-}\underset{\underset{\displaystyle CH_2CH_3}{|}}{\overset{\overset{\displaystyle H}{|}}{C}}{-}\overset{\overset{\displaystyle O}{\|}}{C}{-}OEt$$

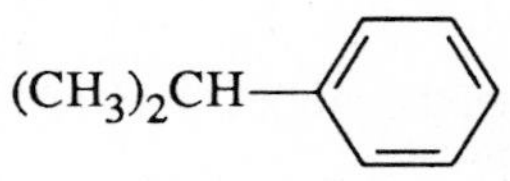

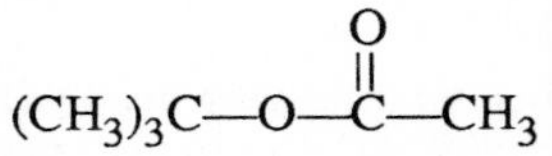

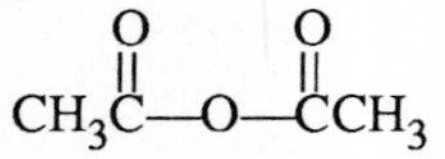

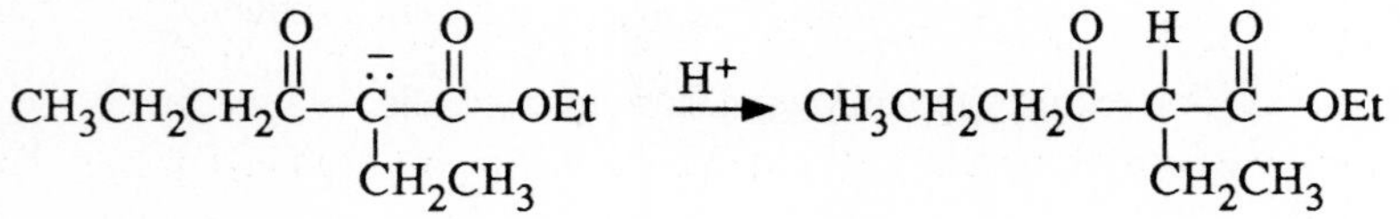

23. Hydroxide is *not* a suitable base for the Claisen condensation because it saponifies esters. The resulting carboxylate ions do not undergo the Claisen condensation (why?).

24. (a) Compound *A* has no especially acidic α-hydrogen. Hence, the ethoxide attacks the ketone carbonyl and brings about a reverse Diekmann condensation. The resulting open-chain diester then recloses to give the alternate Dieckmann product *B* as its anion, from which *B* itself is recovered by acidification. Formation of the conjugate-base anion of *B* drives this reaction to completion. To summarize:

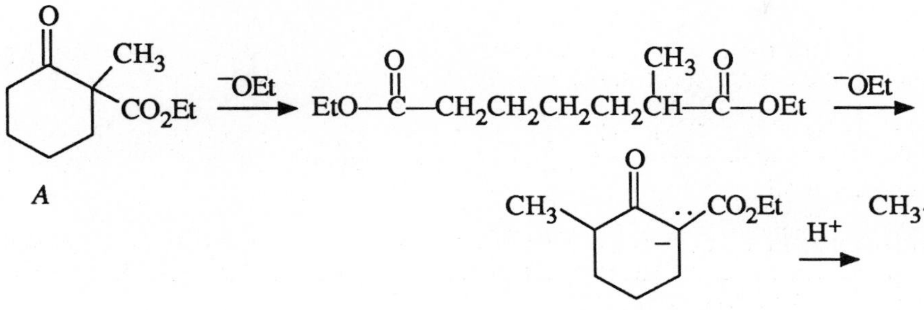

(b) There are in principle two Dieckmann products possible, but only one contains an acidic α-proton that can ionize to drive the reaction to completion. [If the other Dieckmann product forms it does so reversibly, by analogy to the solution to part (a).] The product formed is as follows:

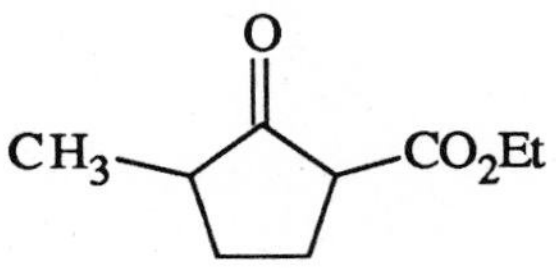

25. (a)   (b)   (c)   (d)

$$Me_3CCCH_2COEt \qquad PhCCH_2CPh \qquad CH_3CCH_2COEt$$

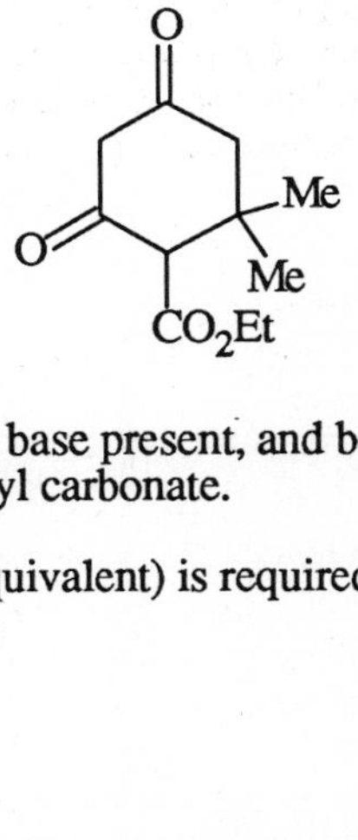

The product in (c) does not react further because it is ionized by the base present, and because the resulting anion is too weak a base to be an effective nucleophile toward diethyl carbonate.

26. In each case below, a suitable base such as sodium ethoxide (one equivalent) is required in addition to the starting materials shown.

(a) There are two possible combinations of starting materials:

$$PhCH_2CO_2Et \ + \ CH_3CH_2CH_2CH_2CO_2Et \quad \text{or} \quad PhCH_2CCH_2CH_2CH_2CH_3 \ + \ EtO\!-\!C\!-\!OEt$$

Neither is satisfactory, since the most acidic hydrogen in both cases is the one α to the phenyl group. The product is not derived from this enolate ion.

(b) There are two possible combinations of starting materials:

$$2 \ CH_3CH_2C\!-\!OEt \quad \text{or} \quad CH_3CH_2CCH_2CH_3 + EtO\!-\!C\!-\!OEt$$

Either is satisfactory, although the reaction of ethyl propionate avoids having to separate the product from an excess of diethyl carbonate at the end of the reaction.

(c) The starting material required is:

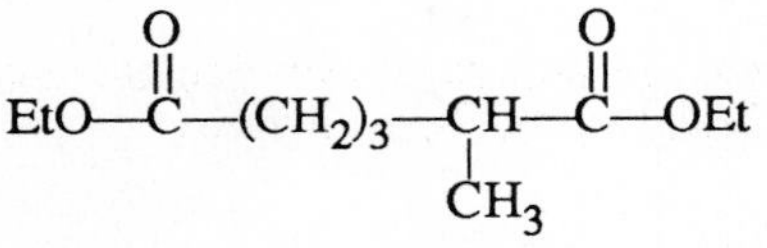

$$\text{EtO—C(=O)—(CH}_2)_3\text{—CH(CH}_3\text{)—C(=O)—OEt}$$

Unfortunately, this starting material would not give the desired product. [What product would it give? See Problem 24(b).]

(d) There are two possible combinations of starting materials:

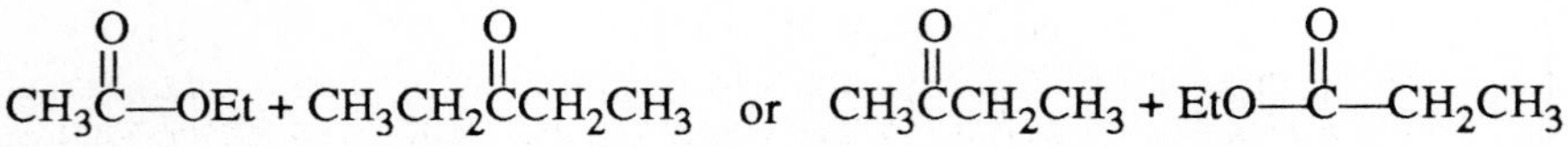

$$\text{CH}_3\text{C(=O)—OEt} + \text{CH}_3\text{CH}_2\text{C(=O)CH}_2\text{CH}_3 \quad \text{or} \quad \text{CH}_3\text{C(=O)CH}_2\text{CH}_3 + \text{EtO—C(=O)—CH}_2\text{CH}_3$$

Only the first pair is satisfactory, since the ketone in the second pair can form two different enolate ions. Thus, the second pair of reactants would give a mixture of products.

27. (a) (b) 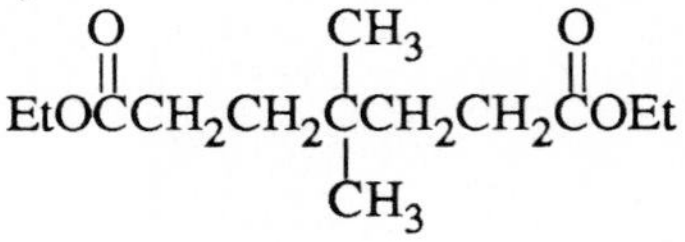 (c)

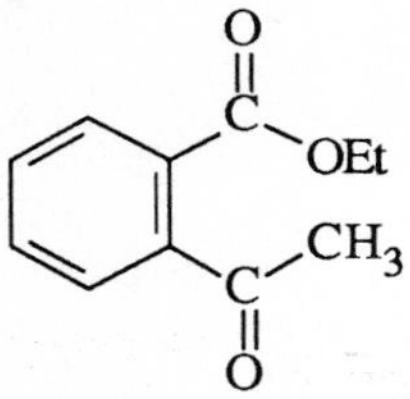

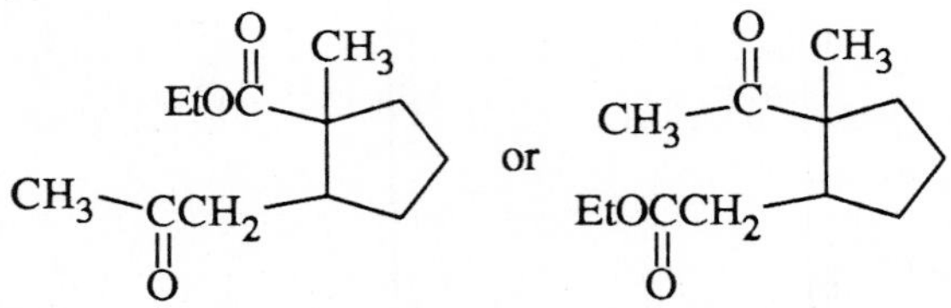

Sodium ethoxide is required as a base in each case.

28. (a) 2-Ethylbutanoic acid can be prepared by the following malonic ester synthesis:

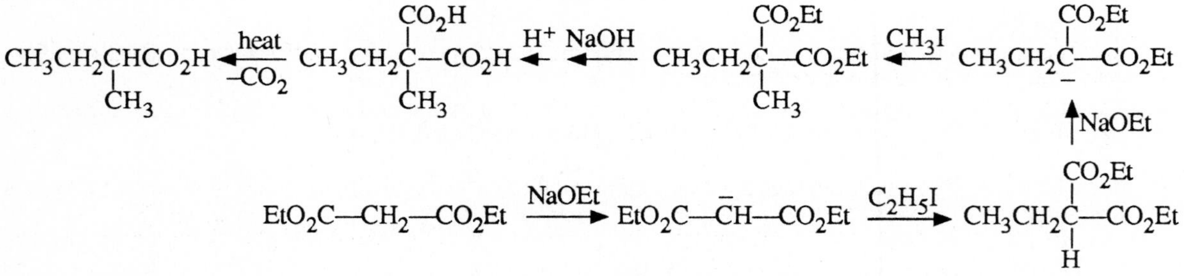

➤ From now on we'll use some conventions to abbreviate reaction schemes involving malonic ester syntheses. The last three steps — saponification, acidification, and decarboxylation, will be shown as follows:

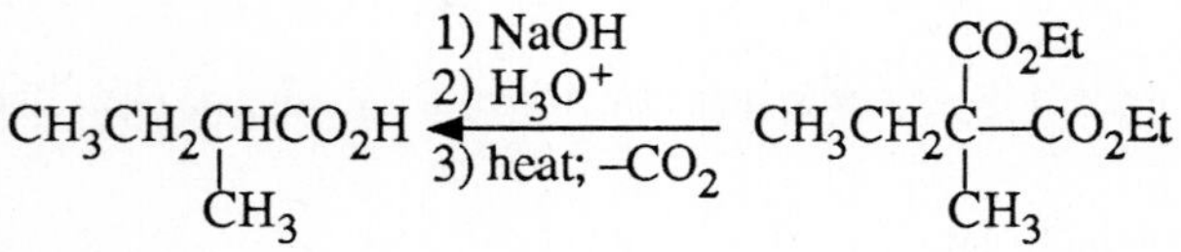

The ionization and alkylation of a malonic ester derivative — for example, the first two steps above — will be abbreviated as follows:

$$CH_2(CO_2Et)_2 \xrightarrow[\text{2) } C_2H_5I]{\text{1) NaOEt}} CH_3CH_2\overset{\overset{\displaystyle CO_2Et}{|}}{CH}-CO_2Et$$

(b) 3,3-Dimethylbutanoic acid cannot be made by the malonic ester synthesis because it would require that *t*-butyl chloride be used as the alkylating agent. *t*-Butyl chloride does not undergo S_N2 reactions.

would have to be derived
from *t*-butyl chloride

$$CH_3-\overset{\overset{\displaystyle CH_3}{|}}{\underset{\underset{\displaystyle CH_3}{|}}{C}}-CH_2-CO_2H$$

29. The molecular formula shows that the product has not only a carboxylic acid group, but also either a ring or double bond. A cyclobutane ring can be formed by an *intramolecular* alkylation reaction of compound *A*, which is an intermediate in the reaction; the final product is *B*:

$$\overset{\overset{\displaystyle CO_2Et}{|}}{\underset{\underset{\displaystyle CO_2Et}{|}}{CH}}-CH_2CH_2CH_2-Cl \qquad\qquad \square\!\!-CO_2H$$

A   *B*

30. **(a)**

$$CH_2=CHCH_2\overset{\overset{}{|}}{\underset{\underset{\displaystyle CH_3}{|}}{CH}}CO_2H \xleftarrow[\substack{\text{2) } H_3O^+ \\ \text{3) heat; } -CO_2}]{\text{1) NaOH}} CH_2=CHCH_2\overset{}{\underset{\underset{\displaystyle CH_3}{|}}{C}}(CO_2Et)_2 \xleftarrow[\text{2) } CH_2=CHCH_2Cl]{\text{1) NaOEt}} CH_3CH(CO_2Et)_2$$

$$\Big\uparrow \substack{\text{1) NaOEt} \\ \text{2) } CH_3I}$$

$$CH_2(CO_2Et)_2$$

In this and other malonic ester syntheses involving more than one alkylation, the order in which the alkyl groups are introduced can be reversed.

(b)

$$CH_2=CHCH_2\overset{\overset{\displaystyle C_2H_5}{|}}{\underset{\underset{\displaystyle C_2H_5}{|}}{C}}CO_2H \xleftarrow{CH_2=CHCH_2Cl} \overset{(CH_3)_2CH}{\underset{}{\bigcirc\!\!-N^-\,Li^+}} \xleftarrow{} (C_2H_5)_2CHCO_2Et \xleftarrow{EtOH, H^+}$$

$$\Big\downarrow \substack{\text{1) NaOEt} \\ \text{2) } C_2H_5I}$$

$$C_2H_5CH(CO_2Et)_2 \xrightarrow[\text{2) } C_2H_5I]{\text{1) NaOEt}} (C_2H_5)_2C(CO_2Et)_2 \xrightarrow[\substack{\text{2) } H_3O^+ \\ \text{3) heat; } -CO_2}]{\text{1) NaOH}} (C_2H_5)_2CHCO_2H$$

$$CH_2(CO_2Et)_2$$

(c)

$$(Pr)_2CHCO_2H \xleftarrow[\substack{\text{2) } H_3O^+ \\ \text{3) heat; } -CO_2}]{\text{1) NaOH}} (Pr)_2C(CO_2Et)_2 \xleftarrow[\text{2) Pr}-\text{Br}]{\text{1) NaOEt}} PrCH(CO_2Et)_2 \xleftarrow[\text{2) Pr}-\text{Br}]{\text{1) NaOEt}} CH_2(CO_2Et)_2$$

31. This is an aldol condensation reaction in which the enolate ion of *t*-butyl acetate reacts with acetone:

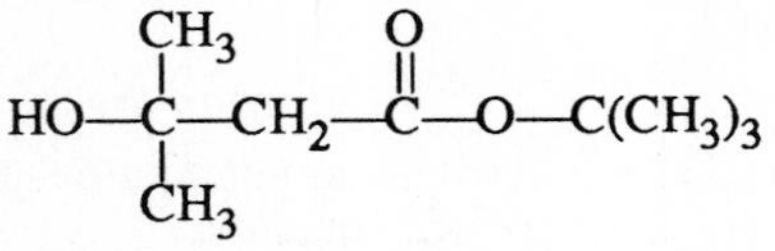

$$HO-\underset{\underset{CH_3}{|}}{\overset{\overset{CH_3}{|}}{C}}-CH_2-\overset{\overset{O}{\|}}{C}-O-C(CH_3)_3$$

32. (a)

$$CH_3-\overset{\overset{O}{\|}}{C}-CH_2CH_2\underset{\underset{CH_3}{|}}{CH}CH_3 \xleftarrow[\text{2) } H_3O^+, -CO_2]{\text{1) NaOH}} CH_3-\overset{\overset{O}{\|}}{C}-\overset{\overset{CO_2Et}{|}}{C}HCH_2CH(CH_3)_2 \xleftarrow[\text{2) } (CH_3)_2CHCH_2Br]{\text{1) NaOEt}}$$

$$CH_3\overset{\overset{O}{\|}}{C}CH_2CO_2Et$$

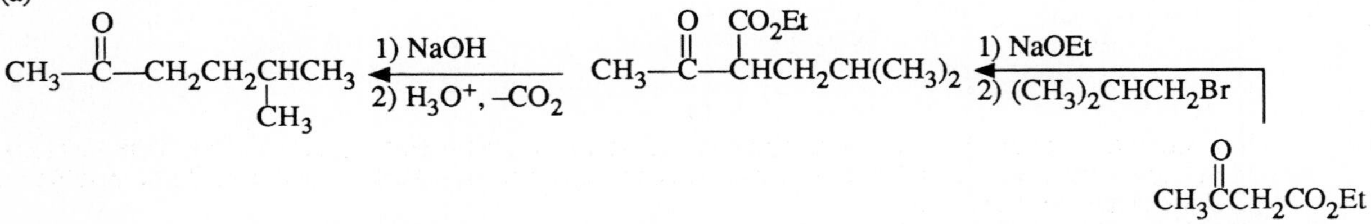

(b) Use exactly the same sequence of reactions as in (a), except use benzyl bromide (PhCH₂Br) instead of isobutyl bromide as the alkylating agent.

33. Compound *A* is the desired β-keto ester:

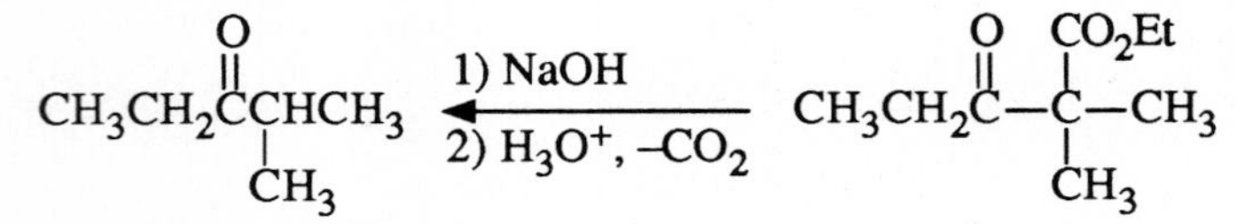

$$CH_3CH_2\overset{\overset{O}{\|}}{C}\underset{\underset{CH_3}{|}}{C}HCH_3 \xleftarrow[\text{2) } H_3O^+, -CO_2]{\text{1) NaOH}} CH_3CH_2\overset{\overset{O}{\|}}{C}-\overset{\overset{CO_2Et}{|}}{\underset{\underset{CH_3}{|}}{C}}-CH_3$$

4-methyl-3-pentanone   *A*

This cannot be prepared *directly* by a Claisen condensation, but it can be prepared in several steps from another β-keto ester that *can* be prepared by a Claisen condensation of ethyl propionate:

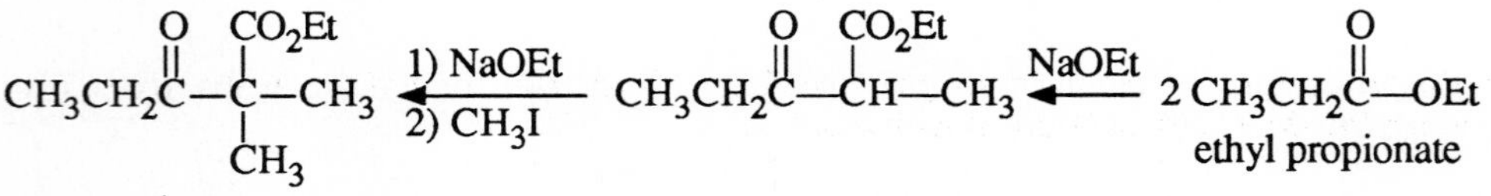

$$CH_3CH_2\overset{\overset{O}{\|}}{C}-\overset{\overset{CO_2Et}{|}}{\underset{\underset{CH_3}{|}}{C}}-CH_3 \xleftarrow[\text{2) } CH_3I]{\text{1) NaOEt}} CH_3CH_2\overset{\overset{O}{\|}}{C}-\overset{\overset{CO_2Et}{|}}{C}H-CH_3 \xleftarrow{\text{NaOEt}} 2\ CH_3CH_2\overset{\overset{O}{\|}}{C}-OEt$$

A   ethyl propionate

34. Species *A* is simply the conjugate-base anion of diethyl malonate. Like most nucleophiles, this one can attack an epoxide to give a ring-opened product; attack occurs at the less hindered carbon to give compound *B*:

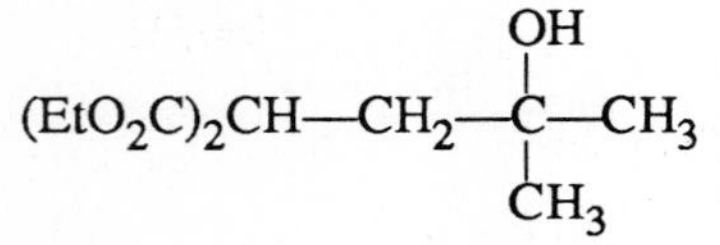

$$(EtO_2C)_2CH-CH_2-\overset{\overset{OH}{|}}{\underset{\underset{CH_3}{|}}{C}}-CH_3 \quad B$$

From the formula of the final product, we see that compound *B* has lost two carbons and one oxygen — that is, a C₂H₅O— group. This suggests an intramolecular transesterification reaction to form a lactone:

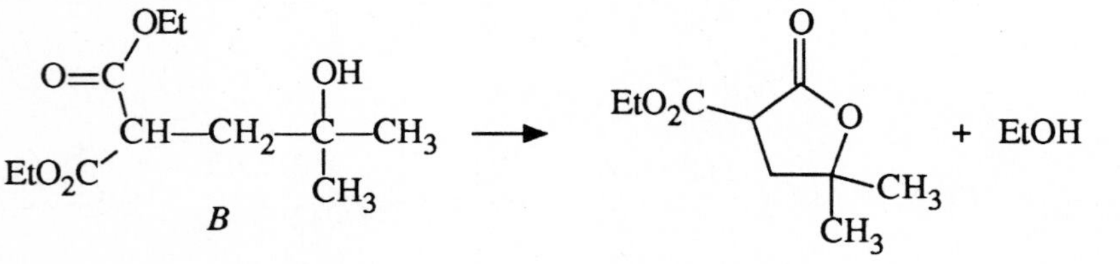

(Be sure to write the mechanism of the reaction if what is happening is not clear to you!)

35. First, we write the starting material in its diketone form *A*. Then we analyze the formation of *A* by the aldol condensation of a polyketide *B*. (The symbol ⇨ means "implies as a starting material.")

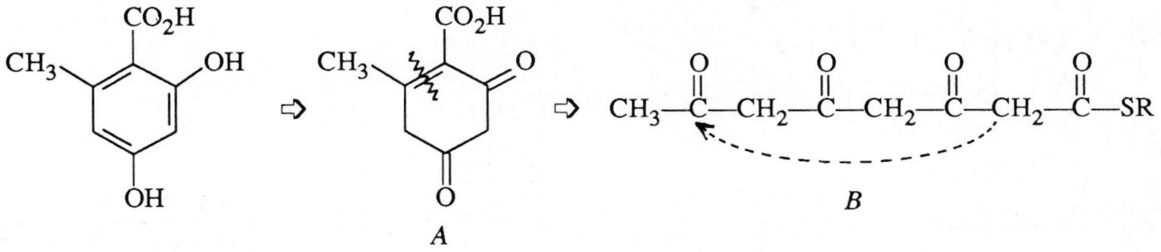

Compound *B* is identical to, and is formed in the same way as, the product of Eq. 22.78a in the text for $n = 2$. From this analysis, you should now write the detailed steps that show the conversion of *B* into orsellinic acid if you have not already done so.

36. HMG-CoA is the product of an aldol condensation between acetoacetyl-CoA (Eq. 22.77a with —SR = —SCoA) and malonyl-CoA (structure at the top of text page 956). The enolate ion is formed by decarboxylation of malonyl-CoA, as in Eq. 22.77a:

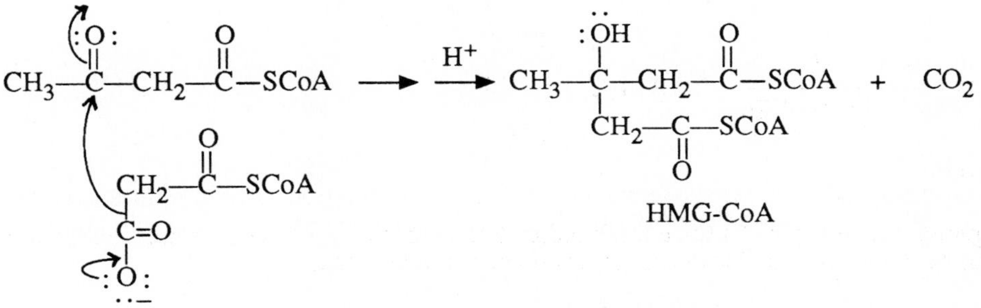

37. In parts (a)–(c), the product results from a conjugate addition. In part (d), the product results from ester saponification, an *irreversible* carbonyl-substitution reaction.

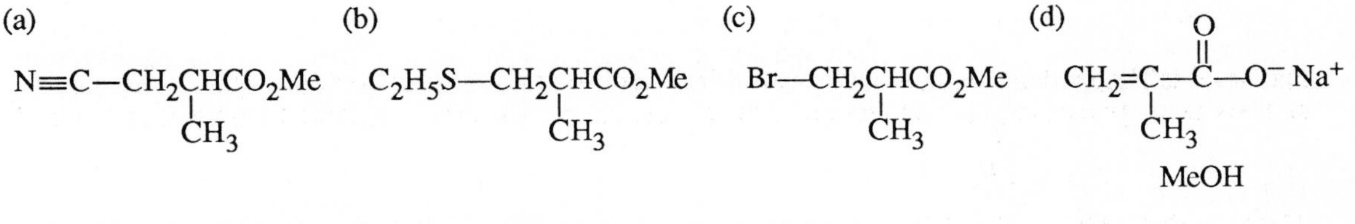

(a)   (b)   (c)   (d)

38. (a) The product results from a conjugate addition to the α,β-unsaturated lactone:

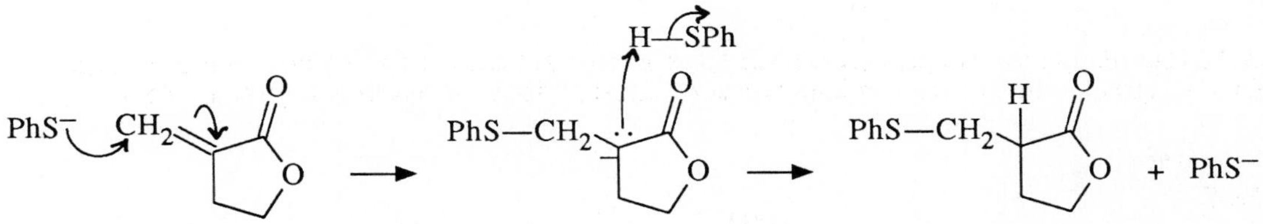

(b) The product is the result of two consecutive conjugate additions involving two equivalents of the α,β-unsaturated ester:

$$MeNH_2 \quad CH_2=CH-CO_2Me \longrightarrow \xrightarrow{\text{proton transfer}} Me\ NH-CH_2-CH_2-CO_2Me \longrightarrow \xrightarrow{\text{proton transfer}}$$

$$\searrow CH_2=CH-CO_2Me$$

$$Me\ \overset{..}{N}-CH_2-CH_2-CO_2Me$$
$$\overset{|}{C}H_2-CH_2-CO_2Me$$

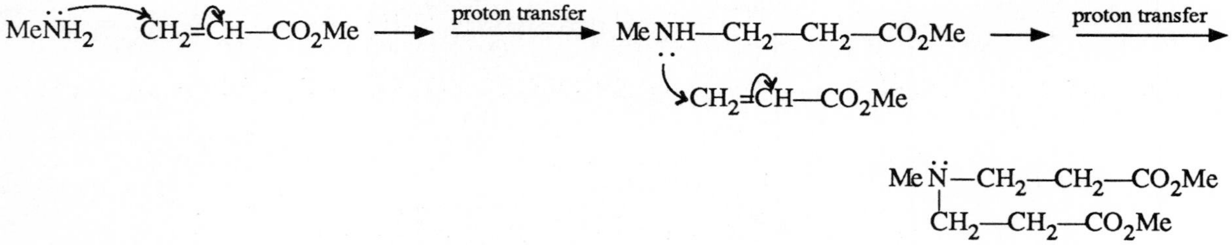

(c) Conjugate addition converts the α,β-unsaturated ester into a compound in which there is no carbon–carbon double bond. Internal rotation and elimination by a *reverse* conjugate addition gives the *trans* isomer of the α,β-unsaturated ester.

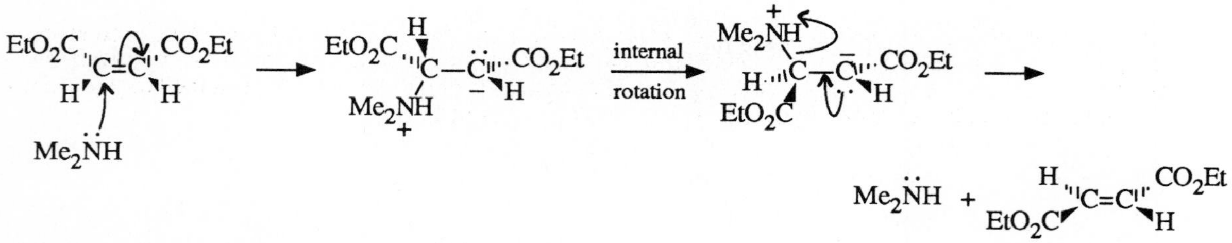

39. (a) The conjugate-base anion of diethyl malonate undergoes conjugate addition to the α,β-unsaturated ester to give a triester A. Saponification of the triester followed by decarboxylation of the malonic acid portion gives a dicarboxylic acid B.

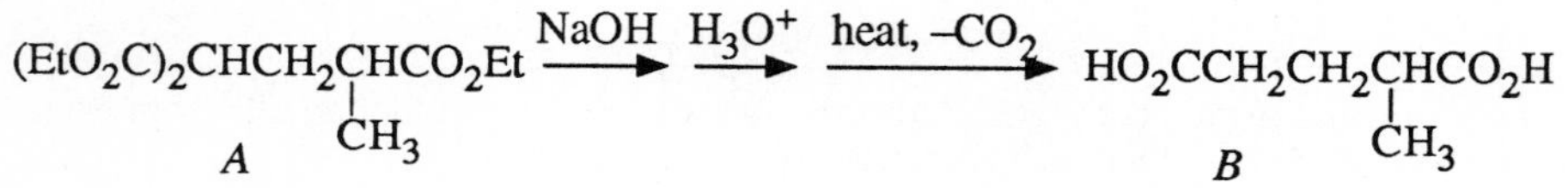

$$(EtO_2C)_2CHCH_2\underset{\underset{CH_3}{|}}{C}HCO_2Et \xrightarrow{NaOH} \xrightarrow{H_3O^+} \xrightarrow{\text{heat},\ -CO_2} HO_2CCH_2CH_2\underset{\underset{CH_3}{|}}{C}HCO_2H$$
$$\qquad\qquad A \qquad\qquad\qquad\qquad\qquad\qquad\qquad\qquad\qquad\qquad\qquad B$$

(b) The formula of the product tells us that *two* equivalents of acrylonitrile ($CH_2=CH-CN$) have been added. (Be sure you see why this is so.) Each addition is a conjugate addition in which the conjugate-base anion of the β-keto ester acts as a nucleophile:

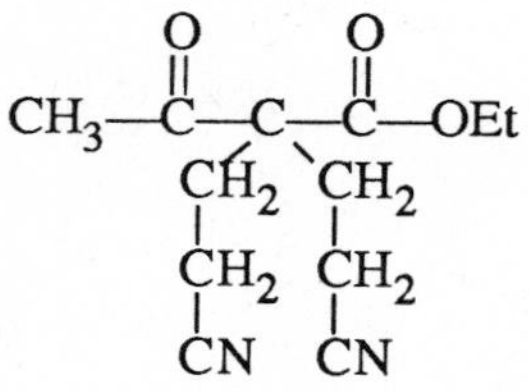

40. (a) Intermediate *A* results from the Michael addition of the conjugate-base anion of diethyl malonate. The product results from a Dieckmann condensation of *A*.

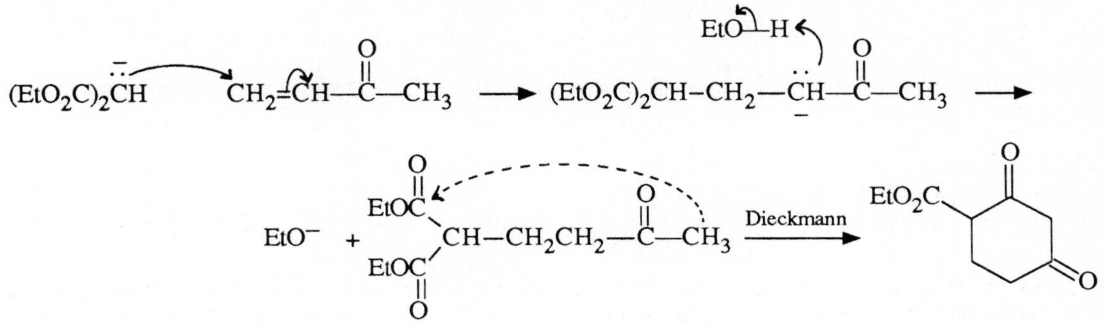

The mechanism of the Dieckmann condensation is discussed on text page 944.

(b) This reaction is a Michael addition of the conjugate-base enolate ion of the α-formyl ketone to give compound *B*. Because this compound has no α-hydrogens between the formyl-group carbonyl and the ketone carbonyl, it undergoes a reverse Claisen condensation when one equivalent of ^-OH is added to give compound *C*. An intramolecular aldol condensation of *C* gives the final product.

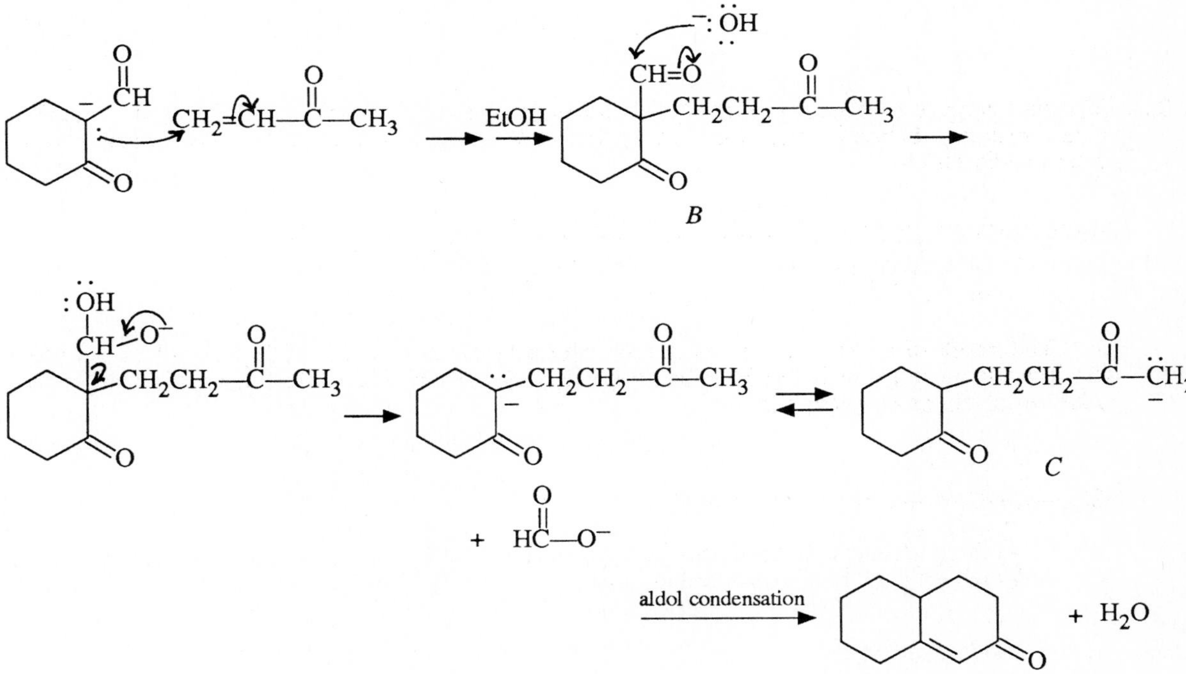

We leave it to you to supply the details of the aldol condensation.

41. (a)

$$CH_3CH{=}CHC({=}O){-}OEt \xrightarrow{H_2,\ \text{catalyst}} CH_3CH_2CH_2C({=}O){-}OEt$$

(b)

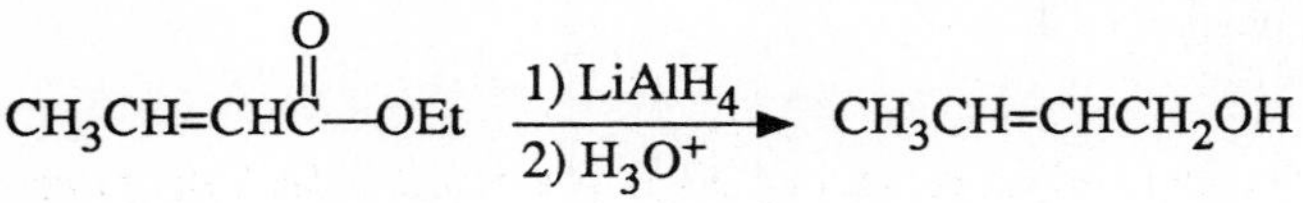

$$CH_3CH=CH\overset{\overset{\displaystyle O}{\|}}{C}-OEt \xrightarrow[\text{2) }H_3O^+]{\text{1) LiAlH}_4} CH_3CH=CHCH_2OH$$

42. Mesityl oxide is the starting material for each of these syntheses. The preparation of mesityl oxide is given in Eq. 22.44 on text page 935.

(a)

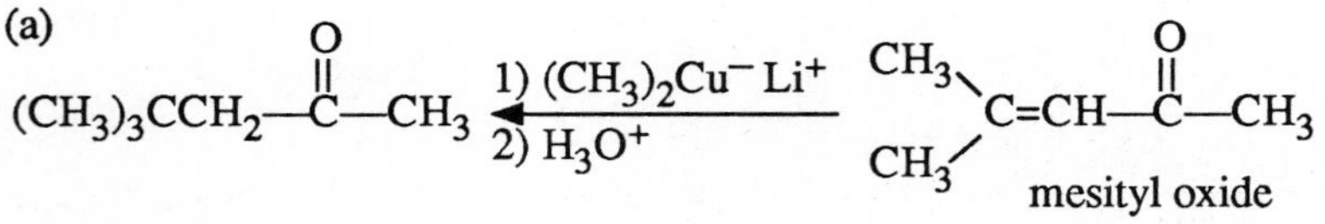

$$(CH_3)_3CCH_2-\overset{\overset{\displaystyle O}{\|}}{C}-CH_3 \xleftarrow[\text{2) }H_3O^+]{\text{1) }(CH_3)_2Cu^-\,Li^+} \underset{CH_3}{\overset{CH_3}{>}}C=CH-\overset{\overset{\displaystyle O}{\|}}{C}-CH_3$$
mesityl oxide

(b)

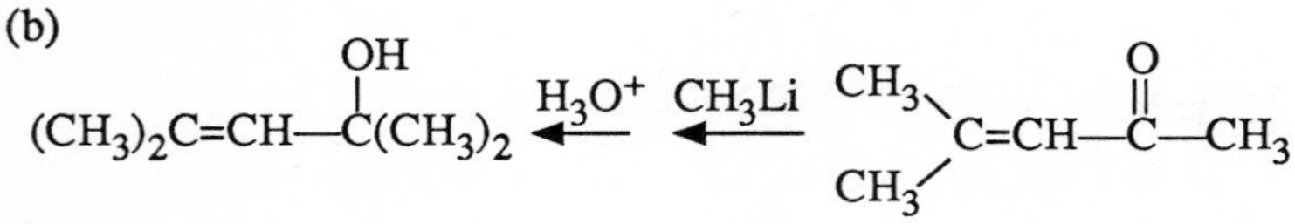

$$(CH_3)_2C=CH-\overset{\overset{\displaystyle OH}{|}}{C}(CH_3)_2 \xleftarrow{H_3O^+} \xleftarrow{CH_3Li} \underset{CH_3}{\overset{CH_3}{>}}C=CH-\overset{\overset{\displaystyle O}{\|}}{C}-CH_3$$

(c)

$$C_2H_5-\overset{\overset{\displaystyle CH_3}{|}}{\underset{\underset{\displaystyle CH_3}{|}}{C}}-CH=C(CH_3)_2 \xleftarrow[-H_2O]{H_3PO_4} C_2H_5-\overset{\overset{\displaystyle CH_3}{|}}{\underset{\underset{\displaystyle CH_3}{|}}{C}}-CH_2-\overset{\overset{\displaystyle OH}{|}}{C}(CH_3)_2 \xleftarrow[\text{2) }H_2O]{\text{1) CH}_3Li} C_2H_5-\overset{\overset{\displaystyle CH_3}{|}}{\underset{\underset{\displaystyle CH_3}{|}}{C}}-CH_2-\overset{\overset{\displaystyle O}{\|}}{C}-CH_3$$

$$\underset{CH_3}{\overset{CH_3}{>}}C=CH-\overset{\overset{\displaystyle O}{\|}}{C}-CH_3 \xrightarrow[\text{2) }H_2O]{\text{1) }(C_2H_5)_2CuLi}$$

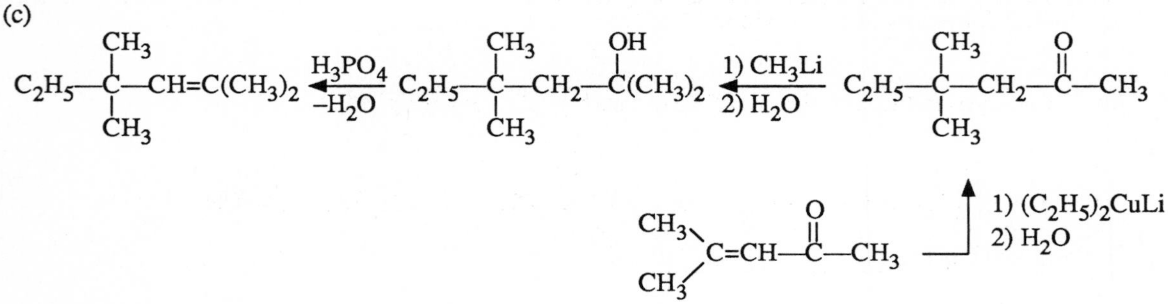

43. (a) In this case, conjugate addition could give a 1,4- or a 1,6-addition product:

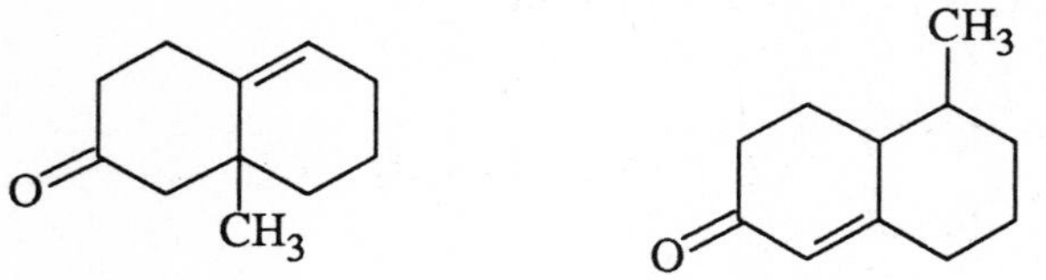

1,4-addition product　　　　1,6-addition product

The 1,6-addition product is favored because the enolate ion formed in the 1,6-addition has more resonance structures, and is therefore more stable and formed more readily, than the one formed in the 1,4-addition:

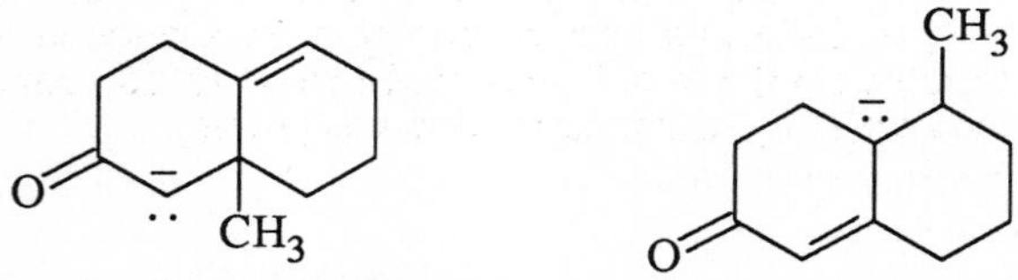

enolate ion from 1,4-addition:　　enolate ion from 1,6-addition:
fewer resonance structures　　　more resonance structures

We leave it to you to verify this point by drawing the resonance structures of the enolate ions.

(b) Conjugate addition to an acetylenic ester gives a substituted α,β-unsaturated ester:

$(CH_3)_2C{=}CH{-}CO_2Me$

44. (a) We start with an α,β-unsaturated ketone and add the remaining alkyl group with a dialkylcuprate reagent:

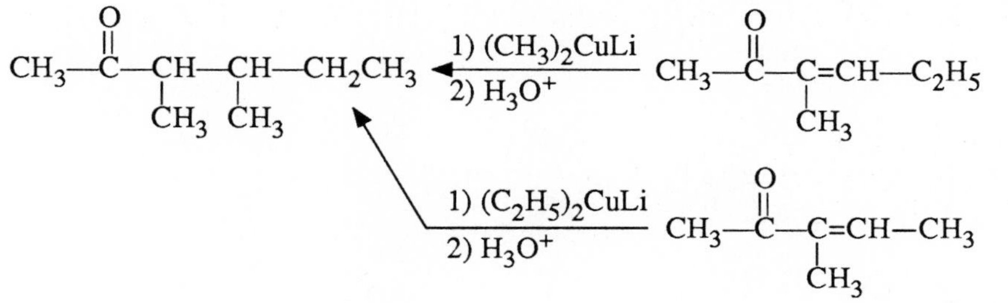

(b) Add cyanide to an α,β-unsaturated ester:

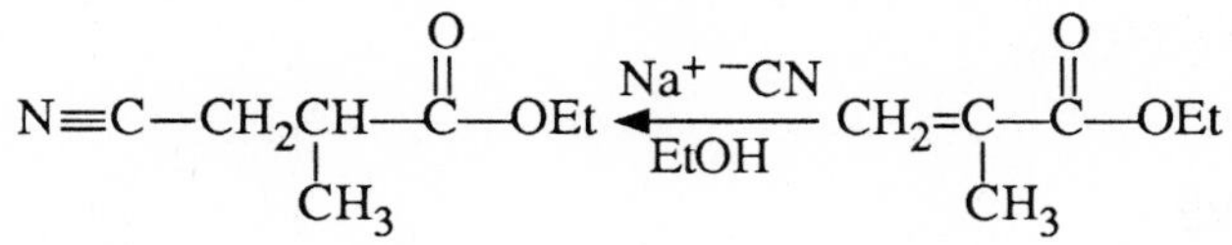

(c) The analysis in the text (Eq. 22.107) suggests the following reactants:

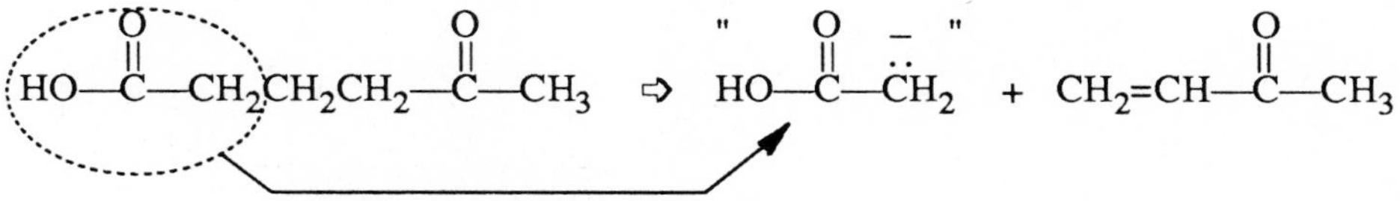

The anion is in quotation marks because this anion could not exist (why?). However, an anion that can yield equivalent results is the conjugate-base anion of diethyl malonate. Addition of this anion to the ketone shown above, saponification of the esters, and decarboxylation gives the desired compound:

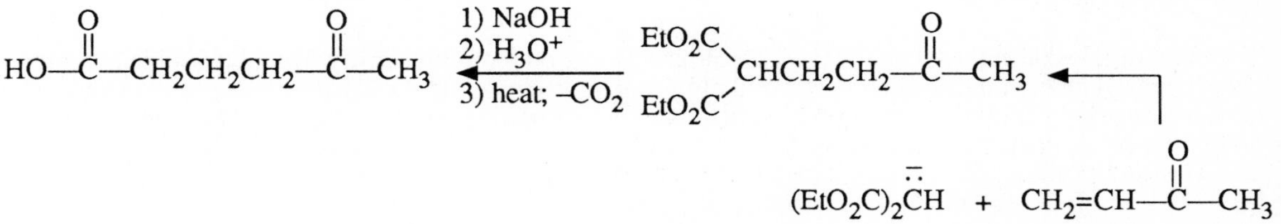

➤ You might ask, "How am I supposed to see this for myself?" Notice that the desired compound is really a substituted acetic acid in the sense shown on text page 949, Eq. 22.65. The malonic ester synthesis is used to prepare "substituted acetic acids." On text page 949, we focused on the reaction of malonic ester anion with alkyl halides and tosylates. However, epoxides (Problem 34) and α,β-unsaturated carbonyl compounds are also alkylating agents and can be adapted to a malonic ester-type synthesis, as in this problem.

Solutions to Additional Problems

45. (a)

$$CH_3-\overset{\overset{\displaystyle O}{\|}}{C}-CH_2CH_2Br$$

(b)

$$CH_3-\overset{\overset{\displaystyle O}{\|}}{C}-\underset{\underset{\displaystyle Br}{|}}{C}HCH_2Br$$

(c)

$$CH_3-\underset{\underset{\displaystyle }{|}}{\overset{\overset{\displaystyle OH}{|}}{C}}H-CH=CH_2$$

(d)

$$CH_3-\overset{\overset{\displaystyle O}{\|}}{C}-CH_2CH_2CN \ + \ CH_3-\underset{\underset{\displaystyle CN}{|}}{\overset{\overset{\displaystyle OH}{|}}{C}}-CH_2CH_2CN$$

(e)

$$CH_3-\overset{\overset{\displaystyle O}{\|}}{C}-CH_2CH_2CH_2CH_3$$

(f)

$$CH_3\overset{\overset{\displaystyle O}{\|}}{C}CH_2CH_2CH(CO_2Et)_2$$

(g)

(h)

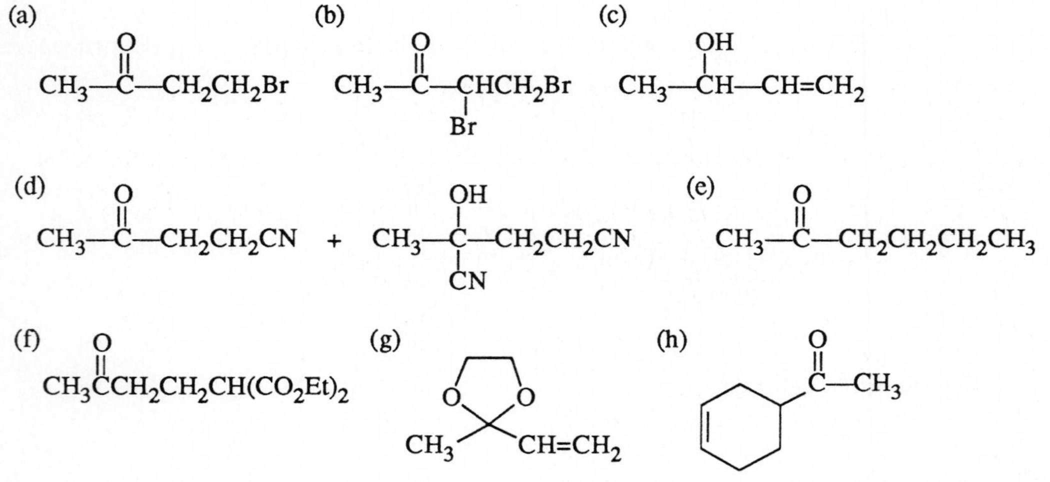

46. (a)

$$HO\overset{\overset{\displaystyle O}{\|}}{C}\underset{\underset{\displaystyle CH_3}{|}}{C}HCH_2\overset{\overset{\displaystyle O}{\|}}{C}OH$$

(b)

$$CH_3\underset{\underset{\displaystyle NMe_2}{|}}{C}HCH_2\overset{\overset{\displaystyle O}{\|}}{C}-OEt$$

(c)

(d)

(e)

$$CH_3CH_2CH_2CO_2Et$$

(f)

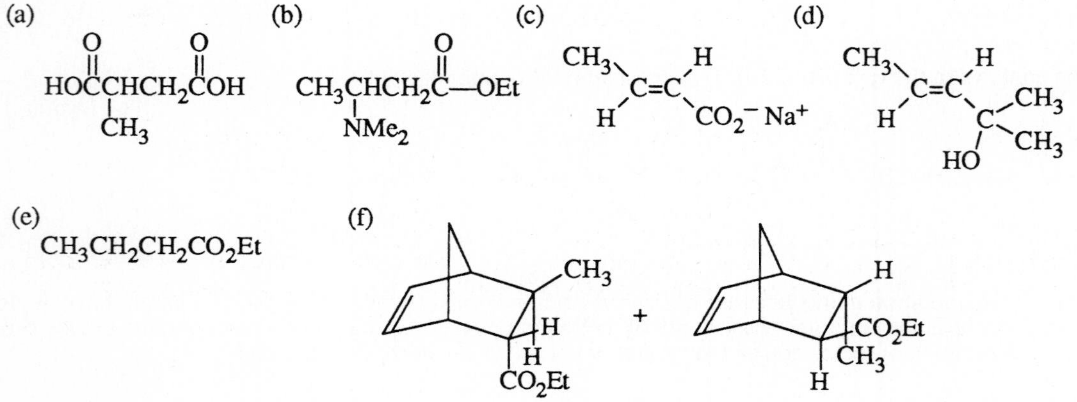

47. The bond dipoles of the —Cl and the —CO$_2$Et groups are both oriented *away* from the double bond toward the groups. Hence, in the *E* isomer the bond dipoles tend to cancel; in the *Z* isomer they tend to add. The *Z* isomer is the one with the higher dipole moment and higher boiling point. (Why does the isomer with higher boiling dipole moment have the higher boiling point?)

48. (a)

$$CH_3\underset{\underset{\displaystyle C_2H_5}{|}}{C}H\overset{\overset{\displaystyle O}{\|}}{C}CH_3$$

(b)

CH$_3$ ... —OH   or $$CH_2=CHCH_2CH_2CH_3$$ (with OH)

(c)

$$CH_3\underset{\underset{\displaystyle C_2H_5}{|}}{C}HCH_2CH=O$$

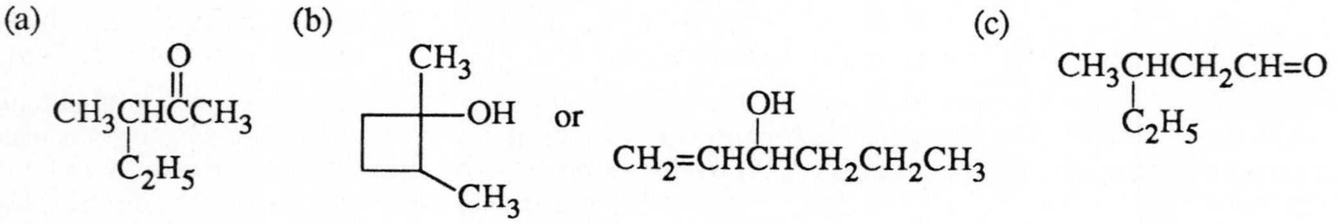

(d)

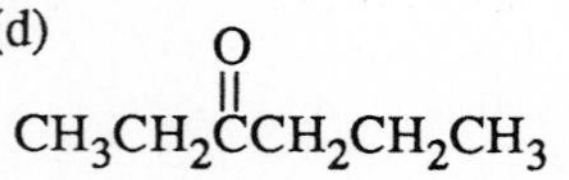

$$CH_3CH_2\overset{\overset{\displaystyle O}{\|}}{C}CH_2CH_2CH_3 \quad \text{(or many other compounds)}$$

A compound that racemizes in base must have an exchangeable α-proton on an asymmetric carbon. The Tollens' test requires that a compound be an aldehyde. Be sure you understand how the compounds above meet the indicated criteria. There are in some cases other answers that fit the data.

49. A compound that gives a 2,4-DNP derivative must be an aldehyde or ketone. A compound that gives a positive haloform test must be either a methyl ketone or a methyl carbinol [a compound with the partial structure CH_3—$CH(OH)$—].

(a) $CH_3CH_2CH_2CH$=O

(b) $CH_3\overset{\overset{O}{||}}{C}CH_2CH_3$

(c) CH_2=$CHCH_2CH_2OH$

(d) $CH_3\overset{\overset{OH}{|}}{C}HCH$=$CH_2$

50. (a) This compound is an ynol (the alkyne analog of an enol), and isomerizes to the carbonyl compound CH_3CH=C=O.
(b) This is the hydrate of benzaldehyde; it decomposes to benzaldehyde (Ph—CH=O) and water.
(c) This compound is an acetal and is stable (unless aqueous acid is present).
(d) This is the triketone form of the phenol phloroglucinol (1,3,5-benzenetriol).

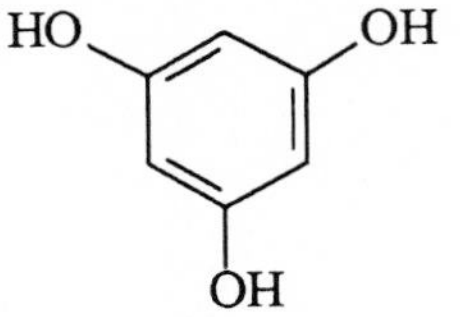

phloroglucinol

The phenol form is more stable because it is aromatic.
(e) This is a hemiacetal, which breaks down to acetaldehyde and an enol, which in turn is transformed spontaneously into an aldehyde:

$CH_3\overset{\overset{OH}{|}}{C}HOCH$=$CHCH_3$ $\longrightarrow$ CH_3CH=O + $HOCH$=$CHCH_3$ $\longrightarrow$ O=$CHCH_2CH_3$
                                                                         an enol

51. In each set, we number the compounds with numbers increasing from left to right.
(a) Compound (2) is most acidic, because the conjugate-base anion is stabilized not only by resonance interaction with the two carbonyl groups, but also by resonance interaction with the phenyl group.

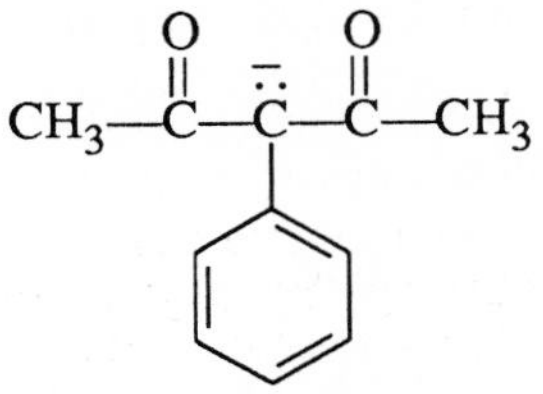

conjugate-base anion of (2)

(b) Compound (1) is more acidic, because the conjugate-base anion is stabilized not only by resonance interaction with the carbonyl group, but also by resonance interaction with the carbon–carbon double bond.

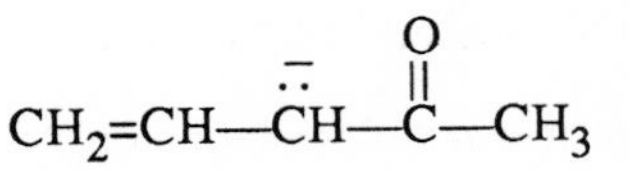

conjugate-base anion of (1)

(c) Compound (2) is most acidic, because the conjugate-base anion is stabilized by resonance interaction not only with the carbonyl group, but also with the very electronegative nitro group.

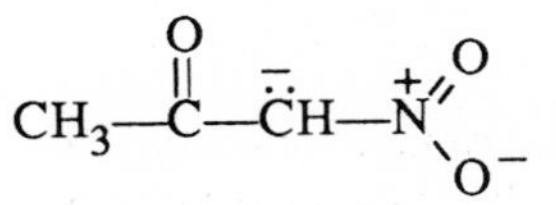

conjugate-base anion of (2)

The conjugate-base anion of (3) is also highly resonance-stabilized, but the charge is not delocalized to any additional electronegative atoms as it is in a nitro group. That is, a nitro group stabilizes negative charge more effectively than a phenyl group.

➤ You should be sure to draw the resonance structures for the anions in each part of this problem.

52. The order of acidity and approximate pK_a values are:

    (c) [42] < (d) ≈ (e) [25] < (a) [15] < (f) [10] < (b) [4.5]

53. Because there are two asymmetric carbons in the product, a mixture of diastereomers is formed. Since diastereomers have different physical properties, a mixture of diastereomers behaves like a mixture of ordinary compounds — that is, the melting point is depressed and broadened.

54. Conjugate addition of the organocuprate reagent can in principle occur to give two stereoisomers. Their structures and the Clemmensen reduction of each are as follows:

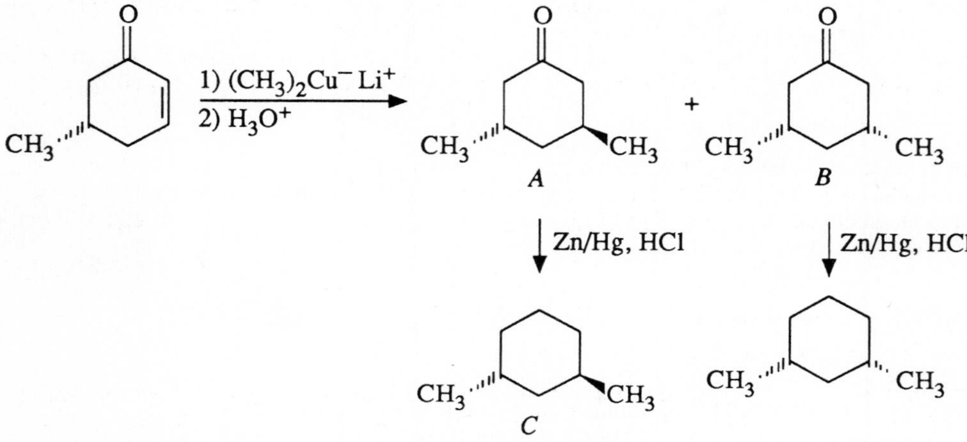

Only product A and its reduction product C could be optically active. Compound B and its reduction product are *meso* compounds, and are therefore not chiral. The data therefore show that the identities of compounds A and C are as indicated above.

55. (a) Bromobenzene does not undergo S_N2 reactions (see Section 18.1), and therefore cannot work in the malonic ester synthesis.
    (b) Sodium ethoxide promotes the Claisen condensation of ethyl propionate. A direct alkylation such as the one proposed requires a strong amide base (see Sections 22.5A and 22.6B).
    (c) Dehydration of this alcohol would require formation of a carbocation at a carbon that is α to a carbonyl group. Such carbocations do not form. (See Eq. 22.36, text page 933.)
    (d) Cringe is trying to form a Grignard reagent from an α-bromo acid formed in the first step. Even if such a Grignard reagent formed, it would be immediately destroyed by reaction with the acidic proton of the carboxylic acid group.
    (e) This is a crossed aldol condensation between an aldehyde and a ketone. What would occur instead is an aldol condensation between two aldehyde molecules.
    (f) In addition to bromination of the benzene ring, we would expect acid-catalyzed α-halogenation of the methyl group of the ketone (see Section 22.3A). Lewis acids, in their roles as "fat protons," can catalyze such halogenations just as protons can.

56. The α-hydrogen can ionize under the basic conditions to an enolate ion; the enolate ion can protonate from the top face to give back starting material A, or from the bottom face to give compound B, as shown in the following equation:

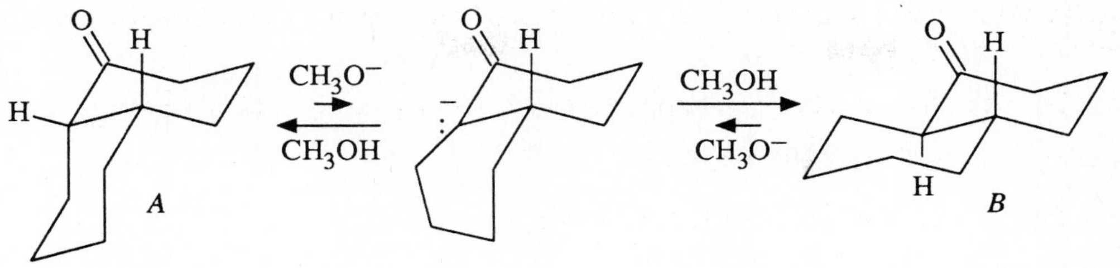

Compound *B* is favored at equilibrium because *trans*-decalin derivatives are more stable than their *cis*-isomers (see text page 242). Because compound *C* lacks the acidic proton — its α-position is blocked by a methyl group — it cannot undergo this isomerization.

57. (a) The α,β-unsaturated ketone is favored at equilibrium because it is conjugated. Just as conjugated dienes are more stable than unconjugated ones because of the π-electron overlap associated with conjugation, α,β-unsaturated carbonyl compounds are also favored over β,γ-unsaturated ones.
    (b) The mechanism involves formation of the enolate ion. Its resonance structures show that its negative charge is shared by both carbon-2 and carbon-4. Protonation at carbon-4 gives the conjugated ketone.

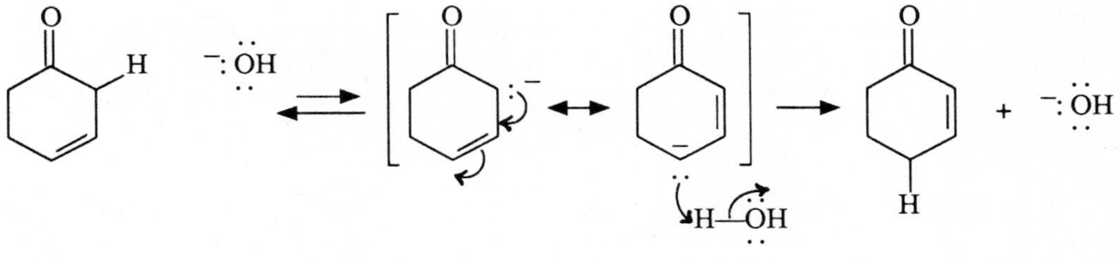

(c) Formation of the enol 1,3-cyclohexadien-1-ol, protonation to give a resonance-stabilized carbocation, and loss of a proton account for the isomerization. We begin our mechanism with the enol; formation of the enol occurs by the mechanism shown in Eq. 22.16b, text page 926.

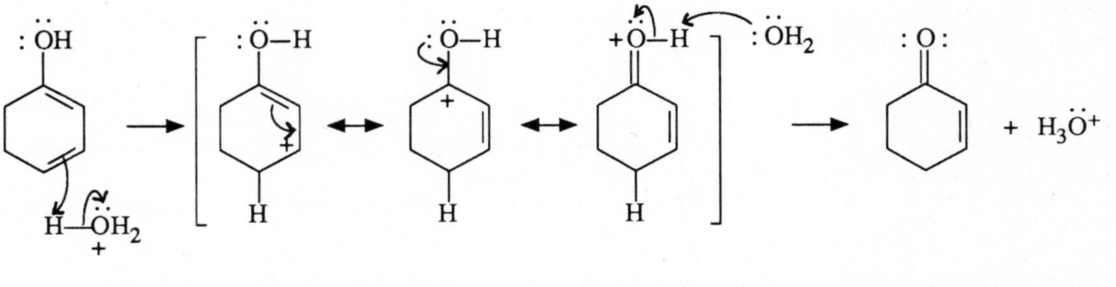

(d) The equilibrium constant for isomerization of 4-methyl-3-cyclohexen-1-one should favor the β,γ-unsaturated ketone more than the equilibrium constant for isomerization of 3-cyclohexen-1-one because the former compound has a more highly substituted double bond. Formation of the conjugated isomer gives a compound that has a less substituted double bond.

58. (a) The mechanism of exchange of protons H^a is identical to the mechanism shown in the solution to Problem 3, page 526 of this manual. The conjugate-base anion formed when either proton H^c or H^d is ionized is resonance-stabilized, and is simply a conjugated enolate anion. Protonation of this anion by deuterated solvent gives the exchange. In the following equation we show exchange of protons H^d; we leave it to you to show the exchange of protons H^c by an analogous mechanism. (B :⁻ = base.)

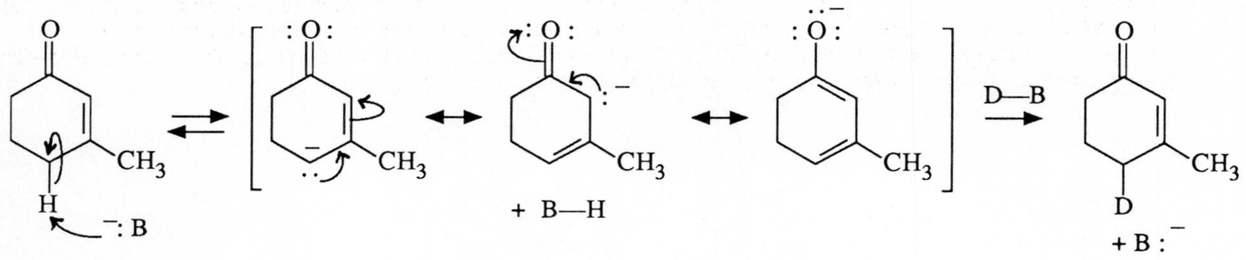

(b) The electron pair in the conjugate-base anion is in an orbital perpendicular to the π-electron system of the carbonyl group:

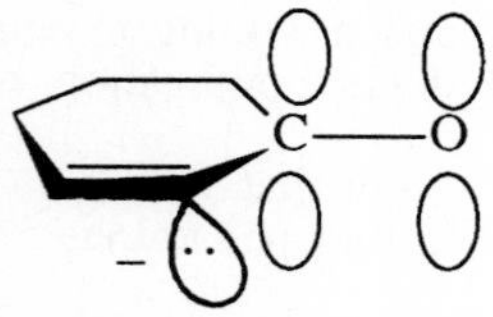

Hence, this anion is not resonance-stabilized. Looking at the situation another way, the resonance structures that we might draw for this anion are highly strained (why?), and therefore not important:

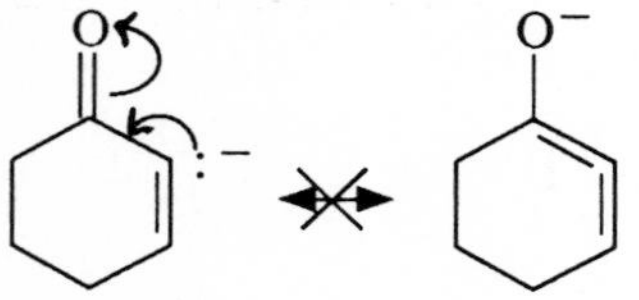

(c) The exchange of proton H^b begins with the ionization of H^d. This anion has resonance structures which show that it can be protonated at carbon-2. Following this protonation by *deuterated* solvent, the proton at H^b is removed by base. Reprotonation of the resulting anion at carbon-4 gives a deuterium at that position also.

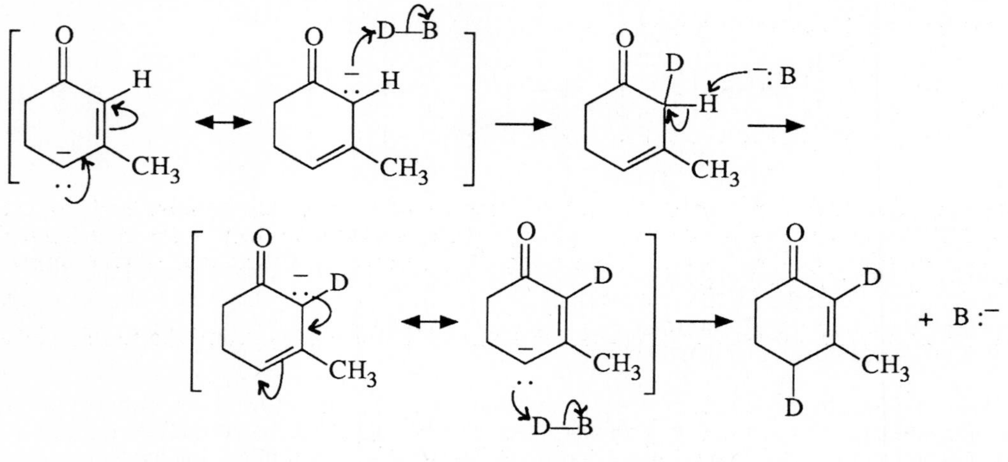

This shows that exchanges at carbon-2 and carbon-4 occur by the same mechanism.

59. (a) Compound *A*, γ-pyrone, protonates on the carbonyl oxygen, because the resulting carbocation is aromatic, and therefore especially stable. Protonation of this compound on the ether oxygen, in contrast, gives a conjugate acid that is not resonance-stabilized. Compound *B* protonates on the ether oxygen because ethers are more basic than aldehydes and ketones (see discussion on text pages 772–773).

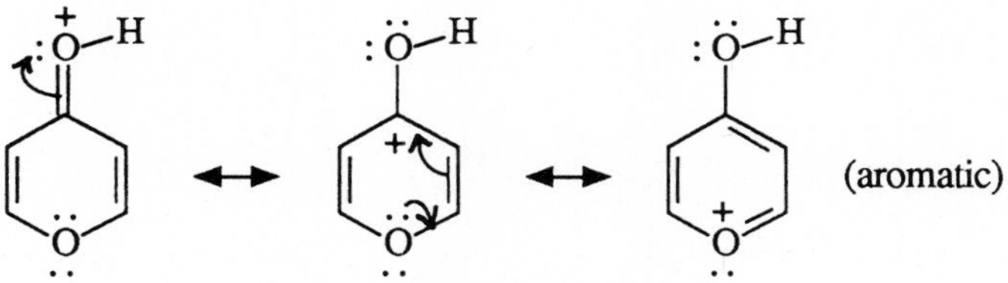

conjugate acid of *A*

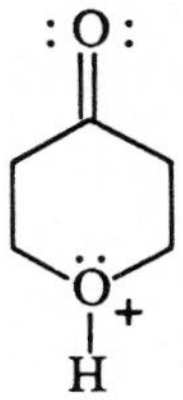

(aromatic)

conjugate acid of *B*

(b) The conjugate acid of tropone is particularly stable because its resonance structure shows that it is an aromatic cation; it has six π-electrons and fulfills the criteria for aromaticity.

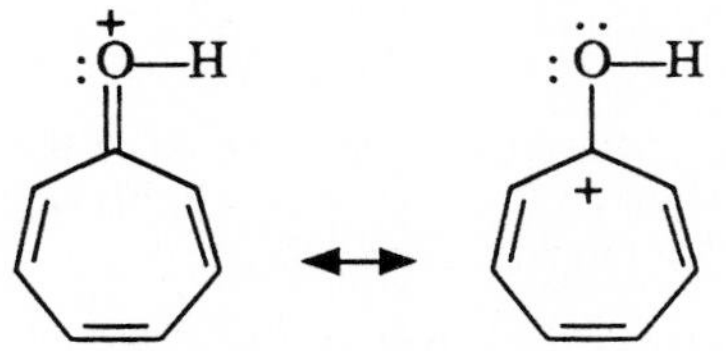

conjugate acid of tropone

60. The white powder is the lithium enolate of the ester:

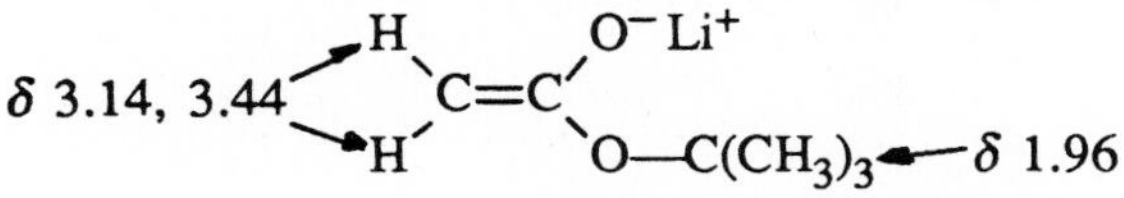

δ 3.14, 3.44

We have drawn the resonance form that has the carbon–carbon double bond. This form is clearly important, because the NMR spectrum shows that the two vinylic hydrogens are nonequivalent — that is, rotation about the double bond between the carbonyl carbon and the α-carbon is slow. Slow rotation is expected about a bond with significant double-bond character.

61. (a) The three forms include two structural isomers; one structural isomer can exist as diastereomers, labeled *B* and *C*:

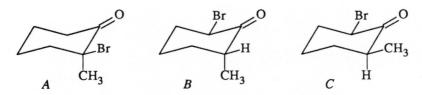

(b) Compound *A* is formed because the enol leading to it has a more highly substituted double bond than the enol leading to compounds *B* and *C*. (Draw the structure of the two enols and confirm this conclusion. The effect of substitution on alkene stability is discussed on text pages 106–108.) Compound *A* can exist as enantiomers; since the starting materials are achiral, the racemate of *A* is formed.

62. Let us analyze the mechanism by working backward from the product. The lactone unit in alternariol comes from transesterification of a phenol and a thiol ester:

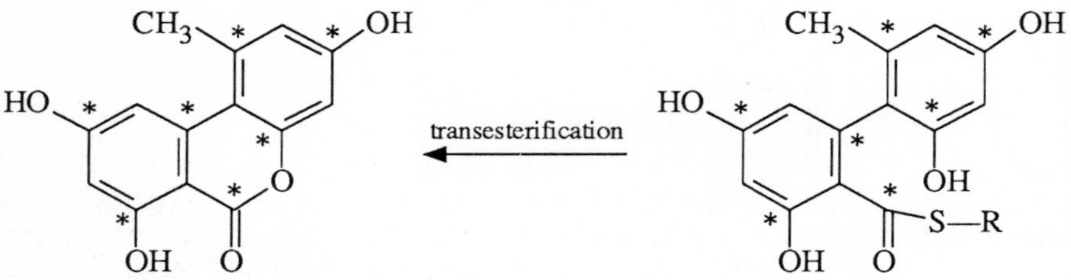

The phenols can be viewed as the aromatic tautomers of ketones that, in turn, are formed from dehydration of intermediates derived from aldol condensation reactions of a polyketide:

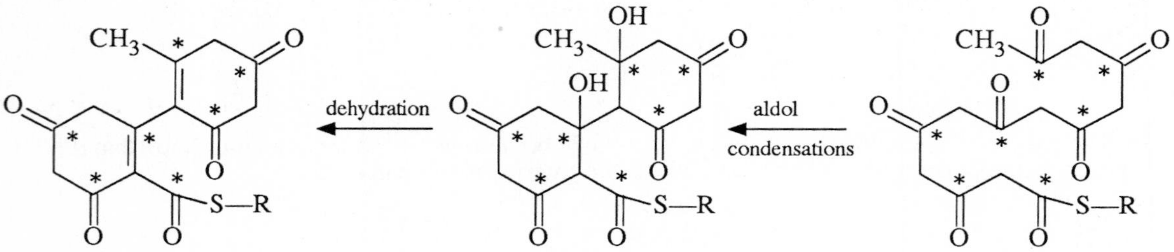

The asterisks trace the label from the polyketide to the final product. The positions of the asterisks in the polyketide follow from the mechanism of polyketide formation, which is given in the text. With this outline, you should now be able to provide the detailed mechanism if you have not already done so.

63. In each case, the label can be introduced by the conjugate addition of cyanide to an α,β-unsaturated ester. Hydrolysis of the ester and nitrile groups gives the labeled acids.

$$\overset{*}{N}C^- + CH_3{-}CH{=}CH{-}\overset{O}{\overset{\|}{C}}{-}OEt \longrightarrow \xrightarrow{H_3O^+,\ heat} HO{-}\underset{*}{\overset{O}{\overset{\|}{C}}}{-}\underset{CH_3}{\underset{|}{CH}}{-}CH_2{-}\overset{O}{\overset{\|}{C}}{-}OH$$

$$\overset{*}{N}C^- + CH_2{=}\underset{CH_3}{\underset{|}{C}}{-}\overset{O}{\overset{\|}{C}}{-}OEt \longrightarrow \xrightarrow{H_3O^+,\ heat} HO{-}\underset{*}{\overset{O}{\overset{\|}{C}}}{-}CH_2{-}\underset{CH_3}{\underset{|}{CH}}{-}\overset{O}{\overset{\|}{C}}{-}OH$$

64. From the discussion on text page 844, we know that decarboxylation of β-keto acids involves an enol intermediate. Bromination of the enol by the usual mechanism (text pages 928–929) gives the bromoketone.

$$CH_3{-}\overset{O}{\overset{\|}{C}}{-}CH_2{-}\overset{O}{\overset{\|}{C}}{-}OH \xrightarrow{-CO_2} CH_3{-}\overset{OH}{\overset{|}{C}}{=}CH_2 \xrightarrow{Br_2} CH_3{-}\overset{O}{\overset{\|}{C}}{-}CH_2{-}Br \ + \ HBr$$

The rate law suggests that decarboxylation is the rate-limiting step. If bromination were the rate-limiting step, the rate law would contain a term in $[Br_2]$.

65. The source of the iodoform must be the central carbon:

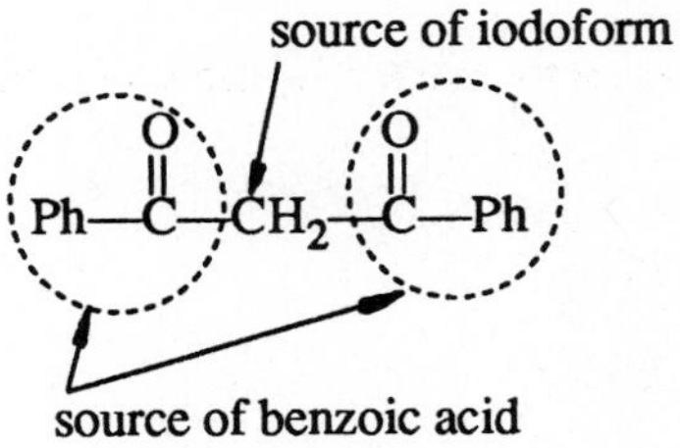

source of iodoform

source of benzoic acid

Base-promoted iodination occurs at the central carbon by the usual mechanism. The molecule is then cleaved by base to give benzoic acid with the enolate ion of a diiodoketone as the leaving group. This enolate iodinates to give triiodoacetophenone, which is then cleaved in the same manner as other trihaloketones to give iodoform and the conjugate base of benzoic acid.

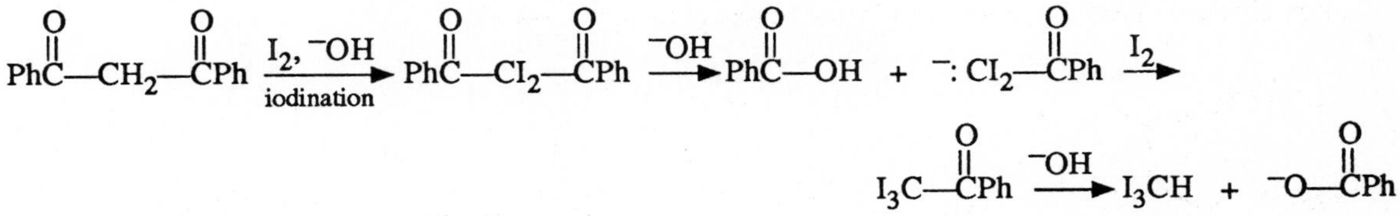

66. (a)

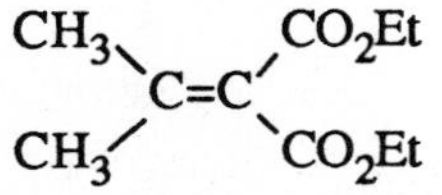

(b) Because diethyl malonate is considerably more acidic than acetone, its conjugate-base enolate ion is formed quantitatively in the presence of ethoxide. Hence, it is the only enolate ion in the reaction mixture. Acetone, then, is the only un-ionized carbonyl compound present. As a result, there is only one possible aldol condensation. The reaction is driven to completion by dehydration of the alcohol intermediate.

(c) Reaction of the product of (a) with lithium dimethylcuprate followed by saponification and decarboxylation gives the desired compound.

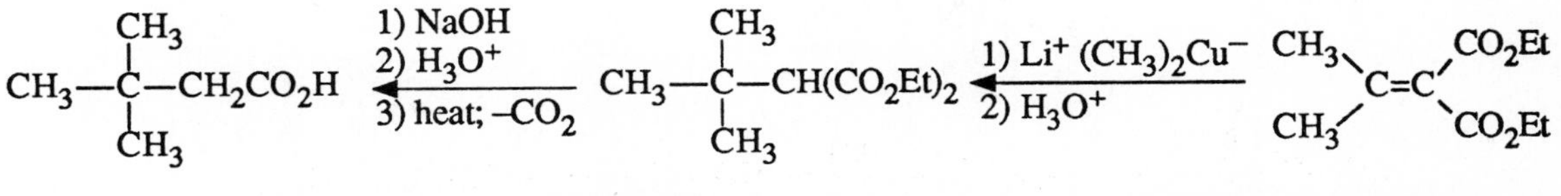

67. This sequence is a Claisen condensation of a ketone with an ester (ethyl formate), followed by a Robinson annulation (a conjugate addition followed by an intramolecular aldol condensation). We outline the mechanism below, and leave it to you to provide the details.

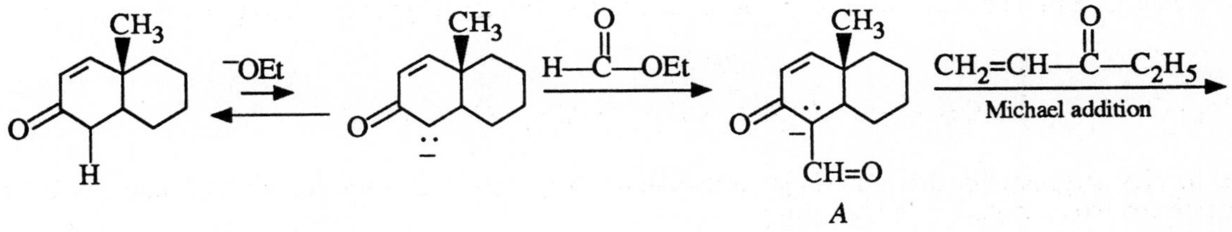

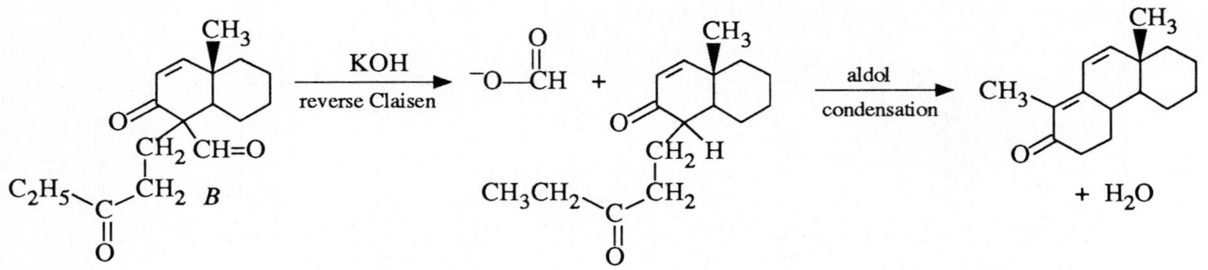

68. The structure of pulegone suggests that the most likely source of acetone is the isopropenyl branch. Indeed, conjugate addition of ⁻OH followed by a reverse aldol condensation affords acetone and 3-methyl-1-cyclohexanone:

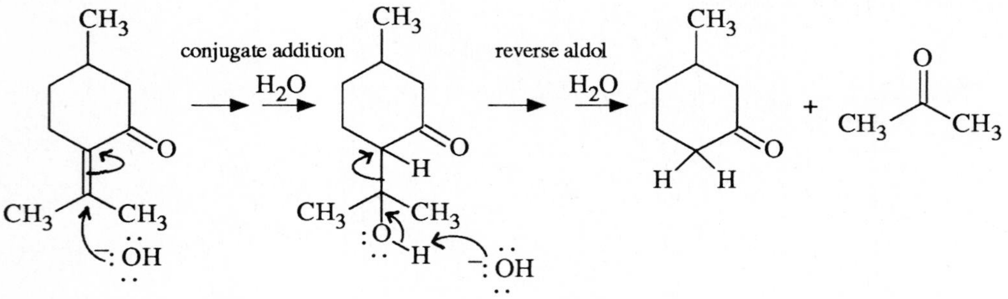

69. (a) One equivalent of base is required in the Claisen or Dieckmann condensation because ionization of the product is required to drive the reaction to completion. (See text pages 941–943.)
    (b) Sodium phenoxide, the conjugate base of phenol, is about 10^{-5} as basic as sodium ethoxide. Phenol, with a pK_a of 10, is not basic enough to ionize fully the α-hydrogen of a Claisen condensation product, which typically has a pK_a of 10.7 (see Eq. 22.51c, text page 942). Hence, the Claisen condensation reaction is not driven to completion. Moreover, sodium phenoxide is not nearly as effective as the more basic ethoxide in formation of the initial ester enolate ion required for the condensation to occur.

70. (a)

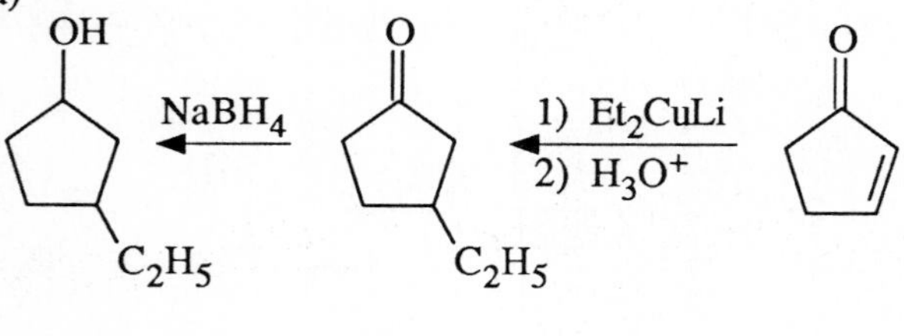

    (b)

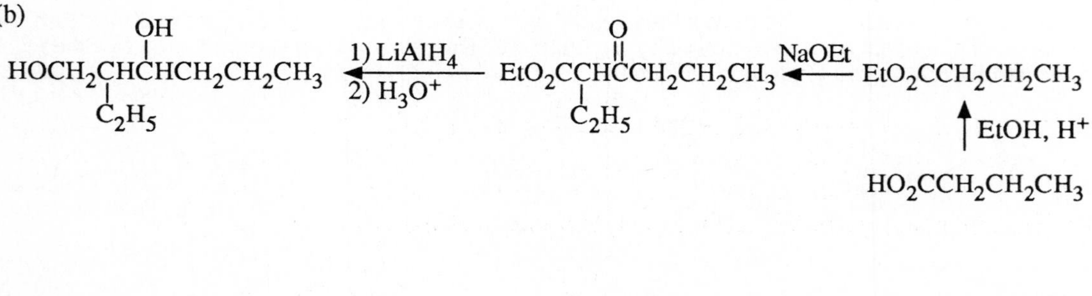

(c)

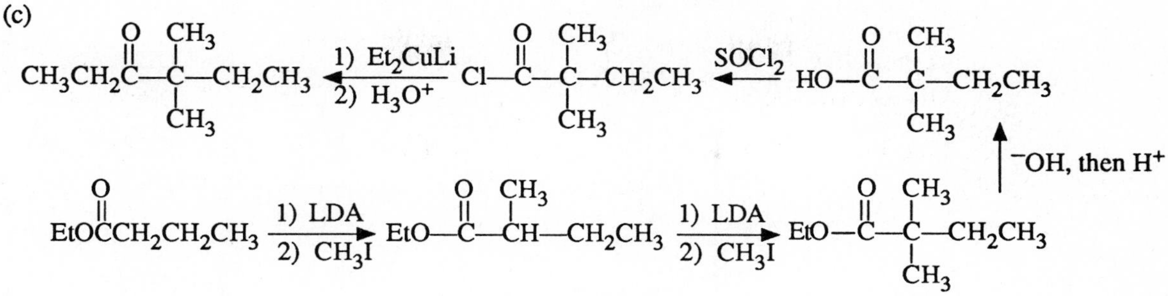

(d)

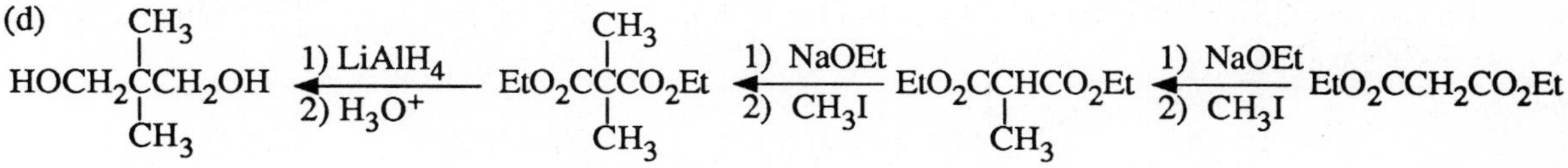

(e)

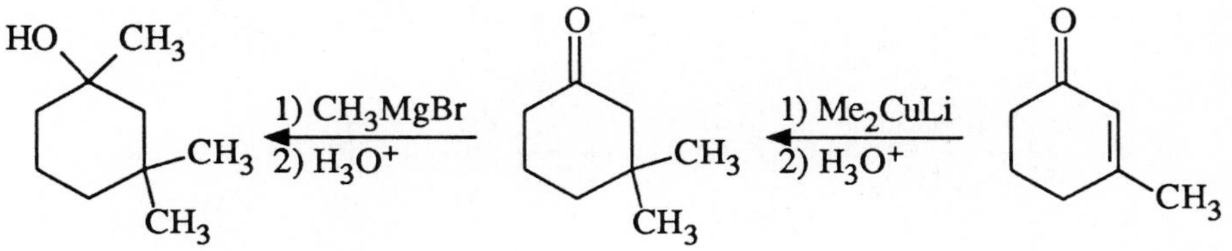

(f)

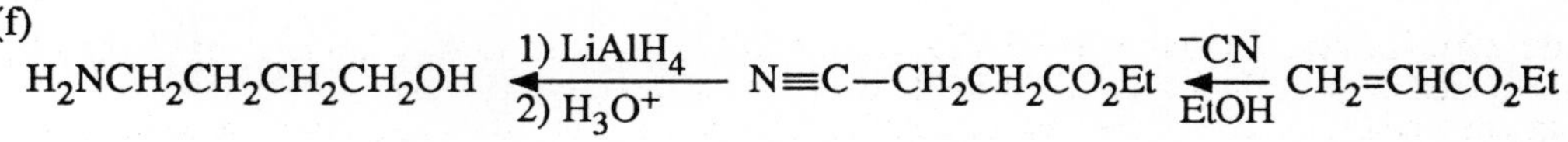

(g)

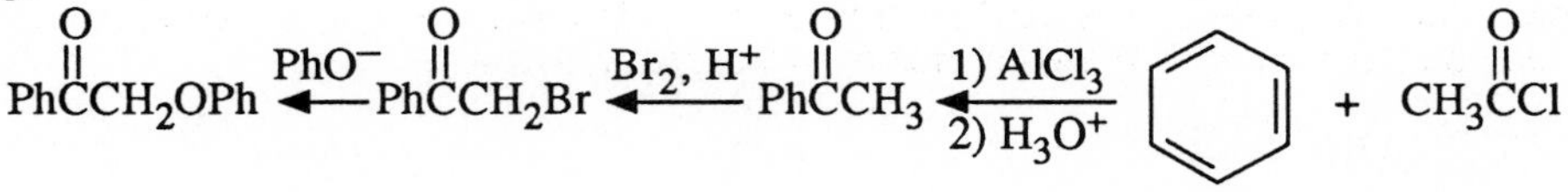

(h)

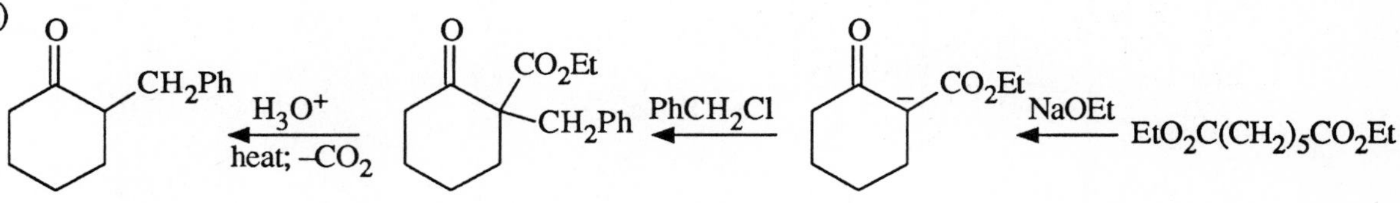

(i)

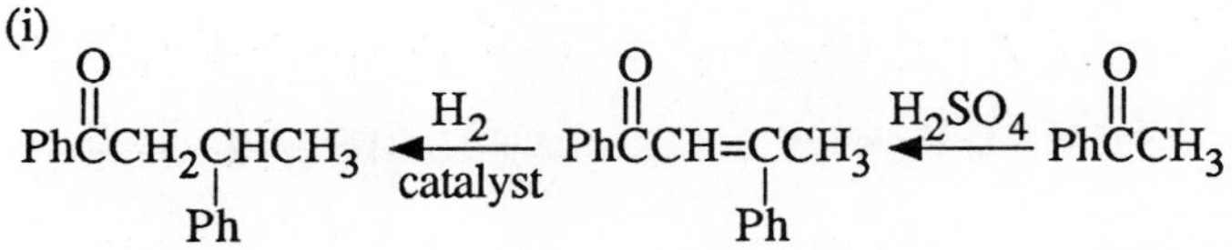

(The first step of this synthesis is an acid-catalyzed aldol condensation.)

(j)

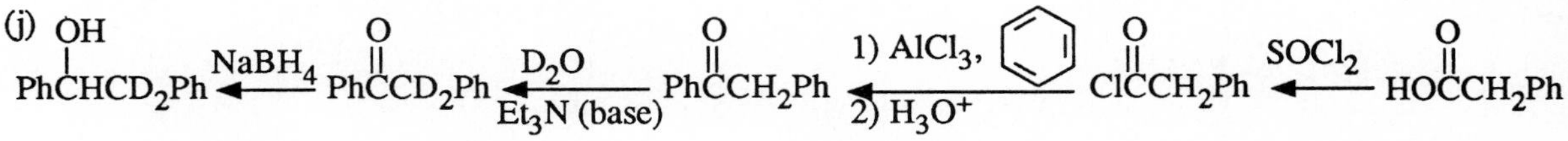

(k)

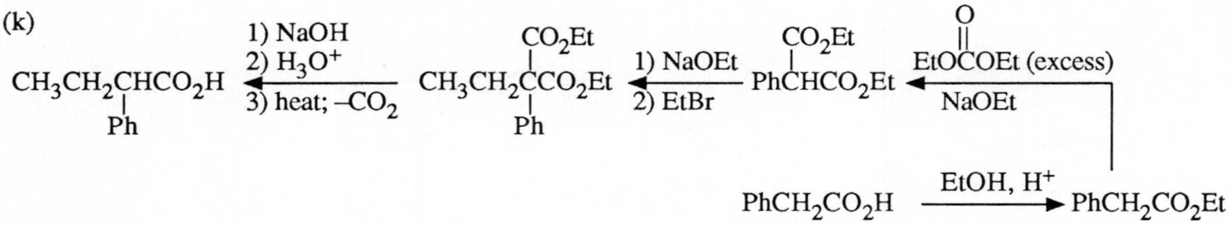

$$CH_3CH_2\underset{\underset{Ph}{|}}{CH}CO_2H \xleftarrow[\substack{1)\ NaOH \\ 2)\ H_3O^+ \\ 3)\ heat;\ -CO_2}]{} CH_3CH_2\underset{\underset{Ph}{|}}{\overset{\overset{CO_2Et}{|}}{C}}CO_2Et \xleftarrow[\substack{1)\ NaOEt \\ 2)\ EtBr}]{} Ph\overset{\overset{CO_2Et}{|}}{CH}CO_2Et \xleftarrow[NaOEt]{\overset{\overset{O}{\|}}{EtOCOEt}\ (excess)}$$

$$PhCH_2CO_2H \xrightarrow{EtOH,\ H^+} PhCH_2CO_2Et$$

(l)

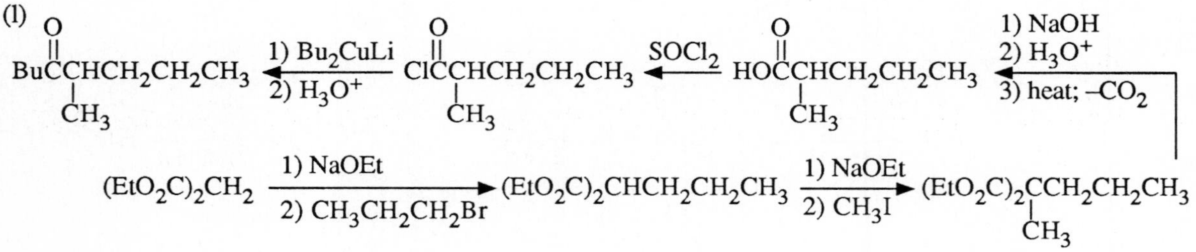

$$Bu\overset{\overset{O}{\|}}{C}\underset{\underset{CH_3}{|}}{CH}CH_2CH_2CH_3 \xleftarrow[\substack{1)\ Bu_2CuLi \\ 2)\ H_3O^+}]{} Cl\overset{\overset{O}{\|}}{C}\underset{\underset{CH_3}{|}}{CH}CH_2CH_2CH_3 \xleftarrow{SOCl_2} HO\overset{\overset{O}{\|}}{C}\underset{\underset{CH_3}{|}}{CH}CH_2CH_2CH_3 \xleftarrow[\substack{1)\ NaOH \\ 2)\ H_3O^+ \\ 3)\ heat;\ -CO_2}]{}$$

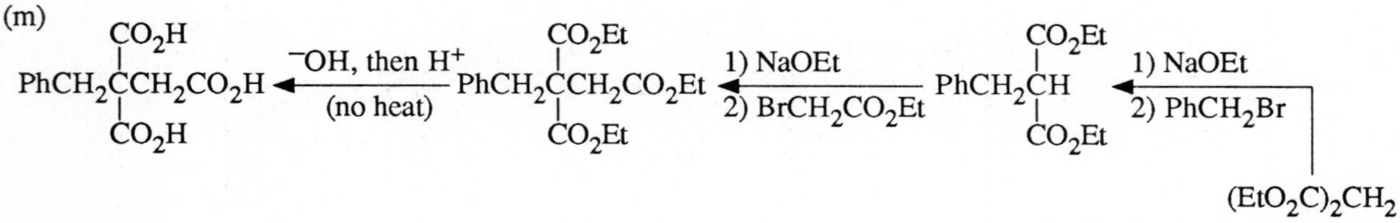

$$(EtO_2C)_2CH_2 \xrightarrow[\substack{2)\ CH_3CH_2CH_2Br}]{1)\ NaOEt} (EtO_2C)_2CHCH_2CH_2CH_3 \xrightarrow[\substack{2)\ CH_3I}]{1)\ NaOEt} (EtO_2C)_2\underset{\underset{CH_3}{|}}{C}CH_2CH_2CH_3$$

(m)

$$PhCH_2\underset{\underset{CO_2H}{|}}{\overset{\overset{CO_2H}{|}}{C}}CH_2CO_2H \xleftarrow[\text{(no heat)}]{^-OH,\ then\ H^+} PhCH_2\underset{\underset{CO_2Et}{|}}{\overset{\overset{CO_2Et}{|}}{C}}CH_2CO_2Et \xleftarrow[\substack{2)\ BrCH_2CO_2Et}]{1)\ NaOEt} PhCH_2\underset{\underset{CO_2Et}{|}}{\overset{\overset{CO_2Et}{|}}{C}}H \xleftarrow[\substack{2)\ PhCH_2Br}]{1)\ NaOEt}$$

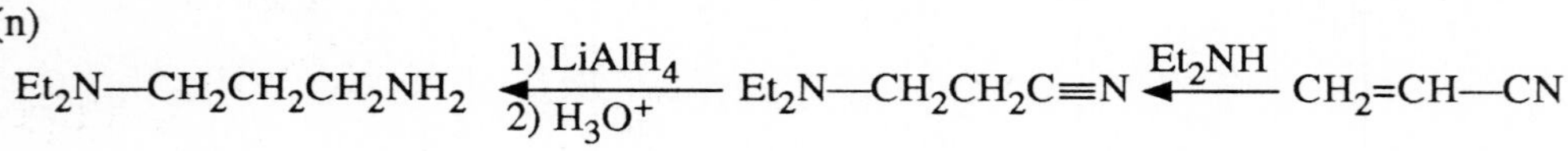

$$(EtO_2C)_2CH_2$$

(n)

$$Et_2N-CH_2CH_2CH_2NH_2 \xleftarrow[\substack{2)\ H_3O^+}]{1)\ LiAlH_4} Et_2N-CH_2CH_2C\equiv N \xleftarrow{Et_2NH} CH_2=CH-CN$$

(o)

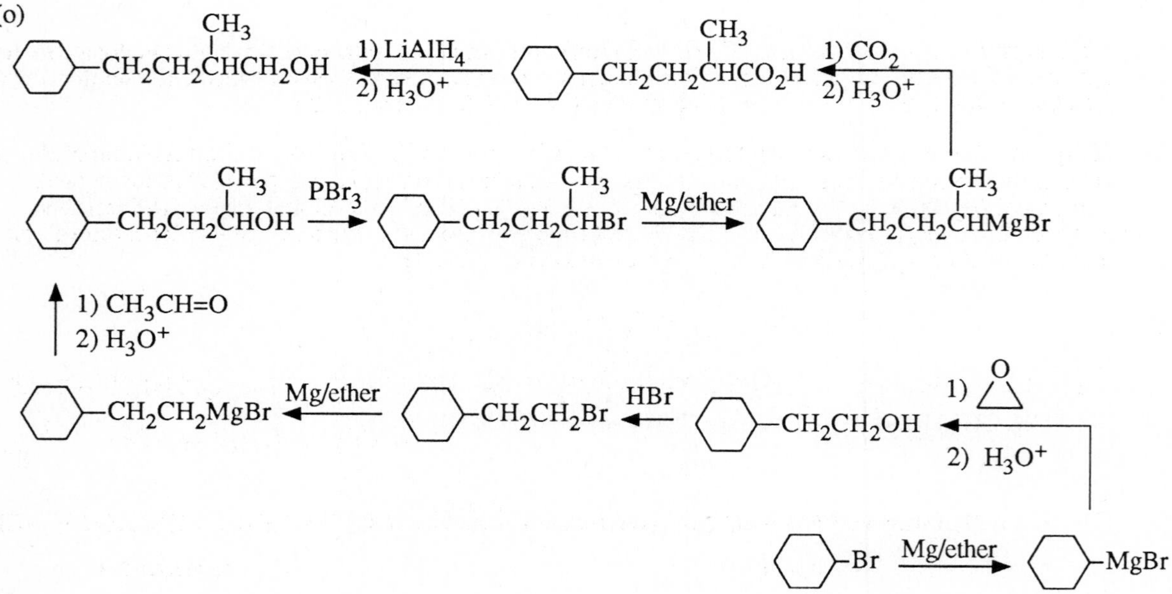

(p)

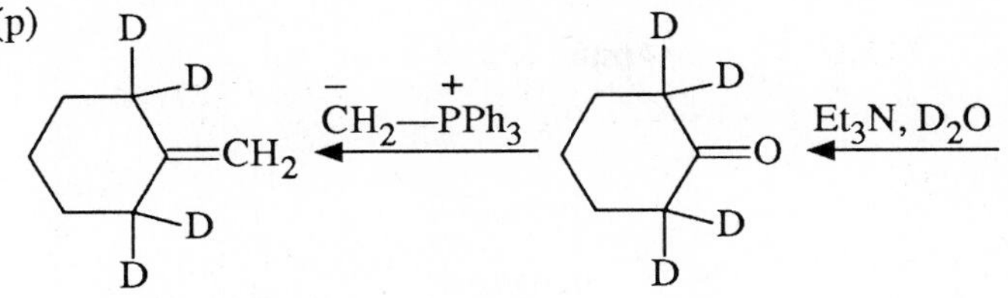

The preparation of the ylid is given on text page 802.

(q)

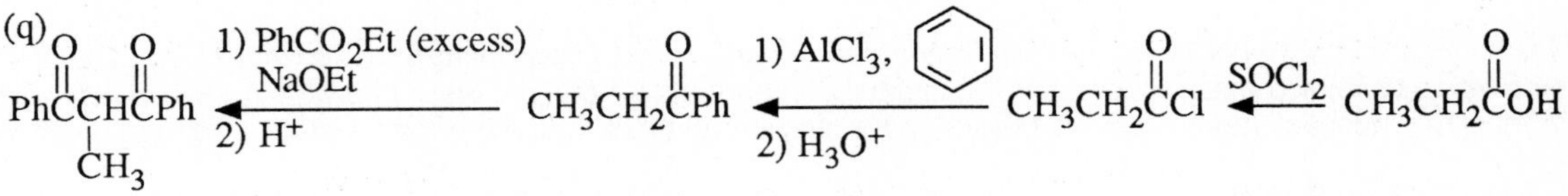

(r)

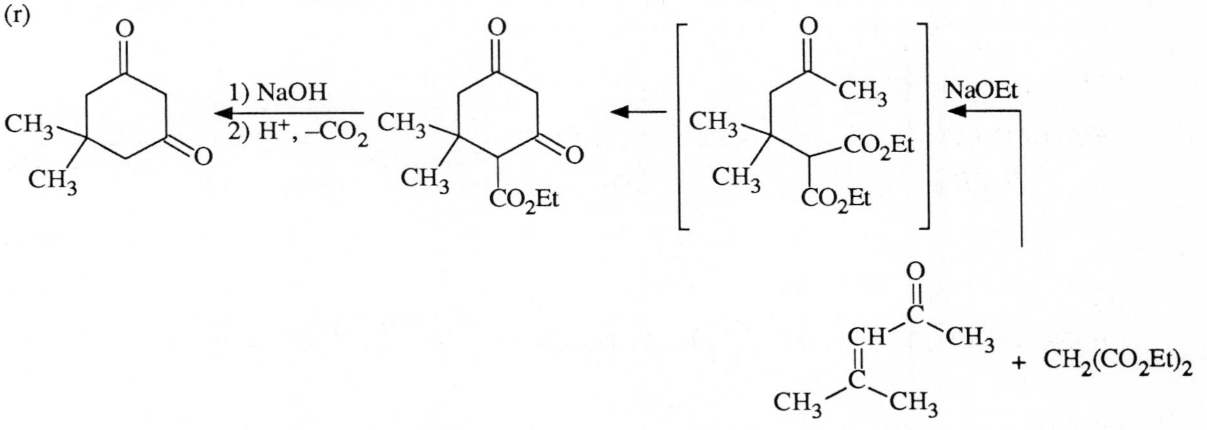

The first step in this synthesis is a Michael addition of the conjugate-base anion of diethyl malonate to the α,β-unsaturated ketone. Under the basic conditions, a Dieckmann condensation occurs to establish the carbon skeleton. Hydrolysis of the ester and decarboxylation complete the synthesis.

71. Compound B is an aldehyde; therefore, compound A is a primary alcohol. The carbon skeleton of B is the same as that of octanoic acid (an unbranched chain of eight carbons), and compound B is conjugated. Compound B is therefore 2-octenal, $CH_3CH_2CH_2CH_2CH_2CH=CH—CH=O$. In order to form this compound, the "butyl anion" of the dibutylcuprate reagent must add to the terminal vinylic carbon of the epoxide. In other words, this is a *conjugate addition to an epoxide*:

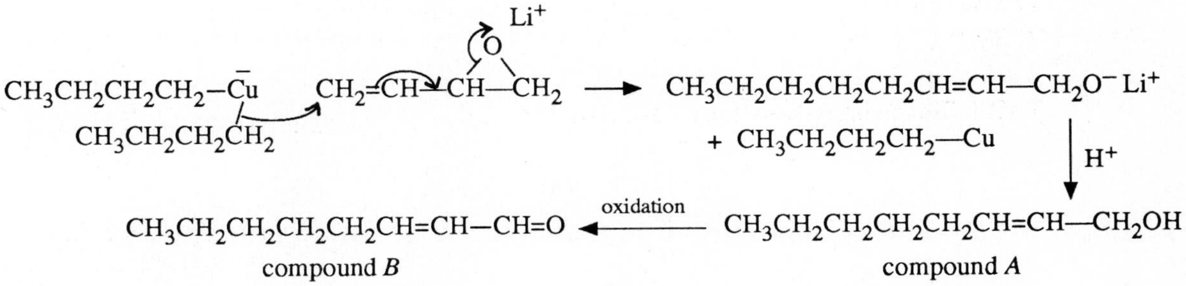

72. The deuterium incorporation results show that the carbon–carbon double bond is protonated. As a result, a resonance-stabilized carbocation is formed that is attacked by water to give a hemiacetal. Hemiacetals decompose to aldehydes or ketones in the presence of water:

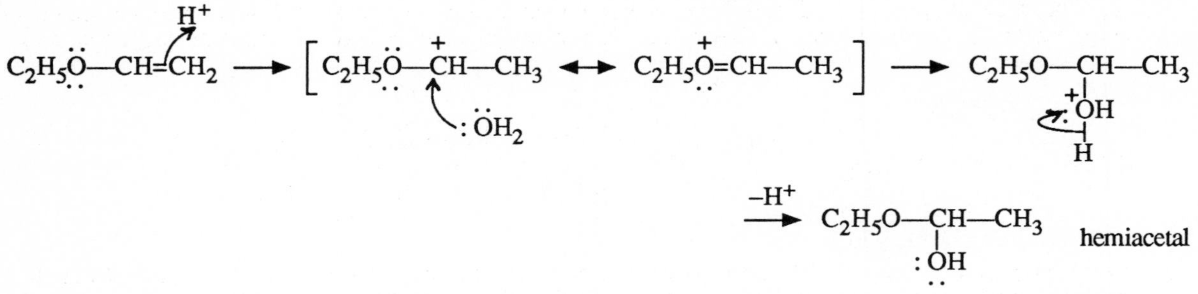

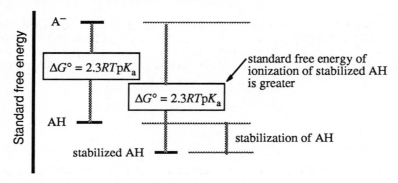

We leave it to you to complete the conversion of the hemiacetal to acetaldehyde. (See text pages 788–790 for a discussion of hemiacetals.) Compare the mechanism above with that for ether cleavage on text pages 424–425. Why is the mechanism above more favorable for ethyl vinyl ether than the ordinary ether-cleavage mechanism?

73. (a) This type of resonance interaction stabilizes the un-ionized form of an acid. Stabilization of an acid relative to its conjugate base *increases* the $\Delta G°$ for its ionization, and therefore *raises* its pK_a, as shown by the following energy diagram (AH = acid, A⁻ = conjugate base):

(b) There are two effects on acidity: the resonance effect indicated in part (a) and the inductive effect. In the compound on the left (3-butenoic acid), there can be no resonance effect — the double bond is not conjugated with the carbonyl group. The pK_a of this compound is lower than that of butanoic acid, the compound on the right, by about 0.5 unit. Since inductive effects are most important in charged species, we assume that the inductive effect acts to stabilize the conjugate base. (If this is not clear to you, see the discussion of inductive effects on acidity on text pages 300–302.) This implies, then, that a double bond is inductively electron-withdrawing — that is, it behaves as if it is an electronegative group.
(c) Inductive effects are more important when the two interacting groups are closer together. The double bond in the middle compound, *trans*-2-butenoic acid, is closer to the carboxy group than the double bond in 3-butenoic acid. Since we have already concluded that the inductive effect of a double bond enhances acidity, it follows that if the inductive effect were the only thing affecting the pK_a of 2-butenoic acid, its acidity should be greater than that of 3-butenoic acid. Yet the acidity of 2-butenoic acid is less. Therefore, some acidity-reducing effect must be offsetting the inductive effect. This is consistent with the operation of the resonance effect discussed in part (a).

74. (a) Species *A* is the conjugate-base enolate ion:

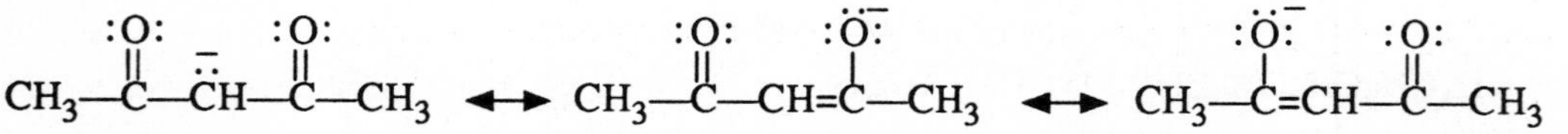

(The gas is H_2.) According to the resonance structures, the nucleophilic atoms should be the ones that share the negative charge: the carbonyl oxygens and the central carbon.

(b) The three compounds B, C, and D are the compound methylated on carbon, and two stereoisomers of the compound methylated on oxygen. (Reaction at either oxygen gives the same mixture of stereoisomers.)

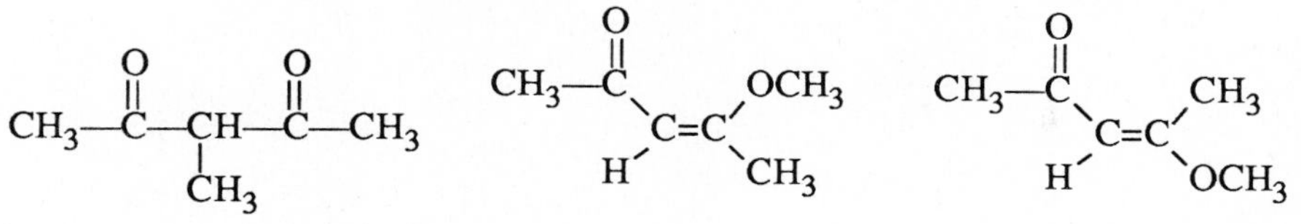

75. Removal of an α-proton from the bromo ester, attack of the resulting enolate anion on benzaldehyde, and intramolecular attack of the oxygen anion thus formed on the carbon bearing the bromide ion leads to epoxide formation. We begin with the attack of the enolate ion on benzaldehyde:

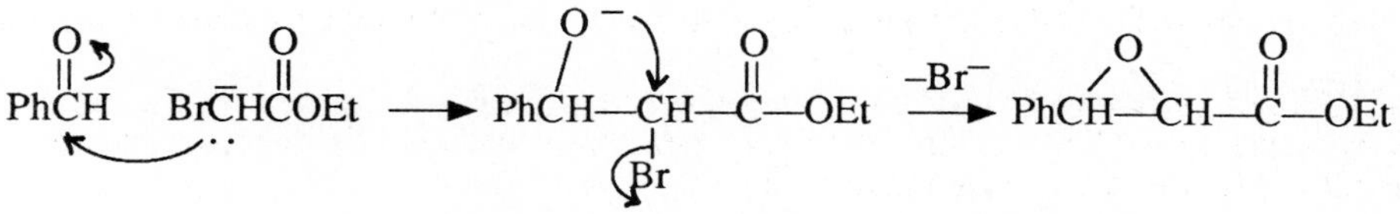

76. (a) The formula is consistent with the addition of four carbons (from the dihalide) to the β-keto ester followed by hydrolysis of the ester and decarboxylation — that is, a net addition of one carbon. The formula also indicates two degrees of unsaturation. Since there is only one carbonyl group left in the product, there must be a ring. This results from S_N2 reactions of intermediate enolate ions at both ends of the alkyl dihalide. The product is:

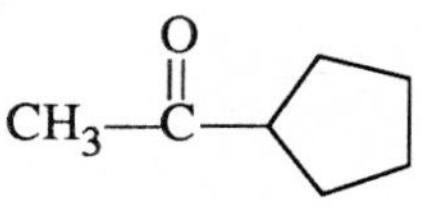

(b) This reaction is a nucleophilic aromatic substitution (Sec. 18.4A) with the enolate ion as the nucleophile:

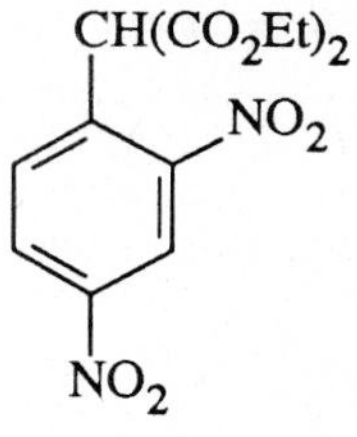

(c) This is an ester alkylation (Sec. 22.6B); the ester is cyclic (that is, it is a lactone):

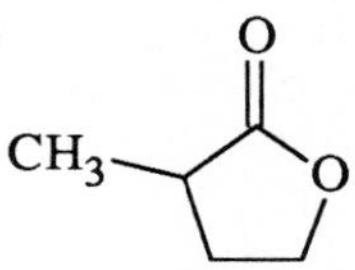

(d) Lithium aluminum hydride reduces carbonyl groups of α,β-unsaturated ketones:

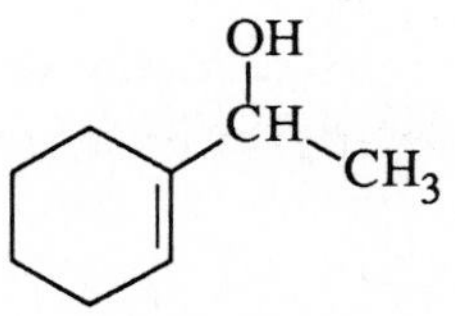

(e) This is a Michael addition in which the conjugate-base anion of the diethyl malonate derivative acts as the nucleophile:

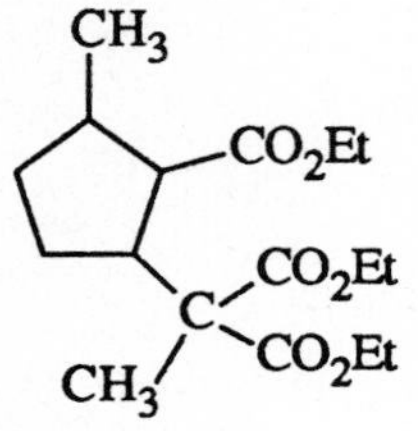

CH$_3$, cyclopentane ring with CO$_2$Et substituent, and a carbon bearing CH$_3$, CO$_2$Et, CO$_2$Et groups

(f) And here we have another Michael addition:

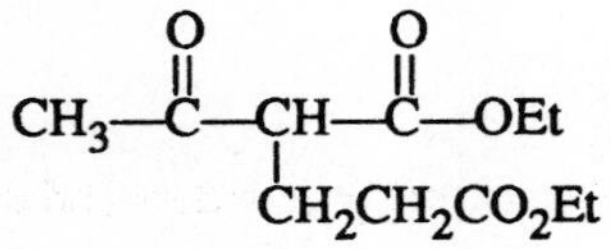

$$CH_3-\overset{\overset{O}{\|}}{C}-\underset{\underset{CH_2CH_2CO_2Et}{|}}{CH}-\overset{\overset{O}{\|}}{C}-OEt$$

(g) The product results from a conjugate addition of an "alkyl anion" from a cuprate reagent formed from the Grignard reagent and CuCl. The attacking group enters from the face of the molecule opposite the methyl group; that is, the entering group and the methyl group are *trans*.

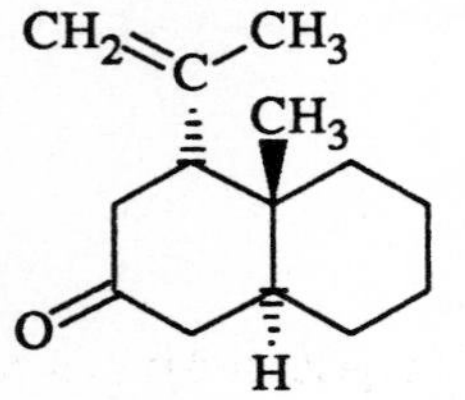

CH$_2$=C(CH$_3$) group on a decalone (fused bicyclic) system with CH$_3$, O, and H substituents

(h) We know that aluminum chloride, as a Lewis acid, should complex with a ketone at its carbonyl group. In this case, such a complex has a resonance structure in which positive charge is delocalized to the β-carbon:

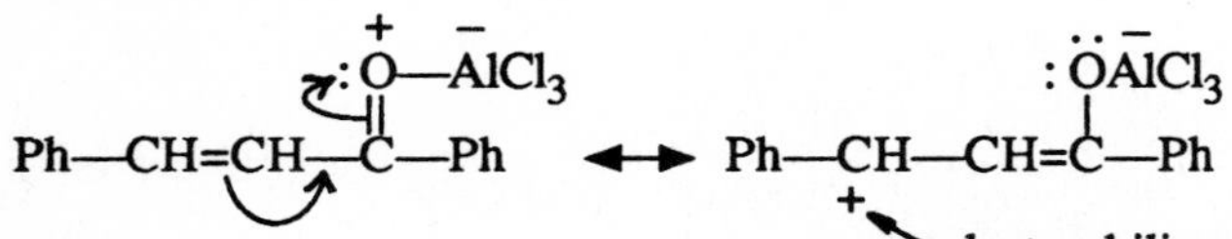

$$Ph-CH=CH-\overset{\overset{+}{\overset{:O-AlCl_3}{\|}}}{C}-Ph \longleftrightarrow Ph-CH-CH=\overset{\overset{:\overset{..}{O}AlCl_3}{|}}{\underset{+}{C}}-Ph$$

electrophilic carbon atom

This carbon acts as an electrophile in an aromatic substitution reaction on benzene. Addition of water to the reaction mixture affords an enol, which is rapidly transformed into the product ketone:

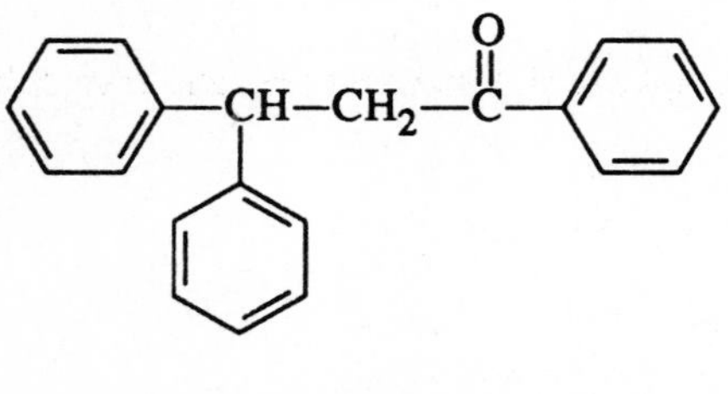

Ph—CH(Ph)—CH$_2$—C(=O)—Ph structure drawn with benzene rings

(i) The Mg in the presence of CuBr forms a magnesium dialkylcuprate reagent from the alkyl halide. This undergoes a conjugate addition to the α,β-unsaturated ketone to give the following addition product, which hydrolyzes to an aldehyde under the aqueous acidic conditions of protonolysis:

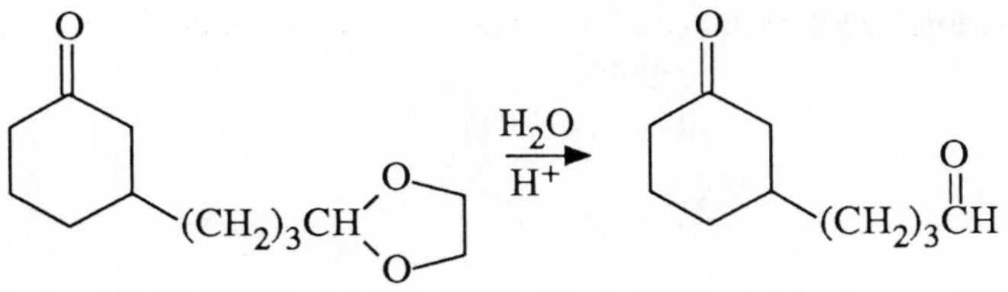

This aldehyde then undergoes an acid-catalyzed aldol condensation to give the final product:

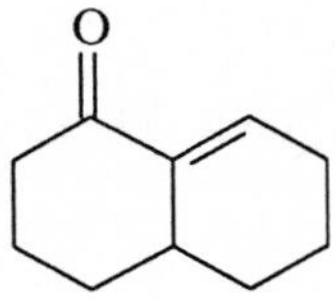

➤ If you did not get some of the products in these reactions, you should be certain that you understand the processes by which the correct products do form.

77. (a) The nitro group stabilizes the conjugate-base anion by both a resonance and inductive effect:

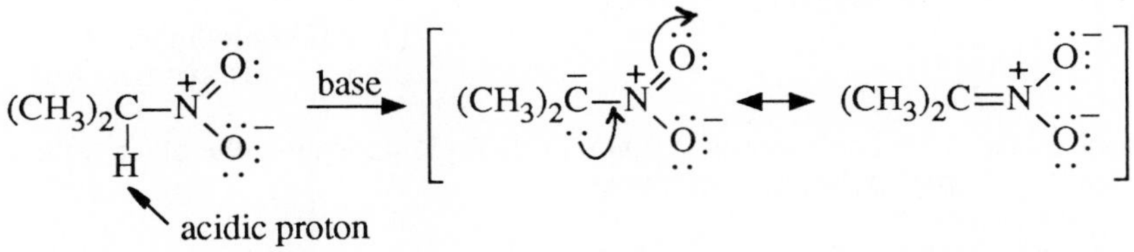

(b) The resonance structures above show that negative charge is shared by both the oxygens and the carbon of 2-nitropropane anion. Reprotonation on carbon gives back 2-nitropropane; protonation of an oxygen gives the nitro analog of an enol (called an *aci*-nitro compound):

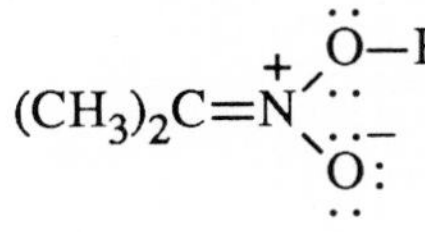

(c) Like other enolate ions, this "enolate" ion undergoes Michael additions:

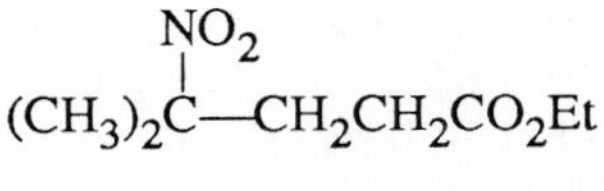

$$NO_2$$
$$(CH_3)_2C-CH_2CH_2CO_2Et$$

78. (a) An enolate ion acts as a nucleophile in an intramolecular nucleophilic displacement reaction to give the cyclopropane:

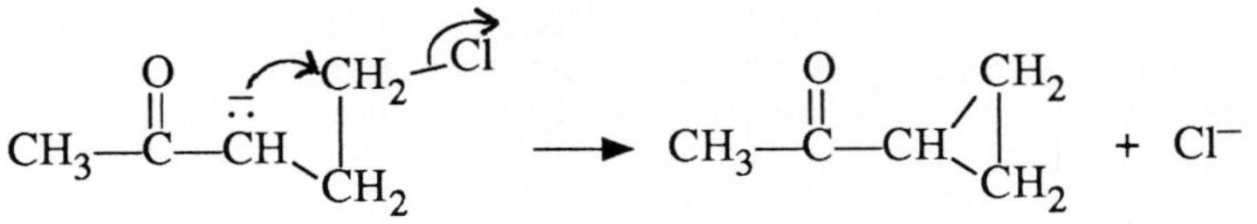

(b) As the hint suggests, the reaction is a reverse aldol condensation:

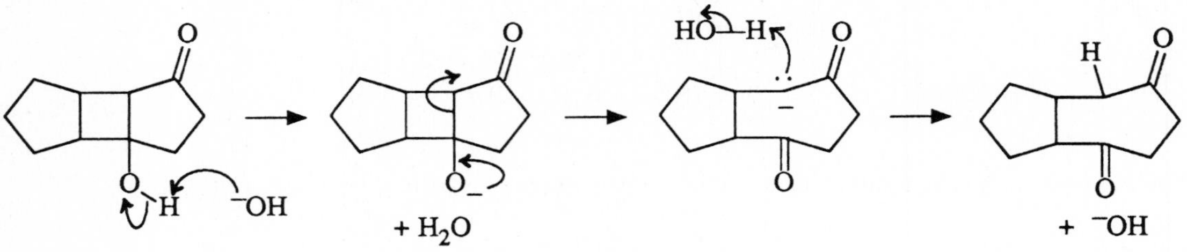

(c) In this case, we outline the mechanism by providing key intermediates and leave it to you to fill in the details. The conjugate-base enolate of diethyl malonate attacks the epoxide to give the conjugate base of an alcohol A which undergoes hydrolysis and decarboxylation to give hydroxy acid B. Under the acidic conditions, compound B lactonizes to give the first product:

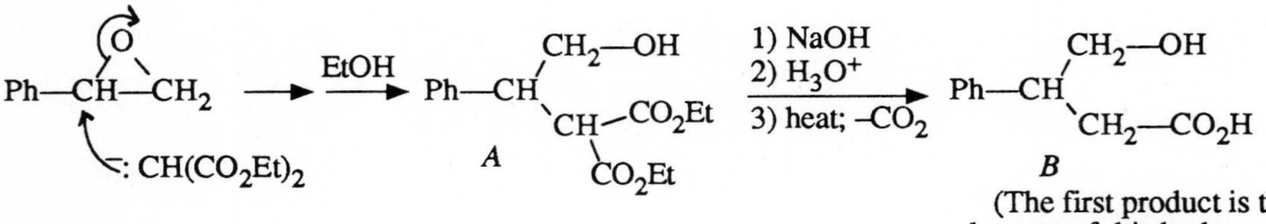

(The first product is the lactone of this hydroxy acid.)

The second product arises from attack of the conjugate-base anion of diethyl malonate at the other carbon of the epoxide. (Give the structures of the corresponding intermediates.)

➤ Normally basic reagents attack epoxides at the less substituted carbon. However, the more substituted position is activated in this case because it is benzylic. Benzylic displacements are activated for epoxides as they are for alkyl halides (Sec. 17.4). Hence, products of attack at both positions are observed.

(d) A benzyne intermediate is formed by the reaction of $NaNH_2$ with bromobenzene (see Sec. 18.4B). This intermediate is attacked by the two bases present: the amide ion ($^-NH_2$) and the conjugate-base anion of diethyl malonate, which is itself formed by reaction of diethyl malonate with the amide ion:

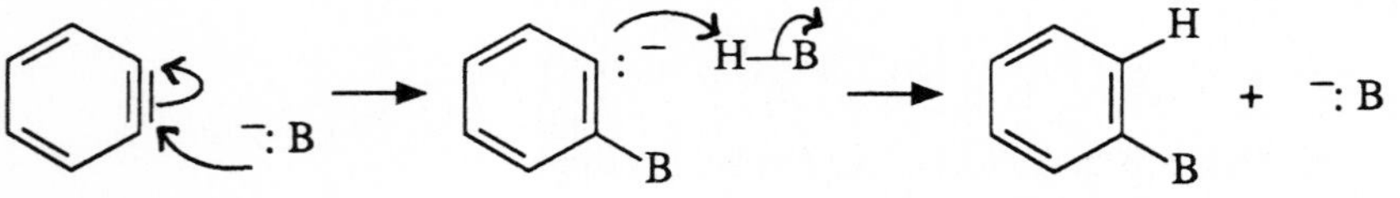

[B $:^- = \ ^-: CH(CO_2Et)_2$ accounts for one product; B $:^- = \ ^-: \ddot{N}H_2$ accounts for the other.] The reason that the same reaction is not observed with sodium ethoxide is that sodium ethoxide is not a strong enough base to form benzyne. Under the basic conditions the product derived by attack of diethyl malonate actually exists as an anion; addition of acid (not shown) is required to neutralize it. Can you see why four equivalents of $NaNH_2$ are required?

(e) This is a Claisen condensation followed by the reversal of a different Claisen condensation. The reaction is driven to completion by removal of the volatile by-product ethyl acetate. The mechanism is outlined below beginning with the conjugate-base anion of the starting material; you provide the details.

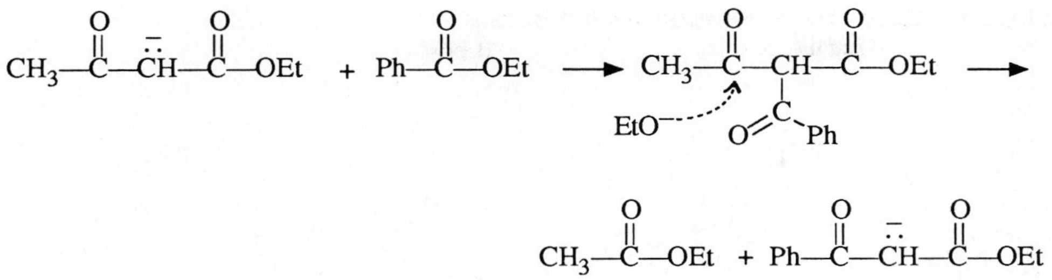

Protonation of the last anion affords the product.

79. (a) The product arises from attack of the conjugate-base anion of urea on an ester group, then loss of ethoxide. Repetition of a similar process closes the ring:

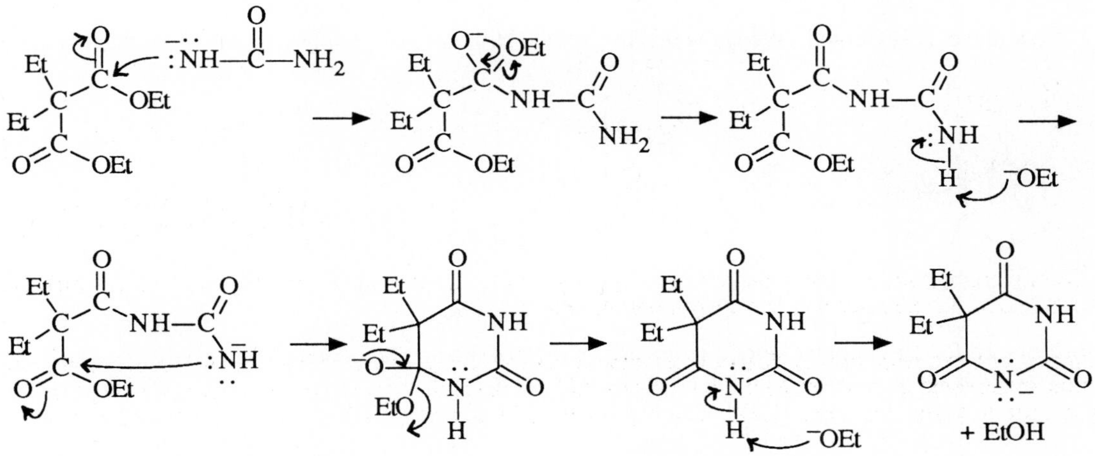

Protonation of the last anion to give the product occurs when acid is added.

(b)

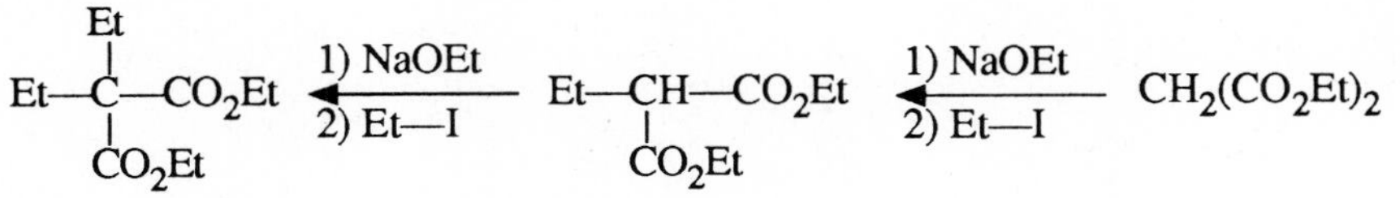

80. (a) This is an intramolecular aldol condensation. We begin the mechanism with the enolate ion:

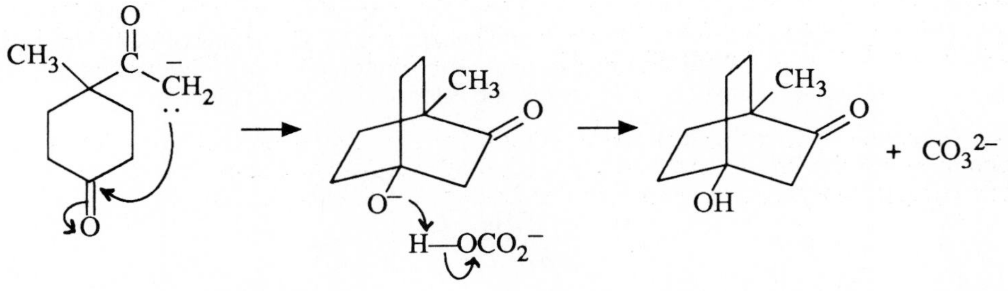

(b) The product results from four successive aldol condensations. The mechanism is outlined with the key intermediates below; you provide the details.

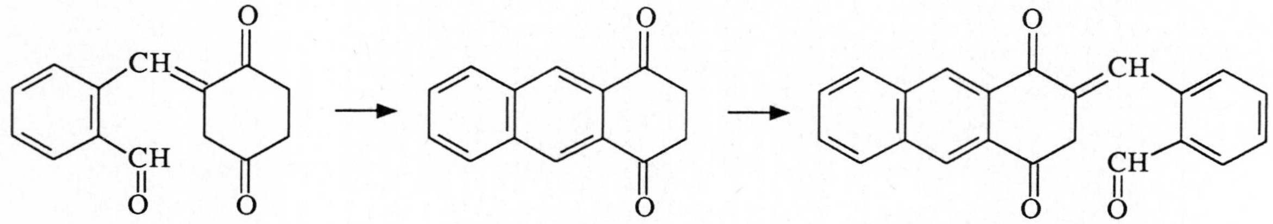

product of first
aldol condensation

product of second
aldol condensation

product of third aldol condensation

A fourth aldol condensation affords the final product.

(c) First, a dienol A is formed. We show this in a partial structure, beginning with the protonated ketone:

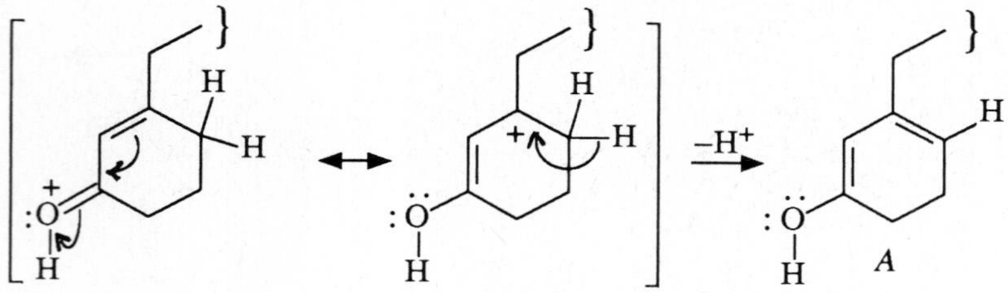

The protonated form of another ketone group adds to one of the double bonds of A to give a resonance-stabilized carbocation. Loss of a proton affords the product:

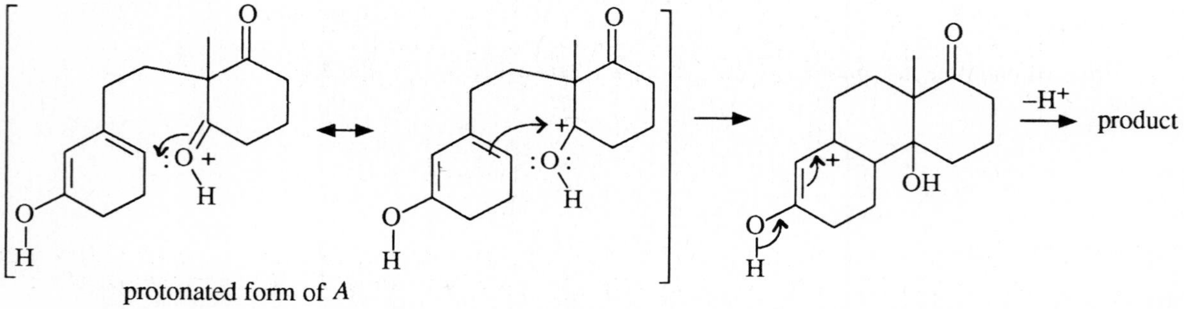

protonated form of A

(d) This process begins as a double Claisen condensation of one molecule of acetone with two of diethyl oxalate (the diester) to give intermediate anion A. (You should be able to give the details of this reaction.) Addition of the anionic oxygen of this enolate ion to a carbonyl group within the same molecule affords an alcohol that undergoes base-catalyzed dehydration to give B, the ester of chelidonic acid.

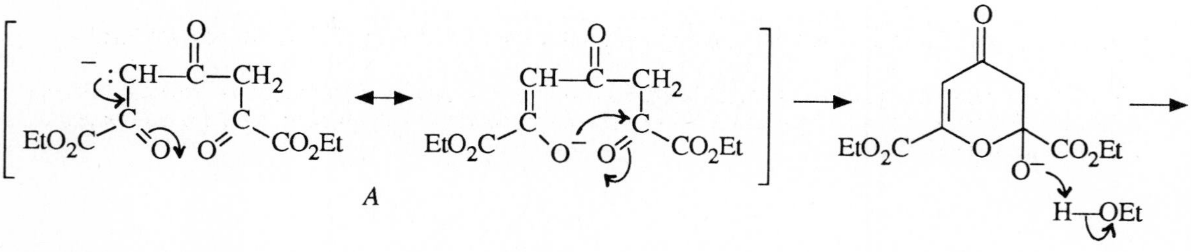

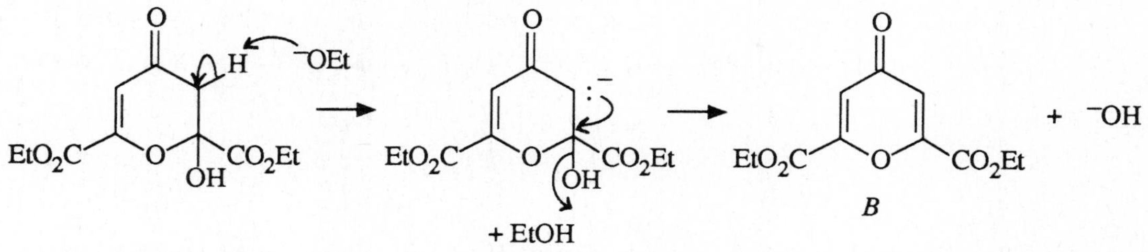

The conversion of *A* to *B* is just an aldol condensation in which the *oxygen* of an enolate ion is the nucleophile. The oxygen rather than carbon acts as the nucleophilic atom in this case because a six-membered ring is formed. (What size ring would be formed if the anionic carbon were the nucleophile?) Hydrolysis of the ester affords chelidonic acid.

(e) An intramolecular nucleophilic displacement reaction followed by an E2 elimination accounts for the product. We begin the mechanism with an enolate ion:

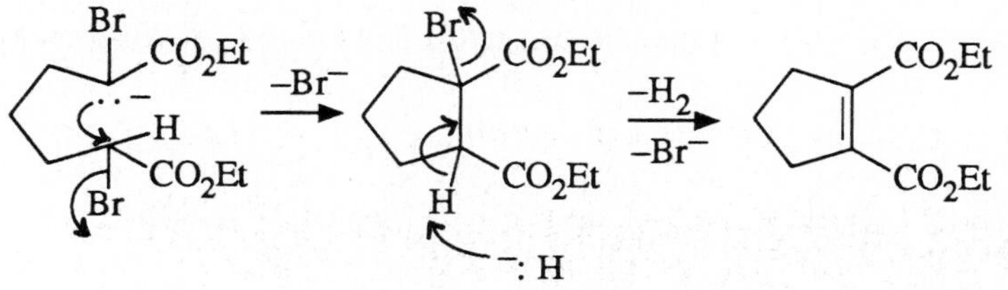

(f) A double Claisen condensation gives intermediate *A*. (The dashed arrows show the bond connections; you provide the details.) Hydrolysis of the ester groups and decarboxylation give the product.

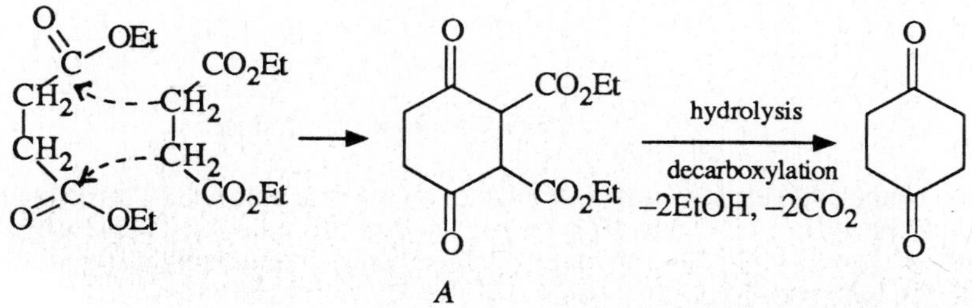

81. (a) A Michael addition of ⁻OH followed by a "reverse Michael addition" in which phenoxide is eliminated gives an enol, which then reverts to the aldehyde by the usual mechanism (Eq. 22.16a, text page 926):

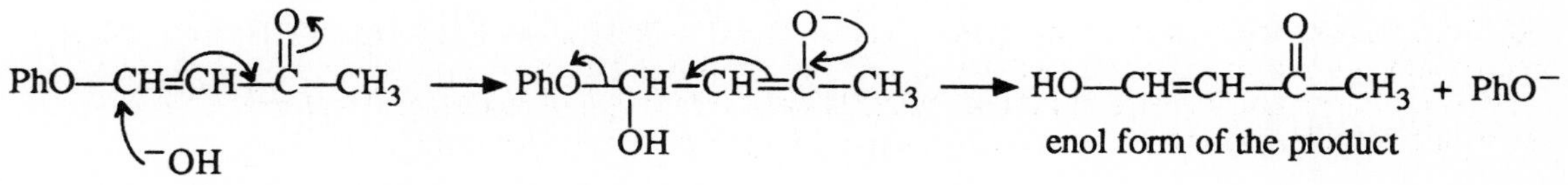

(Because the product is a β-dicarbonyl compound, a substantial fraction remains in the enol form.)

(b) This is an acid-catalyzed Michael addition, followed by elimination of phenol in a "reverse Michael addition." As in the preceding part, an enol is formed that reverts to the product by the usual mechanism (Eq. 22.16b, text page 926):

$$\left[\ PhO-CH=CH-\overset{\overset{+}{\underset{|}{:}O-H}}{C}-CH_3 \longleftrightarrow PhO-\overset{+}{C}H-CH=\overset{\overset{:\ddot{O}-H}{|}}{C}-CH_3\ \right] \longrightarrow PhO-CH-CH=\overset{\overset{:\ddot{O}-H}{|}}{C}-CH_3$$

$$\xrightarrow[\text{transfer}]{\text{proton}}\ PhO-CH-CH=\overset{\overset{O-H}{|}}{C}-CH_3 \xrightarrow{-Ph\ddot{O}H} +\ddot{O}=CH-CH=\overset{\overset{OH}{|}}{C}-CH_3 \xrightarrow{-H^+} O=CH-CH=\overset{\overset{OH}{|}}{C}-CH_3$$

enol form of the
product

(c) This is a base-catalyzed isomerization to an enol, which then reverts to the product ketone by the usual mechanism. The equilibrium is driven to the right by the very favorable equilibrium constant for enol-to-ketone conversion. The proton that is removed in the initial step is fairly acidic because the resulting anion is resonance-stabilized by interaction with both the phenyl ring and the double bond, and by the electron-withdrawing inductive effect of the oxygen. The O—H proton is also acidic, but removal of this proton does not lead to any reaction.

$$Ph-\overset{\overset{OH}{|}}{\underset{\underset{H}{|}}{C}}-CH=CH-CH_3 \longrightarrow \left[\ Ph-\overset{\overset{OH}{|}}{C}-CH=CH-CH_3 \longleftrightarrow Ph-\overset{\overset{OH}{|}}{C}=CH-CH-CH_3\ \right]$$

$$\longrightarrow Ph-\overset{\overset{OH}{|}}{C}=CH-\overset{\underset{H}{|}}{C}H-CH_3\ +\ {}^-OH$$

enol form of the product

(d)   The first step is the formation of the ethyl ester by attack of ethanol on the acid chloride. The mechanism is analogous to that in the solution to Problem 11a, Chapter 21, on page 487 of this manual. HCl is a by-product of this reaction. HCl then undergoes a conjugate addition by a mechanism completely analogous to that shown for HBr addition in Eq. 22.89, text page 961.

(e) Conjugate addition of the amino group is followed by an intramolecular transesterification.

$$CH_3-CH=CH-\overset{\overset{O}{||}}{C}-OCH_3 \longrightarrow CH_3-CH-CH=\overset{\overset{O^-}{|}}{C}-OCH_3 \longrightarrow CH_3-CH-CH_2-\overset{\overset{O}{||}}{C}-OCH_3 \longrightarrow$$

$$\qquad CH_3\ddot{N}H-OH \qquad\qquad CH_3-\overset{+}{\underset{\underset{OH}{|}}{N}}H \qquad\qquad CH_3-\overset{\underset{:\ddot{O}H}{|}}{N}\ \ddot{:}$$

(f) The starting material has a resonance structure in which there is a positive charge on the carbon adjacent to the oxygen (an α-alkoxy carbocation). This carbon is attacked by the amine. A cyclic shift of electrons (a *pericyclic reaction*; see text pages 141 and 592) gives a ketone, which is attacked intramolecularly by the amino group. Loss of water affords the final product.

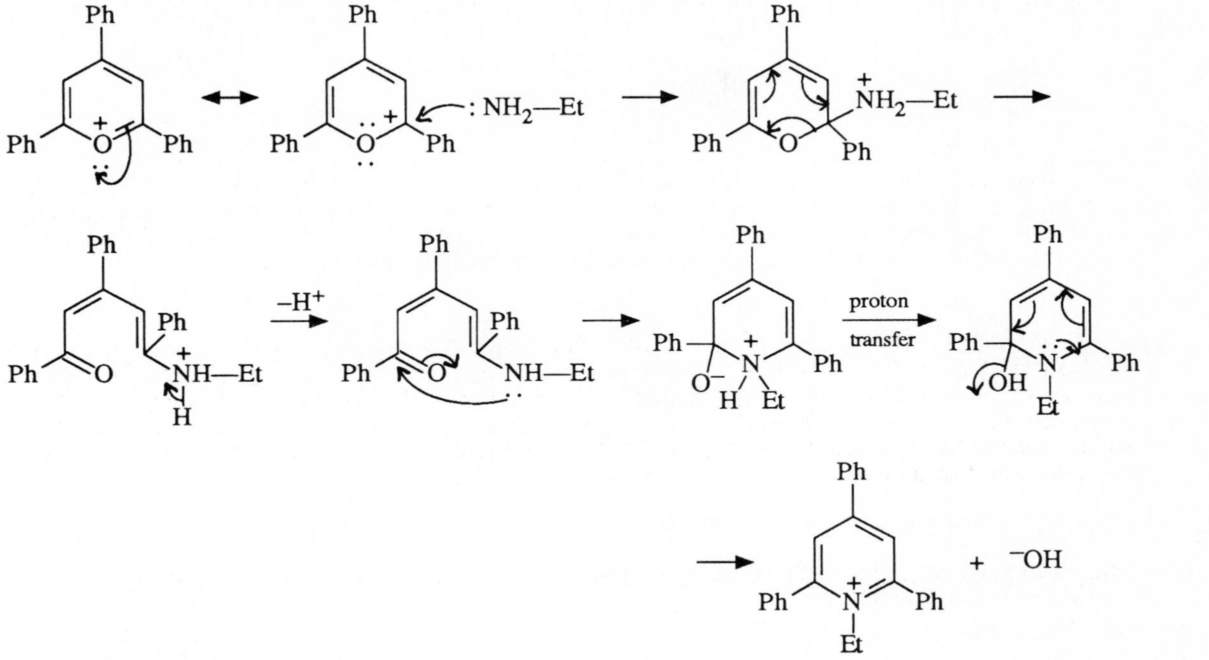

(g) An aldol condensation resulting from attack of the enolate ion of the cyano ester on the aldehyde is followed by dehydration. The resulting α,β-unsaturated ester undergoes a conjugate addition with cyanide ion:

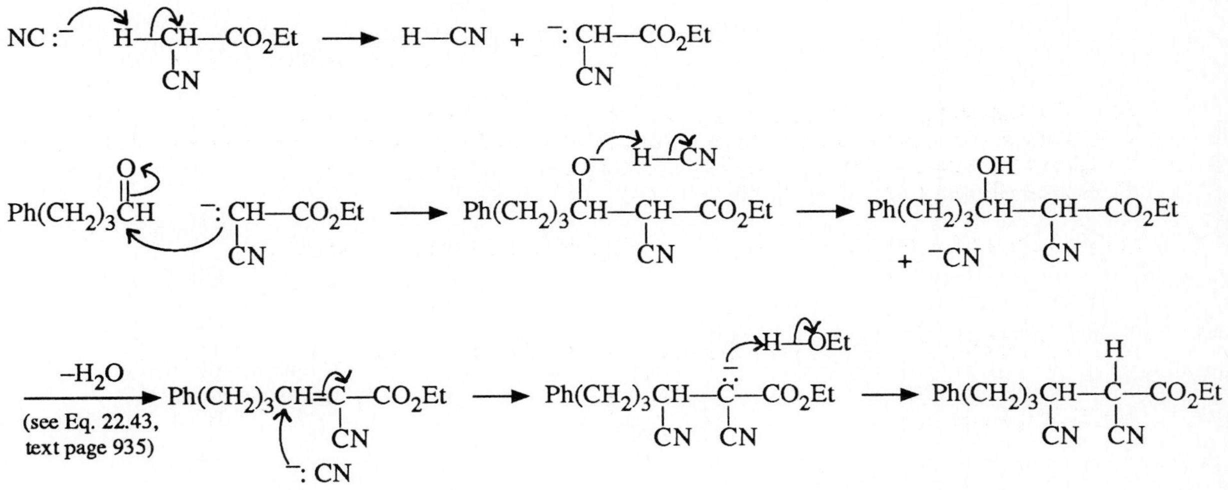

The $^-$OH saponifies the ester group; esters are more reactive than nitriles. Under acidic conditions, the carboxylic acid decarboxylates to give the final product. (β-Cyano acids decarboxylate in the same sense as β-keto acids.)

(h) This reaction is a Michael addition to a cyclopropyl ketone:

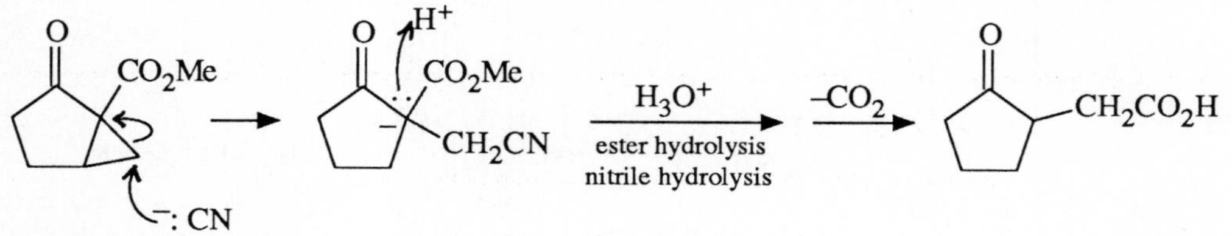

(i) Conjugate addition of triphenylphosphine and proton transfer gives an ylid (see text page 801). This then reacts with the aldehyde in a Wittig reaction. We show formation of the ylid; the mechanism of the Wittig reaction is analogous to that shown in Eq. 19.74a and b on text page 801.

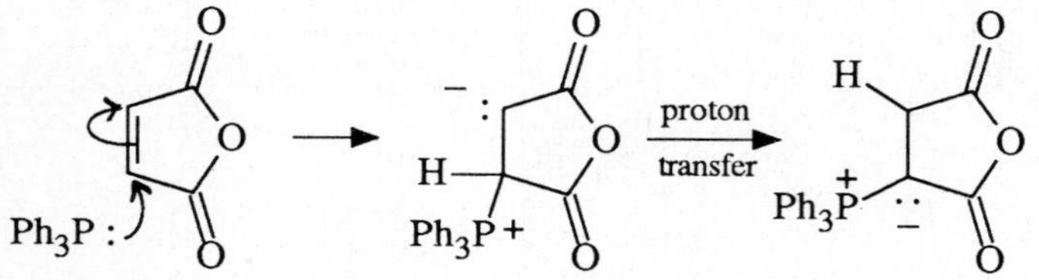

Hydrolysis of the anhydride to a dicarboxylic acid also occurs under the aqueous conditions of the final step.

82. This reaction is a sequence that involves a Michael addition, a Dieckmann condensation, and a reverse Dieckmann condensation:

protonation by solvent
gives the product

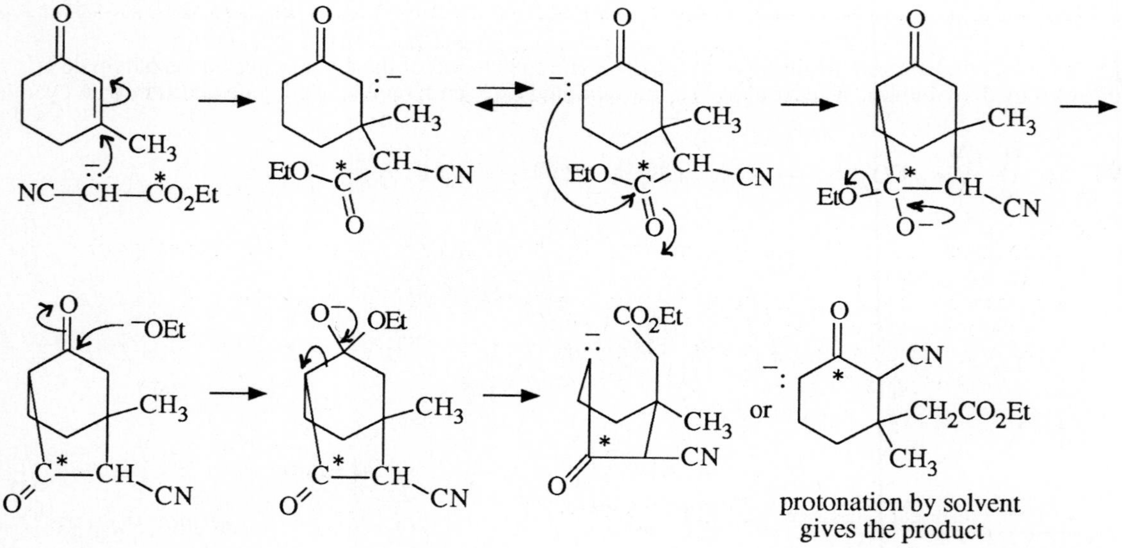

Chapter 23 / Chemistry of Amines

CHAPTER 23 TERMS

acyl azide 23.11C
acyl hydrazide 23.11C
alkaloid 23.12B
amide base 23.5E
amine .... Introduction
amino group 23.1B
ammonium salt 23.5A
azo dye 23.10C
basicity constant 23.5A
carbamate ester 23.11C
Curtius rearrangement 23.11B
diazoic acid 23.10
diazonium salt 23.10
diazotization 23.10
exhaustive methylation 23.7A
Gabriel synthesis 23.11A
Hofmann rule 23.8

Hofmann elimination 23.8
Hofmann hypobromite reaction 23.11C
Hofmann rearrangement 23.11C
isocyanate 23.11C
neurotransmitter 23.12B
nitrosamine 23.10D
nitrosyl cation (nitrosonium ion) 23.10
optical resolution 23.5D
primary amine .... Introduction
quaternary ammonium salt 23.6
quaternization 23.7A
reductive amination 23.7B
Sandmeyer reaction 23.10B
Schiemann reaction 23.10B
secondary amine .... Introduction
tertiary amine .... Introduction

CHAPTER 23 CONCEPTS

I. Introduction to Amines:

A. <u>General</u>:
1. **Amines** are organic derivatives of ammonia in which the ammonia protons are formally substituted with organic groups.
2. Amines are classified according to the number of hydrogens on the amine *nitrogen*.
   a) A primary amine has two N—H protons.
   b) A secondary amine has one N—H proton.
   c) A tertiary amine has *no* N—H protons.

$CH_3-\ddot{N}H_2$
a primary amine

:N—H
a secondary amine

$-\dot{N}Me_2$
a tertiary amine

B. <u>Common Nomenclature</u>:
1. In common nomenclature an amine is named by appending the suffix *amine* to the name of the alkyl group; the name of the amine is written as one word.
2. When two or more alkyl groups in a secondary or tertiary amine are different, the compound is named as an *N*-substituted derivative of the larger group (an *N* or <u>N</u> designates that the substituent is on the amine nitrogen).
3. Aromatic amines are named as derivatives of aniline; those with a methyl group on the benzene ring are called toluidines.

N,*N*diethyl-*p*-toluidine

CH_3-〈〉$-\dot{N}Me_2$

CH_2CH_3
$H-N\ddot{:}$
$CH_2CH_2CH_2CH_3$

*N*ethylbutylamine

C. Systematic Nomenclature:
1. The most widely used system of amine nomenclature is that of *Chemical Abstracts*.
   a) In this system, an amine is named systematically in the same manner as the analogous alcohol, except that the suffix *amine* is used.
   b) In diamine nomenclature, the final *e* of the hydrocarbon name is retained.

NH₂ on cyclohexane ring

$$\overset{..}{N}H_2\overset{\overset{\displaystyle CH_3}{|}}{C}HCH_2CH_2CH_2\overset{..}{N}H_2$$

cyclohexanamine   1,4-pentanediamine

2. The priority for citation of amine groups as principal groups is just below that of alcohols (a complete list of group priorities is given in Appendix I, text page A-1).

$$-CO_2H \text{ and derivatives} > -CH=O, \ \backslash C=O > -OH > -NR_2$$

3. When cited as a substituent, the —NH₂ group is called the **amino group.**

$$\overset{..}{N}H_2CH_2CH_2OH$$ $CH_3CH_2\overset{..}{N}H$—⟨benzene ring⟩—CO_2H

   2-aminoethanol   4-(ethylamino)benzoic acid

4. There are many important nitrogen-containing heterocyclic compounds, most of which are known by specific names that must be **learned**. In these compounds, numbering generally begins with the heteroatom:

aziridine   pyrrolidine   piperidine   morpholine

D. Structure of Amines:
1. The C—N bonds of aliphatic amines are longer than the C—O bonds of alcohols, but shorter than the C—C bonds of alkanes.
2. Aliphatic amines have a pyramidal shape (or approximately tetrahedral shape, if the electron pair is regarded as a group).
   a) Most amines undergo rapid inversion at nitrogen; this occurs through a planar transition state and converts an amine into its mirror image.
   b) Because of this inversion, amines in which the only asymmetric atom is the amine nitrogen cannot be resolved into enantiomers.

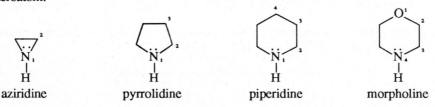

3. The C—N bond in aniline is shorter than that in aliphatic amines because of:
   a) *sp²* hybridization of the adjacent carbon.
   b) **overlap** of the unshared electrons on nitrogen with the π-electron system of the ring; this overlap **gives** double-bond character to the C—N bond.

E. Physical Properties of Amines:
1. Most amines are somewhat polar liquids with unpleasant odors.
2. The boiling points of amines depend on whether they are primary, secondary, or tertiary.
   a) Primary and secondary amines, which can both donate and accept hydrogen bonds, have higher boiling points than isomeric tertiary amines, which cannot donate hydrogen bonds.
   b) Primary and secondary amines have higher boiling points than ethers but lower boiling points than alcohols (alcohols are better hydrogen-bond donors).
3. Most primary and secondary amines with four or fewer carbons, as well as trimethylamine, are miscible with water; amines with large carbon groups have little or no water solubility.

II. Spectroscopy of Amines:

A. IR Spectroscopy:
1. The most important absorptions in the infrared spectra of primary amines are the N—H stretching absorptions, which usually occur as two or more peaks at 3200–3375 cm^{-1}.
2. Primary amines show an NH_2 scissoring absorption near 1600 cm^{-1}.
3. Most secondary amines show a single N—H stretching absorption rather than the multiple peaks observed for primary amines.
4. Tertiary amines obviously show no N—H absorptions.

B. NMR Spectroscopy:
1. The characteristic resonances in the NMR spectra of amines are those of the protons adjacent to the nitrogen (the α-protons) and the N—H protons.
   a) In alkylamines, the α-protons are observed in the δ 2.5–3.0 region of the spectrum.
   b) In aromatic amines, the α-protons of *N*-alkyl groups are somewhat further downfield near δ 3.
2. The chemical shift of the N—H proton depends on the concentration of the amine, and on the conditions of the NMR experiment.
   a) In alkylamines, this resonance typically occurs at rather high field, typically around δ 1.
   b) In aromatic amines, this resonance is at considerably lower field.
3. The N—H proton of amines under most conditions undergoes rapid exchange.
   a) The N—H absorption can be obliterated from the spectrum by exchange with D_2O.
   b) In some amine samples the N—H resonance is broadened.
   c) Splitting between the amine N—H and adjacent C—H groups is usually not observed.
4. In aromatic amines the absorptions of the ring protons *ortho* and *para* to the nitrogen are shifted to higher field than other aromatic-ring protons; this shift reflects the donation of electrons by resonance from nitrogen onto the *ortho* and *para* carbons of the ring.

C. Mass Spectrometry:
1. Compounds containing an odd number of nitrogens have odd molecular weights.
2. α-Cleavage is a particularly important fragmentation mode of aliphatic amines.
3. The parent ion occurs at an odd mass if the amine contains an odd number of nitrogens.
   a) Odd-electron ions containing an odd number of nitrogens are observed at odd mass.
   b) Even-electron ions containing an odd number of nitrogens are observed at even mass.

III. Acidity and Basicity of Amines:

A. Acidity of Amines:
1. The conjugate base of an amine, called an **amide base**, is a very strong base.
2. The pK_a of a typical amine is about 35 (that's $R_2\overset{..}{N}$—H $\rightarrow$ $R_2\overset{..}{N}{:}^-$ + H^+ not $R_3\overset{+}{N}$—H $\rightarrow$ $R_3N{:}$ + H^+).

B. Basicity of Amines:
1. Amines are good bases and are completely protonated in dilute mineral acids.
2. Protonated amines are called ammonium salts.
   a) The ammonium salts of simple alkylamines are named as substituted derivatives of the ammonium ion.
   b) Other ammonium salts are named by replacing the final *e* in the name of the amine with the suffix *ium*.
3. Ammonium salts are fully ionic compounds—the N—H bonds are covalent, but there is no covalent bond between the nitrogen and the counter ion.

4. The dissociation constant K_a is defined by the following expression:

$$RNH_3^+ + H_2O \; \leftrightarrow \; RNH_2 + H_3O^+$$

$$K_a = \frac{[R-NH_2][H_3O^+]}{[R-NH_3^+]}$$

5. The basicity of an amine is conveniently expressed by the pK_a of its conjugate-acid ammonium salt; the higher the pK_a of the ammonium ion, the more basic is its conjugate-base amine.

C. Factors Effecting Amine Basicity:
    1. Three effects influence the basicity of amines (the same effects that govern the acidity and basicity of other compounds):
        a) The effect of alkyl substitution.
        b) The inductive effect.
        c) The resonance effect.
    2. Alkyl substitution:
        a) There are two factors involved:
            (1) The first is a tendency of alkyl groups to stabilize charge through a polarization effect.
                (a) The polarization of alkyl groups can act to stabilize either positive or negative charge.
                (b) This effect governs the pK_a values of ammonium ions in the gas phase, in which the pK_a values of ammonium ions increase regularly with increasing alkyl substitution.
            (2) The second factor is a solvent effect (stabilization of the conjugate acid by hydrogen-bond donation to the solvent).
                (a) Primary ammonium ions are stabilized by hydrogen bonding more than tertiary ones—primary ammonium salts have three hydrogens that can be donated to form hydrogen bonds, but a tertiary ammonium salt has only one.
                (b) There is probably some steric hindrance to hydrogen bonding in a tertiary ammonium ion.
        b) Most common alkylamines are somewhat more basic than ammonia in aqueous solution.
        c) A dialkylamine is typically more basic than a trialkylamine or monoalkylamine.
    3. Inductive effect:
        a) An electronegative group destabilizes an ammonium ion because of a repulsive electrostatic interaction between the positive charge on the ammonium ion and the positive end of the substituent bond dipole.
        b) The base-weakening effect of electron-withdrawing groups falls off rapidly with distance.
        c) An electron-withdrawing inductive effect of the aromatic ring also contributes significantly to the reduced basicity of aromatic amines.
    4. Resonance effect:
        a) Aniline is stabilized by resonance interaction of the lone pair on nitrogen with the aromatic ring.
            (1) When aniline is protonated, this resonance stabilization is no longer present, because the lone pair is bound to a proton.
            (2) The stabilization of aniline relative to its conjugate acid reduces its basicity.
        b) The resonance stabilization of aniline adds to the energy required for its protonation and lowers its basicity relative to that of cyclohexylamine.
    5. The pK_a of an ammonium ion is directly related to the standard free-energy difference $\Delta G°$ between it and its conjugate base.

$$\Delta G° = 2.3RT \, pK_a$$

        a) If a substituent stabilizes the ammonium ion more than the amine, the free energy of the ammonium ion is lowered, $\Delta G°$ is increased, and the pK_a is raised.
        b) If a substituent destabilizes the ammonium ion relative to the amine, the opposite effect is observed: the pK_a is lowered.
        c) If a substituent group stabilizes the amine relative to the ammonium ion, the pK_a of the ammonium ion is also lowered.

D. Quaternary Ammonium Salts:
    1. Closely related to ammonium salts are compounds in which all four protons of $^+NH_4$ are replaced by organic groups; such compounds are called quaternary ammonium salts.
    2. Quaternary ammonium salts are fully ionic compounds.
    3. Many quaternary ammonium salts containing large organic groups are soluble in nonaqueous solvents.

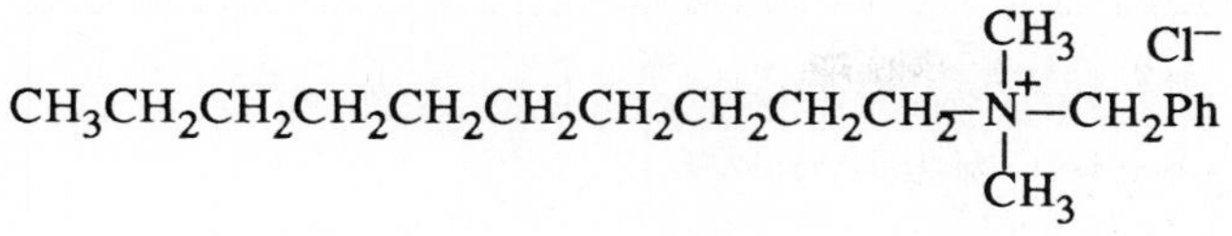

$$CH_3CH_2CH_2CH_2CH_2CH_2CH_2CH_2CH_2CH_2\overset{\overset{\displaystyle CH_3}{|}}{\underset{\underset{\displaystyle CH_3}{|}}{\overset{+}{N}}}\!\!-CH_2Ph \quad Cl^-$$

benzyldecyldimethylammonium chloride

IV. Utilization of Amine Basicity:

A. <u>Separations Using Amine Basicity</u>:
   1. Because ammonium salts are ionic compounds, many have appreciable water solubilities.
      a) When a water-insoluble amine is treated with dilute aqueous mineral acid, the amine dissolves as its ammonium salt.
      b) Upon treatment with base, an ammonium salt is converted back into the corresponding amine.
   2. This property of ammonium salts can be used to design separations of amines from other compounds.

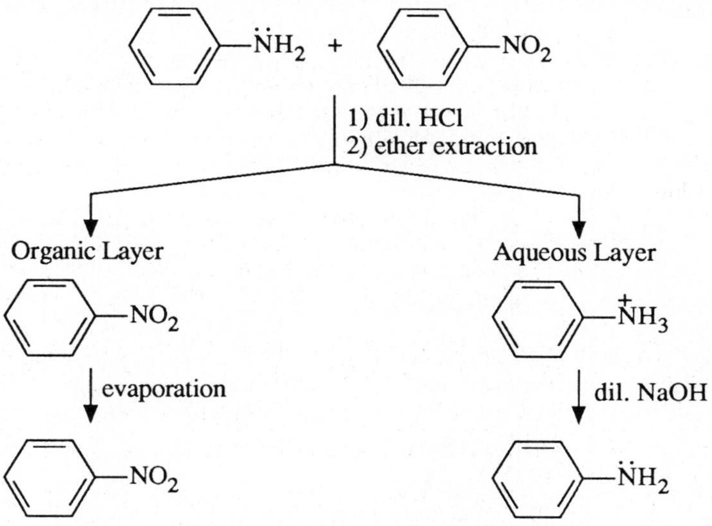

B. <u>Use of Amine Basicity in Optical Resolution</u>:
   1. The separation of a racemate into its enantiomeric components presents special problems because a pair of enantiomers have identical physical properties; the separation of an enantiomeric pair of compounds is called an **optical resolution**.
   2. Salt formation is such a rapid, quantitative, and easily reversed reaction that it is often used for the optical resolution of carboxylic acids and amines.
      a) If an optically pure carboxylic acid is allowed to react with a racemic amine, a mixture of two salts is formed.
      b) The salt is a mixture because the starting amine is a mixture of enantiomers.
      c) The salt is a mixture of two diastereomers; diastereomers have different physical properties.

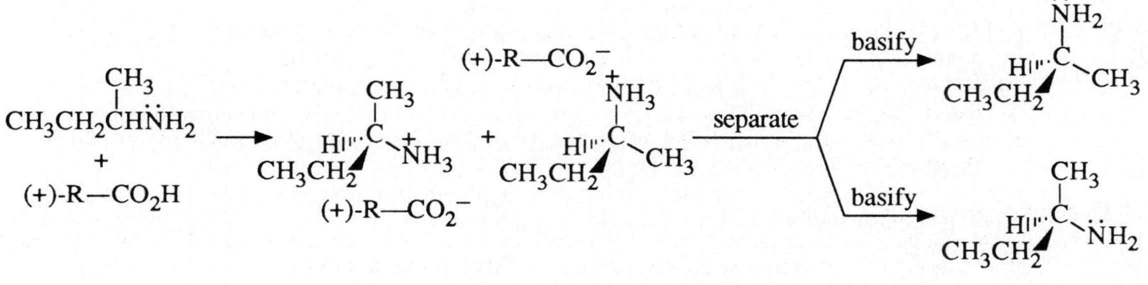

CHAPTER 23 REACTIONS

I. Synthesis of Amines—Alkylation Reactions:

A. General:
1. Amines are good nucleophiles (Lewis bases).
2. Three reactions of nucleophiles have been studied in previous sections:
   a) S_N2 reaction with alkyl halides, sulfonate esters, or epoxides (Secs. 9.1, text page 320, and 11.4, text page 427).
   b) Addition to aldehydes and ketones and related reactions (Sec. 19.11, text page 792, and Sec. 22.8, text page 959).
   c) Substitution at the carbonyl groups of carboxylic acid derivatives (Sec. 21.8, text page 884).

B. Direct Alkylation of Amines:
1. Treatment of ammonia or an amine with an alkyl halide or other alkylating agent results in alkylation on the nitrogen—an example of an S_N2 reaction in which the amine acts as the nucleophile.
   a) The immediate product of the reaction is an ammonium ion.
   b) If this ammonium ion has N—H bonds, however, further alkylations can take place to give a complex product mixture.

$$\ddot{N}H_3 \ + \ RX \ \longrightarrow \ R\ddot{N}H_2 \ + \ R_2\ddot{N}H \ + \ R_3\ddot{N}$$

   c) A mixture of products is formed because the alkylammonium ion produced initially is partially deprotonated by the amine starting material.
2. Epoxides, as well as α,β-unsaturated carbonyl compounds and α,β-unsaturated nitriles, also react with amines and ammonia; multiple alkylation can be a problem with these alkylating agents as well.
3. In an alkylation reaction, the exact amount of each product obtained depends on the precise reaction conditions and on relative amounts of starting amine and alkyl halide; the utility of alkylation as a preparative method for amines is limited.

C. Quaternization of Amines:
1. Amines can be converted into quaternary ammonium salts with excess alkyl halide under forcing conditions.
   a) This process, called **quaternization**, is one of the most important synthetic applications of amine alkylation.
   b) The reaction is particularly useful when especially reactive alkyl halides are used.
2. Conversion of an amine into a quaternary ammonium salt with excess methyl iodide is called **exhaustive methylation**.

D. Reductive Amination:
1. Primary and secondary amines form imines and enamines, respectively, when they react with aldehydes and ketones; in the presence of a reducing agent, imines and enamines are reduced to amines.
   a) Reduction of the C=N double bond is analogous to reduction of the C=O bond.
   b) The imine or enamine does not have to be isolated; because imines and enamines are reduced much more rapidly than carbonyl compounds, reduction of the carbonyl compound is not a competing reaction.
2. The formation of an amine from the reaction of an aldehyde or ketone with another amine and a reducing agent, usually NaBH$_4$ or sodium cyanoborohydride (NaBH$_3$CN), is called **reductive amination**.

        a) An iminium ion is formed in the reductive amination of a secondary amine and formaldehyde (no imine or enamine is formed); this ion is rapidly and irreversibly reduced.

        b) The reaction of an amine with an excess of formaldehyde is a useful way to introduce methyl groups to the level of a tertiary amine; quaternization does not occur in this reaction.

   3. To determine the required starting materials:
        a) Work in reverse, starting with the desired compound.
        b) Mentally reverse the reductive amination process.
        c) Break one of the C—N bonds:
            (1) On the nitrogen side, form an N—H bond.
            (2) On the carbon side, remove a hydrogen from the carbon and add a carbonyl oxygen.
        d) Repeat this process for each C—N bond and evaluate the best pathway.

II. Other Syntheses of Amines:

   A. Gabriel Synthesis of Primary Amines:
      1. Multiple alkylation of amines can be avoided by protecting the amine nitrogen so that it can react only once with alkylating agents.
      2. One approach of this sort begins with the imide phthalimide; the nitrogen in phthalimide has only one acidic hydrogen, and the ion formed when this proton is removed can thus be alkylated only once.
        a) The conjugate base of phthalimide is easily formed with KOH or NaOH.
        b) The phthalimide anion is alkylated by alkyl halides or sulfonate esters (primary or unbranched secondary) in an S_N2 reaction.
        c) The N-alkylated phthalimides formed are converted into free amines by amide hydrolysis in either strong acid or base.

      3. The alkylation of phthalimide anion followed by hydrolysis of the alkylated derivative to the primary amine is called the **Gabriel synthesis**.

   B. Reduction of Nitro Compounds:
      1. Nitro compounds can be reduced to amines under a variety of conditions.
        a) The nitro group is usually reduced very easily by catalytic hydrogenation.
        b) The reduction of aromatic nitro compounds to primary amines can be accomplished with finely divided metal powders and HCl; iron or tin powder is frequently used.

        c) Aromatic nitro compounds do react with $LiAlH_4$, but the reduction products are azobenzenes, not amines.
        d) Nitro groups do not react at all with $NaBH_4$ under the usual conditions.

C. Hofmann Rearrangement:
  1. When a primary amide is treated with bromine in base, the amide is converted into an amine with one fewer carbon atom, and the carbonyl carbon of the amide is lost as CO_2.
     a) A rearrangement has taken place in this reaction because the alkyl group originally attached to the carbonyl carbon in the amide is bound to the amine nitrogen of the product.
     b) This reaction is called the **Hofmann rearrangement** or **Hofmann hypobromite reaction**.

$$R-\overset{\overset{O}{\parallel}}{C}-\ddot{N}H_2 \quad \xrightarrow[\text{2) } H_3O^+]{\text{1) } Br_2/OH^-} \quad R-\ddot{N}H_2$$

  2. The first step in the mechanism is ionization of the amide N—H proton; the resulting anion is then brominated.
     a) The *N*-bromoamide product is more acidic than the amide starting material and ionizes.
        (1) The *N*-bromo anion undergoes a fast rearrangement to an **isocyanate**.
        (2) Isocyanates are very reactive, and are attacked by nucleophiles at the carbonyl carbon.
     b) Attack of hydroxide on the carbonyl carbon of the isocyanate leads to the formation of a carbamate ion,.
        (1) The overall reaction with the isocyanate is an addition across the carbon–nitrogen bond.
        (2) The carbonyl group is left intact because the C=O bond is a stronger bond than the C=N bond.
     c) When the reaction mixture is acidified, the carbamate decarboxylates to give the amine.
  3. The Hofmann rearrangement can be summarized by the following steps:

     amide → *N*-bromoamide → isocyanate → carbamic acid → amine + CO_2

  4. When an alcohol solvent is used for the Hofmann rearrangement, the nucleophile that attacks the isocyanate is the conjugate-base anion of the alcohol, and a carbamate ester is formed; carbamate esters are stable compounds and do not decarboxylate.

$$R-\overset{\overset{O}{\parallel}}{C}-\ddot{N}H_2 \quad \xrightarrow[\substack{\text{EtOH}\\\text{NaOEt}}]{Br_2} \quad R-\ddot{N}H-\overset{\overset{O}{\parallel}}{C}-OEt$$
$$\text{a carbamate ester}$$

  5. The Hofmann rearrangement takes place with retention of stereochemical configuration in the migrating alkyl group; optically active carboxylic acid derivatives can be used to prepare optically active amines and carbamic acid derivatives of known stereochemical configuration.

$$\underset{\substack{H^{\prime\prime}\blacktriangle\\Et}}{\overset{Me}{\diagdown}}C-\overset{\overset{O}{\parallel}}{C}-\ddot{N}H_2 \xrightarrow[OH^-]{Br_2} \underset{\substack{H^{\prime\prime}\blacktriangle\\Et}}{\overset{Me}{\diagdown}}C-\overset{\overset{O}{\parallel}}{C}-\underset{Br}{\overset{H}{N}}: \xrightarrow{\text{rearrangement}} \underset{\substack{H^{\prime\prime}\blacktriangle\\Et}}{\overset{Me}{\diagdown}}C-\ddot{N}CO \xrightarrow[\text{2) } H_3O^+]{\text{1) } OH^-} \underset{\substack{H^{\prime\prime}\blacktriangle\\Et}}{\overset{Me}{\diagdown}}C-\overset{+}{N}H_3 + CO_2$$

D. Curtius Rearrangement:
  1. Closely related to the Hofmann rearrangement is an analogous reaction of **acyl azides**—an acyl azide has an azido (—N_3) group attached to a carbonyl carbon.
  2. When acyl azides are heated, they are transformed, with loss of nitrogen, into isocyanates; this reaction is called the **Curtius rearrangement**.

$$R-\overset{\overset{O}{\parallel}}{C}-N_3 \quad \xrightarrow{\text{heat}} \quad R-N{=}C{=}O \; + \; N_2\uparrow$$

  3. The mechanistic similarity between the Curtius and Hofmann rearrangements can be seen by the following comparison.
     a) In the Hofmann rearrangement, bromide ion is the leaving group.
     b) In the Curtius rearrangement, molecular nitrogen is the leaving group.
     c) Other than this difference, the two rearrangement reactions are formally identical.
  4. Despite the similarity between the Hofmann and Curtius rearrangements, there are important practical differences.
     a) The Curtius rearrangement can be run in inert aprotic solvents such as benzene or toluene, and can be used to prepare pure isocyanates.

b) If isolation of the isocyanate is not desired, the Curtius rearrangement may also be run in protic solvents.

c) The isocyanate formed in the Curtius reaction may be treated with other nucleophiles such as amines, phenols, alcohols, and so on, to give carbamate derivatives.

5. There are two ways to prepare acyl azides:

    a) Reaction of an acid chloride with sodium azide (NaN_3).

$$R-\overset{\overset{\displaystyle O}{\|}}{C}-Cl \; + \; NaN_3 \longrightarrow R-\overset{\overset{\displaystyle O}{\|}}{C}-N_3 \; + \; NaCl$$

    b) Reaction of an ester with hydrazine (NH_2—NH_2), followed by diazotization of the derivative thus formed.

$$R-\overset{\overset{\displaystyle O}{\|}}{C}-OR \xrightarrow{\ddot{N}H_2\ddot{N}H_2} R-\overset{\overset{\displaystyle O}{\|}}{C}-\ddot{N}H-\ddot{N}H_2 \xrightarrow[\text{HCl}]{NaNO_2} R-\overset{\overset{\displaystyle O}{\|}}{C}-N_3$$

6. The Curtius rearrangement takes place with retention of stereochemical configuration in the migrating alkyl group; optically active carboxylic acid derivatives can be used to prepare optically active amines and carbamic acid derivatives of known stereochemical configuration.

$$\underset{Et}{\overset{Me}{\underset{H}{\diagdown\!\!\diagup}}}C-\overset{\overset{\displaystyle O}{\|}}{C}-N_3 \xrightarrow[\text{via rearrangement}]{\text{heat}} \underset{Et}{\overset{Me}{\underset{H}{\diagdown\!\!\diagup}}}C-\ddot{N}CO \xrightarrow{H_3O^+} \underset{Et}{\overset{Me}{\underset{H}{\diagdown\!\!\diagup}}}C-\overset{+}{N}H_3$$

E. <u>Aromatic Substitution Reactions of Aniline Derivatives</u>:

1. Although electrophilic aromatic substitution reactions of aniline derivatives occur on the aromatic ring, their outcome is strongly influenced by the activating and directing effects of the amino nitrogen, an *ortho*, *para*-directing group.

    a) The amino group is one of the most powerful activating groups in electrophilic aromatic substitution.

    b) Protonated aniline no longer has the free nitrogen electron pair responsible for the activation of the *ortho* and *para* positions; ammonium salts are largely *meta*-directing groups.

2. Nitration of aniline can be performed at only the *para* position if the amino nitrogen is protected so that it cannot be protonated easily.

    a) Conversion of the aniline into an amide, which is much less basic than the amine, is accomplished with acetic anhydride.

    b) Nitration of acetanilide can be stopped after a single substitution has occurred, because the acetamido group is not so strong an activating group as the free amino group.

    c) Following the nitration reaction, the acetyl group is removed to afford the nitrated aniline, *p*-nitroaniline.

    (1) The amide group of acetanilide is a protecting group in this sequence of reactions.

    (2) The acetamido group (—NHAc) is an *ortho*, *para*-directing group even under the strongly acidic conditions of nitration.

F. <u>Synthesis of Amines—Summary</u>:

1. To summarize:

    a) Reduction of amides with $LiAlH_4$ (Sec. 21.9B, text page 891).

    b) Reduction of nitriles with $LiAlH_4$ (Sec. 21.9C, text page 893).

    c) Direct alkylation of amines (Sec. 23.7, text page 1001). This reaction is of limited utility, but is useful for preparing quaternary ammonium salts.

    d) Reductive amination (Sec. 23.7B, text page 1003).

e) Aromatic substitution reactions of anilines (Sec. 23.9, text page 1009).
f) Gabriel synthesis of primary amines (Sec. 23.11A, text page 1020).
g) Reduction of nitro compounds (Sec. 23.11B, text page 1021).
h) Hofmann and Curtius rearrangements (Sec. 23.11C, text page 1023).
2. Methods c), d), and e) are methods of preparing amines from other amines.
3. Method f) is limited to the preparation of primary amines.
4. Methods a), b), g), and h) can be used for obtaining amines from other functional groups.

III. Syntheses of Organic Compounds with Amines:

A. Hofmann Elimination of Quaternary Ammonium Hydroxides:
   1. Alkenes can be formed from amines by a three-step process:
      a) Exhaustive methylation.
      b) Conversion of the ammonium salt to the hydroxide.
      c) Hofmann elimination.

2. The **Hofmann elimination** reaction involves a quaternary ammonium hydroxide as the starting material; the amine acts as the leaving group.
   a) When a quaternary ammonium hydroxide is heated, a β-elimination reaction takes place to give an alkene, which distills from the reaction mixture.
   b) A quaternary ammonium hydroxide is formed by treating a quaternary ammonium salt with silver hydroxide (formed from water and silver oxide).
   c) The Hofmann elimination is formally analogous to the E2 reaction of alkyl halides, in which a proton and a halide ion are eliminated; in the Hofmann elimination, a proton and a tertiary amine are eliminated.
   d) Hofmann elimination occurs with *anti* stereochemistry.
   e) The conditions of the Hofmann elimination are typically harsh.
3. The elimination reactions of alkyl halides and quaternary ammonium salts show distinct differences in regiochemistry.
   a) E2 elimination of most alkyl halides gives a predominance of the alkene with the greatest amount of branching at the double bond.
   b) However, elimination of a trialkylammonium salt generally occurs in such a way that the base abstracts a proton from the β-carbon atom with the least branching—the **Hofmann rule**.

   c) This behavior is accounted for by the preference for *anti*-elimination and the minimization of steric repulsions in the transition state of the reaction.
4. When there are especially acidic β-hydrogens, violation of the Hofmann rule can occur.
   a) Since base must abstract a proton in the elimination, the acidity of the β-hydrogen plays an important role in determining the direction of elimination.

   b) For a similar reason, protons adjacent to carbonyl groups are also preferentially abstracted in the Hofmann elimination.

B. <u>Reactions of Amines with Nitrous Acid—Reactions of Diazonium Ions</u>:
   1. The conversion of a primary amine into a **diazonium salt**, called **diazotization**, is a reaction that is brought about by nitrous acid (HNO$_2$).
      a) Because nitrous acid is unstable, it is generated as it is needed from the reaction of sodium nitrite (NaNO$_2$) and a mineral acid.

benzenediazonium chloride

      b) Nitrite esters (compounds of the form R—O—N=O) can also be used to generate diazonium salts.
   2. In solution, nitrous acid is in equilibrium with its anhydride, dinitrogen trioxide (N$_2$O$_3$).
      a) Dinitrogen trioxide is the actual diazotizing reagent and contains a good leaving group, nitrite.
      b) It reacts as if it were a salt of the nitrosyl cation (nitrosonium ion) and the nitrite anion.
   3. The first mechanistic step in diazotization is the attack of the amine nitrogen on the electron-deficient nitrogen of N$_2$O$_3$ to form a **nitrosamine**.
      a) The nitrosamine is in equilibrium with a tautomer called a **diazoic acid**.
      b) Under the acidic conditions of diazotization, diazoic acids dehydrate to diazonium ions.

   4. Alkanediazonium salts are very unstable and decompose under the reaction conditions; aryldiazonium salts are more stable and undergo several important reactions.

C. <u>Reactions of Alkanediazonium Salts</u>:
   1. Diazonium ions incorporate one of the best leaving groups, molecular nitrogen.
   2. Alkanediazonium ions are unstable and decompose spontaneously with the evolution of nitrogen gas to give carbocations.
      a) The carbocation undergoes typical carbocation reactions to give a mixture of products.
      b) The evolution of nitrogen during diazotization is a good qualitative test for aliphatic primary amines.
   3. Because a complex mixture of products is obtained, the diazotization of most primary alkylamines is *not generally* a useful synthetic procedure.

D. <u>Aromatic Substitution with Diazonium Ions</u>:
   1. Aryldiazonium ions react with aromatic compounds containing strongly activating substituent groups, such as tertiary amino groups and phenols, to give substituted **azobenzenes**; this is an electrophilic aromatic substitution reaction in which the terminal nitrogen of the diazonium ion is the electrophile.

an azobenzene

   2. The mechanism follows the usual pattern of electrophilic aromatic substitution.
      a) First the electrophile is attacked by the π-electrons of the aromatic compound to give a resonance-stabilized carbocation.
      b) This carbocation then loses a proton to give the substitution product.
   3. Because the azobenzene derivatives formed in these reactions have extensive conjugated π-electron systems, most of them are colored.
   4. Some of these compounds are used as dyes and indicators; as a class they are known as **azo dyes**.

E. <u>Substitution Reactions of Aryldiazonium Salts</u>:
   1. Aryldiazonium salts decompose much more slowly than alkanediazonium salts, because loss of N$_2$ from an aryldiazonium salt would yield a very unstable aryl cation.
   2. Aryldiazonium salts can be prepared in solution and used in subsequent reactions.
   3. Addition of cuprous chloride or cuprous bromide to a solution of an aromatic diazonium salt gives products in which the nitrogen is replaced by halide.

a) An analogous reaction occurs with CuCN.
  (1) This reaction is another way of forming a carbon–carbon bond, in this case to an aromatic ring.
  (2) The resulting nitrile can be converted into a carboxylic acid.
b) The reaction of an aryldiazonium ion with a cuprous salt is called the **Sandmeyer reaction**.
c) This reaction is an important method for the synthesis of aryl halides and nitriles.

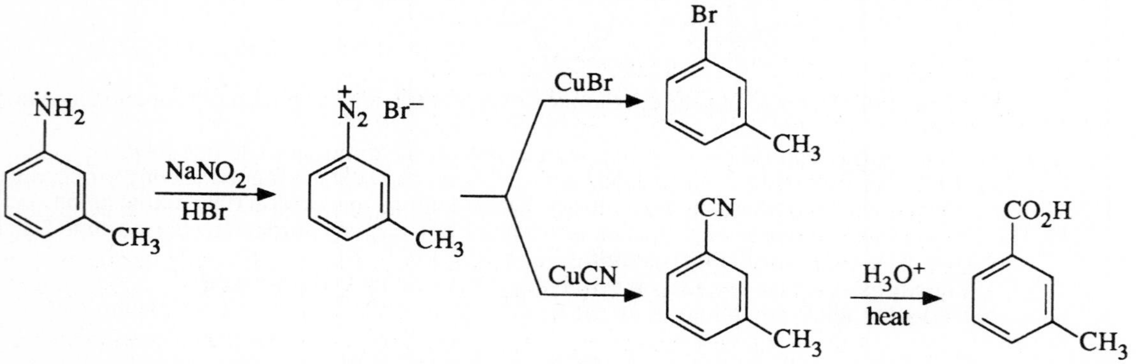

4. Aryl iodides can also be made by the reaction of diazonium salts with potassium iodide; cuprous salts are not required.

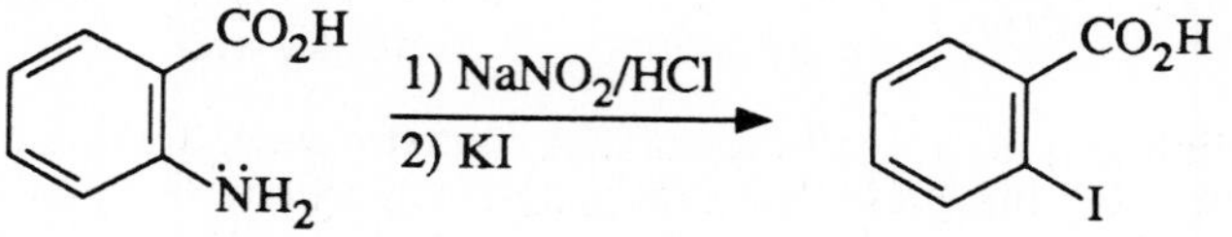

5. Replacement of the diazonium group with fluoride can be effected by heating the diazonium salt with fluoroboric acid (HBF_4); this reaction is called the **Schiemann reaction**.

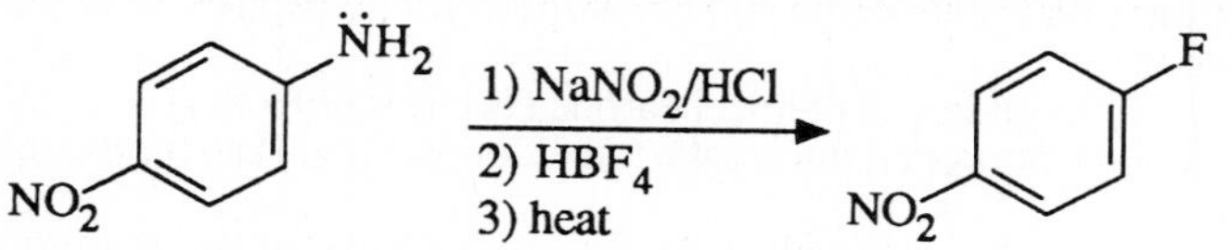

6. Diazonium salts can also be hydrolyzed to phenols by heating them with water.

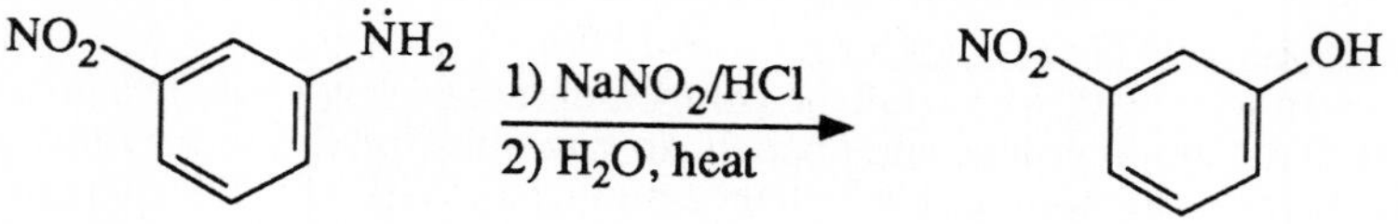

7. The diazonium group is replaced by hydrogen when the diazonium salt is treated with hypophosphorous acid, H_3PO_2.

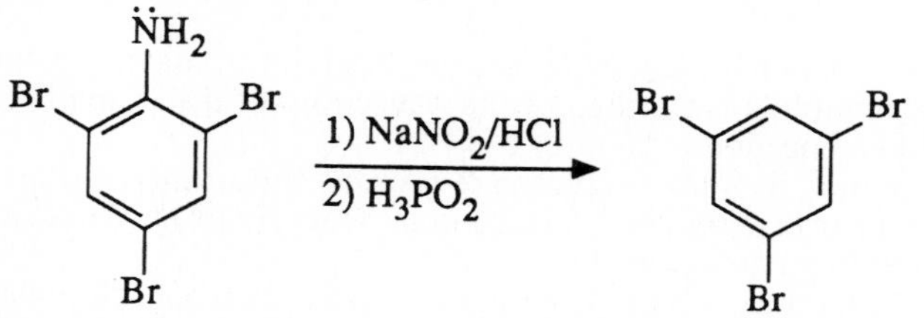

8. All of the diazonium salt reactions are substitution reactions and occur by a variety of mechanisms.
  a) The Sandmeyer reaction cannot be an S_N2 reaction of halide ion with the diazonium ion, because aromatic compounds do not undergo S_N2 reactions.
    (1) Copper(I) has a catalytic effect in the Sandmeyer reaction somewhat like its effect in lithium dialkylcuprate additions to α,β-unsaturated carbonyl compounds.
    (2) The Sandmeyer reaction is believed to involve radical or radical-like species.

b) The Schiemann reaction and the hydrolysis of diazonium salts to phenols are not free-radical reactions; they probably involve aryl cations as intermediates.
    (1) Despite the instability of aryl cations, they can be formed from diazonium salts because nitrogen is such a good leaving group.
    (2) Both the Schiemann reaction and the hydrolysis reaction require heating.
c) The reaction of diazonium salts with H_3PO_2 is a free-radical chain reaction.
9. The substitution reactions of diazonium salts achieve ring-substitution patterns that cannot be obtained in other ways.

F. Reactions of Secondary and Tertiary Amines with Nitrous Acid:
1. Secondary amines react with nitrous acid to yield *N*-nitrosoamines, usually called simply **nitrosamines**, and are known potent carcinogens.

$$R_2\ddot{N}H \;+\; HNO_2 \;\longrightarrow\; R_2\ddot{N}-\dot{N}{=}O \qquad \text{a nitrosamine}$$

a) The mechanism of this reaction is almost identical to that of the first step in the diazotization of primary amines.
b) Since the nitrosamine derivative of a secondary amine has no N—H protons, it cannot react further, as a primary amine can; therefore, secondary nitrosamines can be isolated as stable compounds.
2. The nitrogen of tertiary amines does not react under the strongly acidic conditions used in diazotization reactions.
3. *N*,*N*-disubstituted aromatic amines react with the electrophilic reagent N_2O_3 generated during diazotization in conventional electrophilic substitution reactions; the products are nitrosated on the aromatic ring.

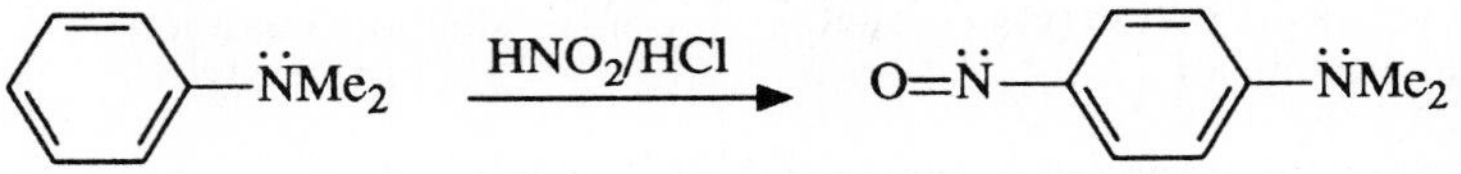

CHAPTER 23 SOLUTIONS

Solutions to In-Text Problems

1. (a)

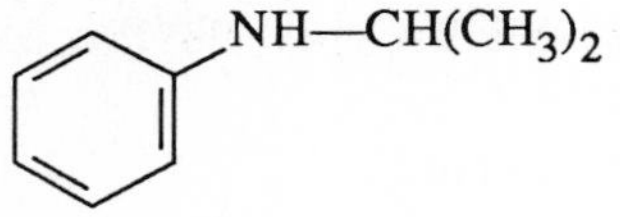

NH—CH(CH$_3$)$_2$

(b) (CH$_3$)$_3$C—NH$_2$

(c)

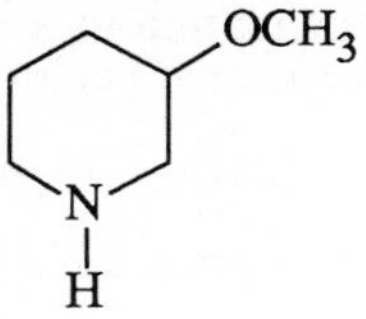

OCH$_3$

N
H

(d) (CH$_3$)$_3$C—CH—CH$_2$CH$_2$CH$_3$
                    |
                    NH$_2$

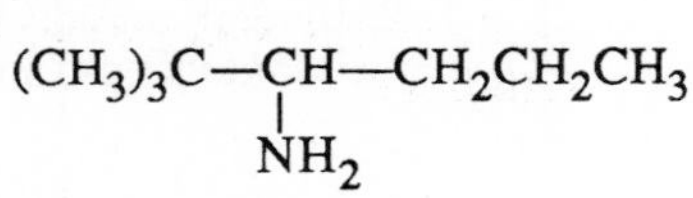

(e)

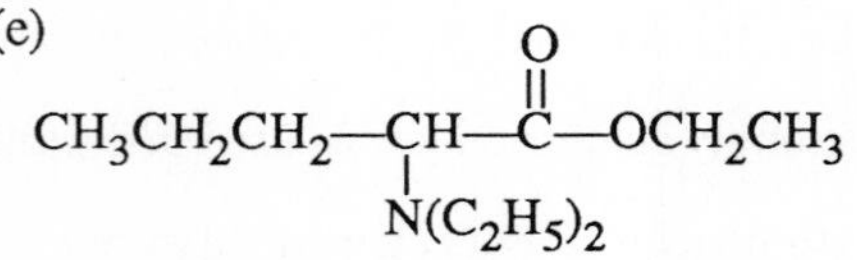

$$CH_3CH_2CH_2—CH—\overset{\overset{\displaystyle O}{\|}}{C}—OCH_2CH_3$$
                    |
                    N(C$_2$H$_5$)$_2$

(f)

CH$_3$CH$_2$CHCH$_2$CH$_2$CH$_2$CH$_3$
        |
        N(C$_2$H$_5$)$_2$

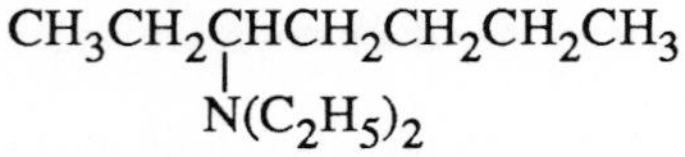

2. (a) *N*-ethyl-*N*,2-dimethyl-1-propanamine (systematic) or *N*-ethyl-*N*-methylisobutylamine (common)
    (b) 1-dimethylamino-4-nitrobenzene (systematic) or *p*-nitro-*N*,*N*-dimethylaniline (common)
    (c) *N*-cyclohexylcyclohexanamine (systematic) or dicyclohexylamine (common)
    (d) 3-methylamino-1-pentanol

3. Compounds with double-bond character have shorter C—N bonds than those with *partial* double-bond character, which have shorter C—N bonds than compounds with C—N single bonds. The order is:

    (a) < (c) < (b)

    The C—N bond of compound (c) has some double-bond character because of overlap of the nitrogen unshared electron pair with the *p* orbitals of the carbon–carbon double bond:

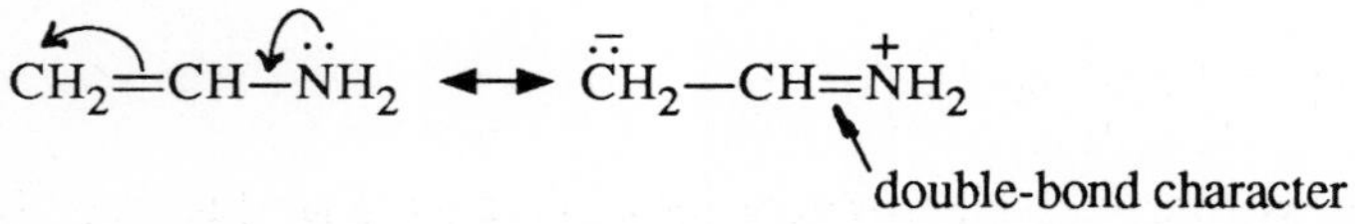

    CH$_2$=CH—ṄH$_2$ ⟷ C̄H$_2$—CH=N̟H$_2$
                                    double-bond character

4. The IR spectrum suggests that the compound is an amine. The NMR spectrum indicates that the compound has three unsplit methyl groups, two of which are equivalent; in addition the compound has two equivalent aromatic hydrogens. Compound (b), 2,4,6-trimethylaniline, is the only compound that fits the data.

5. *N*-Ethylbenzylamine fits the data:

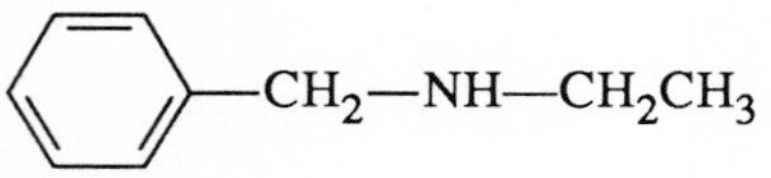

    —CH$_2$—NH—CH$_2$CH$_3$

    The *m/e* = 120 peak comes from loss of a methyl radical by α-cleavage; and the peak at *m/e* = 91 is attributable to the benzyl cation, formed by inductive cleavage. (Show these cleavage mechanisms.)

6. The peaks arise from α-cleavage of the parent ions derived from the respective amines. 2-Methyl-2-heptanamine can form a cation of mass 58 by this mechanism, and is therefore compound *B*. *N*-ethyl-4-methyl-2-pentanamine can form a cation of mass 72 by this mechanism, and is therefore compound *A*. We show the α-cleavage mechanism for *B*; you show it for *A*.

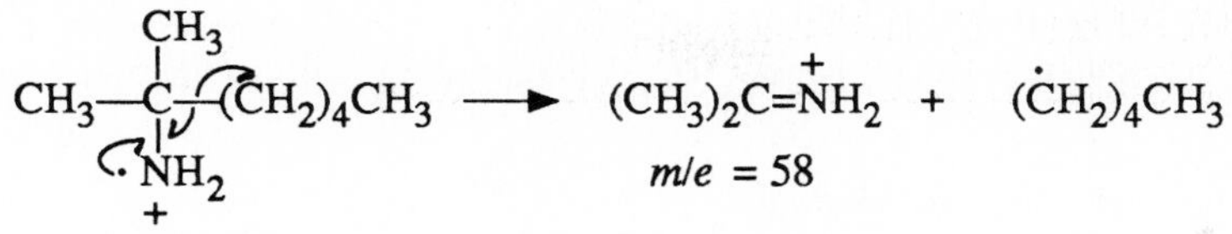

parent ion from
compound *B*

7. The inductive effect of the nitro group destabilizes the conjugate acid of the last two amines; hence, they are weaker bases than aniline itself (Figure 23.3). The *p*-nitro group in addition stabilizes *p*-nitroaniline by resonance:

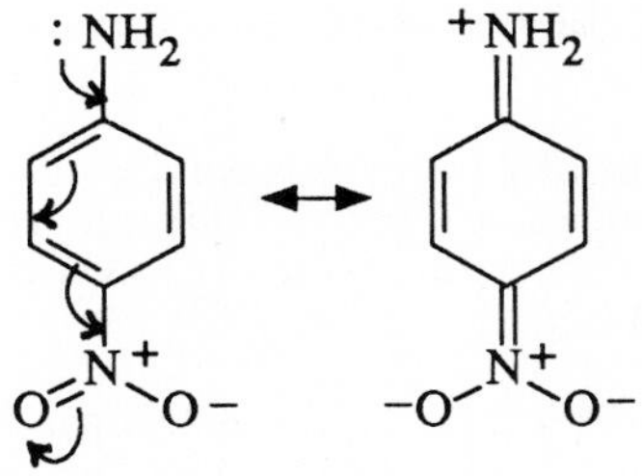

This makes the amine a weaker base. Hence, its conjugate acid is a stronger acid.

8. (a) Secondary amines are more basic than primary amines, which are more basic than ammonia (alkyl-group substitution effect). Hence, the correct order is:

ammonia < propylamine < dipropylamine

(b) The full positive charge in the last compound interacts repulsively with a second positive charge introduced by protonation to form the conjugate acid, and therefore reduces basicity. The inductive effect of the bond dipoles of the ester group in the first compound also reduces basicity. There is no such inductive effect in the second compound. The correct order is:

$$H_3\overset{+}{N}CH_2CH_2NH_2 < H_2NCH_2CH_2\overset{O}{\overset{\|}{C}}—OEt < CH_3\overset{NH_2}{\overset{|}{C}}HCH_2CH_3$$

(c) The ester group is inductively electron-withdrawing, and therefore destabilizes protonated amines. Hence, the last two compounds are less basic than the first. In the third compound, the amine is stabilized by resonance interaction of the nitrogen unshared electron pair with the ester carbonyl group:

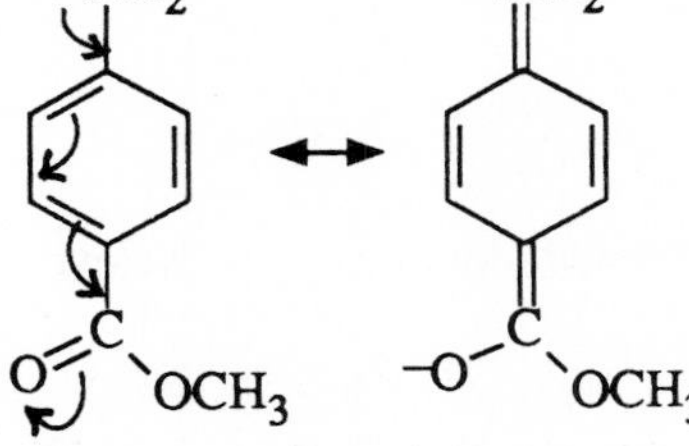

This interaction further reduces the basicity of this amine relative to that of aniline. Hence, the correct order is:

methyl *p*-aminobenzoate < methyl *m*-aminobenzoate < aniline.

(d) Because of the resonance effect, aniline is a weaker base than any of the alkylamines. Because of the inductive effect of the nitro group, *p*-nitrobenzylamine is a weaker base than benzylamine. The phenyl group exerts an electron-withdrawing inductive effect that reduces the basicity of a benzylamine derivative relative to that of an ordinary alkylamine. (See last sentence on text page 997.) This reasoning leads to the following order:

aniline < p-nitrobenzylamine < benzylamine < cyclohexylamine.

➤ Be sure you understand the difference between benzylamine, Ph—CH₂—NH₂, and aniline, Ph—NH₂. There is no resonance effect in a benzylamine derivative.

9. We begin with all three compounds in solution in a water-insoluble organic solvent, such as ether or methylene chloride. We extract with aqueous NaHCO₃. This extraction removes *p*-chlorobenzoic acid as its sodium salt. Adding HCl to the aqueous solution liberates the free carboxylic acid. Next, we extract our organic solution with dilute HCl. This removes *p*-chloroaniline as its hydrochloride salt. Adding base to the water layer gives the neutral amine. To recover *p*-chlorotoluene we simply dry the organic solution and evaporate the solvent. (The order of the extractions with acid and NaHCO₃ could be reversed.)

10. We take either enantiomer of the amine and form the salt with the racemate of 2-phenylpropanoic acid. This yields a mixture of diastereomeric salts. We then selectively crystallize one diastereomer of this salt, leaving the other in solution. Addition of HCl to the salt gives an aqueous solution of the amine (as its HCl salt) and leaves a pure enantiomer of the free carboxylic acid as a precipitate (assuming it is not soluble in water).

11. If we use the racemate of tartaric acid, then we get not only the diastereomeric salts shown on text page 999, but also their enantiomers. Since enantiomers have identical solubilities in achiral solvents, crystallization would afford both enantiomers. Liberation of the amine would therefore yield the racemic amine, and all our work would have accomplished nothing.

12. Compound *B* can form an amine by loss of a proton:

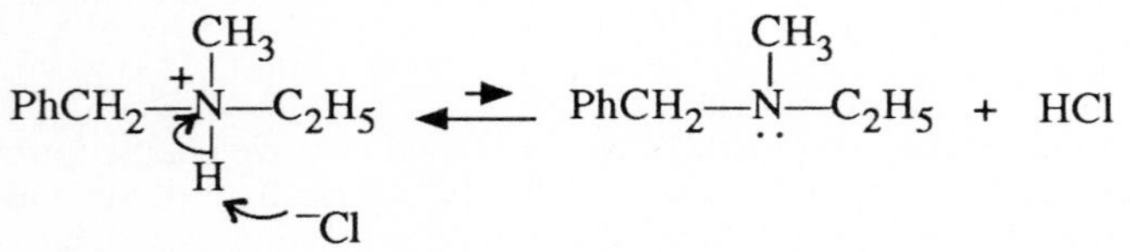

Rapid inversion of the amine brings about loss of optical activity. Compound *A* cannot lose a proton to form the free amine; hence, its optical activity is not lost.

13. Either alkyl group — the ethyl group or a cyclohexyl group — can be derived from a carbonyl compound.

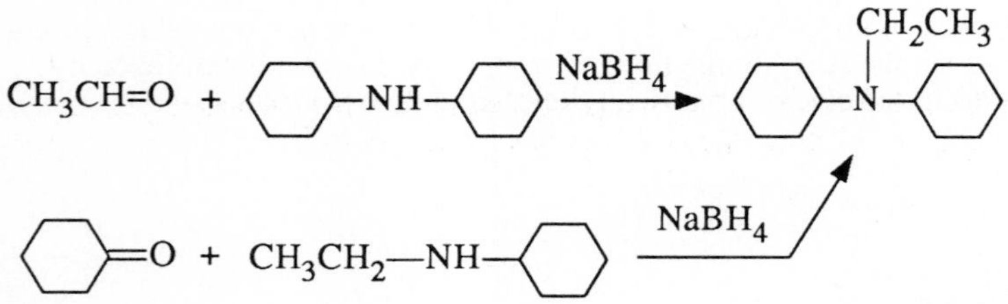

14. First, we carry out a reductive amination of benzaldehyde to give benzyldimethylamine. Then we quaternize with methyl iodide. (We do *not* react first with an alkyl halide; why?)

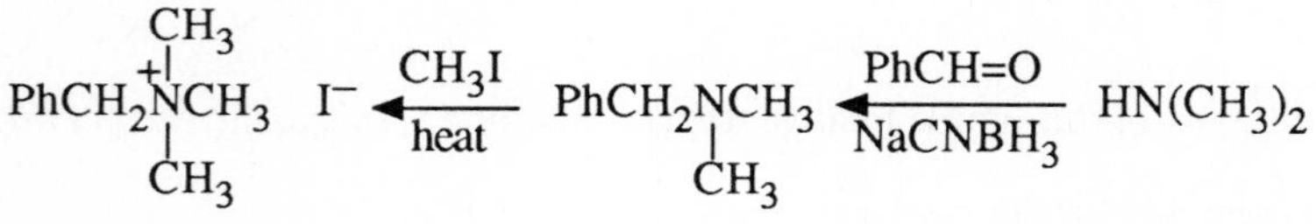

15. Mada undoubtedly produced some of the desired compound, but it too underwent reductive amination:

$$C_4H_9CH=O \ + \ NH_3 \xrightarrow{H_2/cat} \ \underset{\text{desired compound}}{C_4H_9CH_2NH_2} \ \xrightarrow[H_2/cat]{C_4H_9CH=O} \ \underset{\text{(could also react further)}}{C_4H_9CH_2-NH-CH_2C_4H_9}$$

16. This reaction cannot succeed, because bromobenzene does not undergo S_N2 reactions. (See Sec. 18.1.)

17. (a) The approach to this problem is, first, to draw the compounds in a conformation corresponding to the Fischer projection, and then put the molecule in a conformation in which the β-proton to be lost and the amine leaving group are *anti*.

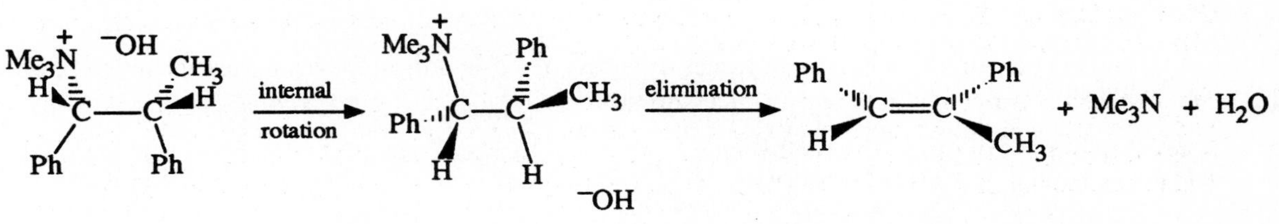

In the second structure above, in which the hydrogen and the leaving group are *anti*, the phenyl groups are on the same side of the molecule. Hence, in the product alkene, the phenyl groups will be *cis*, as shown in the last structure.

(b) The product in this case is the (*E*)-isomer of the same alkene. (You should establish this point for yourself by going through an analysis similar to the one above.)

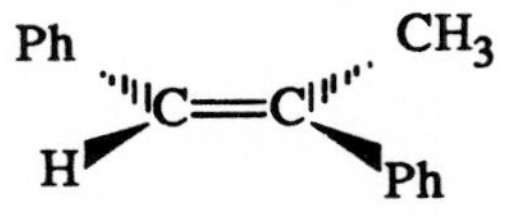

18. (a) In this case, all hydrogens have comparable acidity. Hence, the proton is lost from the least substituted carbon (the methyl group) to give the following product:

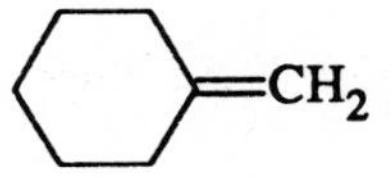

(b) In this case, one hydrogen is particularly acidic — the hydrogen that is α to the carbonyl group. (Why is this hydrogen acidic?) The elimination takes place with loss of this hydrogen as follows:

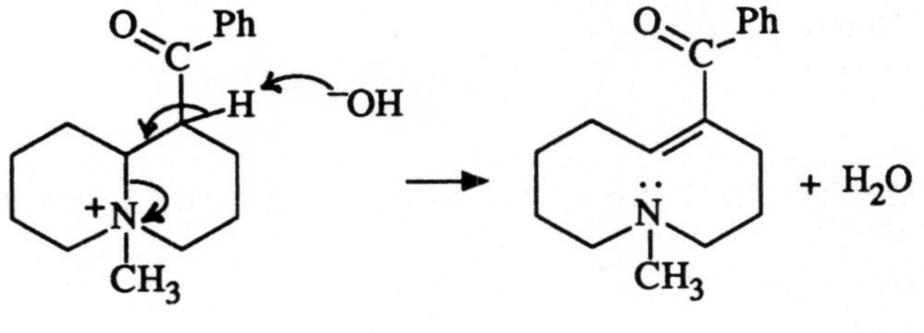

19. Since there are three distinguishable *β*-hydrogens, there are three possible alkenes:

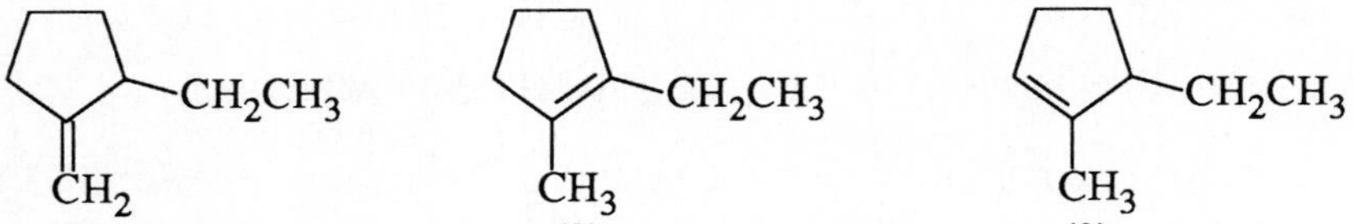

(1) (2) (3)

The relative amounts of each are predicted to be in the following order:

(1) > (3) > (2).

Compound (1) predominates because it comes from loss of a *β*-hydrogen from the least substituted carbon — the methyl carbon.

20. It takes two rounds of exhaustive methylation to liberate a nitrogen from a *cyclic* secondary amine. Hence, the data are consistent with the presence of a heterocyclic amine. There are five carbons in a piperidine ring. The carbons bearing the nitrogen are the ones to which a double bond is formed in the Hofmann elimination steps. The two elimination products are evidently derived from two competing *β*-eliminations of the same tetraalkylammonium ion. From the structures of the alkenes, it follows that the nitrogen is connected between carbon-1 and carbon-5. (This is the only connection that could give *both* alkenes from the same starting material.)

1,4-octadiene

$CH_2{=}CHCH_2CH{=}CHCH_2CH_2CH_3$

N connected here

1,5-octadiene

$CH_2{=}CHCH_2CH_2CH{=}CHCH_2CH_3$

N connected here

The only structure of coniine consistent with this information is that of 2-propylpiperidine:

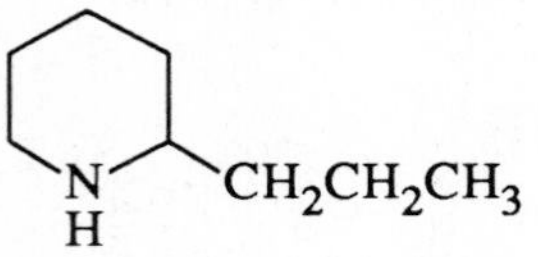

2-propylpiperidine (coniine)

(If you did not get the correct answer, you should be sure to show how the transformations of coniine given in the problem can lead to the dienes above.)

21. The product of the chlorosulfonic acid reaction would polymerize by reaction of the amino group of one molecule with the chlorosulfonyl group of another:

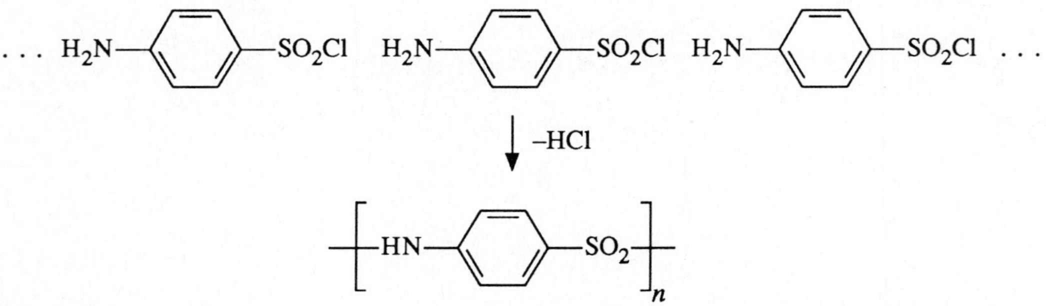

Another side reaction is sulfonation of the amino nitrogen by chlorosulfonic acid.

22. (a) The synthesis of 2,4-dinitroaniline begins with the synthesis of *p*-nitroacetanilide, the preparation of which is shown on text page 1010.

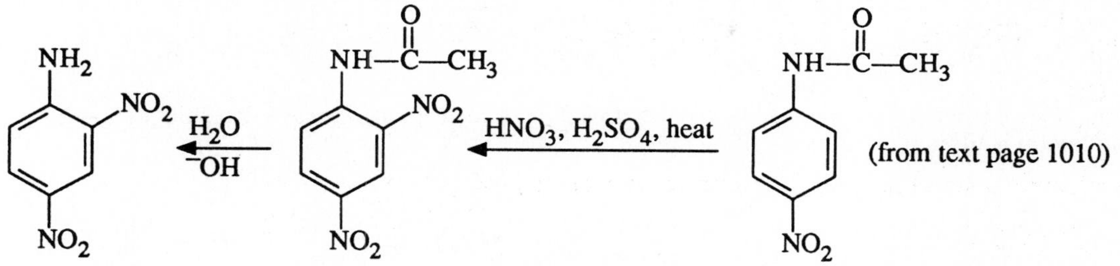

(b) The synthesis of sulfathiazole begins with *p*-(chlorosulfonyl)acetanilide, the synthesis of which is given as the first reaction in Eq. 23.49 on text page 1011.

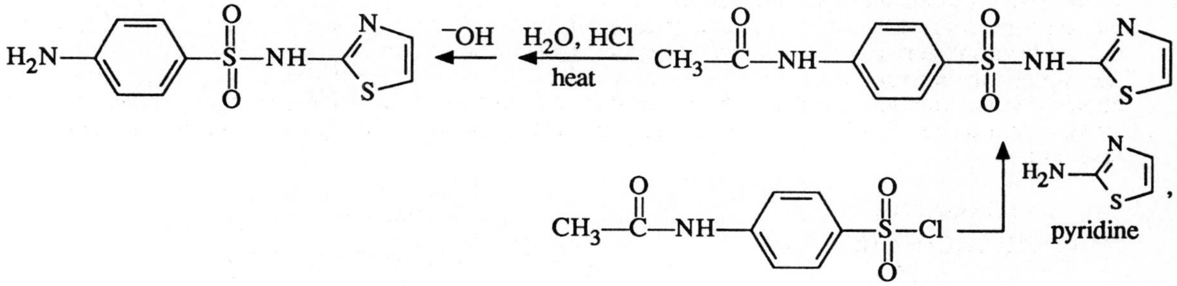

23. Reaction (a) is cyanohydrin formation, which takes place with HCN in a protic solvent with a base catalyst. Reaction (b) is reduction of a nitrile to a primary amine, which can be effected with either catalytic hydrogenation or with LiAlH$_4$ followed by protonolysis. (The —OH proton would be removed by LiAlH$_4$, but would be restored in the protonolysis step.) Diazotization in step (c) affords the diazonium ion, which spontaneously loses nitrogen to give a primary carbocation. This ion rearranges to give the ketone:

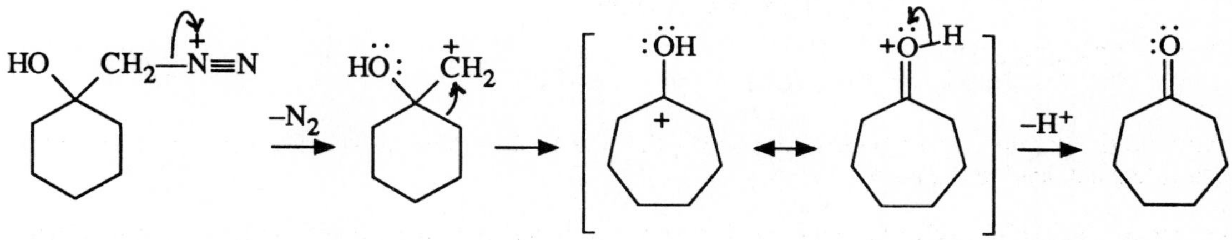

24. (a)

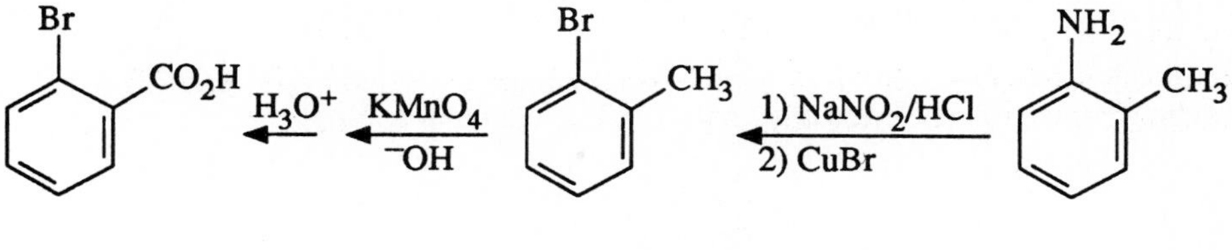

(b)

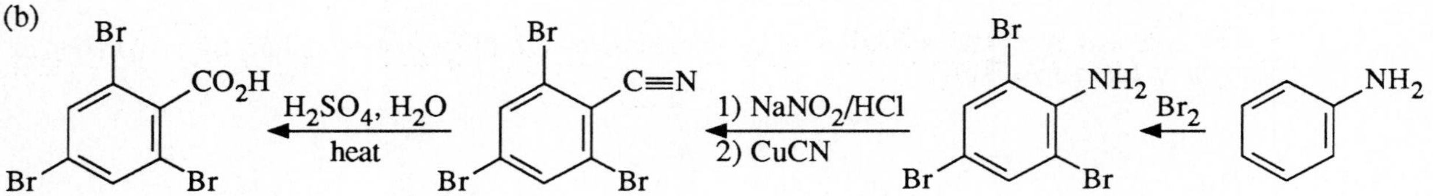

25. Methyl orange itself can be prepared by the reaction of a *para*-substituted benzenediazonium ion with *N,N*-dimethylaniline:

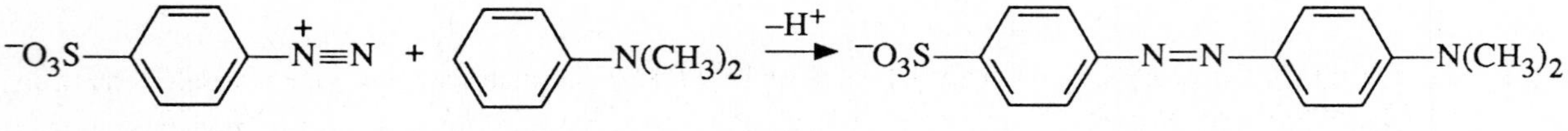

The diazonium ion, in turn, can be prepared from the appropriately substituted aniline, which comes from aniline itself by protection and sulfonation:

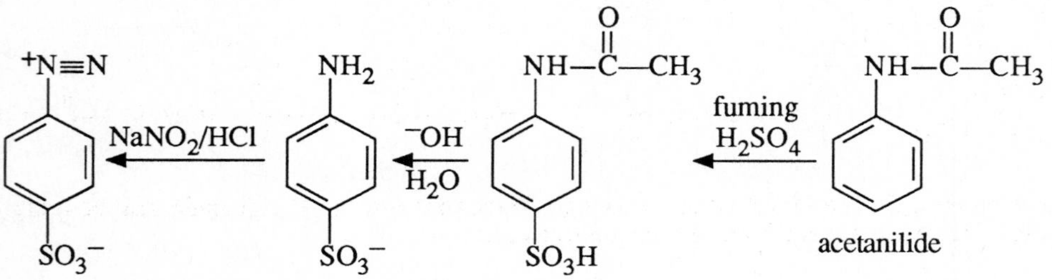

The preparation of acetanilide from aniline is shown in Eq. 23.48, text page 1010. *N,N*-Dimethylaniline is prepared by a reductive amination reaction of formaldehyde and aniline:

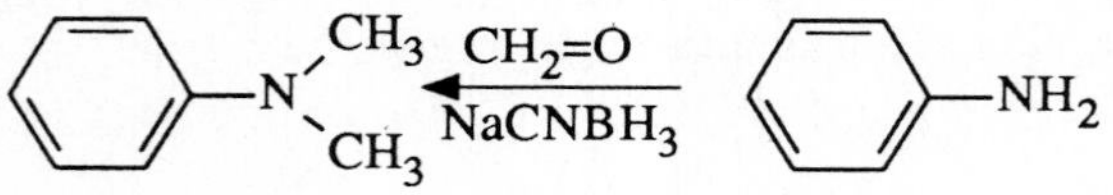

26. The following two compounds would react to give FD & C #6:

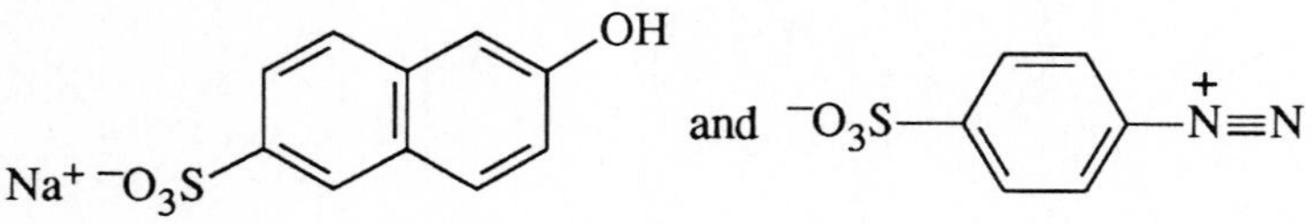

The preparation of the diazonium compound is shown in the previous problem.

27. The key to this problem is to recognize that the iodine is introduced by a Sandmeyer reaction; the amino group on which the Sandmeyer reaction is carried out comes from reduction of a nitro group:

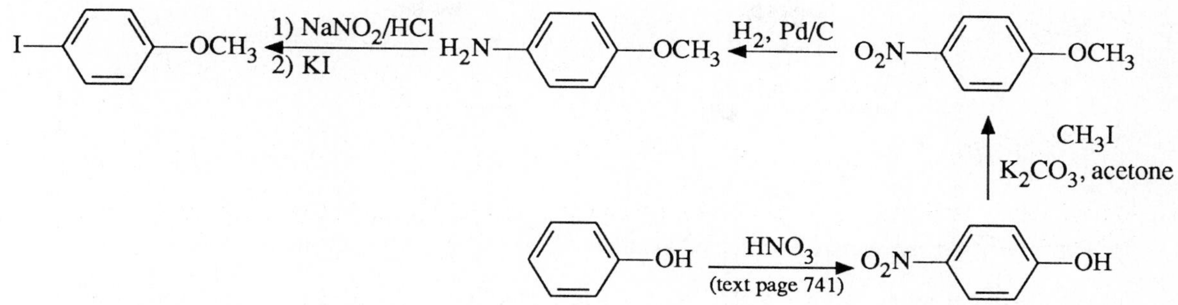

28. (a) *t*-Butylamine *cannot* be prepared by the Gabriel synthesis, because such a synthesis would require that *t*-butyl bromide undergo an S_N2 reaction. Tertiary alkyl halides do not undergo S_N2 reactions.
     (b) This amine can be prepared by either the Hofmann or Curtius reaction.

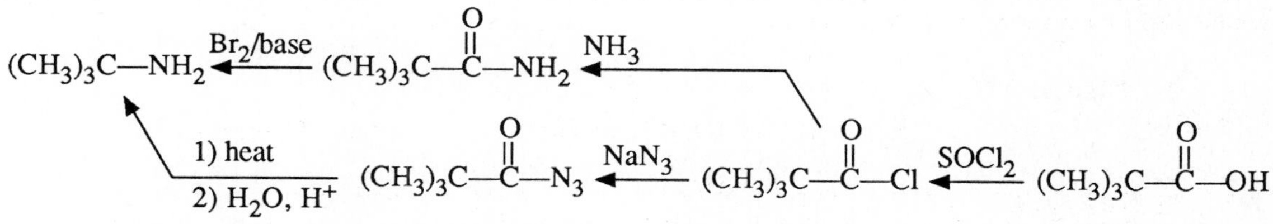

29. In each case we run either a Hofmann or Curtius rearrangement on the amide or acyl azide, respectively, of 3-methylbenzoic acid. These reactions afford isocyanate *A*, as follows:

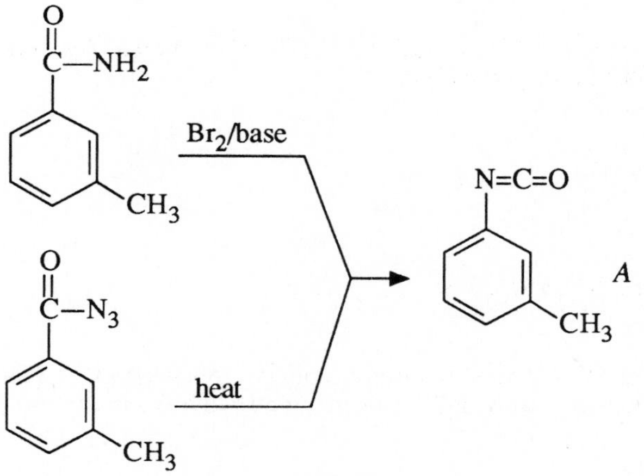

In the Hofmann rearrangement, *A* is an *intermediate* that reacts with nucleophiles present in the reaction mixture; in the Curtius rearrangement, the isocyanate can be isolated if desired. Reaction of isocyanate *A* in different ways leads to the three compounds in the problem, as follows:

(a) Reaction of *A* with methanol gives the carbamate ester. In the Hofmann rearrangement, we would use methanol as the solvent; in the Curtius rearrangement, we would add the isocyanate to methanol.

(b) Reaction of *A* with water gives the amine *B*. The amine is then acetylated with acetic anhydride:

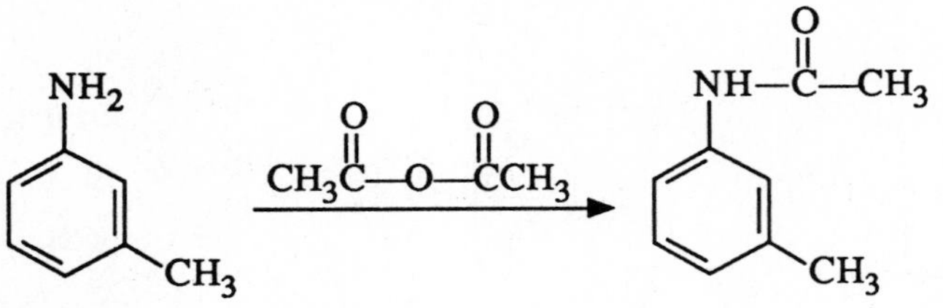

B

(c) Reaction of the isocyanate *A* with methylamine (CH₃NH₂) gives the substituted urea.

Preparation of the amide and acyl azide shown above is as follows. The acyl azide can be prepared by reaction of the corresponding acid chloride with sodium azide (Eq. 23.87, text page 1026), and the amide can be prepared by reaction of the same acid chloride with an excess of NH_3. The acid chloride can be prepared by treating the corresponding carboxylic acid with PCl_5 or $SOCl_2$.

30. The desired product has the following structure, which we shall abbreviate *P* in the interest of space:

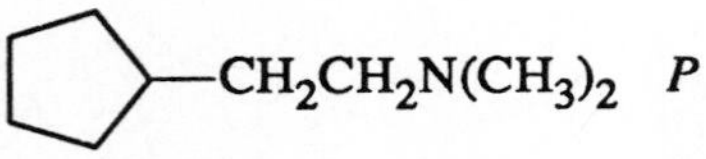

(a)

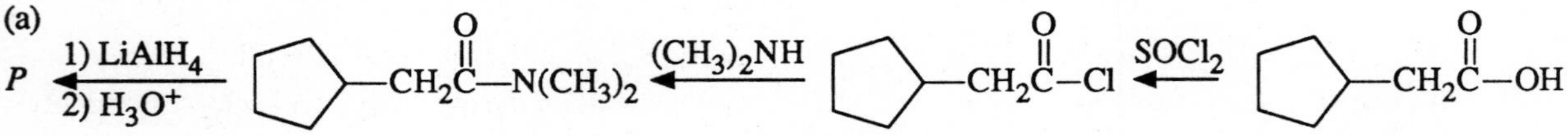

(b)

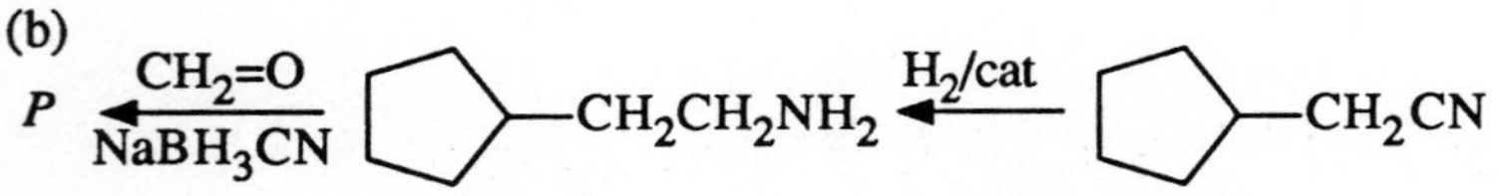

(c) The first synthesis involves a reductive amination:

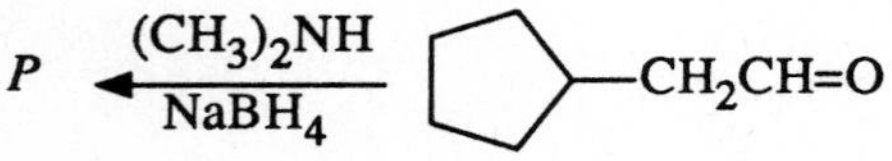

For the second synthesis, the aldehyde can be oxidized with any of several oxidizing reagents (Ag^+, HNO_3, $KMnO_4$, chromic acid, etc.) to the carboxylic acid starting material in part (a). The synthesis in part (a) is used from this point.

(d)

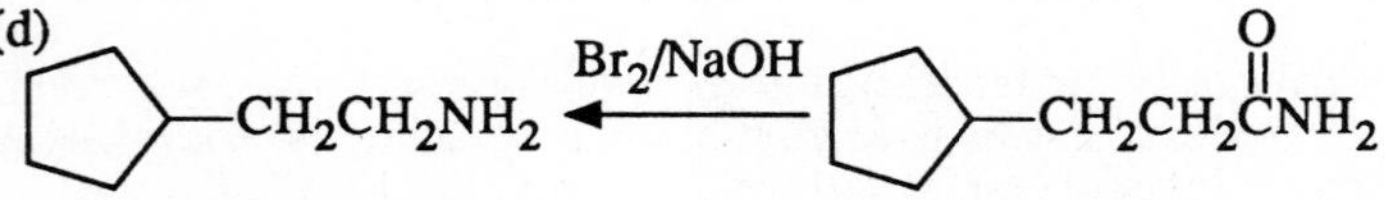

amine used in part (b)

The amine prepared in this equation is then used as shown in part (b).

31. In both alkaloids it is the nitrogen that is basic. In both cases, the nitrogen is part of a tertiary amine. As we have learned, tertiary amines are readily protonated.

Solutions to Additional Problems

32. (a)   (b)   (c)   (d)   (e)

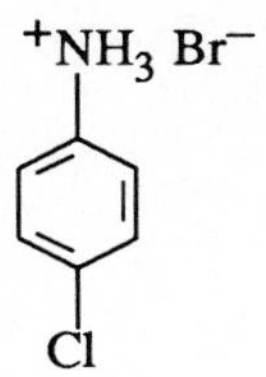

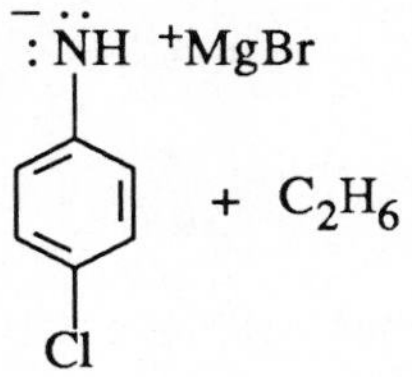

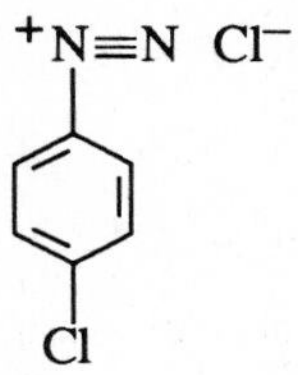

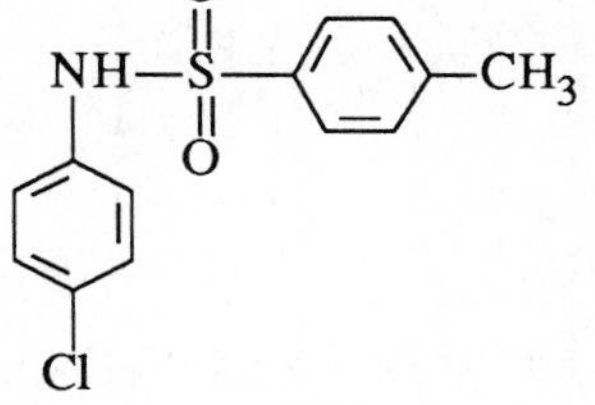

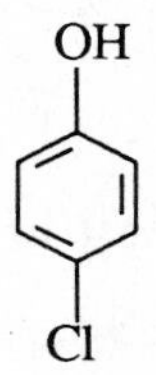

$^+NH_3$ Br$^-$ $^-:\ddot{N}H$ $^+$MgBr $^+N{\equiv}N$ Cl$^-$ NH—SO₂—⟨ ⟩—CH₃   OH

(on chlorobenzene rings; (b) + C₂H₆)

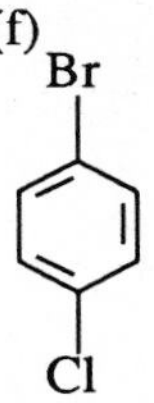

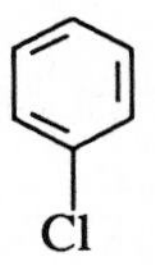

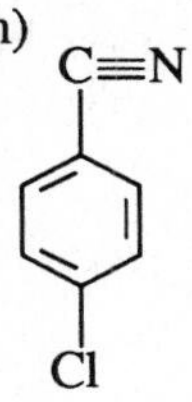

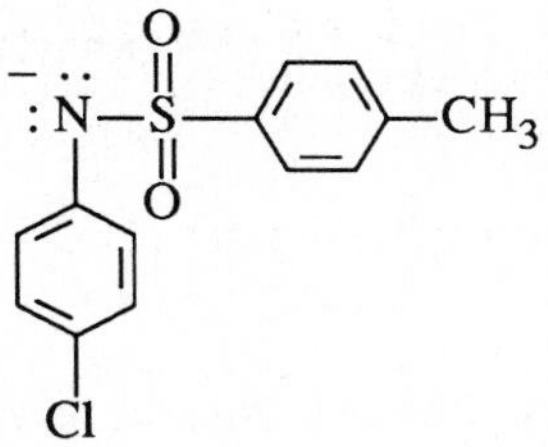

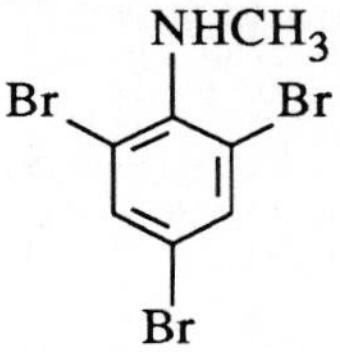

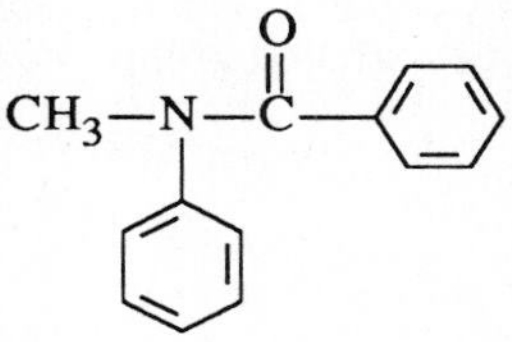

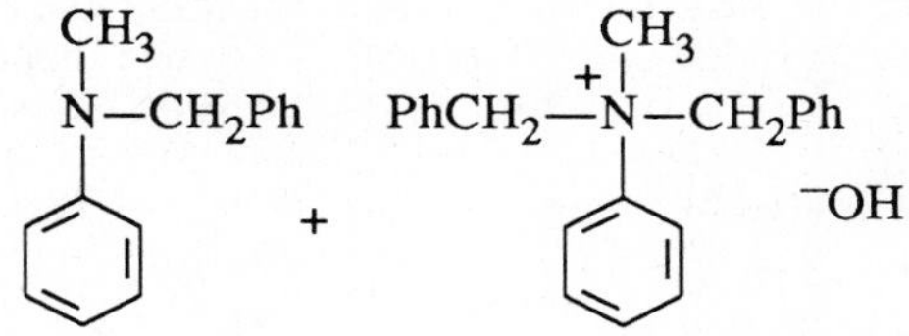

(f) Br   (g)   (h) C≡N   (i) F   (j) $^-:\ddot{N}$—SO₂—⟨ ⟩—CH₃

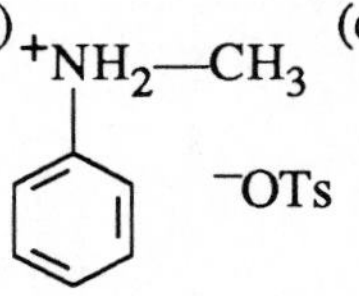

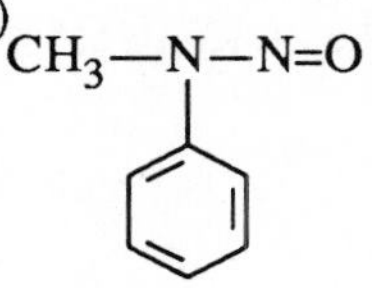

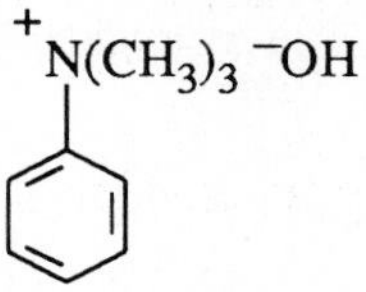

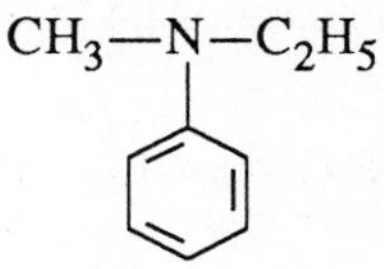

(on 4-chloro rings)

33. (a)

NHCH₃ (2,4,6-tribromo ring, Br at positions)

(b) CH₃—N(Ph)—C(=O)—Ph

(c) CH₃—N(Ph)—CH₂Ph   +   PhCH₂—$\overset{+}{N}$(CH₃)(Ph)—CH₂Ph $^-$OH

(d) $^+$NH₂—CH₃ (on phenyl) $^-$OTs

(e) CH₃—N(Ph)—N=O

(f) $^+$N(CH₃)₃ (on phenyl) $^-$OH

(g) CH₃—N(Ph)—C₂H₅

34. (a)   (b) no reaction   (c)

(CH₃)₂CH$\overset{+}{N}$H₃ HSO₄$^-$ (CH₃)₂CHN$\overset{-}{H}$ Li$^+$ + CH₃CH₂CH₂CH₃

(d)   O   (e)

(CH₃)₂CHNH$\overset{\|}{C}$CH₃   (CH₃)₂CHBr + (CH₃)₂CHOH + CH₃CH=CH₂

(f)   (g)   (h)   O

(CH₃)₂CH—NH—CH(CH₃)₂   (CH₃)₂CH$\overset{+}{N}$(CH₃)₃ I$^-$ (CH₃)₂CH$\overset{+}{N}$H₃ $^-$O$\overset{\|}{C}$Ph

(i) (CH₃)₂CHN(CH₃)₂   (j) CH₃CH=CH₂ + (CH₃)₃N   (k) (CH₃)₂CH—NH—CH₂CH₃

35. (a) *sec*-butylamine, or 2-butanamine:

CH₃CHCH₂CH₃
        |
        NH₂

(b) 2-cyclobuten-1-amine

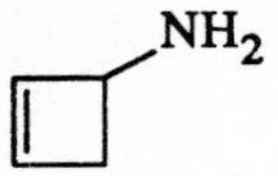
NH_2

(c)

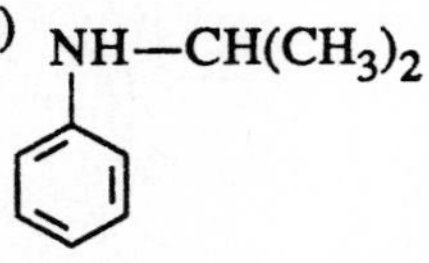
NH—CH(CH$_3$)$_2$

and

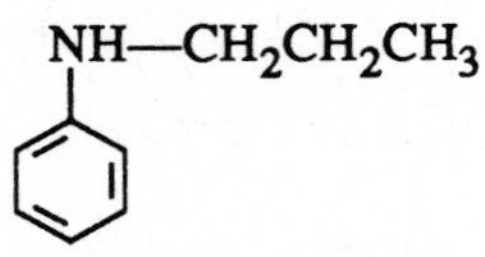
NH—CH$_2$CH$_2$CH$_3$

N-isopropylaniline *N*-propylaniline

(d)

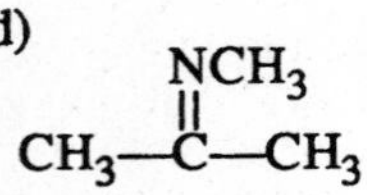
NCH$_3$
CH$_3$—C—CH$_3$

This compound is the imine derived from the reaction of methylamine and acetone.

36. Protonation occurs on the topmost nitrogen because this is a secondary amine. The nitrogen adjacent to the benzene ring is less basic because anilines are less basic than alkylamines. The unshared electron pair in the rightmost nitrogen is delocalized through the double bond into the carbonyl group, thus:

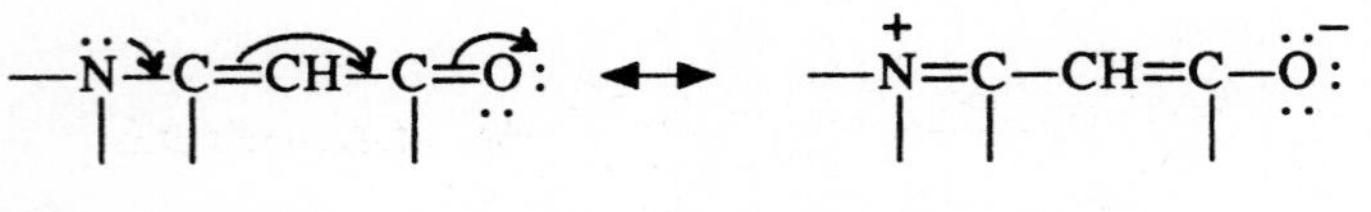

This type of resonance reduces the basicity of this part of the molecule (in the same sense that the resonance in an aniline derivative reduces its basicity). The protonated form of the molecule is:

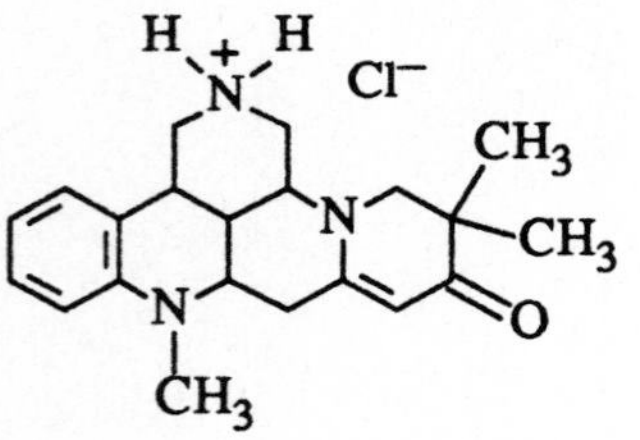
Cl$^-$
CH$_3$
CH$_3$
O
N
N
CH$_3$

37. (a) Methyl red is the product of diazo coupling:

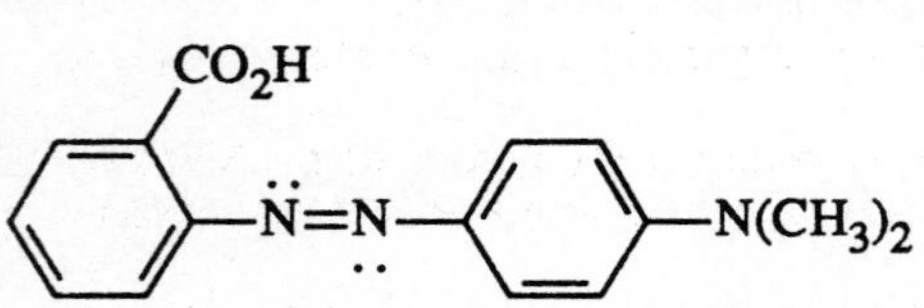
CO$_2$H
N=N
N(CH$_3$)$_2$

methyl red

(b) In *acidic* solution, methyl red is protonated to give its conjugate acid — but where is it protonated? Because amines are basic, one's first tendency might be to suggest that protonation occurs on the dimethylamino group. However, protonation occurs instead on a diazo nitrogen, because the resulting conjugate acid is resonance-stabilized:

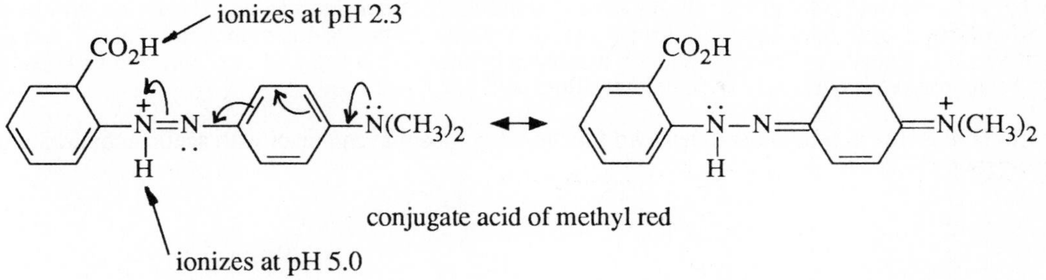

conjugate acid of methyl red

Why are there *two* ionizations? There are two acidic groups, the carboxylic acid group and the protonated diazo group. Which ionization occurs at which pH? We can see from the resonance structures above that protonation of the diazo group affects the electronic characteristics of the conjugated system. In particular, the positive charge in the diazo-protonated form (shown above) is extensively delocalized. Since color is associated with delocalization of electrons (text pages 589–590), it is reasonable that the deprotonation that affects the color of methyl red is the one associated with the conjugated π-electron system. Hence, the protonated diazo group has the higher pK_a. Ionization of the carboxy group gives an anion that is *not* delocalized into the π-electron system. (In this anion, the diazo group remains protonated.) Hence, this ionization does not affect the color. (Draw the structure of the species that exists between pH 2.3 and pH 5.0.)

38. Base is required in the Hofmann rearrangement, first, to form the nitrogen anion that is brominated, and second, to form the anion that undergoes rearrangement:

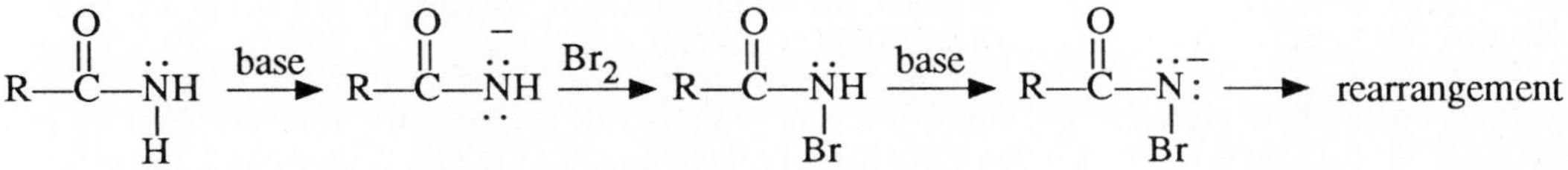

In an acyl azide, both the leaving group and the negative charge required for the Curtius rearrangement are in place:

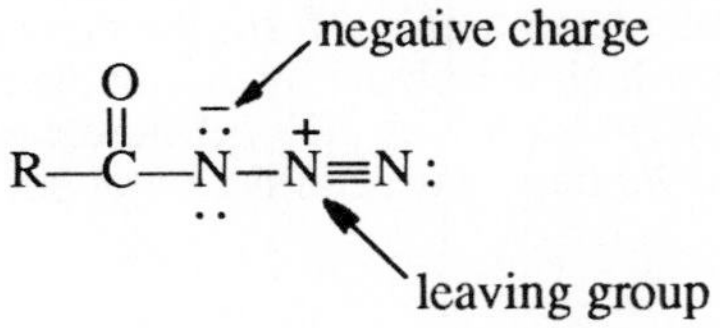

39. (a) Edy is trying to carry out a Friedel–Crafts acylation. Unfortunately, the amino group is acylated much more readily than the ring; furthermore, under the acidic conditions of the reaction, the amino group will either be protonated or will react with $AlCl_3$. As a result, no acylation at all may occur.
(b) It is difficult to stop alkylation reactions at the introduction of only one group; a mixture of products will very likely occur. (See Sec. 23.7A.)
(c) Under the acidic conditions of the reaction the dimethylamino group will be protonated. A protonated amino group is a *meta* director. Hence, substantial *meta*-substitution product will be formed. (See text pages 1009–1010.)
(d) Edy is trying to effect the displacement of an —OH group with an amine under acidic conditions. Although acid converts the —OH group into a good leaving group by protonation, acid also protonates the amine. Hence, under the reaction conditions, the amine cannot act as a nucleophile. No reaction will occur.
(e) Although $LiAlH_4$ reduces aldehydes to primary alcohols, it also reduces nitro groups. (See Eq. 23.78, text page 1022.) Hence, the nitro group would not survive this reaction unscathed. (Reduction with $NaBH_4$ would work, however.)
(f) Following exhaustive methylation, Edy is trying to effect a Hofmann elimination. Unfortunately, the product shown would not be the major elimination product. (What would be the product?)
(g) Edy is trying to carry out an S_N2 reaction on a tertiary halide. Such folly!

40. (a) The two amines will dissolve in dilute HCl, whereas the amide will not. 1-Octanamine, a primary amine, will liberate a gas (N_2) when it reacts with nitrous acid. The tertiary amine will not.

    (b) Only benzylamine and *p*-toluidine will dissolve in dilute HCl. Benzylamine, an *alkylamine*, will liberate a gas (N_2) when treated with cold aqueous nitrous acid. *p*-Toluidine forms a diazonium salt that will not liberate nitrogen unless it is heated. *p*-Cresol, a phenol, dissolves in base; the amines do not. Since anisole has neither acidic nor basic groups, it will dissolve in neither dilute acid nor dilute base.

41. The problem here is that *p*-aminophenol has two functional groups that can react with acetic anhydride: the phenol group and the amino group.

    This reaction involves a competition between the —OH group and the —NH_2 group acting as a nucleophile. We expect the better base to be the better nucleophile. The conjugate acid of the —NH_2 group has a pK_a of about 4.5; the conjugate acid of the —OH group has a pK_a of about –6 (that's *minus* 6!). Because the —NH_2 group is the better base (and better nucleophile), it reacts with acetic anhydride much more rapidly than the —OH group. Hence, compound *B* is acetaminophen, the product formed. Because it is a phenol, it dissolves in NaOH solution.

42. We begin with a solution of all four compounds in a water-immiscible solvent such as ether. First we extract with aqueous HCl. Aniline is taken into the water layer as its hydrochloride salt. The water layer is separated and made basic with NaOH to afford free aniline, which forms a separate layer and can be removed in a separatory funnel. Next, we extract the ether solution with aqueous $NaHCO_3$. This solution is basic enough to dissolve *p*-nitrobenzoic acid as its sodium salt, but not the phenol. Isolation of the water layer and addition of HCl to it affords the free carboxylic acid, which precipitates. Next we extract the ether solution with aqueous NaOH, which removes *p*-chlorophenol as its sodium salt. Making the water layer acidic affords the neutral phenol. The only compound remaining in the ether layer is nitrobenzene, which is isolated by drying the ether solution and boiling away the ether on a steam bath. (Whether we do the extraction with HCl before the two basic extractions, or vice versa, is immaterial. However, the order of the two basic extractions cannot be reversed; why?)

43. (a)

    (b)

(c)

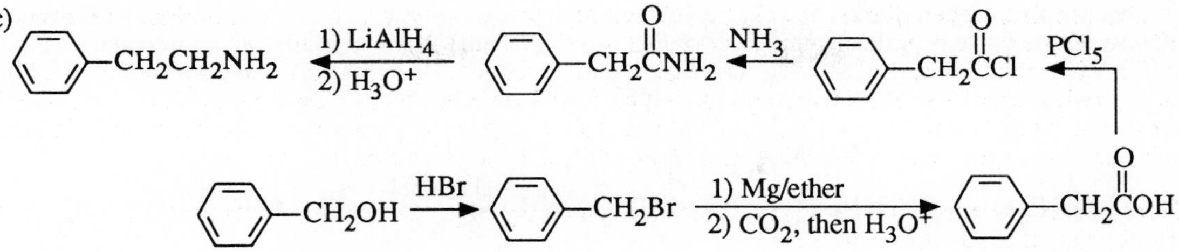

from part (b)

(d)

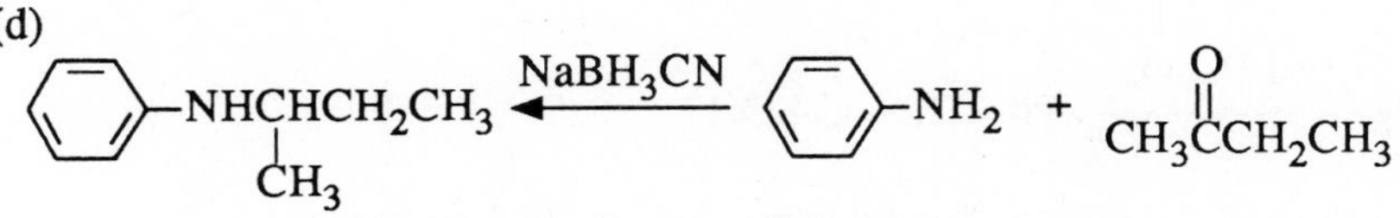

(e)

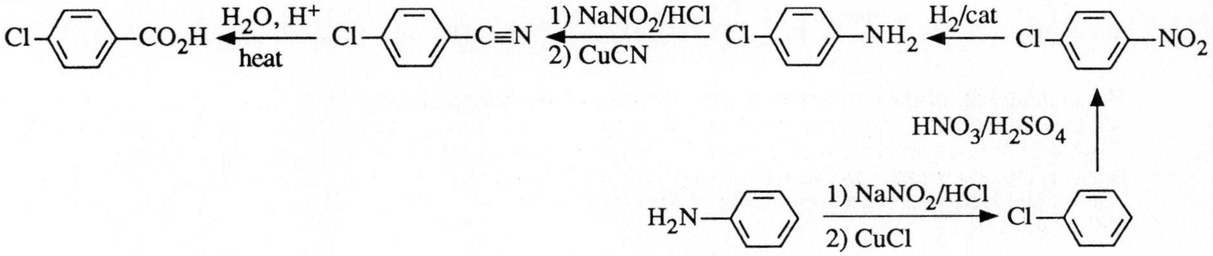

(f)

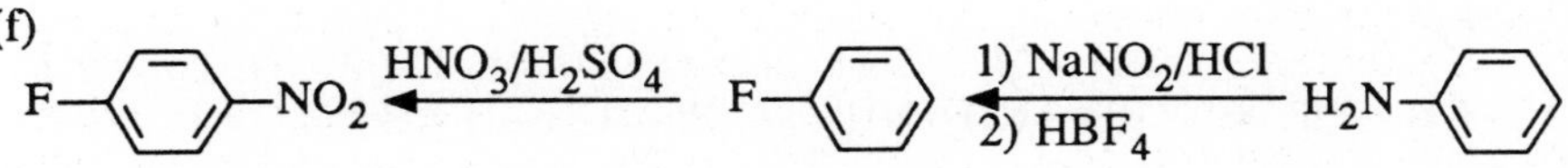

44. Reaction of methyl isocyanate with 1-naphthol yields carbaryl:

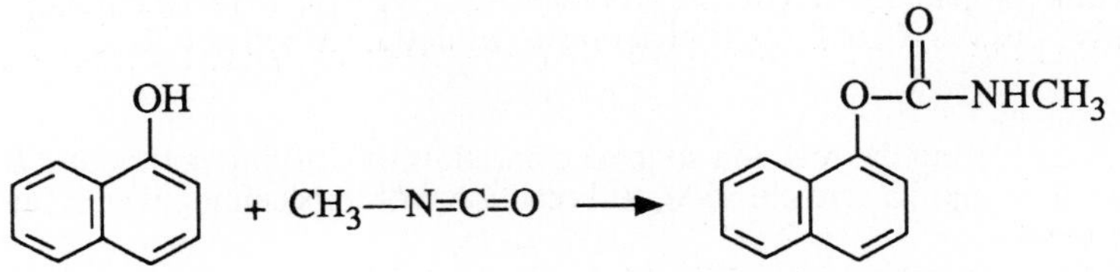

45. Compounds *A* and *B* are primary alkylamines, because they give off nitrogen (the gas) on diazotization. Furthermore, compound *A* is the racemate of a chiral compound. From the oxidation data, compound *A* has a benzene ring with one substituent, and compound *B* contains a *para*-disubstituted benzene ring. Finally, compound *C* is an aniline derivative with a *para* substituent. The following structures of *A*, *B*, and *C* fit the data:

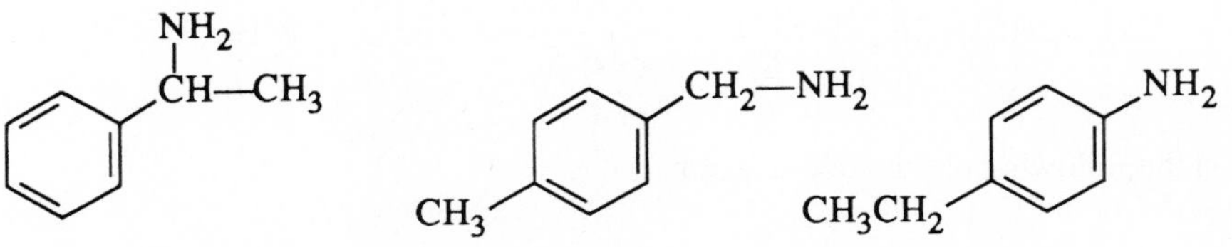

46.   First, we resolve 2-phenylbutanoic acid into enantiomers using an optically active amine as the resolving agent. Then we allow the appropriate enantiomer of this carboxylic acid to undergo the following reactions.

(a) In this synthesis we begin with the (R)-enantiomer of the acid.

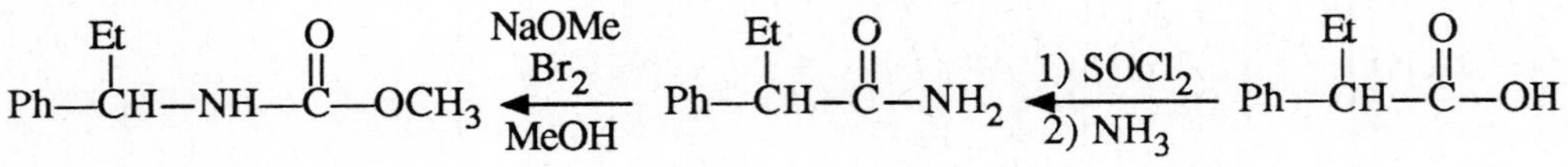

$$\text{Ph—CH—NH—C—OCH}_3 \xleftarrow[\text{MeOH}]{\substack{\text{NaOMe} \\ \text{Br}_2}} \text{Ph—CH—C—NH}_2 \xleftarrow[\text{2) NH}_3]{\text{1) SOCl}_2} \text{Ph—CH—C—OH}$$

(b) The (S)-enantiomer of the acid is esterified to give the desired product:

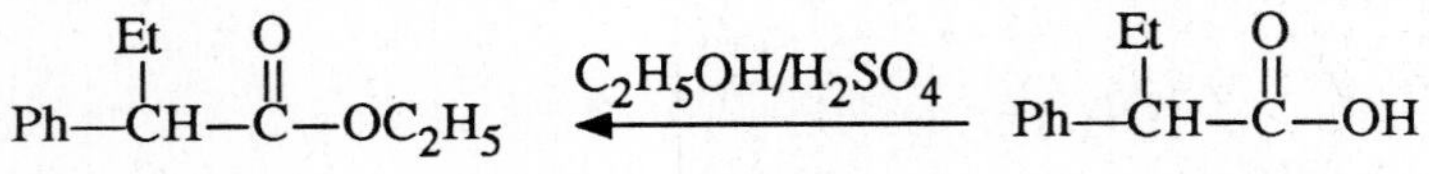

$$\text{Ph—CH—C—OC}_2\text{H}_5 \xleftarrow{\text{C}_2\text{H}_5\text{OH/H}_2\text{SO}_4} \text{Ph—CH—C—OH}$$

(c) First, we use the (R)-enantiomer of the carboxylic acid to prepare the (R)-isocyanate:

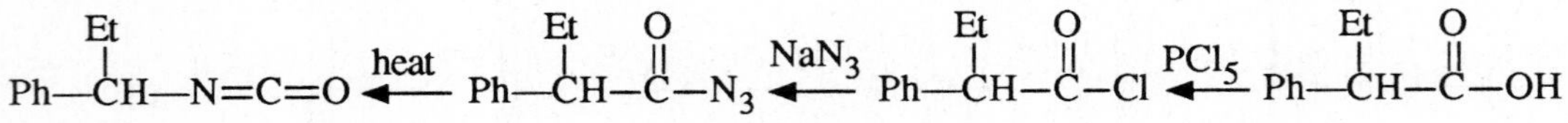

$$\text{Ph—CH—N=C=O} \xleftarrow{\text{heat}} \text{Ph—CH—C—N}_3 \xleftarrow{\text{NaN}_3} \text{Ph—CH—C—Cl} \xleftarrow{\text{PCl}_5} \text{Ph—CH—C—OH}$$

We then let half of the isocyanate react with water to give the (R)-amine:

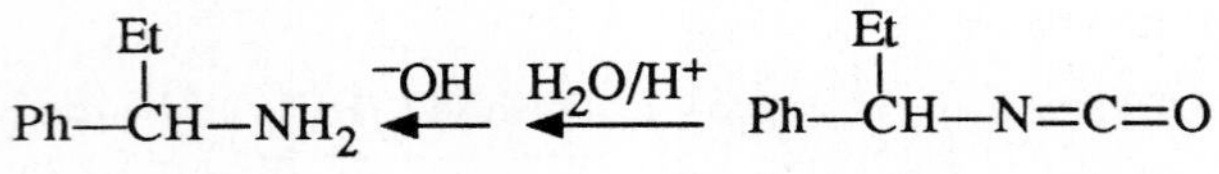

$$\text{Ph—CH—NH}_2 \xleftarrow{^-\text{OH}} \xleftarrow{\text{H}_2\text{O/H}^+} \text{Ph—CH—N=C=O}$$

This amine is then allowed to react with the remaining isocyanate:

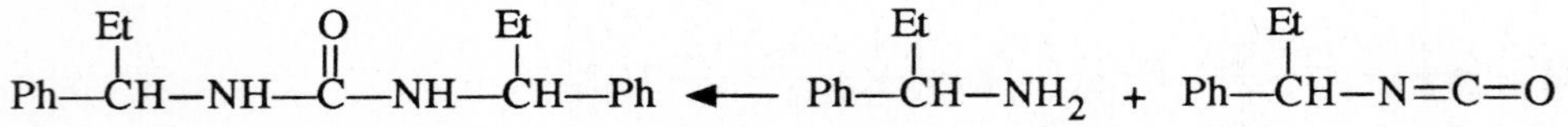

$$\text{Ph—CH—NH—C—NH—CH—Ph} \xleftarrow{} \text{Ph—CH—NH}_2 + \text{Ph—CH—N=C=O}$$

(d) Starting with the (S)-enantiomer of 2-phenylbutanoic acid, we prepare the (S)-amine using the same reactions that we used for the (R)-amine in the previous problem. We then allow the (S)-amine to react with the (R)-isocyanate. [Alternatively, we could prepare the (R)-amine and let it react with the (S)-isocyanate.] The point is that the desired *meso* derivative has the R configuration at one asymmetric carbon and the S configuration at the other.

47.   Let us begin solving this problem by completing the reaction sequence and thus identifying compound B. Thionyl chloride converts 4-pentenoic acid into its acid chloride, and reaction with piperidine gives an amide. Reduction of this amide gives the amine B:

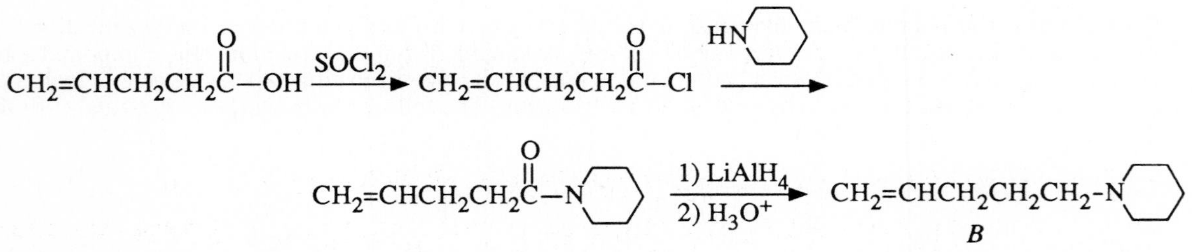

$$\text{CH}_2\text{=CHCH}_2\text{CH}_2\text{C—OH} \xrightarrow{\text{SOCl}_2} \text{CH}_2\text{=CHCH}_2\text{CH}_2\text{C—Cl} \xrightarrow{\text{HN}\langle\rangle}$$

$$\text{CH}_2\text{=CHCH}_2\text{CH}_2\text{C—N}\langle\rangle \xrightarrow[\text{2) H}_3\text{O}^+]{\text{1) LiAlH}_4} \text{CH}_2\text{=CHCH}_2\text{CH}_2\text{CH}_2\text{—N}\langle\rangle$$
$$\textit{B}$$

Compound B is formed in the following elimination reaction:

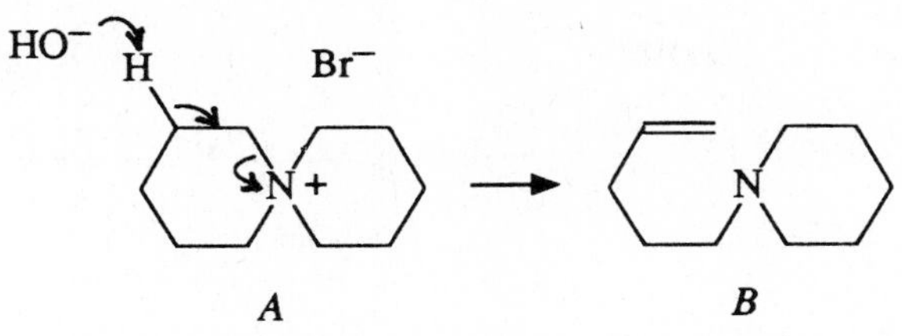

Compound *A* gives a precipitate with $AgNO_3$ because it is an ionic halide. It is formed in four successive alkylation reactions with two equivalents of 1,5-dibromopentane:

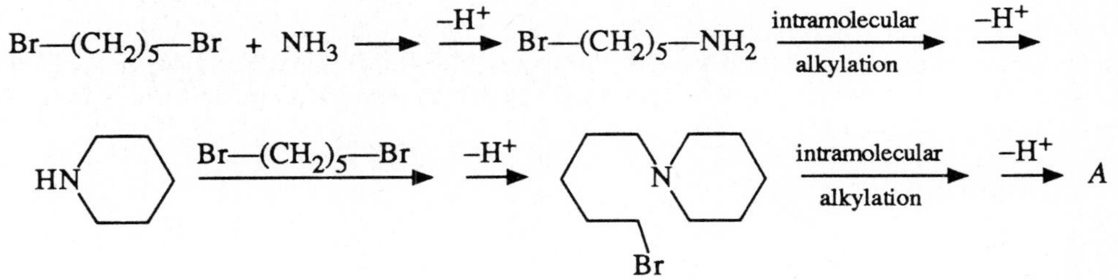

48. (a) Delocalization of the amine unshared electron pair into the nitro group imparts double-bond character in the *N*-phenyl bond:

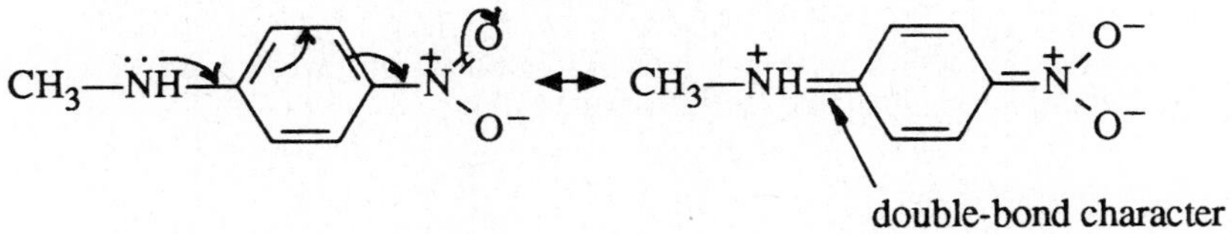

(Notice that this type of resonance is consistent with the amine as an electron-donating group, and the nitro group as an electron-withdrawing group.) Delocalization of the nitrogen unshared pair is less significant in *N*-methylaniline itself, in which the *p*-nitro group is not present. Internal rotation is more difficult (requires more energy) when the bond involved has a greater amount of double-bond character.

(b) Amine inversion interconverts *cis*- and *trans*-1,3-dimethylpyrrolidine:

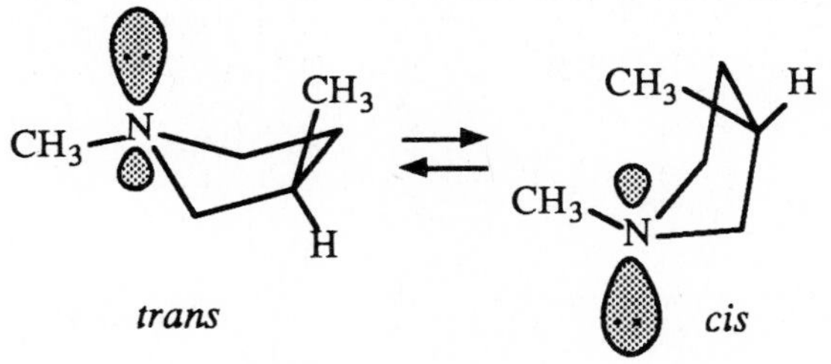

Because this process is rapid, the two stereoisomers cannot be separately isolated.

(c) The compound is the nitrogen analog of an acetal, and spontaneously hydrolyzes to formaldehyde and two equivalents of methylamine:

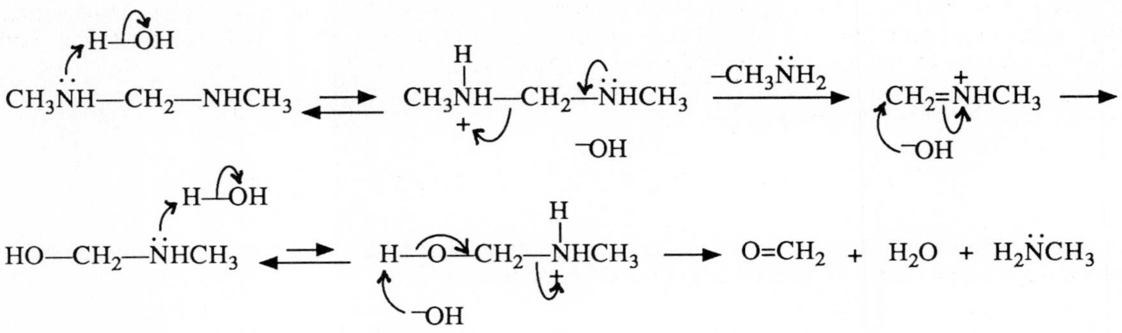

(d) This compound exists as an enamine for the same reason that β-diketones contain a high percentage of enol: Internal hydrogen bonding and conjugation associated with the enamine form increase the stability of the molecule:

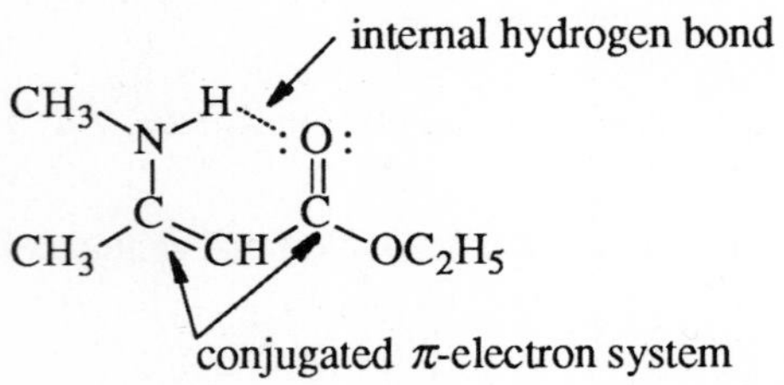

(e) Loss of nitrogen from the diazonium ion would give a carbocation that has four π-electrons. Thus, this cation is *antiaromatic*, and therefore particularly unstable (see text page 622):

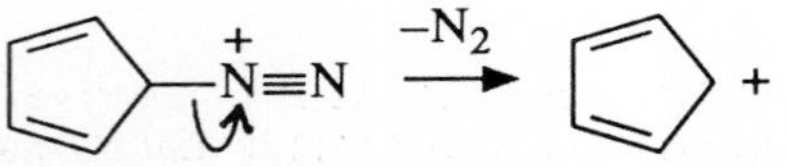

49. (a) Since diazotization of R—NH$_2$ gives R—$\overset{+}{N}$≡N, which then decomposes to R$^+$ (a carbocation) and N$_2$, by analogy diazotization of H—NH$_2$ should give H$^+$ and N$_2$.

(b) This is an exhaustive methylation followed by a Hofmann elimination. The product is formed by proton removal from the angular methyl group:

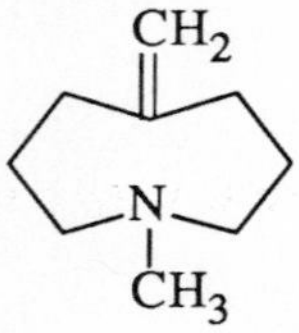

(c) Because amines are nucleophiles, they can attack epoxides at the less substituted carbon:

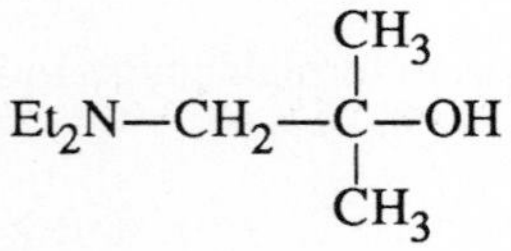

(d) The organolithium reagent acts as a base to remove a proton from the amine to form the amide anion. This anion then removes a proton from the alkyne to give the acetylide ion, which, in turn, reacts with the alkyl halide to give the following substituted alkyne (see Sec. 14.7):

$$C_2H_5-C\equiv C-CH_2CH(CH_3)_2$$

(e) Cuprous nitrite introduces a nitro group in a variant of the Sandmeyer reaction:

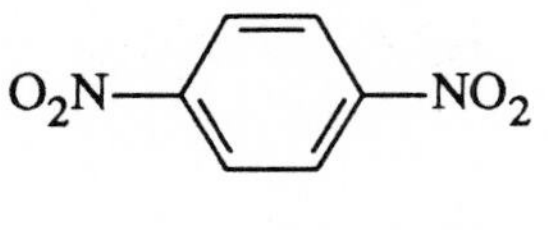

➤ *p*-Dinitrobenzene would be hard to prepare by ordinary electrophilic aromatic substitution reactions. Can you see why?

(f) The amine reacts with two equivalents of the epoxide to give $CH_3CH_2CH_2CH_2-N(CH_2CH_2OH)_2$.

(g) Nitrobenzene is reduced to aniline by hydrogenation. The aniline reacts with the aldehyde to form an imine, which is also reduced. The resulting secondary amine reacts again in a second reductive amination reaction. The sequence can be summarized as follows:

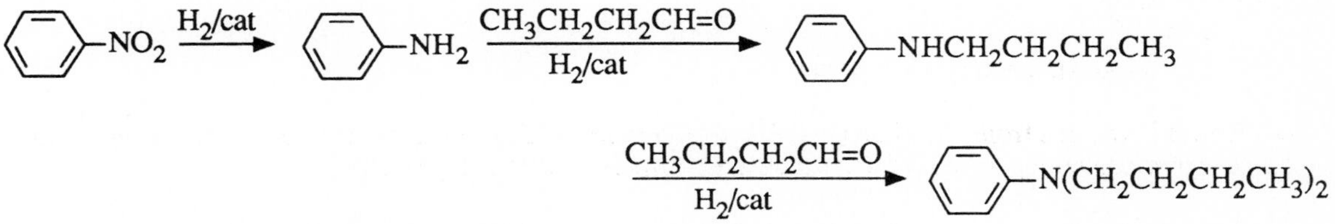

(h) The amine can attack either carbon of the epoxide with inversion of configuration. Attack at one carbon gives one enantiomer; attack at the other carbon gives the other enantiomer. Since attack at both carbons is equally likely, the racemate is formed:

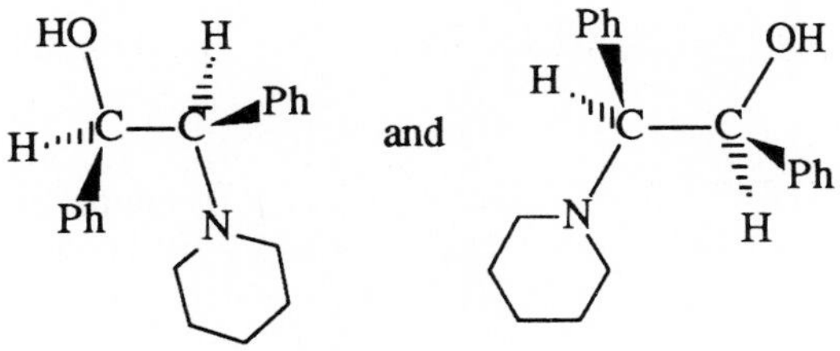

(i) This is an S$_N$2 reaction with the amine as the nucleophile. The *allylic* bromine is displaced, but the *vinylic* bromine survives:

$$CH_2=\overset{|}{\underset{Br}{C}}-CH_2-\overset{+}{N}H_2Et \quad Br^-$$

Recall that allylic halides are especially reactive in the S$_N$2 reaction (Sec. 17.4), whereas vinylic halides are especially unreactive (Sec. 18.1).

(j) Although the Gabriel synthesis usually involves alkyl halides, there is no reason that an epoxide cannot also be used. Hydrolysis of the product in base avoids dehydration of the alcohol that might occur in acidic solution.

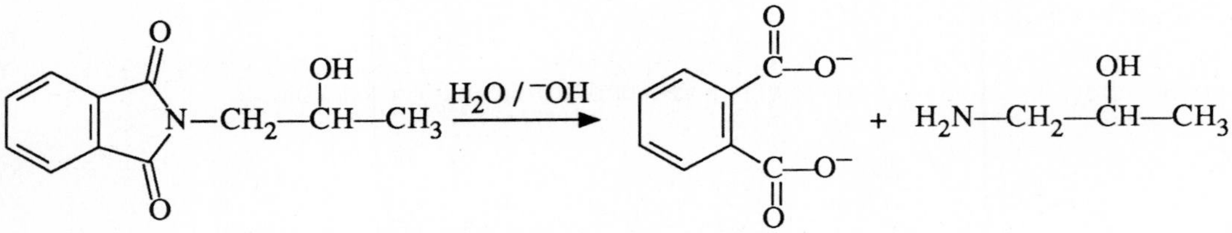

(k) The respective conversions are as follows, beginning with the product of the first reaction:

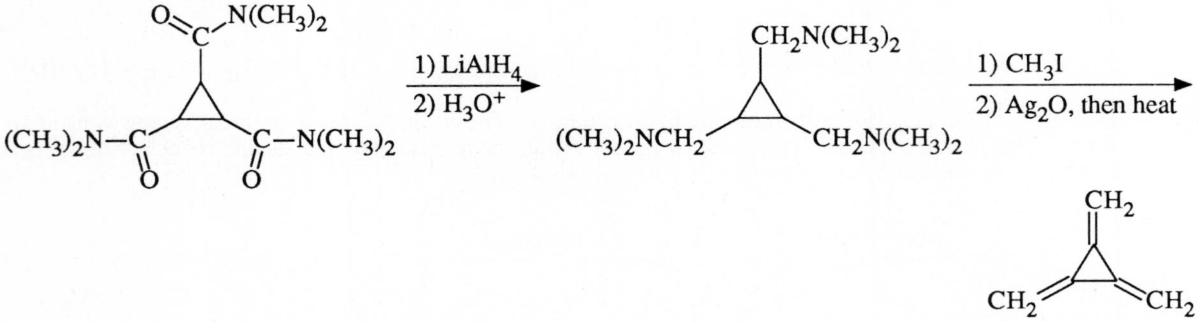

the isomer of benzene

(l) Reduction of aromatic nitro compounds by LiAlH$_4$ gives azobenzenes (Eq. 23.78, text page 1022). The fact that the product has twelve carbons shows that the reaction in this case is intramolecular:

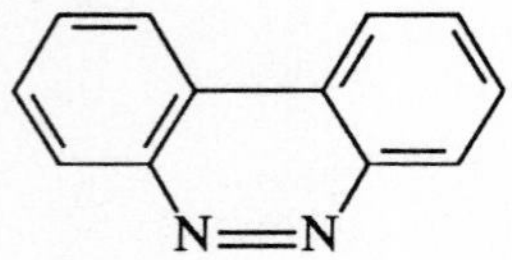

(m) We learned that acidic sodium nitrite is a source of " $^+$NO " . Just as nitrous acid can effect nitrosation of tertiary aromatic amines in the ring (Eq. 23.72, text page 1020), it can also bring about ring nitrosation of phenols:

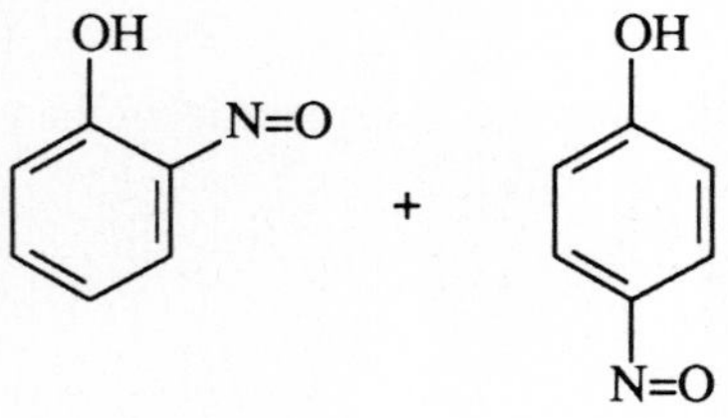

50. As we learn more chemistry, we can conceive of more acceptable ways to carry out a given synthesis. Hence, it is possible to have a correct solution that does not correspond to one of those below.

(a)

$$CH_3NH(CH_2)_5CH_3 \xleftarrow[\text{2) } H_3O^+]{\text{1) LiAlH}_4} CH_3NH\overset{O}{\overset{\|}{C}}(CH_2)_4CH_3 \xleftarrow[\text{2) } CH_3NH_2 \text{ (excess)}]{\text{1) SOCl}_2} HO\overset{O}{\overset{\|}{C}}(CH_2)_4CH_3$$

$$\uparrow H_3O^+, \text{heat}$$

$$CH_3(CH_2)_3CO_2H \xrightarrow[\text{2) } H_3O^+]{\text{1) LiAlH}_4} HO-(CH_2)_4CH_3 \xrightarrow{\text{HBr}} Br-(CH_2)_4CH_3 \xrightarrow{\text{NaCN}} N\equiv C-(CH_2)_4CH_3$$

(b) We show two syntheses for this compound:

$$(CH_3)_2N(CH_2)_4CH_3 \xleftarrow[\text{NaBH}_4]{\substack{\text{excess} \\ CH_2=O}} H_2N(CH_2)_4CH_3 \xleftarrow[\text{2) } H_3O^+]{\text{1) LiAlH}_4} H_2N\overset{O}{\overset{\|}{C}}(CH_2)_3CH_3 \xleftarrow[\text{2) } NH_3]{\text{1) SOCl}_2}$$

$$\xleftarrow[\text{2) } H_3O^+]{\text{1) LiAlH}_4} (CH_3)_2N\overset{O}{\overset{\|}{C}}(CH_2)_3CH_3 \xleftarrow[\text{2) } (CH_3)_2NH]{\text{1) SOCl}_2} HO\overset{O}{\overset{\|}{C}}(CH_2)_3CH_3$$

(c) Pentylamine was prepared as an intermediate in the previous synthesis.

(d)

$$H_2N(CH_2)_3CH_3 \xleftarrow{\text{Br}_2/\text{NaOH}} H_2N\overset{O}{\overset{\|}{C}}(CH_2)_3CH_3 \quad \text{[from part (b)]}$$

(e)

$$H_2N(CH_2)_5CH_3 \xleftarrow[\text{2) } H_3O^+]{\text{1) LiAlH}_4} H_2N\overset{O}{\overset{\|}{C}}(CH_2)_4CH_3 \xleftarrow[\text{2) } NH_3]{\text{1) SOCl}_2} HO\overset{O}{\overset{\|}{C}}(CH_2)_4CH_3 \quad \text{[from part (a)]}$$

(f)

$$EtNH(CH_2)_3Ph \xleftarrow[\text{2) } H_3O^+]{\text{1) LiAlH}_4} EtNH\overset{O}{\overset{\|}{C}}(CH_2)_2Ph \xleftarrow[\text{2) } EtNH_2]{\text{1) SOCl}_2} HO\overset{O}{\overset{\|}{C}}(CH_2)_2Ph \xleftarrow{\text{dil. HNO}_3} HO(CH_2)_3Ph$$

$$\uparrow \begin{array}{l} \text{1) Mg/ether} \\ \text{2) } \triangle\!\!\!\!\triangle O \\ \text{3) } H_3O^+ \end{array}$$

$$CH_3-Ph \xrightarrow[\text{peroxides}]{\text{NBS}} BrCH_2Ph$$

(NBS is *N*-bromosuccinimide; see text page 693.)

(g)

$$PhCH_2-\overset{\overset{\displaystyle CH_3}{|}}{\underset{\underset{\displaystyle CH_3}{|}}{\overset{+}{N}}}-CH_2CH_2CH_2CH_3 \;\; Br^- \xleftarrow{\text{PhCH}_2\text{Br}} (CH_3)_2NCH_2CH_2CH_2CH_3 \xleftarrow[\text{NaBH}_3\text{CN}]{(CH_3)_2NH}$$

$$CH_3CH_2CH_2CH=O$$

(h)

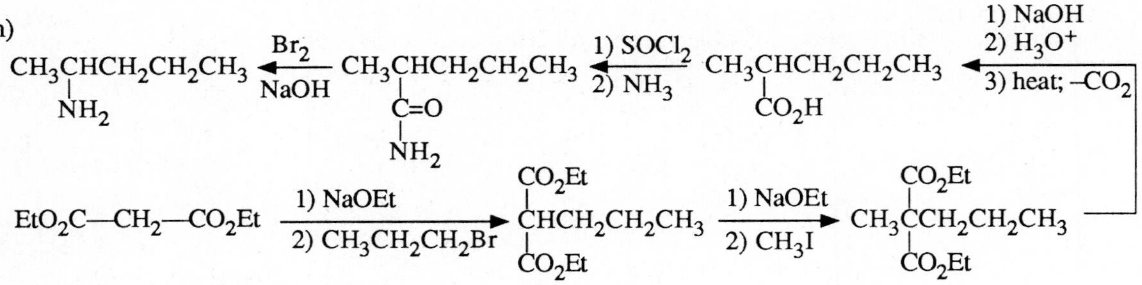

(i)

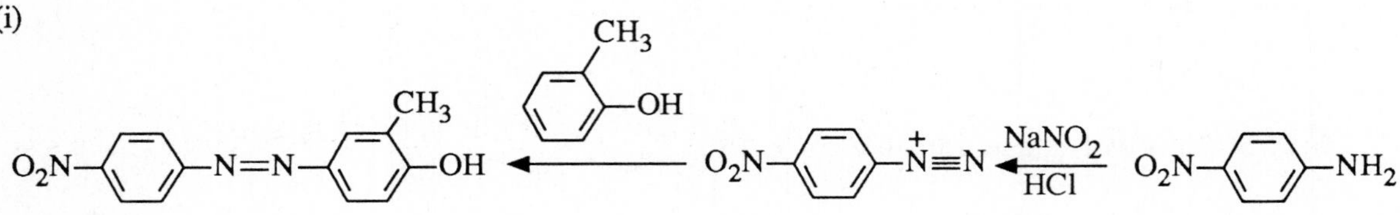

The preparation of *p*-nitroaniline is shown on text page 1010.

(j)

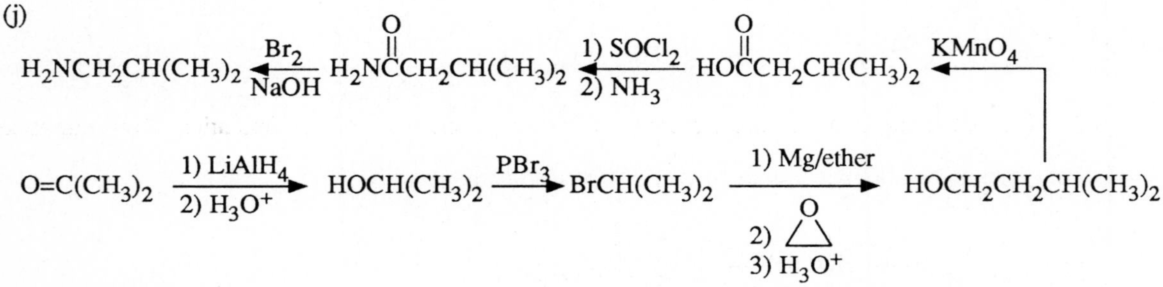

(k)

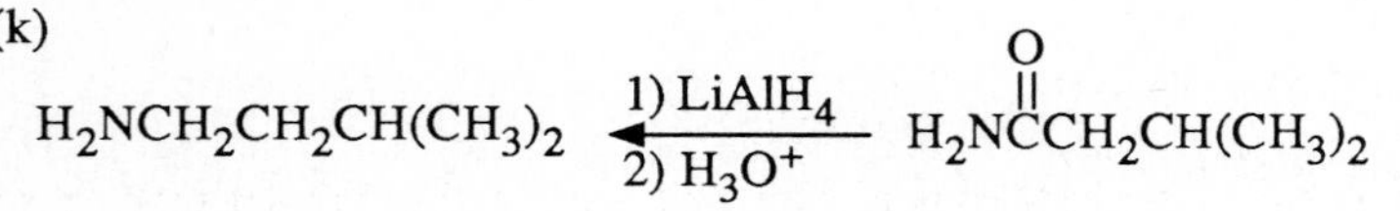

[from part (j)]

(l)

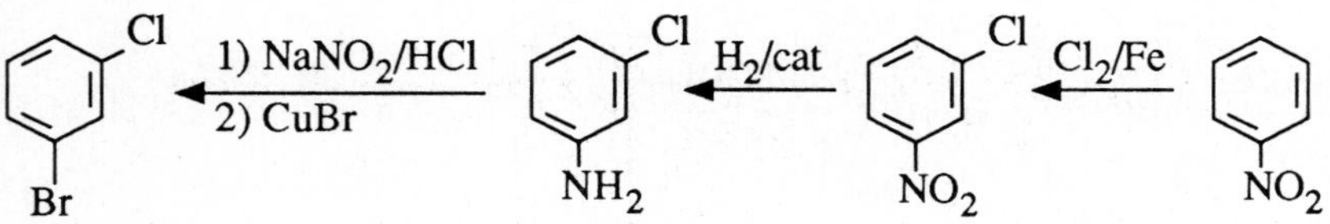

(m)

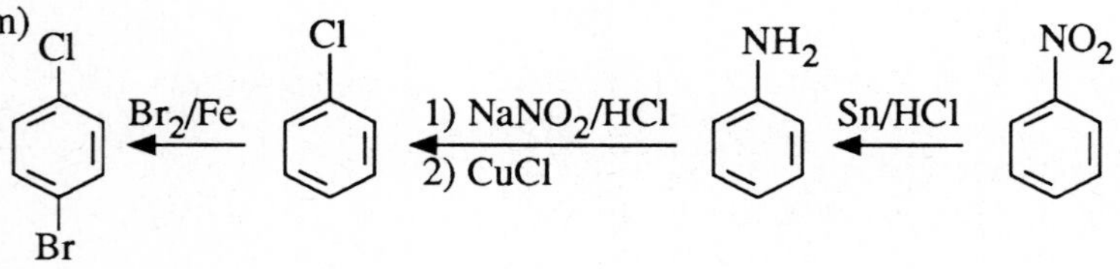

(n)

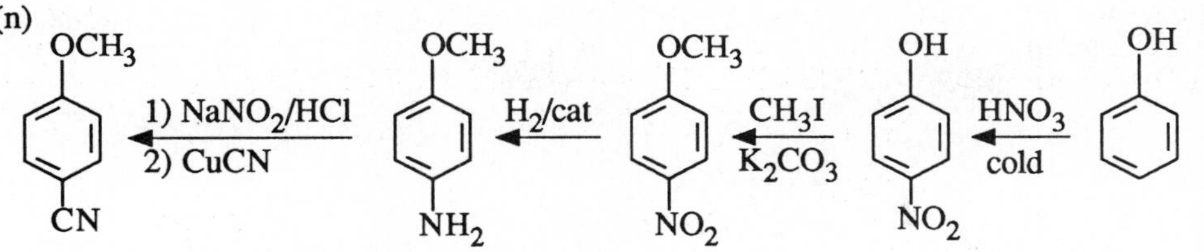

(o)

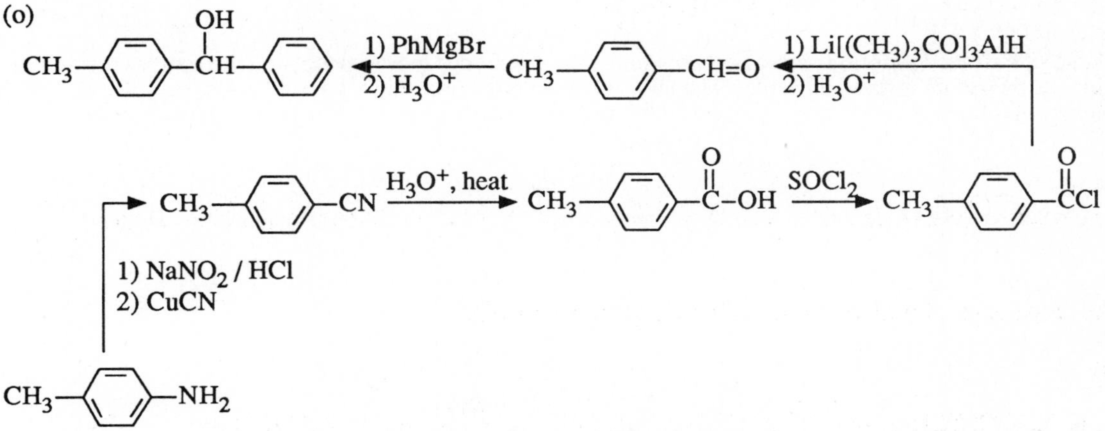

(p) We first determine whether the transformation involves overall inversion or retention of configuration at the asymmetric carbon.

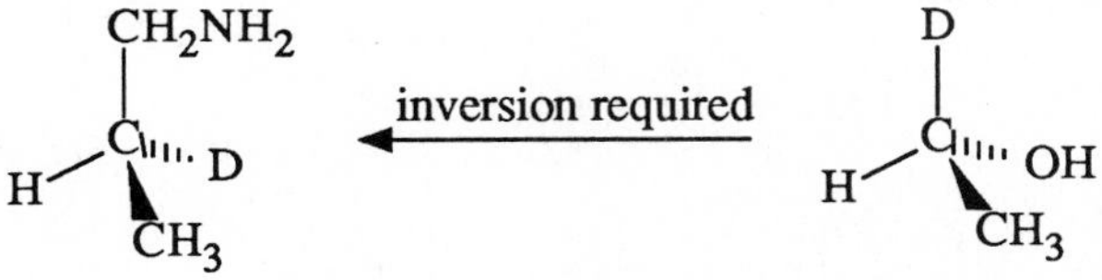

The following reaction scheme incorporates one S_N2 reaction at the asymmetric carbon; this reaction provides the required inversion.

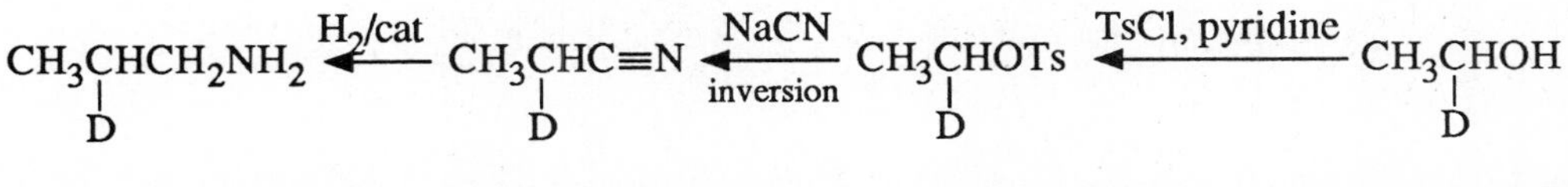

Recall (Sec. 10.3A) that TsCl is the abbreviation for p-toluenesulfonyl chloride ("tosyl chloride").

(q)

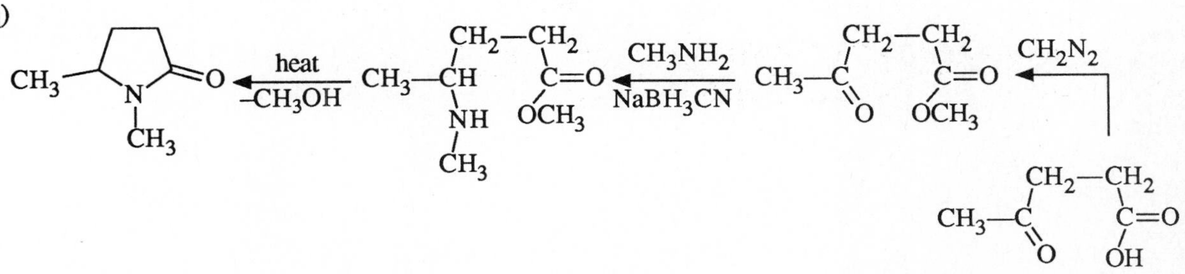

51. In order for a proton and the trimethylammonium group to be *anti*, the R-group and the leaving group must assume a *gauche* relationship:

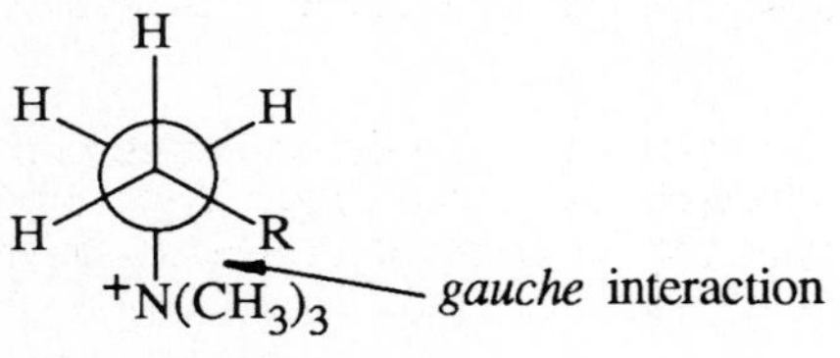

As the size of the R-group is increased, this interaction becomes more severe, and the transition state for elimination becomes more unstable. The less stable the transition state, the smaller the rate. Hence, the relative rates for the Hofmann rearrangements in question are inversely related to the size of the R-group:

relative rate: $B > C > A$

52. (a) Protonation of enamines occurs on *carbon* because the resulting cation is resonance-stabilized:

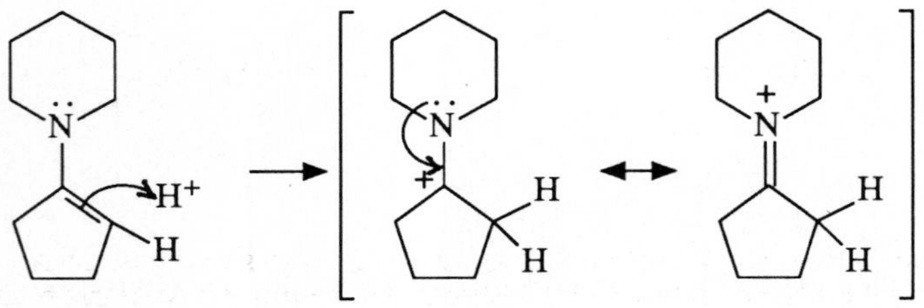

(Protonation on nitrogen gives a cation that is *not* resonance-stabilized.)

(b) Reaction with CH_3—I is much like reaction with a proton:

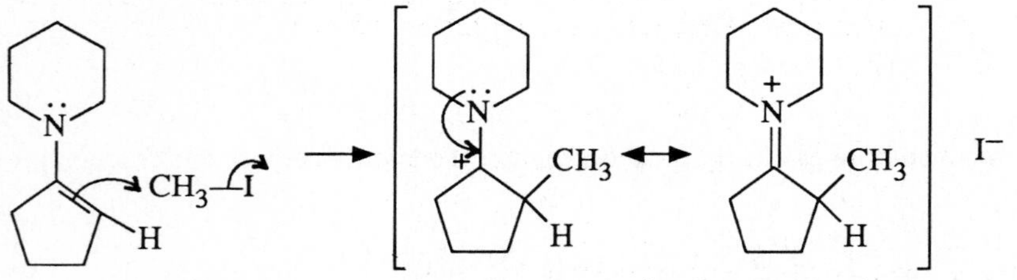

A

and

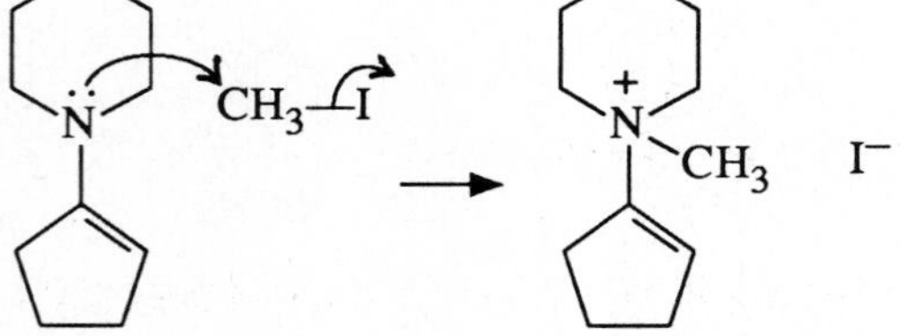

B

(c) The reaction to give *B* simply reverses by attack of I⁻ on the methyl group and expulsion of the enamine as a leaving group. Since this is an S$_N$2 reaction with I⁻ as the nucleophile, it should be first order in [I⁻]. Notice that compound *A* is favored at equilibrium for the same reason that the conjugate acid above is favored: it is a resonance-stabilized cation.

53. Compound *A* is an amide of benzoic acid. Compound *B* is the amine from which *A* is derived by reaction with benzoyl chloride. Compound *B* must be a secondary amine; if it were a primary amine, a gas (N$_2$) would be liberated when it is treated with nitrous acid, and if it were a tertiary amine, it would not form an amide. Alkene *D* is:

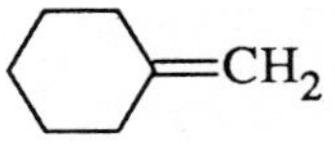

Hence amine *B* is a compound that gives styrene and *D* on successive exhaustive-methylation/Hofmann-elimination sequences. It follows that the identities of compounds *A*, *B*, and *C* are as follows:

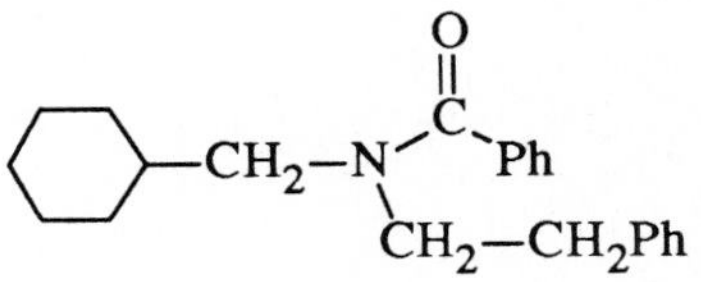

If you did not get the correct answers, you should work back through the reactions to show how these structures are consistent with the data. Why is styrene rather than *D* formed on the *first* cycle of methylation–elimination?

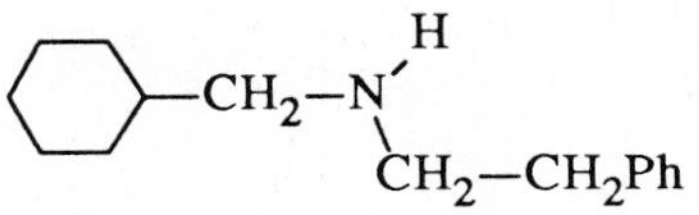

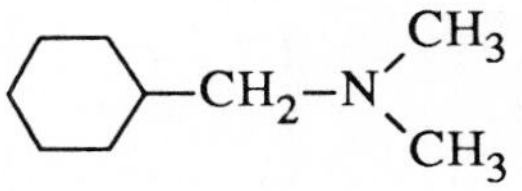

54. Aniline absorbs at a longer wavelength than benzene because of the conjugation between the unshared electron pair on nitrogen and the ring; this conjugation is symbolized by the resonance structures in Eq. 23.3, text page 989. When aniline is protonated, the electron pair on nitrogen is bound to a proton and is no longer available for interaction with the ring. Thus, the conjugated π-electron system in protonated aniline is just the benzene ring itself. Hence, the UV absorption of protonated aniline is like that of benzene.

55. (a)   (b)

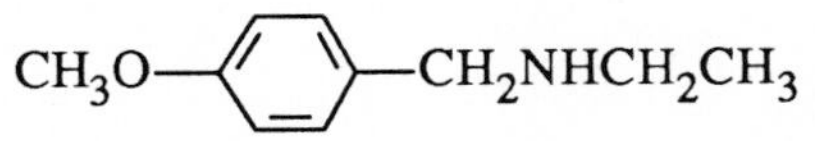

$$CH_3O—\langle\!\!\bigcirc\!\!\rangle—CH_2NHCH_2CH_3 \qquad CH_3NH—CH_2CH_2—OH$$

56. These rearrangements are all related to the Hofmann hypobromite reaction.

(a) The mechanism of this reaction, called the *Lossen rearrangement*, is identical to that of the Hofmann rearrangement, except that benzoate ion rather than bromide ion is the leaving group. We begin the mechanism with the conjugate-base anion of the starting material, which is formed by reaction of the starting material with KH:

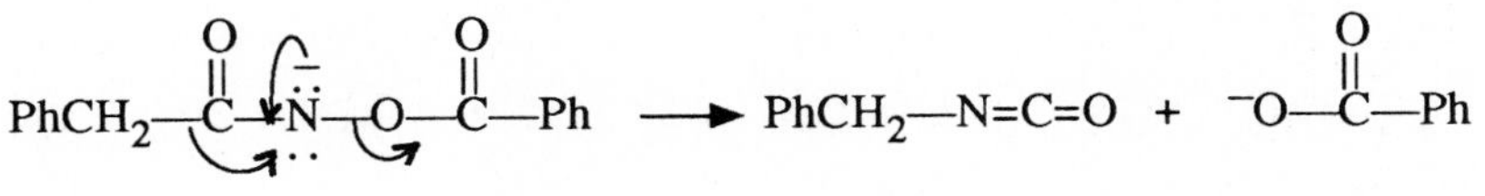

Conversion of the isocyanate to the amine follows the mechanism in Eqs. 23.81e and f, text page 1024.

(b) Reaction of the imide with hydroxide generates an *N*-bromo anion, which is an intermediate in the Hofmann rearrangement:

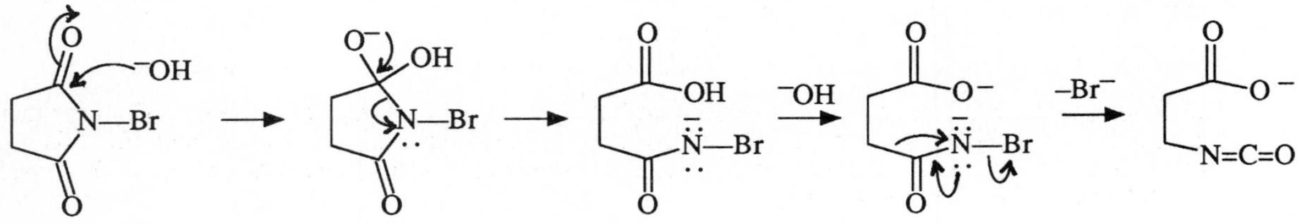

Hydrolysis of the isocyanate in the usual manner affords the amine.

(c) In this reaction a Hofmann rearrangement is possible at each amide group of the molecule. After one Hofmann rearrangement takes place, the intermediate contains an amide group and an isocyanate group at each end of the molecule. Attack of the amide on the isocyanate gives the product:

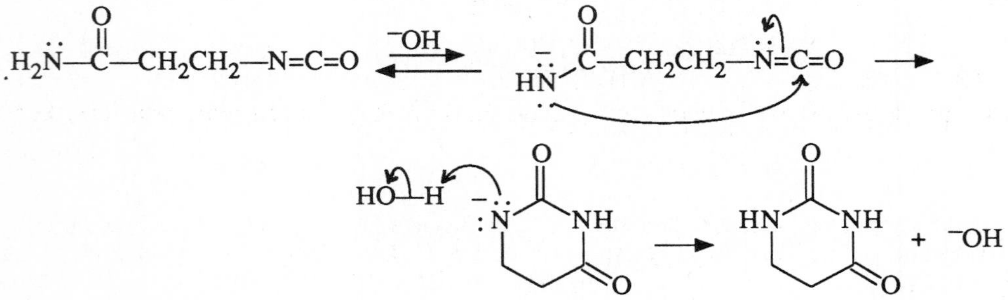

57. Compound *A* is the HCl salt of *B*; because *A* is an ionic halide, it rapidly gives a precipitate with acidic silver nitrate solution. Compound *B* is a primary alkylamine, because it gives off a gas (N_2) upon diazotization. The elemental analysis translates into the formula $C_{6.65}H_{9.62}N_{0.74}$, or $C_9H_{13}N$. A compound with this formula has an unsaturation number of 4. Since the elimination products contain a benzene ring, we can hypothesize that compound *B* is aromatic, and that its benzene ring fully accounts for its unsaturation. From our knowledge of the Wolff–Kishner reaction, we conclude that compound *D* is propylbenzene:

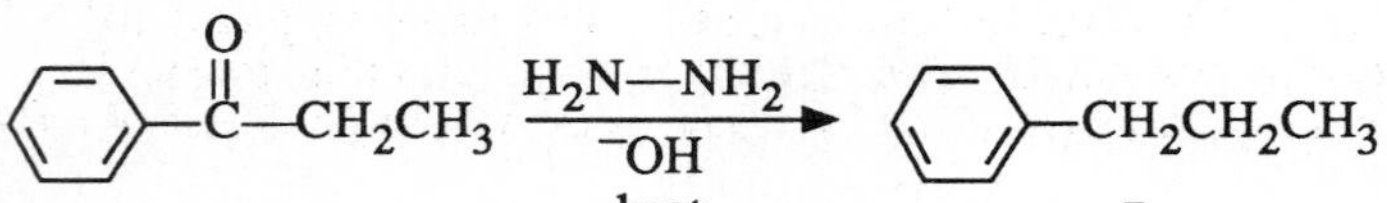

A mixture of compounds that would hydrogenate to propylbenzene is the mixture of the following alkenes:

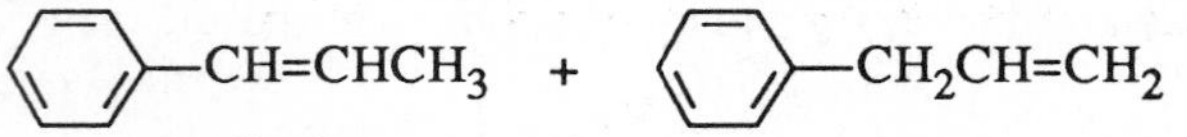

The chiral primary amines that could give these alkenes upon exhaustive methylation followed by Hofmann elimination are either *B1* or *B2*:

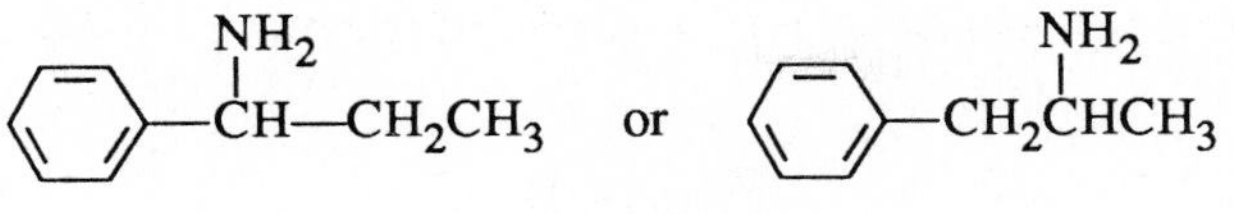

B1   B2

The doublet in the NMR spectrum is consistent with the presence of a group split *only* by a single proton; the chemical shift suggests that this might be a methyl group. Only compound *B2* is consistent with this information. Therefore, the structure of *B* is *B2*, and compound *A* is the conjugate-acid salt of *B* formed with HCl. (Compound *B* is amphetamine.)

58. (a) Amides, like amines, can be diazotized. The result is an acyl diazonium ion, which rapidly hydrolyzes to carbamic acid and N_2. As we learned in Eq. 20.48, text page 846, carbamic acid decarboxylates to ammonia and CO_2. The ammonia is itself diazotized to N_2, as discussed in the solution to Problem 49(a).

(b) The secondary amine group and the ketone react intramolecularly to give an enamine, which is reduced by $NaBH_4$.

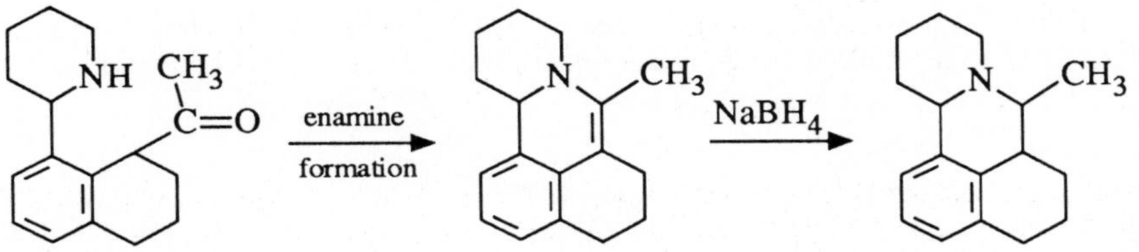

The mechanism of enamine formation is given in Sec. 19.11B, and sodium borohydride reduction of enamines is discussed in Sec. 23.7B.

(c) In this reaction, a diazonium ion intermediate is formed by the usual mechanism (text pages 1012–1013); this ion then decomposes to a primary carbocation, which rearranges by hydride migration to a tertiary carbocation. The products are derived respectively from attack of water (from solvent) and loss of a β-proton:

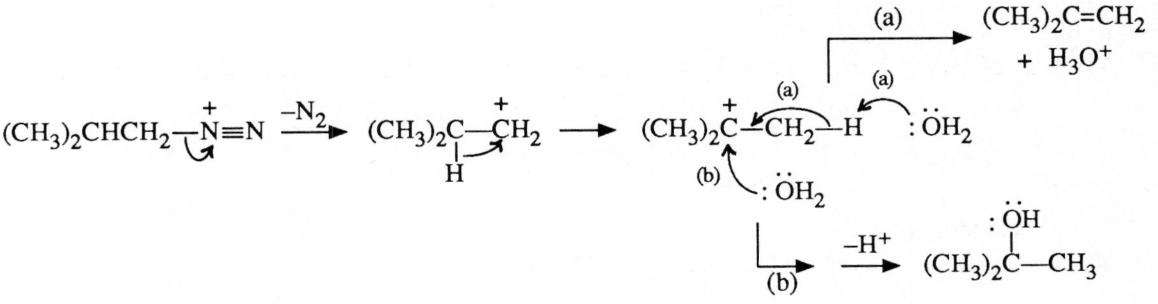

(d) Cyanide ion, acting as a base, initiates an elimination to give an α,β-unsaturated carbonyl compound, to which cyanide then adds in a conjugate-addition reaction to form the product:

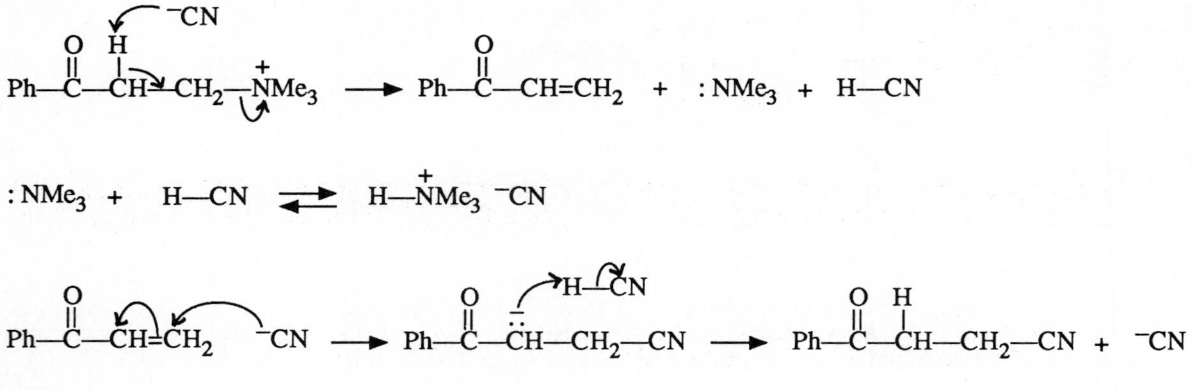

(e) The reaction with sodium azide gives the acyl azide:

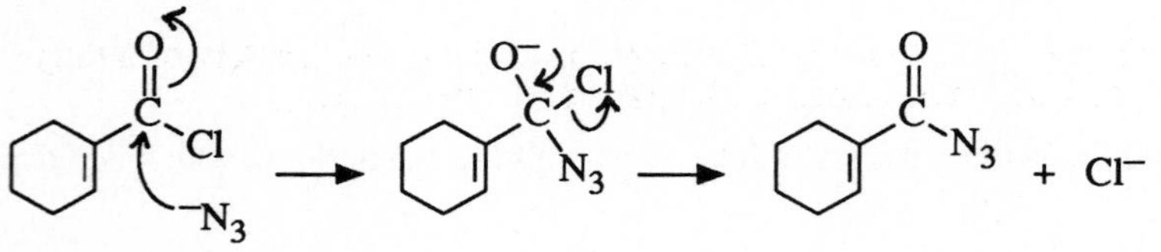

The acyl azide then undergoes the Curtius rearrangement by the usual mechanism (Eq. 23.85, text page 1025) to give the isocyanate, which, under the aqueous acidic reaction conditions, hydrolyzes to the amine:

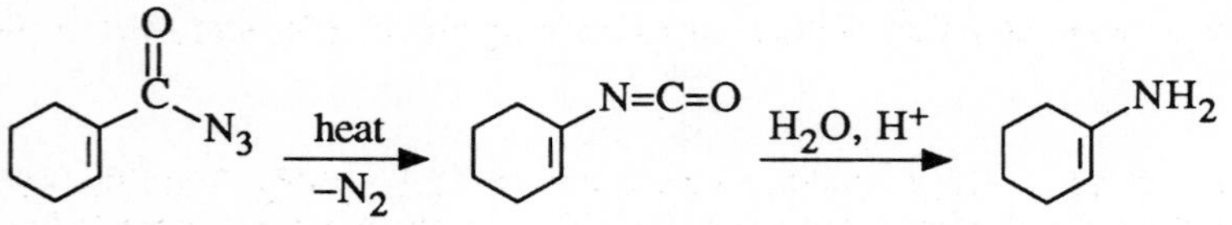

However, this is not an ordinary amine but is instead an enamine. This enamine, like others, hydrolyzes to its parent "amine" (NH_3) and carbonyl compound under the aqueous acidic conditions. This mechanism is the exact reverse of enamine formation. We provide the key intermediates; you provide the arrow formalism, if you have not already done so:

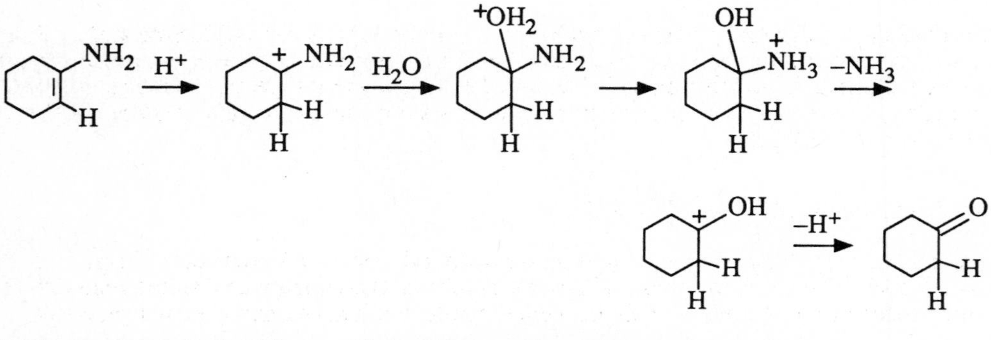

(f) The product is derived from a Diels–Alder reaction of furan and benzyne:

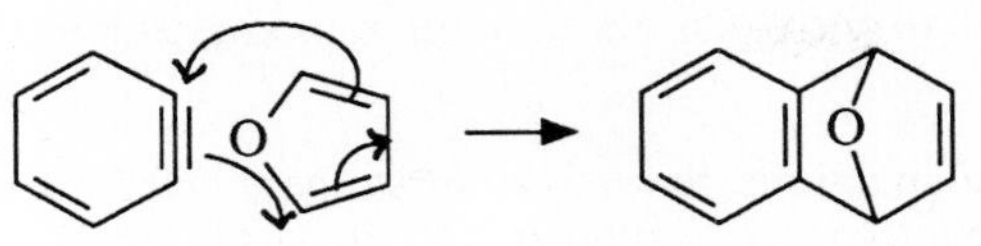

Benzyne is generated by decarboxylation of the diazonium salt that, in turn, is formed by diazotization of the starting material by the mechanism shown on text pages 1012–1013. We begin with the diazonium ion:

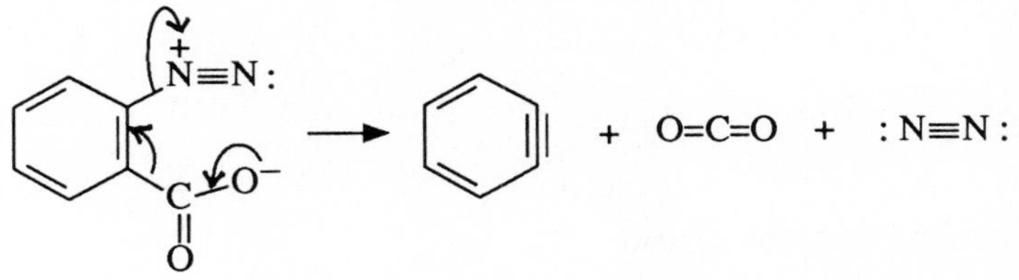

(g) This reaction is related to the pinacol rearrangement. Diazotization of the amine and loss of nitrogen generate the same carbocation intermediate that is formed in the pinacol rearrangement:

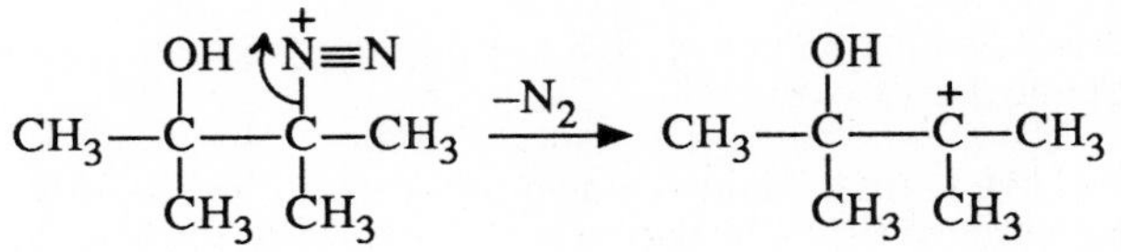

From this point on, the mechanism is identical to that of the pinacol rearrangement. (See Eqs. 10.9 b and c on text page 372.)

59.   At pH 1, methylamine exists almost completely as the methylammonium ion, $CH_3{-}\overset{+}{N}H_3$. Provided that chemical exchange of the N—H protons is sufficiently slow, we would expect the methyl protons to be split into a quartet by the N—H protons, according to the $n + 1$ splitting rule. The only reasonable mechanism for exchange of the N—H protons is for water, acting as a base, to remove them:

$$CH_3{-}\overset{+}{N}H_3 \ + \ H_2O \ \rightleftharpoons \ CH_3{-}\overset{..}{N}H_2 \ + \ H_3O^+$$

Evidently, this reaction is sufficiently slow that exchange is not observed on the NMR time scale. (That is, exchange occurs, but more slowly than can be detected by NMR.) Because hydroxide is a much stronger base than water, the rate constant for its reaction with the methylammonium ion is greater than the corresponding rate constant for reaction of water, but the reaction exact rate depends not only on the rate *constant* but also on the concentration of the hydroxide ion:

rate of exchange = $k[CH_3{-}\overset{+}{N}H_3][^-OH]$

At low pH, there is not enough hydroxide ion present for hydroxide-catalyzed exchange to occur with a significant rate. However, at pH 9, the amine still exists largely as its conjugate-acid ammonium ion, and there is enough hydroxide present that reaction with the methylammonium ion, and hence exchange, is fast:

$$CH_3{-}\overset{+}{N}H_3 \ + \ {}^-OH \ \rightleftharpoons \ CH_3{-}\overset{..}{N}H_2 \ + \ H_2O$$

Because exchange is very fast on the NMR time scale, the splitting of the methyl group by the N—H protons is obliterated. (A similar effect of exchange on splitting is described for alcohols on text pages 524 and 528.)

➤ How would you expect the splitting of the methyl group to change as the solution of methylamine is made *very* basic?

60. There are two effects of the phenyl group on the basicity of an aniline derivative. First, there is the resonance effect, discussed on text page 997. Second, there is the inductive effect, alluded to in the last sentence on text page 997. The basicities of the amines in this problem allow us to evaluate each effect independently. Amine *C* provides the standard of comparison; all effects of the phenyl group are absent. In amine *B*, the bicyclic structure forces the nitrogen unshared electron pair to lie *in the plane of the benzene ring*; that is, it *cannot* overlap with the π-electron system of the ring:

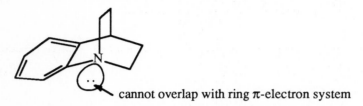

cannot overlap with ring π-electron system

Hence, the effect of the phenyl group on the basicity of compound *C* can be due only to its inductive effect. We can see that this effect is about 2.8 pK_a units. In compound *A*, there is unrestricted rotation about the ring–nitrogen bond. Hence, the nitrogen unshared pair can overlap with the ring π-electron system. Therefore, the basicity of this compound reflects both resonance and inductive effects. We see that resonance accounts for another 2.6 pK_a units. Evidently, the resonance effect and the inductive effect of the phenyl group are about equally important in determining the basicity of aniline derivatives.

61. The data show that both cyclic and bicyclic amines have normal conjugate-acid pK_a values. Hence, there is no unusual pK_a effect caused by the ring itself when a nitrogen becomes part of a ring. The pK_a of amide *A* is rather typical for an amide; it is only about one unit higher than that of acetamide (see Eq. 21.4b, text page 871). Furthermore, recall that amides protonate on *oxygen*, not on nitrogen (why?). Hence, the conjugate-acid pK_a of compound *D* is clearly unusual; it is 4–5 units higher than that of a typical amide. As in the previous problem, the bicyclic structure prevents the nitrogen unshared pair from overlap with an adjacent π-electron system — in this case, the π-electron system of the carbonyl group:

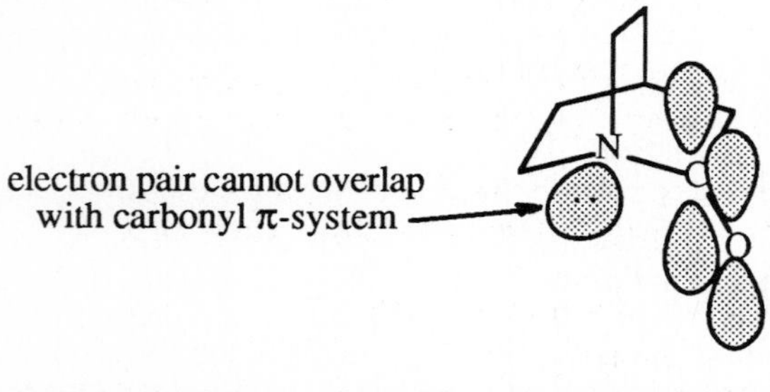

electron pair cannot overlap
with carbonyl π-system

As a result, this nitrogen is more like an amine nitrogen than an amide nitrogen. The energetic advantage due to resonance of amide protonation on the oxygen is lost; hence, protonation occurs on nitrogen:

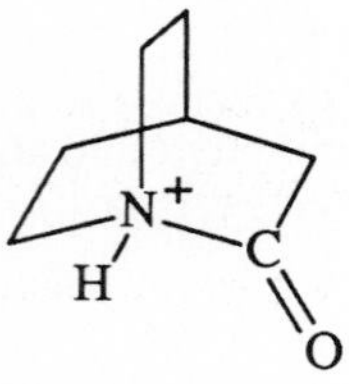

The pK_a of this species is that of an amine with an adjacent electron-withdrawing group. In other words, it is about like that of aniline. Why does this amide hydrolyze so readily? Recall (Sec. 21.7F) that the resonance in neutral amides is one reason that they hydrolyze so slowly. Since amide resonance is absent in this carboxylic acid derivative, it reacts more like an acid chloride!

Chapter 24 / Chemistry of Naphthalene and the Aromatic Heterocycles

CHAPTER 24 TERMS

bridgehead carbon 24.1B
Chichibabin reaction 24.5B
Fischer indole synthesis 24.4B
heteroatom .... Introduction
heterocyclic compound .... Introduction
Hückel $4n + 2$ rule 24.2B, 15.6D
naphthyl group 24.1B

peri interaction 24.1C
phenylhydrazone 24.4B, 19.11A
polycyclic aromatic hydrocarbon .... Introduction
pyridinium salts 24.5C
Reissert synthesis 24.4B
resonance energy 24.2B, 15.7C
Skraup synthesis 24.5E

CHAPTER 24 CONCEPTS

I. Introduction to Polycyclic Aromatic Hydrocarbons:

    A. <u>General</u>:
        1. **Polycyclic aromatic hydrocarbons** are hydrocarbons with more than one aromatic ring.
            a) Polycyclic aromatic hydrocarbons generally consist of planar six-membered rings with formal alternating single and double bonds.
            b) Naphthalene is the simplest example; others are shown in Figure 24.3, text page 1045.
        2. Naphthalene can be represented by three resonance structures, two of which are equivalent.

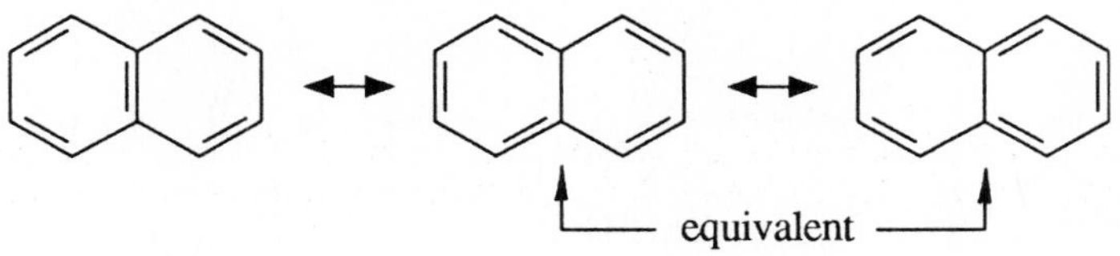

    B. <u>Nomenclature of Naphthalene Derivatives</u>:
        1. In systematic nomenclature, carbon-1 of naphthalene is the carbon adjacent to the **bridgehead carbon** (a vertex at which the rings are fused); substituents are given the lowest numbers consistent with this scheme and their relative priorities.
        2. Naphthalene also has a common nomenclature that uses Greek letters—the 1-position is designated as α and the 2-position as β.
        3. Common and systematic nomenclature should *never* be mixed.

4. As a substitutent, the naphthalene ring is called the **naphthyl group**.

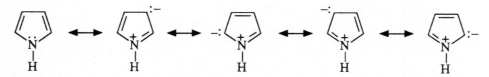

β-chloronaphthalene   1-bromo-8-nitronaphthalene   2-naphthyl benzoate

II. Introduction to the Aromatic Heterocycles:

A. General:
   1. **Heterocyclic compounds** are compounds with rings that contain more than one type of atom; the heterocyclic compounds of greatest interest to organic chemists have carbon rings containing one or two **heteroatoms** (atoms other than carbon).
   2. The chemistry of many *saturated* heterocyclic compounds is analogous to that of their open-chain counterparts.
   3. A significant number of *unsaturated* heterocyclic compounds exhibit aromatic behavior.

B. Nomenclature of the Heterocycles:
   1. The names and structures of some of the common aromatic heterocyclic compounds are given in Figure 24.1, text page 1044.
   2. The same rules used in numbering and naming saturated heterocyclic compounds are used for numbering and naming aromatic heterocyclic compounds.
      a) In all but a few cases, a heteroatom is given the number 1 (isoquinoline is an exception).
      b) Oxygen and sulfur are given a lower number than nitrogen when a choice exists.
      c) Substituent groups are given the lowest number consistent with this scheme.

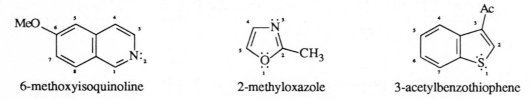

6-methoxyisoquinoline   2-methyloxazole   3-acetylbenzothiophene

C. Structure and Aromaticity of the Heterocycles:
   1. The aromatic heterocyclic compounds furan, thiophene, and pyrrole can be written as resonance hybrids.

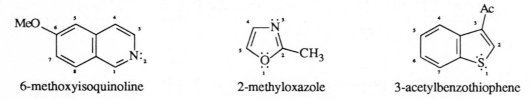

   a) The importance of the charge-separated structures is evident in comparing the dipole moments of furan and tetrahydrofuran.
      (1) Electrons in the σ-bonds are pulled toward the oxygen because of its electronegativity.
      (2) The resonance delocalization of the oxygen unshared electrons into the ring tends to push electrons away from the oxygen into the π-electron system of the ring.
   b) These two effects nearly cancel in furan; thus furan has a very small dipole moment.
   2. Pyridine can be represented by two equivalent neutral resonance structures; three additional structures, although involving separation of charge, have some importance because they reflect the relative electronegativity of nitrogen.

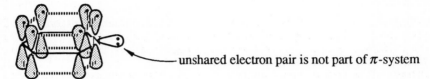

minor contributors

3. Heteroatoms involved in formal double bonds (such as the nitrogen of pyridine) contribute one
π-electron to the six π-electron aromatic system; the orbital containing the unshared electron pair of
the pyridine nitrogen is perpendicular to the *p* orbitals of the ring and is therefore not involved in π-
bonding.

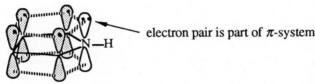

4. An unshared electron pair of a heteroatom in a formally allylic position (such as the unshared pair on
the nitrogen of pyrrole) is part of the aromatic π-system; the hydrogen of pyrrole lies in the plane of
the ring.

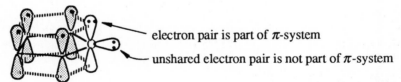

5. The oxygen of furan contributes one unshared electron pair to the aromatic π-electron system; the other
unshared electron pair occupies a position analogous to that of the hydrogen of pyrrole (in the ring
plane, perpendicular to the *p* orbitals of the ring).

electron pair is part of π-system

unshared electron pair is not part of π-system

III. Basicity and Acidity of the Nitrogen Heterocycles

A. Basicity:
1. Pyridine and quinoline act as ordinary aromatic amine bases; they are less basic than aliphatic tertiary
amines because of the sp^2 hybridization of their nitrogen unshared electron pairs.
   a) Protonation of the pyridine unshared electron pair occurs because this electron pair is *not* part of
   the π-electron system.
   b) Protonation of this electron pair does not destroy aromaticity.
2. Pyrrole and indole are not basic.
   a) These compounds are protonated only in strong acid, and protonation occurs on carbon, *not*
   nitrogen. Although protonation of the carbon of pyrrole disrupts the aromatic π-electron
   system, the resulting cation is resonance-stabilized.
   b) Protonation of the pyrrole nitrogen disrupts the aromatic six π-electron system by taking the
   nitrogen's unshared pair out of circulation; furthermore, the positive charge in nitrogen-
   protonated pyrrole cannot be delocalized by resonance.
3. Imidazole is basic and is protonated to give a conjugate acid.
   a) Imidazole has two nitrogens:
      (1) One has the electronic configuration of pyridine.
      (2) The other has the electron configuration of pyrrole.

b) Protonation of imidazole occurs on the pyridine-like nitrogen—the one whose electron pair is not part of the aromatic sextet.

c) Once imidazole is protonated, its two nitrogens both share the positive charge because of the resonance structures of the protonated form.

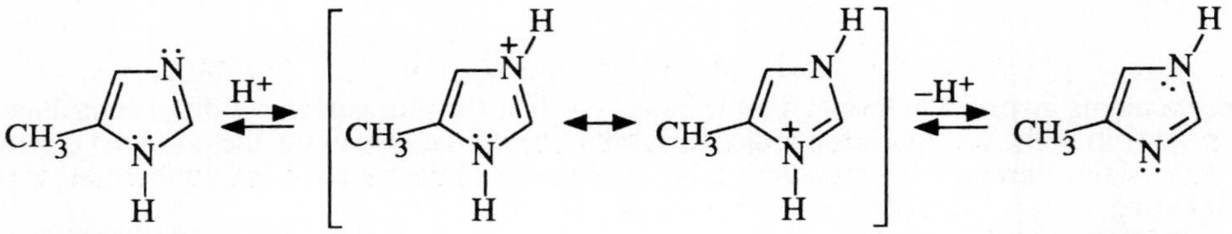

5-methylimidazole   4-methylimidazole

d) Because the protonated form is resonance-stabilized, imidazole is more basic than pyridine.

B. Acidity:

1. Pyrrole and indole are weak acids.

a) The N—H protons of pyrrole and indole are about as acidic as alcohol O—H protons.

b) Pyrrole and indole behave as acids toward basic organometallic compounds.

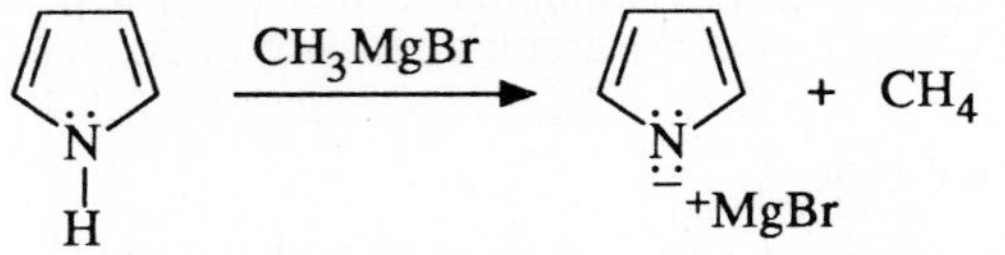

2. The greater acidity of these compounds, relative to the acidity of amines, is a consequence of the resonance stabilization of the conjugate-base anions.

CHAPTER 24 REACTIONS

I. Electrophilic Aromatic Substitution Reactions of Naphthalene and Its Derivatives:

A. Electrophilic Aromatic Substitution Reactions of Naphthalene:
  1. Naphthalene is an aromatic compound that undergoes electrophilic aromatic substitutions (much like those of benzene), generally at the 1-position.
  a) Seven resonance structures for the carbocation intermediate in electrophilic aromatic substitution at the 1-position are possible.

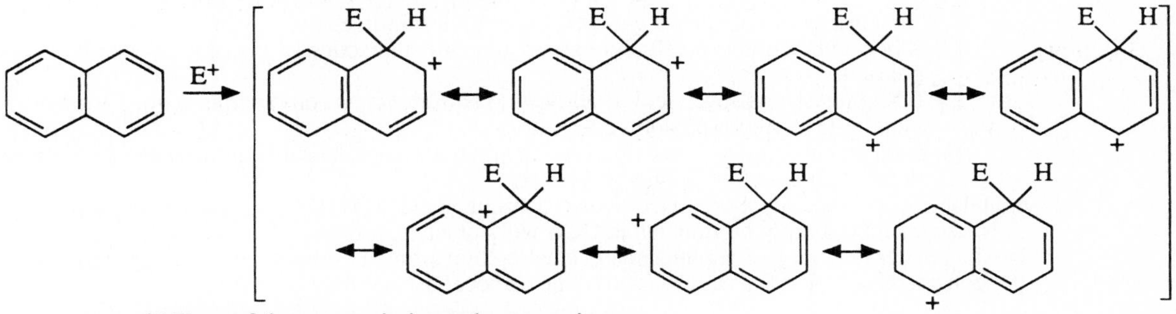

  b) Four of these contain intact benzene rings.
   (1) Structures in which benzene rings are left intact are more important than those in which the formal double bonds are moved out of the ring.
   (2) Structures lacking the intact benzene rings are formally not aromatic, and are thus less stable.
  c) Six resonance structures for the carbocation intermediate in electrophilic aromatic substitution at the 2-position are possible—only two contain intact benzene rings.

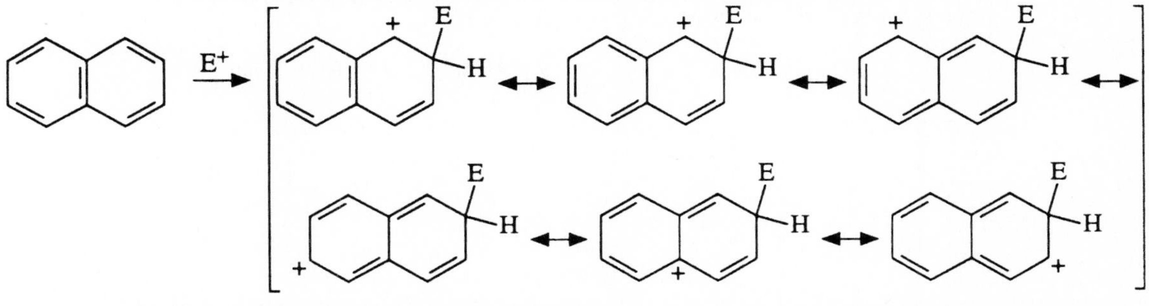

  d) There is nothing wrong with the 2-substitution; 1-substitution is simply more favorable.
  2. As with benzene, sulfonation of naphthalene is a reversible reaction.
  a) Sulfonation of naphthalene under mild conditions gives mostly 1-naphthalenesulfonic acid; under vigorous conditions, sulfonation yields mostly 2-naphthalenesulfonic acid.

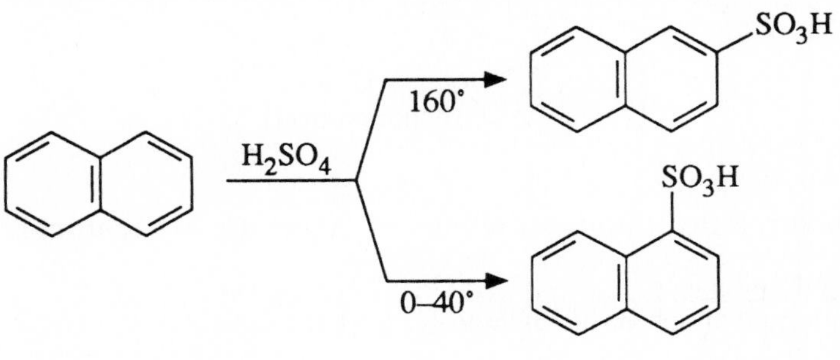

b) This is a case of kinetic *vs.* thermodynamic control of a reaction.
  (1) At low temperature, substitution at the 1-position is observed because it is faster.
  (2) At higher temperature, formation of 1-naphthalenesulfonic acid is reversible, and 2-naphthalenesulfonic acid is the more stable product.
c) In the 1-position, the large sulfonic acid group interacts unfavorably with the adjacent hydrogen of the 8-position.

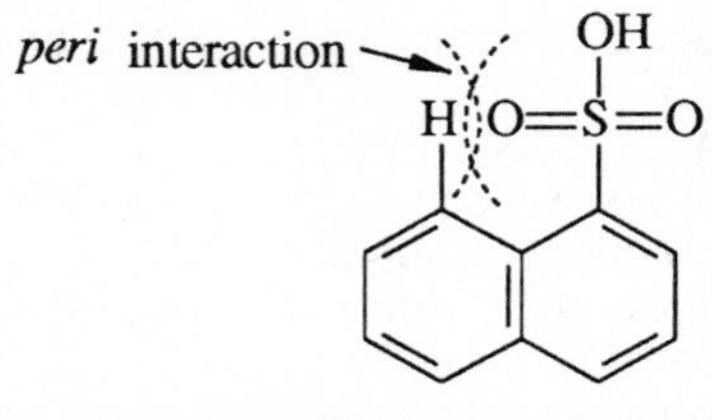

peri interaction

  (1) This interaction, called a ***peri* interaction**, destabilizes the 1-isomer.
  (2) A *peri* interaction is much more severe than the interaction of the same two groups in *ortho* positions.
  (3) 1-Naphthalenesulfonic acid, if allowed to equilibrate, is converted into the 2-isomer to avoid this unfavorable steric interaction.
  (4) Such an equilibrium is not observed in other electrophilic substitution reactions because these other reactions are not reversible.
3. Naphthalene is considerably more reactive than benzene in electrophilic aromatic substitution.
  a) Naphthalene is readily brominated in CCl₄ without a catalyst.
  b) The greater reactivity of naphthalene in electrophilic aromatic substitution reactions reflects the considerable resonance stabilization of the carbocation intermediate.

B. Electrophilic Aromatic Substitution Reactions of Substituted Naphthalenes:
  1. The position of a second substitution on a monosubstituted naphthalene depends on the substituent present.
  2. The following trends are observed in most cases:
    a) When one ring of naphthalene is substituted with deactivating groups, further substitution occurs in the *unsubstituted* ring at an open α-position (if available).
    b) When one ring of naphthalene is substituted with activating groups, further substitution occurs in the substituted ring at the *ortho* or *para* positions.

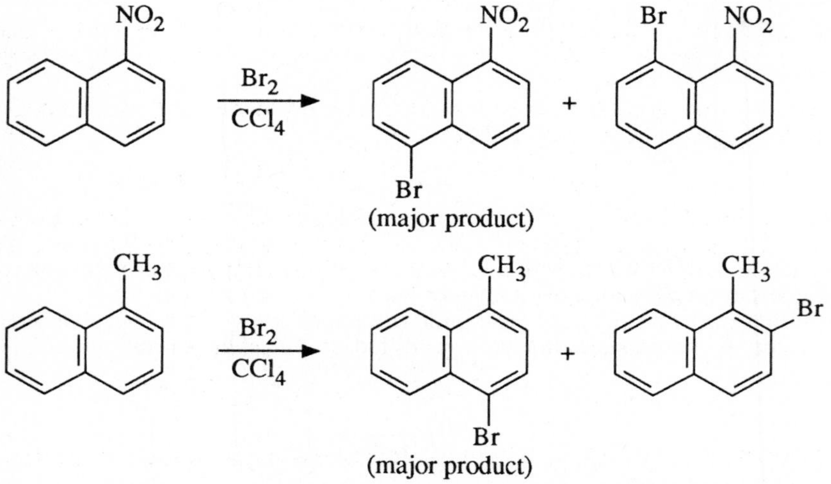

II. Electrophilic Aromatic Substitution Reactions of Aromatic Heterocyclic Compounds:

A. Furan, Pyrrole, and Thiophene:
  1. Furan, pyrrole, and thiophene all undergo electrophilic substitution predominantly in the 2-position of the ring.

a) The carbocation resulting from attack of the electrophile at carbon-2 has more important resonance structures, and is therefore more stable, than the carbocation resulting from attack at carbon-3.

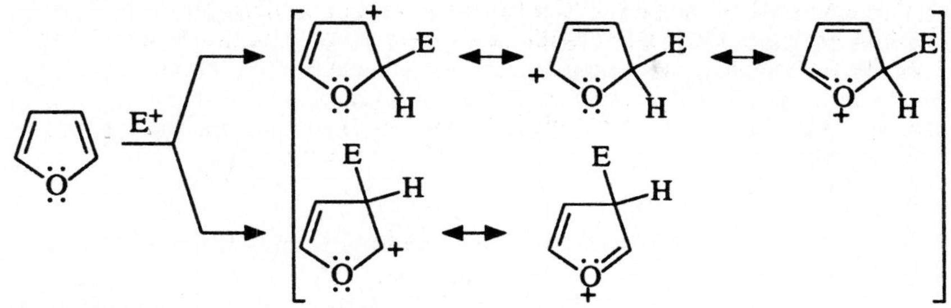

b) There is nothing wrong with reaction at carbon-3; reaction at carbon-2 is simply more favorable.
c) Some carbon-3 substitution product accompanies the major carbon-2 substitution product in many cases.
d) If both carbon-2 and carbon-5 are substituted, substitution at carbon-3 occurs.

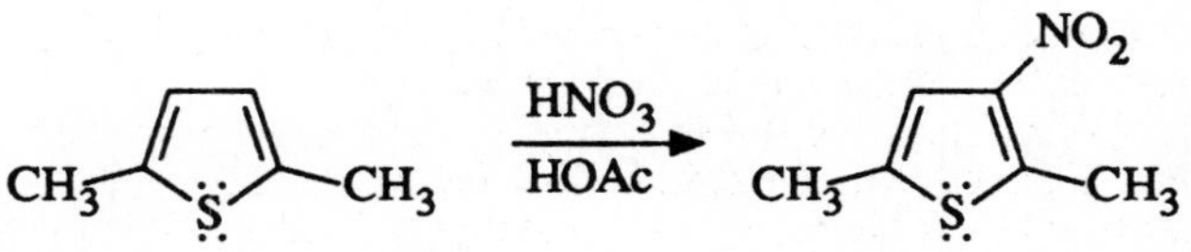

2. Furan, pyrrole, and thiophene are all much more reactive than benzene in electrophilic aromatic substitution reactions.
   a) Precise reactivity ratios depend on the particular reaction.
   b) Milder reaction conditions must be used with more reactive compounds.
   c) The reactivity order of the heterocycles is a consequence of the relative stabilities of the heteroatoms to stabilize positive charge in the intermediate carbocations.

$$pyrrole \, > \, furan \, > \, thiophene \, \gg \, benzene$$

   (1) Both pyrrole and furan have heteroatoms from the first row of the periodic table.
   (2) Because nitrogen is better than oxygen at delocalizing positive charge (it is less electronegative), pyrrole is more reactive than furan.
   (3) The sulfur of thiophene is a second row element; although it is less electronegative than oxygen, its $3p$ orbitals overlap less efficiently with the $2p$ orbitals of the aromatic π-electron system.
3. The reactivity order of the heterocycles in aromatic substitution parallels the reactivity order of the corresponding substituted benzene derivatives:

$$(CH_3)_2N—Ph \, > \, CH_3O—Ph \, > \, CH_3S—Ph$$

4. The usual activating and directing effects of substituents in aromatic substitution apply; superimposed on these effects is the normal effect of the heterocyclic atom in directing substitution to the 2-position.
   a) Count around the carbon framework of the heteroatom compound, not through the heteroatom, when using the *ortho*, *meta*, *para* analogy.

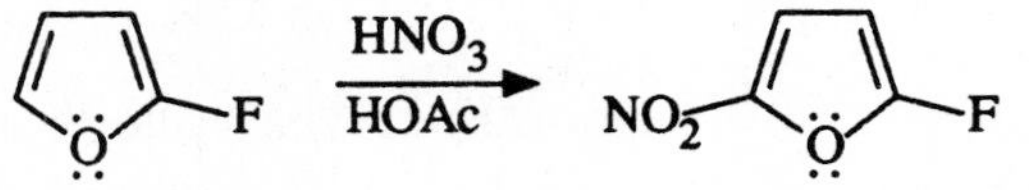

   b) When the directing effects of substituents and the ring compete, it is not unusual to observe mixtures of products.
   c) If both 2-positions are occupied, 3-substitution takes place.

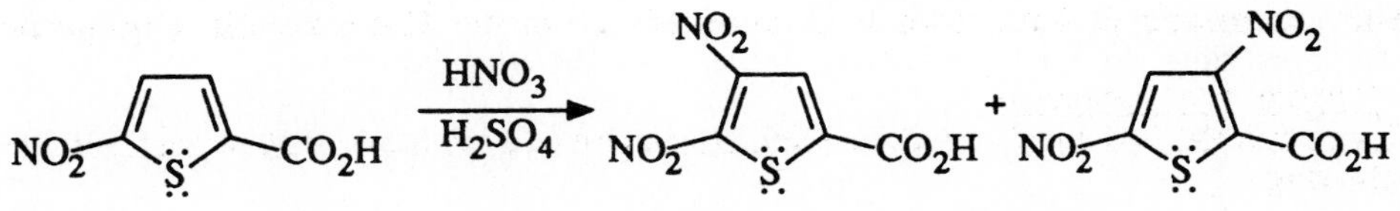

B. Indole, Benzofuran, and Benzothiophene:
   1. Substitution occurs on the heterocyclic ring rather than on the benzene ring of benzofuran, benzothiophene, and indole.
   2. The relative reactivity of the 2- and 3-positions is more closely balanced in indole, benzofuran, and benzothiophene than it is in pyrrole, furan, or thiophene.
      a) Benzothiophene and indole show predominant substitution in the 3-position.
      b) Benzofuran substitutes predominately at the 2-position.
   3. Benzofuran, benzothiophene, and indole are less reactive than furan, thiophene, or pyrrole, respectively, but more reactive than benzene.

C. Pyridine:
   1. In general, pyridine has very low reactivity in electrophilic aromatic substitutions; it is much less reactive than benzene.
      a) Consider the ring nitrogen of pyridine as if it were a nitro group attached to a benzene ring.
      b) When substitution in pyridine does occur, it takes place at the 3-position, and the yields are in some cases poor.
      c) The preference for 3-substitution in pyridines can be understood by considering the resonance structures for the possible carbocation intermediates.
         (1) Substitution in the 3-position gives a carbocation with three resonance structures.

         (2) Substitution at the 2-position also involves an intermediate with three resonance structures, but one is particularly unfavorable because the nitrogen is not only positively charged, but also electron deficient (without an electronic octet).

         (3) The electronegative nitrogen destabilizes the positive charge in the structures.
      d) Most methods of electrophilic aromatic substitution involve highly acidic conditions.
         (1) An acid can coordinate with the unshared electron pair of pyridine to give a positively charged nitrogen.
         (2) Introducing a further positive charge into the ring by electrophilic substitution is then especially difficult.
   2. Pyridine-N-oxide is much more reactive than pyridine and undergoes useful aromatic substitution reactions; substitution occurs in the 4-position.
      a) Pyridine-N-oxide is formed by oxidation of pyridine with 30% hydrogen peroxide.

      b) The N-oxide function can be removed by catalytic hydrogenation, which will also reduce any nitro groups present.
      c) Reaction with trivalent phosphorous compounds removes the N-oxide function without reducing nitro groups.

D. Quinoline:
   1. The pyridine ring of quinoline is deactivated; as with naphthalene, substitution occurs in the more activated ring—in this case, the benzene ring—at the α-positions.

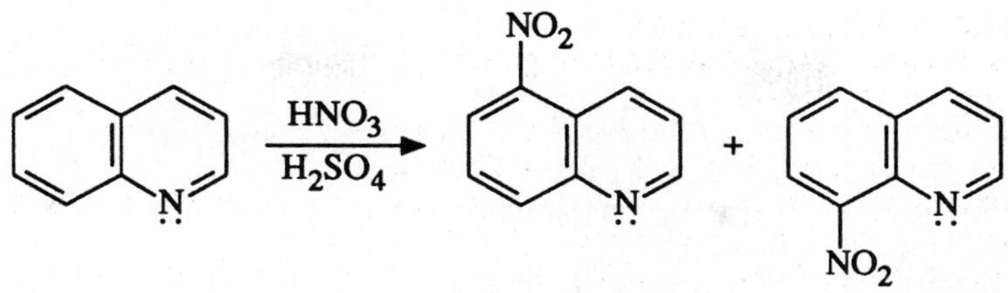

a) Because two nonequivalent α-positions are available, a mixture of compounds is obtained.
b) Because most electrophilic substitution reactions of quinoline give mixtures, substituted quinolines are generally synthesized from acyclic compounds.
2. Quinoline-*N*-oxide undergoes reactions similar to pyridine-*N*-oxide.

III. Nucleophilic Aromatic Substitution Reactions of Aromatic Heterocyclic Compounds:

A. Pyridine:
   1. The reaction of a pyridine derivative with the strong base (nucleophile) sodium amide ($Na^+\ ^-NH_2$) brings about a nucleophilic substitution of an amino group for a ring hydrogen; this reaction is called the **Chichibabin reaction**.

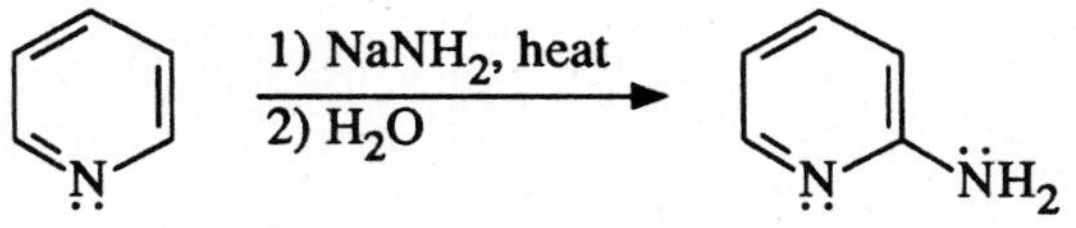

   a) In the first step of the mechanism, the amide ion attacks the 2-position of the ring to form a tetrahedral addition intermediate.
      (1) The C=N linkage of the pyridine ring is somewhat analogous to the C=O of a carbonyl group.
      (2) Carbon at the 2-position has some of the character of a carbonyl carbon and can be attacked by nucleophiles.
      (3) The C=N group of pyridine is much less reactive than a carbonyl group because it is part of an aromatic system.
   b) In the second step of the mechanism, the leaving group, a hydride ion, is lost.
      (1) Hydride ion is a very poor leaving group because it is very basic.
      (2) There are two reasons why this reaction is driven to completion.
         (*a*) The aromatic pyridine ring is re-formed; aromaticity that was lost in the formation of the tetrahedral addition intermediate is regained when the leaving group departs.
         (*b*) The basic sodium hydride produced in the reaction reacts with the —NH₂ group irreversibly to form hydrogen gas and the resonance-stabilized conjugate-base anion of 2-aminopyridine.
      (3) The neutral 2-aminopyridine is formed when water is added in a separate step.

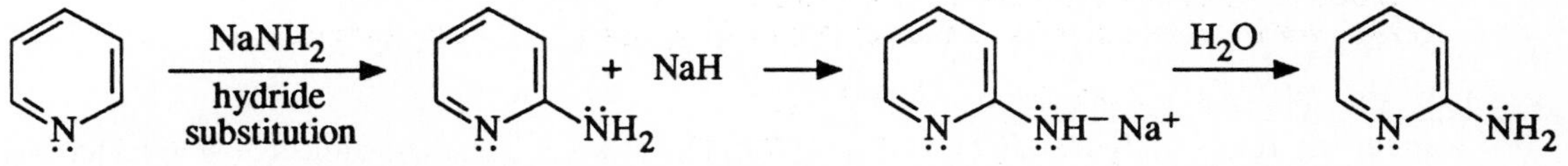

   c) A reaction similar to the Chichibabin reaction occurs with organolithium reagents.

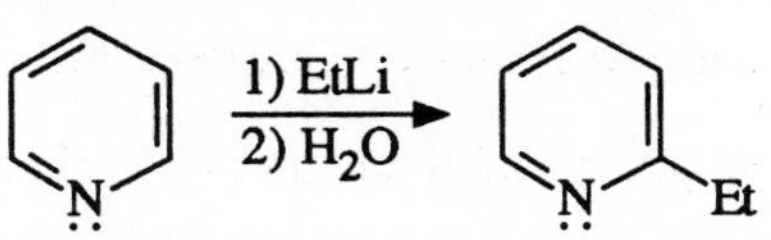

   2. When pyridine is substituted with a better leaving group than hydride at the 2-position or 4-position, it reacts more rapidly with nucleophiles; thus, the 2-halopyridines and 4-halopyridines readily undergo substitution of the halogen by other nucleophiles under conditions milder than those used in the Chichibabin reaction.

3. Nucleophilic substitution reactions on pyridine rings are not S_N2 reactions, because aryl halides cannot undergo S_N2 reactions; these reactions are analogous to nucleophilic aromatic substitution reactions.
   a) The electron-withdrawing group in the reaction of pyridines is the pyridine nitrogen itself; consider the ring nitrogen of pyridine as if it were a nitro group attached to a benzene ring.
   b) The tetrahedral addition intermediate is analogous to the Meisenheimer complex of nucleophilic aromatic substitution.
   c) Negative charge in the addition intermediate is delocalized onto the electronegative pyridine nitrogen.
4. The 2-aminopyridines formed in the Chichibabin reaction serve as starting materials for a variety of other 2-substituted pyridines.
5. 3-Substituted pyridines are *not* reactive in nucleophilic substitution because negative charge in the addition intermediate *cannot* be delocalized onto the electronegative nitrogen.
6. Although 2-pyridone exists largely in the carbonyl form, it nevertheless undergoes some reactions reminiscent of hydroxy compounds.

B. Pyridinium Salts and Their Reactions:
   1. Pyridine is a nucleophile and reacts in S_N2 reactions with alkyl halides or sulfonate esters to form quaternary ammonium salts, called **pyridinium salts**.

   2. Pyridinium salts are activated toward nucleophilic displacement of groups at the 2- and 4-positions of the ring much more than pyridines themselves, because the positively charged nitrogen is much more electronegative than the neutral nitrogen of a pyridine.
      a) When the nucleophiles in such displacement reactions are anions, charge is neutralized.
      b) Pyridine-*N*-oxides are formally pyridinium ions, and they react with nucleophiles in much the same way as quaternary pyridinium salts.

IV. Other Reactions of Heterocyclic Aromatic Compounds:

A. Addition Reactions to Furan:
   1. Furan, pyrrole, or thiophene can be viewed formally as a 1,3-butadiene molecule with its terminal carbons tied down by a heteroatom bridge.

formal butadiene unit

   2. Of the three heterocyclic compounds furan, pyrrole, and thiophene, furan has the least resonance energy.
      a) Furan has the greatest tendency to behave like a conjugated diene.
      b) Furan undergoes some 1,4-addition reactions, such as Diels–Alder reactions with reactive dienophiles.

B. Side-Chain Reactions of Furan, Pyrrole, and Thiophene:
   1. Many reactions occur at the side chains of heterocyclic compounds without affecting the rings.
   2. Decarboxylation of carboxylic acid groups at the 2-position of heterocyclic rings is effected by strong heating (in some cases with a catalyst).

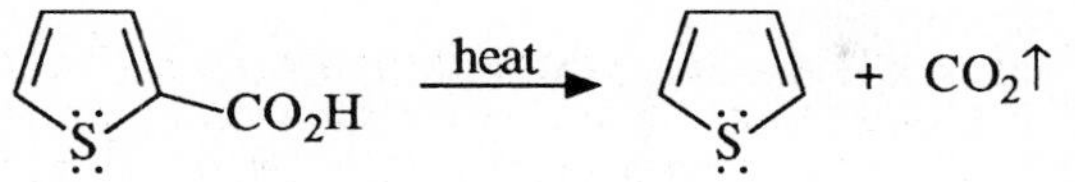

C. Side-Chain Reactions of Pyridine Derivatives:
   1. The benzylic protons of an alkyl group at the 2- or 4-position of a pyridine ring are especially acidic because the electron pair (and charge) in the conjugate-base anion is delocalized onto the electronegative pyridine nitrogen.
      a) Strongly basic reagents such as organolithium reagents or $NaNH_2$ abstract the benzylic proton from 2- or 4-alkylpyridines.

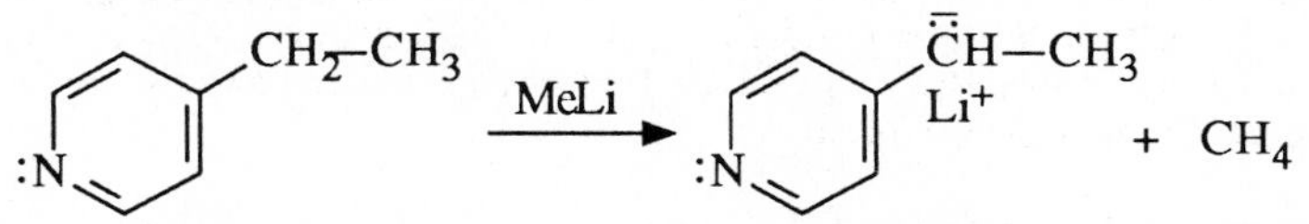

   b) The anion formed in this way has a reactivity much like that of other organolithium reagents.
   c) These anions undergo some of the reactions of enolate anions, such as aldol condensations.
   2. The benzylic protons of 2- or 4-alkylpyridinium salts are much more acidic than those of the analogous pyridines.
      a) One resonance form of the conjugate-base is a neutral compound.
      b) The conjugate base can be formed in useful concentrations by aqueous NaOH or amines.

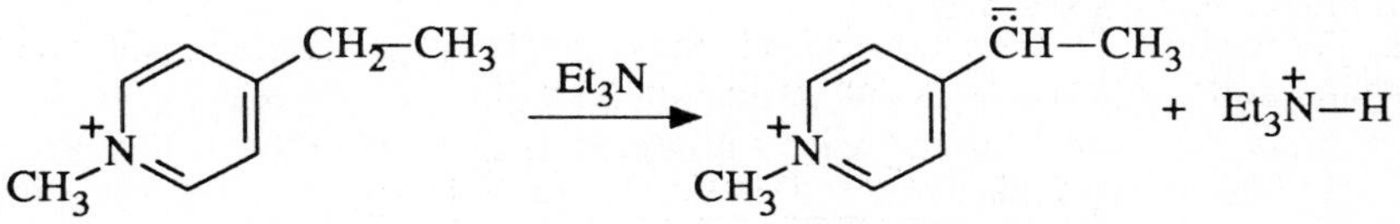

   3. Many side-chain reactions of pyridines are analogous to those of the corresponding benzene derivatives.

V. Synthesis of Indole and Quinoline from Acyclic Starting Materials:

A. Synthesis of Indoles—the Fischer and Reissert Syntheses:
   1. The **Fischer indole synthesis** occurs under acidic conditions; the key starting materials for this synthesis are a phenylhydrazine and an aldehyde or ketone with an α- —CH_2— group.

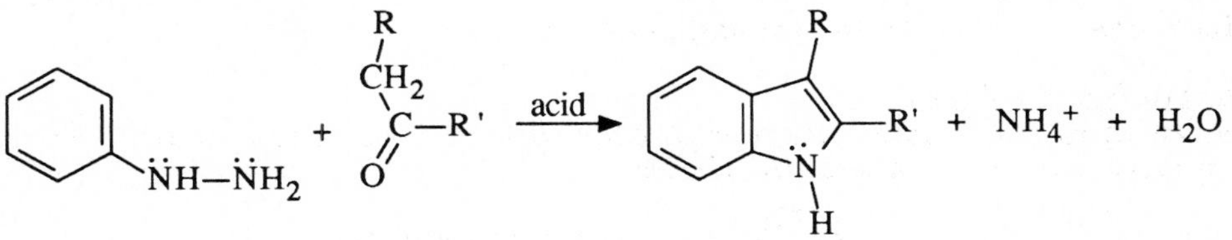

   a) A variety of Brønsted and Lewis acid catalysts can be used.
   b) The reaction works with many different substituted phenylhydrazines and carbonyl compounds.
   c) Acetaldehyde, however, does not work in this reaction, probably because it polymerizes under the reaction conditions.
   2. The mechanism of the Fischer indole synthesis begins with the conversion of the carbonyl compound into a phenylhydrazone, a type of imine.
      a) The phenylhydrazone, which is protonated under the reaction conditions, is in equilibrium with a small amount of its enamine tautomer, which is also protonated.

b) The latter species undergoes a cyclic shift of three electron pairs (six electrons) to give a new intermediate in which the N—H bond of the phenylhydrazone has been broken.
    (1) This step occurs by the cyclic flow of electrons—a pericyclic reaction.
    (2) The intermediate formed is an imine.
c) After protonation on the imine nitrogen, the imine undergoes nucleophilic addition with the amine group in the same molecule.
d) The resulting enamine derivative is the product indole.

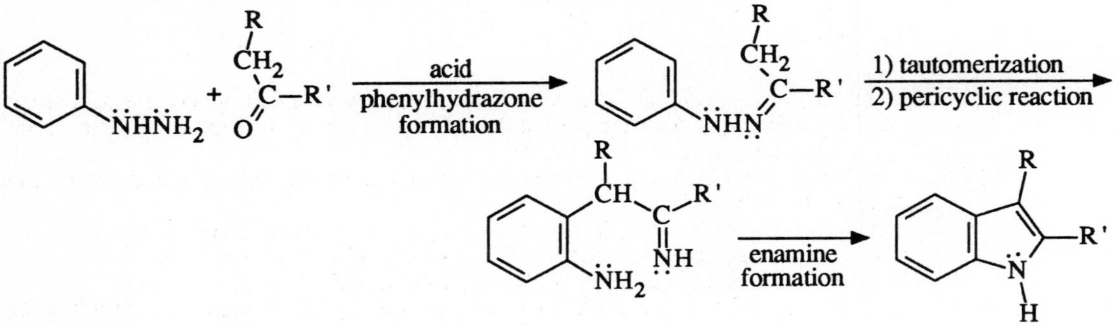

3. The **Reissert synthesis** occurs under basic conditions; the key starting materials for this synthesis are diethyl oxylate and *o*-nitrotoluene or a substituted derivative.

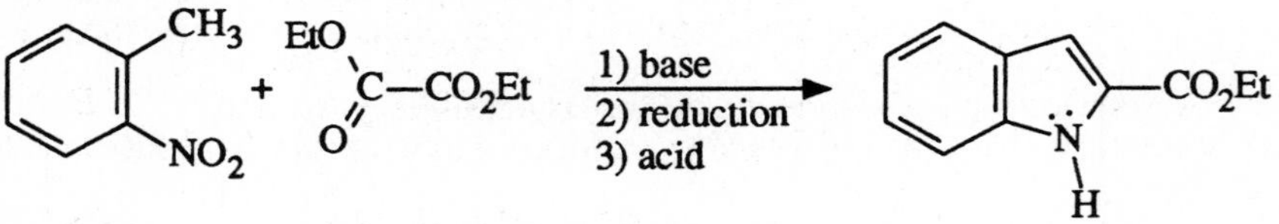

a) The *o*-nitro group is an essential element in the success of this reaction because it stabilizes by resonance the anion formed when a proton is removed from the methyl group.
    (1) This nucleophilic anion attacks a carbonyl group of diethyl oxylate, displacing ethanol; the reaction is a variation of the Claisen condensation.
    (2) Because this reaction is driven to completion by ionization of the product, at least one equivalent of the base must be used.
b) The anion is neutralized by protonation in acetic acid, and the nitro group is converted into an amino group in a separate reduction step.
c) The amino group thus formed reacts with neighboring ketone to yield, after acid–base equilibria, an enamine, which is the product indole.
d) Indole-2-carboxylic acid can be decarboxylated to prepare indole itself.

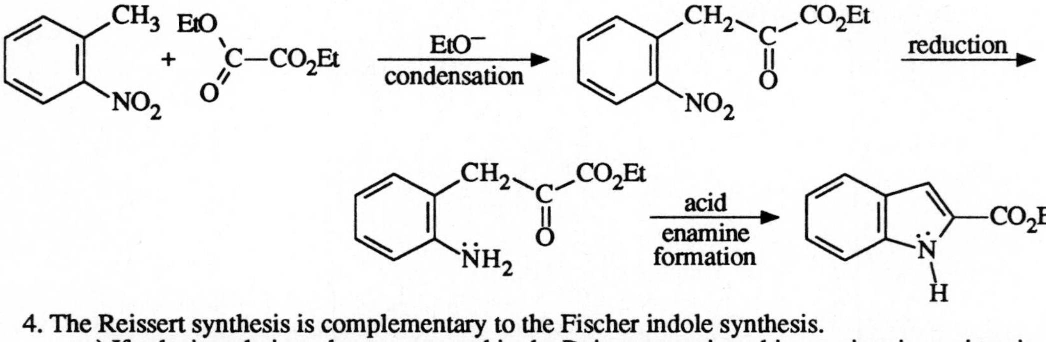

4. The Reissert synthesis is complementary to the Fischer indole synthesis.
    a) If substituted nitrotoluenes are used in the Reissert reaction, this reaction, in conjunction with the final decarboxylation step, can be used to prepare indoles that are substituted in the benzene ring and unsubstituted at the 2- or 3-positions.
    b) Although many substituted phenylhydrazines work in the Fischer synthesis, some are difficult to prepare; thus, the Fischer synthesis is most often used to prepare indoles that are substituted at the 2- or 3-positions.

B. <u>Synthesis of Quinolines</u>:
 1. The **Skraup synthesis** occurs under acid catalysis; the key starting materials for this reaction are glycerol and an aniline derivative.

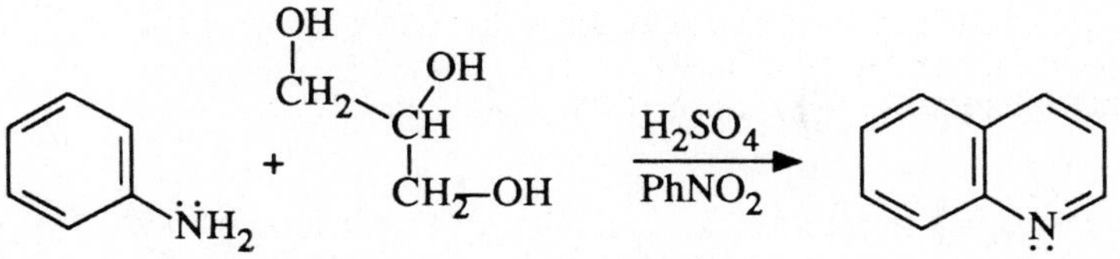

 a) Glycerol undergoes an acid-catalyzed dehydration to provide a small but continuously replenished amount of acrolein, an α,β-unsaturated aldehyde (if acrolein itself were used as a reactant at high concentrations, it would polymerize).
 b) Aniline undergoes a Michael-type conjugate addition with the acrolein and, under the influence of acid, the resulting aldehyde protonates.
 c) The protonated aldehyde has carbocation character, and its electron-deficient carbon serves as the electrophile in an intramolecular electrophilic aromatic substitution reaction.
 d) Dehydration of the resulting alcohol yields a 1,2-dihydroquinoline.
 e) The 1,2-dihydroquinoline product differs from quinoline by only one degree of unsaturation, and is readily oxidized to the aromatic quinoline by mild oxidants.

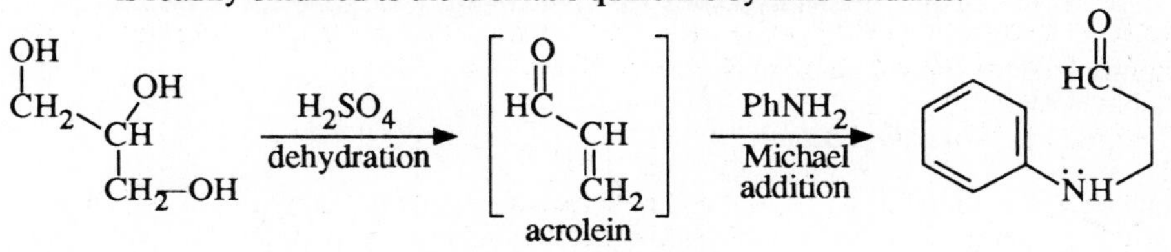

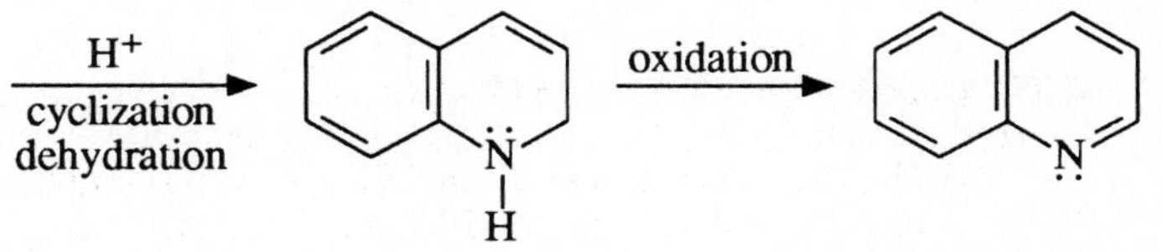

 2. α,β-Unsaturated aldehydes and ketones that are less prone to polymerize than acrolein can be used instead of glycerol in the Skraup synthesis to give substituted quinolines.

CHAPTER 24 SOLUTIONS

Solutions to In-Text Problems

1. In two-thirds of the resonance structures (Eq. 24.1), bond (b) is a double bond:

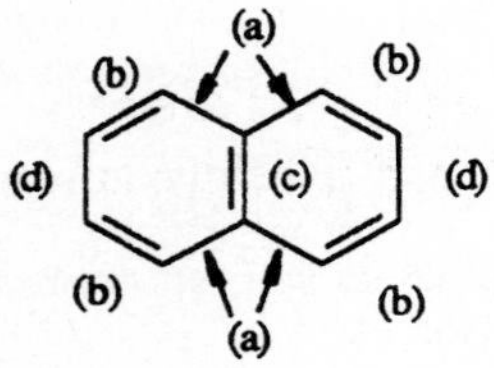

Since no other bond has so much double-bond character, and since double bonds are shorter than single bonds, then bond (b) is the shortest bond. (This hypothesis is confirmed by the data in Figure 24.2.)

2. (a) 2-bromonaphthalene, or β-bromonaphthalene
    (b) 1,8-naphthalenediol
    (c) 2-naphthyl acetate, or β-naphthyl acetate.

    ➤ Although "acetate" is a common name, IUPAC nomenclature allows the mixing of systematic and common nomenclature when the common name is preferred. (Virtually no one would name this compound by its fully systematic name, 2-naphthyl ethanoate, although such a name is certainly correct.)

    (d) 5,8-dinitro-2-naphthalenecarboxylic acid

3. (a)   (b)   (c)

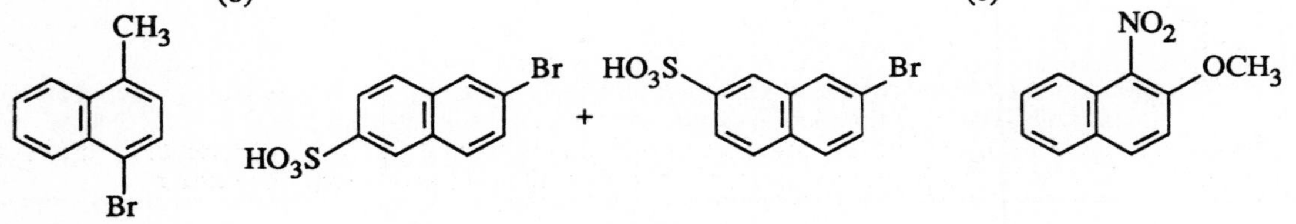

In (c), there might also be some nitration in the 3-position because of the steric crowding in the 1-position.

    (d)

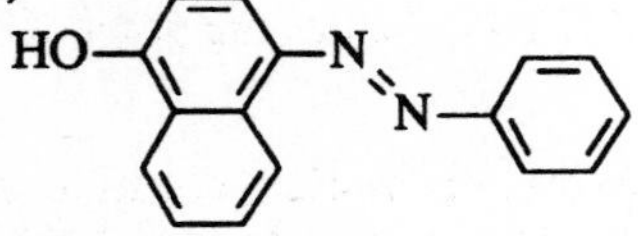

4.

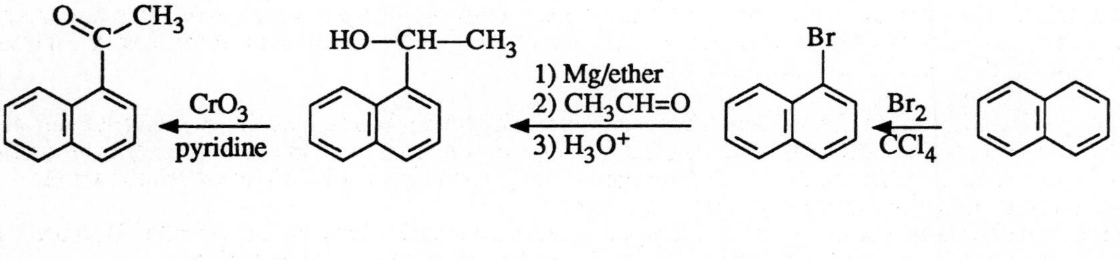

5. (a)   (b)

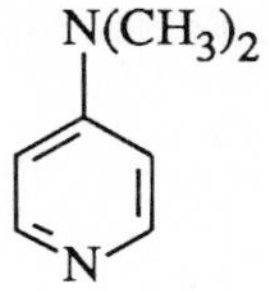

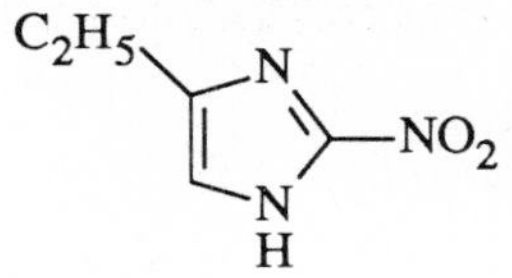

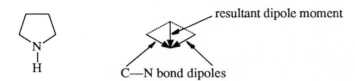

6. (a) 5-bromo-2-methylthiazole
    (b) 2-bromo-4-nitropyrrole
    (c) 8-methoxyquinoline

7. (a) Because nitrogen is an electronegative atom, the C—N bond dipoles in pyrrole are directed toward nitrogen; hence, pyrrole has an overall dipole moment vector that is directed toward the nitrogen:

The same effect of the C—N bonds exists in pyrrole. However, there is in addition a resonance interaction of the nitrogen unshared pair with the ring π-electron system that gives a dipole-moment contribution directed *away* from the nitrogen:

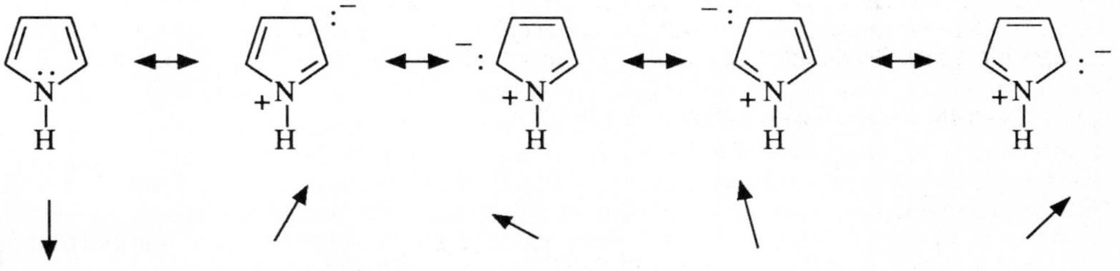

The contributions of the last four structures are sufficiently important that they outweigh the contribution of the first; hence, the overall dipole moment vector in pyrrole is directed away from the nitrogen.

(b) Furan has resonance structures exactly analogous to those for pyrrole above. (See Eq. 24.13.) The electronegativity of oxygen is such that the dipole-moment contribution of the first structure dominates. As a result, the dipole-moment vector of furan is oriented *toward* the oxygen. However, the various dipole vectors nearly cancel; the dipole moment of furan is only 0.7 D, whereas that of tetrahydrofuran is 1.7 D. The weak dipole moment of furan is reflected in its comparatively low boiling point of 31.4°; the boiling point of tetrahydrofuran, by comparison, is 67°.

8. Because pyrrole and pyridine are aromatic compounds, their ring hydrogens have downfield chemical shifts. Hence, the δ 2.82 chemical shift is that of the nonaromatic amine pyrrolidine; this shift is about like that for the α-hydrogens of a typical amine. The resonance structures for pyrrole (see solution to the previous problem) show that there is considerable negative charge delocalized to the 2-position of the ring. This is reflected in an upfield chemical shift of the 2-protons of pyrrole relative to that of the 2-protons of pyridine, whose resonance structures do not place negative charge at the 2-position. Hence, the chemical shift of the pyrrole 2-protons is δ 6.41; that of the pyridine 2-protons is δ 8.51.

9. (a) The pyridine nitrogen is basic. Since bases can accept hydrogen bonds, pyridine can accept hydrogen bonds from water. This hydrogen-bonding capacity helps to solubilize pyridine in water. Pyrrole, on the other hand, is not basic. In addition, the N—H hydrogen is not particularly acidic. Hence, pyrrole cannot hydrogen-bond, and it is therefore insoluble in water.
    (b) Imidazole has both a basic nitrogen, like pyridine, and a nonbasic nitrogen, like pyrrole. Because it is basic, it can accept hydrogen bonds; therefore, imidazole has substantial water solubility.

10. (a) There are two nitrogens on which protonation might occur. However, protonation on the ring nitrogen is observed because it gives a resonance-stabilized cation:

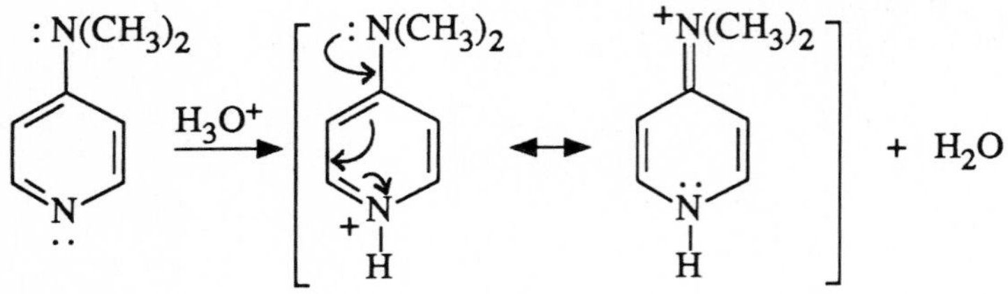

Protonation on the amine nitrogen, in contrast, gives a conjugate acid that is not resonance-stabilized.

(b) By analogy to the protonation results in part (a), we expect methyl iodide to react at the ring nitrogen, because a resonance-stabilized cation is formed:

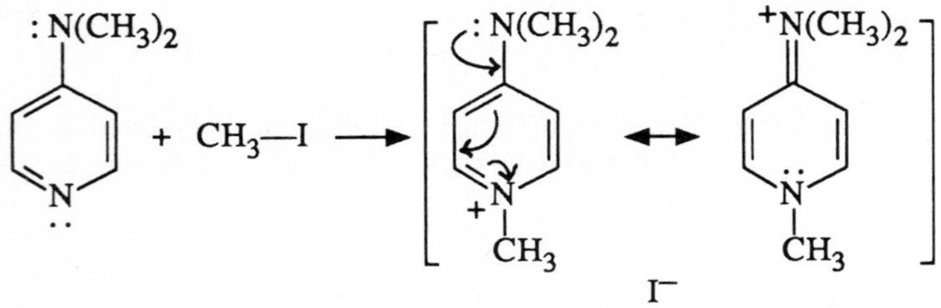

11. The unshared electron pair on the nitrogen of aniline is conjugated with the ring, as shown by the resonance structures in Eq. 23.3, text page 989. When aniline is protonated, the electron pair on nitrogen is bound to a proton and is no longer available for resonance interaction with the ring. The resulting loss of conjugation causes a shift to lower wavelength in its UV spectrum. (See the solution to Problem 54, Chapter 23, on page 601 of this manual for a further discussion of this effect.) The unshared electron pair on the nitrogen of pyridine is not part of the pyridine π-electron system. Hence, protonation of this electron pair does not affect the conjugation in pyridine, and therefore also does not affect the UV spectrum.

12. (a)   (b) 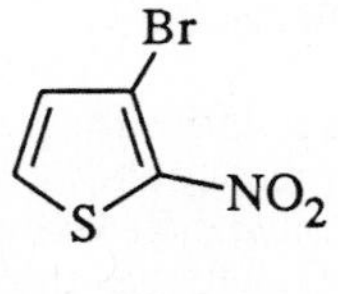   (c) 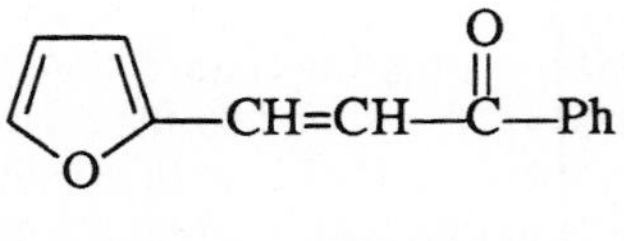   (d)

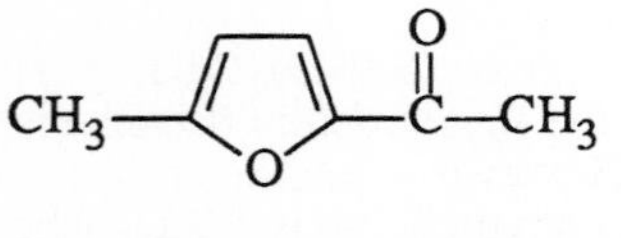

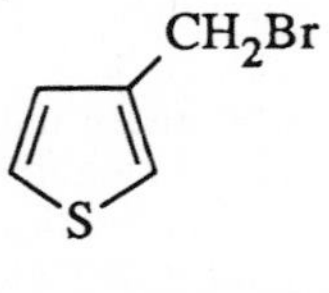

Reaction (a) is a Friedel–Crafts reaction with acetic anhydride as the acylating agent. In reaction (b), the nitro group goes to the 2-position because it satisfies the directing effects of both the sulfur and the bromine. Reaction (c) is a Claisen–Schmidt condensation, a variation of the aldol condensation (see text page 937). Reaction (d) is a free-radical bromination (see Sec. 17.2).

13. (a) The product is derived from a Diels–Alder reaction of furan with benzyne, which is generated from an organometallic intermediate by β-elimination:

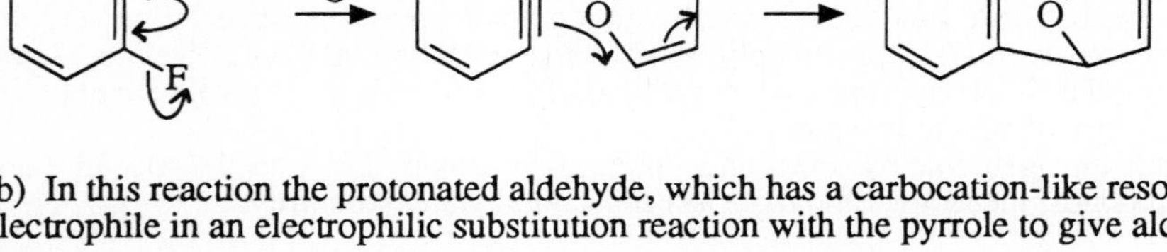

(b) In this reaction the protonated aldehyde, which has a carbocation-like resonance structure, acts as an electrophile in an electrophilic substitution reaction with the pyrrole to give alcohol *A*. The —OH group of *A* is protonated and lost as water to give a stable carbocation, which is the product of the reaction:

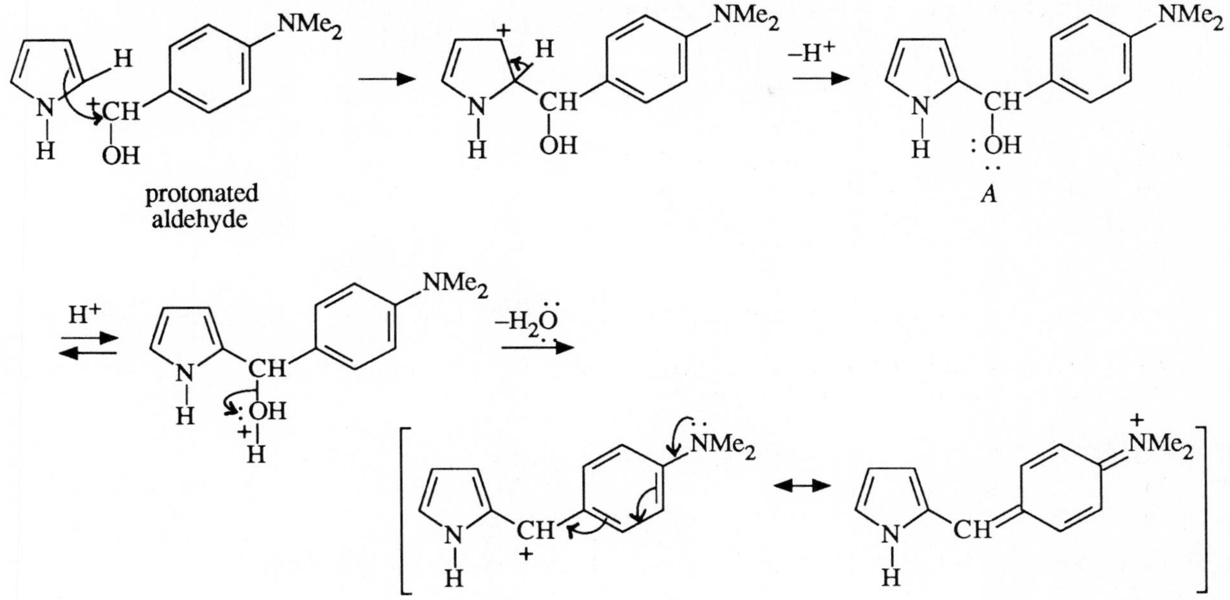

protonated
aldehyde

A

14. (a)   (b)   (c)

$$PhNHNH_2 \;+\; H\!-\!\overset{O}{\overset{\|}{C}}\!-\!CH_2CH(CH_3)_2 \qquad PhN\!-\!NH_2 \;+\; CH_3\!-\!\overset{O}{\overset{\|}{C}}\!-\!Ph \qquad PhNHNH_2 \;+\;$$

with CH_3 on the N of $PhN-NH_2$, and a cyclohexanone structure at right.

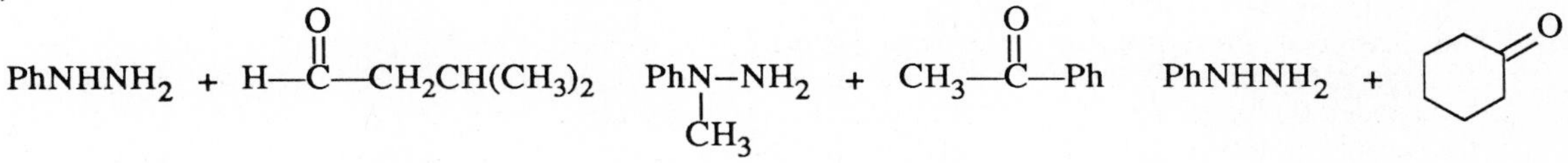

15. In the mechanistic step shown in Eq. 24.41b, a protonated enamine is involved. When 2-butanone is used as the ketone, there are two possible enamines which lead, respectively, to 2-ethylindole and 2,3-dimethylindole:

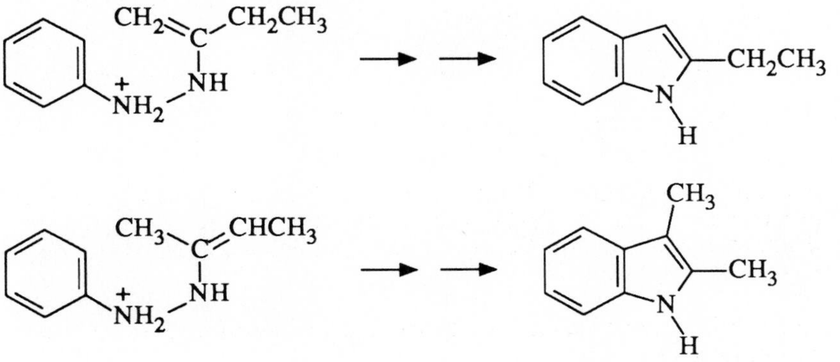

16. The following synthesis involves preparation of 4-bromo-2-methyl-1-nitrobenzene followed by a Reissert synthesis:

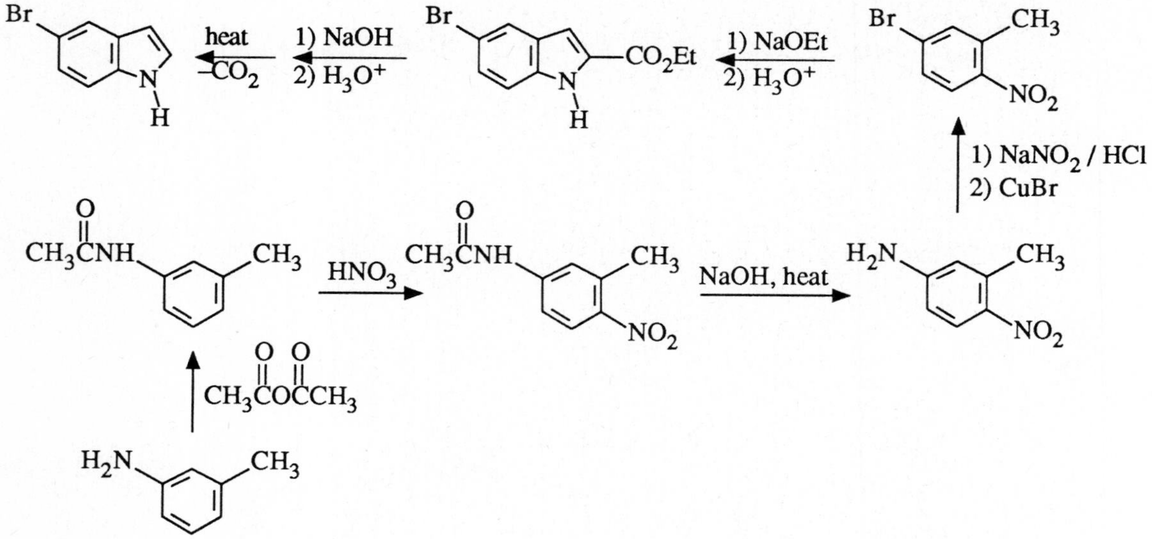

17. The carbocation intermediate for nitration of pyridine-*N*-oxide at carbon-4 is as follows:

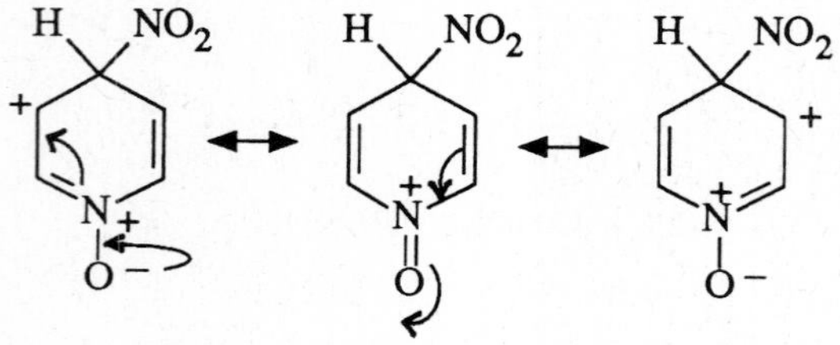

The second structure shows that the positive charge in the ring is stabilized by the *N*-oxide group. Nitration at the 3-position gives a carbocation with resonance structures in which the positive charge *cannot* be stabilized by the *N*-oxide group. (Draw these structures if you have not already done so.) Therefore, nitration occurs at the 4-position because 4-nitration gives the more stable intermediate.

18.

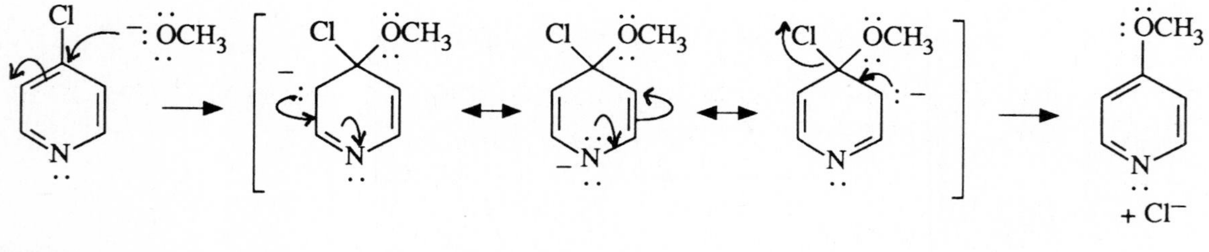

19. (a) 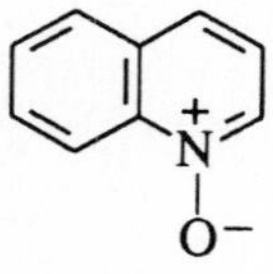   (b) 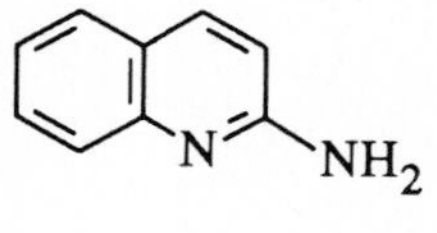   (c)

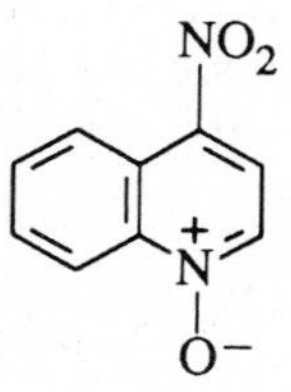

20. (a)

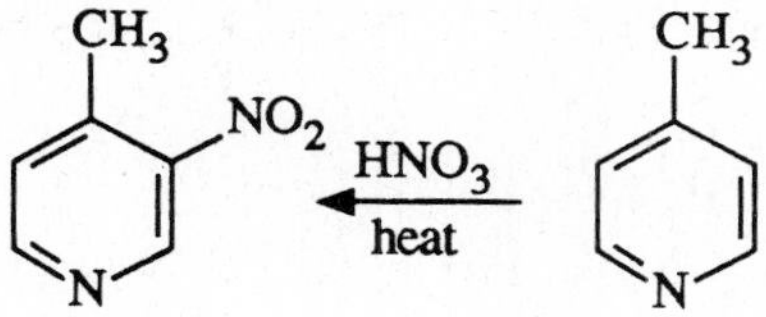

(b)

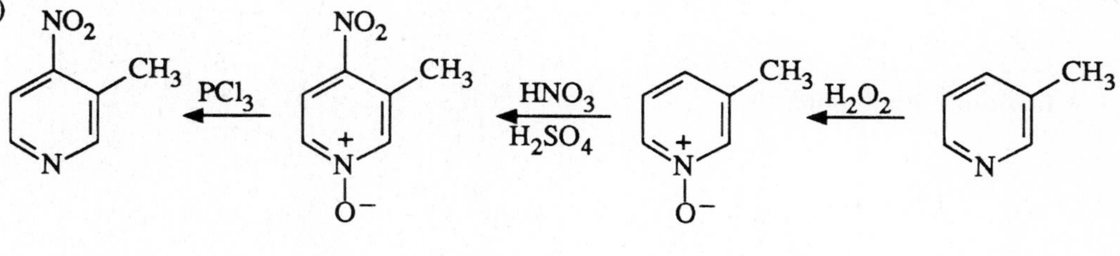

(c)

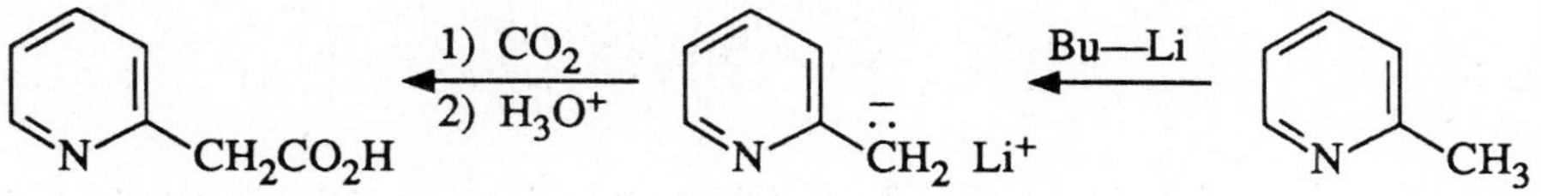

(d)

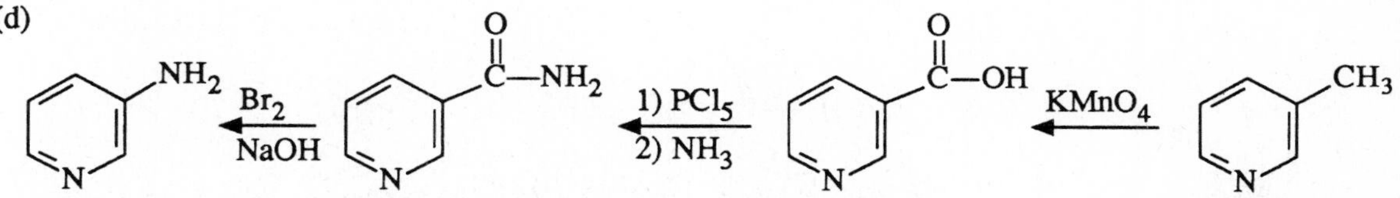

21. (a) From the formula of the product, one methyl group has been introduced. This comes from reaction of methyl iodide with the anion formed by proton removal from the 4-methyl group. The 4-methyl hydrogens are more acidic than the 3-methyl hydrogens (why?).

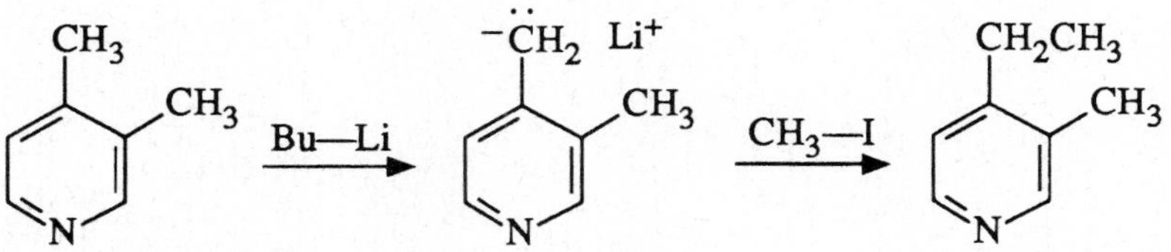

(b) The 4-bromo group is displaced in a nucleophilic aromatic substitution reaction. The 3-bromo group is inert (why?).

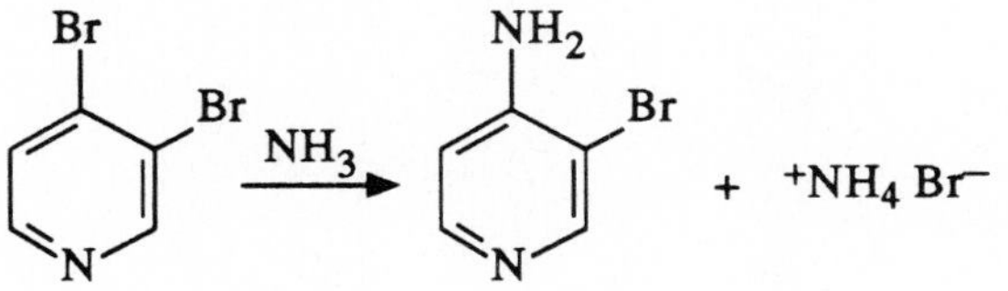

22. (a)   (b)

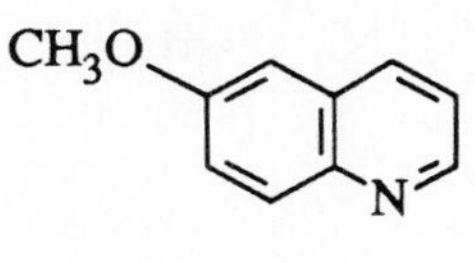

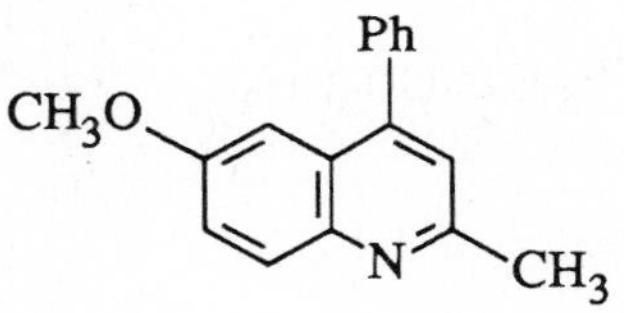

23. The reactants required are *p*-chloroaniline, 3-methyl-3-buten-2-one, and an oxidant:

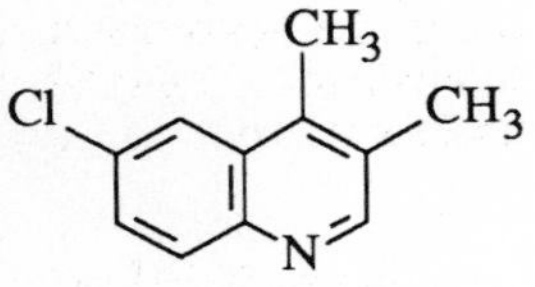
requires
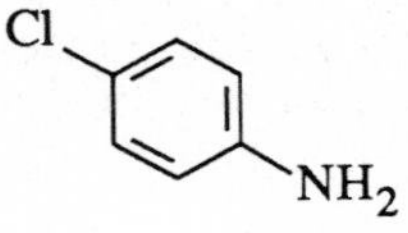
and
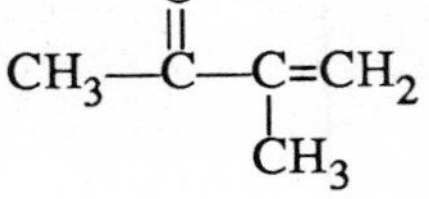

Solutions to Additional Problems

24. (a)

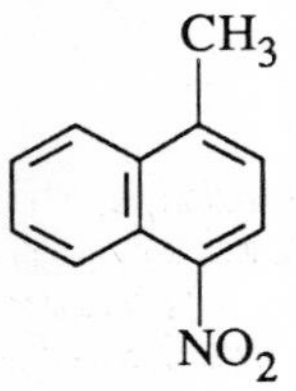

(b)

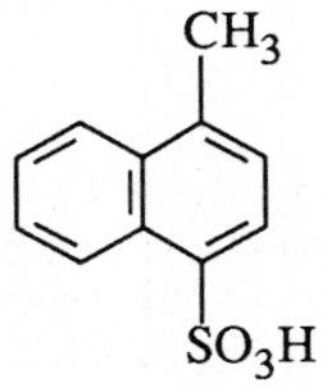

(c)

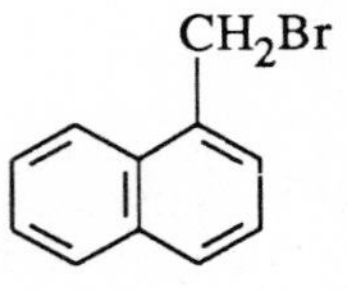

(d)

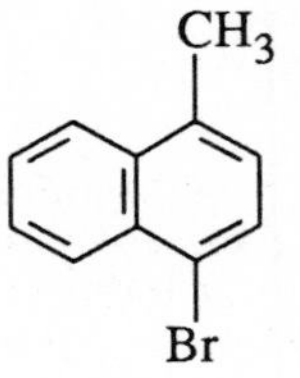

25. (a)

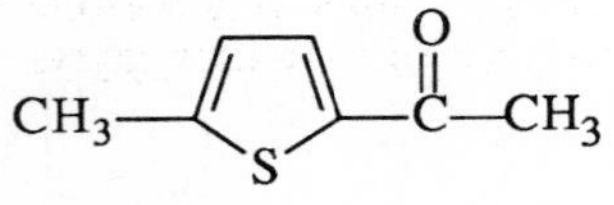

(b)

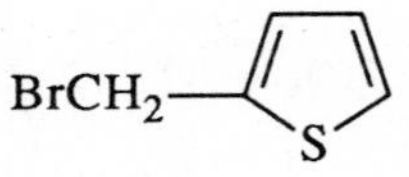

(c)

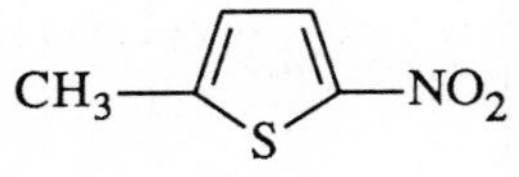

(d) no reaction

(e) no reaction

(f)

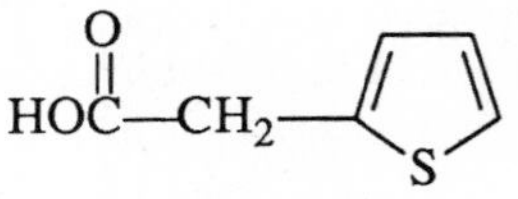

(g)

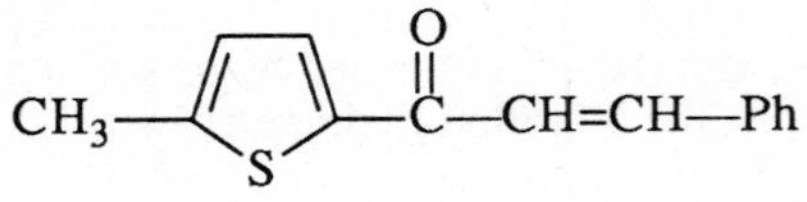

26. (a)

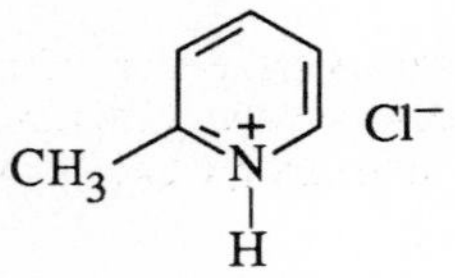

(b) no reaction

(c)

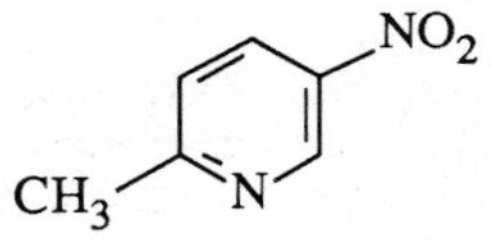

(d)

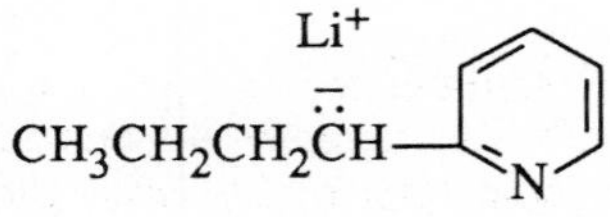

(e)

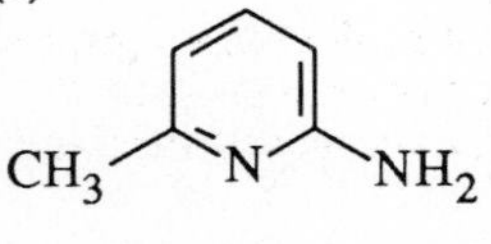

(f)

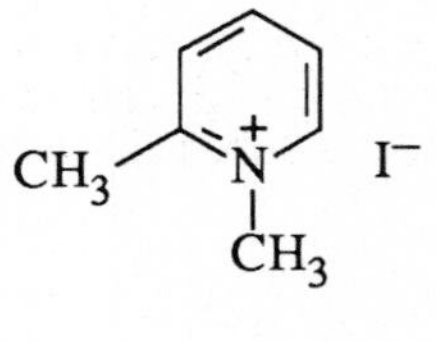

(g)

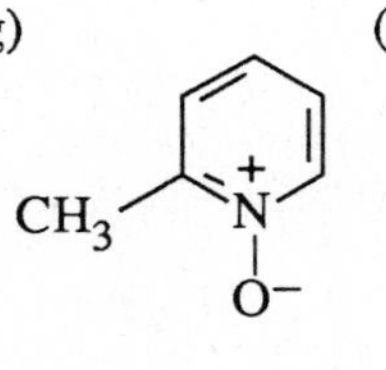

(h)

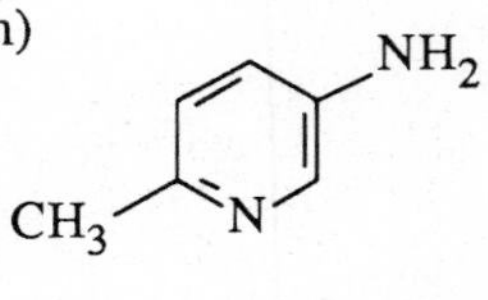

(i)

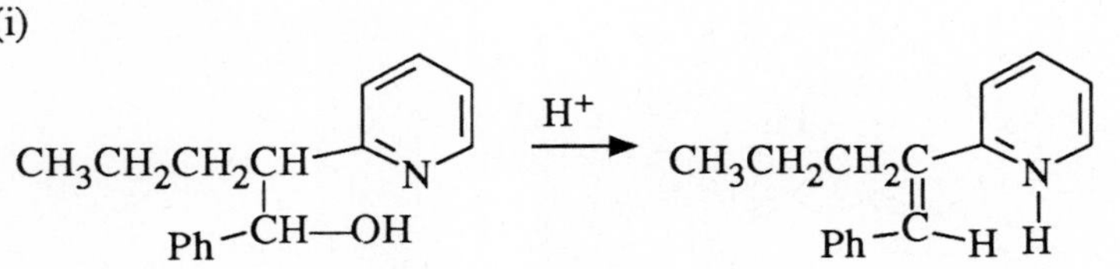

(j)

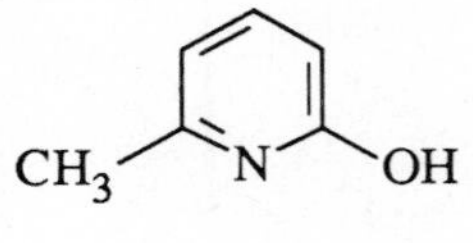

27. Naphthalene is most reactive; quinoline is next most reactive; and pyridine is least reactive. The reasons for pyridine's low reactivity and naphthalene's high reactivity are discussed in the text on pages 1049 and 1068, respectively. The α-positions of the benzene ring of a quinoline are more reactive than the 3-position of pyridine because of the many resonance structures possible for the carbocation intermediate. On the other hand, these structures are not as attractive as those for naphthalene itself. (Draw these structures and show why!)

28. The following three compounds are formed as products in the bromination of 1,6-dimethylnaphthalene:

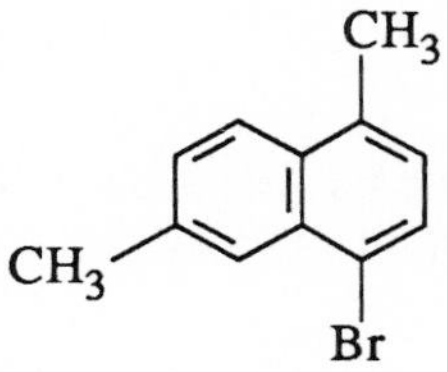

$$A \qquad\qquad B \qquad\qquad C$$

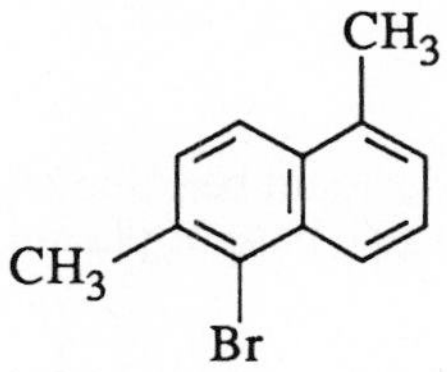

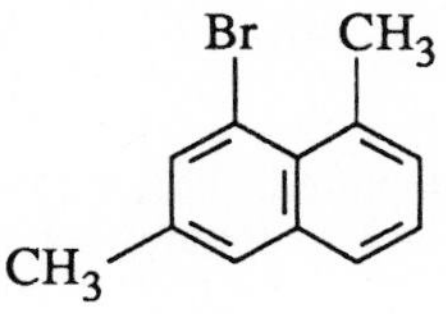

Both compounds A and B are brominated in α-positions that are activated by the methyl groups. (The resonance structures for the carbocation intermediate in each case show that positive charge is placed adjacent to each methyl group.) Compound C is brominated in an α-position, but this α-position is less activated by the methyl groups; furthermore, there is a severe *peri* interaction between the methyl group and the bromine. Hence, compound C is formed in smallest amount.

29. (a) 5-Methoxyindole is not basic. The inductive effect of the 3-methoxy group in 3-methoxy pyridine weakens the basicity of this derivative relative to that of pyridine itself. The congugate acid of 4-methoxypyridine, however, is stabilized by resonance:

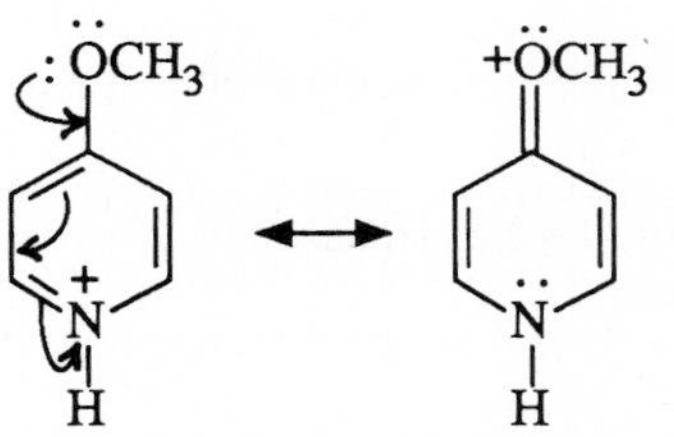

This increases the basicity of 4-methoxypyridine relative to that of pyridine. The base-weakening inductive effect of the methoxy group is present as it is in the 3-methoxy derivative; but by now we should realize that resonance effects generally outweigh inductive effects. In summary, the order of increasing basicity — that is, increasing pK_a for the conjugate acids — is:

5-methoxyindole < 3-methoxypyridine < pyridine < 4-methoxypyridine

(b) The electron-withdrawing inductive effect of the nitro group is greater than that of the chloro group, as we can see from the ammonium-ion pK_a values in Table 23.1, page 995 (compare 3-chloroaniline with 3-nitroaniline). The same effect operates in pyridine basicity, and there is no compensating resonance effect. Hence, the basicity order is:

3-nitropyridine < 3-chloropyridine < pyridine

(c) The first compound is actually a neutral compound:

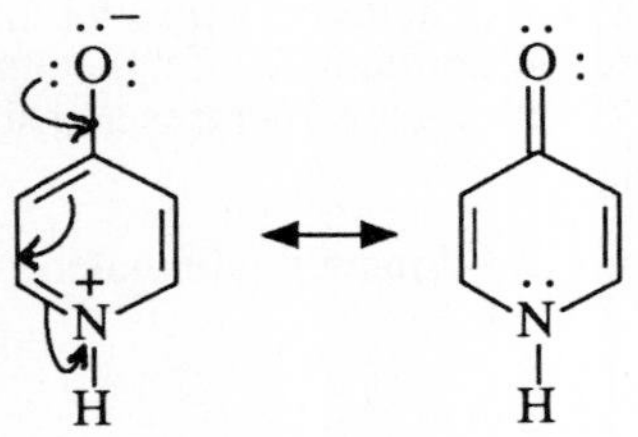

That is, this is really a carbonyl compound. This compound should be somewhat more basic than an amide (conjugate-acid $pK_a \cong 1$). The second compound, the conjugate base of phenol, is much more basic; the pK_a of phenol is about 10.

(d) The resonance structures of protonated imidazole are shown in Eq. 24.19, text page 1056. There are similar structures for the conjugate acid of oxazole:

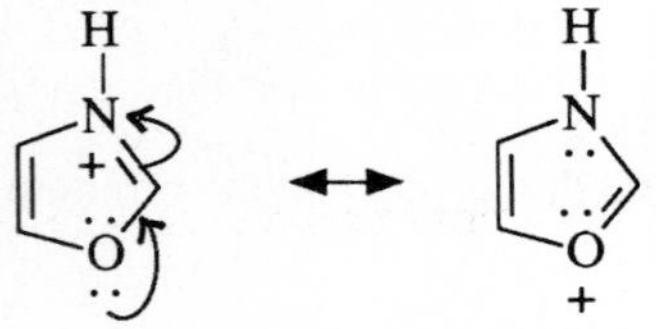

In oxazole, the positive charge is shared by an oxygen; in imidazole, it is shared by a second nitrogen. Since nitrogen supports positive charge more effectively (it is less electronegative), it takes less energy to protonate imidazole. Hence, imidazole is more basic.

30. (a) The explanation for the tendency of naphthalene to substitute in the 1-position is found on text pages 1047–1048.
(b) Because benzene rings are more reactive than pyridine rings, we would expect quinoline to substitute preferentially in the "benzene ring" part of quinoline. The reactivity of the 1-position has the same reason as the reactivity of naphthalene (of which quinoline is an analog) at the 1-position.
(c) The explanation for the tendency of pyridine to substitute at the 3-position is found on text pages 1067–1068.
(d) When a nucleophile attacks the 2- and 4-positions of a pyridine ring, as it would in the nucleophilic aromatic substitution reactions of 2- and 4-bromopyridine, negative charge is delocalized onto the electronegative nitrogen in the anionic intermediate. This favorable situation does not exist when nucleophilic attack occurs at carbon-3 of 3-bromopyridine. (See Eqs. 10.63a–c, text pages 1073.)
(e) The explanation for the relative basicities of pyridine and pyrrole are considered in detail on text pages 1054–1055.

31. (a) Since the C=N group of pyridine has chemical behavior much like that of a carbonyl group, we can expect, by analogy with aldehyde and ketone chemistry, that exchange of α-hydrogens will take place:

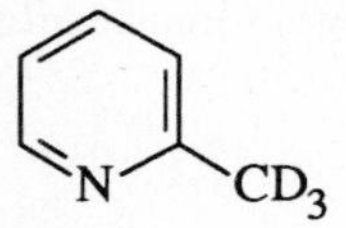

(b) The reaction is aromatic nitration, but at which ring does it occur? Since naphthalene is more reactive than benzene, the reaction takes place on the naphthalene ring. Furthermore, the phenyl group activates the naphthalene ring because it can stabilize the carbocation intermediate by resonance. (You should draw the appropriate resonance structures to demonstrate this point.) Hence, substitution occurs *para* to the phenyl ring. The product is 1-nitro-4-phenylnaphthalene:

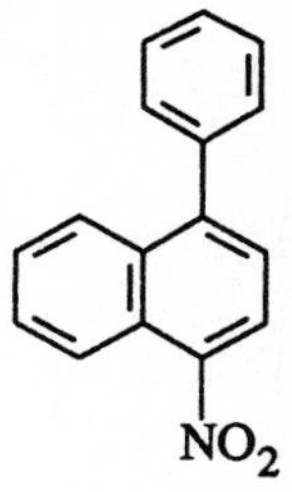

(c) Under the mild conditions, substitution occurs at the α-position of the unsubstituted ring that has the least severe *peri* interaction. The product is 1,5-naphthalenedisulfonic acid:

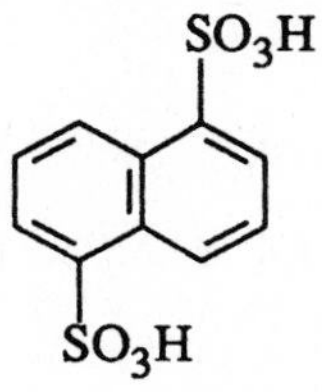

(d) Under more severe conditions, substitution takes place at both of the β-positions of the unsubstituted ring, and the sulfonic acid group already present rearranges to a β-position:

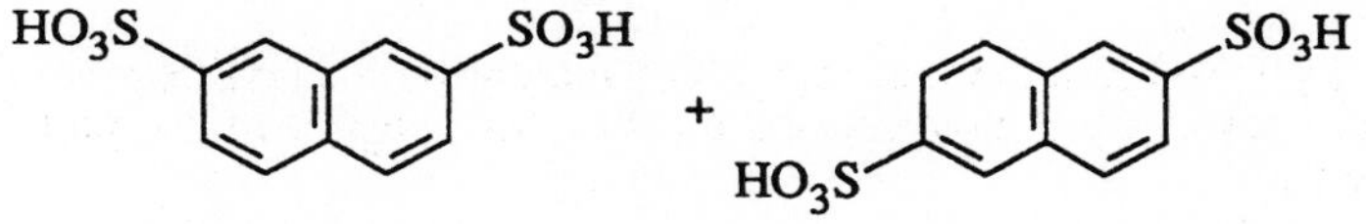

(e) This compound reacts like an aniline derivative, and brominates *para* to the amino group.

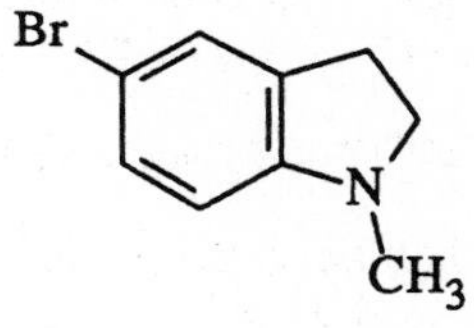

(f) The amide nitrogen directs substitution to the *para* position, which is also the position that is normally substituted in a pyridine derivative:

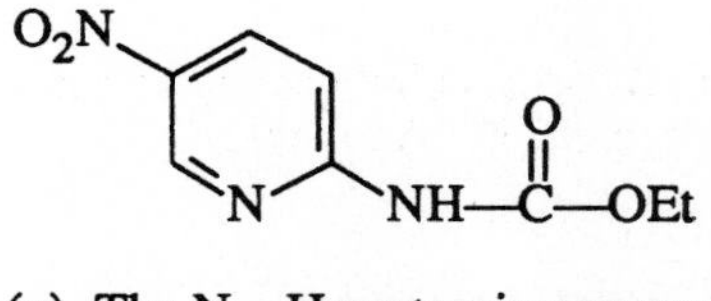

(g) The N—H proton is removed in an acid–base reaction (see Eqs. 24.20 and 24.21, text page 1056):

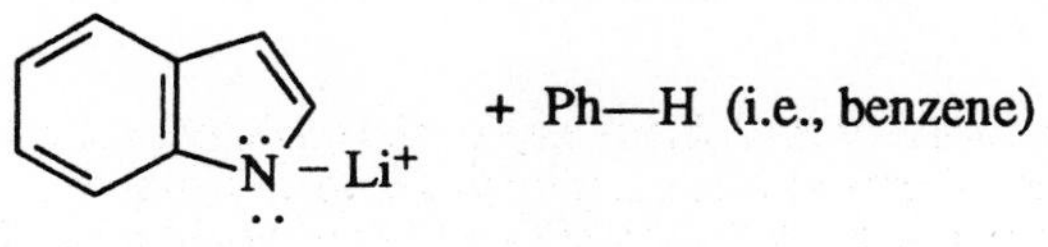

+ Ph—H (i.e., benzene)

(h) This is an ordinary Wolff–Kishner reaction:

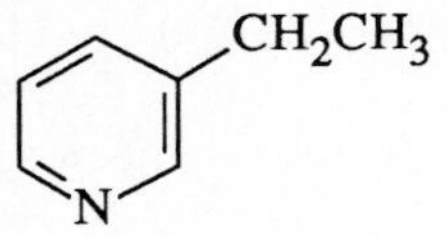

(i) Nitration occurs in the 4-position of the substituted ring:

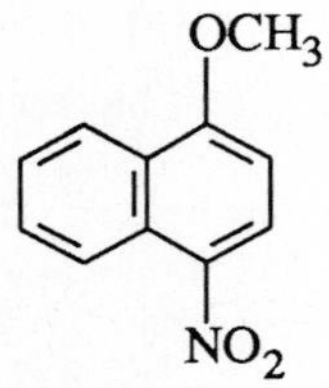

(j) Pyridine-*N*-oxides undergo electrophilic aromatic substitution in the 4-position. (See Eq. 24.52, text page 1069.) Although the methyl group is an *ortho, para* director, it does not deactivate the 4-position, whereas the position *para* to the methyl group is strongly deactivated by the *N*-oxide group (why?). The product is as follows:

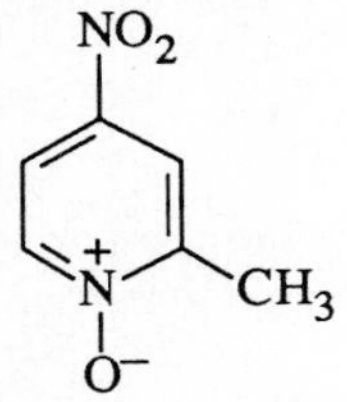

(k) This is a Fischer indole synthesis. If we work through the mechanism, we see that the product has to be 1,2-dimethylindole:

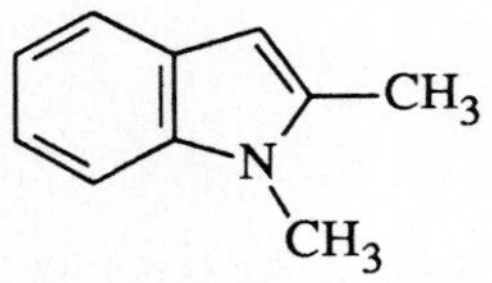

(l) Since furans are more reactive than thiophenes, substitution occurs in the furan ring:

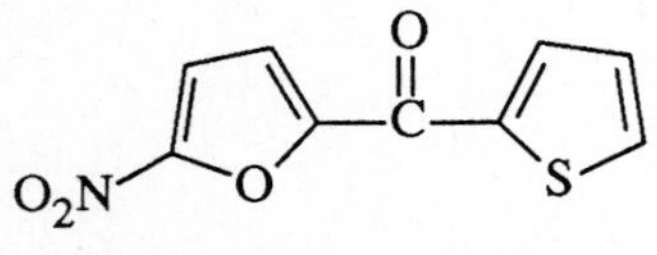

(m) Diazotization of *p*-nitroaniline affords 4-nitrobenzenediazonium chloride. This diazonium salt then undergoes diazo coupling with indole. Since this is an electrophilic aromatic substitution reaction, it occurs at the same position of the indole ring that other electrophilic aromatic substitution reactions occur: the 3-position. The product is:

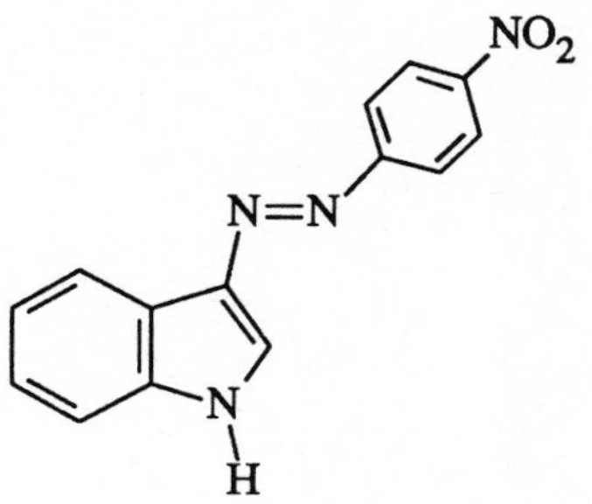

(n) There is no reason why the starting amine in the Skraup synthesis cannot itself be a quinoline derivative:

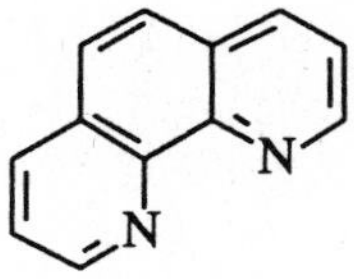

phenanthroline

32. (a)

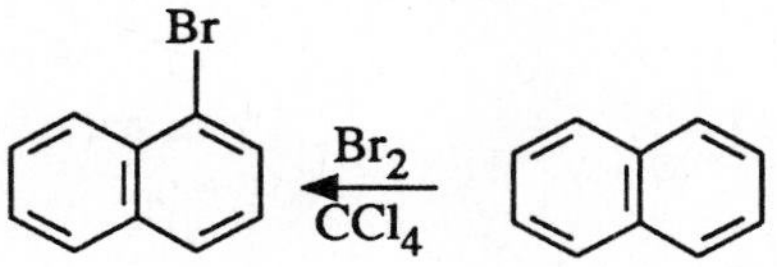

(b)

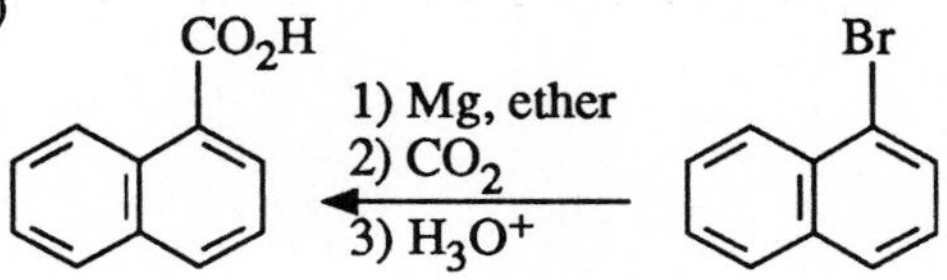

[from part (a)]

(c)

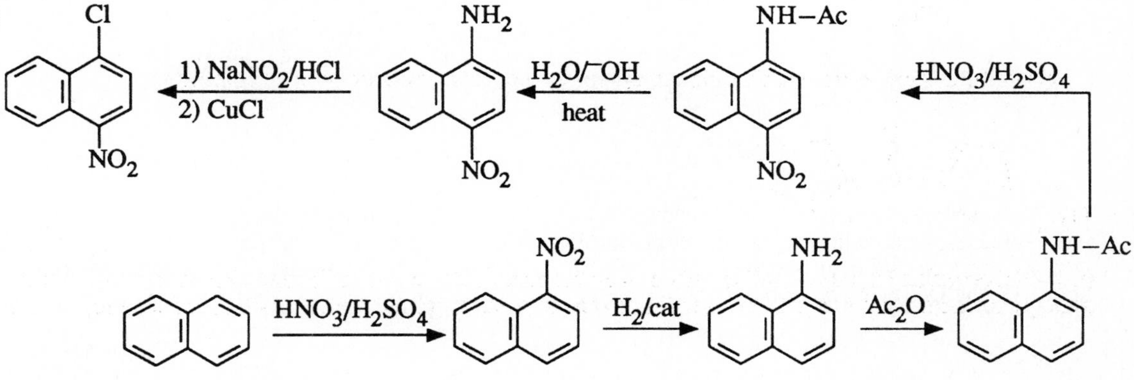

In this synthesis, Ac— is an abbreviation for the acetyl group; see Table 22.1, text page 940.

(d)

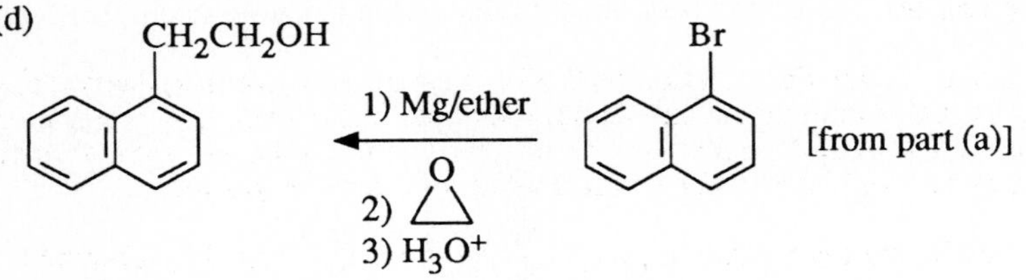

(e)

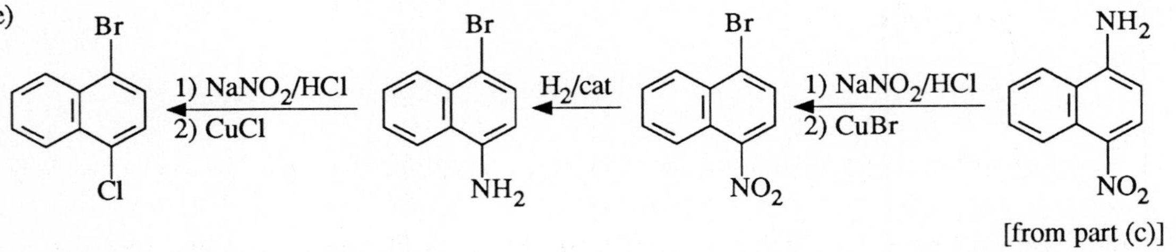

[from part (c)]

(f)

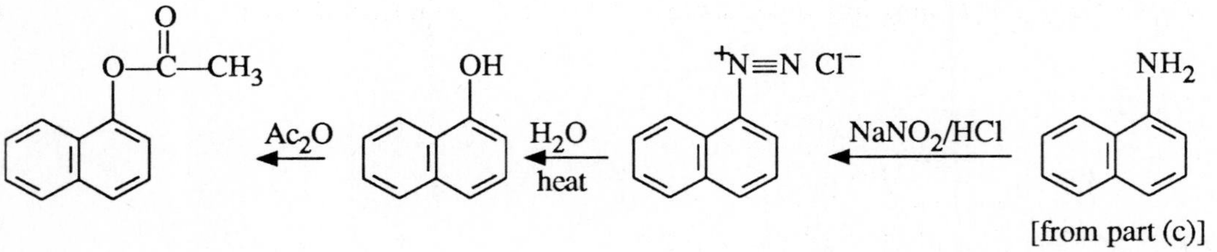

[from part (c)]

(g)

[from part (c)]

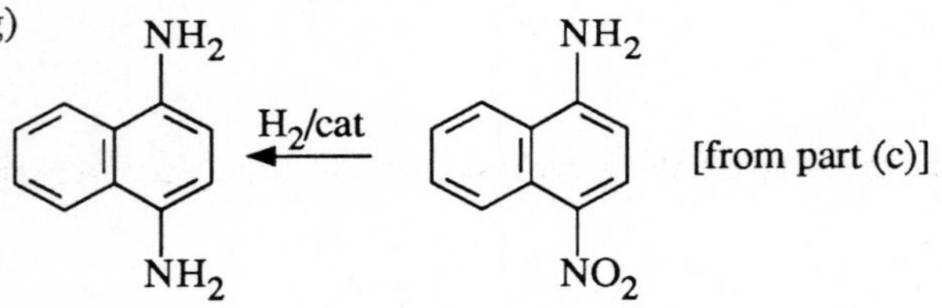

(h)

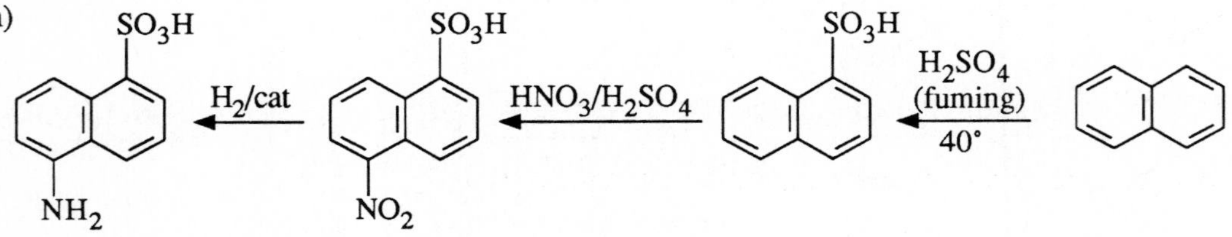

33. (a) There are two reasons why this reaction will not work. First, attack of the amide anion at the 2-position of indole does not delocalize negative charge onto the indole nitrogen. More important, however, is the fact that another reaction will occur instead. Since the pK_a of the indole N—H is about 17, and that of ammonia is about 35, the following acid–base reaction will go to completion:

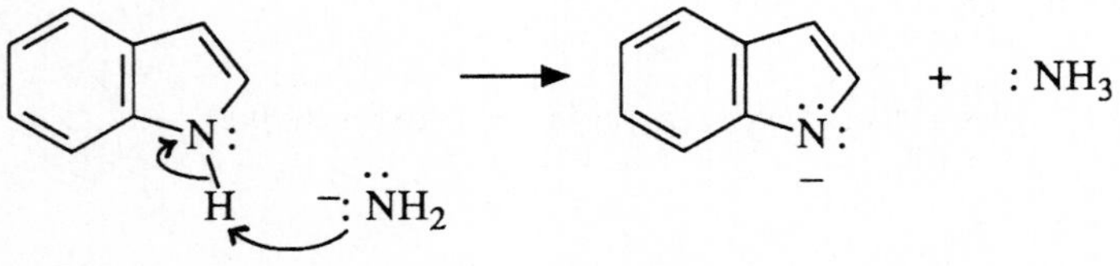

This destroys the amide anion and makes introduction of a second negative charge into the indole ring —

already unlikely — a ludicrous possibility.

(b) Doreen is attempting to carry out a Chichibabin reaction on 2-chloropyridine. Were this reaction to go as planned, it would mean that attack at the 6-position and expulsion of hydride ion as a leaving group would occur in preference to attack at the 2-position and expulsion of chloride ion. Since chloride ion is a vastly superior leaving group, the reaction that would occur, then, is formation of 2-aminopyridine.

34. (a) Since the indole ring is not basic, the nitrogen of the primary amino group is selectively protonated:

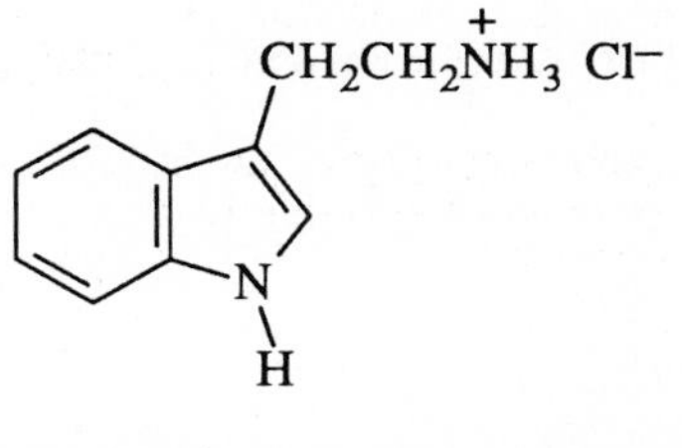

(b) There are two basic nitrogens in quinine; the more basic one will be protonated by one equivalent of HCl. Since the pK_a of protonated quinoline is 4.9, and that of a protonated tertiary amine is about 10.5, the bridgehead nitrogen is about a million times more basic than the quinoline nitrogen:

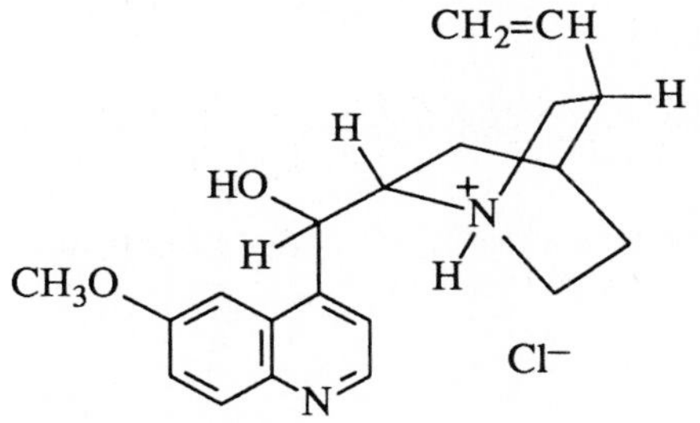

(c) The nitrogen of the tertiary alkylamino group is considerably more basic than the nitrogen of a pyridine ring:

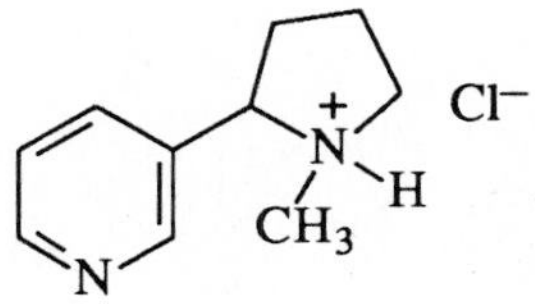

(d) Protonation occurs on the more basic tertiary alkylamino group:

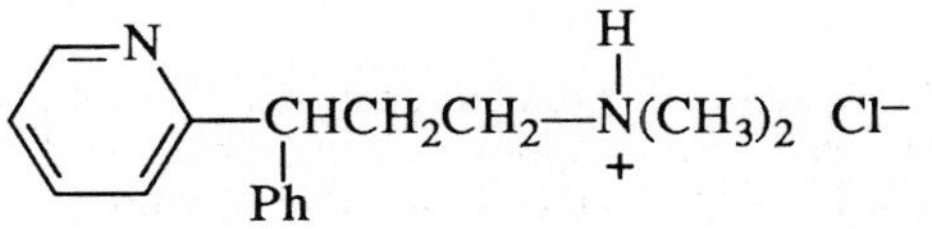

(e) There are three nitrogens that we must consider. Protonation of the pyridine nitrogen occurs because the resulting conjugate acid is resonance-stabilized:

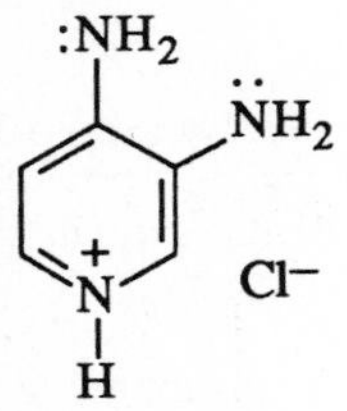

(You should draw resonance structures for this cation; see the solution to Problem 10(a) for a very similar situation.) In contrast, protonation of the 3- or 4-amino group gives a cation that is *not* resonance-stabilized.

(f) One nitrogen is an indole-like nitrogen; protonation of this nitrogen, like protonation of the indole nitrogen, would destroy aromaticity; hence, this nitrogen is not basic. The other nitrogen is a pyridine-like nitrogen and can be protonated in dilute HCl:

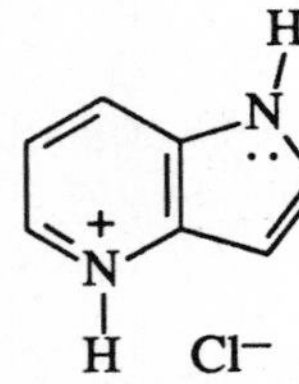

Furthermore, the positive charge in this cation is delocalized to the other nitrogen by resonance. (Draw the resonance structure that shows this delocalization.)

35. The first steps of the mechanism involve formation of the protonated enamine A; the mechanism of enamine formation is described in Sec. 19.11B. Subsequent mechanistic steps are as follows:

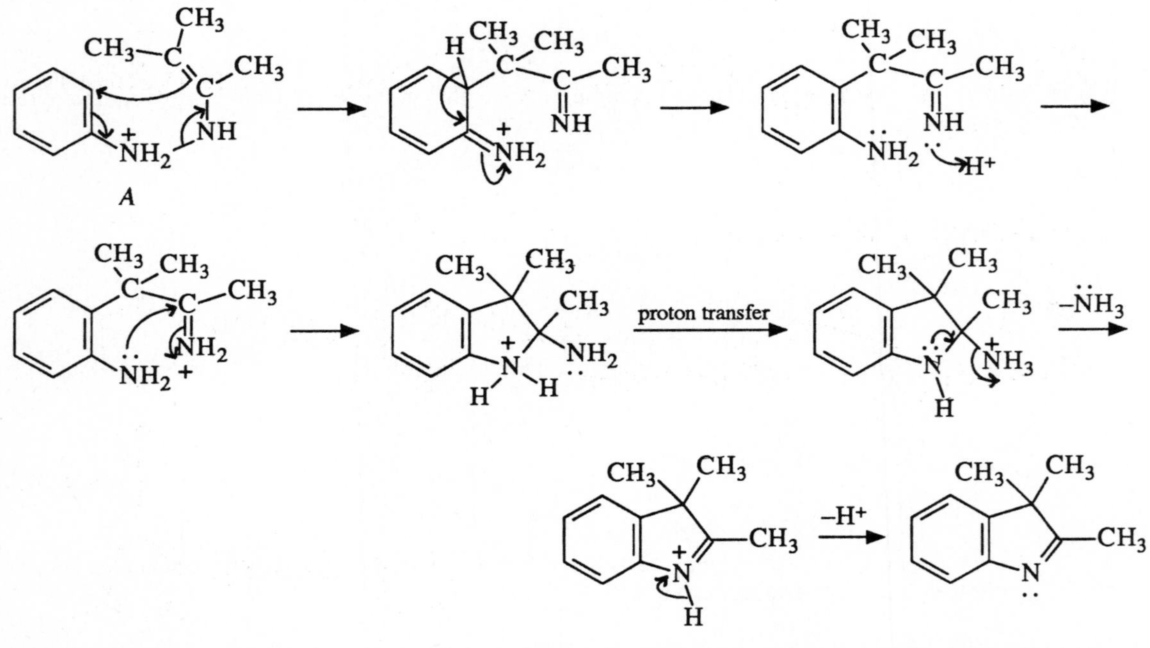

Since the product has no proton that can be lost from the 3-position, the double bond in the five-membered ring is "trapped" between the nitrogen and carbon.

➤ Intermediate A is not the only protonated enamine that could have formed. Draw the other possibility. Evidently A is preferred because it has the more substituted double bond. What indole would have been produced if the other enamine had formed?

36. (a) An indole substituted in the "benzene ring" can be formed by the Reissert synthesis:

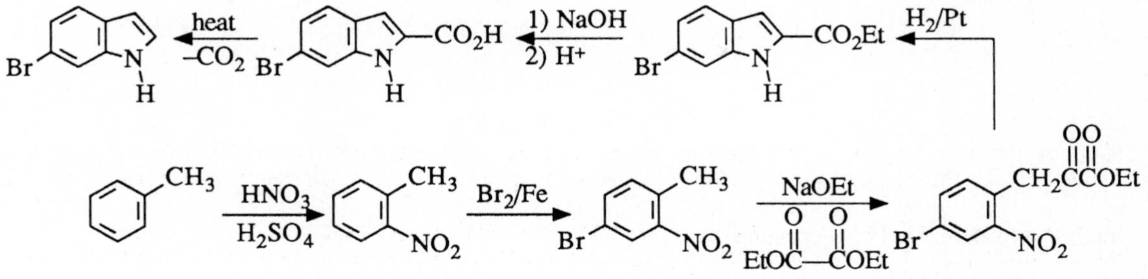

Ortho-nitrotoluene must be separated from the *para* isomer in the first step of the synthesis.

(b)

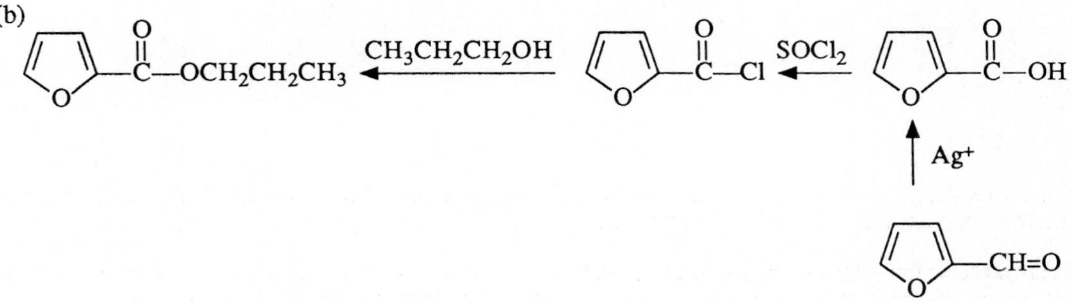

(c)

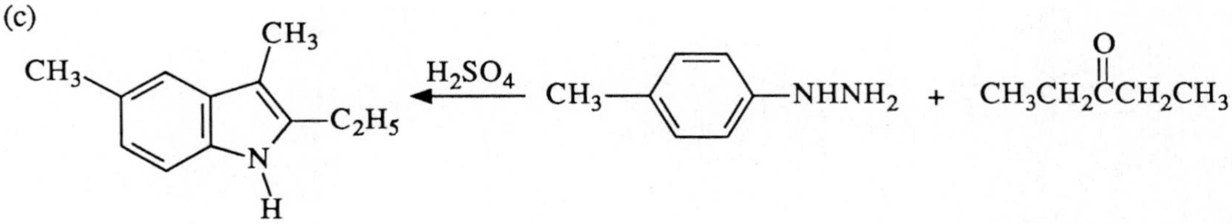

(This is a Fischer indole synthesis.)

(d)

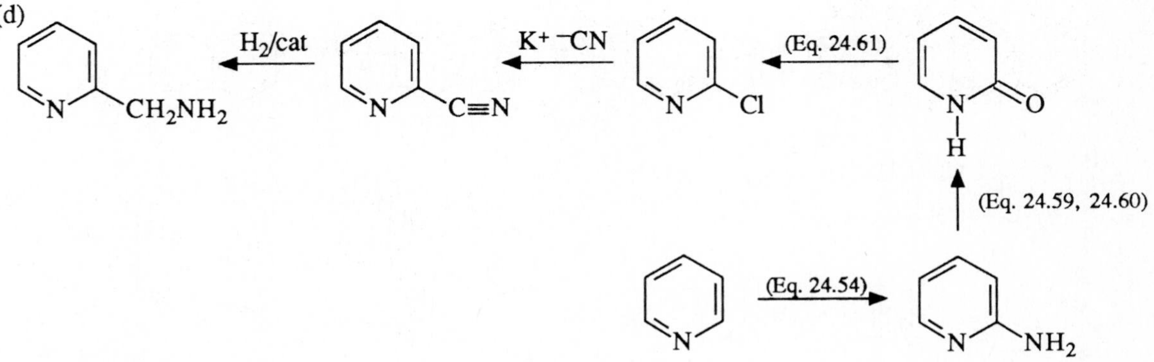

(e)

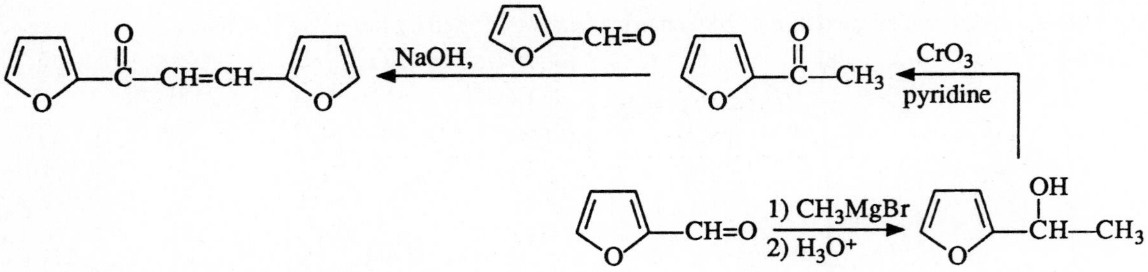

$\xleftarrow{\text{NaOH,}}$ (furan-CH=O)   (furan)-CO-CH$_3$ $\xleftarrow[\text{pyridine}]{\text{CrO}_3}$

(furan)-CH=O $\xrightarrow[\text{2) H}_3\text{O}^+]{\text{1) CH}_3\text{MgBr}}$ (furan)-CH(OH)-CH$_3$

The last step is an aldol condensation.

(f)

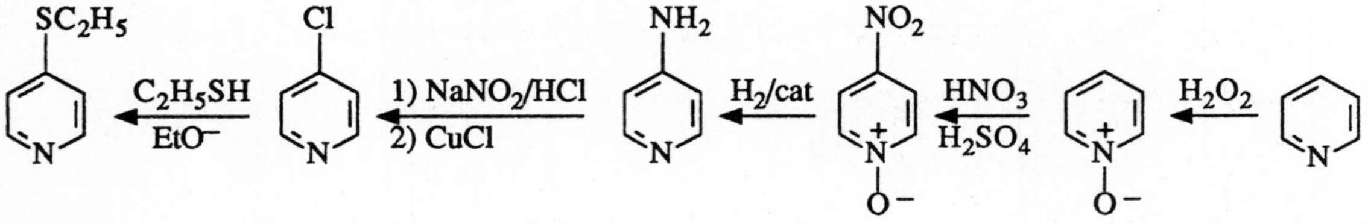

(4-SC$_2$H$_5$-pyridine) $\xleftarrow[\text{EtO}^-]{\text{C}_2\text{H}_5\text{SH}}$ (4-Cl-pyridine) $\xleftarrow[\text{2) CuCl}]{\text{1) NaNO}_2/\text{HCl}}$ (4-NH$_2$-pyridine) $\xleftarrow{\text{H}_2/\text{cat}}$ (4-NO$_2$-pyridine N-oxide) $\xleftarrow[\text{H}_2\text{SO}_4]{\text{HNO}_3}$ (pyridine N-oxide) $\xleftarrow{\text{H}_2\text{O}_2}$ (pyridine)

(g)

(pyridin-3-yl)-NH-CO-NH-(pyridin-3-yl) $\longleftarrow$ (3-NH$_2$-pyridine) + (3-N=C=O-pyridine) $\xleftarrow{\text{heat; } -\text{N}_2}$

$\underset{\text{then } ^-\text{OH}}{\xrightarrow{\text{H}_2\text{O, H}^+}}$

(3-CH$_3$-pyridine) $\xrightarrow{\text{KMnO}_4}$ (3-CO-OH-pyridine) $\xrightarrow[\text{2) NaN}_3]{\text{1) SOCl}_2}$ (3-CO-N$_3$-pyridine)

(h)

(benzo[h]quinoline) $\xleftarrow[\text{As}_2\text{O}_5]{\substack{\text{H}_2\text{SO}_4 \\ \text{glycerol}}}$ (1-NH$_2$-naphthalene) $\xleftarrow{\text{H}_2/\text{cat}}$ (1-NO$_2$-naphthalene) $\xleftarrow{\text{HNO}_3}$ (naphthalene)

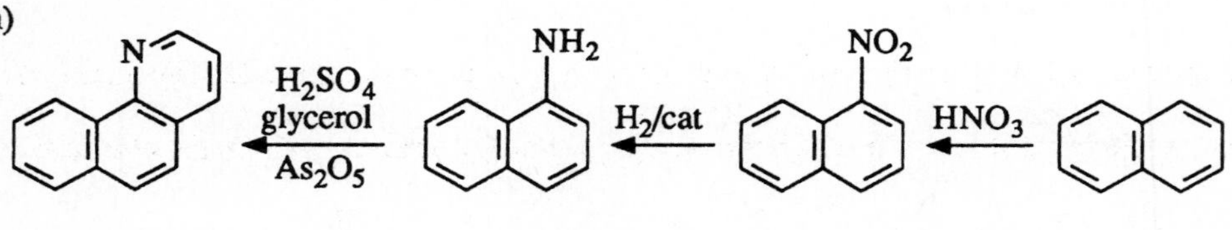

(i)

(pyridin-2-yl)-CH(CH$_2$CH$_2$CH$_3$)-CO$_2$H $\xleftarrow[\text{2) H}_3\text{O}^+]{\text{1) CO}_2}$ (pyridin-2-yl)-$\overset{..}{\text{C}}$HCH$_2$CH$_2$CH$_3$ Li$^+$ $\xleftarrow{\text{CH}_3\text{CH}_2\text{CH}_2\text{CH}_2\text{Li}}$

(2-CH$_3$-pyridine) $\xrightarrow{\text{CH}_3\text{CH}_2\text{CH}_2\text{CH}_2\text{Li}}$ (pyridin-2-yl)-$\overset{..}{\text{C}}$H$_2$ Li$^+$ $\xrightarrow{\text{I}-\text{CH}_2\text{CH}_2\text{CH}_3}$ (pyridin-2-yl)-CH$_2$CH$_2$CH$_2$CH$_3$

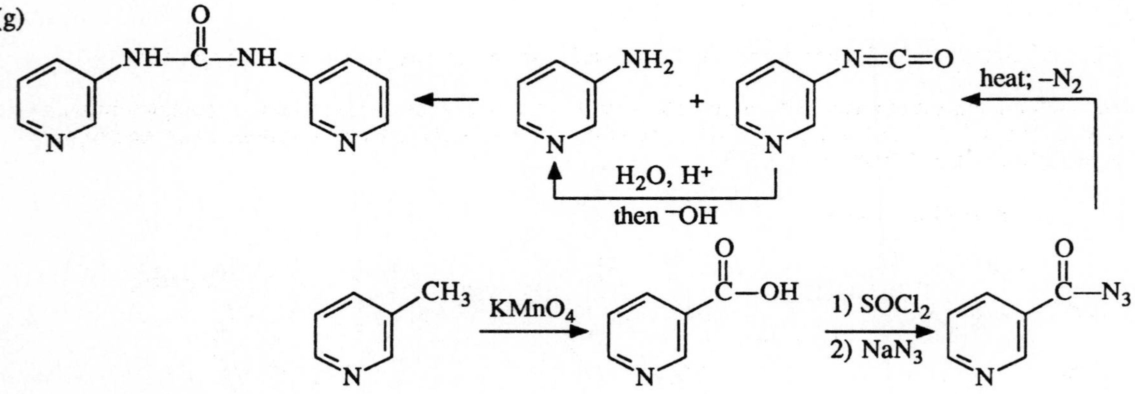

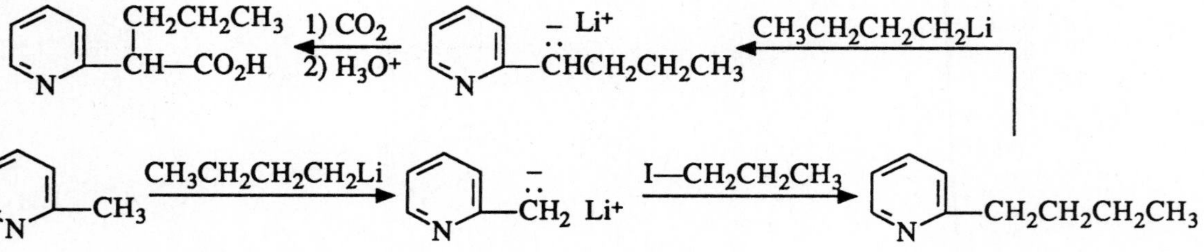

(j)

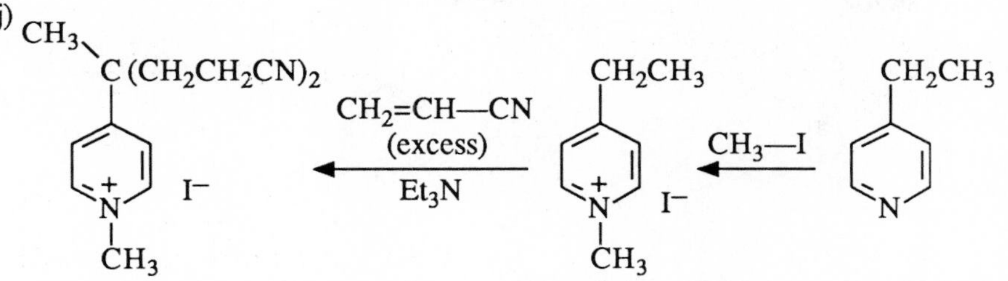

37. As we learned on text page 688, the groups that activate electrophilic aromatic substitution also activate S_N1 solvolysis reactions at benzylic positions. Hence, the reactivity order is the same as in the electrophilic aromatic substitution reactions of the corresponding aromatic hydrocarbons:

pyridine < benzene < thiophene < furan, or (b) < (a) < (d) < (c)

Synthesis of the thiophene derivative:

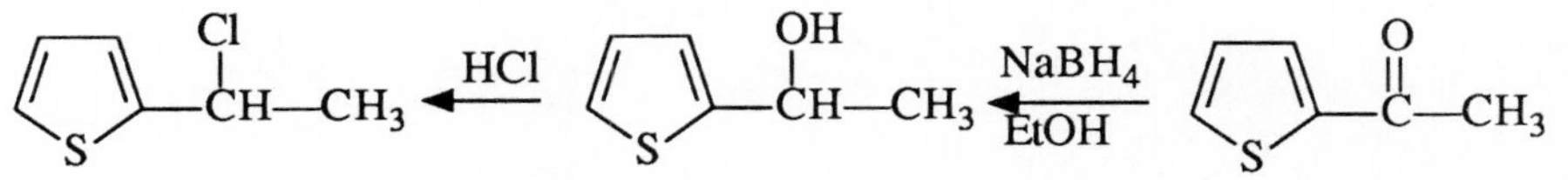

The preparation of the ketone from thiophene itself is shown in Eq. 24.27b on text page 1059.

38. (a) Diethylamine and formaldehyde react to form an immonium ion by a mechanism completely analogous to that shown in Eq. 23.32, text page 1004. The immonium ion acts as the electrophile in an electrophilic substitution at the 3-position of indole:

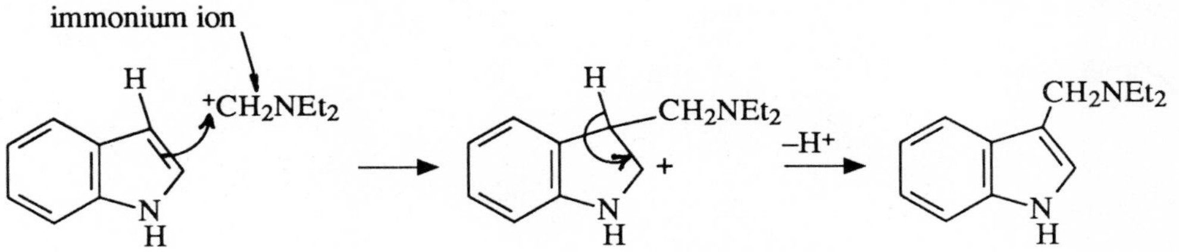

The carbocation intermediate *A* is resonance-stabilized; draw the resonance structures for this intermediate.

(b) This is an electrophilic substitution in which the isotopic proton (D^+) from D_2SO_4 is the electrophile:

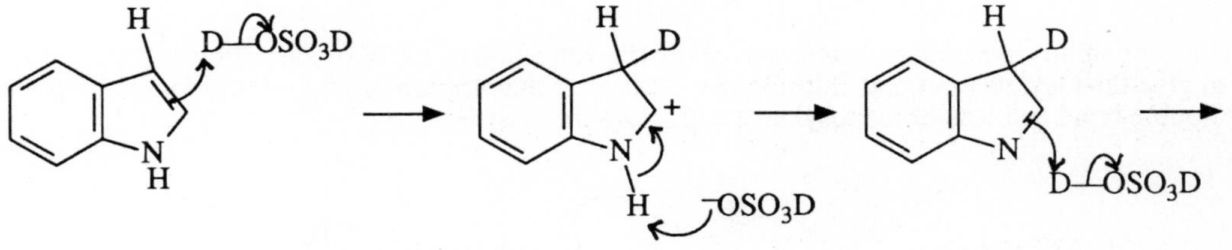

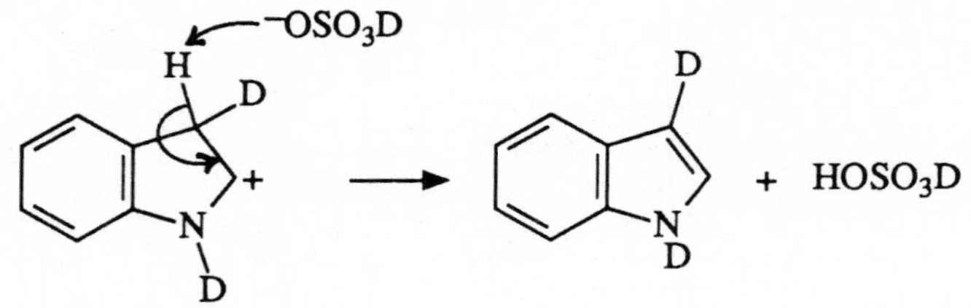

(c) Protonation of the nitrogen gives a carbocation that undergoes rearrangement. Notice that protonation of the nitrogen can occur because the starting material, called an *indolenine*, is *not* aromatic.

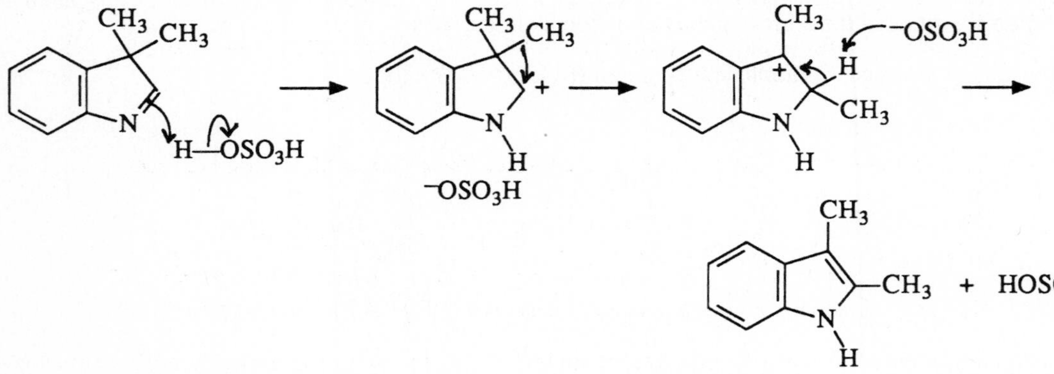

(d)

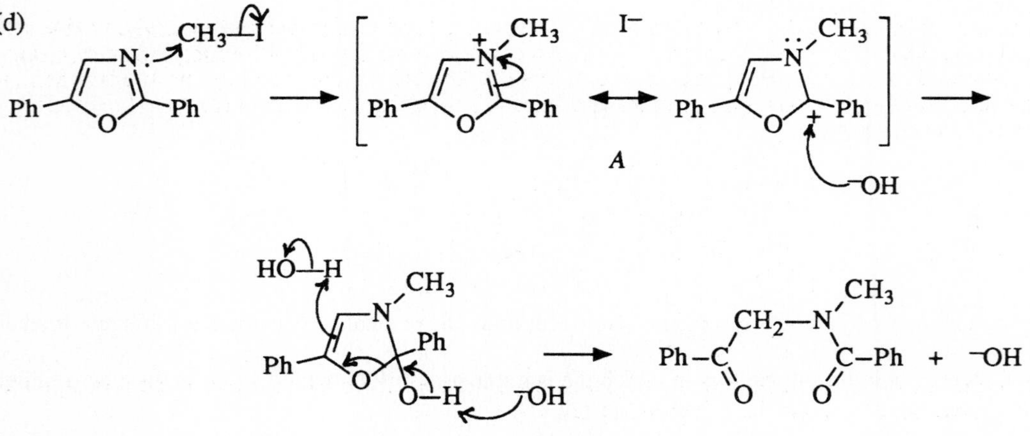

(e) The first step in this mechanism is reaction of the oxygen anion of the *N*-oxide with *p*-toluenesulfonyl chloride to give the tosylate ester and chloride ion. This ester then loses a proton. Attack of chloride ion on the resulting double bond and loss of the tosylate group gives the product:

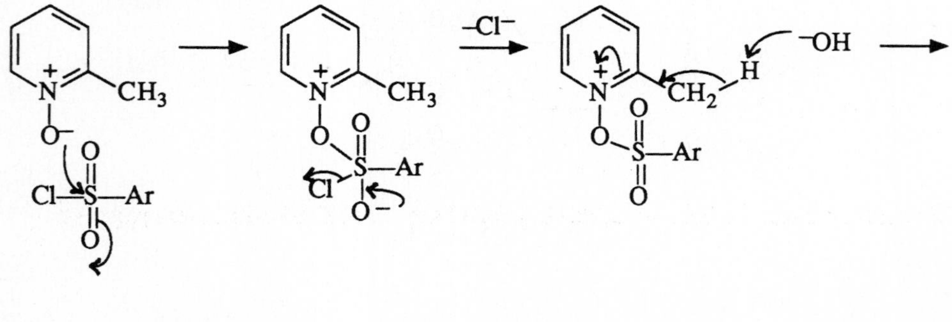

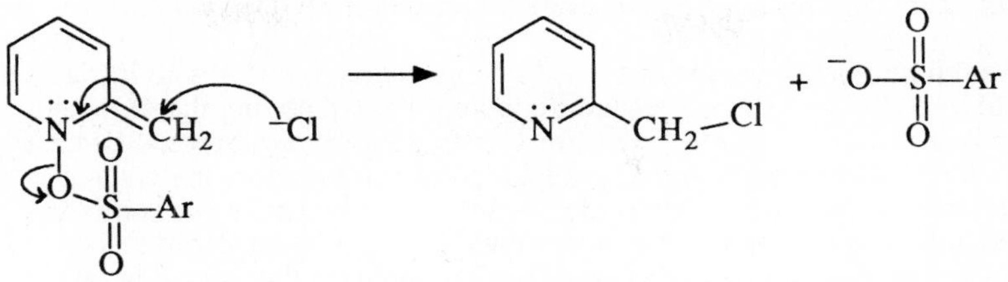

(f) The pyrrole ring is nucleophilic enough to react with this very reactive acid chloride:

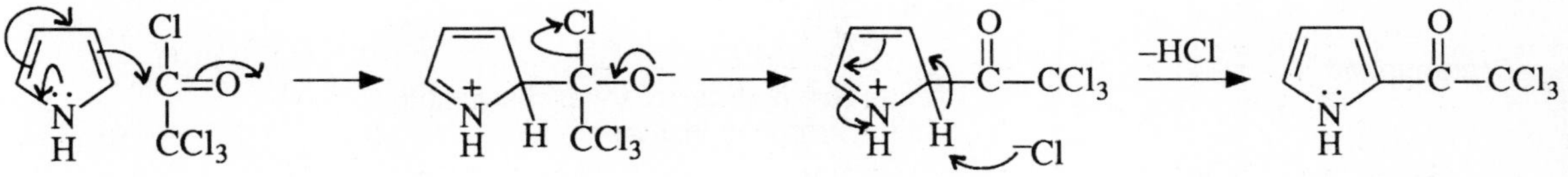

The product, a trichloromethyl ketone, reacts in a haloform-like reaction when base is added:

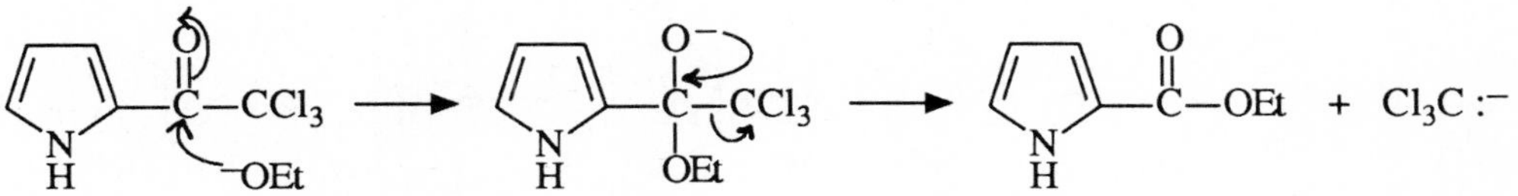

Protonation of the $Cl_3C\!:\!^-$ by ethanol gives the chloroform by-product.

39. The reaction of thiophene with chlorosulfonic acid gives compound A, 2-thiophenesulfonyl chloride (see Eq. 20.32, text page 840). Because the chlorosulfonyl group exerts a strong *meta*-directing effect, nitration of A gives the 4-nitro derivative B. Heating B in water converts the sulfonyl chloride into the sulfonic acid, which then loses its sulfonyl group to give 3-nitrothiophene, C. (Recall that sulfonation is reversible; see Eq. 24.4, text page 1048.)

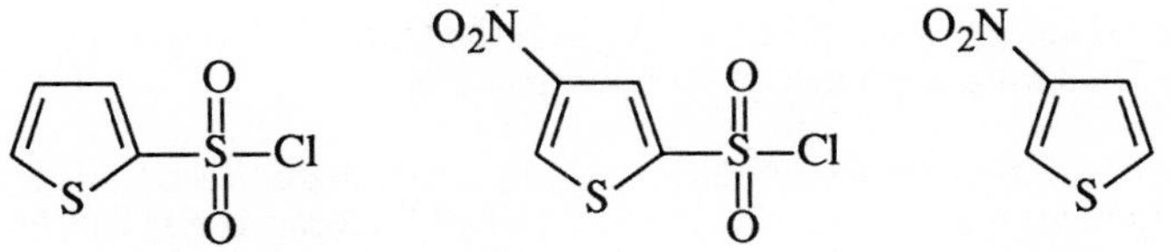

3-Nitrothiophene cannot be made directly from thiophene, because thiophene nitrates in the 2-position to give mostly 2-nitrothiophene. (See Eq. 24.23, text page 1057.)

➤ Notice that the chlorosulfonyl group is used as a *protecting group* in this reaction; it blocks the 2-position of the thiophene ring, forcing nitration into the 4-position. It is then removed when it is no longer needed.

40. The conjugate acid of this compound is resonance-stabilized:

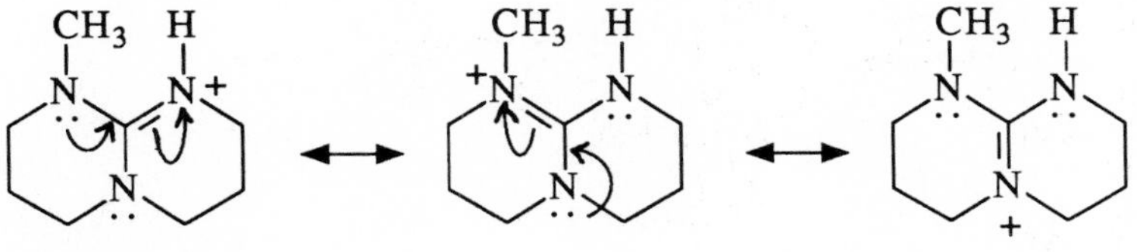

Stabilization of an acid increases the basicity of its conjugate base. (See Figure 23.3, text page 995.)

Protonation occurs on the nitrogen with the double bond because protonation on either of the other nitrogens gives a cation that is *not* resonance-stabilized, and is therefore less stable.

41. The unsaturation number of compound *A* is 4. Since oxidation of *A* with nitric acid gives nicotinic acid, it is reasonable to hypothesize that compound *A* contains a pyridine ring that is substituted in the 3-position. Since pyridine has five carbons, the side-chain contains a total of three carbons. Since the pyridine ring accounts for the nitrogen, there is no primary amino group, and we can therefore understand why the diazotization reaction does not liberate nitrogen. Since compound *A* is oxidized by CrO_3 to a compound that incorporates deuterium in base — an aldehyde or ketone — then compound *A* must be an alcohol. The only chiral alcohol that can be oxidized to a ketone that incorporates five deuterium atoms is the following one:

compound *A*:

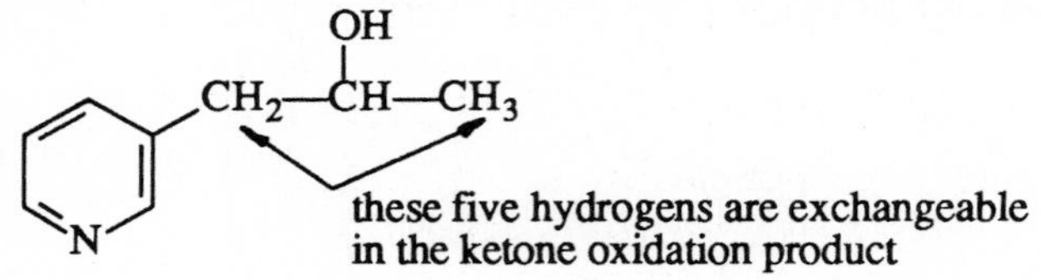

these five hydrogens are exchangeable in the ketone oxidation product

42. In the Chichibabin reaction, the first product formed is the conjugate-base anion of 2-aminopyridine (Eq. 24.55d, text page 1071). Reaction of this anion in a Chichibabin-like reaction gives the by-product:

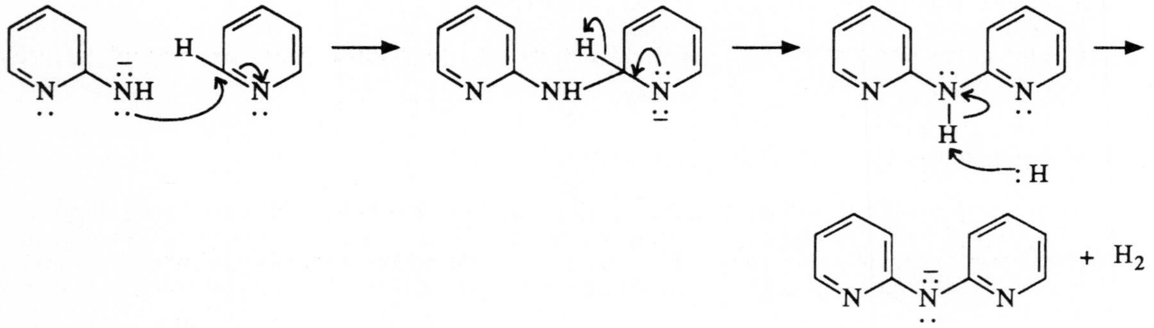

Protonation of the last anion when water is added gives the product. As with the Chichibabin reaction itself, this reaction is driven to completion by the final ionization that gives hydrogen gas.

➤ One might ask why this isn't the *major* reaction under the conditions of the Chichibabin reaction. The reason is that the starting anion is much less basic than the amide ion itself (why?). Because it is less basic, it is less nucleophilic, and therefore less reactive. Hence, the side reaction is slower than the Chichibabin reaction itself.

43. (a) The enolate ion derived from the β-keto diester reacts with the α-chloro ketone. An internal aldol condensation of the resulting derivative affords the product. We begin with the enolate ion:

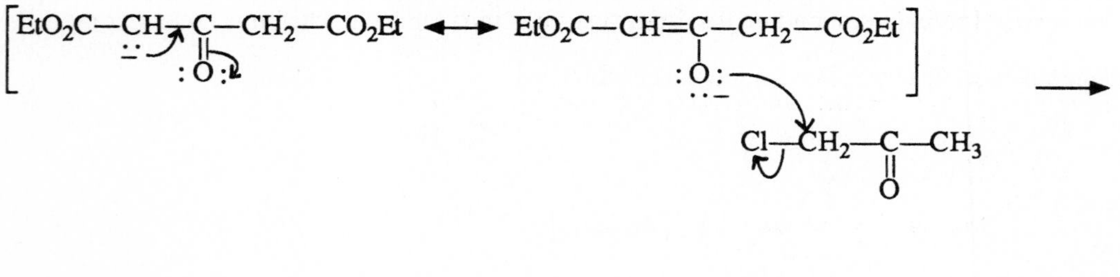

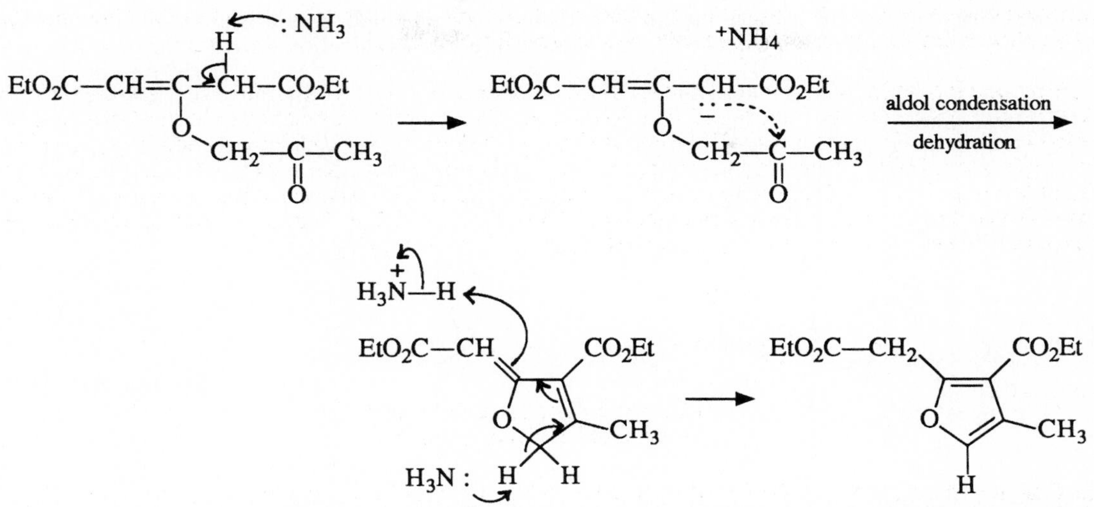

We leave it to you to supply the details of the aldol condensation–dehydration. It is also conceivable that the aldol condensation and S_N2 steps occur in reverse order.

(b) This reaction is two successive aldol condensations. We shall outline these, beginning with an enolate anion; you provide the details:

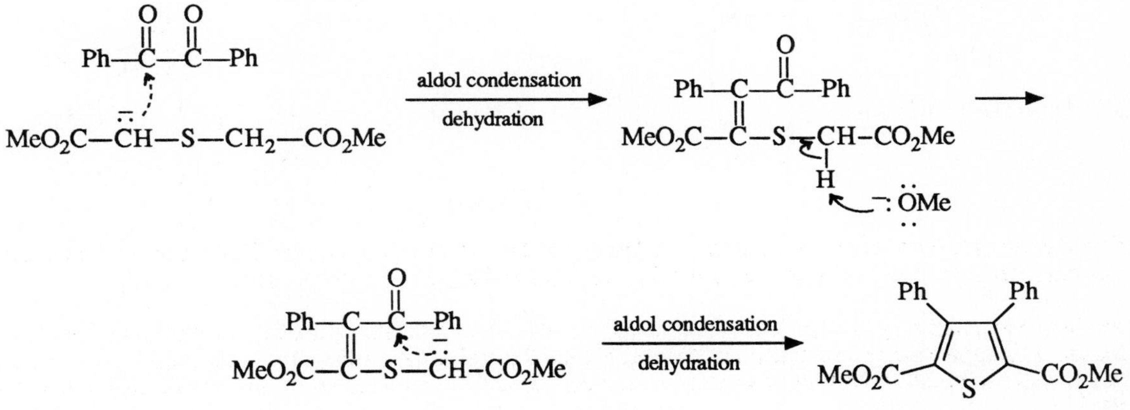

(c) Analyzing the relationship between the product and the starting material, we see that the ester (lactone) bond is broken; the carbonyl carbon of the lactone becomes the carbon of the carboxylic acid group; and the ester oxygen becomes bonded to the α-carbon:

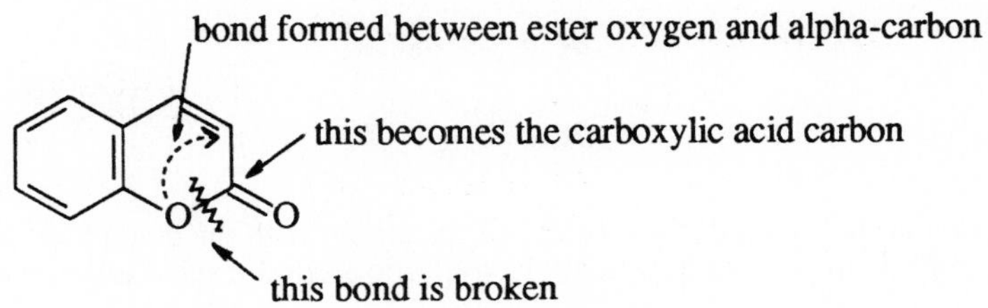

bond formed between ester oxygen and alpha-carbon

this becomes the carboxylic acid carbon

this bond is broken

The KOH, by saponifying the lactone, breaks the carbonyl–oxygen bond. Bromination of the double bond provides an α-bromo acid, which reacts with the phenolic oxygen. Elimination provides the product:

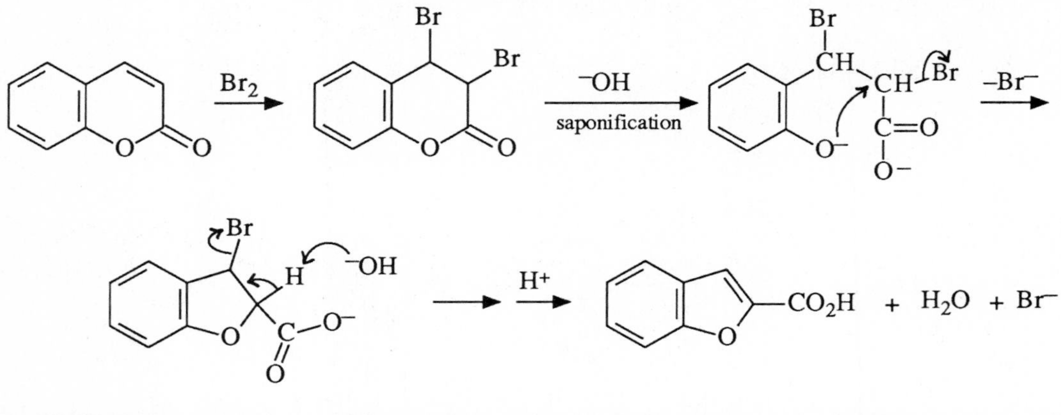

(d) The first step of this synthesis is formation of an imine, which forms its "enol," an enamine. This is followed by an aldol condensation–dehydration. We begin with the imine:

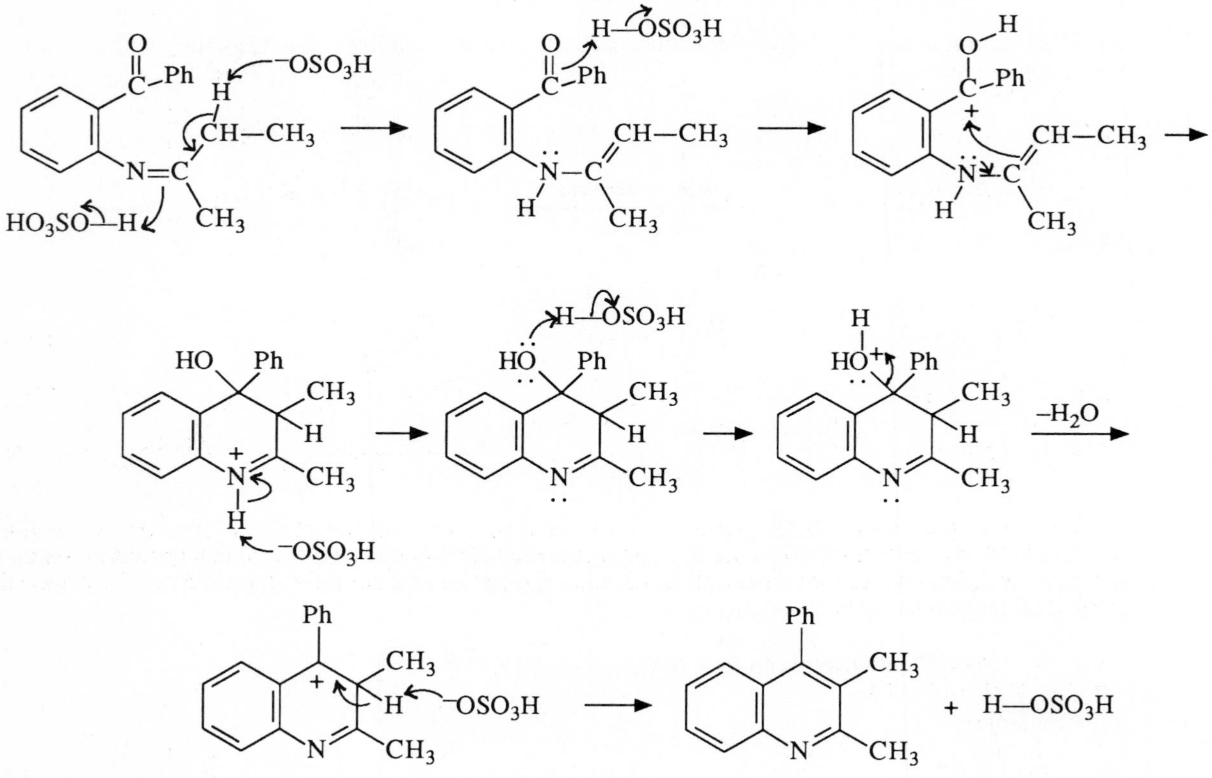

(e) In this synthesis, the first step is formation of an amide by reaction of the amine with the acid chloride. The protonated amide then serves as the electrophile in an intramolecular electrophilic aromatic substitution reaction:

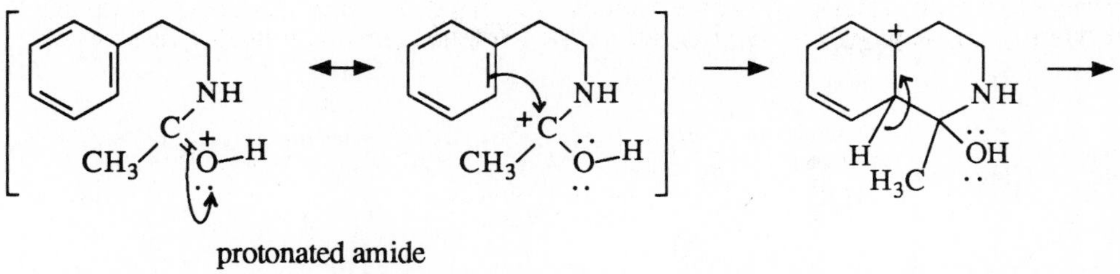

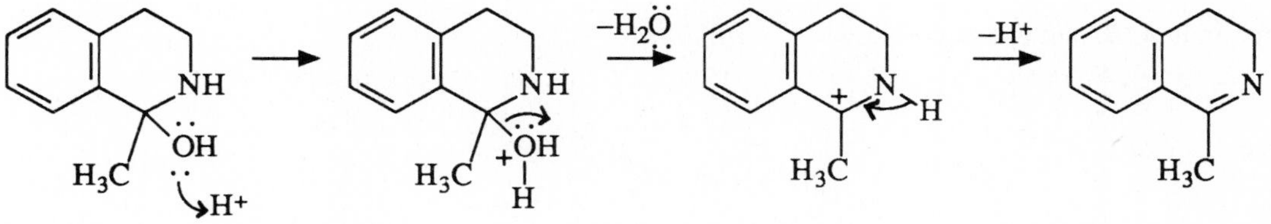

protonated amide

(f) The amine reacts with one carbonyl group to form an imine. Protonation of the other carbonyl group then generates a carbocation that serves as the electrophile in an intramolecular electrophilic aromatic substitution reaction. We begin the mechanism with the imine:

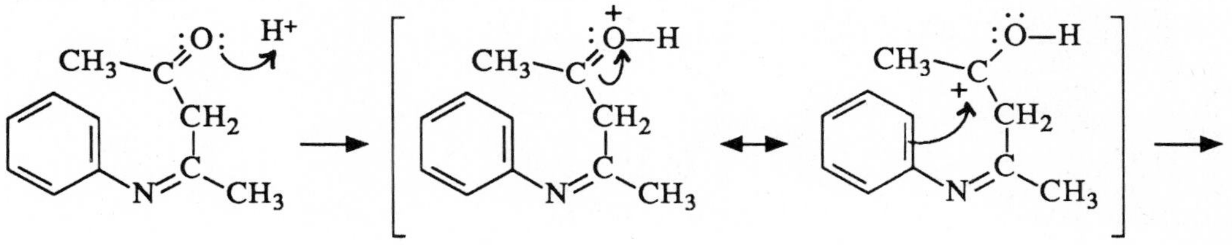

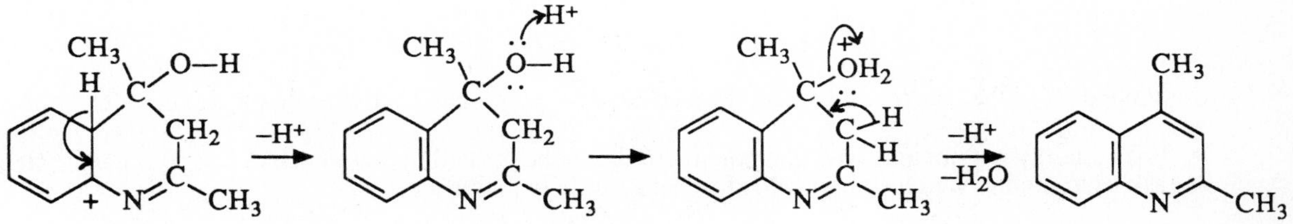

(g) The first step in this synthesis is an aldol condensation of ethyl acetoacetate with formaldehyde to give an α,β-unsaturated β-keto ester. The enolate of a second equivalent of ethyl acetoacetate then undergoes a conjugate addition with this intermediate. Two enamine-forming reactions give the product. We begin with the aldol condensation product:

aldol condensation product
of ethyl acetoacetate and
formaldehyde

conjugate-base
enolate of
ethyl acetoacetate

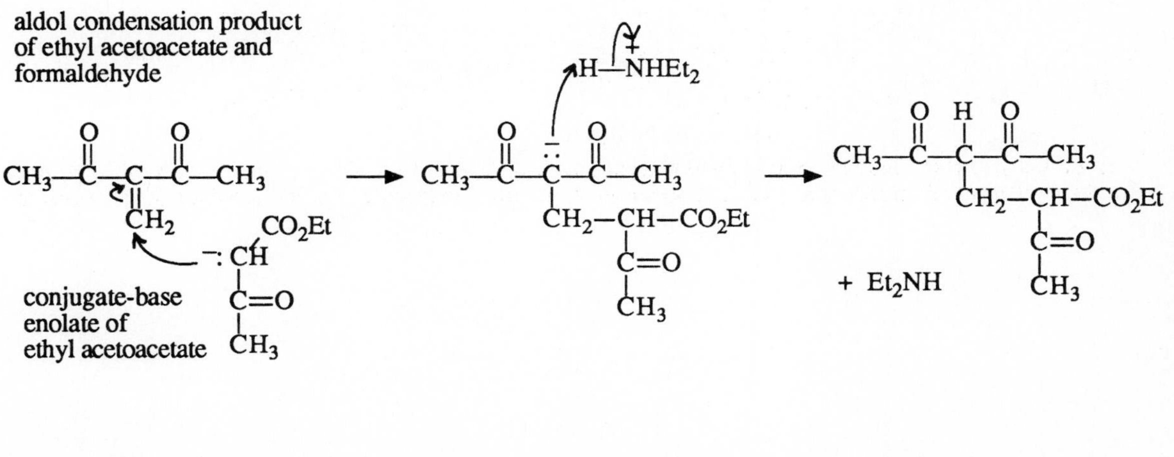

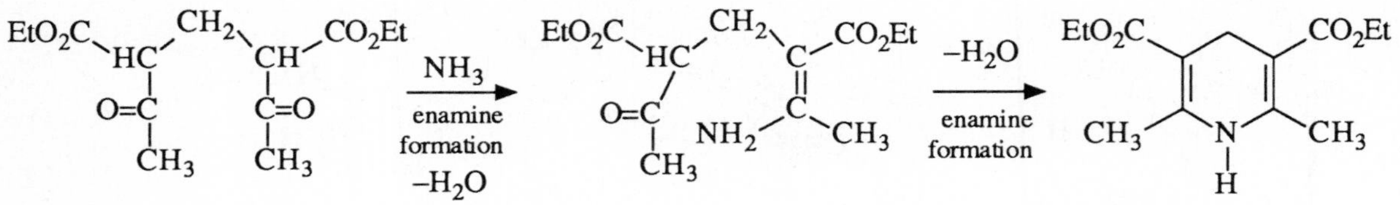

We leave it to you to supply the details of the aldol condensation and the enamine-forming reactions. (See Sections 22.4 and 19.11.)

44. Compounds *A*, *B*, and *C* are as follows:

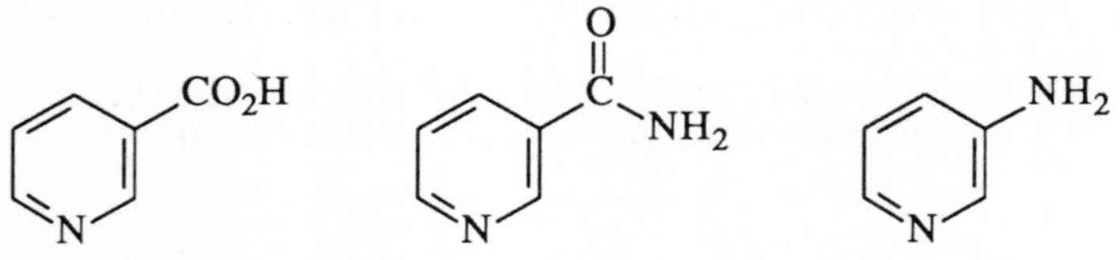

A   *B*   *C*

The last reaction is a Skraup synthesis. There are two possibilities for the product, depending on whether cyclization occurs to the 2- or 4-position:

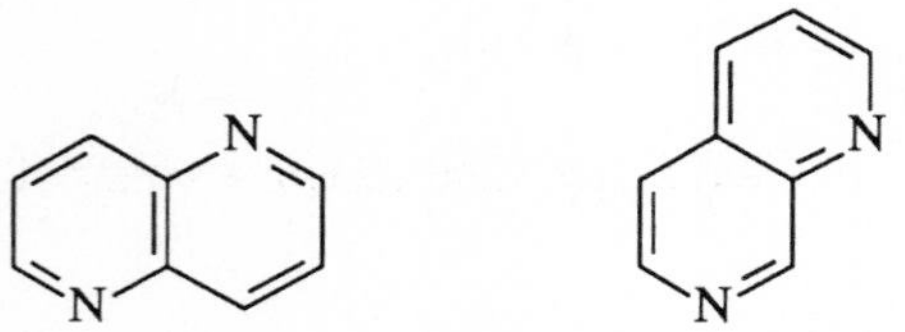

D1   *D2*

Compound *D1* is the compound actually formed because only it can have zero dipole moment.

➤ It is certainly not obvious why compound *D1* should be formed in preference to *D2*. But the problem does not ask us to predict which compound is formed — only to identify it.

45. The product is a dicarbonyl compound with the carbon skeleton of hexane. Since all hydrogens are exchangeable, all hydrogens are α-hydrogens. These deductions, plus the NMR spectrum, which implies a high degree of symmetry, are consistent with only 2,5-hexanedione as the product *A*. The mechanism of its formation is as follows:

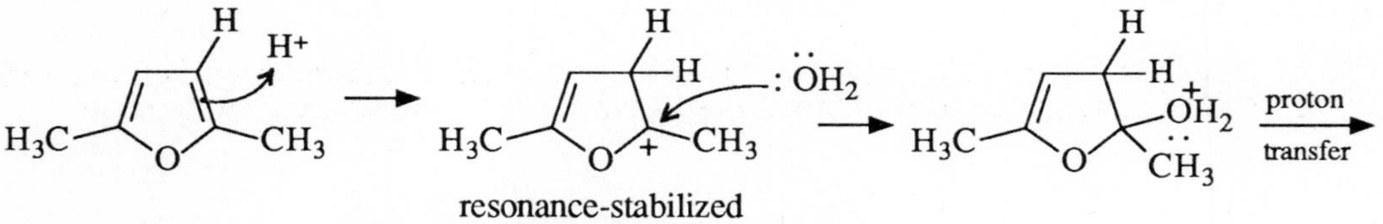

resonance-stabilized
carbocation

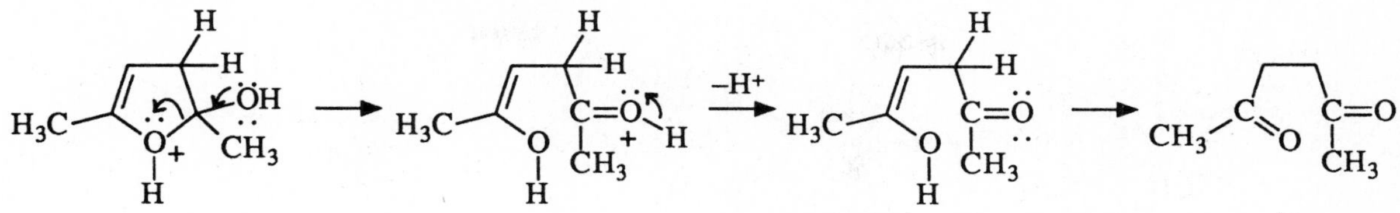

enol form of the product

A

46. (a) 4-Chloropyridine undergoes nucleophilic aromatic substitution to give 4-aminopyridine. This reaction takes place readily because attack of the nucleophile ammonia on the 4-position of the pyridine ring places negative charge on the pyridine nitrogen, an electronegative atom. (See Eq. 24.63b on text page 1073.) When ammonia attacks the 3-position in 3-chloropyridine, however, the negative charge in the ring *cannot* be delocalized to nitrogen. Hence, the reaction is much slower — so much slower, in fact, that it does not occur. (See the solution to Problem 30d.)

(b) 4-Aminopyridine is a *cine*-substitution product (see text page 727). This and the strongly basic conditions suggest that the products are derived from a benzyne (or more accurately, *pyridyne*) intermediate:

A

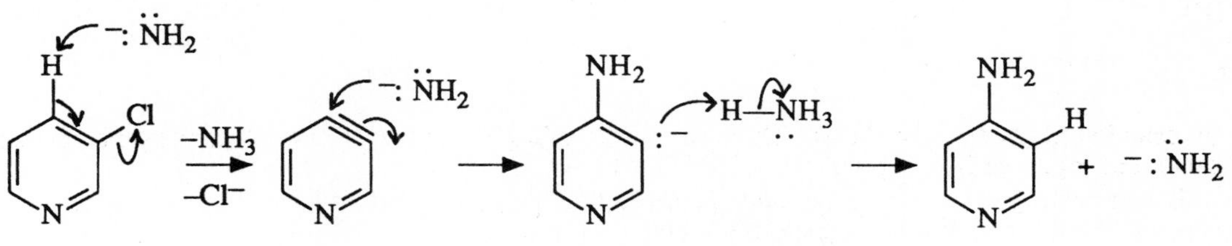

We have shown the formation of 4-aminopyridine; the formation of 3-aminopyridine occurs by attack of the amide ion on the 3-position of the pyridyne intermediate *A*.

47. (a) 2-Pyridone ionizes readily in base because the anion is *aromatic*:

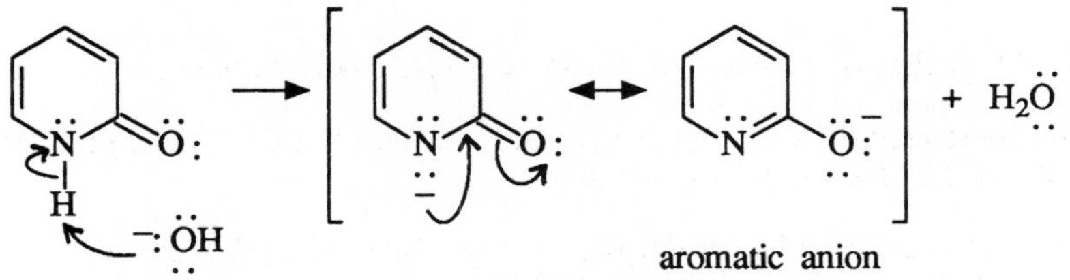

aromatic anion

This anion resists nucleophilic attack by ⁻OH because such attack would introduce a second negative charge into the ring. Under the same conditions, δ-butyrolactam does not ionize, and it is therefore readily attacked at the carbonyl group by ⁻OH.

(b) The colored protons are more acidic because the "anion" formed when they are removed is delocalized to nitrogen in such a way that all charge is neutralized. That is, the "anion" is in fact a neutral molecule:

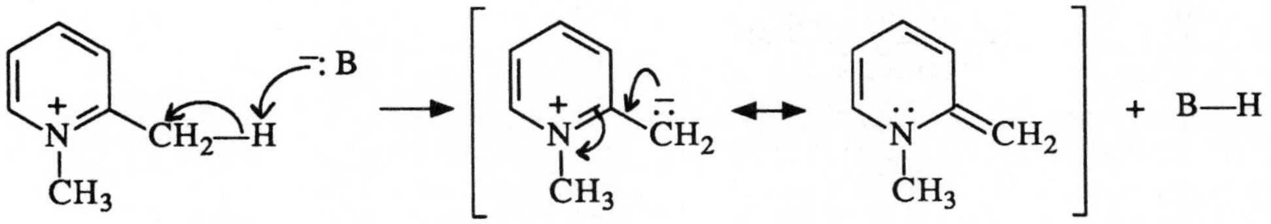

(c) The reaction is very much like a carbonyl substitution reaction. Hydroxide ion attacks carbon-2 of the benzimidazole ring because the positively charged nitrogen is a particularly good electron acceptor:

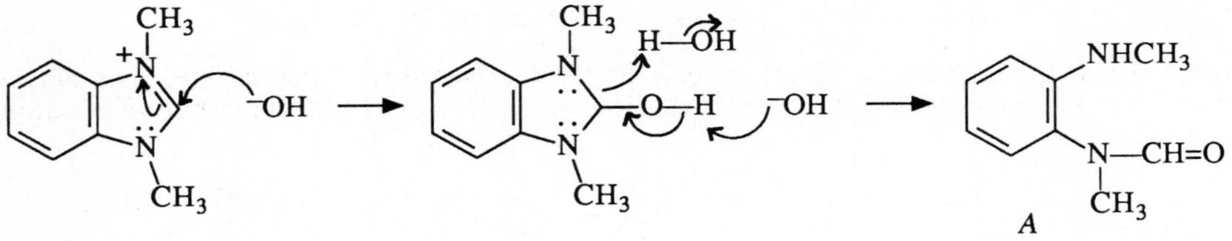

Amide *A* hydrolyzes to give the final products.

(d) Arsenic is much more electropositive (that is, much less electronegative) than nitrogen. Thus, introduction of a positive charge into an arsabenzene ring is much less difficult than introduction of a positive charge into a pyridine ring. Indeed, arsenic is sufficiently electropositive that resonance structures such as the following are important (E = an electrophile):

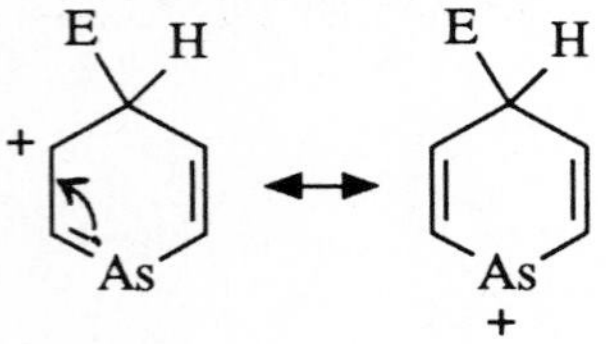

A positive charge can reside on arsenic only if substitution occurs in the 2- or 4-position. (Analogous resonance structures for pyridine are *not* important; see Eq. 24.48b.)

(e) Exchange occurs when the conjugate-base anion is formed by abstraction of one of the protons shown in color; this anion then reacts with the deuterated solvent to form the deuterium-substituted compound. The anion involved in this exchange is readily formed because it is resonance-stabilized in such a way that negative charge is delocalized onto both a nitrogen and an oxygen, which are electronegative atoms:

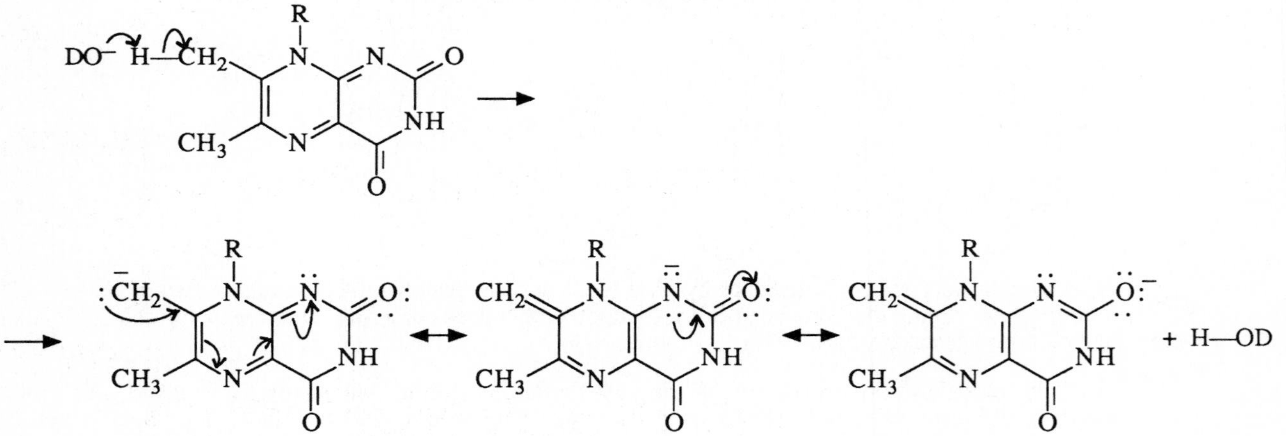

Analogous delocalization to electronegative atoms is not possible for the anion derived by proton abstraction from the other methyl group. Hence, this anion is less stable, and it does not form.

48. Step (1) is an aromatic nitration, which can be effected with HNO_3 and H_2SO_4. Nitration in the open position is activated by the unshared electron pair on the ring nitrogen. Step (2) is analogous to the reaction shown in Eq. 24.61, text page 1072, and therefore requires PCl_5. Step (3) is a reduction of both the nitro group and the nitrile; catalytic hydrogenation is called for here. Evidently, this hydrogenation also removes the 2-chloro group. If we recall that a 2-chloropyridine derivative has reactivity that is similar to that of an acid chloride, we see that this reaction resembles the reduction of an acid chloride to an aldehyde (Rosenmund reduction; Eq. 21.62, text page 895). Step (4) is an ether cleavage, which is brought about by concentrated aqueous HBr.

Step (5) involves a diazotization with $NaNO_2/H_2SO_4$. The diazonium ion that is formed reacts with solvent water to give the alcohol. (Elimination is not possible; there are no β-hydrogens.)

49. (a) In this reaction, sodium methoxide forms the enolate of the β-keto ester. This enolate ion attacks the diazonium ion at its terminal nitrogen. A reverse Dieckmann condensation and protonation afford the product.

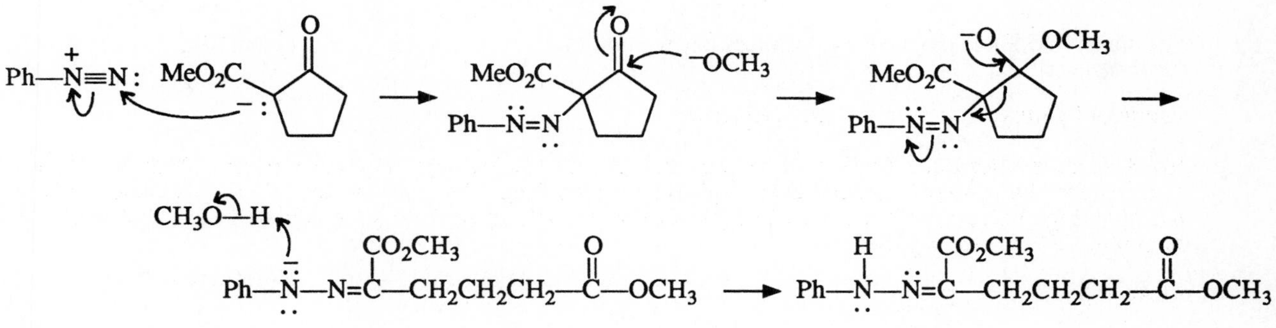

(b) The following indole would be formed:

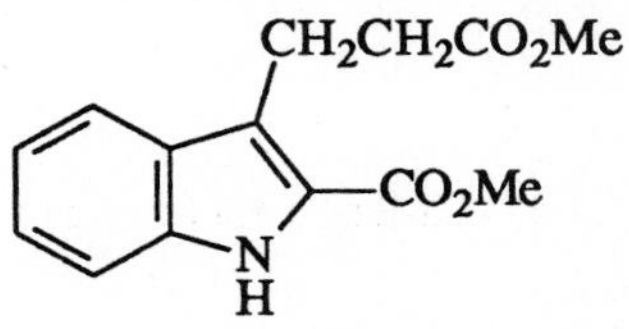

(c) A Fischer indole synthesis and the required arylhydrazine are as follows:

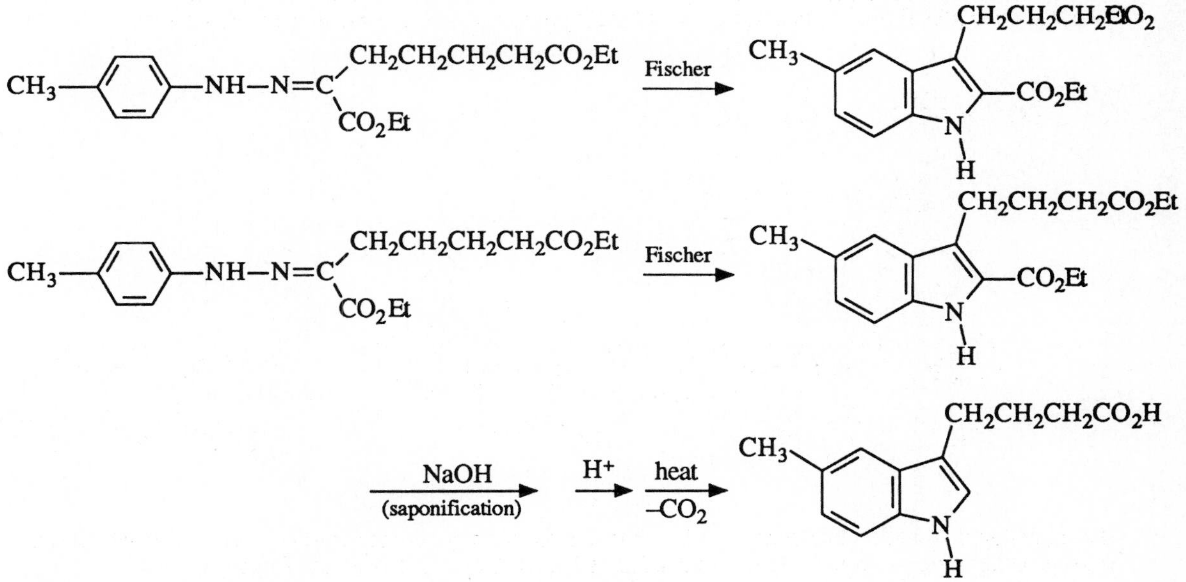

The arylhydrazine is prepared, by analogy with the reaction shown in the problem, as follows:

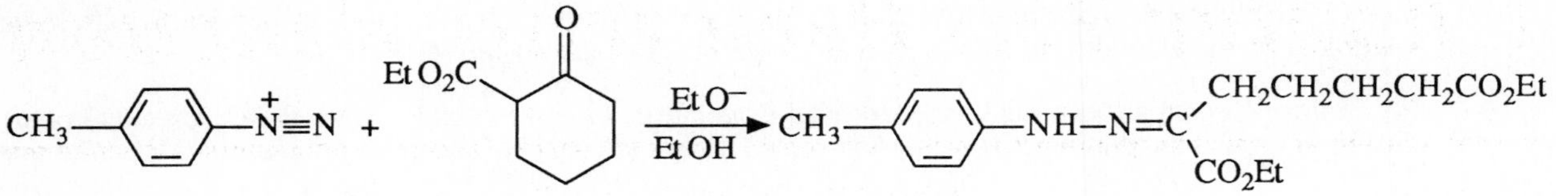

The diazonium ion is prepared by diazotization of *p*-toluidine, which, in turn, comes from toluene by way of nitrobenzene:

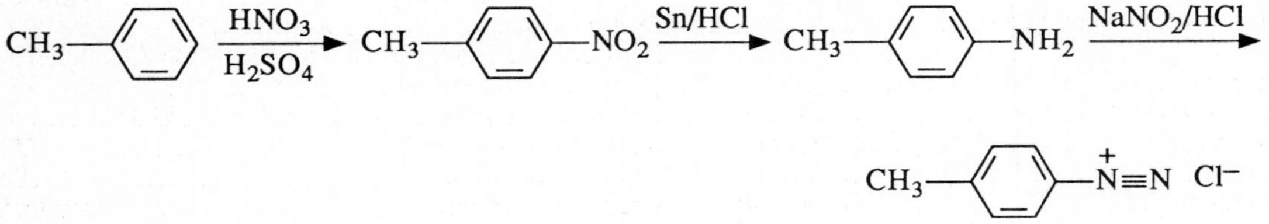

Finally, ethyl 2-oxo-1-cyclohexanecarboxylate (the β-keto ester required in the synthesis of the phenylhydrazine derivative) is prepared by a Dieckmann condensation of diethyl pimelate in the presence of one equivalent of sodium ethoxide.

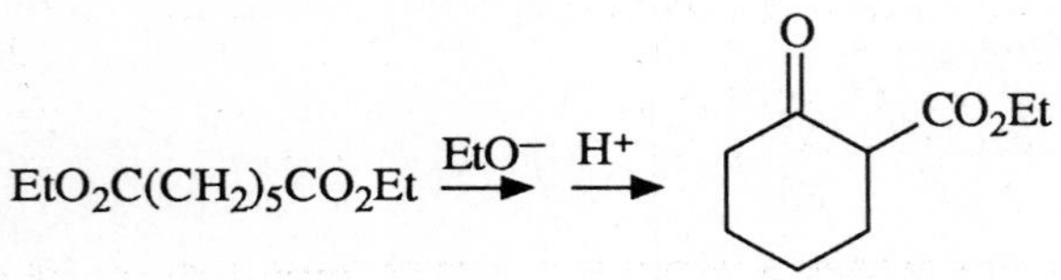

$$EtO_2C(CH_2)_5CO_2Et \xrightarrow{\; EtO^- \;} \xrightarrow{\; H^+ \;}$$

Chapter 25 / Pericyclic Reactions

CHAPTER 25 TERMS

allowed transition 25.2A
antarafacial 25.3
antibonding molecular orbital (ψ^*) 25.1A
antisymmetric MO (A) 25.1A
bonding molecular orbital (ψ) 25.1A
Claisen rearrangement 25.4B
concerted reaction .... Introduction
conrotatory 25.2A
Cope rearrangement 25.4B
[2 + 2] cycloaddition 25.3
[2s + 4a] cycloaddition 25.3
[2s + 4s] cycloaddition 25.3
[4 + 2] cycloaddition 25.3
cycloaddition reaction .... Introduction
disrotatory 25.2A
electrocyclic reaction .... Introduction
excited state 25.1C
fluxional molecule 25.6

forbidden transition 25.2A
frontier–orbital theory .... Introduction
ground state 25.1C
highest occupied molecular orbital (HOMO) 25.1A
[1,3] hydrogen shift 25.4A
lowest unoccupied molecular orbital (LUMO) ... 25.1A
nonbonding molecular orbital 25.1B
oxyCope reaction 25.4B
pericyclic reaction .... Introduction
pericyclic selection rules 25.2B
photochemical reaction 25.2B
reference plane 25.1A
[1,5] sigmatropic migration 25.4A
sigmatropic reaction 25.4A
[3,3] sigmatropic rearrangement 25.4B
suprafacial 25.3
symmetric MO (S) 25.1A
thermal reaction 25.2B

CHAPTER 25 CONCEPTS

I. Molecular Orbitals of Conjugated π-Electron Systems:

A. <u>Molecular Orbitals of Conjugated Alkenes</u>:
   1. The overlap of p orbitals to give π-molecular orbitals is described by quantum-theory mathematics.
   2. The π-molecular orbitals for ethylene and ordinary conjugated alkenes can be constructed according to the following generalizations:
      a) A π-electron system derived from the interaction of a number m of p orbitals contains m π-molecular orbitals (MOs) that differ in energy.
      b) Conjugated alkenes have two types of π-molecular orbitals:
         (1) **Bonding π-molecular orbitals** (half of the π-molecular orbitals) that have lower energy than the isolated p orbitals.
         (2) **Antibonding π-molecular orbitals** (half of the π-molecular orbitals) that have higher energy than the isolated p orbitals.

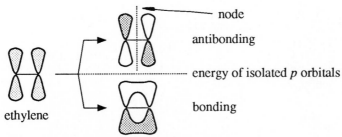

[See Fig. 25.1, text page 1094, and Fig. 25.2, text page 1095.]

c) The bonding π-molecular orbital of lowest energy, ψ_1, has no nodes *between* the atoms; each π-molecular orbital of increasingly higher energy has one additional node.

(1) The nodes occur *between* atoms and are arranged symmetrically with respect to the center of the π-electron system.

(2) A plane through the center of the π-electron system and perpendicular to the plane of the molecule is called the **reference plane**.

     (*a*) **Symmetric π-molecular orbitals (S)** have peaks that reflect through the reference plane into peaks, and troughs into troughs.

     (*b*) **Antisymmetric π-molecular orbitals (A)** have peaks that reflect through the reference plane into troughs, and troughs that reflect into peaks.

(3) The first π-molecular orbital (ψ_1) is symmetric with respect to the reference plane; π-molecular orbitals of progressively higher energy alternate in symmetry.

d) Electrons are placed pairwise into each π-molecular orbital, beginning with the orbital of lowest energy.

3. There are two π-molecular orbitals of particular importance in understanding pericyclic reactions:

a) The **highest occupied π-molecular orbital (HOMO)**.

b) The **lowest unoccupied π-molecular orbital (LUMO)**.

c) The HOMO and LUMO of any given compound have opposite symmetry.

HOMO   1,3-butadiene   LUMO   [See Fig. 25.2, text page 1096, Fig. 25.4, text page 1098, and Fig. 25.5, text page 1099.]

antisymmetric   symmetric

B. Molecular Orbitals of Conjugated Ions and Radicals:

1. Conjugated unbranched ions and radicals have an odd number of carbon atoms.

2. The π-molecular orbitals of such species follow many of the same patterns as those of conjugated alkenes, with two important differences:

a) One π-molecular orbital is neither bonding nor antibonding, but has the same energy as the isolated p orbitals; this is called a **nonbonding π-molecular orbital**.

b) In some of the π-molecular orbitals, nodes pass *through* carbon atoms.

3. The charge in a conjugated carbanion can be associated with the electrons in its HOMO.

4. Cations, radicals, and anions involving the same π-system have the same π-molecular orbitals; they differ only in the *number* of π-electrons.

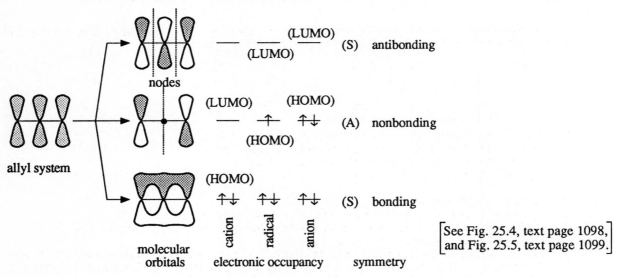

allyl system

nodes

       (LUMO)   (LUMO)   (S)   antibonding

       (LUMO)   (HOMO)   (A)   nonbonding

       (HOMO)

       (HOMO)   (S)   bonding

molecular orbitals   cation radical anion   [See Fig. 25.4, text page 1098, and Fig. 25.5, text page 1099.]

              electronic occupancy   symmetry

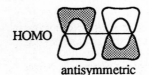

C. <u>Excited States</u>:
   1. The normal electronic configuration of a compound is called the **ground state**.
   2. Some molecules and ions can absorb energy from light of certain wavelengths to promote an electron from the HOMO of the ground state to the LUMO.
      a) The species with the promoted electron is in an **excited state**.
      b) The HOMOs of the ground state and the excited state have opposite symmetries.

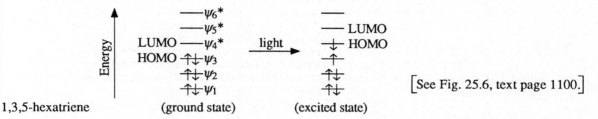

1,3,5-hexatriene   (ground state)   (excited state) $\Big[$See Fig. 25.6, text page 1100.$\Big]$

II. Pericyclic Reactions:

A. <u>Introduction</u>:
   1. **Pericyclic reactions** are defined as reactions that occur by a concerted cyclic shift of electrons— reactant bonds are broken and product bonds are formed at the same time, without intermediates.
   2. There are three major types of pericyclic reactions:
      a) **Electrocyclic reactions**—a ring is closed at the expense of a conjugated double (or triple) bond.

      b) **Cycloaddition reactions**—two or more discrete π-electron systems react to form a ring at the expense of one double (or triple) bond in each of the reacting partners.

      c) **Sigmatropic reactions**—a σ-bond formally migrates from one end to the other of a π-electron system and the net number of double (or triple) bonds remains the same.

   3. Three features of any pericyclic reaction are intimately interrelated:
      a) The manner in which the reaction is activated (heat or light).
      b) The number of π-electrons involved in the reaction.
      c) The stereochemistry of the reaction.

B. <u>Excited-State Pericyclic Reactions</u>:
   1. When a molecule absorbs light, it is transformed into an excited state.
      a) Photochemical reactions are reactions that occur through electronically excited states.
      b) Thermal reactions occur through the ground state.
   2. The mode of ring closure in photochemical electrocyclic and cycloaddition reactions is opposite to that of pericyclic reactions that occur through electronic ground states; the HOMO of the excited state is different from the HOMO of the ground state and therefore has different symmetry.

C. Classification of Sigmatropic Reactions:
  1. In a sigmatropic reaction, a σ-bond formally migrates from one end of a π-system to the other, and the number of double or triple bonds remains the same.
  2. Sigmatropic reactions are classified by using bracketed numbers to indicate the number of atoms over which a σ-bond formally migrates.
      a) In some reactions, both ends of a σ-bond migrate; count the point of original attachment as atom 1.
      b) In other reactions, one end of a σ-bond remains fixed to the same group and the other end formally migrates.

D. Fluxional Molecules:
  1. A number of compounds continually undergo rapid sigmatropic rearrangements at room temperature.
  2. Molecules that undergo rapid bond shifts are called **fluxional molecules**; their atoms are in a continual state of motion associated with the rapid changes in bonding.

E. Pericyclic Selection Rules—Summary:
  1. The allowed stereochemistry of a pericyclic reaction follows from the phase relationships within the molecular orbitals involved.
  2. The selection rules are summarized in Tables 25.1, 25.2, and 25.3 on text pages 1103, 1108, and 1118, respectively.
  3. An aid to remembering the selection rules is to assign either a +1 or a –1 to each of the following aspects of the reaction:
      a) The mode of activation:
          (1) For a thermal reaction, +1.
          (2) For a photochemical reaction, –1.
      b) The number of reacting electrons:
          (1) For $4n + 2$ electrons, +1.
          (2) For $4n$ electrons, –1.
          (3) The number of electrons involved in the reaction is determined by counting the electron pairs when the mechanism is written with curved arrows.

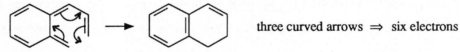

three curved arrows $\Rightarrow$ six electrons

      c) The stereochemistry of each component:
          (1) For a suprafacial or disrotatory reaction, +1.
          (2) For an antarafacial or conrotatory reaction, –1.
      then multiply together the resulting numbers:
      a) If the result is +1, the reaction is allowed.
      b) If the result is –1, the reaction is forbidden.
  4. The selection rules refer to the *rates* of pericyclic reactions and not the *position of the equilibria* involved.
      a) The selection rules do not tell which component of an equilibrium will be favored—only whether the equilibrium will be established in the first place at a reasonable rate.
      b) It is common for a photochemical reaction to favor the less stable isomer of an equilibrium because the energy of light is harnessed to drive the equilibrium energetically uphill.
  5. The principle of microscopic reversibility assures us that selection rules apply equally well to the forward and reverse of any pericyclic reaction, because the reaction in both directions must proceed through the same transition state.
      a) An electrocyclic ring opening *must* follow the same selection rules as its reverse, an electrocyclic ring closure.
      b) Allowed reactions are sometimes prevented from occurring for reasons having nothing to do with the selection rules. For example, steric crowding can prevent a formally allowed reaction from taking place.

CHAPTER 25 REACTIONS

I. Electrocyclic Reactions:

A. <u>Stereochemistry of Electrocyclic Reactions</u>:
    1. Electrocyclic reactions incorporate a ring closure at the expense of a double or triple bond; the carbons at each end of the conjugated π-system turn in a concerted fashion so that the *p* orbitals can overlap (and rehybridize) to form the σ-bond that closes the ring.
    2. The turning can occur in two stereochemically distinct ways.
        a) In a **conrotatory** closure the two carbon atoms turn in the same direction, either both clockwise or both counterclockwise.

conrotatory closure      or   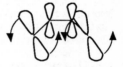

        b) In a **disrotatory** closure, the two carbon atoms turn in opposite directions; either the upper lobes of the *p* orbitals overlap, or the lower lobes of the *p* orbitals overlap.

disrotatory closure      or   

    3. The HOMO of the conjugated alkene contains the π-electrons of highest energy and governs the course of pericyclic reactions.
    4. When the ring closure takes place, the two *p* orbitals on the ends of the π-system must overlap in phase.
        a) The wave peak on one carbon must overlap with the wave peak on the other, or a wave trough must overlap with a wave trough.
        b) If a peak were to overlap with a trough, the electron waves would cancel and no bond would form.
    5. It is the relative orbital phase at the terminal carbon atoms of the HOMO (the orbital symmetry) that determines whether the reaction is conrotatory or disrotatory.
        a) Conjugated alkenes with $4n$ π-electrons (n = any integer) have antisymmetric HOMOs and undergo conrotatory ring closure. Conrotatory ring closure is *allowed* for systems with $4n$ π-electrons; it is *forbidden* for systems with $4n + 2$ π-electrons.
        b) Conjugated alkenes with $4n + 2$ π-electrons have symmetric HOMOs and undergo disrotatory ring closure. Disrotatory ring closure is *allowed* for systems with $4n + 2$ π-electrons; it is *forbidden* for systems with $4n$ π-electrons.

II. Cycloaddition Reactions:

A. <u>Stereochemisty of Cycloaddition Reactions</u>:
    1. Cycloaddition reactions involve the formation of a ring from two or more π-electron systems at the expense of one double or triple bond in each of the reacting partners.
    2. Cycloadditions are classified, first, by the number of electrons involved in the reaction with respect to each component.
        a) The number of electrons involved is determined by writing the reaction mechanism in the curved-arrow notation.
        b) The number of electrons contributed by each given reactant is equal to twice the number of curved arrows originating from that component.

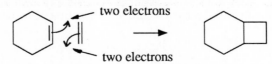

3. Cycloadditions are also classified by their stereochemistry with respect to the plane of each reacting molecule and may in principle occur either across the same face, or across opposite faces, of the planes in each reacting component.

   a) If the reaction occurs across the same face of a π-system, the reaction is said to be **suprafacial** with respect to that π-system—a *syn* addition that occurs in a single mechanistic step. A [2s + 4s] cycloaddition occurs suprafacially (or *syn*) on both the 2π component and the 4π component.

   b) If the reaction bridges opposite faces of a π-system, it is said to be **antarafacial**— an *anti* addition that occurs in one mechanistic step. A [2s + 4a] cycloaddition occurs suprafacially on the 2π component, but antarafacially (or *anti*) on the 4π component.

4. In order for a cycloaddition to occur, there must be bonding overlap between the *p* orbitals at the terminal carbons of each π-electron system.

   a) One component will donate the electrons in its HOMO, the other component will accept these electrons to form the new bond into the lowest *empty* molecular orbital, its LUMO.

   b) The two molecular orbitals used must have matching phases if bonding overlap is to be achieved.

5. The [2s + 2s] cycloaddition is forbidden by orbital symmetry under thermal conditions, but it is allowed under photochemical conditions.

   a) Under these conditions, it is the excited state of one alkene that reacts with the ground state of the other.

   b) The HOMO of the excited state has the proper symmetry to interact in a bonding way with the LUMO of the reacting partner.

   c) A [2 + 2] addition that is suprafacial on one component but antarafacial on the other is allowed by orbital symmetry, but is geometrically more difficult to accomplish.

6. All-suprafacial cycloadditions are allowed thermally for systems in which the total number of reacting electrons is 4n + 2, and photochemically for systems in which the number is 4n.

III. Sigmatropic Reactions:

A. <u>Stereochemistry of Sigmatropic Reactions</u>:

   1. Sigmatropic reactions can be classified by their stereochemistry; consider whether the migrating bond moves over the same face, or between opposite faces, of the π-electron system.

      a) If the migrating bond moves across one face of the π-system, the reaction is said to be **suprafacial**.

      b) If the migrating bond moves from one face of the π-system to the other, the reaction is said to be **antarafacial**.

      c) When both ends of a σ-bond migrate, the reaction can be suprafacial or antarafacial with respect to either π-system.

   2. The stereochemistry of sigmatropic reactions is a simple function of the number of electrons involved which, in turn, can be determined from the curved-arrow formalism by counting the curved arrows and multiplying by two. (See Table 25.3, text page 1118.)

      a) All-suprafacial sigmatropic reactions occur when there are 4n + 2 electrons involved in the reaction (an odd number of electron pairs, or curved arrows).

All-suprafacial
sigmatropic reaction

three curved arrows   keto form of a phenol

      b) A sigmatropic reaction must be antarafacial on one component and suprafacial on the other when 4n electrons are involved (an even number of electron pairs, or curved arrows).

c) When a single carbon migrates, the term "suprafacial" is taken to mean "retention of configuration," and the term "antarafacial" is taken to mean "inversion of configuration."

B. [1,3] and [1,5] Sigmatropic Rearrangements:
   1. The interaction of the LUMO of the migrating group with the HOMO of the π-system, or vice versa, controls the stereochemistry of the reaction.
      a) In the migration of a hydrogen, the orbital involved is a $1s$ orbital, which has no nodes.
      b) In the migration of a carbon, the orbital involved is a $2p$ orbital, which has one node.
      c) The shift of a carbon can occur in two stereochemically distinct ways:
         (1) Migration with retention of configuration.
         (2) Migration with inversion of configuration.
   2. In the allyl anion, the HOMO is antisymmetric:

   allyl anion

      a) The suprafacial [1,3] shift of a hydrogen is *forbidden.*
      b) The antarafacial [1,3] migration of hydrogen is *allowed* but not observed.
      c) The suprafacial [1,3] shift of a carbon is *allowed* with inversion of configuration.
      d) The antarafacial [1,3] shift of a carbon is *allowed* with retention of configuration but is not observed.
   3. In the 2,4-pentadienyl anion, the HOMO is symmetric:

                                                          2,4-pentadienyl anion

      a) The suprafacial [1,5] migration of a hydrogen is *allowed.*
      b) The antarafacial [1,5] migration of a hydrogen is *forbidden.*
      c) The suprafacial [1,5] migration of a carbon is *allowed* with retention of configuration.
      d) The antarafacial [1,5] migration of a carbon is *allowed* with inversion of configuration.

C. [3,3] Sigmatropic Rearrangements—Cope and Claisen Rearrangements:
   1. A [3,3] sigmatropic rearrangement is a reaction in which *two* groups migrate.
      a) The transition state of a [3,3] sigmatropic rearrangement can be thought of as the interaction of two allylic systems, one a cation and one an anion.

      b) The two molecular orbitals involved achieve bonding overlap when the [3,3] sigmatropic rearrangement occurs suprafacially on both components.
   2. The **Cope rearrangement** is a [3,3] sigmatropic rearrangement in which a hydrocarbon isomerizes.

                              $\xrightarrow{165-185°}$

3. The **oxyCope reaction** involves the initial formation of an enol; tautomerization of the enol into the corresponding carbonyl compound is a very favorable equilibrium that drives the reaction to completion.

4. In the **Claisen rearrangement**, an allylic ether undergoes a [3,3] sigmatropic rearrangement. If both *ortho* positions of an aryl allylic ether are blocked by substituent groups, the *para*-substituted derivative is obtained by a sequence of two Claisen rearrangements, followed by tautomerization of the product to the phenol.

CHAPTER 25 SOLUTIONS

Solutions to In-Text Problems

1. (a) An electrocyclic reaction. The arrow formalism:

or

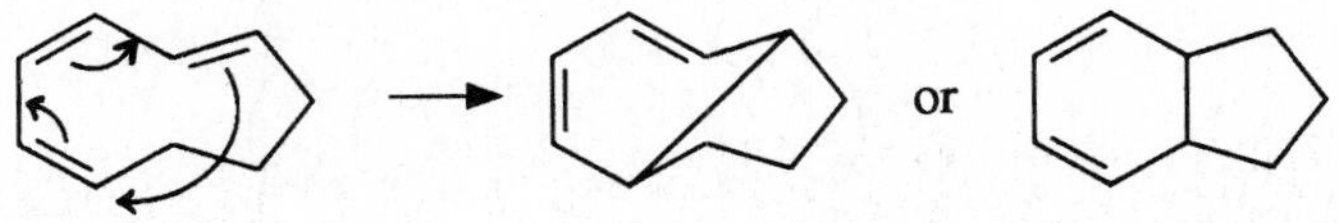

(b) A sigmatropic reaction. The arrow formalism:

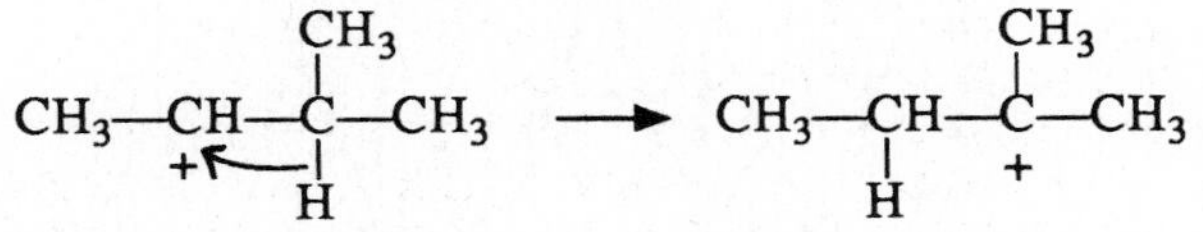

(c) A sigmatropic reaction. The arrow formalism:

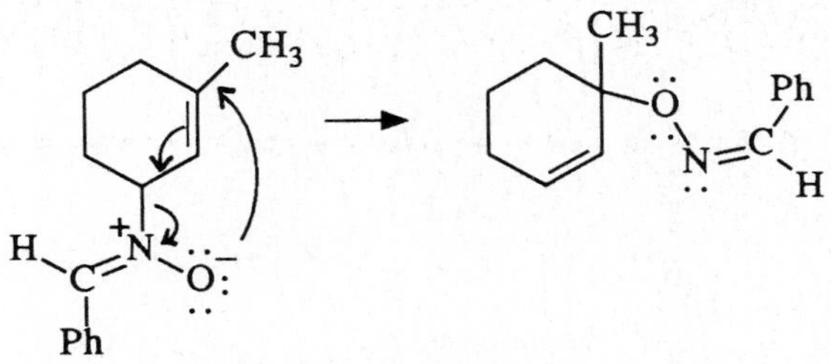

(d) An intramolecular cycloaddition reaction. The arrow formalism:

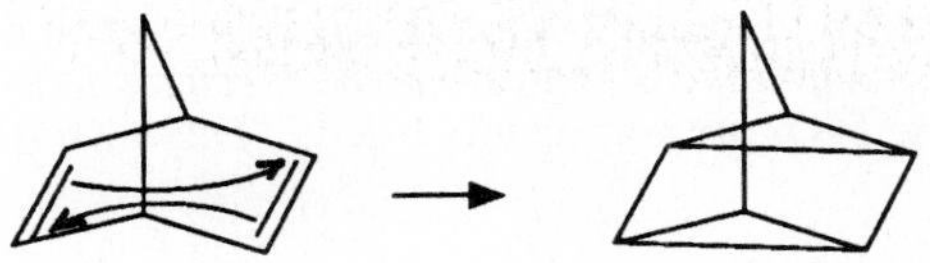

Why isn't this an electrocyclic reaction? Because an electrocyclic reaction closes a ring at the expense of a *conjugated* double bond. The double bonds in the starting material aren't conjugated.

(e) An electrocyclic reaction. The arrow formalism:

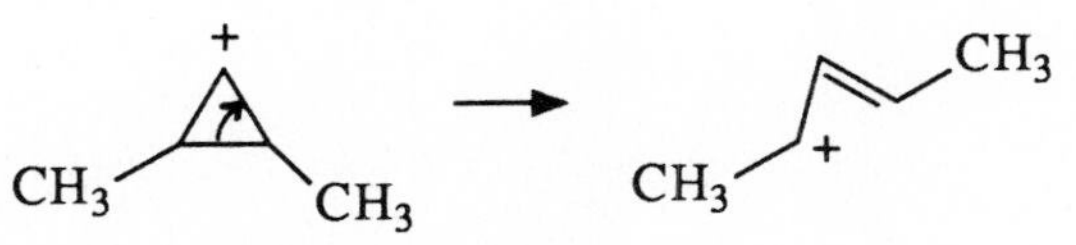

2.   In the following diagram, the bonding MOs are on the left, and are at lower energy than the antibonding MOs, which are on the right. Energy increases from bottom to top. Nodes are shown as dotted lines. Overlap occurs between adjacent orbitals when there is no node. Notice that nodes are placed symmetrically about the center of the π-electron system; the number of nodes increases by one as the energy increases; the symmetry of successive MOs alternates; and, since there are six component p orbitals, there are six π-molecular orbitals. The HOMO is ψ_3 and the LUMO is ψ_4^*.

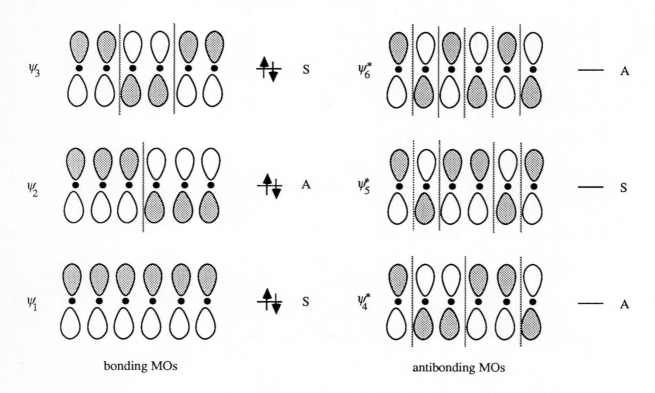

          bonding MOs   antibonding MOs

3.   (a) There are three bonding MOs. As in the solution to Problem 2, energy increases from bottom to top. Notice that the requirement for one node and an antisymmetric MO forces the node *through* the carbon in the middle of the π-electron system. This node means that electrons in this MO contribute *no electron density* at this carbon! In the heptatrienyl cation, radical, and anion these MOs are completely filled. (These MOs are diagrammed on the following page.)

➤ How did we know in the third MO to place the nodes between the second and third carbons from the end? Why not between the third and fourth carbons? The answer is that the mathematics of quantum mechanics tells us where to place the nodes. Since the appropriate formulas are not familiar to you, any placement of the nodes can be considered satisfactory for the purposes of this problem *provided* that the MO has the correct number of nodes and the correct symmetry. It will turn out for our purposes that the relative phases of the orbitals at the *ends* of the π-electron system will prove to be particularly important; the placement of nodes in the middle will not affect our conclusions.

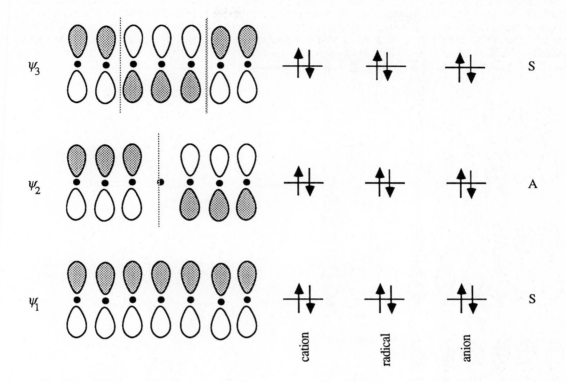

There is a nonbonding MO that lies at higher energy than the bonding MOs:

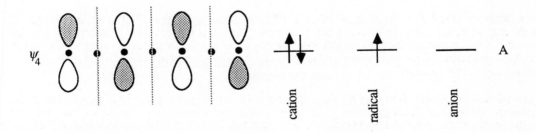

In the cation, this MO is empty; in the radical, this MO contains one electron; and in the anion, this MO contains two electrons. Finally, there are three antibonding MOs that lie at higher energy than the nonbonding MO. (These are shown on the next page.)

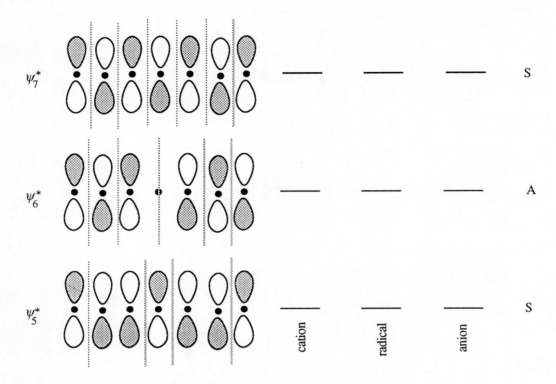

These MOs contain no electrons in either the cation, the radical, or the anion.

(b) The heptatrienyl cation is charged because the nonbonding MO lacks an electron. Hence, the distribution of the positive charge is dictated by the characteristics of this MO. In effect, there is positive charge wherever the MO has a nonzero value. Since there are nodes through carbons 2, 4, and 6, it follows that this cation has positive charge at carbons 1, 3, 5, and 7. Indeed, this is consistent with the resonance formalism:

4.   The MOs for the allyl system are shown in Figure 25.4. In the excited state of the allyl anion, ψ_1 contains two electrons; ψ_2 contains one electron; and ψ_3^* contains one electron.

5.   (a) There are six π-electrons involved, and the reaction as shown is disrotatory. The selection rules in Table 25.1 show that this process is allowed.
(b) There are also six π-electrons involved in this reaction, but the reaction as shown is conrotatory. Hence, it is not allowed, and therefore, if it occurs at all, does not take place by a concerted mechanism.

6.   The two conrotatory modes of ring opening are as follows:

(2)

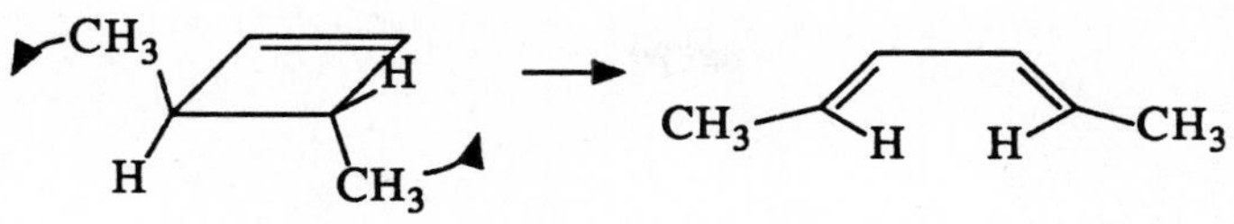

Mode (1) gives a product with substantial steric hindrance between the methyl groups. Hence, mode (2) is the observed reaction.

7.   The product is (1*E*,3*Z*)-1,3-cyclodecadiene, which is formed in a conrotatory ring opening. The *trans* double bond does not introduce significant strain into a large ring.

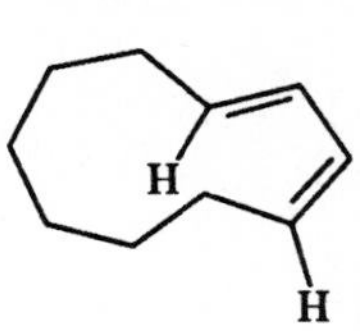

8.   The product is the following compound:

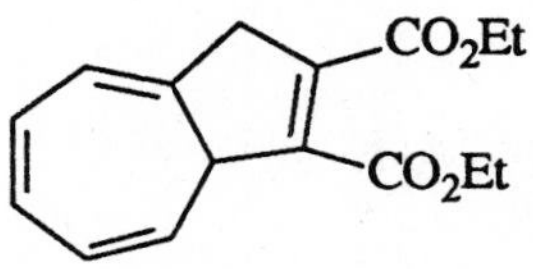

9.   The four products are the stereoisomeric 1,2,3,4-tetramethylcyclobutanes:

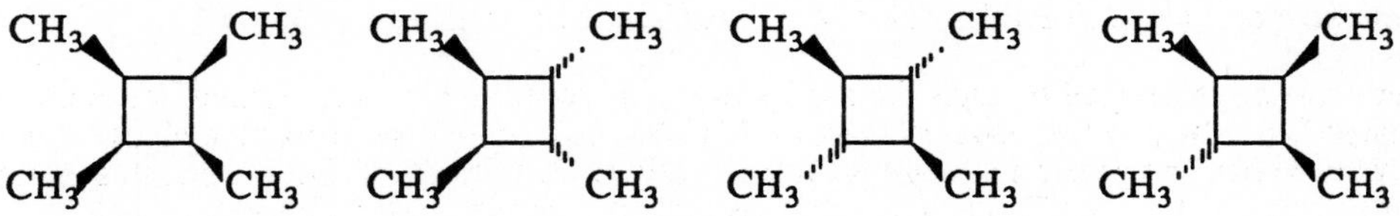

All are formed in photochemical [2*s* + 2*s*] cyclizations.

10.   This reaction is a [1,7] sigmatropic reaction in which a hydrogen migration occurs with antarafacial stereochemistry.

11.   (a) [1,4]   (b) [2,3]   (c) [5,5]

12.   (a) [1,5] suprafacial sigmatropic hydrogen shifts can account for the observed reaction:

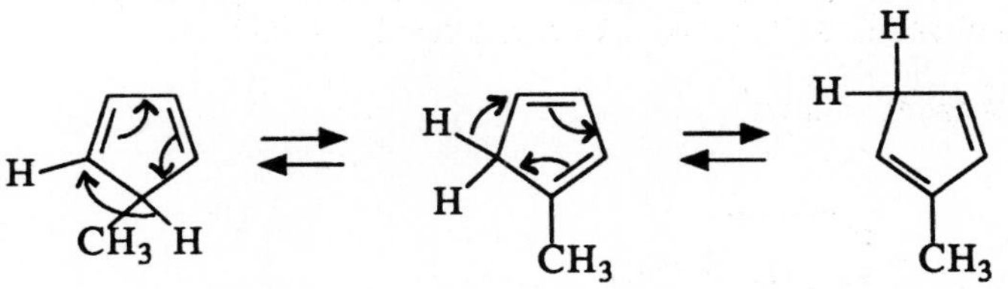

Be sure you understand why this is a [1,5] and not a [1,2] shift: We must take into account *all* the carbons involved in the π-electron system.

(b) Similar hydrogen migrations in 2,3-dimethyl-1,3-cyclopentadiene would give a mixture of three compounds:

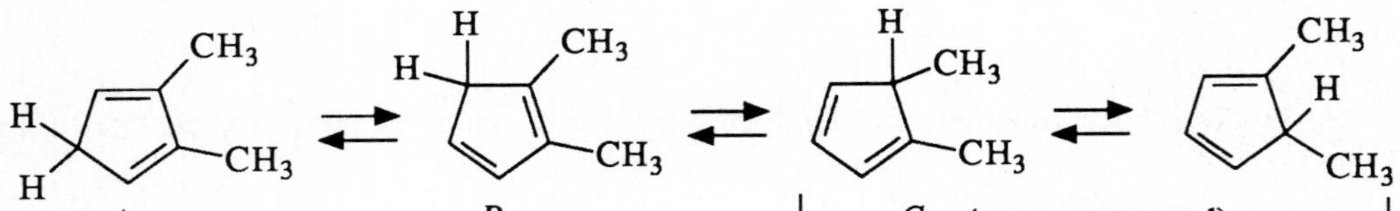

Products A and B would be expected to be the predominant products since they have more highly substituted double bonds than product C.

13. (a) Using skeletal formulas, the [3,3] sigmatropic rearrangement can be represented in the following way:

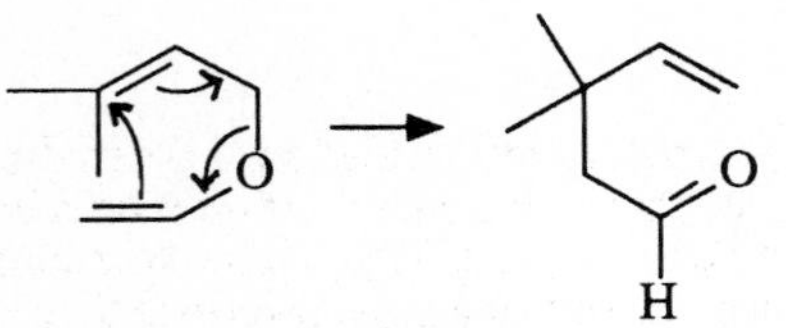

(b) If we think of a Claisen rearrangement analogous to the one in part (a) *in reverse*, we arrive at the following analysis:

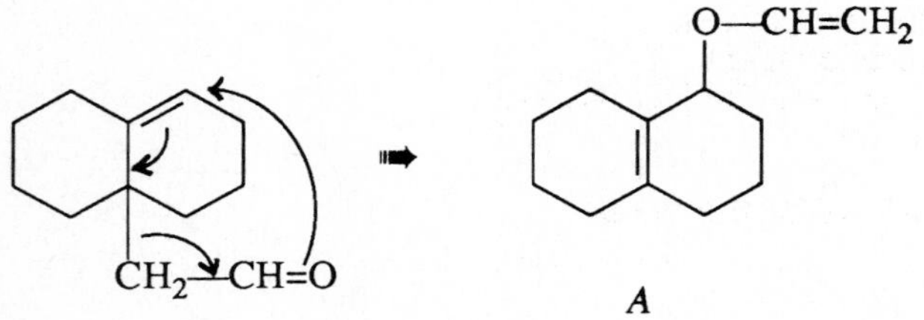

Compound A is therefore the required starting material.

14. (a) A [1,5]-suprafacial migration of carbon can be envisioned as the migration of a carbocation across the ends of a pentadienyl anion:

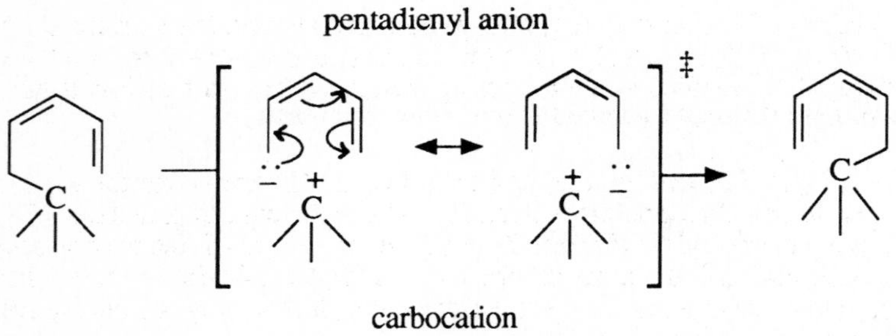

pentadienyl anion

carbocation

In the transition state, the HOMO of the pentadienyl anion (the nonbonding MO ψ_3 in Figure 25.5) interacts with the LUMO of the migrating carbon, which is simply a p orbital. Since ψ_3 of the pentadienyl system is symmetric, the carbocation p orbital must migrate with retention:

HOMO of pentadienyl anion

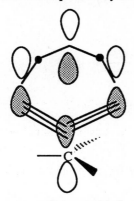

carbon *p* orbital

(b) The reactions are, from left to right, a [1,5]-sigmatropic carbon migration with retention, followed by two [1,5]-hydrogen migrations. Since the methyl group remains "up" in the first reaction, this migration takes place with retention of configuration, a result that is in accord with the analysis in part (a). The stereochemistry of the hydrogen migrations cannot be determined, but we can be confident from the selection rules that these also occur suprafacially.

15. (a) Stereochemistry: (+1)(−1); thermal reaction: (+1); and 4*n* electrons: (−1).
The product is (+1)(−1)(+1)(−1) = +1. The reaction is allowed.
(b) Stereochemistry: (+1); 4*n* electrons: (−1); thermal reaction: (+1).
The product is (+1)(−1)(+1) = −1. The reaction is forbidden.
(c) Stereochemistry: (+1); photochemical reaction: (−1); 4*n* electrons: (−1).
The product is (+1)(−1)(−1). The reaction is allowed.

16. (a) This process is very similar to the one that occurs in bullvalene:

This is an allowed, all-suprafacial [3,3] sigmatropic reaction.

(b) This is the "methyl walk" from Problem 54, Chapter 15. (The reaction is shown in the solution on page 314 of this manual.) This reaction, which involves two electrons (one curved arrow; 4*n* + 2 for *n* = 0) is allowed with suprafacial stereochemistry and retention at the migrating carbon. (Since this carbon is not asymmetric the stereochemistry at the migrating carbon is invisible.)

17. (a) As indicated in the text, previtamin D$_2$ is identical to previtamin D$_3$ (Eq. 25.41) except for the R-group. Ergosterol results from an allowed conrotatory photochemical electrocyclic ring closure of previtamin D$_2$. However, there are *two* conrotatory ring closures of previtamin D$_2$ possible: one in which the methyl and hydrogen groups rotate in a clockwise fashion, and the other in which the methyl and hydrogen rotate in a counterclockwise fashion. One closure gives ergosterol, as the problem states; the other gives lumisterol. Let us imagine an end-on view of the compounds as shown below:

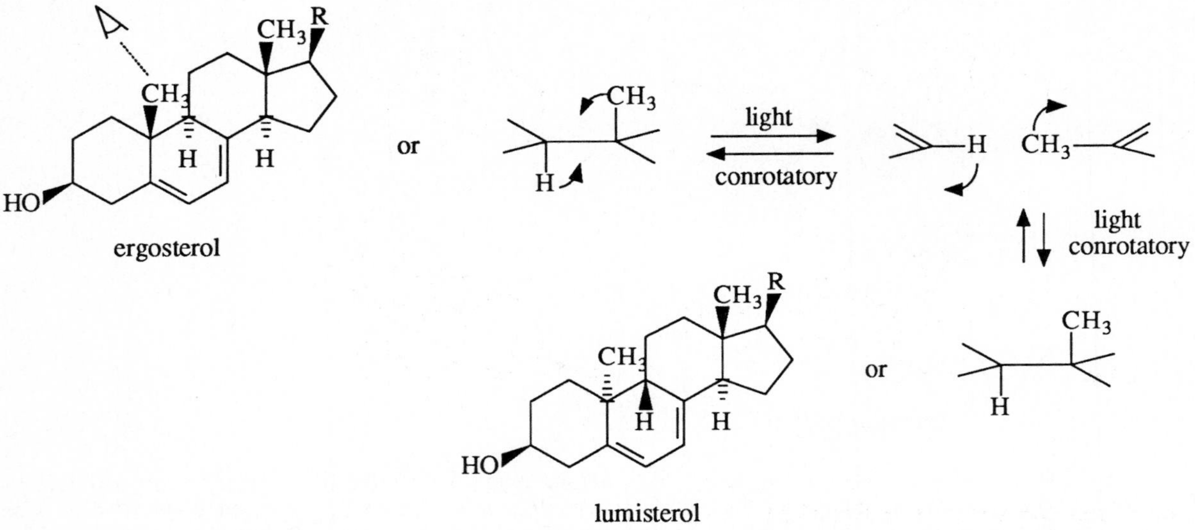

ergosterol

lumisterol

18. Heating previtamin D$_2$ should give the products of *disrotatory* ring closure. There are two such products corresponding to the two modes of disrotatory ring closure. We view the molecule as in Problem 17:

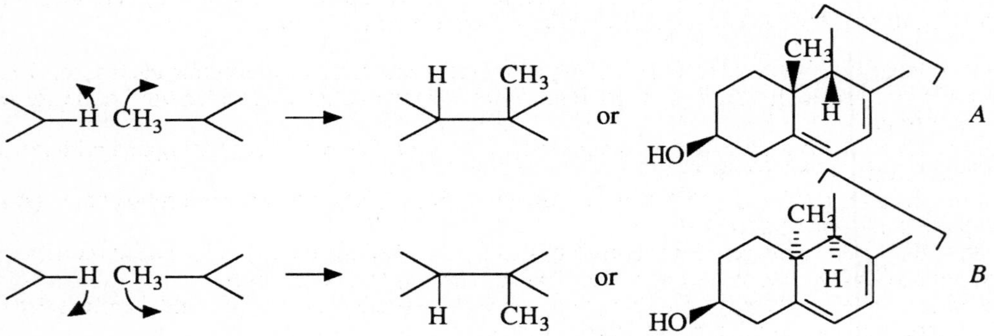

(The structures on the right are partial structures of the two products in which only the first two rings are shown.)

19. First, let us determine why irradiation of *A* and *B* does not give back previtamin D$_2$. Because $4n + 2$ electrons are involved, irradiation must give the product of *conrotatory* ring opening. In both possible conrotatory reactions, products containing a *trans* double bond within a six-membered ring would be obtained:

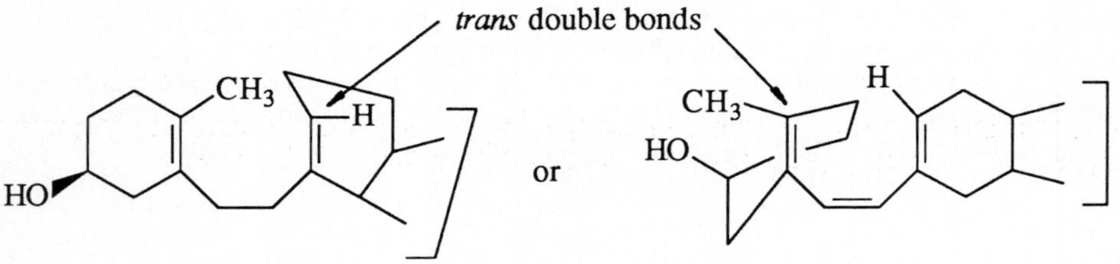

The only alternative to this reaction is a disrotatory process involving four electrons to give the following compounds containing cyclobutane rings:

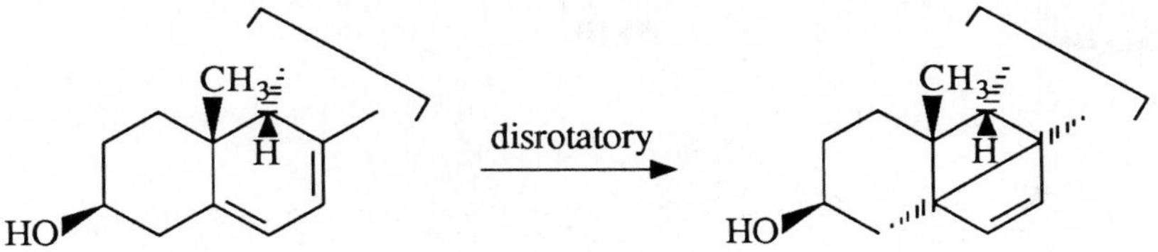

Solutions to Additional Problems

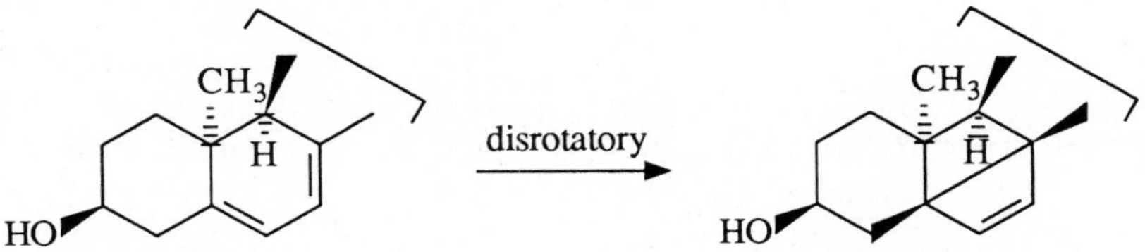

20. (a) Thermal, disrotatory, and $4n$ electrons: $(+1)(+1)(-1) = (-1)$, therefore forbidden.
(b) Photochemical, suprafacial, suprafacial, $4n$ electrons: $(-1)(+1)(+1)(-1) = (+1)$, therefore allowed.
(c) The highest occupied molecular orbital of a conjugated triene is ψ_3. Since orbitals of conjugated dienes alternate in symmetry, this MO is symmetric. (See the solution to Problem 2.) The methyl groups, to a useful approximation, have no effect on the nodal properties of the molecular orbitals.

21. The pericyclic selection rules say *absolutely nothing* about the position of equilibrium in each case. These rules refer to *rates* of reactions, not to equilibrium constants. We have to use other considerations to decide on the position of equilibrium.
(a) Equilibrium favors the right side of the equation because the double bonds are conjugated with the phenyl rings. (Conjugation is a stabilizing effect.)
(b) Equilibrium favors the left side of the equation because the double bonds are more substituted. (Alkyl substitution stabilizes a double bond.)
(c) Equilibrium favors the right side of the equation because a C=O double bond is formed at the expense of a C=C double bond. (C=O bonds are stronger than C=C bonds; see text page 963.)
(d) Equilibrium favors the right side of the equation because one product is aromatic and therefore particularly stable, and the other product is volatile (ethylene is a gas).
(e) Equilibrium favors the left side of the equation because the double bonds are conjugated with the carbonyl group.

22. (a) The formation of compound *B* is a ground-state (thermal) electrocyclic reaction involving eight electrons, and is therefore allowed when it occurs in a conrotatory mode. The methyl groups are therefore *trans*:

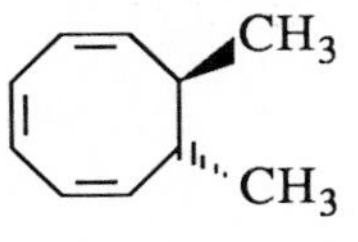

The second reaction is a thermal electrocyclic reaction involving $4n + 2$ electrons. Hence, the ring junction is *cis*. (The stereochemistry of the methyl groups is unaffected; therefore, they remain *trans*.)

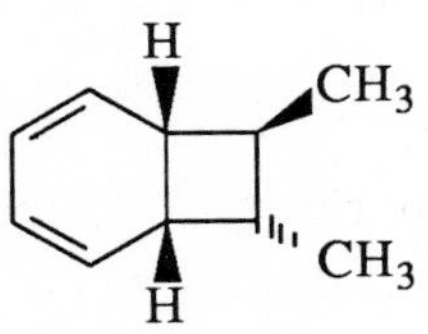

(b) The stereoisomer of A that also gives compound C is the one in which the terminal double bonds *both* have the Z configuration:

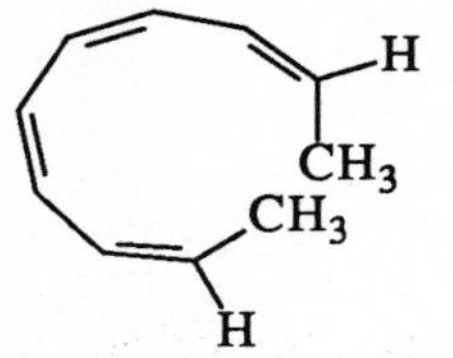

23. This can be viewed as either a [1,9] or a [1,13] sigmatropic rearrangement. In any of these three classifications the reaction is an allowed process that is suprafacial on the π-electron system and occurs with retention at the migrating carbon.

24. (a) The formula of the product indicates that an addition has taken place. A [2s + 2s] cycloaddition is photochemically allowed, and it would give the following product:

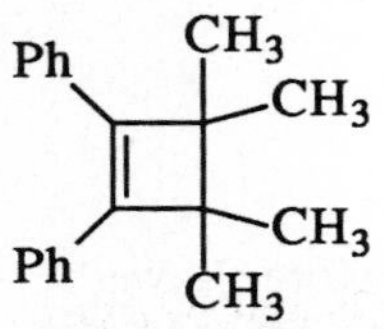

(b) This is an allylic ether. Such ethers undergo the Claisen rearrangement on heating:

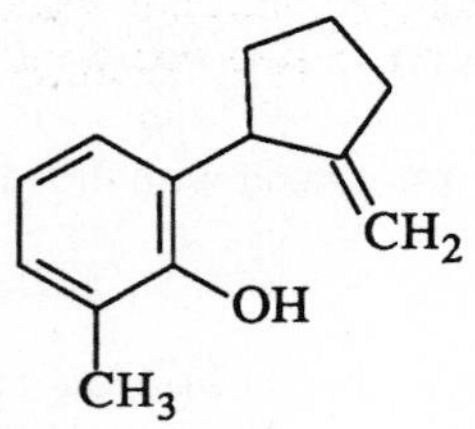

(c) This is a [4s + 2s] all-suprafacial cycloaddition; the exocyclic double bond in the triene is not involved in the reaction:

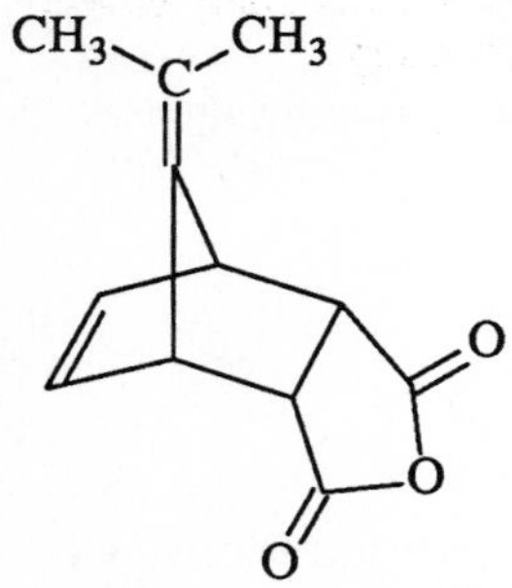

There are two other *formally* allowed reactions. One is a [2s + 6a] cycloaddition to give product A, and the other a [2a + 6s] cycloaddition to give product B:

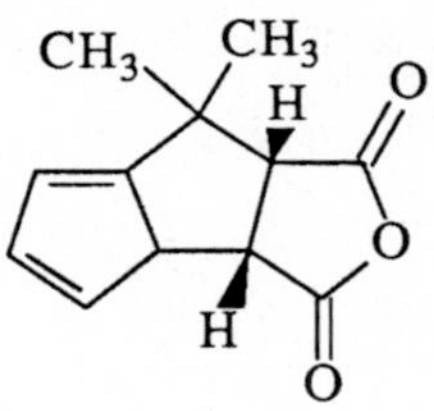

A 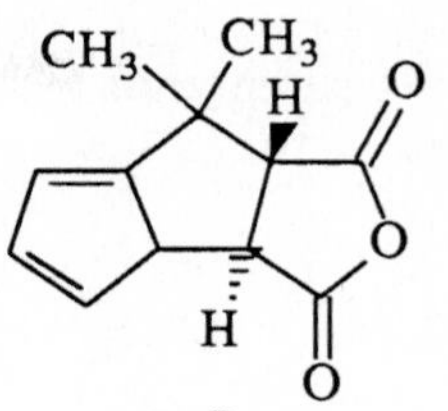   B

The transition states by which both of these compounds would be formed are highly strained and hence very unstable. As a result, the reactions that form these products are slower than the [4s + 2s] process and are therefore not observed.

25. The structure of the ozonolysis product C implies the following structure of B:

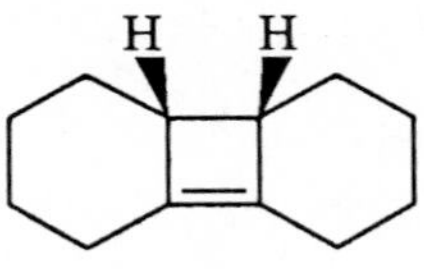

B

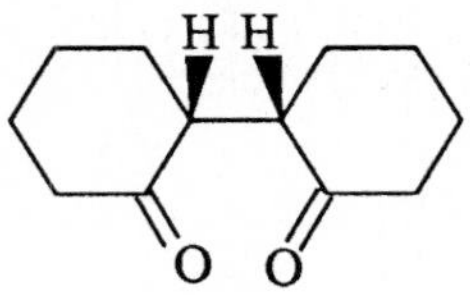

C

Because this is a photochemical electrocyclic reaction involving four electrons, it occurs in a disrotatory manner. As a result, compounds B and C have the stereochemistry shown above.

(b) If compound B were to open on heating, it would have to do so in a conrotatory manner; one of the resulting cyclohexene rings would contain a *trans* double bond. The resulting strain precludes this reaction. However, the following isomer of B, compound D, can open in a conrotatory fashion to give compound A:

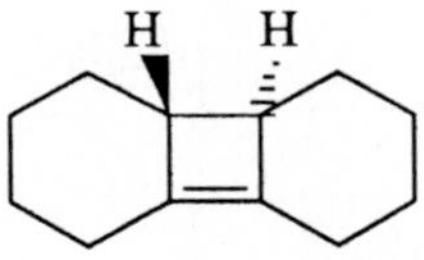

D

26. This reaction involves sixteen electrons. Hence, the reaction must be suprafacial on one component and antarafacial on the other. That is, it must be a [14s + 2a] or a [14a + 2s] cyclization. In fact, a twisting of the heptafulvalene molecule about the central double bond allows this reaction to accur antarafacially on the π-electron system of this molecule. Consequently, the product has *trans* stereochemistry:

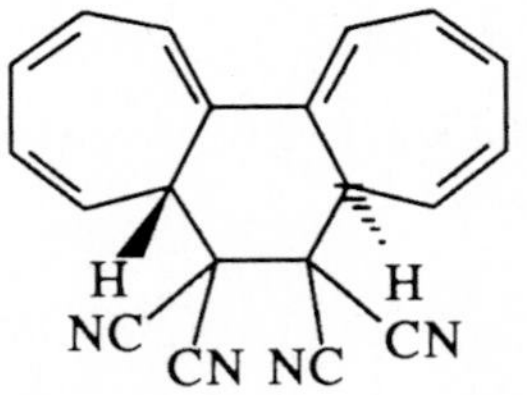

27. (a) This transformation is a sequence of two conrotatory electrocyclic reactions, one a closure, the second an opening:

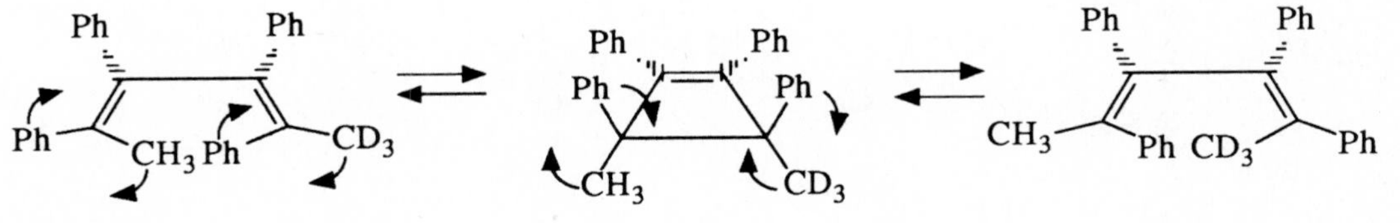

(b) This is a [3,3] sigmatropic rearrangement (a Claisen rearrangement):

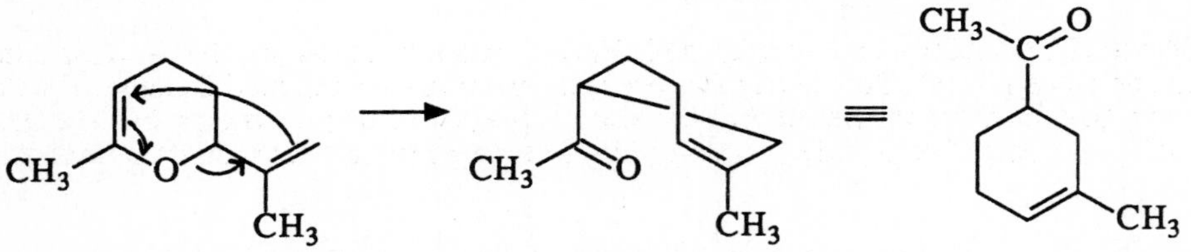

(c) The silver ion assists formation of a cyclopropyl cation (see Sec. 9.5C); this carbocation undergoes a disrotatory electrocyclic ring opening to an allylic cation that reacts with water to give the product.

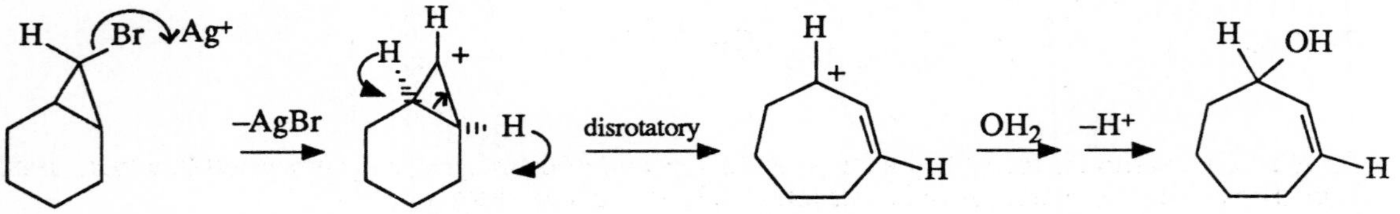

(d) This is a [3,3] all-suprafacial sigmatropic rearrangement in which the product requires a little redrawing!

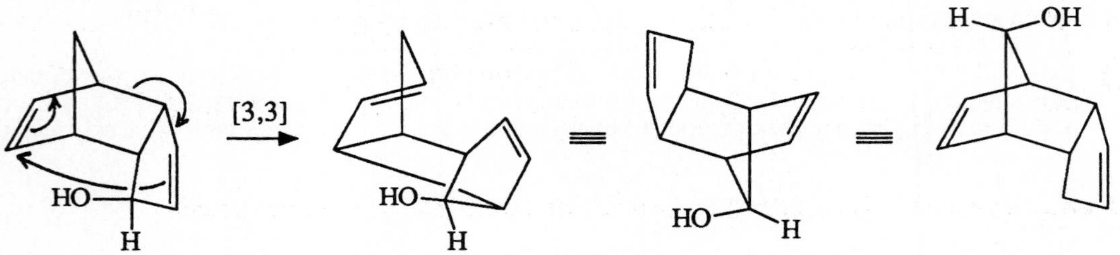

(e) This is a [1,3] suprafacial sigmatropic reaction with inversion in the migrating carbon:

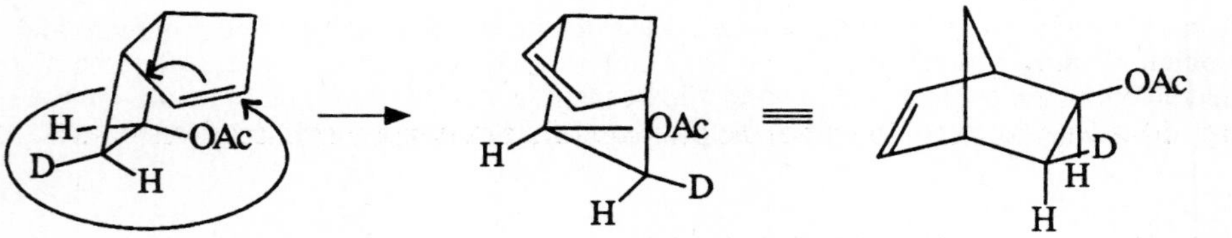

28. The first reaction is a Diels–Alder reaction (another name for a [4s + 2s] cycloaddition) to give compound A. This compound then undergoes a *reverse* Diels–Alder reaction.

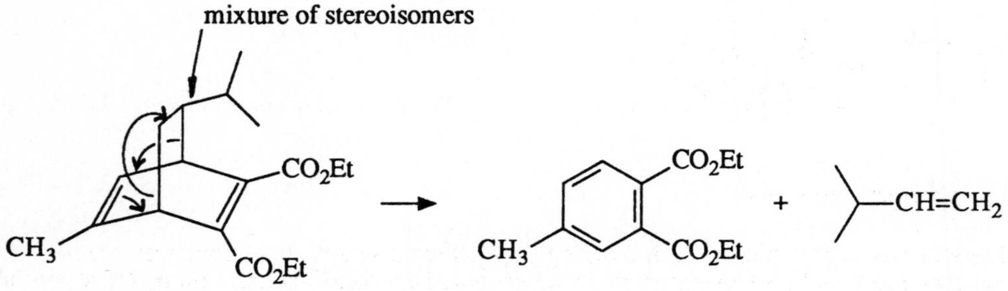

The last reaction is driven to completion by the aromaticity of the product and the formation of a volatile by-product. [See the solution to Problem 21(d) for a similar case.]

29. We start with two compounds: A (C_8H_{10}) and the alkyne ($C_6H_6O_4$). After the reaction, what is left is dimethyl phthalate ($C_{10}H_{10}O_4$) and compound D. Subtracting the formulas, we see that compound D must have the formula C_4H_6, and could be cyclobutene. The pattern here also fits the one in the previous problem: a Diels–Alder reaction followed by a reverse Diels–Alder reaction. The following structure for product C is consistent with the data:

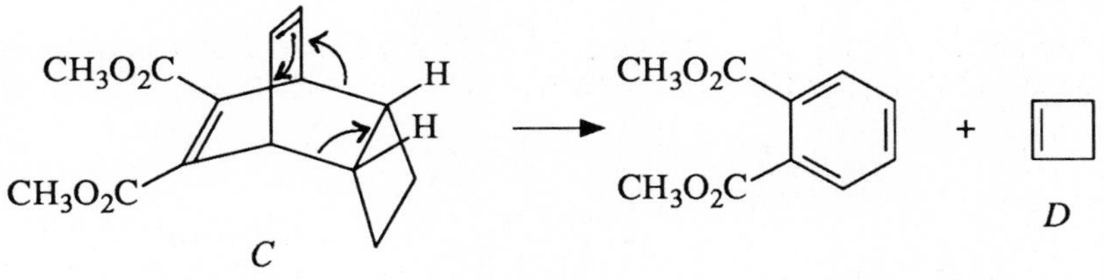

Compound C, in turn, is formed by a Diels–Alder reaction of the alkyne with compound B, which, in turn, is formed by a disrotatory electrocyclic reaction of 1,3,5-cyclooctatriene:

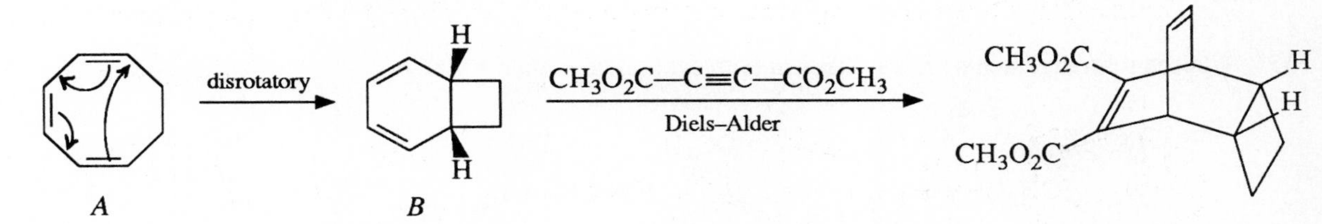

30. When we see an ether that is both allylic and vinylic, we think of a Claisen rearrangement!

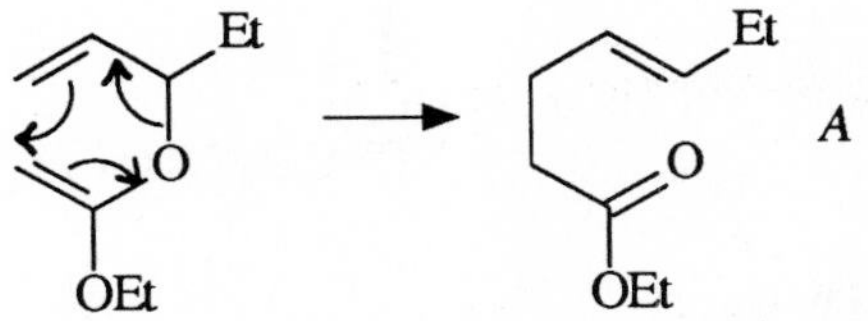

Compound A is ethyl (E)-4-heptenoate. (The E stereochemistry of the double bond is not determined by the data.)

31. A [1,5] sigmatropic hydrogen shift racemizes α-phellandrene:

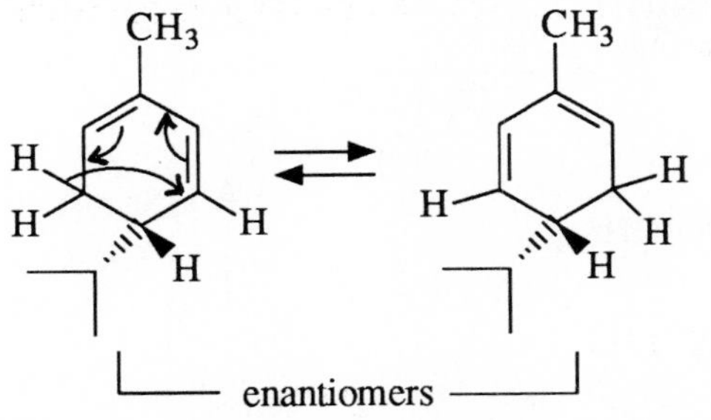

32. Compound A has an unsaturation number of 5. Judging from the structure of D, we conclude that four of the unsaturations are accounted for by a benzene ring; the other could be a double bond. Compound B appears to

be a phenol which forms a methyl ether C when its conjugate-base anion is treated with dimethyl sulfate. Ozonolysis results in the loss of one carbon to give D; hence, compound C has an allyl group that is converted by ozonolysis into the —CH_2CO_2H group. The structures of the unknowns are as follows:

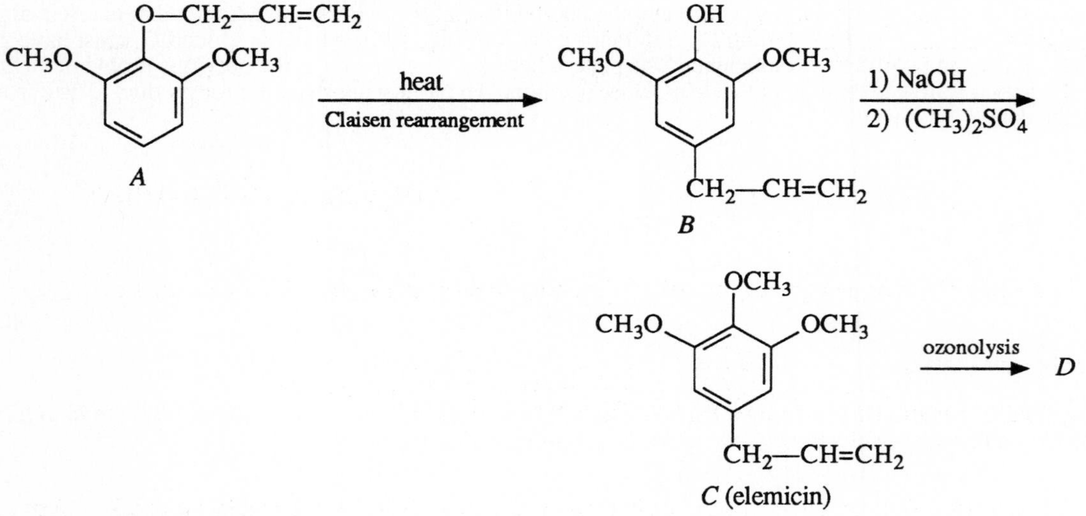

33. Claisen rearrangements are key steps in both syntheses:

(a)

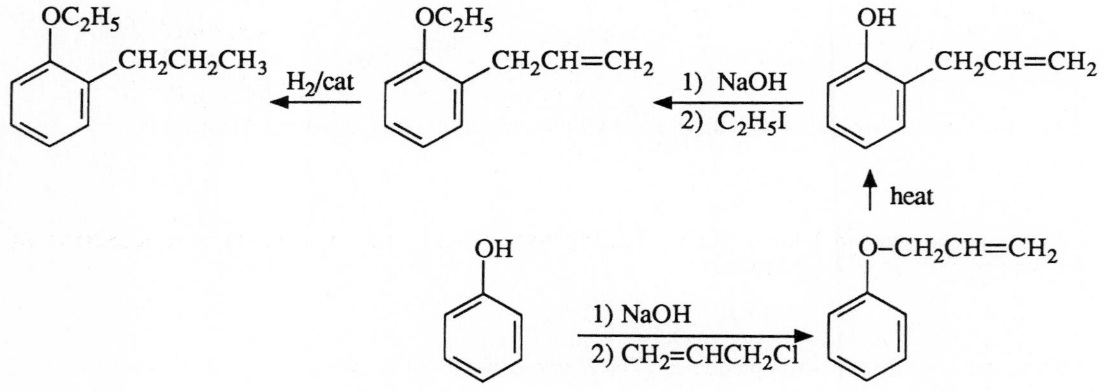

(b)

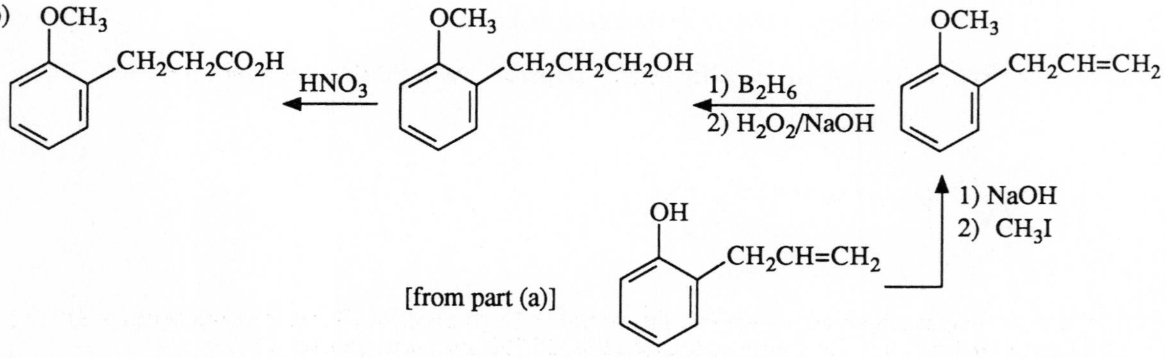

34. Compound *A* is a secondary alcohol, and the aldehyde *B* is formed in an oxyCope reaction by way of the enol intermediate in brackets:

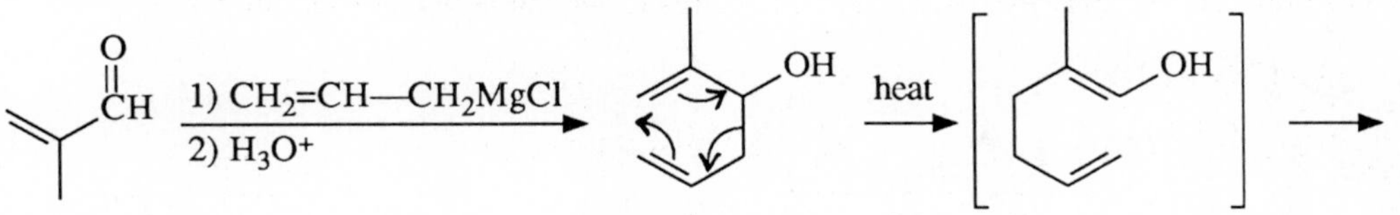

$$CH_2=CHCH_2CH_2\overset{\underset{|}{CH_3}}{CH}-CH=O$$

B

35. (a) Two successive disrotatory photochemical electrocyclic reactions account for the products:

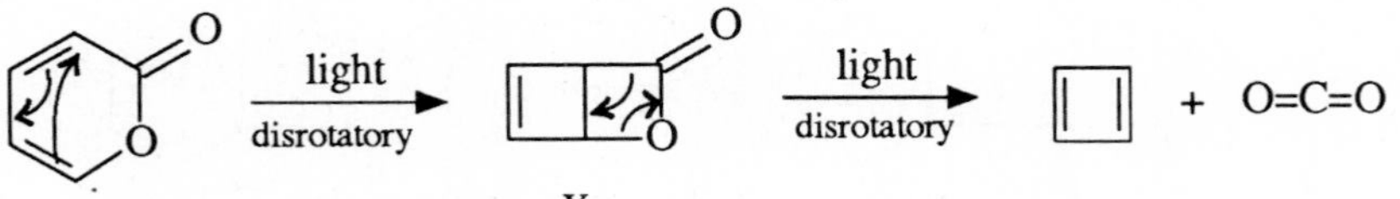

(b) A conrotatory electrocyclic reaction involving four electrons gives the intermediate triene *X*. All six π-electrons of the triene are involved in a subsequent *disrotatory* ring closure to give the final product:

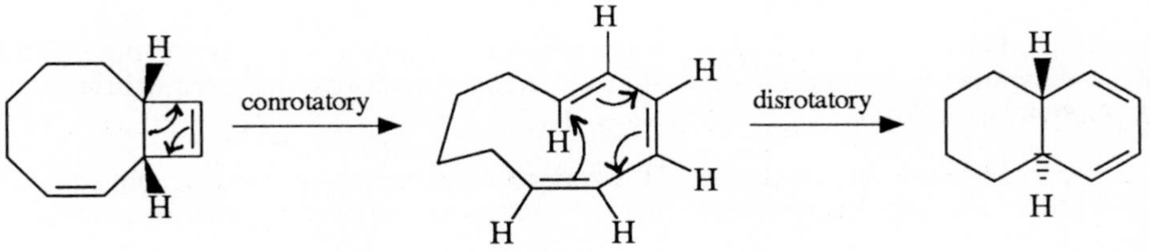

36. (a) The intermediate in this case is the following diene, which is formed from the starting material by a disrotatory electrocyclic ring closure:

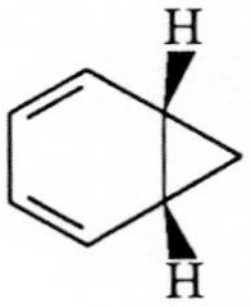

(b) The intermediate is the trienone formed in the first step of the Claisen rearrangement:

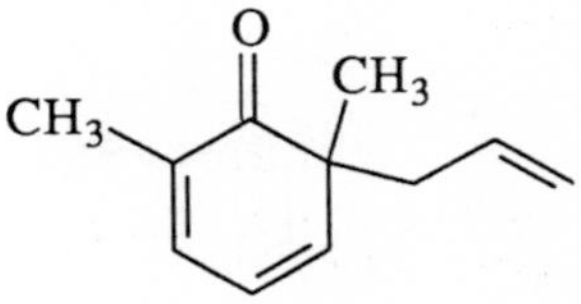

Were the maleic anhydride not present, this would undergo a second Claisen rearrangement to give a phenol with the allyl group in the *para* position (see Eqs. 25.39b and c on text page 1117).

(c) The intermediate trapped by the maleic anhydride is the tetraene formed by a [1,9] sigmatropic hydrogen migration:

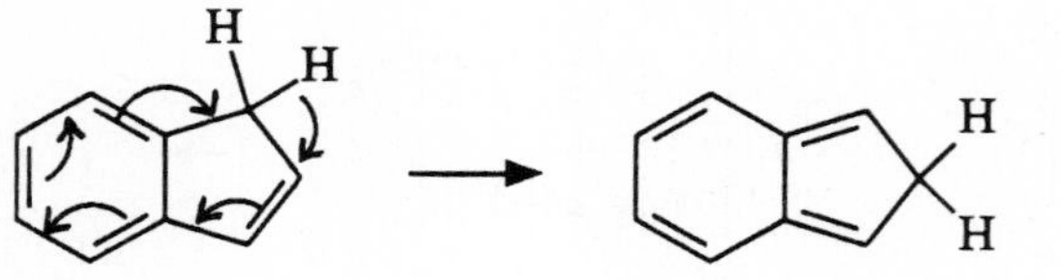

37. A thermal electrocyclic reaction of the carbocation (a protonated ketone) followed by loss of a proton from the resulting carbocation gives an enol. Since four electrons are involved, the reaction is conrotatory, and the methyl groups in the product are therefore *trans*:

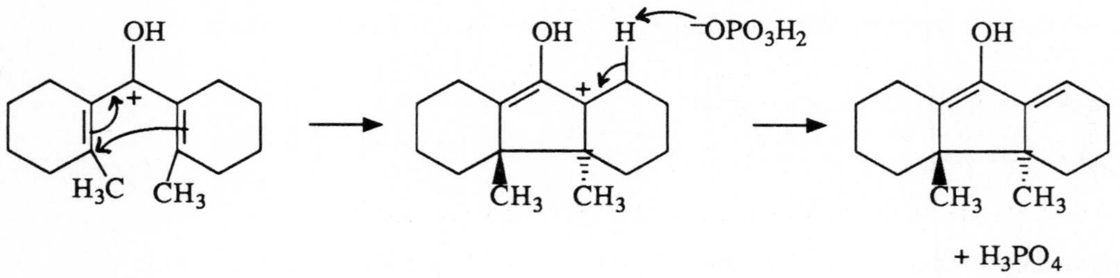

+ H_3PO_4

The product is the ketone corresponding to this enol.

➤ The orbital involved in this reaction is the HOMO of the pentadienyl cation, which is ψ_2 (Figure 25.5). Because this orbital is antisymmetric, a conrotatory twist of the terminal carbons is required to bring about in-phase overlap in the electrocyclic closure.

38. (a) A conrotatory ring opening gives intermediate *A*. This compound is no longer aromatic, but can undergo an intramolecular Diels–Alder reaction that restores aromaticity and forms the product with precisely the desired stereochemistry:

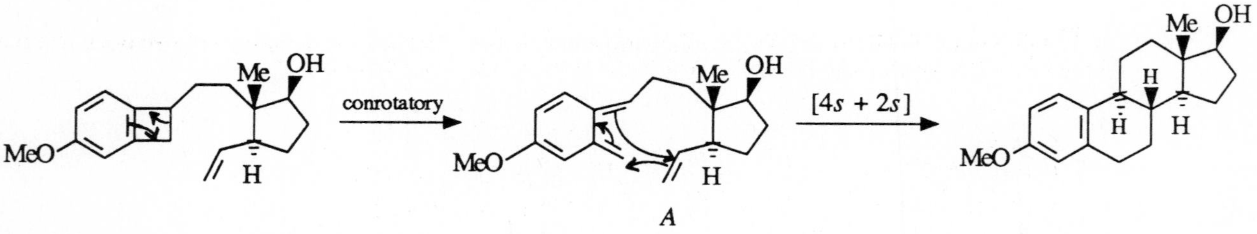

(b) Oxidation of the secondary alcohol and hydrolysis of the ether give estrone:

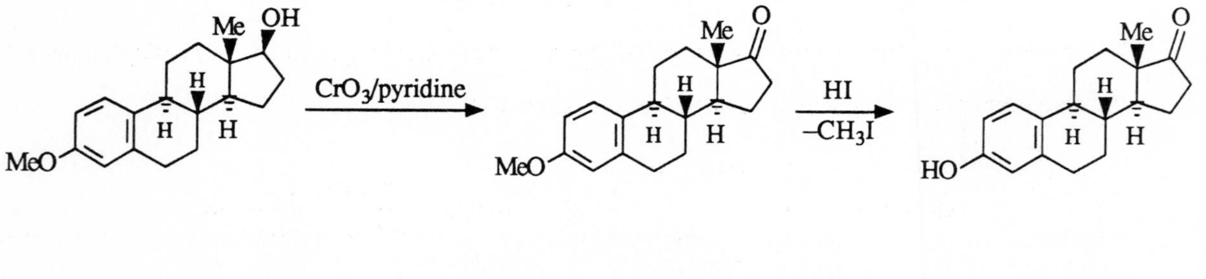

39. (a) Place the first diene in a chairlike conformation. (Models help to be sure that the configurations of the asymmetric carbons are correct.)

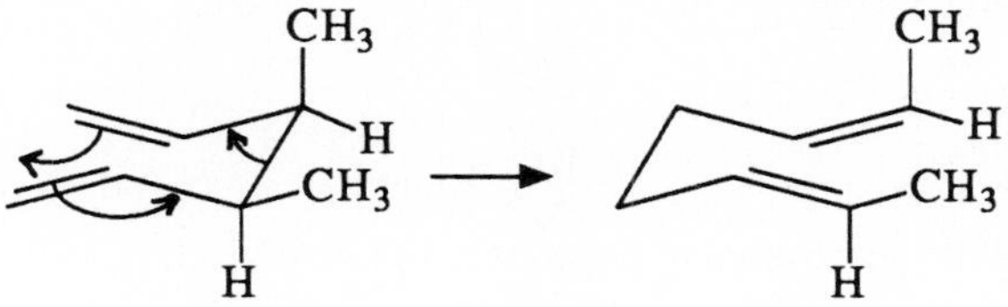

cis, trans (major product)

This indeed gives the major product. However, our job is not done until we ascertain that a boatlike conformation of this diene *does not* give this product:

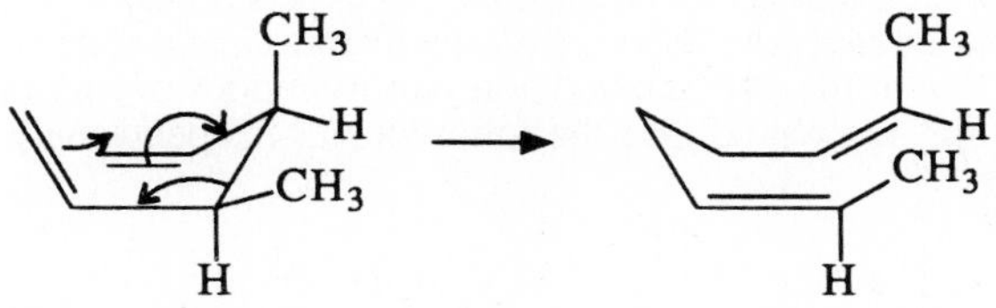

cis, cis diene

A second boatlike conformation is possible, but it gives the all-*trans* diene:

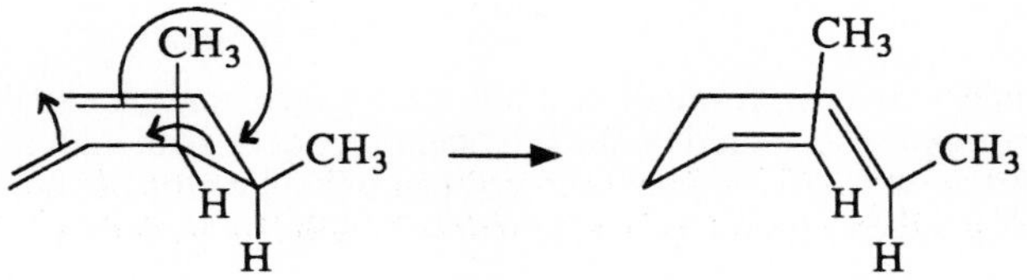

Since the *cis, trans* diene is observed, it seems that the reaction proceeds through the chairlike transition state. We leave it to you to verify a similar conclusion for the other alkene.

➤ Why are experiments with *both* alkenes necessary to establish that a chairlike transition state is preferred?

(b) Given that germacrone assumes a chairlike transition state when it reacts to give β-elemenone, we can deduce the structure of germacrone by mentally reversing the Cope rearrangement:

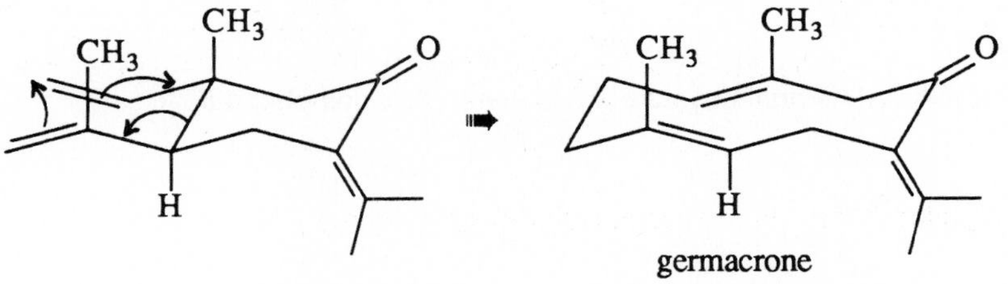

germacrone

➤ This is a very elegant synthesis of a compound containing a large ring from one containing a smaller ring.

40. The transformations leading to compound *C* are as follows:

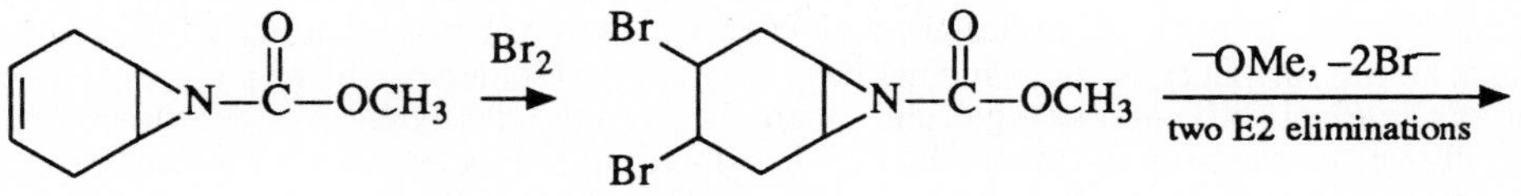

A

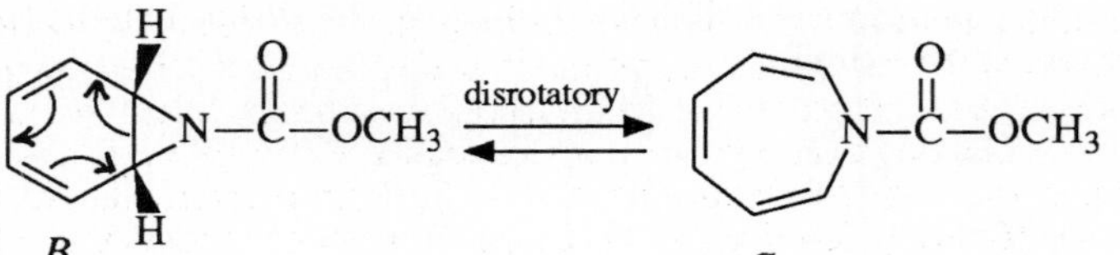

Reaction of compound *C* as a diene with the dienophile tetracyanoethylene gives the final product.

41. (a) If compound *A* is indeed aromatic, then it must be planar. If it is planar, the two inner hydrogens (shown in the structure of *A*) lie on top of one another. The high energy from the resulting steric repulsion is not outweighed even by the aromaticity of *A*.
    (b) The conclusions of part (a) remain as speculation until tested by experiment. An experimental test is to prepare compound *A* by a *stereochemically unambiguous reaction*. Naturally, a photochemical electrocyclic reaction fits the bill. Were compound *B* to undergo one of the two allowed conrotatory modes of ring opening, product *A* would form. (The other conrotatory ring opening would give the following all-*cis* pentaene:)

    (c) The formation of *C* suggests that compound *A* may have formed. If it did indeed form and then underwent an allowed *thermal* electrocyclic ring closure, compound *C* would be the predicted product! Although the all-*cis* pentaene shown above could in principle also close to give *C* in an allowed electrocyclic closure, it probably would not do so spontaneously, since the all-*cis* pentaene should be a reasonably stable compound.

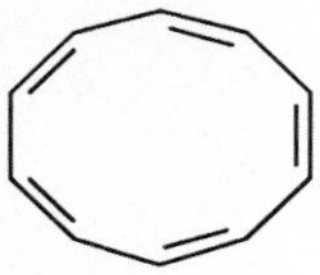

42. This sequence of reactions represents an effort (and a successful one) to prepare the 10π-electron system in the previous problem. In this case, the offending hydrogens are replaced by a —CH₂— bridge. The reactions leading to compound *A* are as follows:

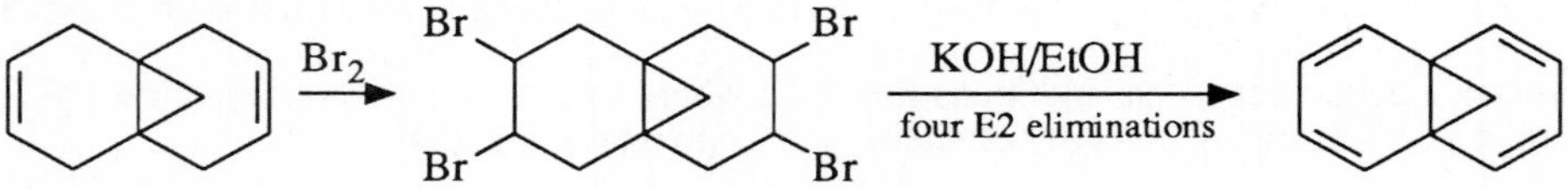

Compound *A* then reacts in an allowed thermal disrotatory reaction to give compound *B*:

The large ring in *B* — the pentaene unit — is nearly planar and should show evidence of aromatic behavior. The existence of a ring current was used as a test for aromaticity (see Sec. 16.3B). The eight protons that absorb at low field have chemical shifts very similar to the chemical shift of benzene protons. These protons are evidently the ones on the periphery of the pentaene ring; they are deshielded by the ring current. The two hydrogens at negative chemical shift — very high field — are those on the methylene bridge, shown explicitly in the structure of *B* above. These protons are shielded. This shielding is exactly what we would expect for protons situated in the *face* of an aromatic ring current. (See Figure 16.2 and Problem 4, Chapter 16 for a similar case.)

43. Bullvalene (text page 1120) should have distinguishable allylic and vinylic resonances. However, if the interconversion of the various forms of bullvalene is fast on the NMR time scale, these signals should average to one signal, because all protons of bullvalene are equivalent when averaged over all the possible forms. (You'll have to take our word that we examined all 1,209,600 forms to verify this conclusion; that's why it took so long to write this solutions manual.) At high temperature, the interconversion of the many forms of bullvalene is sufficiently fast that the NMR spectrometer cannot distinguish between the different types of protons. (See Sec. 13.7 for a discussion of this phenomenon.) Were this interconversion *not* occurring, the NMR spectrum should not change with temperature. Hence, the signal averaging observed for bullvalene in the NMR spectrometer at high temperature is strong evidence in support of the equilibration shown in Eq. 25.40.

Chapter 26 / Amino Acids, Peptides, and Proteins

CHAPTER 26 TERMS

acidic amino acid 26.4B
active site 26.10
acyl-enzyme 26.10
α-amino acid .... Introduction
amino acid .... Introduction
amino acid analysis 26.7A
amino acid sequence 26.7B
amino terminus (Pep^N) 26.1B, 7B
amphoteric 26.4B
anion-exchange resin 26.4C
antiparallel pleated sheet 26.9B
basic amino acid 26.4B
tert-butyloxycarbonyl (*t*-Boc) group 26.8B
carboxy terminus (Pep^C) 26.1B, 7B
cation-exchange resin 26.4C
coenzyme 26.10
cyanogen bromide 26.7C
D,L system 26.2
denaturation 26.9C
disulfide bond 26.9A
Edman degradation 26.7B
Edman reagent 26.7B
endopeptidase 26.7C
enzyme 26.10
enzyme-substrate complex 26.10
exopeptidase 26.7C
α-helix, right-handed 26.9B
homoserine lactone 26.7C
hydrophilic residue 26.9C
hydrophobic bond 26.9C

hydrophobic residue 26.9C
ion-exchange chromatography 26.4C
ion-exchange resin 26.4C
isoelectric point, pI 26.4B
isoelectric pH 26.4B
neutral amino acid 26.4B
ninhydrin 26.6B
parallel pleated sheet 26.9B
peptidase 26.7C
peptide .... Introduction
peptide backbone 26.1B
peptide bond .... Introduction
phenylthiohydantoin (PTH) 26.7B
primary sequence 26.7B
primary structure 26.9A
protease 26.7C
protein .... Introduction
proteolytic enzyme 26.7C
quaternary structure 26.9C
random coil 26.9B
residue 26.1B
Ruhemann's purple 26.6B
secondary structure 26.9B
solid-phase peptide synthesis 26.8B
Strecker synthesis 26.5C
β-structure (pleated sheet) 26.9B
substrate 26.10
tertiary structure 26.9C
zwitterions 26.4A

CHAPTER 26 CONCEPTS

I. Introduction to Amino Acids and Peptides:

    A. <u>General</u>:

        1. Compounds that contain both an amino group and a carboxylic acid group are called **amino acids**.

           a) The neutral amino group is basic, and can formally accept a proton from the acidic carboxylic acid group.

           b) When two groups of opposite charge are contained within the same molecule, the molecule is called a **zwitterion**.

2. The α-**amino acids** have an amino group at the α-carbon—the carbon adjacent to the carboxylic acid group.

$$\overset{+}{N}H_3-CH-\overset{\displaystyle O}{\overset{\|}{C}}-O^-$$
$$\underset{R}{|}$$

           an α-amino acid in zwitterionic form

3. **Peptides** are biologically important polymers in which α-amino acids are joined into chains through amide bonds (**peptide bonds**); **proteins** are large peptides.

$$\xi-NH-CH-\overset{\displaystyle O}{\overset{\|}{C}}-NH-CH-\overset{\displaystyle O}{\overset{\|}{C}}-NH-CH-\overset{\displaystyle O}{\overset{\|}{C}}-NH-CH-\overset{\displaystyle O}{\overset{\|}{C}}-\xi$$
$$\underset{R}{|}\qquad\underset{R}{|}\qquad\underset{R}{|}\qquad\underset{R}{|}$$

B. Nomenclature of Amino Acids:
     1. Some amino acids are named systematically as carboxylic acids with amino substituents.
     2. Twenty α-amino acids occur commonly as constituents of most proteins and are known by widely accepted traditional names; these names and their structures are given in Table 26.1 of the text.
         a) With the exception of proline, all α-amino acids have the same general structure, differing only in the identity of the side chain R.
         b) Proline is the only naturally occurring amino acid with a secondary amino group.

$$H-\overset{\displaystyle \overset{H}{|}}{\overset{+}{N}}-CH-\overset{\displaystyle O}{\overset{\|}{C}}-O^-$$

            proline in zwitterionic form

         c) The amino acids can be organized into six groups according to the nature of their side chains:
            (1) Hydrogen or aliphatic hydrocarbon groups.
            (2) Aromatic groups.
            (3) Thiol, sulfide, or alcohol groups.
            (4) Carboxylic acid or amide groups.
            (5) Basic side chains.
            (6) Proline.
     3. The α-amino acids are often designated by abbreviations; the generally accepted three-letter abbreviations for the naturally occurring amino acids and the standard single-letter abbreviations are given in Table 26.1, text page 1136.

C. Stereochemistry of the α-Amino Acids:
     1. With the exception of glycine, the α-amino acids have at least one asymmetric carbon atom; the naturally occurring chiral amino acids all have the S configuration at the α-carbon.
     2. The stereochemistry of α-amino acids is often described with an older system, the D,L **system**.
         a) In this system, the naturally occurring amino acids are said to have the L configuration.
         b) The L designation refers to the configuration of a reference carbon—the α-carbon—in each amino acid, regardless of the number of asymmetric carbons in the molecule.

$$\underset{S\text{-configuration}}{\overset{\displaystyle CO_2^-}{\overset{\overset{+}{N}H_3\diagup\;\;\overset{|}{C}_{\text{\tiny||}}\cdot R}{\underset{H}{}}}}\;=\;\underset{\text{L-amino acid}}{\overset{\displaystyle CO_2^-}{\overset{+}{N}H_3-\!\!\!\!\!\!\!\!-\!\!\!\!\!-H}}\;\bigg|\;\underset{\text{D-amino acid}}{\overset{\displaystyle CO_2^-}{H-\!\!\!\!\!\!\!\!-\!\!\!\!\!-\overset{+}{N}H_3}}$$

                                        mirror plane

         c) In the D,L system, diastereomers are given *different* names.

D. Nomenclature of Peptides:
     1. The peptide backbone is the repeating sequence of nitrogen, α-carbon, and carbonyl groups.
         a) Each amino acid unit in the peptide is called a **residue**.

b) The ends of a peptide are labeled as the amino end or **amino terminus (Pep^N)** and the carboxy end or **carboxy terminus (Pep^C)**.
2. A peptide is conventionally named by giving successively the names of the amino acid residues, starting at the amino end.
   a) The names of all but the carboxy-terminal residue are formed by dropping the final ending of the amino acid and replacing it with *yl*.
   b) This type of nomenclature is used for the smallest peptides.
3. Peptides can be represented by connecting with hyphens the three-letter (or one-letter) abbreviations of the component amino acid residues beginning with the amino-terminal residue.

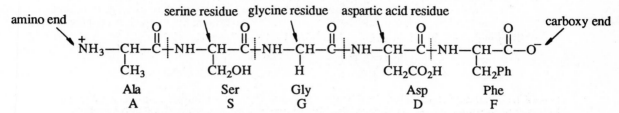

alanylserylglycylaspartylphenylalanine   (abbreviated Ala-Ser-Gly-Asp-Phe or A-S-G-D-F)

4. Large peptides and proteins of biological importance are known by common names.

E. <u>UV Spectra of Amino Acids and Peptides</u>:
   1. Most amino acids have negligible UV absorption, but tyrosine and tryptophan have an appreciable absorption near 280 nm, and phenylalanine near 260 nm.
   2. The absorbance at 280 nm, called A_{280} by protein chemists, is an important physical characteristic of a protein and is large for a protein or peptide that contains a substantial number of tryptophan and/or tyrosine residues.

II. Acid–Base Properties of Amino Acids and Peptides:

A. <u>Zwitterionic Structures of Amino Acids and Peptides</u>:
   1. The major neutral form of any α-amino acid is the zwitterion.
      a) The high melting points of amino acids and their greater solubility in water than in ether are characteristics of charged species.
      b) Water is the best solvent for most amino acids because it solvates the ionic groups of the amino acids.
      c) The dipole moments of the amino acids are very large—much larger than those of similar-sized molecules with only a single amine or a carboxylic acid group.
      d) The pK_a values for amino acids are what we would expect for the zwitterionic forms of the neutral molecules.
   2. Peptides also exist as zwitterions; at neutral pH, the terminal amino group is protonated and the terminal carboxylic acid group is ionized.

B. <u>Isoelectric Points of Amino Acids and Peptides</u>:
   1. Amino acids and peptides are **amphoteric** substances—they contain both acidic and basic groups.
   2. An important measure of the acidity or basicity of an amino acid or peptide is its **isoelectric point,** or **isoelectric pH**; this is the pH of a dilute aqueous solution of the amino acid or peptide at which it is exactly neutral. (The isoelectric points of the α-amino acids are given in Table 26.1, text page 1136.)
   3. At the isoelectric point, two conditions are met:
      a) The concentration of positively charged amino acid or peptide molecules equals the concentration of negatively charged ones.
      b) The relative concentration of neutral amino acid or peptide molecules is greater than at any other pH.
   4. The isoelectric point, pI, of an amino acid is the average of the two pK_a values of an amino acid:

$$\text{isoelectric point} = \text{p}I = \frac{\text{p}K_{a1} + \text{p}K_{a2}}{2}$$

5. The isoelectric point indicates not only the pH at which the amino acid or peptide has zero charge, but also the net charge at any pH.
   a) At pH values below the isoelectric point, an amino acid or peptide is positively charged.
   b) At pH values above the isoelectric point, an amino acid or peptide is negatively charged.
6. When an amino acid or peptide has a side chain containing an acidic or basic group, the isoelectric point is markedly changed.
   a) With a basic group, the isoelectric point is the average of the two highest pK_a values.
   b) With an acidic group, the isoelectric point is the average of the two lowest pK_a values.
      (1) Amino acids with high isoelectric points are classified as **basic amino acids**.
      (2) Amino acids with low isoelectric points are classified as **acidic amino acids**.
      (3) Amino acids with isoelectric points near 6 are classified as **neutral amino acids**.
7. A peptide can be classified as acidic, basic, or neutral by examining the number of acidic and basic groups that it contains.

C. Separation of Amino Acids and Peptides Using Acid–Base Properties:
   1. The isoelectric point is a useful criterion of which the separation of amino acids and peptides can be designed.
      a) Most peptides and amino acids are more soluble in their ionic forms and least soluble in their neutral forms.
      b) Some peptides, proteins, and amino acids precipitate from water if the pH is adjusted to their isoelectric points; these same compounds are more soluble at pH values far from their isoelectric points because at these pH values they bear a net charge.
   2. A separation technique used extensively in amino acid and peptide chemistry is **ion-exchange chromatography**, which depends on the isoelectric points of amino acids and peptides.
      a) In this technique, a hollow tube or column is filled with a buffer solution in which is suspended a finely powdered, insoluble polymer called an **ion-exchange resin**; the resin bears acidic or basic groups.
         (1) Ion-exchange resins that bear negatively charged pendant groups (usually sulfonic acids) absorb cations and are called **cation-exchange resins**.
         (2) Ion-exchange resins that bear positively charged pendant groups (typically ammonium ions) absorb anions and are called **anion-exchange resins**.
      b) Whether an amino acid or peptide is absorbed by the column depends on its charge, which, in turn, depends on the relationship of its isoelectric point to the pH of the buffer.

III. Structures of Peptides and Proteins:

A. Primary Structure:
   1. The simplest level at which a peptide or protein structure can be described is its **covalent structure**, or **primary structure**.
   2. The most important aspect of any primary structure is the amino acid sequence.
   3. Disulfide bonds link the cysteine residues in different parts of a sequence and serve as crosslinks between different parts of a peptide chain.

$$\xi\text{—Val—Ala—Cys—Arg—}\xi$$
$$|$$
$$S$$
$$| \longleftarrow \text{disulfide linkage}$$
$$S$$
$$|$$
$$\xi\text{—Asn—Ser—Cys—His—Lys—}\xi$$

   a) The disulfide bonds of a protein are readily reduced to free cysteine thiols by other thiols.
   b) Two commonly used thiol reagents are 2-mercapto-1-ethanol ($HSCH_2CH_2OH$), and dithiothreitol (DTT, or Cleland's reagent), $HSCH_2CH(OH)CH(OH)CH_2SH$.

B. Secondary Structure:
   1. The description of a peptide or protein in terms of the configuration of its amino acid residues is called **secondary structure**.
   2. Three conformations occur commonly:
      a) In a **right-handed α-helix**, the side-chain groups are positioned on the outside of the helix, and the helix is stabilized by hydrogen bonds between the amide N—H of one residue and the carbonyl oxygen four residues away.

right handed α-helix ⟶  ⟵ helix axis

      b) In a **β-structure (pleated sheet)**, the peptide chain adopts an open, zigzag conformation, and is engaged in hydrogen bonding with another peptide chain (or a different part of the chain) in a similar conformation.
         (1) The successive hydrogen-bonded chains can run (in the amino-terminal to carboxy-terminal sense) in the same direction (parallel pleated sheet) or in opposite directions (antiparallel pleated sheet).
         (2) The side-chain R-groups alternate between positions above and below the sheet.

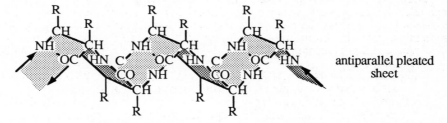 antiparallel pleated sheet

      c) Peptides that adopt a **random coil** conformation show no discernible pattern in their conformation.

   3. Some peptides and proteins exist entirely as α-helix or pleated sheet; however, most proteins contain different types of secondary structure in different parts of their peptide chains.

C. Tertiary and Quaternary Structures:
   1. The complete three-dimensional description of protein structure at the atomic level is called **tertiary structure** and is determined by X-ray crystallography.
   2. The tertiary structure of any given protein is an aggregate of α-helix, β-sheet, random-coil, and other conformations.
   3. Generally, the tertiary structure of a protein is stabilized by three types of noncovalent interactions:
      a) Hydrogen bonds.
         (1) Hydrogen bonds stabilize both the α-helix and the β-structure as well as other conformations.
         (2) Protein conformations are also stabilized in part by hydrogen bonding of certain groups to solvent water.
      b) Van der Waals interactions.
         (1) Van der Waals interactions, or dispersion forces, are the same interactions that provide the cohesive force in a liquid hydrocarbon, and can be regarded as examples of the like-dissolves-like phenomenon.
         (2) The van der Waals interactions of this type between hydrocarbonlike residues are sometimes called **hydrophobic bonds**, because the hydrocarbon groups would rather be near each other than water.
      c) Electrostatic interactions, which are noncovalent interactions between charged groups governed by the electrostatic law.

4. A protein adopts a tertiary structure in which favorable interactions are maximized and unfavorable interactions are minimized.
   a) Although there are exceptions, most soluble proteins are globular and compact rather than extended, because a near-spherical shape minimizes the amount of protein surface exposed to water.
   b) The reason for minimizing the exposed surface is that the majority of the residues in most proteins are hydrophobic, and the interactions of hydrophobic side chains with solvent water is unfavorable.
      (1) The hydrocarbonlike amino acid residues tend to be found on the interior of a protein, away from solvent water.
      (2) The polar residues tend to be on the exterior of a protein.
5. When a protein is denatured, it is converted entirely into a random-coil structure; denaturation of a protein is brought about typically by breaking its disulfide bonds with thiols, such as DTT or 2-mercaptoethanol, and treating it with $8M$ urea, detergents, or heat.
6. The amino acid sequence of a protein specifies its conformation; that is, the native structure is the most stable structure. In many cases it appears that primary structure dictates tertiary structure.
7. Some proteins are aggregates of other individual proteins, called **subunits**; the description of subunit arrangement in a protein is called **quaternary structure**.

D. <u>Enzymes—Biological Catalysts</u>:
   1. Many of the proteins that occur naturally are **enzymes**—catalysts for biological reactions.
      a) Enzymes are true catalysts; their concentrations are typically much lower than the concentrations of the compounds in the reactions they catalyze.
      b) They do not affect the equilibrium constants of the reactions they catalyze.
      c) They catalyze both the forward and reverse reactions of an equilibrium.
   2. Two characteristics of all enzymes are:
      a) Catalytic efficiency.
      b) Specificity.
   3. When an enzyme catalyzes a reaction of a certain compound, called a **substrate** for the enzyme, they act on the substrate in at least three stages:
      a) The substrate binds to the enzyme in a noncovalent enzyme-substrate complex.
         (1) The binding occurs at a part of the enzyme called the **active site**.
         (2) Within the active site are groups that attract the substrate by noncovalent interactions:
            (*a*) Electrostatic interactions.
            (*b*) Hydrogen bonding.
            (*c*) Van der Waals interactions (hydrophobic bonds).
      b) The enzyme promotes the appropriate chemical reaction(s) on the bound substrate to give an enzyme-product complex.
         (1) The necessary chemical transformations are brought about by groups in the active site of the enzyme.
         (2) In some cases, other molecules, called **coenzymes**, are also required.
      c) The product(s) departs from the active site, leaving the enzyme ready to repeat the process on a new substrate molecule.

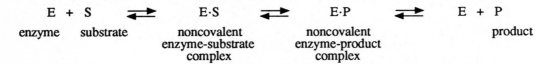

$$E + S \rightleftharpoons E{\cdot}S \rightleftharpoons E{\cdot}P \rightleftharpoons E + P$$

enzyme   substrate   noncovalent   noncovalent   product
                       enzyme-substrate   enzyme-product
                       complex   complex

4. A chiral enzyme reacts with a chiral substrate to form first an enzyme-substrate complex.
   a) The enzyme-substrate complex derived from the enantiomer of the substrate is a diastereomer of the one derived from the substrate itself.
   b) This is an example of differentiation of enantiomers by a chiral reagent.

CHAPTER 26 REACTIONS

I. Synthesis and Optical Resolution of α-Amino Acids:

A. Alkylation of Ammonia:

1. Some α-amino acids can be prepared by alkylation of ammonia with α-bromocarboxylic acids.

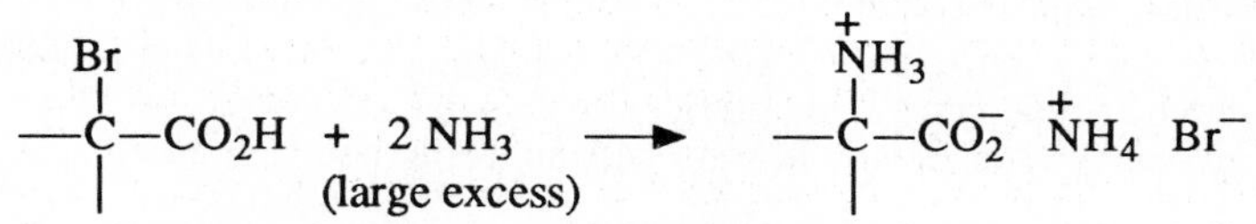

$$—\overset{\overset{\displaystyle Br}{|}}{\underset{|}{C}}—CO_2H \;+\; 2\,NH_3 \;\longrightarrow\; —\overset{\overset{\displaystyle \overset{+}{N}H_3}{|}}{\underset{|}{C}}—CO_2^- \;\; \overset{+}{N}H_4 \;\; Br^-$$

(large excess)

   a) This is an S_N2 reaction with ammonia acting as the nucleophile.
   b) The use of a large excess of ammonia in the synthesis favors monoalkylation.
2. Amino acids are less reactive toward further alkylation with alkylating agents than simple alkylamines because amino acids are less basic and more sterically hindered.

B. Alkylation of Aminomalonate Derivatives:

1. One of the most widely used methods for amino acid synthesis is a variation of the malonic ester synthesis.
2. α-Amino acids can be prepared from a malonic ester derivative in which a protected amino group is already in place: diethyl α-acetamidomalonate.
   a) Treatment of α-acetamidomalonate with sodium ethoxide in ethanol forms the ester–enolate ion, which is then alkylated with an alkyl halide.
   b) The resulting compound is then treated with hot aqueous HCl or HBr; this treatment accomplishes three things:
      (1) The ester groups are hydrolyzed to carboxylic acids, yielding a substituted malonic acid.
      (2) The malonic acid derivative decarboxylates under the reaction conditions.
      (3) The acetamido group, an amide, is also hydrolyzed.
   c) Neutralization affords the α-amino acid.

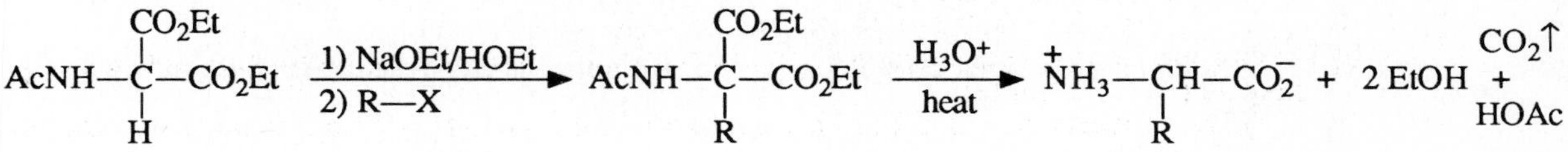

$$AcNH—\overset{\overset{\displaystyle CO_2Et}{|}}{\underset{\underset{\displaystyle H}{|}}{C}}—CO_2Et \quad\xrightarrow[\text{2) R—X}]{\text{1) NaOEt/HOEt}}\quad AcNH—\overset{\overset{\displaystyle CO_2Et}{|}}{\underset{\underset{\displaystyle R}{|}}{C}}—CO_2Et \quad\xrightarrow[\text{heat}]{H_3O^+}\quad \overset{+}{N}H_3—\underset{\underset{\displaystyle R}{|}}{C}H—CO_2^- \;+\; 2\,EtOH \;+\; \overset{\overset{\displaystyle CO_2\uparrow}{}}{HOAc}$$

C. Strecker Synthesis:

1. Hydrolysis of α-amino nitriles to give α-amino acids is called the **Strecker synthesis**; the α-amino nitriles can be prepared by treatment of aldehydes with ammonia in the presence of cyanide ion.

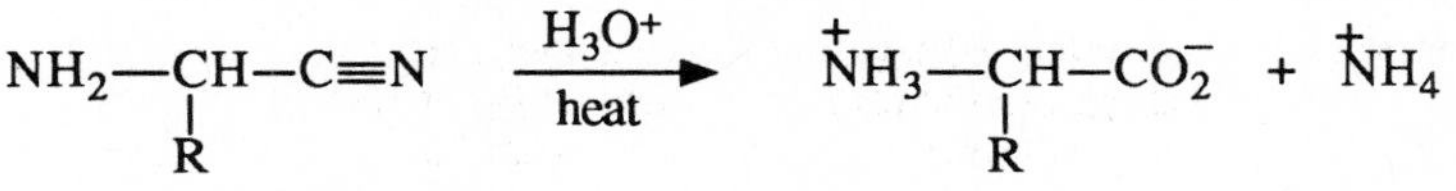

$$NH_2—\underset{\underset{\displaystyle R}{|}}{C}H—C{\equiv}N \quad\xrightarrow[\text{heat}]{H_3O^+}\quad \overset{+}{N}H_3—\underset{\underset{\displaystyle R}{|}}{C}H—CO_2^- \;+\; \overset{+}{N}H_4$$

2. α-Amino nitriles are made through a reaction that probably involves the transient formation of an imine.
   a) The conjugate acid of the imine reacts with cyanide to give the α-amino nitrile.
   b) The addition of cyanide to an imine is analogous to the formation of a cyanohydrin from an aldehyde or ketone.

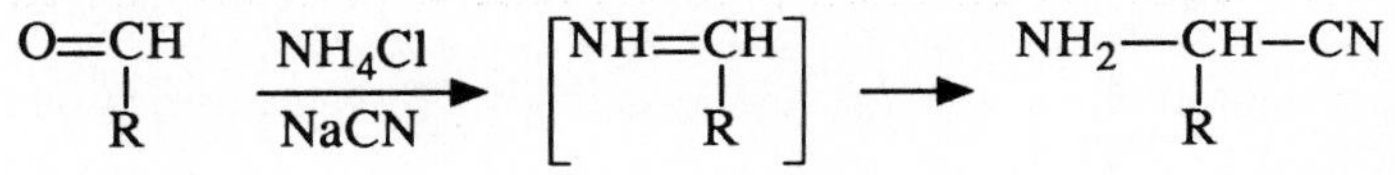

$$O{=}\underset{\underset{\displaystyle R}{|}}{C}H \quad\xrightarrow[\text{NaCN}]{NH_4Cl}\quad \left[NH{=}\underset{\underset{\displaystyle R}{|}}{C}H \right] \quad\longrightarrow\quad NH_2—\underset{\underset{\displaystyle R}{|}}{C}H—CN$$

D. Optical Resolution of α-Amino Acids:
    1. Amino acids synthesized by common laboratory methods are racemic; since many applications require the pure enantiomers, the racemic compounds must be optically resolved.
    2. An alternative approach to the preparation of optically pure amino acids used industrially is the synthesis of amino acids by microbiological techiques—**fermentation**.
    3. Certain enzymes can also be used to resolve racemic amino acids into enantiomers.

II. Reactions of Amino Acids:

A. Acylation and Esterification:
    1. Amino acids undergo many of the characteristic reactions of both amines and carboxylic acids.
       a) They can be acylated by acid chlorides or anhydrides.
       b) They are easily esterified by heating with an alcohol and a mineral acid catalyst.

B. Reaction with Ninhydrin:
    1. α-Amino acids react with **ninhydrin**, the hydrate of a tricarbonyl compound, to form a dye called **Ruhemann's purple** that is used to detect small amounts of amino acids; the same dye is formed from all α-amino acids with *primary* amino groups.

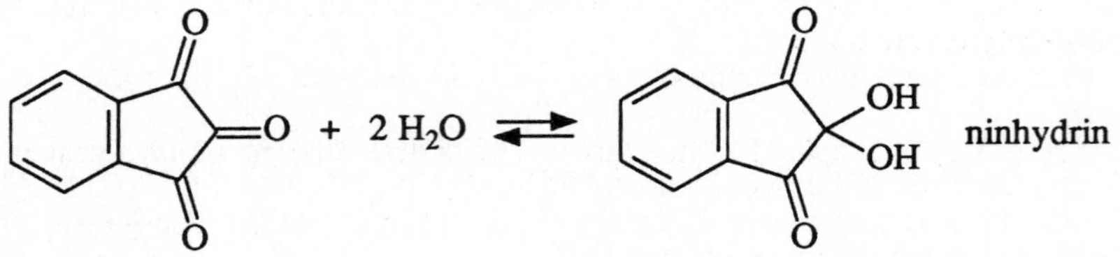

       a) The formation of the dye can be used for the quantitative analysis of amino acids and peptides in the laboratory.
       b) Secondary amines cannot react in this way with ninhydrin; proline reacts to give a different adduct, which has a different color and absorbs light at a different wavelength.
    2. The mechanism of the ninhydrin reaction involves two molecules of ninhydrin per molecule of amino acid, and is a combination of simpler reactions.
       a) An imine is formed between the tricarbonyl form of ninhydrin and the amine of the amino acid.
       b) This imine is converted into a different imine by the loss of CO_2 (decarboxylation).
       c) The new imine hydrolyzes to an aldehyde and an amine; the aldehyde carries the amino acid side chain.
       d) The resulting amine then forms yet another imine with a second molecule of ninhydrin; this is the final product.

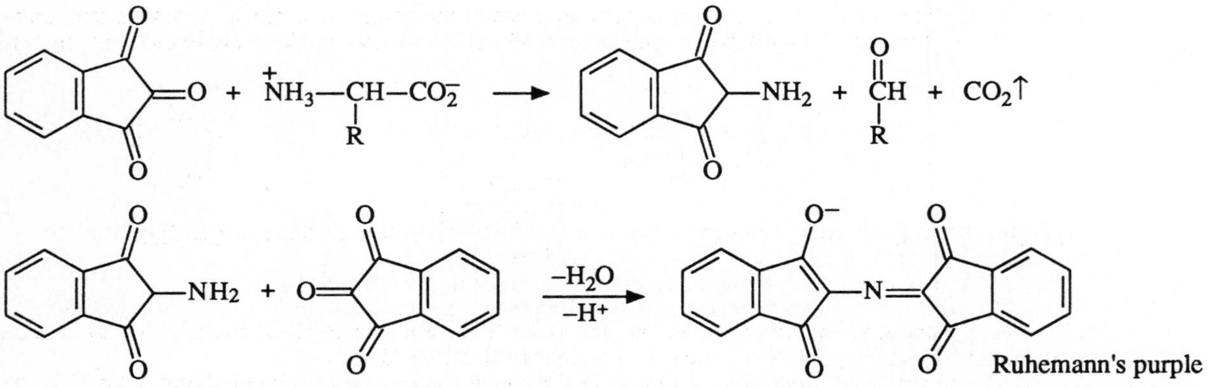

    3. Simple primary amines also react with ninhydrin to give the same dye, but the reaction with α-amino acids is particularly efficient.

III. Synthesis of Peptides:

A. Strategy of Peptide Synthesis:
   1. Because peptides are linear sequences of amino acid residues, in principle a peptide can be built up from one end to the other by simply forming successive peptide bonds between the amino group of one amino acid and the carboxy group of another.
   2. The desired peptide bond can be formed only if the amino group of one and the carboxy group of the other are blocked with protecting groups; once the protecting groups are no longer needed, they are removed.

B. Solid-Phase Peptide Synthesis:
   1. In a technique called **solid-phase peptide synthesis**, the carboxy-terminal amino acid is covalently anchored to an insoluble polymer, and the peptide is grown, one residue at a time, on this polymer.
      a) Solutions containing the appropriate reagents are allowed to contact the polymer with shaking.
      b) At the conclusion of each step, the polymer containing the peptide is simply filtered away from the solution, which contains soluble by-products and impurities.
      c) The completed peptide is removed from the polymer by a reaction that cleaves its bond to the resin.
   2. In a solid-phase peptide synthesis, the amino group of the amino acids is protected with a special acyl group, the *tert*-**butyloxycarbonyl group** (*t*-**Boc**, or **Boc**).
      a) The Boc group is introduced by allowing an amino acid to react with the anhydride di-*t*-butyldicarbonate.

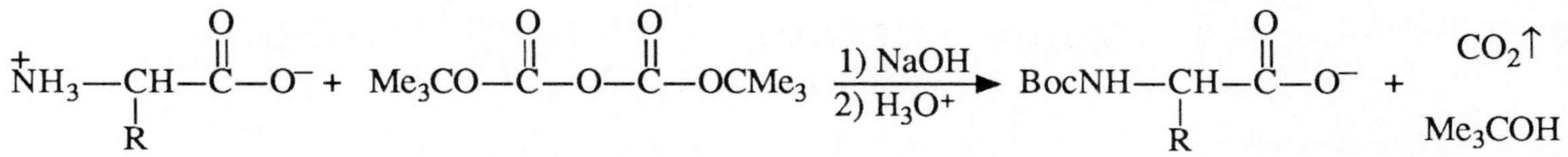

$$\overset{+}{N}H_3{-}CH{-}\overset{\displaystyle O}{\overset{\|}{C}}{-}O^- \;+\; Me_3CO{-}\overset{\displaystyle O}{\overset{\|}{C}}{-}O{-}\overset{\displaystyle O}{\overset{\|}{C}}{-}OCMe_3 \quad \xrightarrow[\text{2) } H_3O^+]{\text{1) NaOH}} \quad BocNH{-}CH{-}\overset{\displaystyle O}{\overset{\|}{C}}{-}O^- \;+\; \begin{array}{l} CO_2\uparrow \\[4pt] Me_3COH \end{array}$$

with R below each CH.

      b) The amino group rather than the carboxylate group reacts with the anhydride because it is the more basic, and therefore more nucleophilic, group.
   3. At the start of the solid-phase peptide synthesis, a Boc-protected amino acid is anchored to the insoluble solid support using the reactivity of its free carboxylic acid group.
      a) An S_N2 reaction between the cesium salt of the Boc-amino acid and the resin results in the formation of an ester linkage to the resin.
      b) Once the Boc-amino acid is anchored to the resin, the Boc protecting group is removed with anhydrous acid (see Sec. 21.7A, text page 875).
         (1) The carboxylic acid group exposed in this reaction is of the carbamic acid type, which decarboxylates under acidic conditions; this decarboxylation exposes the free amino group.
         (2) Since the ester linkage holding the first amino acid residue to the resin is not a *t*-butyl ester, it is not cleaved under the anhydrous acidic conditions.
         (3) This deprotection step, after neutralization of the ammonium salt, exposes the free amino group of the resin-bound amino acid, which is used as a nucleophile in the next reaction.

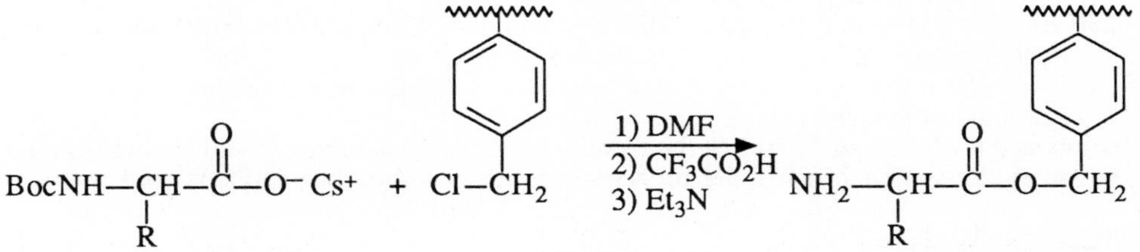

$$BocNH{-}CH{-}\overset{\displaystyle O}{\overset{\|}{C}}{-}O^-\,Cs^+ \;+\; Cl{-}CH_2\text{—(resin)} \quad \xrightarrow[\text{3) } Et_3N]{\substack{\text{1) DMF}\\ \text{2) } CF_3CO_2H}} \quad NH_2{-}CH{-}\overset{\displaystyle O}{\overset{\|}{C}}{-}O{-}CH_2\text{—(resin)}$$

with R below each CH.

   4. Coupling of another Boc-protected amino acid to the free amino group of the resin-bound amino acid is effected by the reagent **N,N'-dicyclohexylcarbodiimide (DCC)**.
      a) Markovnikov addition of the amino acid carboxylic acid group to a double bond of DCC gives a derivative called an *O*-**acylisourea**.
      b) This derivative behaves somewhat like an anhydride, and is an excellent acylating agent.
         (1) It can react directly with the amino group of the resin-bound amino acid to form the peptide bond; the by-product of this reaction is the enol form of *N,N*-dicyclohexylurea (DCU), which is spontaneously transformed into DCU itself.

(2) The *O*-acylisourea can react with the carbonyl group of another equivalent of the protected amino acid, giving an anhydride; this anhydride can also acylate the amino group of the resin-bound amino acid to complete the formation of the peptide bond.

c) The by-product DCU is washed away from the peptide—it is not attached covalently to the resin.

$$
\underset{R}{\text{BocNH—CH—}}\overset{\overset{\displaystyle O}{\|}}{\text{C}}\text{—OH} \quad + \quad \underset{R}{\text{NH}_2\text{—CH—CO}_2\text{CH}_2} \quad \xrightarrow[\substack{\text{2) CF}_3\text{CO}_2\text{H} \\ \text{3) Et}_3\text{N}}]{\text{1) DCC/CH}_2\text{Cl}_2} \quad \underset{R}{\text{NH}_2\text{—CH—}}\overset{\overset{\displaystyle O}{\|}}{\text{C}}\text{—NH—}\underset{R}{\text{CH—CO}_2\text{CH}_2}
$$

5. Completion of the peptide synthesis requires deprotection of the resin-bound dipeptide in the usual way and a final coupling step with the final Boc-amino acid and DCC.

   a) The ester linkage that connects the peptide to the resin, like most esters, is more easily cleaved than the peptide (amide) bonds, and is typically broken by liquid HF or a mixture of CF_3SO_3H (trifluoromethanesulfonic acid) and trifluoroacetic acid.

   b) These acidic reagents also remove the Boc group from the product peptide.

$$
\underset{R}{\text{BocNH—CH—CO}_2\text{H}} \quad + \quad \text{NH}_2\text{—Pep}\overset{\overset{\displaystyle \text{resin}}{\wedge\!\wedge\!\wedge}}{\text{C}} \quad \xrightarrow[\substack{\text{2) CF}_3\text{CO}_2\text{H} \\ \text{3) HF}}]{\text{1) DCC/CH}_2\text{Cl}_2} \quad \overset{+}{\text{NH}_3}\underset{R}{\text{—CH—}}\overset{\overset{\displaystyle O}{\|}}{\text{C}}\text{—NH—Pep}\overset{\text{C}}{} \quad + \quad \overset{\text{resin}}{\wedge\!\wedge\!\wedge}
$$

6. The advantage of the solid-phase method is the ease with which dissolved impurities and by-products are removed from the resin-bound peptide by simple filtration.

   a) The same reagents used in solid-phase peptide synthesis can also be used in solution, but removal of the DCU from the product peptide is sometimes difficult.

   b) In order to avoid impurities, each step in the solid-phase synthesis must occur with virtually 100% yield.

IV. Analytically Important Reactions of Peptides:

A. <u>Hydrolysis of Peptides—Amino Acid Analysis</u>:

1. Peptides can be hydrolyzed under the conditions of amide hydrolysis—moderately concentrated aqueous acid (or base) and heat.

2. When a peptide or protein is hydrolyzed, the product amino acids can be separated, identified, and quantitated by a technique called **amino acid analysis.**

   a) The amino acids in the hydrolyzed mixture are separated by passing them through a cation-exchange column under very carefully defined conditions; the time at which each amino acid emerges from the column is accurately known.

   b) As each amino acid emerges, it is mixed with ninhydrin; the intensity of the resulting color is proportional to the amount of the amino acid present.

   c) The color intensity is recorded as a function of time; the area of the peak is proportional to the amount of the amino acid.

3. Amino acid analysis can determine the identity and relative amounts of amino acid residues in a peptide; however, the relative order of the amino acid residues within the peptide is not known.

B. <u>Sequential Degradation of Peptides</u>:

1. The actual arrangement, or sequential order, of amino acid residues in a peptide is called its **amino acid sequence** or **primary sequence.**

2. It is possible to remove one residue at a time from the amino end of the peptide, identify it, and then repeat the process sequentially on the remaining peptide; the standard method for implementing this strategy is called the **Edman degradation.**

   a) The peptide is treated with phenyl isothiocyanate (**Edman reagent**) with which it reacts at its amino-terminal group to give a thiourea derivative.

   b) Any remaining phenyl isothiocyanate is removed, and the modified peptide is then treated with anhydrous trifluoroacetic acid.

c) The sulfur of the thiourea, which is nucleophilic, displaces the amino group of the adjacent residue to yield a five-membered heterocycle called a **thiazoline**; the other product of the reaction is a peptide that is *one residue shorter*.

d) When treated subsequently with aqueous acid, the thiazolinone derivative forms an isomer called a **phenylthiohydantoin (PTH)**; this probably occurs by a reversible reopening of the thiazolinone to the thiourea, followed by ring formation involving the thiourea nitrogen.

e) Because the phenylthiohydantoin derivative carries the characteristic side chain of the amino-terminal residue, the structure of the PTH derivative tells us immediately which amino acid residue has been removed.

3. In practice, because the yields at each step are not perfectly quantitative, an increasingly complex mixture of peptides is formed with each successive step in the cleavage, and after a number of such steps the results become ambiguous.

C. Specific Cleavage of Peptides:

1. The amino acid sequence of most large proteins is determined by breaking the protein into a number of smaller peptides, and sequencing these peptides individually; the sequence of the protein is reconstructed from the sequences of the peptides.

2. When breaking a larger protein into smaller peptides, it is desirable to use reactions that cleave the protein in high yield at well-defined points so that a relatively small number of peptides are obtained.

3. One method uses ordinary chemical reagents; another method involves the use of enzymes to catalyze peptide-bond hydrolysis.

D. Peptide Cleavage at Methionine with Cyanogen Bromide:

1. When a peptide reacts with cyanogen bromide (Br—C≡N) in aqueous HCl, a peptide bond is cleaved *specifically* at the carboxy side of each methionine residue.

a) The amino-terminal fragment from the cleavage has a carboxy-terminal homoserine lactone residue instead of the starting methionine.

b) Methionine is a relatively rare amino acid; hence, when a typical protein is cleaved with BrCN, relatively few cleavage peptides are obtained, and all of them are derived from cleavage at methionine residues.

2. Although cyanogen bromide has the character of an acid chloride, under acidic conditions only its reaction at methionine leads to a peptide cleavage.

a) The sulfur in the methionine side chain acts as a nucleophile, displacing bromide from cyanogen bromide to give a type of sulfonium ion.

b) The sulfonium ion, with its electron-withdrawing cyanide, is an excellent leaving group, and is displaced by the oxygen of the neighboring amide bond to form a five-membered ring; only methionine has a nucleophilic group in a side chain that can form a five-membered ring.

c) Hydrolysis of the resulting iminium ion cleaves the peptide bond.

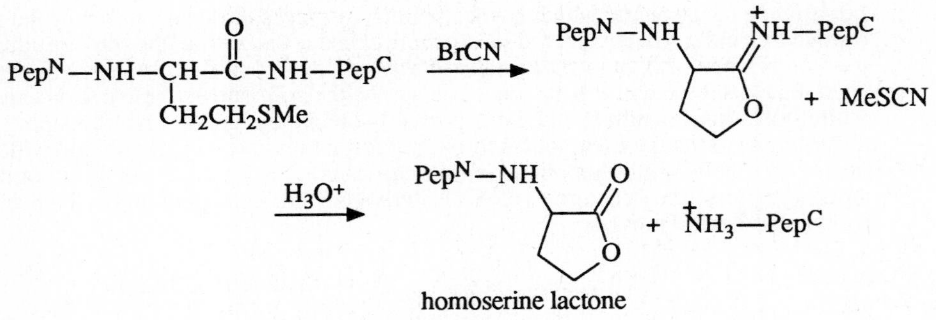

$$PepN—NH—CH—C—NH—PepC \xrightarrow{\text{BrCN}}$$

with the structure showing the O double bond on the carbonyl carbon and CH$_2$CH$_2$SMe side chain, yielding:

$$PepN—NH \quad \overset{+}{N}H—PepC + \text{MeSCN}$$

(cyclic lactone intermediate with O in the ring)

$$\xrightarrow{\text{H}_3\text{O}^+} \quad PepN—NH \quad \text{(lactone with O)} + \overset{+}{N}H_3—PepC$$

homoserine lactone

E. Peptide Cleavage with Proteolytic Enzymes:
   1. There are a number of enzymes that catalyze the hydrolysis of peptide bonds at specific points in an amino acid sequence; such peptide-hydrolyzing enzymes are called **proteases, peptidases,** or **proteolytic enzymes.**
   2. One of the most widely used proteases is the enzyme trypsin which catalyzes the hydrolysis of peptides or proteins at the carbonyl group of arginine or lysine residues:
      a) These residues must not be at the amino end of the protein.
      b) These residues must not be followed by a proline residue.
   3. Because trypsin catalyzes the hydrolysis of peptides at internal rather than terminal residues, it is called an **endopeptidase**; enzymes that cleave peptides only at terminal residues are termed **exopeptidases.**
   4. Chymotrypsin, a protein related to trypsin, is used to cleave peptides at amino acid residues with aromatic side chains and, to a lesser extent, residues with large hydrocarbon side chains; thus, chymotrypsin cleaves peptides at Phe, Trp, Tyr, and occasionally Leu and Ile residues.

CHAPTER 26 SOLUTIONS

Solutions to In-Text Problems

1.   (a)

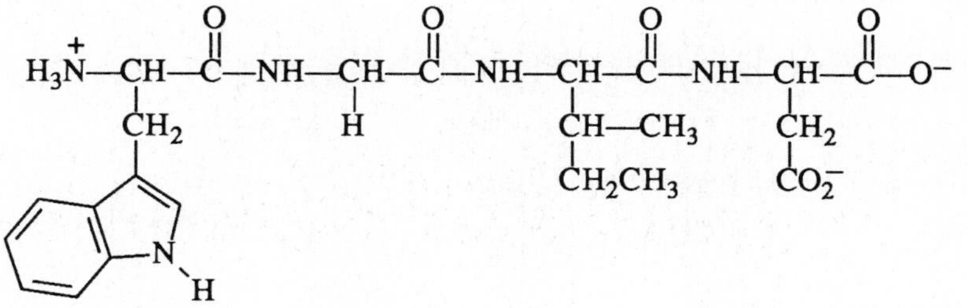

(b)

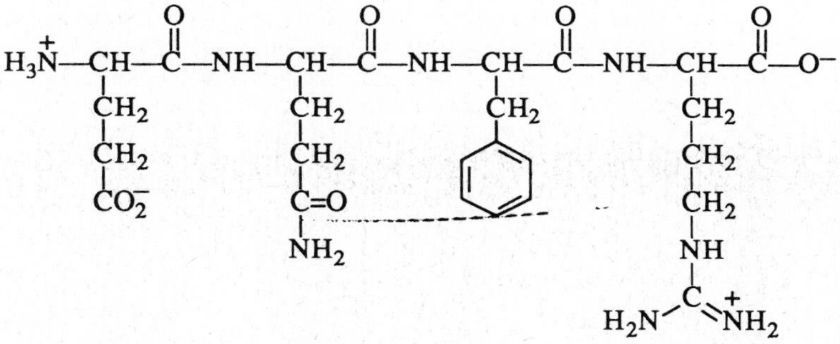

2.   His-Ile-Tyr-Met-Ser, or H-I-Y-M-S

3.   (a) A Fischer projection of L-isoleucine:

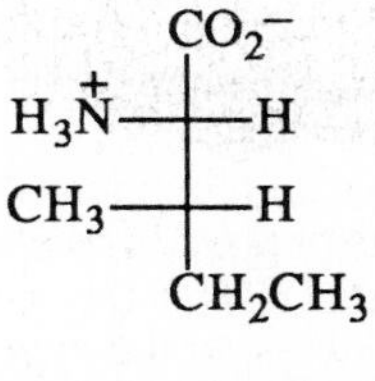

➤ Remember that there are many possible Fischer projections for this compound. If yours differs from this one, see whether you can convert yours into this one by the allowed manipulations of the Fischer projections (Sec. 6.9).

(b)

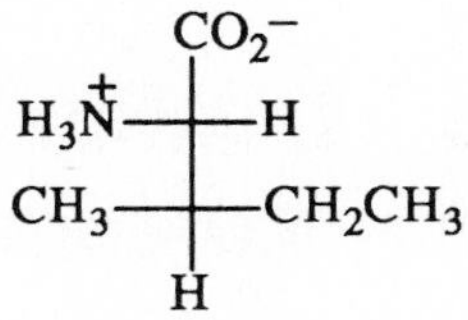

L-alloisoleucine 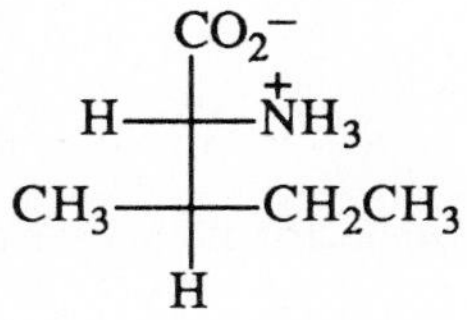   D-alloisoleucine

4. First, we calculate the number of moles per liter in a lysozyme concentration of 0.1 mg/mL:

$$\text{mol/L} = \frac{0.1 \text{ mg/mL} \times 10^{-3} \text{ g/mg} \times 10^3 \text{ mL/L}}{14,100 \text{ g/mol}} = 7.09 \times 10^{-6}$$

There are three equivalents of tyrosine and six of tryptophan in this protein. Using Beer's law (see Eq. 15.3, text page 587) we obtain

$$A = [3(1,100) + 6(5,200)] \times [7.09 \times 10^{-6}] = 0.245.$$

5. The major neutral form of the peptide Ala-Lys-Val-Glu-Met:

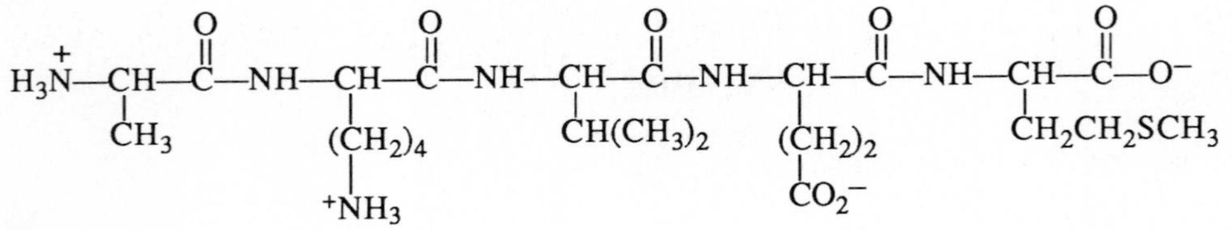

6. (a) The ionizable groups on the amino acid tyrosine (drawn in its most acidic form):

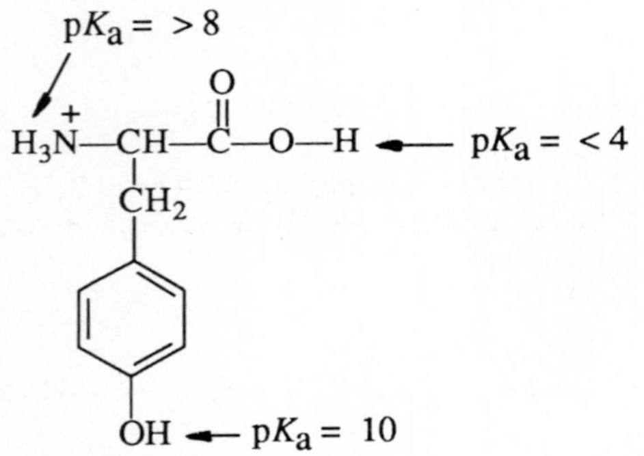

(b) A pH value of 6 is well above the pK_a of only one of these groups: the carboxy group. Hence, only this group is missing its acidic proton at this pH. Hence, the net charge of tyrosine at pH = 6 is zero.

7. (a) Gly-Leu-Val is neutral because it has the same number of acidic and basic groups (the terminal carboxy and amino groups, respectively). The net charge at pH = 6 is zero.
    (b) Leu-Trp-Lys-Gly-Lys has more basic groups (the terminal amino group and the two side-chain amino groups of the Lys residues) than acidic groups (the terminal carboxy group). Hence, this peptide is basic, and its net charge at pH = 6 is +2.
    (c) Ac-Asp-Val-Ser-Arg-Arg has two basic groups (the guanidino groups of the Arg residues) and two acidic groups (the terminal carboxy group and the side-chain carboxy group of the Asp residue). The peptide is neutral. At pH = 6 it has a net charge of zero.

8. We use Eq. 26.5, letting the concentration of form A equal that of form B. Multiplication of the two equalities gives

$$\frac{K_{a1}K_{a2}}{[H_3O^+]^2} = \frac{[N][B]}{[A][N]}$$

At the particular H_3O^+ concentration of the isoelectric point, which we shall call $[H_3O^+]_i$, $[A] = [B]$. Under this condition the equation above becomes

$$\frac{K_{a1}K_{a2}}{[H_3O^+]_i^2} = 1 \qquad \text{or} \quad K_{a1}K_{a2} = [H_3O^+]_i^2$$

Taking negative logs of both sides, we have $pK_{a1} + pK_{a2} = (-\log [H_3O^+]_i^2) = 2$ (isoelectric pH). Division by 2 gives Eq. 26.7.

9. At pH 6 the ion-exchange column is negatively charged, since it bears strongly acidic sulfonic acid pendant groups. At this pH, the peptide Ac-Leu-Gly bears a negative charge; Lys-Gly-Arg has a net charge of +2; and Lys-Gly-Leu has a net charge of +1. Hence, Ac-Leu-Gly will emerge from the column earliest; Lys-Gly-Leu will emerge next; and Lys-Gly-Arg will emerge last.

10. (a) We follow the pattern for synthesis of phenylalanine in Eqs. 26.10a and b, except that we use isobutyl bromide as the alkyl halide:

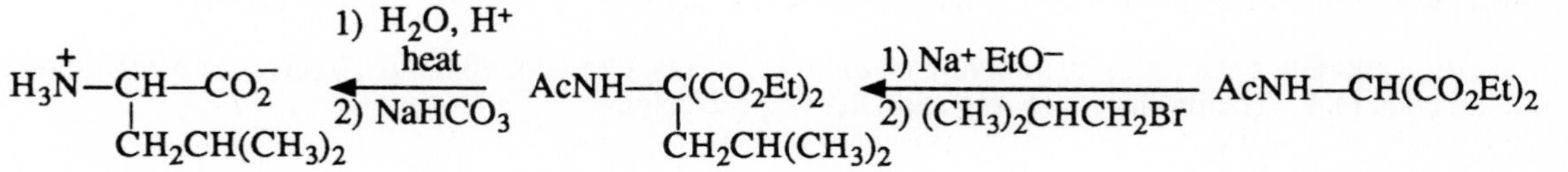

(b) A Strecker synthesis is called for in this case:

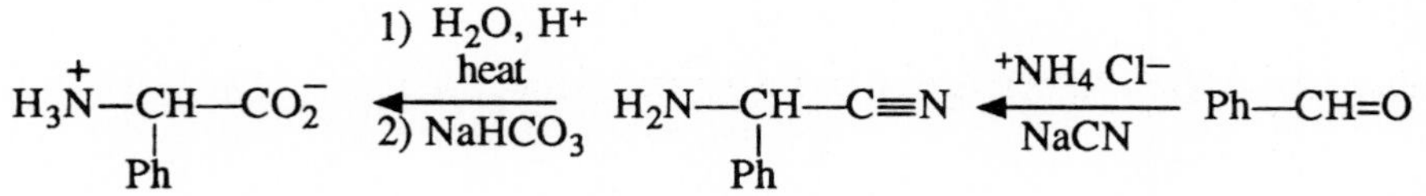

11. The α-amino group is nucleophilic, and could itself react with the alkyl halide. (See Sec. 23.7A.)

12. The amino group of glycine, like any other amine, reacts with esters to form amides. (See Sec. 21.8C.) When the amino group of one glycine molecule reacts with the ester group of another, two glycine molecules are "connected." This process can continue indefinitely to give a polymer:

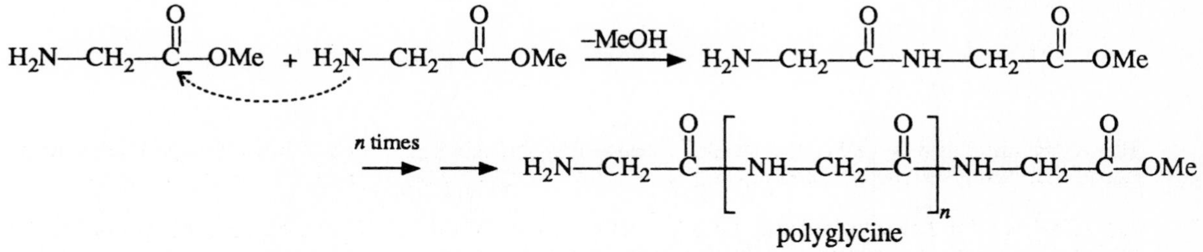

polyglycine

When the amino group is protonated, however, it is no longer nucleophilic; hence, this reaction cannot occur.

13. (a) The first step is the formation of a protonated carbinolamine (Sec. 19.11), which loses first the elements of water, and then CO_2. We begin with the protonated carbinolamine:

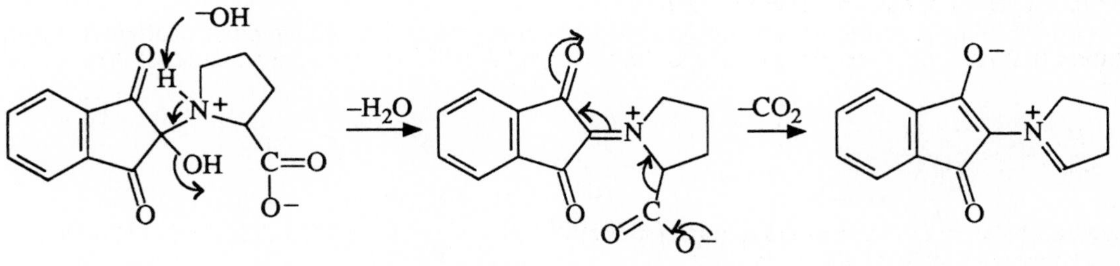

(b) Assuming for simplicity an amine of the form $R-CH_2-NH_2$, we begin with an imine, analogous to the one formed in Eq. 26.21b. Loss of a proton rather than CO_2 gives an imine identical to the second structure in Eq. 26.21c:

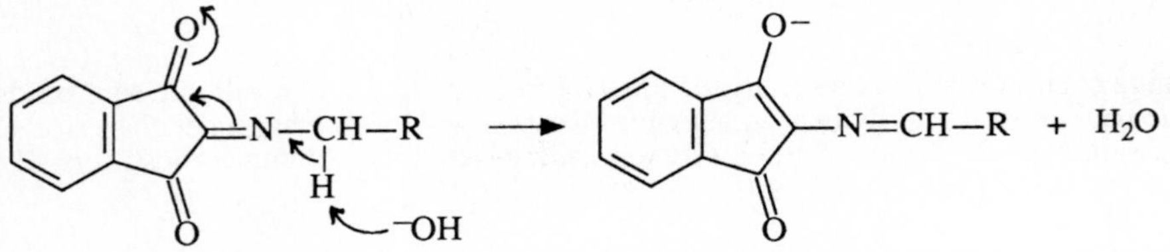

From this point on, the mechanism is identical to that shown in Eqs. 26.21c and d. It would appear from this mechanism that the primary amine has to have at least one α-hydrogen to react with ninhydrin.

14. Since Asn and Gln are amides, their side-chain amide groups, like peptide bonds, hydrolyze when treated with hot aqueous HCl. The products are Asp and Glu, respectively:

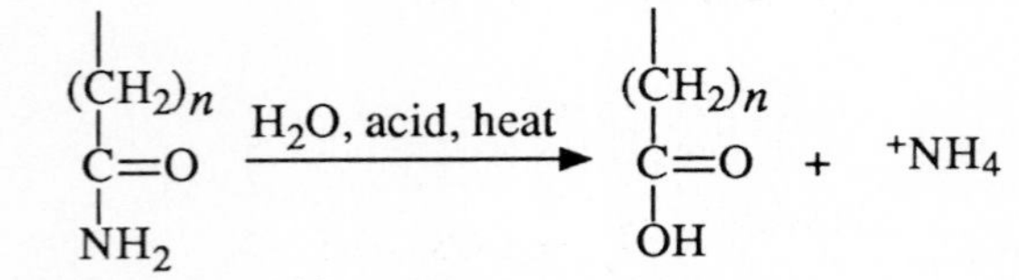

$n = 1$ Asn
$n = 2$ Gln

$n = 1$ Asp
$n = 2$ Glu

Hence, Asn cannot be distinguished from Asp, nor Gln from Glu, because an acid hydrolysis step is involved in amino acid analysis.

15. (a) The reaction in Eq. 26.24a is an addition to the C=N of an isothiocyanate. The mechanism parallels that for carbonyl addition or, more specifically, for addition to an isocyanate. (See text pages 1024–1025.) We represent the peptide as NH_2—Pep:

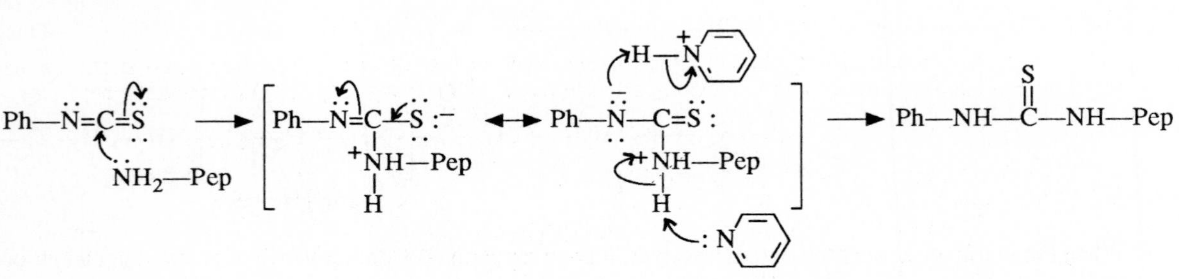

➤ Although the proton transfers in the last step are shown for convenience as *simultaneous* processes, such proton-transfer steps typically occur as separate events.

(b) In Eq. 26.24b, the sulfur acts as a nucleophile and attacks the protonated amide in a carbonyl-substitution reaction:

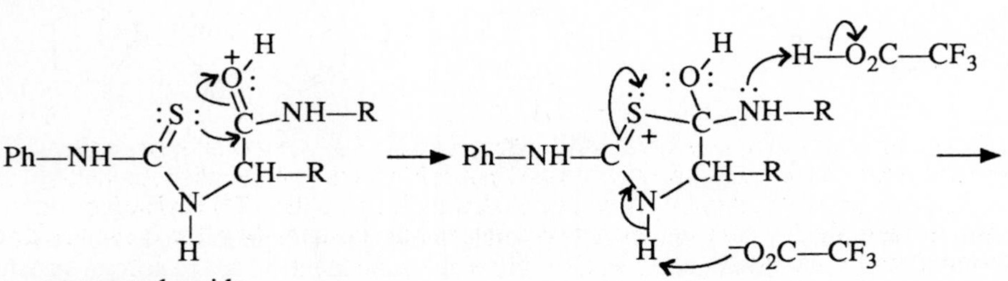

protonated amide

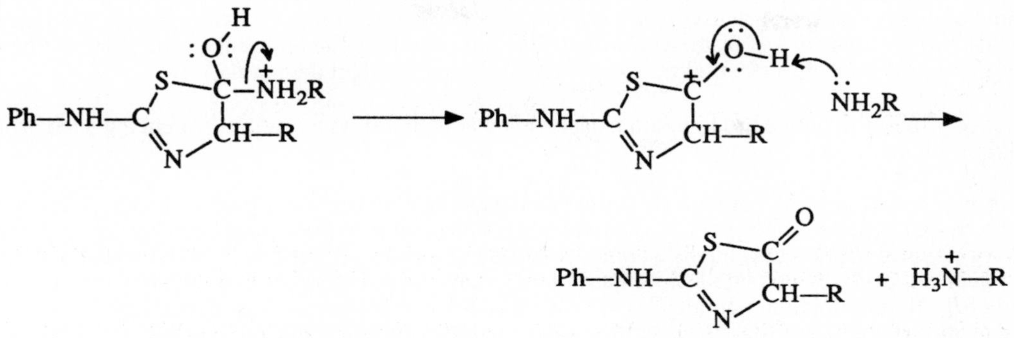

(c) In the first part of Eq. 26.24c, water hydrolyzes the product of the previous equation back to the thiourea derivative. We begin this mechanism with the carbonyl-protonated starting material:

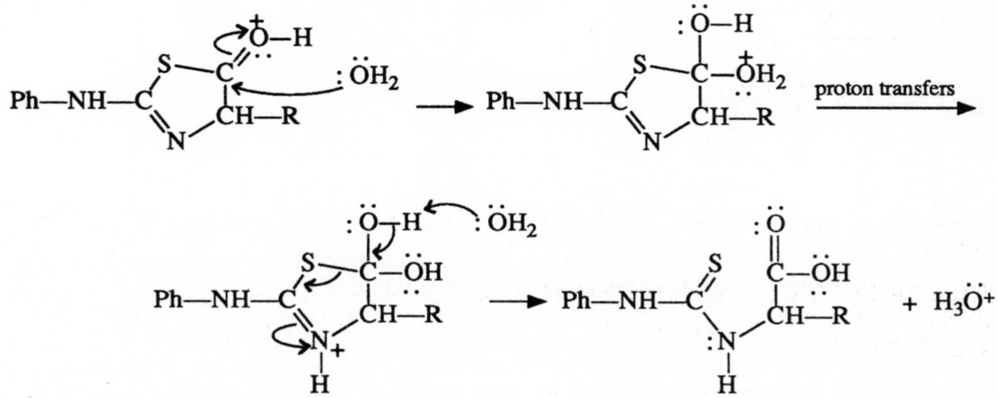

In the last transformation in Eq. 26.24c, the nitrogen of the thioamide effects a carbonyl substitution reaction on the carboxylic acid; in this reaction water is lost. We begin with the carbonyl-protonated thiourea:

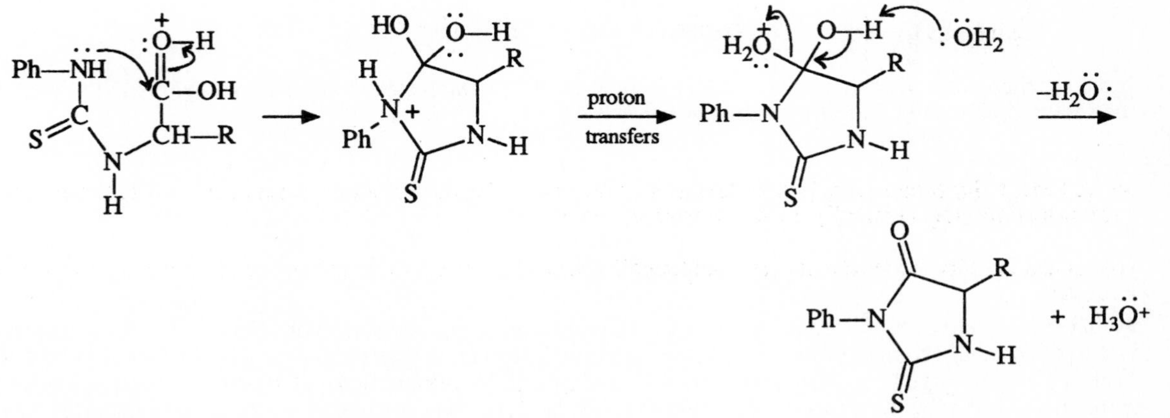

➤ Students have asked why one bothers to convert the thiazolinone into a PTH derivative; since the thiazolinone derivative carries the side chain of the amino-terminal residue, why not identify it directly? The reason is that the thiazolinone is unstable, and slowly converts on standing into the PTH derivative and/or the thiourea. Such a mixture is a nuisance to analyze. Hence, complete conversion to the PTH is used because it affords a single pure compound for analysis.

16. Peptides with an amino-terminal acyl group (such as the acetyl group in the problem) cannot undergo the Edman degradation, because a free amino group is required for reaction with the Edman reagent. (Notice in Eq. 26.24b that two protons are lost from the nitrogen that was originally the terminal amino group. An amide lacks one of these protons and, furthermore, is *much* less nucleophilic than the amine.)

➤ A number of proteins in nature are found to be acetylated at their amino termini. Sequencing such proteins poses special problems.

17. (a) Peptide *A* was known from the previously presented data to be at the amino terminus; hence, either *C* or *D* is the amino-terminal peptide. Since peptide *C* contains a lysine residue, it must have been located at the amino-terminal end of *A*; since peptide *D* contains a homoserine lactone residue, it must have been located at the carboxy-terminal end of *A*. Since peptide *E* contains an arginine, it must have been located at the amino-terminal end of *B*. By elimination, peptide *F* is the carboxy-terminal peptide of *B*, and hence of *P* itself.
(b) Because reactions were used that break peptides at the carboxy-terminal side of Lys, Arg, and Met residues, it follows that these residues are the first ones on the *amino-terminal side of the break*, and hence, at the carboxy-terminal ends of their respective peptides.

18. (a) Since cyanogen bromide is the acid halide of HC≡N, it reacts much like an acid chloride. Thus, it can react with amides to give amides. Reaction with the side-chain amino group of lysine would give a *cyanamide*:

$$(\overset{|}{C}H_2)_4 \;+\; Br{-}C{\equiv}N \;\longrightarrow\; (\overset{|}{C}H_2)_4 \;+\; H{-}Br$$
$$\underset{NH_2}{} \qquad\qquad\qquad\qquad \underset{NH{-}C{\equiv}N}{}$$
$$\text{a cyanamide}$$

(b) Very acidic conditions are used in the cyanogen bromide reaction. Under these conditions amino groups are completely protonated and therefore not nucleophilic. On the other hand, the sulfur of a methionine residue is not very basic, and is therefore nucleophilic under the reaction conditions.

19. We know the peptide *C* is derived from the amino end of *Q* because it contains Leu, the amino-terminal residue of *Q* itself. We know that peptide *D* must be at the carboxy end of *Q* because it contains no Lys or Arg, and therefore must have resulted from cleavage at its amino-terminal residue only. The order of *A* and *B*, however, must be established by other data; the required order is provided by cleavage with chymotrypsin. Peptide *E* shows that the Lys residue in *Q* is followed by a Gly residue; since the other Gly residue follows a Pro (peptide *B*), this establishes that peptide *A* follows peptide *C* in the sequence of *Q*. The Arg-Ser sequence in peptide *F* confirms that peptide *D* follows peptide *B* in the sequence of *Q*. The final sequence of *Q*, then, is *C-A-B-D*, or

Leu-Lys-Gly-Arg-Ile-Trp-Phe-Pro-Gly-Arg-Ser-Glu-Ile

20. If the average yield of each step is *Y*, then the yield of the first step (assuming it is average) is *Y*; the yield of the second is $Y \cdot Y$; and that of the *n*th step is Y^n. Hence,

$$Y^{369} = 0.17$$
$$369 \log Y = \log 0.17 = -0.7696$$
$$\log Y = -0.0021, \text{ or } Y = 0.995.$$

Hence, the average yield of each step is 99.5%!

➤ The high yield of each step demonstrates two points about peptide synthesis. First, it has been developed into a remarkably efficient process. The second point, however, is that even with yield in excess of 99%, the overall yields of large proteins prepared by this method will be extremely small. Furthermore, these will be contaminated by large numbers of impurities that will be difficult to separate from the desired material. Fortunately, genetic-engineering methods (which you will study if you take biochemistry) allow scientists to prepare pure naturally occurring proteins in large amounts. At the present time, the chemical synthesis of peptides is most useful for the preparation of peptides containing about 2–50 residues.

21. (a) Because lysine contains two amino groups, both must be protected in order to prevent nucleophilic side reactions, such as the reaction of the amino group of one lysine molecule with the DCC-activated carboxy group of another.

(b) Deprotection removes *both* protecting groups. Hence, both amino groups react in the subsequent acylation reactions. The peptides obtained are the following: (The Lys residue is drawn in detail for clarity.)

$$
\begin{array}{lll}
\text{Gly—NH—CH—C—Ala} & \text{NH}_2\text{—CH—C—Ala} & \text{Gly—NH—CH—C—Ala} \\
\qquad\quad | & \qquad | & \qquad\quad | \\
\qquad (\text{CH}_2)_4 & \quad (\text{CH}_2)_4 & \qquad (\text{CH}_2)_4 \\
\qquad\quad | & \qquad | & \qquad\quad | \\
\qquad\ \text{NH}_2 & \text{NH—Gly} & \quad\ \text{NH—Gly}
\end{array}
$$

(c) The benzyl ester is not removed by trifluoroacetic acid. (The peptide is also attached to the resin by a benzylic ester; were benzylic esters cleaved by acid, the peptide would not remain on the resin during the first deprotection step.) Hence, the side-chain amino group of Lys remains protected until the end of the synthesis. The benzyl ester, like the benzylic-ester linkage to the resin, is cleaved by the final HF step. As a result, only the first peptide, the desired one, is obtained.

22. Since the four chains of hemoglobin are held together by the same noncovalent forces that account for the tertiary structures of the individual chains, the subunits of hemoglobin would dissociate, and would unfold into two random-coil α-chains and two random-coil β-chains.

Solutions to Additional Problems

23. (a)

$$
\begin{array}{l}
\overset{+}{\text{H}_3\text{N}}\text{—CH—CO}_2\text{Et}\quad \text{HSO}_4^- \\
\qquad\quad | \\
\qquad \text{CH(CH}_3)_2
\end{array}
$$

(b)

$$
\begin{array}{l}
\qquad\ \ \text{O} \\
\qquad\ \ \| \\
\text{Ph—C—NH—CH—CO}_2^- \\
\qquad\qquad\quad | \\
\qquad\qquad \text{CH(CH}_3)_2
\end{array}
$$

(c)

$$
\begin{array}{l}
\overset{+}{\text{H}_3\text{N}}\text{—CH—CO}_2\text{H} \\
\qquad\quad | \\
\qquad \text{CH(CH}_3)_2
\end{array}
$$

(d)

$$
\begin{array}{l}
\text{H}_2\text{N—CH—CO}_2^-\ \text{Na}^+ \\
\qquad\quad | \\
\qquad \text{CH(CH}_3)_2
\end{array}
$$

(e)

$$
\begin{array}{l}
\text{Ph—CH—NH—CH—CO}_2^-\ \text{Na}^+ \\
\qquad\ \ | \qquad\qquad | \\
\qquad\ \text{CN} \qquad\quad \text{CH(CH}_3)_2
\end{array}
$$

(f)

$(\text{CH}_3)_2\text{CH—CH}=\text{O}$ +

Ruhemann's purple
(text page 1151)

Reaction (e) is a variation of the Strecker synthesis in which an amine —in this case, the amino acid valine — rather than ammonia is the source of nitrogen.

(g)

$$
\begin{array}{l}
\qquad\qquad\quad \text{O} \\
\qquad\qquad\quad \| \\
(\text{CH}_3)_3\text{CO—C—NH—CH—CO}_2^-\ \overset{+}{\text{HNEt}_3} \\
\qquad\qquad\qquad\qquad\quad | \\
\qquad\qquad\qquad\quad \text{CH(CH}_3)_2
\end{array}
$$

(h)

$$
\begin{array}{l}
\qquad\qquad\quad \text{O} \qquad\qquad\quad \text{O} \qquad\qquad\quad \text{O} \\
\qquad\qquad\quad \| \qquad\qquad\quad \| \qquad\qquad\quad \| \\
(\text{CH}_3)_3\text{CO—C—NH—CH—C—NH—CH}_2\text{—C—O—}t\text{-Bu} \\
\qquad\qquad\qquad\qquad\quad | \\
\qquad\qquad\qquad\quad \text{CH(CH}_3)_2
\end{array}
$$

(i)

$$
\begin{array}{l}
\qquad\qquad\quad \text{O} \qquad\qquad\quad \text{O} \\
\qquad\qquad\quad \| \qquad\qquad\quad \| \\
\text{H}_2\text{N—CH—C—NH—CH}_2\text{—C—O}^-\ \text{Na}^+ \\
\qquad\quad | \\
\qquad \text{CH(CH}_3)_2
\end{array}
$$

(j)

hydrochloride salts of glycine and valine

24. (a) Aspartic acid has the lowest isoelectric point, and is therefore the most acidic amino acid.
(b) Arginine has the highest isoelectric point, and is therefore the most basic amino acid.
(c) Threonine and isoleucine each have two asymmetric carbons, and therefore can exist as diastereomers.
(d) Proline is not a primary amine, and hence does not react with ninhydrin to give Ruhemann's purple.

(e) Glycine is not chiral, and hence is optically inactive under all conditions.

(f) Asparagine and glutamine have amide groups in their side chains that are hydrolyzed to the respective carboxylic acids aspartic acid and glutamic acid, respectively.

25. (a) Because the amino group of leucine is not protected, a certain amount of attachment to the resin will occur by attack of the α-amino group on the chloromethyl groups of the resin. Subsequent peptide synthesis would then not proceed as planned.

(b) Boc-Leu, once attached to the resin, must be deprotected before the subsequent coupling reaction can be expected to succeed.

26. Since lysozyme has many more basic residues (Lys and Arg) than acidic residues (Asp and Glu), lysozyme is expected to be (and is) a basic protein.

27. This amino acid is really a substituted malonic acid. When heated in acid, it decarboxylates to give glutamic acid. (See Sec. 20.11.)

28. Because the taste-sensing apparatus of the body can distinguish between enantiomers, this apparatus is evidently chiral. (In fact, proteins are undoubtedly an integral part of this apparatus.)

29. The presence of two amino-terminal residues suggests that either (a) insulin is an approximately equimolar mixture of two proteins, or (b) it is a single protein containing two peptide chains. In fact, the latter is correct; insulin is two polypeptide chains connected by disulfide bonds. Glycine is the amino-terminal residue of one chain, and phenylalanine is the amino-terminal residue of the other.

30. The conjugate acid of the side-chain sulfonate group is more acidic than a carboxylic acid. Hence, cysteic acid is more acidic than aspartic acid. Therefore (a) is the correct response.

31. (a) We expect trypsin to catalyze the cleavage of glucagon at Lys and Arg residues. The peptides expected are:

$\overset{+}{H_3N}$-His-Ser-Gln-Gly-Thr-Phe-Thr-Ser-Asp-Tyr-Ser-Lys-CO_2^-

$\overset{+}{H_3N}$-Tyr-Leu-Asp-Ser-Arg-CO_2^-

$\overset{+}{H_3N}$-Arg-CO_2^-

$\overset{+}{H_3N}$-Ala-Gln-Asp-Phe-Val-Gln-Trp-Leu-Met-Asn-Thr-CO_2^-

The $\overset{+}{H_3N}$- and -CO_2^- groups at the ends of the peptides indicate the amino and carboxy termini, respectively.

(b) Cyanogen bromide cleavage would yield two peptides:

$\overset{+}{H_3N}$-His-Ser-Gln-Gly-Thr-Phe-Thr-Ser-Asp-Tyr-Ser-Lys-Tyr-Leu-Asp-Ser-Arg-
   Arg-Ala-Gln-Asp-Phe-Val-Gln-Trp-Leu-homoserine lactone

and $\overset{+}{H_3N}$-Asn-Thr-CO_2^-

(c) The products of this Edman cleavage would be the following:

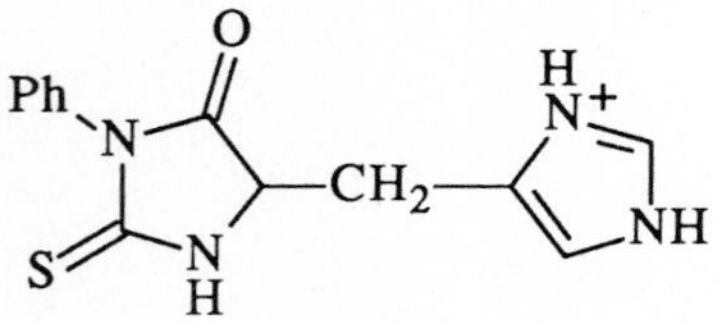

+ Ser-Gln- . . . -Thr (the rest of the glucagon sequence)

Furthermore, the side-chain amino group in the residual peptide would have reacted with the Edman reagent to give the following thiourea:

$$
\begin{array}{c}
\quad\quad\quad\quad O \\
\quad\quad\quad\quad \| \\
-NH-CH-C- \\
\quad\quad | \\
\quad\quad (CH_2)_4 \\
\quad\quad\quad | \\
\quad\quad\quad NH-C-NH-Ph \\
\quad\quad\quad\quad \| \\
\quad\quad\quad\quad S
\end{array}
$$

32. The structure of the derivative (called "dansyl-valine") indicates that the α-amino group of valine was available to react with dansyl chloride. Hence, the amino-terminal residue of the peptide is valine. The other residues are linked in a manner that cannot be determined from the data.

➤ The procedure described in this problem is sometimes used when one desires to determine only the amino-terminal residue of a peptide.

33. (a) Ethylamine reacts with the Edman reagent just as the α-amino groups of peptides do:

$$
\begin{array}{c}
\quad\quad\quad\quad S \\
\quad\quad\quad\quad \| \\
CH_3CH_2NH-C-NH-Ph
\end{array}
$$

(b) This is a variation of the Strecker synthesis in which an amine rather than ammonia serves as the source of nitrogen:

$$
\begin{array}{c}
Ph-CH-NH-CH_3 \\
\quad\quad | \\
\quad\quad C\equiv N
\end{array}
$$

[See Problem 23(e) for a similar case.]

(c) Sodium hydroxide liberates the free amine, which reacts with isobutyraldehyde to give the imine. The imine, in turn, is reduced to an amine by NaBH$_4$. In other words, this is a reductive amination (Sec. 23.7B) in which the amino acid serves as the amine.

$$
\begin{array}{c}
(CH_3)_2CH-CH_2-NH-CH-CO_2^- \\
\quad\quad\quad\quad\quad\quad\quad | \\
\quad\quad\quad\quad\quad\quad\quad CH_3
\end{array}
$$

(d) This is an ester saponification. The question is, which ester is saponified? The answer is that the methyl ester is saponified selectively for two reasons. First, the methyl group provides less steric hindrance toward attack at the carbonyl group than the *t*-butyl group. Second, the *t*-butyl ester is also an amide (it is part of a carbamate group); ester–amides (that is, carbamates) are more resistant to hydrolysis than ordinary esters, just as amides are less reactive than aldehydes and ketones (Eq. 21.65, text page 897).

$$
\begin{array}{c}
\quad\quad\quad\quad\quad O \quad\quad\quad\quad\quad O \\
\quad\quad\quad\quad\quad \| \quad\quad\quad\quad\quad \| \\
(CH_3)_3C-O-C-NH-CH-C-O^- \\
\quad\quad\quad\quad\quad\quad\quad\quad\quad | \\
\quad\quad\quad\quad\quad\quad\quad\quad\quad CH_3
\end{array}
$$

(e) The product is the acyl azide. (See Eq. 23.88, text page 1026.)

$$
\begin{array}{c}
\quad\quad O \quad \ddot{} \quad\quad + \\
\quad\quad \| \quad \cdot\cdot \quad\quad \\
Ph-C-N-N\equiv N: \\
\quad\quad\quad \cdot\cdot
\end{array}
$$

(f) Acyl azides are converted by heating into isocyanates. In this case, the isocyanate is phenyl isocyanate, Ph—N=C=O.

(g) Isocyanates, like iso*thio*cyanates such as the Edman reagent, react with amines. In this case, the product is a substituted urea:

$$
\underset{\substack{| \\ CH(CH_3)_2}}{Ph-NH-\overset{\overset{\displaystyle O}{\|}}{C}-NH-CH-\overset{\overset{\displaystyle O}{\|}}{C}-OMe}
$$

(See also Eq. 23.86 on text page 1025.)

(h) This is like the acetamidomalonate synthesis, except that the protecting group is a formyl group rather than an acetyl group:

$$
\underset{\substack{| \\ CH_2 \\ | \\ H_2C \overset{C}{=} CH_3}}{\overset{+}{H_3N}-CH-CO_2H} \quad + \quad CO_2 \quad + \quad EtOH \quad + \quad H-CO_2H
$$

(i) Reaction with hydrazine forms the hydrazide A; diazotization gives the acyl azide B; heating in ethanol gives the carbamate C; and acid-catalyzed hydrolysis hydrolyzes both the carbamate and the nitrile to give valine, D:

$$
\underset{\substack{| \\ CH(CH_3)_2 \\ \\ A}}{N\equiv C-CH-\overset{\overset{\displaystyle O}{\|}}{C}-NHNH_2} \qquad
\underset{\substack{| \\ CH(CH_3)_2 \\ \\ B}}{N\equiv C-CH-\overset{\overset{\displaystyle O}{\|}}{C}-N_3} \qquad
\underset{\substack{| \\ CH(CH_3)_2 \\ \\ C}}{N\equiv C-CH-NH-\overset{\overset{\displaystyle O}{\|}}{C}-OEt} \qquad
\underset{\substack{| \\ CH(CH_3)_2 \\ \\ D}}{HO-\overset{\overset{\displaystyle O}{\|}}{C}-CH-\overset{+}{NH_3}}
$$

34. The amino-terminal residue of the peptide is lysine. The side-chain amino group of lysine, as well as the α-amino group, reacts with the Edman reagent. (See the solution to Problem 31 for a similar situation.)

35. (a) Alanine (like the other amino acids) is a different compound in HCl, NaOH, and H_2O because its ionization state is different. In acidic solution, the optical rotation is that of the acidic form; in base, the optical rotation is that of the basic form; and in water, the optical rotation is that of the neutral (zwitterion) form.

(b) Lysine has two amino groups, and acetylation of each is possible:

$$
\underset{\substack{| \\ (CH_2)_4 \\ | \\ +NH_3}}{CH_3-\overset{\overset{\displaystyle O}{\|}}{C}-NH-CH-CO_2^-} \quad \text{and} \quad
\underset{\substack{| \\ (CH_2)_4 \\ | \\ NH-\underset{\displaystyle O}{\overset{\|}{C}}-CH_3}}{\overset{+}{H_3N}-CH-CO_2^-}
$$

(c) The peptide is cleaved at the Arg-Ala bond at pH 8. However, in the presence of 8*M* urea, trypsin, like most enzymes, is denatured. Denatured enzymes are devoid of activity because their three-dimensional conformations are disrupted. Because trypsin is inactive, it cannot catalyze the hydrolysis of peptides.

(d) The 2-mercaptoethanol treatment ensures that disulfide bonds are reduced. Aziridine reacts much like an epoxide. Reaction with the thiol group of a cysteine residue gives an amine:

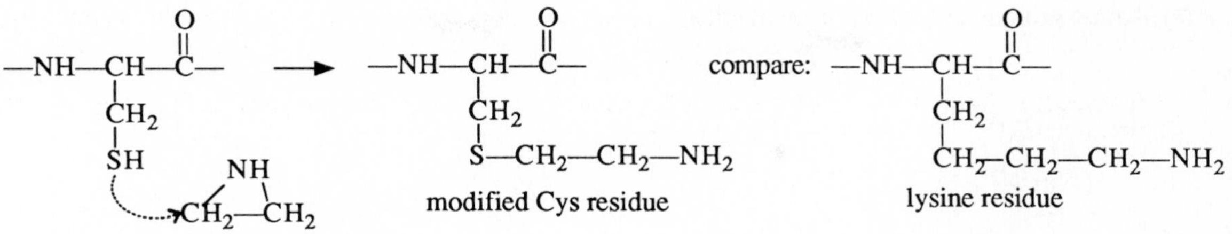

As we can see from the above comparison, the modified Cys residue looks much like a lysine; that is, it contains four atoms separating the peptide backbone from an amino group. Evidently, trypsin also sees the resemblance and hydrolyzes peptides at this modified residue.

(e) The two compounds formed are diastereomers. They both have the same configuration at the α-carbon, but differ in configuration at the sulfur of the sulfoxide group. This sulfur is an asymmetric atom because it has four different "groups" attached: the CH_2, the CH_3, the O, and the electron pair. Evidently, inversion at sulfur in a sulfoxide, unlike amine inversion, is very slow, because the individual diastereomers can be isolated.

(f) Benzamidine contains a functional group that is very much like the guanidino group on the side chain of an arginine. Benzamidine, like an arginine residue in a peptide, is bound in the active site of trypsin. When the active site contains benzamidine, it cannot simultaneously bind a peptide. Hence, benzamidine blocks peptide hydrolysis.

36. Let us number the residues of P from the amino terminus as $1, 2, 3, \ldots$ First, the Edman degradation of P shows that leucine is the amino-terminal residue. The formation of only dipeptides, as well as the dipeptide Leu-Val, shows that DPAP cuts peptide P at every even-numbered residue from the amino terminus. We thus expect this enzyme also to cleave peptide Q at every other residue — the *odd* residues in the numbering of P:

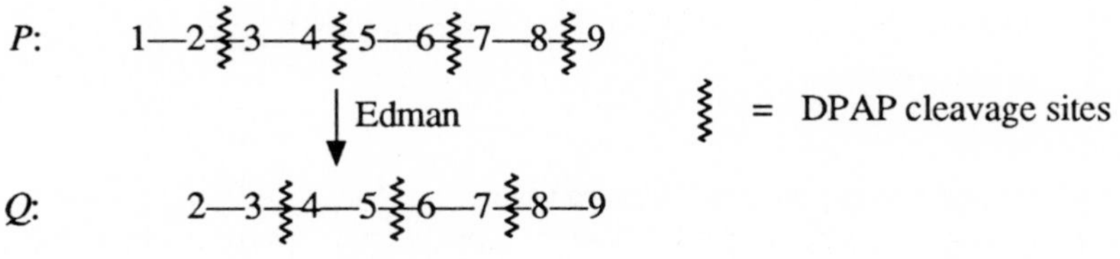

From this analysis, we see that Gly is residue 9, the carboxy-terminal residue of P. To get the order of the dipeptides, we work back and forth between the dipeptides derived from P and those derived from Q. Since Gly has to be at the carboxy terminus of one of the dipeptides from Q, and since the only dipeptide that meets this criterion is Ala-Gly, then Ala is the next residue in from the carboxy terminus. If Ala is in position 8, then position 7, from the P dipeptides, must be Gln; position 6, from the Q dipeptides, must be Asp; and so on. Alternatively, we could work from the amino terminus of P: Leu-Val of P and Val-Arg of Q establish the sequence Leu-Val-Arg; Arg-Gly of P shows that the next residue is Gly; and so on. The final sequence, then is:

$$\overset{+}{H_3N}\text{-Leu-Val-Arg-Gly-Val-Asp-Gln-Ala-Gly-}CO_2^-$$

The ammonia arises from the hydrolysis of Gln.

37. In Figure 26.6, we see that the amino acid side chains extend outward from the periphery of the helix, and are actually rather close to each other in space. Below pH 10, the side-chain amino groups in polylysine are protonated; thus, these side chains are positively charged. The peptide loses its α-helical conformation to avoid repulsive interactions between the adjacent positively charged groups. Above pH 11, the side-chain amino groups are unprotonated and hence uncharged. As a result, there are no charge-charge repulsions in the α-helix. In polyglutamic acid, the side chains are negatively charged at pH values above the pK_a of the carboxy groups. Hence, the repulsion between negative charges causes the helix to be destabilized and thus unfold at high pH. At low pH, the carboxy groups are un-ionized and hence uncharged. Consequently, there are no charge-charge repulsions in the helix at low pH.

38. (a) Amino groups are acylated by anhydrides:

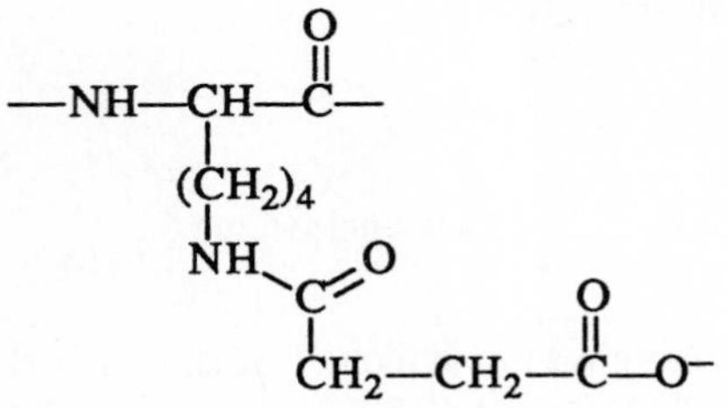

(b) α-Halo carbonyl compounds react rapidly with nucleophiles. The side-chain thiol group of a cysteine residue is partially ionized at pH 8–9, and is therefore an excellent nucleophile:

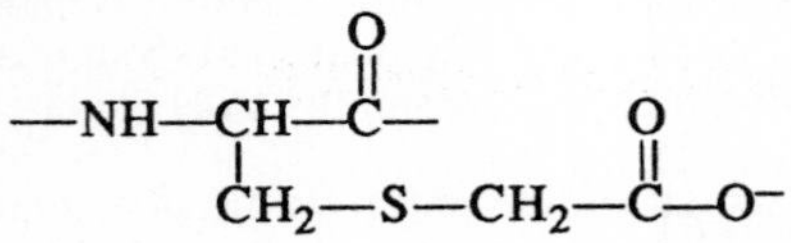

(c) Conjugate addition of the thiol group to the α,β-unsaturated carbonyl compound gives the following product:

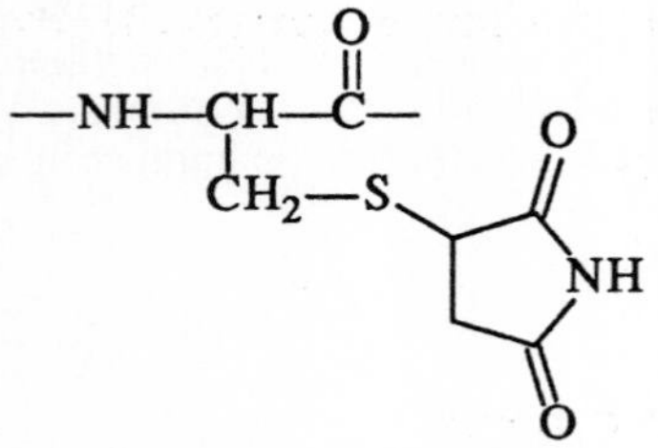

(d) This is a reductive amination that results in the dimethylation of lysine:

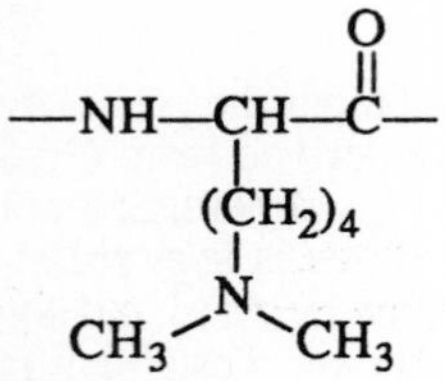

(e) The side-chain carboxy group is coupled to the glycine amino group to give a peptide (amide) bond at the side chain:

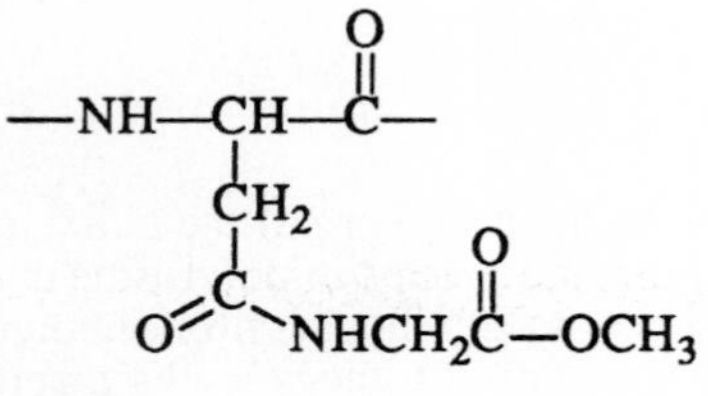

(f) Phenols, including the side-chain phenol group of a tyrosine, undergo diazo coupling with diazonium ions. Since the *para* position of the phenol is blocked, coupling occurs at the *ortho* position:

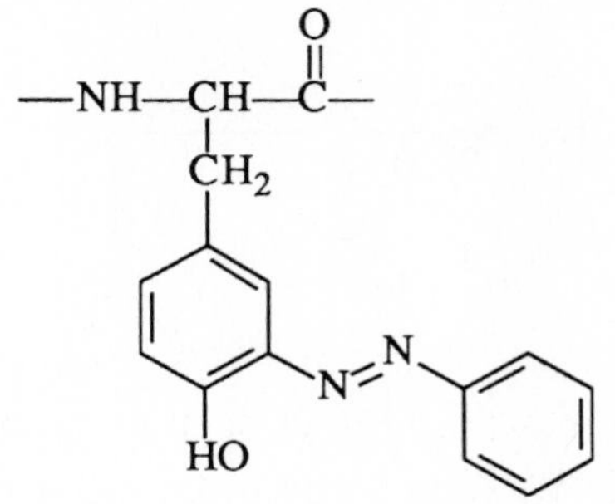

(g) Heavy-metal ions such as mercuric ion form mercaptides with thiols (see text page 300):

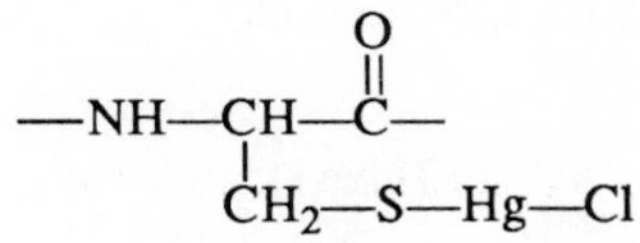

(h) The side-chain amino groups of lysine residues are diazotized, and the products are the typical carbocation-derived materials:

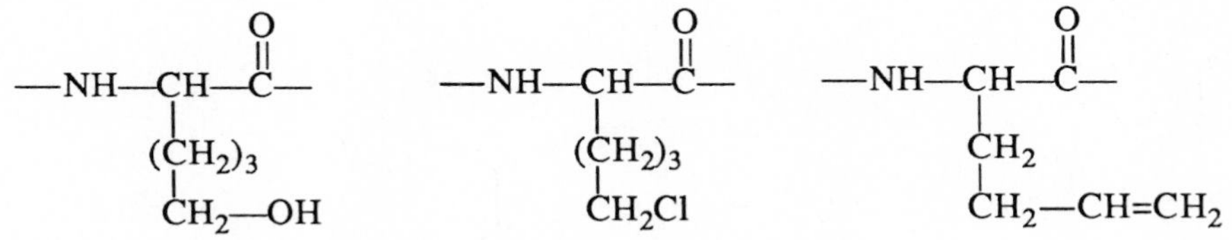

In addition, some rearrangement products can be expected. (See Eq. 23.56 on text page 1014 for a similar situation.)

39. Every synthesis has the same final steps:

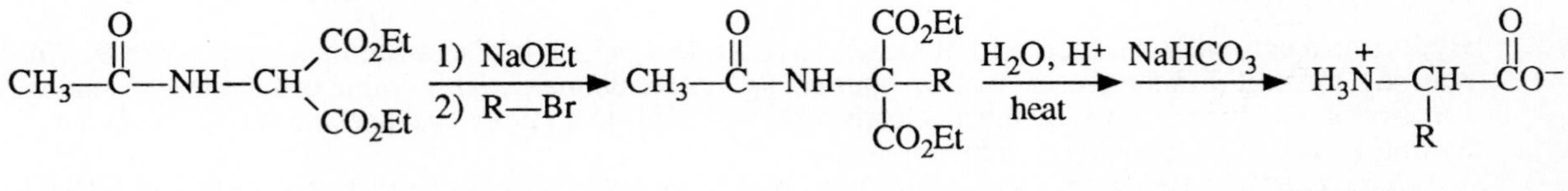

The challenge is to prepare the alkyl halides R—Br that are used in these syntheses. This is accomplished in each case as follows:

(a)

$$(CH_3)_2CDCH_2\text{—}Br \xleftarrow{\text{DBr, peroxides}} (CH_3)_2C{=}CH_2$$

Alternatively, we could hydroborate the same alkene with B_2D_6, oxidize the organoborane with $H_2O_2/{}^-OH$, and then treat the resulting primary alcohol with PBr_3.

(b)

$$Ph\text{—}CHD\text{—}Br \xleftarrow{\text{HBr}} Ph\text{—}CHD\text{—}OH \xleftarrow[\text{2) } H_3O^+]{\text{1) LiAlD}_4} Ph\text{—}CH{=}O$$

(c) In this case, we first prepare the following alkyl halide:

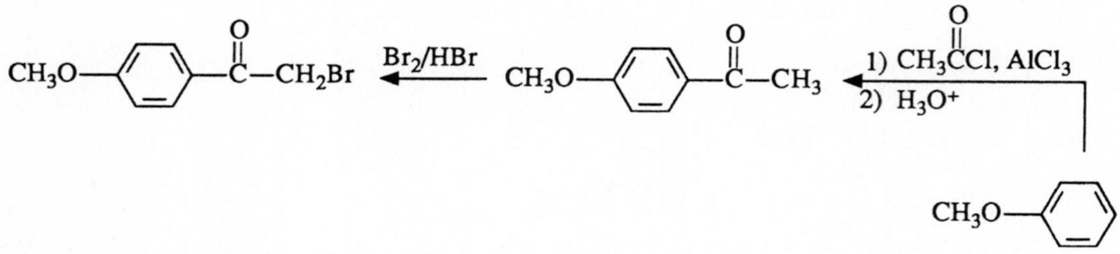

Then we let it react in the acetamidomalonate synthesis as shown above. We carry out the hydrolysis and decarboxylation steps with concentrated HBr, which also demethylates the ether to give the desired amino acid.

40. The reaction is an intramolecular ester aminolysis. Loss of a proton from the terminal amino group gives a free amine; this nucleophile attacks the ester carbonyl group and displaces methoxide as methanol:

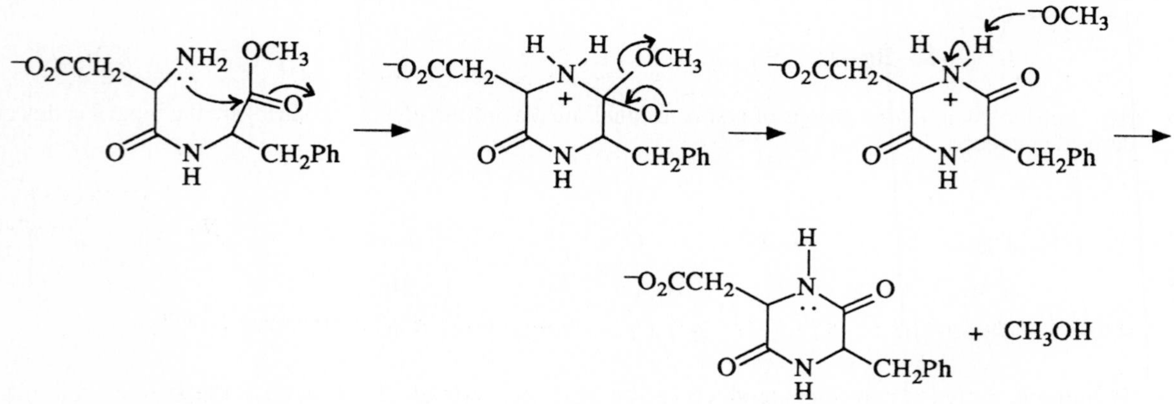

41. The pH of the buffer determines the charge on the peptide. At pH 6, the charge on Gly-Lys is +1, the charge on Gly-Asp is –1, and the charge on Gly-Ala is zero. Hence, Gly-Lys [spot (c)] will migrate toward the cathode, Gly-Asp [spot (a)] toward the anode, and Gly-Ala [spot (b)] will not migrate appreciably.

42. Hydrazine reacts with the ester to form the acyl hydrazide A, which is diazotized to the acyl azide B. Curtius rearrangement of B in the presence of aqueous acid gives the amine C. This amine is the nitrogen analog of a hemiacetal, and breaks down by the mechanism shown below to an imine and acetamide D. The imine hydrolyzes to isobutyraldehyde and ammonia.

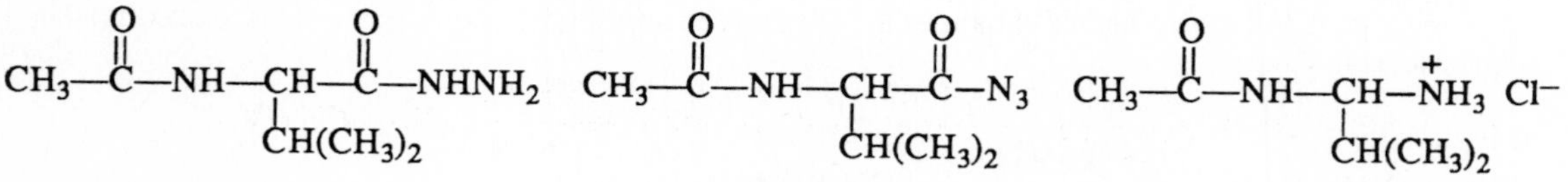

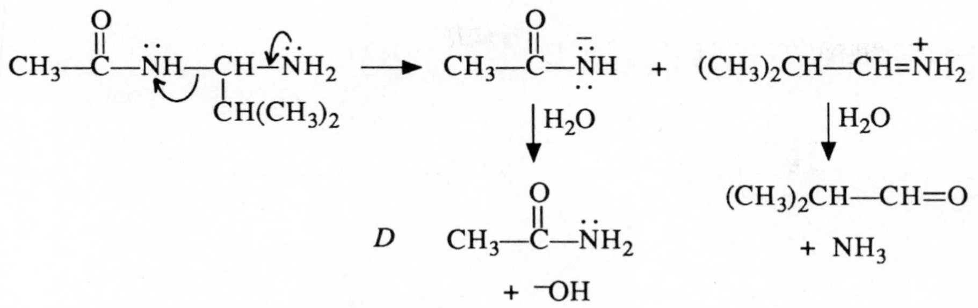

43. (a) Reaction of the Merrifield resin with trimethylamine would give the modified resin indicated. This is an S_N2 reaction of the amine with the benzylic chloride on the resin.

(b) The resin is positively charged and therefore attracts negatively charged groups. That is, the resin is an *anion-exchange* resin. Glutamic acid, which has a charge of −1 at pH 6, is retained on the column; arginine, which has a charge of +1, is repelled; and leucine, with a charge of zero, is neither attracted nor repelled by the column. The order of elution is Arg followed by Leu followed by Glu.

44. (a)

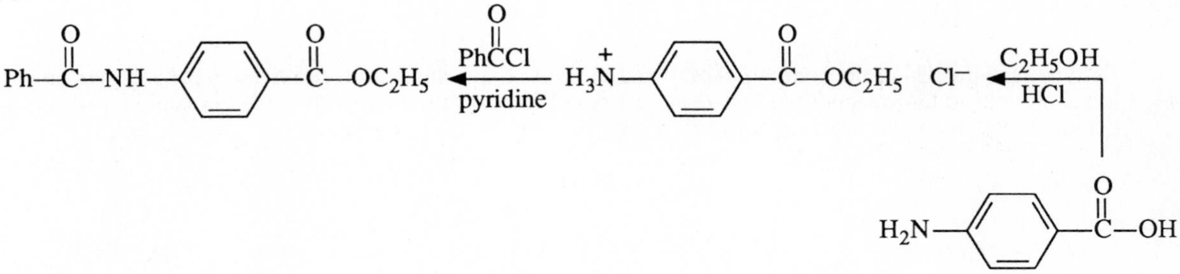

It would probably not be wise to interchange the order of esterification and acylation (why?).

(b)

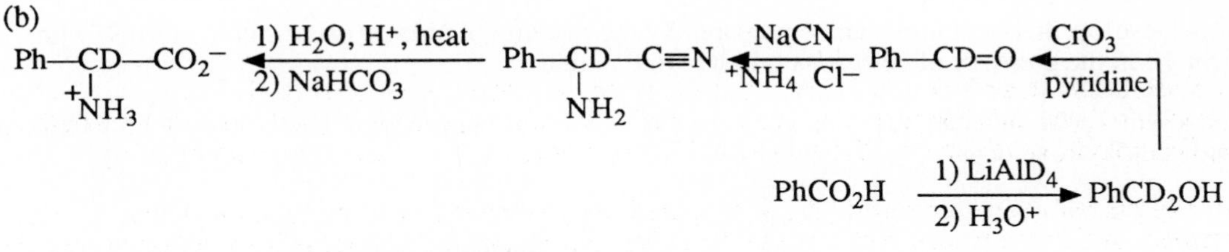

We could also convert benzoic acid into the acid chloride and reduce that directly to the aldehyde using $Li^+ D—\bar{A}l[OC(CH_3)_3]_3$.

(c)

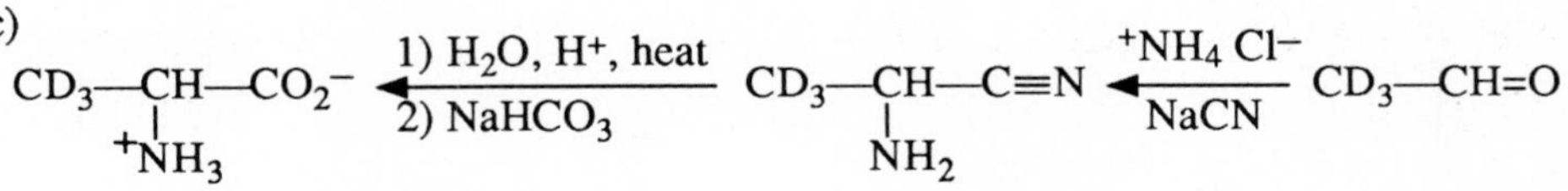

(d)

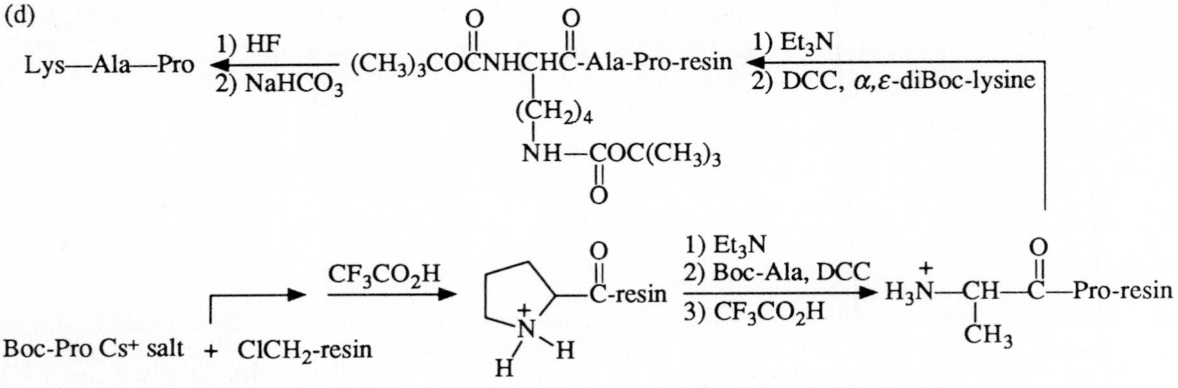

Lys—Ala—Pro $\xleftarrow[\text{2) NaHCO}_3]{\text{1) HF}}$ (CH$_3$)$_3$COCNHCHC-Ala-Pro-resin $\xleftarrow[\text{2) DCC, }\alpha,\varepsilon\text{-diBoc-lysine}]{\text{1) Et}_3\text{N}}$

with (CH$_2$)$_4$ side chain bearing NH—COC(CH$_3$)$_3$

Boc-Pro Cs$^+$ salt + ClCH$_2$-resin $\xrightarrow{}$ $\xrightarrow{\text{CF}_3\text{CO}_2\text{H}}$ (pyrrolidinium)—C-resin $\xrightarrow[\text{3) CF}_3\text{CO}_2\text{H}]{\substack{\text{1) Et}_3\text{N} \\ \text{2) Boc-Ala, DCC}}}$ H$_3$N$^+$—CH(CH$_3$)—C—Pro-resin

(e)

C$_2$H$_5$OCCH(CN)(NH—C—CH$_3$) $\xleftarrow{\text{Ac}_2\text{O}}$ C$_2$H$_5$OCCH(CN)(NH$_2$) $\xleftarrow[\text{NaCN}]{^+\text{NH}_4\text{ Cl}^-}$ C$_2$H$_5$OCCH=O

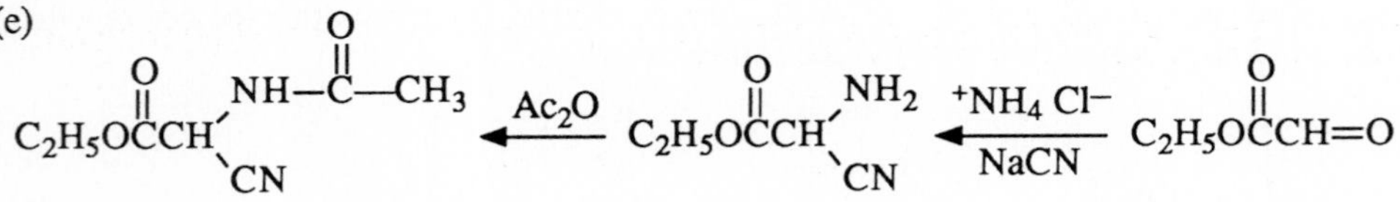

(f) The α-hydrogen of the compound prepared in (e) is acidic, and can be removed in base to give an enolate ion analogous to the acetamidomalonate anion. Alkylation of this anion with the allylic halide 3-bromo-1-cyclopentene, then hydrolysis and decarboxylation, gives the desired product:

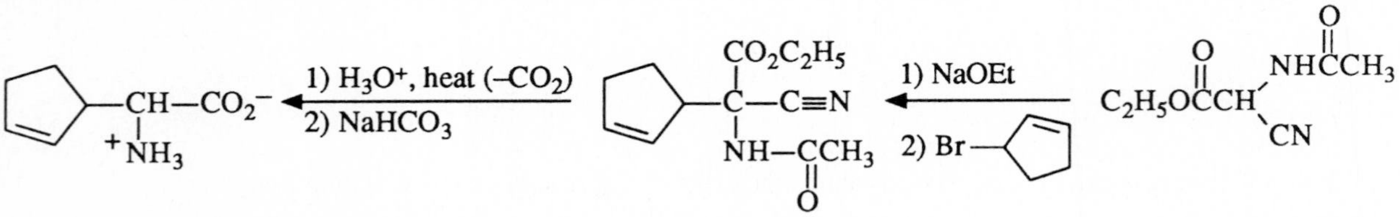

(cyclopentenyl)—CH(CO$_2^-$)($^+$NH$_3$) $\xleftarrow[\text{2) NaHCO}_3]{\text{1) H}_3\text{O}^+\text{, heat (–CO}_2\text{)}}$ (cyclopentenyl)—C(CO$_2$C$_2$H$_5$)(C≡N)(NH—CCH$_3$, =O) $\xleftarrow[\text{2) Br—(cyclopentenyl)}]{\text{1) NaOEt}}$ C$_2$H$_5$OCCH(CN)(NHCCH$_3$, =O)

3-Bromo-1-cyclopentene, in turn, can be prepared by the reaction of *N*-bromosuccinimide (NBS) with cyclopentene in the presence of peroxides (allylic bromination).

(g) The polymer *p*-aramid can be prepared by the reaction of 1,4-benzenediamine with the acid chloride of 1,4-benzenedicarboxylic acid:

H$_2$N—(C$_6$H$_4$)—NH$_2$ + Cl—C(=O)—(C$_6$H$_4$)—C(=O)—Cl $\xrightarrow{\text{Et}_3\text{N}}$ *p*-aramid

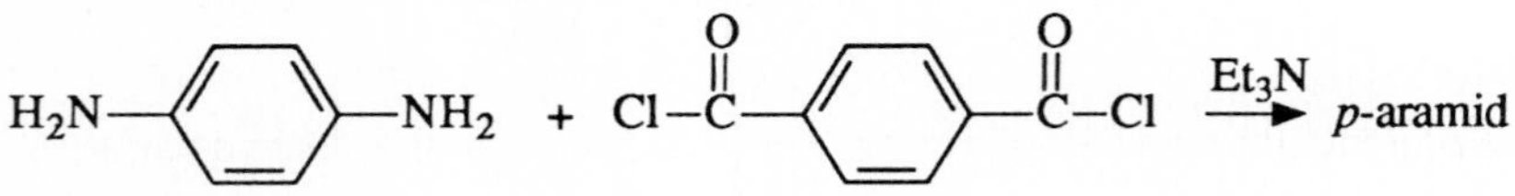

1,4-Benzenediamine is prepared from the acyl azide by a Curtius rearrangement, and the acyl azide is formed from the acid chloride:

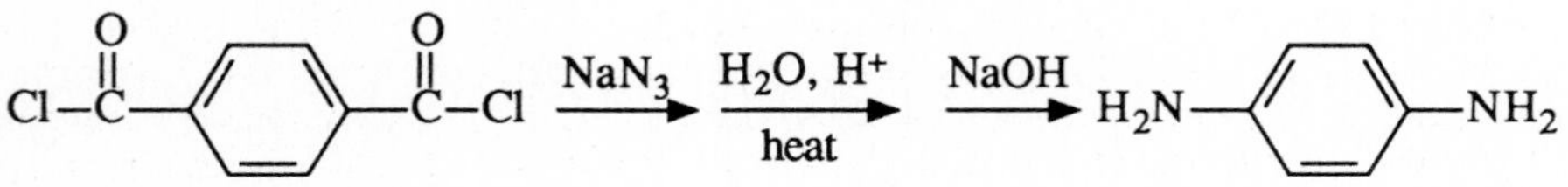

Cl—C(=O)—(C$_6$H$_4$)—C(=O)—Cl $\xrightarrow[\text{heat}]{\text{NaN}_3 \quad \text{H}_2\text{O, H}^+}$ $\xrightarrow{\text{NaOH}}$ H$_2$N—(C$_6$H$_4$)—NH$_2$

And the acid chloride is prepared from 1,4-benzenedicarboxylic acid by any of the usual methods: PCl$_5$, SOCl$_2$, etc.

45. A molecular weight of about 1100 is consistent with the actual composition (Ala$_4$,Arg$_2$,Gly$_2$,Ser$_2$); amino acid analysis gives only the *relative* amounts of each amino acid. The absence of a reaction with the Edman reagent suggests that there is no terminal amino group. A *cyclic* peptide would give these results. Cleavage of a cyclic peptide at two arginine residues would give two peptides unless the two were identical. If the two were

identical, two equivalents of a single peptide would be obtained. The results are in accord with the following structure:

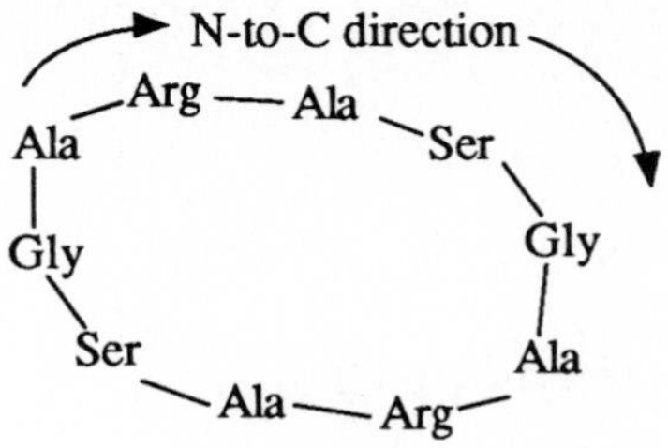

Such a cyclic peptide would be cleaved by trypsin into two identical peptides Ala-Ser-Gly-Ala-Arg. (The position of the second Ala follows from the fact that Arg must be at the carboxy terminus of each peptide.)

46. Triethylamine removes a proton readily to give an aromatic anion. Completion of a β-elimination and loss of CO_2 gives the deprotected peptide:

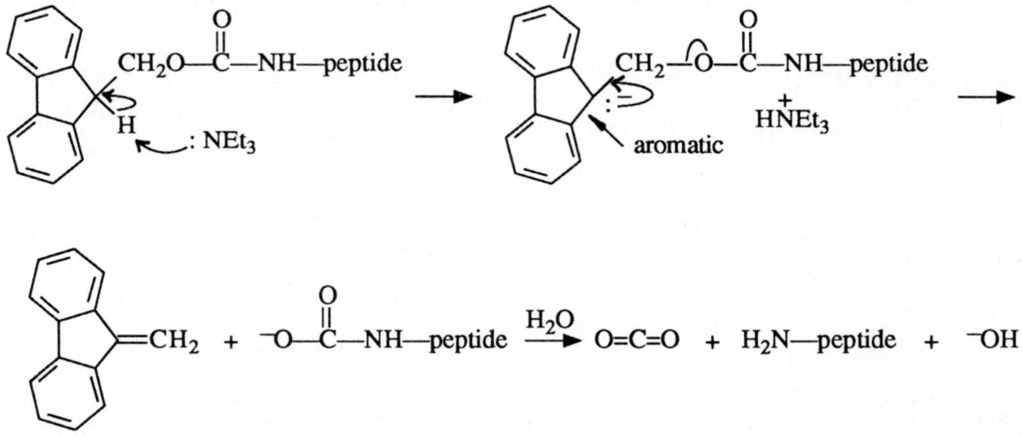

47. Compound A is L-2,4-diaminobutanoic acid:

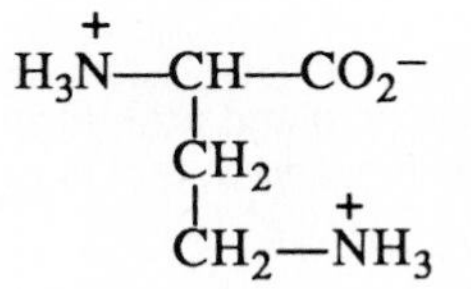

2,4-diaminobutanoic acid

➤ Be sure you can show why this structure is consistent with all the data.

48. The formula for compound A differs from that of N-acetylaspartic acid itself by loss of the elements of water. Treatment of certain dicarboxylic acids with anhydrides gives cyclic anhydrides (text page 842). Hence, compound A is N-acetylaspartic acid anhydride. Like all anhydrides, this can react with amines to give amides. Since the two carbonyl groups of A are not equivalent, two isomeric products are formed when this anhydride reacts with valine:

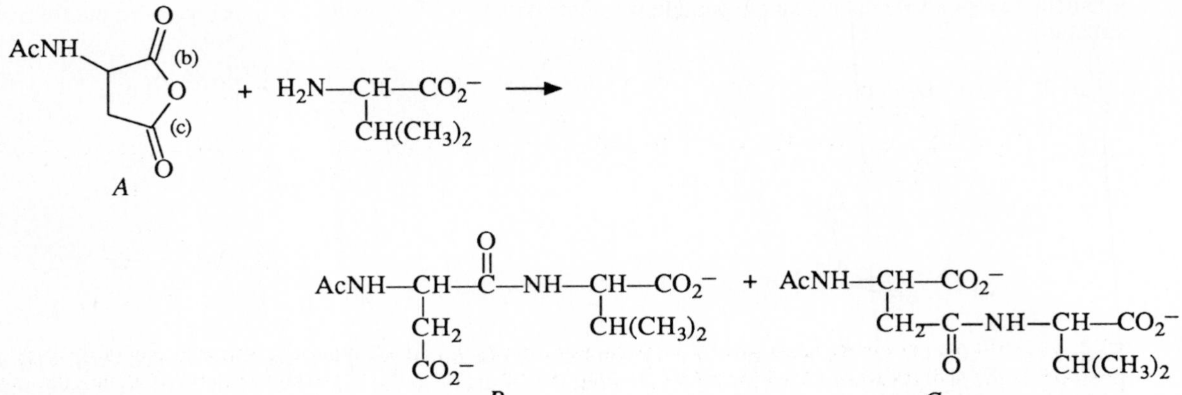

$$AcNH—CH—\overset{\overset{\textstyle O}{\|}}{C}—NH—CH—CO_2^- \quad + \quad AcNH—CH—CO_2^-$$

$$B \qquad\qquad\qquad\qquad C$$

(from reaction at carbonyl b)   (from reaction at carbonyl c)

49. (a) The first step of the mechanism is formation of an imine (Sec. 19.11A). Reaction of this with the conjugate base of the thiol gives an addition product which is eventually transformed into the product. We begin with the imine:

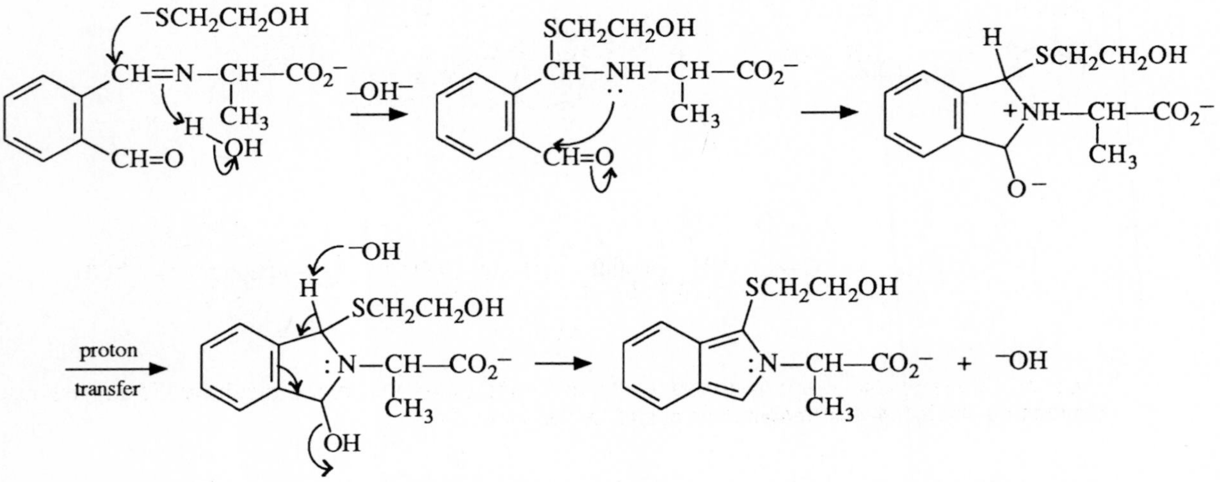

(b) The mechanism is identical to the formation of Ruhemann's purple from an amino acid and ninhydrin, except that alloxan rather than ninhydrin is the triketone starting material. Eqs. 26.21b,c, and d, text pages 1151, give the details of this mechanism.

(c) The conjugate-base amine of the starting material is transformed into the product by an internal nucleophilic aromatic substitution reaction (Sec. 18.4A):

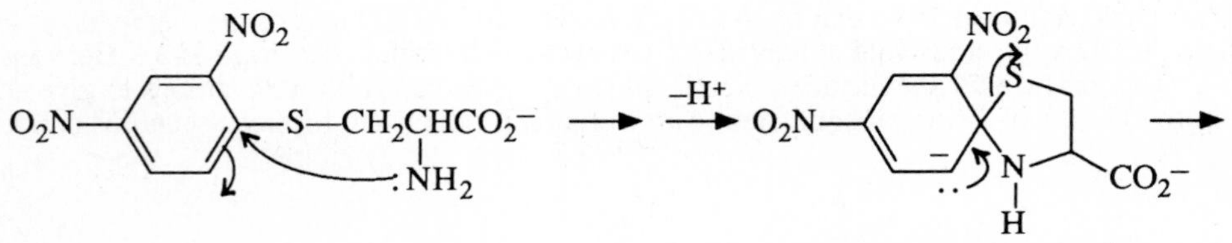

resonance-stabilized anion

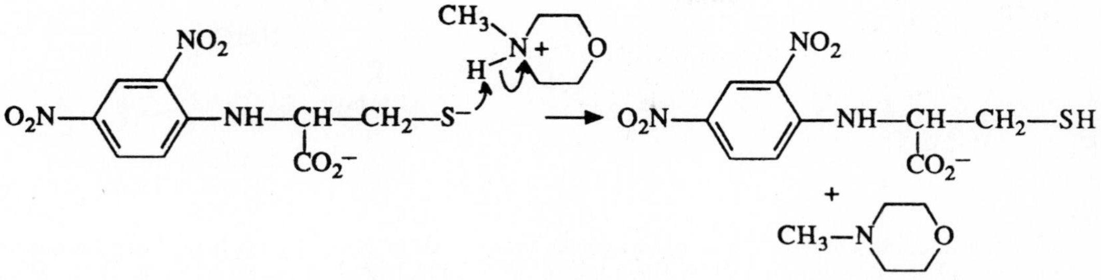

(d) In the first part of the mechanism, ⁻SH displaces chloride in an S_N2 reaction, and ammonia forms an imine by attack on the carbonyl group to give an α-mercapto imine, with which we begin the detailed description of the mechanism. This imine is in equilibrium with an enamine. Addition of both the —SH group and the —NH$_2$ group of this enamine to acetone (in a reaction much like acetal formation) and proton transfers give the first product:

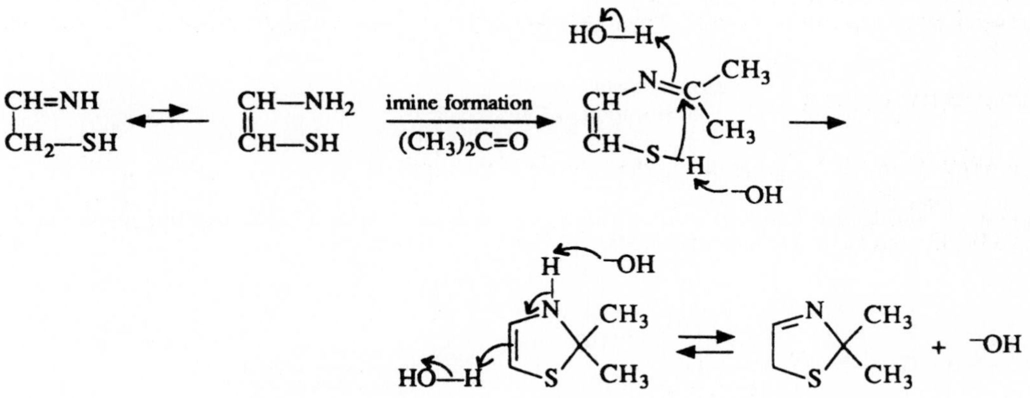

The cyclic imine product reacts with cyanide ion in a variation of the Strecker synthesis. Hydrolysis of the resulting nitrile liberates acetone and gives cysteine as the product:

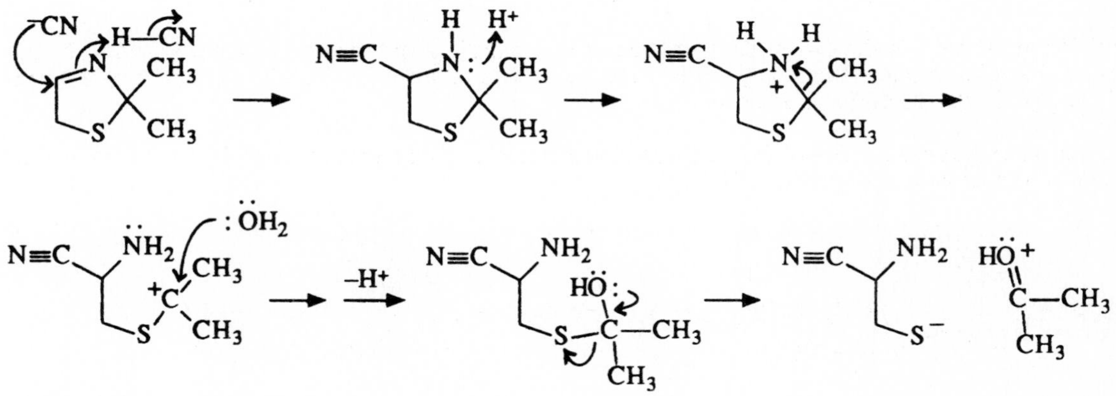

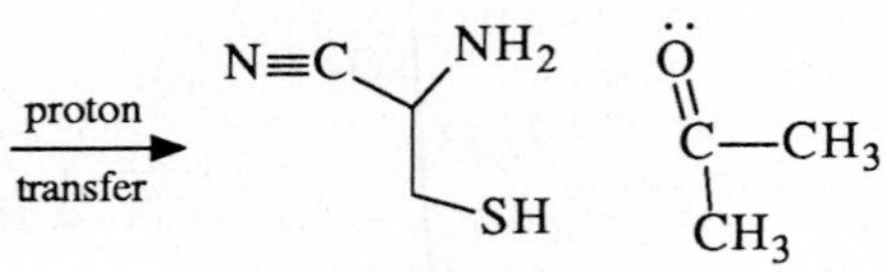

nitrile hydrolysis
gives cysteine

(e) An imine formes between formaldehyde and the amino group of tryptophan. The protonated imine acts as an electrophile in an intramolecular electrophilic aromatic substitution reaction to give the product. We begin with the protonated imine:

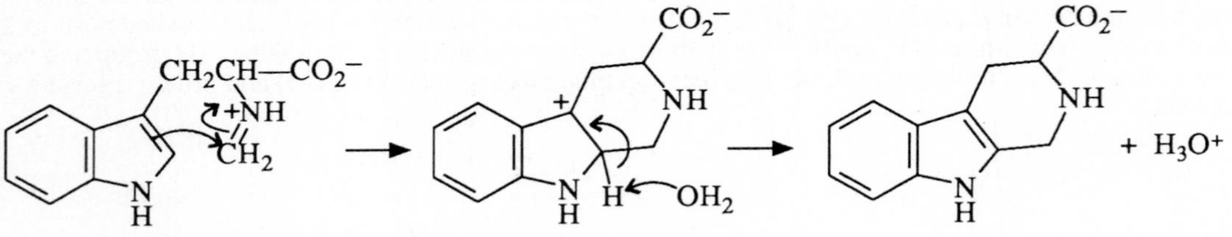

protonated imine

resonance-stabilized
carbocation

Protonation of the amino group gives the product shown in the problem.

(f) The side-chain —OH group adds to the isocyanate intermediate from the Curtius rearrangement to give the product. We begin with the isocyanate intermediate:

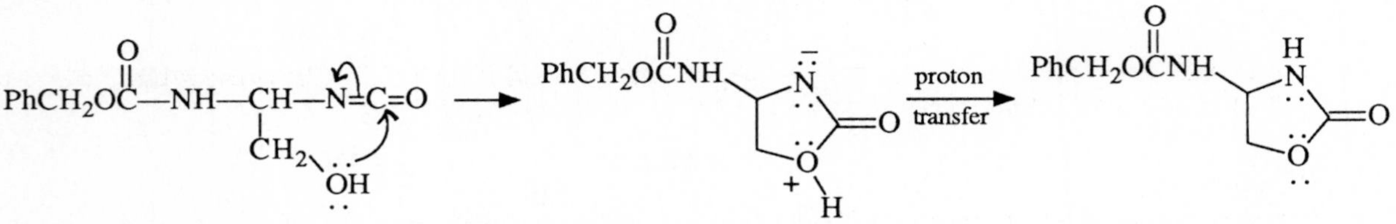

50. The side-chain amino group is acylated because it is more basic than the α-amino group. Remember, better bases make better nucleophiles. The product is the following:

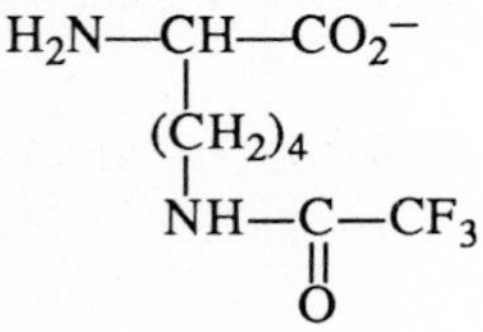

51. (a) An ester can form at either the α-carboxy group or the side-chain carboxy group:

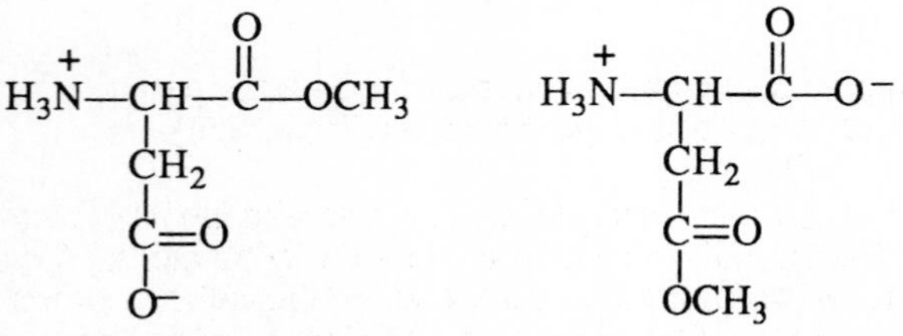

A   B

(b) and (c) According to Table 26.1, the pK_a values of the two carboxy groups in aspartic acid are about 2.1 (for the α-carboxy group) and 3.9 (for the β-carboxy group). (How do we know which is which?) Assuming the carboxy-group pK_a values are about the same for the respective esters, we can postulate that the conjugate acid of compound A has a pK_a of about 3.9, and the conjugate acid of compound B has a pK_a of about 2.1. At pH 3.5, the carboxy group of compound A is largely protonated; at the same pH, the carboxy group of B is mostly ionized. Hence, at pH 3.5, compound A carries a positive charge, whereas B is neutral. Hence, compound B will be retained by an anion-exchange column and will be eluted more slowly than compound A. At pH 7, however, both compounds are negatively charged. Since they have the same charge, they would be retained equally by an anion-exchange column and would therefore not be separated.

52. Consider the following scheme:

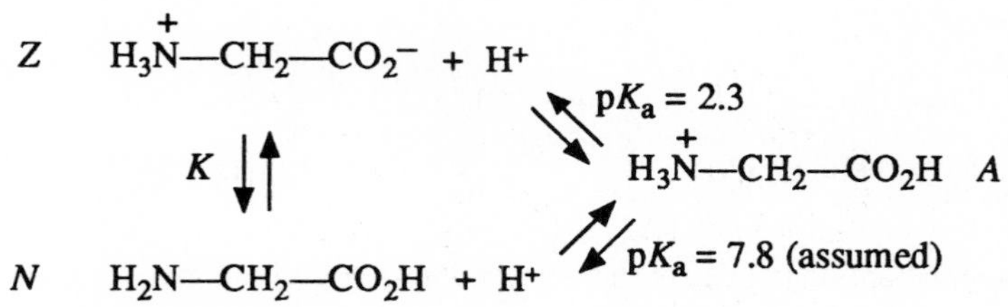

$$Z \quad \overset{+}{H_3N}-CH_2-CO_2^- + H^+$$

$$K \updownarrow$$

$$pK_a = 2.3$$

$$\overset{+}{H_3N}-CH_2-CO_2H \quad A$$

$$N \quad H_2N-CH_2-CO_2H + H^+ \quad pK_a = 7.8 \text{ (assumed)}$$

Notice that the pK_a for dissociation of form A to form N is *not* the experimental pK_a for the amino group of glycine (9.60) from Table 26.1, because that pK_a is for an ammonium ion in which there is an α-carboxylic acid group that is *ionized*. What we need is the pK_a of an ammonium ion in which there is an α-carboxylic acid group that is *not ionized*. The pK_a value of 7.8 given in the problem is valid under the reasonable assumption that the inductive effects of an ester group and an un-ionized carboxylic acid group are about the same. The dissociation expressions for the carboxylic acid and ammonium groups of A are:

$$\frac{[Z][H^+]}{[A]} = 10^{-2.3} \quad \text{and} \quad \frac{[N][H^+]}{[A]} = 10^{-7.8}$$

The equilibrium constant we need to solve the problem is K; and $K = [N]/[Z]$. The two equations above can be divided to arrive at a value of K:

$$\frac{\dfrac{[N][H^+]}{[A]}}{\dfrac{[Z][H^+]}{[A]}} = \frac{[N]}{[Z]} = K = \frac{10^{-7.8}}{10^{-2.3}} = 10^{-5.5}$$

Hence, there is one part in $10^{5.5}$, or about one part per million, of the uncharged form of glycine present in the neutral amino acid.

53. (a) A simple way to look at this problem is to imagine the hydrolysis of the amide bonds to give Phe, Gly, and the following dehydro amino acid:

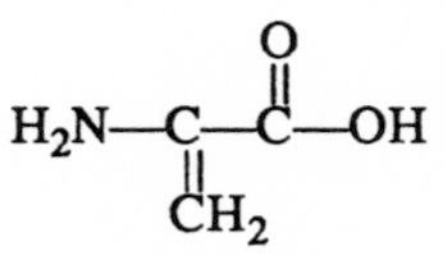

$$H_2N-\underset{\underset{CH_2}{\|}}{C}-\overset{\overset{O}{\|}}{C}-OH \quad \text{dehydroalanine}$$

Dehydroalanine is an enamine, and, under aqueous acidic conditions, an enamine hydrolyzes to the corresponding amine (in this case ammonia) and carbonyl compound (in this case pyruvic acid).

➤ Although this explanation accounts for the data given, it is oversimplified. Dehydroalanine itself is not formed on acid-catalyzed hydrolysis of the peptide. Rather, the amide of phenylalanine (Phe-amide), glycine, and pyruvic acid are formed directly. The key step in the mechanism is protonation of the carbon–carbon double bond. The mechanism is summarized below; you provide the details and the arrow formalism:

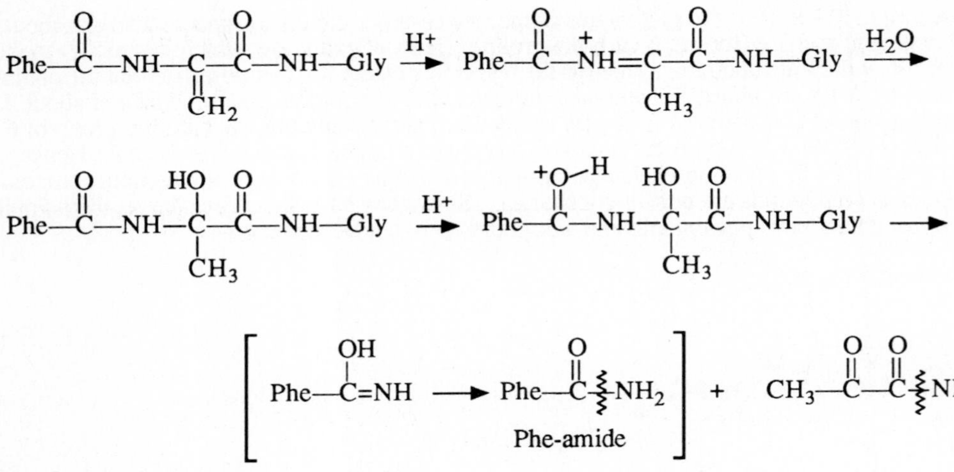

As indicated by the wavy lines, the remaining amide bonds are then cleaved more slowly to give Phe, ammonia, and Gly.

(b) The dehydroalanine-containing peptide is the amide of an enamine and, like enamines themselves, is reduced by sodium borohydride. Reduction of the dehydroalanine residue gives an alanine residue. Since the reducing agent is tritiated, the resulting alanine residue then contains tritium. Since the reduced peptide has the sequence Phe-(^{3}H)Ala-Gly, it follows that hydrolysis yields not pyruvic acid, but the individual amino acids Phe, (^{3}H)Ala, and Gly.

54. The data indicate that a serine residue is modified by phenylmethanesulfonyl fluoride followed by base treatment. The NaBH$_4$ reduction to give an alanine residue suggests (Problem 53) that a dehydroalanine residue has been formed by the reaction with base. The loss of activity suggests that the *active-site serine residue* (Ser$_{195}$; see Figure 26.13) is the one involved. The data are accounted for by the following transformations:

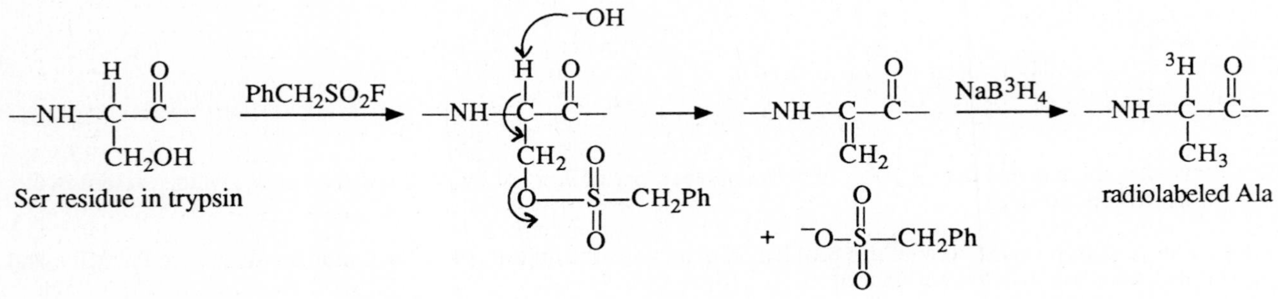

Chapter 27 / Carbohydrates and Nucleic Acids

CHAPTER 27 TERMS

aglycone 27.5
aldaric acid 27.7B
alditol 27.7D
aldohexose 27.1
aldonolactone 27.7A
aldose 27.1
alkylating agent 27.11D
amino sugar 27.10B
amylopectin 27.10B
amylose 27.10B
anomer 27.2B
α-anomer 27.2B
β-anomer 27.2B
anomeric carbon 27.2B
base (in nucleic acids) 27.11B
carbohydrates .... Introduction
cellulose 27.10B
Chargaff's rules 27.11B
chitin 27.10B
cyclic hemiacetal 27.2B
deoxyribonucleic acid (DNA) .... Introduction
deoxyribonucleoside 27.11A
deoxyribonucleotide 27.11A
disaccharide 27.1
double helix 27.11B
enediol 27.4
epimer 27.2A
D-fructose 27.2A
furanose 27.2B
furanoside 27.5
D-galactose 27.2A
genetic code 27.11C
D-glucose 27.2A
glycoside 27.5
Haworth projection 27.2B

hexose 27.1
ketopentose 27.1
ketose 27.1
Kiliani–Fischer synthesis 27.8A
(+)-lactone 27.10A
Lobry de Bruyn–Alberda van Ekenstein reaction .. 27.4
D-mannose 27.2A
messenger RNA (mRNA) 27.11C
monosaccharide 27.1
mutarotation 27.3
nonreducing end 27.10A
nonreducing sugar 27.10A
nucleic acid .... Introduction
nucleotide 27.11A
pentose 27.1
pentulose 27.1
polysaccharide 27.1
purine 27.11A
pyranose 27.2B
pyranoside 27.5
pyrimidine 27.11A
reducing end 27.10A
reducing sugar 27.10A
ribonucleic acid (RNA) .... Introduction
ribonucleoside 27.11A
ribonucleotide 27.11A
D-ribose 27.2A
Ruff degradation 27.8B
starch 27.10B
(+)-sucrose 27.10A
D,L system 27.2A
transcription 27.11C
translation 27.11C
trisaccharide 27.1
Wohl degradation 27.8B

CHAPTER 27 CONCEPTS

I. Introduction to Carbohydrates:

A. <u>Classification and Properties of Sugars</u>:

1. **Carbohydrates** are the sugars and their derivatives.

a) Most common sugars contain an aldehyde or ketone carbonyl group as well as a number of hydroxy groups on an unbranched carbon chain.

b) Many common sugars have formulas that are formally what are expected for a carbon hydrate, $C_m(H_2O)_n$.

c) Modern carbohydrate chemistry also encompasses related compounds.

2. Sugar can be classified using a variety of systems:
   a) By the *type* of carbonyl group in the sugar:
      (1) A sugar with an aldehyde carbonyl group is called an **aldose**.
      (2) A sugar with a ketone carbonyl group is called a **ketose** and can be indicated with the suffix *ulose*.
   b) By the *number* of carbon atoms:
      (1) A six-carbon sugar is called a **hexose**.
      (2) A five-carbon sugar is called a **pentose**.

$$CH_2-CH-CH-CH-CH-\overset{\overset{O}{\|}}{C}-H \qquad CH_2-CH-CH-\overset{\overset{O}{\|}}{C}-CH_2$$
$$\;\;|\quad\;\;|\quad\;|\quad\;|\quad\;| \qquad\qquad\; |\quad\;\;|\quad\;|\qquad\quad\;|$$
$$OH\;\;OH\;OH\;OH\;OH \qquad\quad\; OH\;\;OH\;OH\qquad\; OH$$

an aldose   a ketose

a hexose   a pentose

an aldohexose   a ketopentose or pentulose

c) On the basis of their hydrolysis to simpler sugars:
   (1) **Monosaccharides** contain one sugar unit.
   (2) **Disaccharides** contain two sugar units.
   (3) **Polysaccharides** contain many sugar units.

3. Sugars are very water soluble, but virtually insoluble in nonpolar solvents.

II. Structure of Monosaccharides, Disaccharides, and Polysaccharides:

A. Stereochemistry and Configuration:
   1. A typical class of sugars contains several asymmetric carbons that give rise to 2^n possible stereoisomers (n = the number of asymmetric carbons): these in turn can be divided into two enantiomeric sets of 2^{n-1} diastereomers.
      a) The aldopentoses, for example, have three asymmetric carbons and 2^3 or eight possible stereoisomers.
      b) The aldopentoses can be divided into two enantiomeric sets of four diastereomers.
   2. Each diastereomer is a different sugar with different properties, known by a different name.
   3. Although the *R,S* system could be used to describe the configuration of one or more of the asymmetric carbon atoms, it is more convenient to use the D,L-system, in which the configuration of a sugar enantiomer is specified by applying the following conventions:
      a) The 2*R* enantiomer of the aldotriose glyceraldehyde is arbitrarily said to have the D configuration; the 2*S* enantiomer is then said to have the L configuration.

$$R\text{ configuration} \qquad\qquad\qquad\qquad\qquad\qquad\qquad\qquad CHO \qquad S\text{ configuration}$$

R configuration   CHO   CHO   CHO   CHO   *S* configuration

H—|—OH   HO—|—H

CH₂OH   CH₂OH

a D sugar   an L sugar

b) Aldoses or ketoses are written in a Fischer projection with their carbon atoms in a straight vertical line, and the carbons are numbered consecutively as they would be in systematic nomenclature, so that the carbonyl carbon receives the lowest number.

$$CH_2-CH-CH-\overset{\overset{O}{\|}}{C}-CH_2 \quad = \quad$$

$^1CH_2OH$

$^2\!\!=\!\!O$

$H—^3|—OH$

$H—^4|—OH$

$^5CH_2OH$

c) The asymmetric carbon of highest number is designated as a reference carbon.
   (1) If this carbon has the H, OH, and CH$_2$OH in the same relative configuration as the same three groups of D-glyceraldehyde, the sugar is said to have the D configuration.
   (2) If this carbon has the configuration opposite to that of D-glyceraldehyde, the sugar is said to have the L configuration.

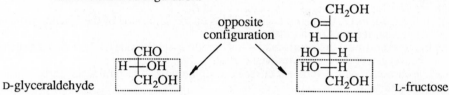

4. There is no general correspondence between configuration and the sign of the optical rotation; there is also no simple relationship between the D,L system and the R,S system.
   a) The R,S system is used to specify the configuration of each asymmetric carbon atom in a molecule; the D,L system specifies a *particular* enantiomer of a molecule that might contain many asymmetric carbons.
   b) The R,S system can be used with systematic nomenclature; in the D,L system, *each* diastereomer is given a *different* name.

5. A few of the aldoses and ketoses are particularly important, and their structures should be learned.

| D-ribose | D-fructose | D-glucose | D-mannose | D-galactose |

6. Compounds that differ in configuration at only one of several asymmetric carbons are called **epimers**.

B. Cyclic Structures of the Monosaccharides:
   1. Aldoses and ketoses exist predominantly as cyclic hemiacetals.
   2. An aldohexose can exist as either a five-membered or six-membered cyclic hemiacetal, depending on which hydroxy group undergoes cyclization.
      a) The five-membered cyclic acetal form of a sugar is called the **furanose** form.
      b) The six-membered cyclic acetal form of a sugar is called the **pyranose** form.

D-fructofuranose   D-glucopyranose

3. When a name such as glucose is used, any or all of the many forms of the sugar are implied.
4. In referring specifically to a cyclic form, use the name that is derived from the size of the hemiacetal ring by inserting the name of the ring before the *ose* suffix.
5. A widely used convention for representing the cyclic forms of sugars is the **Haworth projection**; in this convention, the cyclic form of a sugar is represented as a planar ring at right angles to the page.
   a) In the Haworth projection, the heavy, shaded lines of the ring are meant to be visualized in front of the page; the lighter lines are in back.
   b) The bonds with nothing on the ends bear hydrogen atoms.

D-fructofuranose   D-glucopyranose

C. Anomers and Mutarotation:

1. The furanose or pyranose form of a sugar has one more asymmetric carbon (carbon-1) than the open-chain form; when two cyclic forms of a sugar differ in configuration *only* at the hemiacetal carbon (carbon-1), they are said to be **anomers**.
2. The ring in a Fischer projection of these cyclic compounds is represented as a long bond.
3. Anomers are named with the Greek letters α and β.
   a) In the α-**anomer**, the hemiacetal —OH is on the same side of the Fischer projection as the oxygen at the configurational carbon.
   b) In the β-**anomer**, the hemiacetal —OH group is on the side of the Fischer projection opposite the oxygen at the configurational carbon.
   c) The carbon at which anomers differ in configuration—the hemiacetal carbon—is sometimes referred to as the **anomeric carbon**.

α-anomer α-D-glucopyranose β-anomer β-D-glucopyranose

4. When a pure anomer of a sugar is dissolved in aqueous solution, its optical rotation changes with time; this change, called **mutarotation**, is caused by the acid- or base-catalyzed conversion of the α- and β-anomers into an equilibrium mixture of both.
5. The mechanism of mutarotation begins as the reverse of hemiacetal formation.
   a) A 180° rotation about the bond to the carbonyl group permits attack of the hydroxy group on the opposite face of the carbonyl carbon.
   b) Hemiacetal formation then gives the other anomer.

6. A single hexose can exist in no fewer than five forms (mutarotation allows these forms to come to equilibrium in aqueous solution):
   a) The acyclic aldehyde or keto form.
   b) The α- and β-pyranose forms.
   c) The α- and β-furanose forms.
7. Some general conclusions:
   a) Most aldohexoses exist primarily as pyranoses, although a few have substantial amounts of furanose forms.
   b) There are relatively small amounts of open-chain carbonyl forms of most sugars.
   c) Mixtures of α- and β-anomers are usually found, although the exact amounts of each vary from case to case.

D. Conformational Representations of Pyranoses:

1. The six-membered ring of a pyranose exists in two chair conformations related by the chair–chair interconversion.
2. To go from a Fischer projection to a chair conformation:
   a) Using an allowed manipulation of Fischer projections, first redraw the molecule in an equivalent Fischer projection in which the ring oxygen is in a down position.
   b) Draw the chair conformation with the ring oxygen in a right rear position.
   c) The groups on the left of the Fischer projection are up and those on the right are down.
   d) The —OH group at the anomeric carbon is down in an α-anomer, and up in a β-anomer.

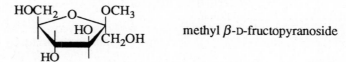

e) If the configuration of the anomeric carbon is uncertain, the bond is represented by a wavy line.

E. Glycosides:

1. Most sugars react with alcohol under acidic conditions to yield cyclic acetals, called **glycosides**, and are named as derivatives of the parent sugar.
   a) The term **pyranoside** indicates that the glycoside ring is a six-membered ring.
   b) The term **furanoside** indicates that the glycoside ring is a five-membered ring.

methyl β-D-fructopyranoside

2. Glycosides are stable to base, but are hydrolyzed in dilute aqueous acid back to their parent sugars.
3. Many compounds occur naturally as glycosides; a glycoside can be hydrolyzed to its component alcohol, called an **aglycone**, and a sugar.

F. Structure of Disaccharides and Polysaccharides:

1. **Disaccharides** consist of two simple sugar residues, or monosaccharides, connected by a glycosidic linkage.
   a) (+)-Lactose (milk sugar) is a disaccharide in which galactose is linked by a β-glycosidic bond to the oxygen at carbon-4 of glucose.
   b) (+)-Sucrose (table sugar) is a disaccharide in which glucose is linked by an α-glycosidic bond to the oxygen at carbon-2 of fructose, and is a nonreducing sugar.

2. Any number of monosaccharide residues can be linked together with glycosidic bonds to form chains; long chains of connected sugars are called **polysaccharides**.
   a) **Cellulose** is a polymer of D-glucopyranose residues connected by β-1,4-glycosidic linkages.

cellulose

b) **Starch** is a polymer of D-glucopyranose. Starch consists of two components:
   (1) **Amylose** has glucose residues connected by α-1,4-glycosidic linkages.
   (2) **Amylopectin** has glucose residues connected by α-1,6-glycosidic linkages.

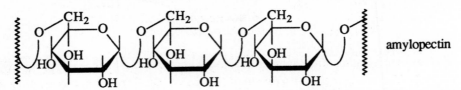

amylopectin

c) **Chitin** is a polysaccharide of *N*-acetyl-D-glucosamine connected by β-1,4-glycosidic linkages.

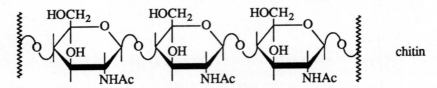

chitin

3. Polysaccharides are mostly long chains with some branches.
   a) There are *no* highly cross-linked, three-dimensional networks.
   b) Cyclic polysaccharides are known.
4. The linkages between monosaccharide units are in every case glycosidic linkages; thus, polysaccharides can be converted into their component monosaccharides by acid hydrolysis.
5. A given polysaccharide incorporates only one stereochemical type of glycoside linkage—the glycoside linkages in cellulose are all β; those in starch are all α.

III. Proof of Glucose Stereochemistry:

A. The Fischer Proof:
   1. Fischer *arbitrarily* assumed that carbon-5 (the configurational carbon in the D,L system) of (+)-glucose has the —OH on the right in the standard Fischer projection.

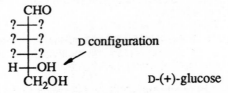

D configuration

D-(+)-glucose

   2. The subsequent logic involved can be summarized in four steps:
      a) (–)-Arabinose is converted into both (+)-glucose and (+)-mannose by a Kiliani–Fischer synthesis.
         (1) (+)-Glucose and (+)-mannose are epimeric at carbon-2.
         (2) (–)-Arabinose has the same configuration at carbons-2, 3, and 4 as that of (+)-glucose and (+)-mannose at carbons-3, 4, and 5, respectively.

(-)-arabinose $\Longrightarrow$ +   (+)-glucose and (+)-mannose

      b) (–)-Arabinose can be oxidized by dilute HNO_3 to an optically active aldaric acid.
         (1) The —OH group at carbon-2 of arabinose must be on the left; otherwise, it would be *meso*, regardless of the configuration of the —OH group at carbon-3.
         (2) The —OH group at carbon-3 of (+)-glucose must therefore be on the left.

```
        CHO                                              CO2H
    ? ──┼── ?        an optically active            ? ──┼── ?
    ? ──┼── ?           aldaric acid                ? ──┼── ?
    H ──┼── OH     ⟹                                H ──┼── OH
        CH2OH         therefore, OH group               CO2H
                      must be on the left side
```

c) Oxidation of both (+)-glucose and (+)-mannose with HNO_3 give optically active aldaric acids.
   (1) The —OH group at carbon-4 is on the right in both (+)-glucose and (+)-mannose.
   (2) The configuration at carbon-4 of (+)-glucose and (+)-mannose is the same as that at carbon-3 of (–)-arabinose.

```
      CHO              CO2H                                   CHO              CO2H
   H──┼──OH         H──┼──OH      optically active        HO──┼──H         HO──┼──H      optically active
  HO──┼──H         HO──┼──H          aldaric acid         HO──┼──H         HO──┼──H         aldaric acid
   ?──┼──?    ⟹     ?──┼──?                                ?──┼──?    ⟹     ?──┼──?
   H──┼──OH         H──┼──OH      OH group must be         H──┼──OH         H──┼──OH      OH group must also
      CH2OH            CO2H        on the right side          CH2OH'           CO2H        be on the right side
  (+)-glucose or                                         (+)-glucose or
  (+)-mannose                                            (+)-mannose
```

d) (+)-Gulose can be oxidized with HNO_3 to the same aldaric acid as (+)-glucose.
   (1) There are only two possible structures that conform to the conclusions of a) through c) above; one is (+)-glucose and one is (+)-mannose.
   (2) The structure with the —OH group at carbon-2 on the left forms a unique aldaric acid upon oxidation with HNO_3; this must be (+)-mannose.

```
                    ┌──────────── same sugar ────────────┐
        CHO                      CO2H                      CH2OH
    HO──┼──H                 HO──┼──H                   HO──┼──H
    HO──┼──H                 HO──┼──H                   HO──┼──H
     H──┼──OH      ⟹          H──┼──OH      ⟸           H──┼──OH
     H──┼──OH                  H──┼──OH                   H──┼──OH
        CH2OH                    CO2H                       CHO
  ∴ (+)-mannose
```

   (3) The structure with the —OH group at carbon-2 on the right forms an aldaric acid upon oxidation with HNO_3 that is identical to the aldaric acid formed by the oxidation of (+)-gulose with HNO_3; this must be (+)-glucose.

```
                    ┌──────────── different sugars ───────────┐
        CHO                      CO2H                      CH2OH
     H──┼──OH                 H──┼──OH                   H──┼──OH
    HO──┼──H                 HO──┼──H                   HO──┼──H
     H──┼──OH      ⟹          H──┼──OH      ⟸           H──┼──OH
     H──┼──OH                  H──┼──OH                   H──┼──OH
        CH2OH                    CO2H                       CHO
  ∴ D-(+)-glucose                                      D-(+)-gulose
```

B. <u>Absolute Configuration of Glucose</u>:
   1. Two cycles of the Ruff degradation convert (+)-glucose into (–)-erythrose.
      a) D-Glyceraldehyde, in turn, is related to (–)-erythrose by a Kiliani–Fischer synthesis.

b) (+)-Glucose, (–)-erythrose,(–)-threose, and (+)-glyceraldehyde are all of the same stereochemical series—the D series.

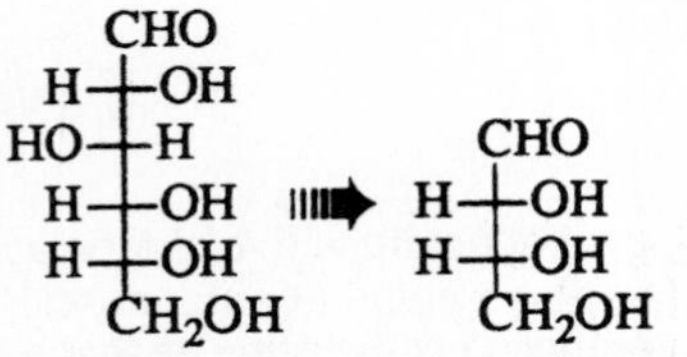

(+)-glucose   (–)-erythrose 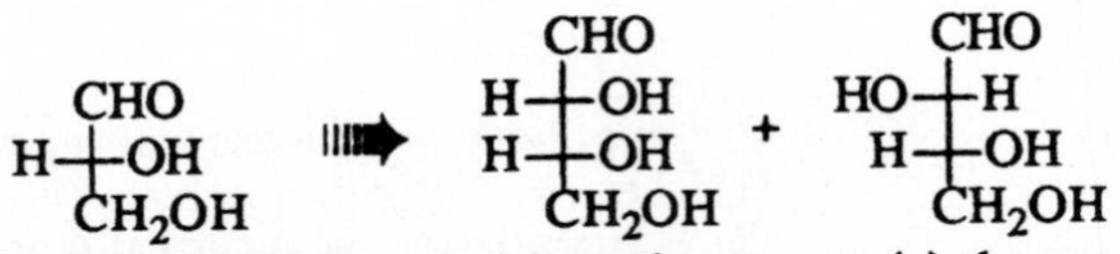   D-(+)-glyceraldehyde   D-(–)-erythrose   D-(–)-threose

2. Oxidation of D-(–)-threose with dilute HNO_3 gives D-(–)-tartaric acid; (+)-tartaric acid was shown by X-ray crystallography to possess the L configuration; hence, (+)-glucose has the D configuration.

D-(–)-threose   D-(–)-tartaric acid

IV. Nucleosides, Nucleotides, and Nucleic Acids:

A. <u>Nomenclature of Nucleosides, Nucleotides, and Nucleic Acids:</u>
  1. A β-glycoside of a heterocyclic nitrogen base is called a **nucleoside**; the base and the sugar ring systems are numbered separately; primes (') are used to refer to the sugar carbon atoms.
    a) A **ribonucleoside** is derived from D-ribose.
    b) A **deoxyribonucleoside** is derived from D-2-deoxyribose; 2-deoxyribose lacks the —OH group at carbon-2 of ribose.

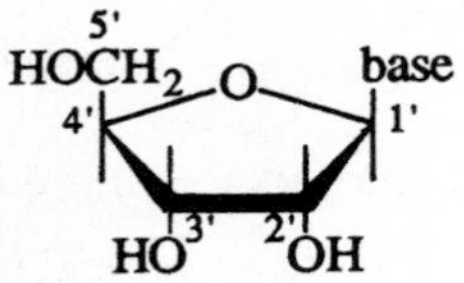

a ribonucleoside 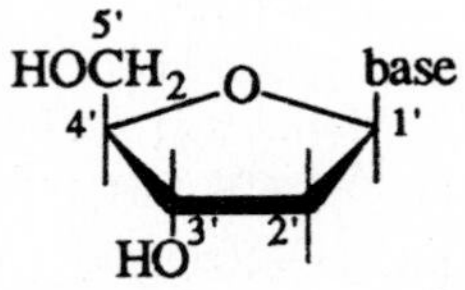   a deoxyribonucleoside

  2. The bases that occur most frequently in nucleosides are derived from two heterocyclic ring systems:
    a) **Pyrimidine**—three pyrimidines occur most commonly and are attached to the sugar at the N-1 position.
    b) **Purine**—two purines occur most commonly and are attached to the sugar at the N-6 position.

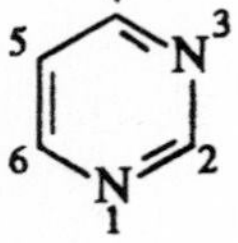

pyrimidine 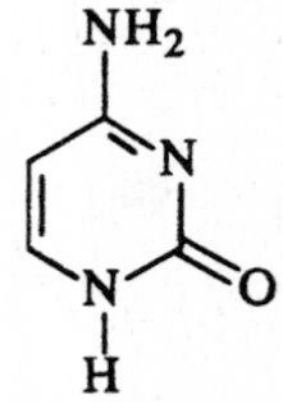   cytosine (C) 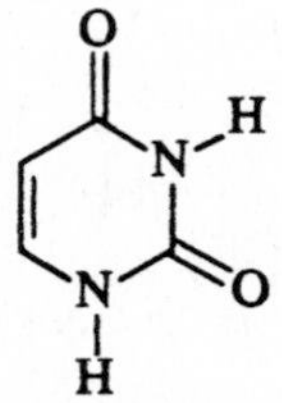   uracil (U) 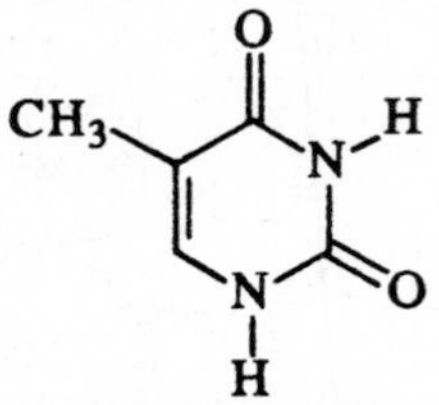   thymine (T)

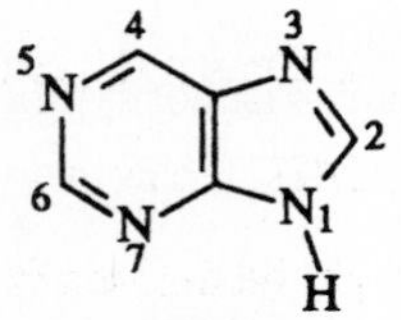

purine 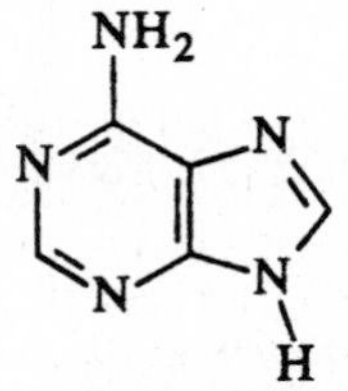   adenine (A) 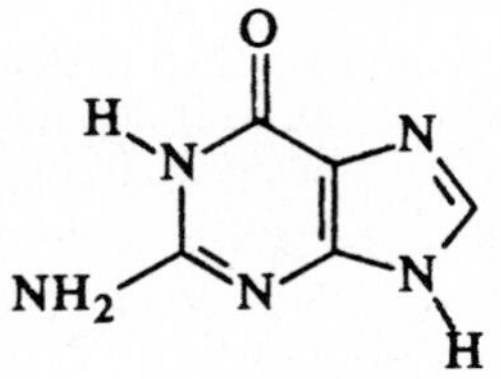   guanine (G)

3. The 5'—OH group of the ribose in a nucleoside is often found esterified to a phosphate group; a 5'-phosphorylated nucleoside is called a **nucleotide**.

    a) A **ribonucleotide** is derived from the D-ribose.

    b) A **deoxyribonucleotide** is derived from 2'-deoxyribose.

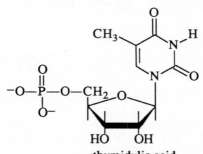

a ribonucleotide   a deoxyribonucleotide

4. Some nucleotides contain a single phosphate group; others contain two or three phosphate groups condensed in phosphoric anhydride linkages.

    a) The names of the mono-, di-, and tri-phosphonucleotide derivatives are often abbreviated—the corresponding deoxy derivatives contain a *d* prefix.

    b) One of the most ubiquitous nucleotides is ATP (adenosine triphosphate), which serves as the fundamental energy source for the living cell.

5. The nomenclature of the five common bases and their corresponding nucleosides and nucleotides is summarized in Table 27.2, text page 1237; the corresponding 2'-deoxy derivatives are named by appending the prefix *2'-deoxy* (or *deoxy*) to the names of the corresponding ribose derivatives, or by appending a *d* prefix to the abbreviation.

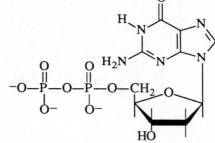

thymidylic acid
or thymidine monophosphate (TMP)   deoxyguanosine diphosphate (*d*GDP)

6. Nucleic acids are a principal component of the cell nucleus and are of two general types:

    a) **Deoxyribonucleic acid (DNA)**—the storehouse of genetic information in the cell.

    b) **Ribonucleic acid (RNA)**—serves various roles in translating and processing the information encoded in the structure of DNA.

B. <u>Structure of DNA and RNA</u>:

    1. Deoxyribonucleic acid (DNA) is a polymer of deoxyribonucleotides.

        a) The individual nucleotide residues are connected by a phosphate group that is esterified both to the 3'—OH group of one ribose and the 5'—OH of another.

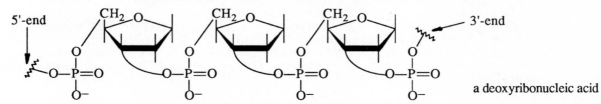

a deoxyribonucleic acid

        b) DNA incorporates adenine, thymine, guanine, and cytidine as the nucleotide bases; each residue in a polynucleotide is distinguished by the identity of its base.

        c) The ratios of adenine to thymine, and guanosine to cytosine, in DNA are both 1.0; these observations are called **Chargaff's rules**.

        d) A typical strand of DNA, which carries genetic information, might be thousands of nucleotides long and is replicated, or copied, during cell reproduction.

2. Ribonucleic acid (RNA) polymers are formally much like DNA polymers, except that ribose is the sugar; RNA incorporates essentially the same bases as DNA, except that uracil occurs in RNA instead of thymine, and some rare bases are found in certain types of RNA.
3. The Watson–Crick structure of DNA has the following important features:
   a) The structure contains two right-handed helical polynucleotide chains that run in opposite directions, coiled around a common axis; the structure is therefore that of a **double helix**.
   b) The sugars and phosphates, which are rich in —OH groups and charges, are on the outside of the helix.
   c) The chains are held together by hydrogen bonds between bases, which are on the inside of the double helix.
      (1) Adenine (**A**) in one chain always hydrogen-bonds to thymine (**T**) in the other.
      (2) Guanosine (**G**) in one chain always hydrogen-bonds to cytosine (**C**) in the other.
   d) The planes of the complementary base pairs are stacked, one on top of the other, and are perpendicular to the axis of the helix.
   e) There is no restriction on the sequence of bases in a polynucleotide; however, the sequence of one polynucleotide strand in the double helix is **complementary** to that of the other strand.
4. The proper sequence of each new DNA strand during cellular reproduction is assured by hydrogen-bonding complementarity.

C. DNA, RNA, and the Genetic Code:
   1. A strand of DNA directs the synthesis of a complementary strand of RNA; this RNA is called messenger RNA (mRNA), and the process by which it is assembled is called **transcription**.
      a) The sequence of the mRNA transcript is complementary to one DNA strand of the gene and runs in the opposite direction to that of its parent DNA.
      b) The mRNA sequence is used by the cell to direct the synthesis of a specific protein from its component amino acids; this process is called **translation**.
         (1) Each successive three-residue sequence of mRNA is translated as a specific amino acid in the sequence of a protein according to the genetic code given in Table 27.3, text page 1244; some amino acids have multiple codes.
         (2) The precise sequence of bases in DNA (by way of its complementary mRNA transcription product) codes for the successive amino acids of a protein.
      c) There is a specific start signal (either of the nucleotide sequences AUG or GUG) at the appropriate point in the mRNA; because mRNA also contains stop signals (UAA, UGA, or UAG), protein synthesis is also terminated at the right place.
      d) It is possible for the change of only one base in the DNA of an organism to cause the change of an amino acid in the corresponding protein.
   2. There are many different types of RNA besides messenger RNA, each with a specific function in the cell.
   3. Methods for the synthesis of DNA and RNA fragments resemble peptide synthesis in that a strand of DNA or RNA is grown from individual nucleotides using a series of protection, coupling, and deprotection steps.

D. DNA Modification and Chemical Carcinogenesis:
   1. There is strong circumstantial evidence that chemical damage to DNA can interfere with its hydrogen-bonding complementarity and can trigger the state of uncontrolled cell division that we call cancer.
      a) One type of chemical damage is caused by **alkylating agents**—compounds that have a significant reactivity with nucleophiles in S_N2 reactions.
      b) The alkylating agents that are the most potent carcinogens also yield the greatest amount of the product alkylated at O-6 of guanosine.
   2. In adjacent positions on a strand of DNA, ultraviolet light promotes the [2 + 2] cycloaddition of the two pyrimidines. People who lack the enzymes to restore the original DNA structure die at an early age.

CHAPTER 27 REACTIONS

I. Reactions of Sugars:

A. Base-Catalyzed Isomerization of Sugars:

1. In base, aldoses and ketoses rapidly equilibrate to mixtures of sugars; this transformation is an example of the **Lobry de Bruyn–Alberda van Ekenstein reaction.**
   a) An aldose can ionize to give a small amount of its enolate ion in base.
   b) Protonation of this enolate ion at one face gives back the aldose; protonation at the other face gives an epimer.
   c) The enolate ion can also protonate on the oxygen to give a new enol, called an **enediol,** which has a hydroxy group at both ends of the double bond—it is the enol of not only an aldose, but also a ketose.

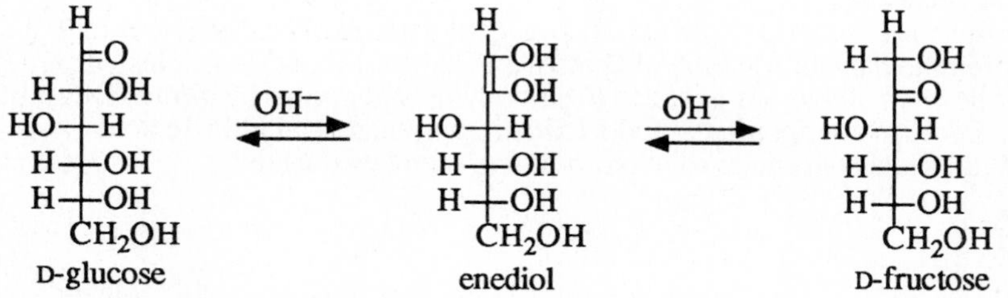

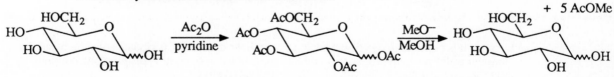

2. Several transformations of this type are important in metabolism.

B. Ether and Ester Derivatives of Sugars:

1. In the presence of concentrated base, sugars are converted into ethers by reactive alkylating agents (Williamson ether synthesis).

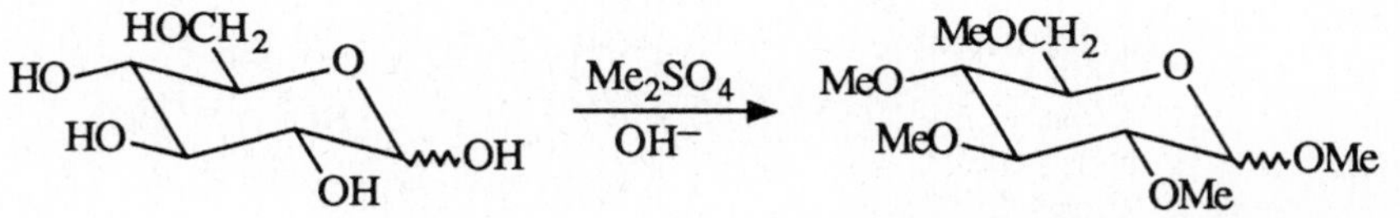

methyl 2,3,4,6-tetra-*O*-methyl-D-glucopyranoside

   a) The hydroxy groups of sugars are more acidic ($pK_a \sim 12$) than those of ordinary alcohols; this enhanced acidity is attributed to the inductive effect of the many neighboring oxygens in the molecule.
   b) Substantial concentrations of their conjugate-base alkoxide ions are formed in concentrated NaOH.
   c) Alkylation of the hydroxy group at carbon-1 is much faster than epimerization; once this oxygen is alkylated, epimerization can no longer occur.
2. It is important to distinguish the ether at carbon-1 from other ether groups in the alkylated sugar.
   a) The ether at carbon-1 is part of a glycosidic linkage.
   b) Since it is an acetal, it can be hydrolyzed in aqueous acid under mild conditions; the other ethers are ordinary ethers and do not hydrolyze under these conditions.
3. The hydroxy groups of sugars can be esterified; these esters can in turn be saponified in base or removed by transesterification with an alkoxide.

4. Ethers and esters are used as protecting groups in organic synthesis with sugars; furthermore, they have broader solubility characteristics and greater volatility than sugars themselves.

C. Oxidation and Reduction Reactions of Sugars:
  1. Treatment of an aldose with bromine water oxidizes the aldehyde group to a carboxylic acid; this reaction is a useful test for aldoses.
      a) Sugars that can be oxidized by bromine water are called **reducing sugars**; the oxidation products are called **aldonic acids**.
      b) Aldonic acids exist in acidic solution as five-membered lactones called **aldonolactones**.

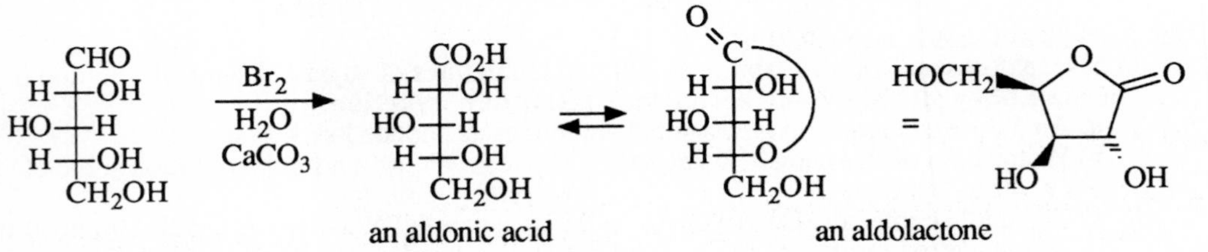

an aldonic acid   an aldolactone

      c) Glycosides are *not* oxidized by bromine water, because the aldehyde carbonyl group is protected as an acetal.
  2. Aldoses can also be oxidized with other reagents; the alkaline conditions of Tollens' test, however, also promote the equilibration of ketoses and aldoses; thus, ketoses also give a positive Tollens' test.
  3. Both ends of an aldose are oxidized to carboxylic acid groups by dilute HNO_3, but the secondary alcohol groups are not affected; the oxidation product is an **aldaric acid**.
      a) Aldaric acids in acidic solution form five-membered lactones.

an aldaric acid

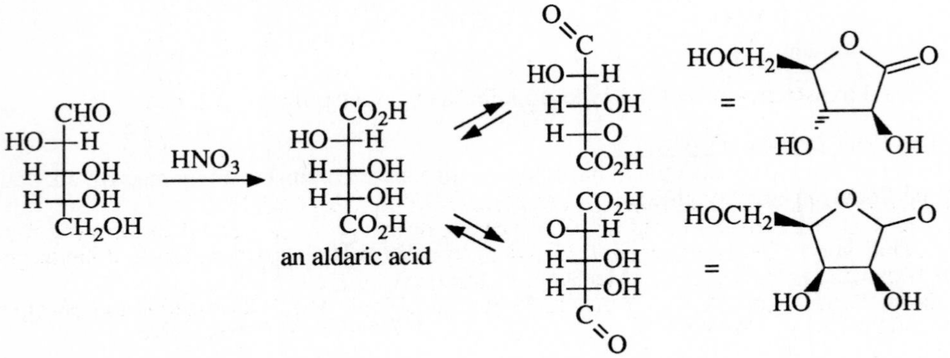

      b) Under certain conditions, some aldaric acids can be isolated as dilactones, in which both carboxylic acid groups are lactonized.
  4. Some compounds that have identical end groups can be derived from either a D or an L sugar; since the two end groups of the molecule are equivalent, the choice is completely arbitrary.
      a) This situation arises because the —OH groups on the endmost asymmetric carbons are on the same side of the Fischer projection.
      b) When these —OH groups are on opposite sides, the configuration is unambiguous.
  5. Many sugars contain vicinal glycol units and are oxidized by periodate.
      a) α-Hydroxy aldehydes are oxidized to formic acid and another aldehyde with one fewer carbon.
      b) α-Hydroxymethyl ketones are oxidized to formaldehyde and a carboxylic acid.

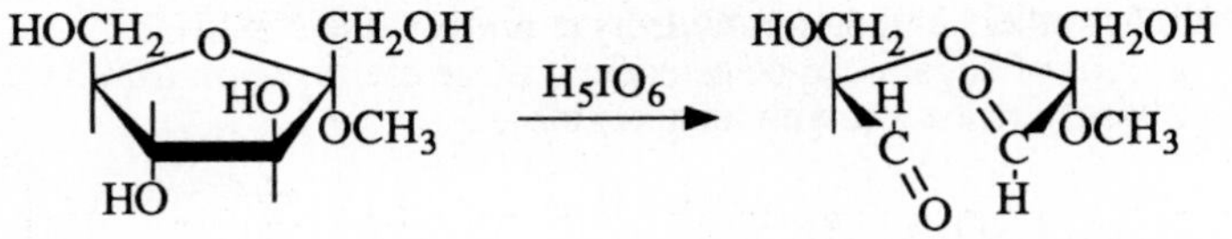

      c) Because it is possible to determine accurately both the amount of periodate consumed and the amount of formic acid produced, periodate oxidation can be used to differentiate between pyranose and furanose structures for saccharide derivatives.

6. Aldoses and ketoses undergo many of the usual carbonyl reductions; an aldose is reduced to a primary alcohol known as an **alditol**.

$$\begin{array}{c} \text{CHO} \\ \text{HO}\!-\!\!|\!-\!\text{H} \\ \text{H}\!-\!\!|\!-\!\text{OH} \\ \text{H}\!-\!\!|\!-\!\text{OH} \\ \text{CH}_2\text{OH} \end{array} \xrightarrow[\substack{\text{RaNi} \\ \text{EtOH}}]{\text{H}_2} \begin{array}{c} \text{CH}_2\text{OH} \\ \text{HO}\!-\!\!|\!-\!\text{H} \\ \text{H}\!-\!\!|\!-\!\text{OH} \\ \text{H}\!-\!\!|\!-\!\text{OH} \\ \text{CH}_2\text{OH} \end{array} \quad \text{an alditol}$$

II. Synthesis of Sugars from Other Sugars:

A. <u>Kiliani–Fischer Synthesis—Increasing the Length of the Aldose Chain</u>:
1. Addition of hydrogen cyanide to aldoses gives cyanohydrins; because cyanohydrin product has an additional asymmetric carbon, it is formed as a mixture of two epimers.
    a) These epimers are diastereomers and are typically formed in different amounts.
    b) The mixture of cyanohydrins can be converted by catalytic hydrogenation into a mixture of aldoses, which can be separated.
    d) The hydrogenation reaction involves reduction of the nitrile to the imine (or a cyclic derivative), which, under the aqueous reaction conditions, hydrolyzes to the aldose and ammonia.
2. The sequence of cyanohydrin formation–reduction converts an aldose into two epimeric aldoses with one additional carbon; this process is known as the **Kiliani–Fischer synthesis**.

$$\begin{array}{c} \text{CHO} \\ \text{H}\!-\!\!|\!-\!\text{OH} \\ \text{H}\!-\!\!|\!-\!\text{OH} \\ \text{CH}_2\text{OH} \end{array} \xrightarrow[\text{2) H}_2/\text{Pd/BaSO}_4]{\text{1) NaCN/H}_2\text{O}} \begin{array}{c} \text{CHO} \\ \text{HO}\!-\!\!|\!-\!\text{H} \\ \text{H}\!-\!\!|\!-\!\text{OH} \\ \text{H}\!-\!\!|\!-\!\text{OH} \\ \text{CH}_2\text{OH} \end{array} + \begin{array}{c} \text{CHO} \\ \text{H}\!-\!\!|\!-\!\text{OH} \\ \text{H}\!-\!\!|\!-\!\text{OH} \\ \text{H}\!-\!\!|\!-\!\text{OH} \\ \text{CH}_2\text{OH} \end{array}$$

B. <u>Ruff and Wohl Degradations—Decreasing the Length of the Aldose Chain</u>:
1. Using either of two reactions, an aldose can be degraded to another aldose with one fewer carbon atom; in both degradations, the aldehyde carbon is removed, and carbon-2 of the original sugar becomes the aldehyde carbon of the lower sugar.
2. In the **Ruff degradation**, the calcium salt of an aldonic acid is oxidized with hydrogen peroxide in the presence of Fe^{3+}.

$$\begin{array}{c} \text{CHO} \\ \text{HO}\!-\!\!|\!-\!\text{H} \\ \text{H}\!-\!\!|\!-\!\text{OH} \\ \text{H}\!-\!\!|\!-\!\text{OH} \\ \text{CH}_2\text{OH} \end{array} \xrightarrow[\substack{\text{2) Ca(OH)}_2 \\ \text{3) Fe(OAc)}_3/\text{30\% H}_2\text{O}_2}]{\text{1) Br}_2/\text{H}_2\text{O}} \begin{array}{c} \text{CHO} \\ \text{H}\!-\!\!|\!-\!\text{OH} \\ \text{H}\!-\!\!|\!-\!\text{OH} \\ \text{CH}_2\text{OH} \end{array}$$

3. In the **Wohl degradation**, an aldose is first converted into its oxime, which is then converted into its per-acetate ester with acetic anhydride.
    a) The sodium acetate present in the reaction mixture acts as a base to convert the oxime by elimination into a nitrile, which is the cyanohydrin of the next lower sugar.
    b) When treated with methoxide ion, the acetate groups are removed by transesterification and the cyanohydrin loses the elements of HCN to form the aldose.

$$\begin{array}{c} \text{CHO} \\ \text{HO}\!-\!\!|\!-\!\text{H} \\ \text{H}\!-\!\!|\!-\!\text{OH} \\ \text{H}\!-\!\!|\!-\!\text{OH} \\ \text{CH}_2\text{OH} \end{array} \xrightarrow[\text{2) Ac}_2\text{O/NaOAc}]{\text{1) NH}_2\text{OH}} \begin{array}{c} \text{CN} \\ \text{AcO}\!-\!\!|\!-\!\text{H} \\ \text{H}\!-\!\!|\!-\!\text{OAc} \\ \text{H}\!-\!\!|\!-\!\text{OAc} \\ \text{CH}_2\text{OAc} \end{array} \xrightarrow{\text{MeO}^-} \begin{array}{c} \text{CHO} \\ \text{H}\!-\!\!|\!-\!\text{OH} \\ \text{H}\!-\!\!|\!-\!\text{OH} \\ \text{CH}_2\text{OH} \end{array}$$

CHAPTER 27 SOLUTIONS

Solutions to In-Text Problems

1. By putting all the sugars in the standard Fischer projection, it becomes easier to see the relative location of corresponding groups:

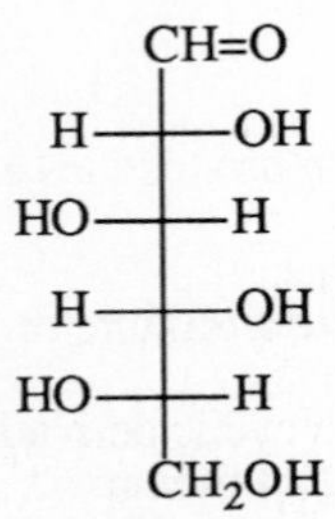

Compounds (b) and (c) are enantiomers. Compound (a) is an epimer of (b) and a diastereomer of (c).

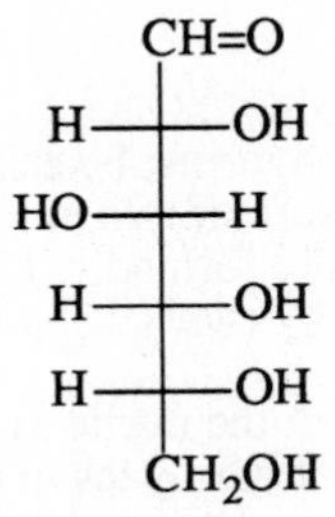

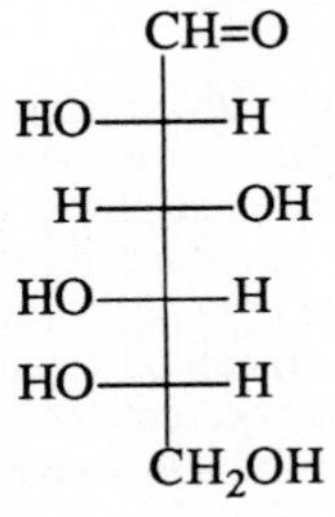

2. (a) After a cyclic permutation of the groups at carbon-5, we see that the —OH is on the right and the —H is on the left. Hence, this sugar has the D-configuration.
    (b) In Figure 27.1, we see that D-glucose has the S configuration at carbon-3. Hence, its enantiomer, L-glucose, must have the R configuration at carbon-3.

3. (a) If we recognize that mannose is epimeric to glucose at carbon-2, the structure of β-D-mannopyranose can be derived from that of β-D-glucopyranose by simply inverting the stereochemistry at carbon-2:

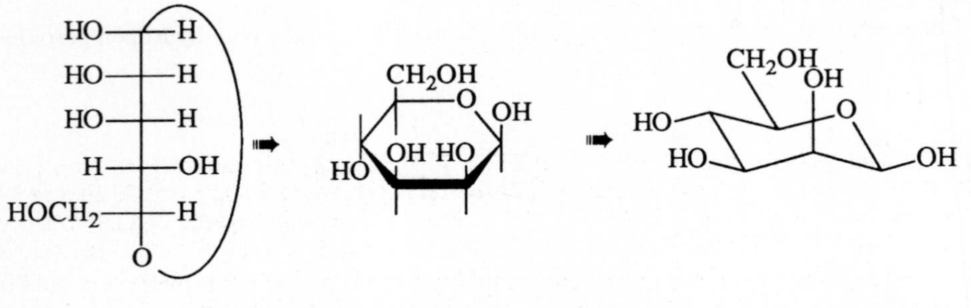

(b) We derive the structure of α-D-fructopyranose as follows:

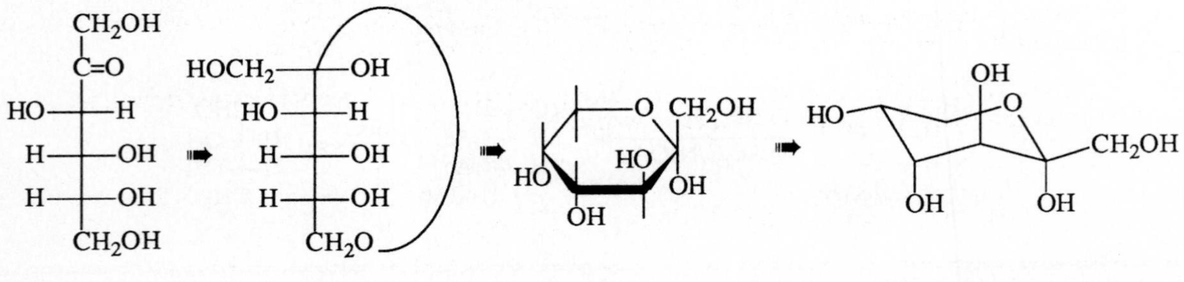

(The chair conformation above is the same as that in Eq. 27.9, text page 1209, except that the chair has been flipped.)

(c) Since xylose is epimeric to ribose at carbon-3, we can draw the structures for xylose by inverting carbon-3 of the ribose structures on text page 1206:

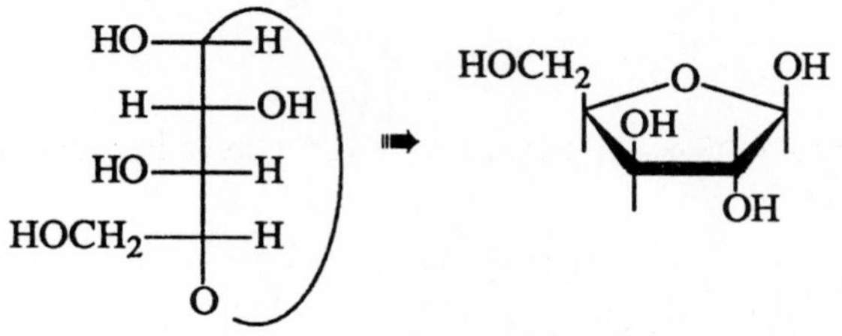

(d) α-L-Glucopyranose is derived by the procedure shown in Figure 27.2:

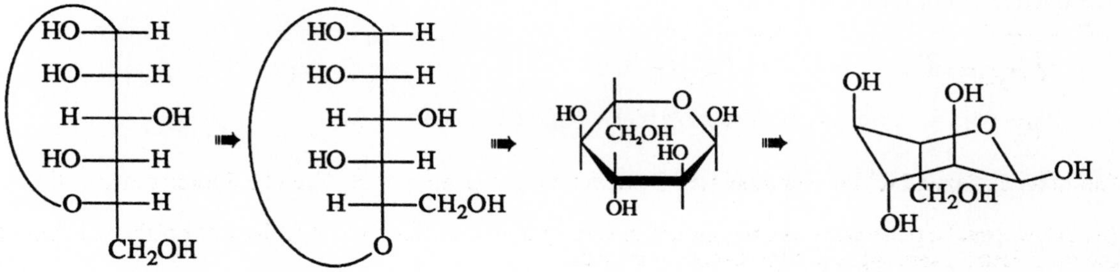

We can turn the chair structure over, then do a chair–chair flip, to show that this structure is the enantiomer of α-D-glucopyranose:

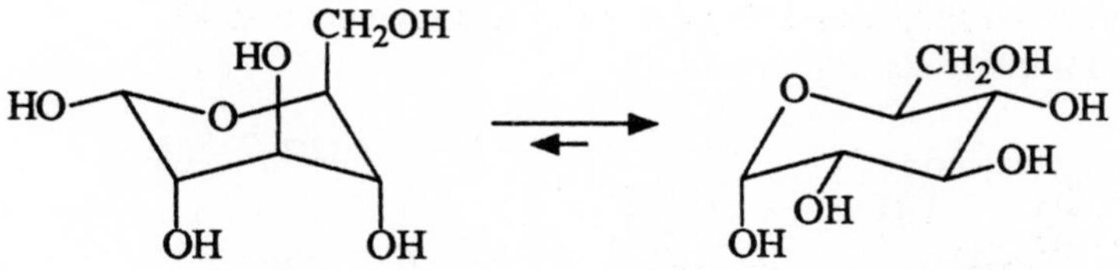

4. (a) This sugar is the anomer of β-D-ribofuranose shown in Eq. 27.7. Hence, this sugar is α-D-ribofuranose.
(b) The configuration of this sugar differs from that of β-D-glucopyranose at carbons 3 and 4. Figure 27.1 shows that the sugar with this relationship to D-glucose is D-gulose. Hence, this sugar is D-gulopyranose.
(c) The configurational carbon is the one with the —CH$_2$OH group. Since this sugar differs in configuration at this carbon from all the D-sugars, it must be an L-sugar. It is an α-anomer because it, like the α-anomer in part (a), has the —CH$_2$OH group and the —OH group on opposite faces of the ring. If we turn the sugar ring over 180° we see that it is the mirror image of α-D-ribofuranose in part (a) *except* for the configuration of carbon-2. The sugar that is epimeric to ribose at carbon-2 is arabinose. Hence, this sugar is α-L-arabinofuranose.

➤ There are many different ways to draw and identify the cyclic forms of sugars. In our solutions above we have used one of the simplest ways: to relate the structures to ones we already know.

5. Since the —OH groups at carbons 2–6 are not directly involved in the mutarotation mechanism, we'll eliminate these for simplicity and focus on what happens at carbon-1:

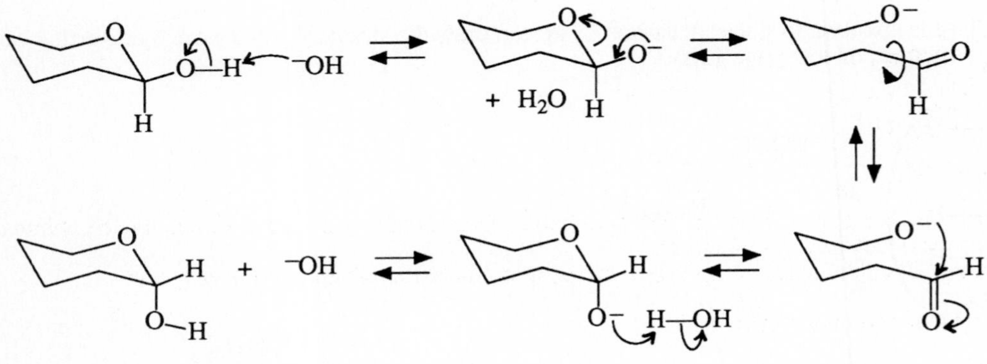

6. Each form of the sugar contributes its own optical rotation in proportion to the amount that is present. Letting N_i = the fraction of form i, we have

$$N_{total} = 52.7° = N_\alpha(112°) + N_\beta(18.7°)$$

Since $N_\alpha + N_\beta = 1$, we can substitute $N_\beta = (1 - N_\alpha)$ and obtain

$$52.7° = N_\alpha(112°) + (1 - N_\alpha)(18.7°)$$

or $N_\alpha(112° - 18.7°) = 52.7° - 18.7° = 34°$

or $N_\alpha = 0.36$ and $N_\beta = 0.64$

Table 27.1 confirms that there is 36% of the α-form and 64% of the β-form of glucopyranose at equilibrium.

7. The β-pyranose forms of D-glucose and D-talose are as follows:

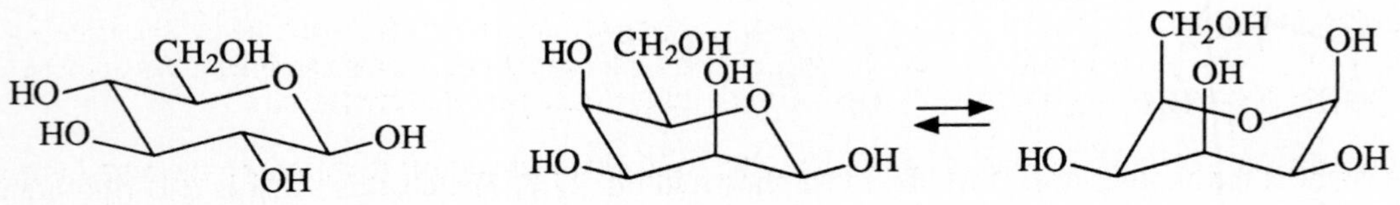

β-D-glucopyranose β-D-talopyranose

The talose molecule has a significantly greater number of 1,3-diaxial interactions in both chair conformations. To relieve these interactions, talose contains a higher percentage of the furanose and aldehyde forms.

8. D-Galactose would be transformed into the aldohexose that is epimeric at carbon-2, namely, D-talose. The ketose formed would be the following (D-tagatose):

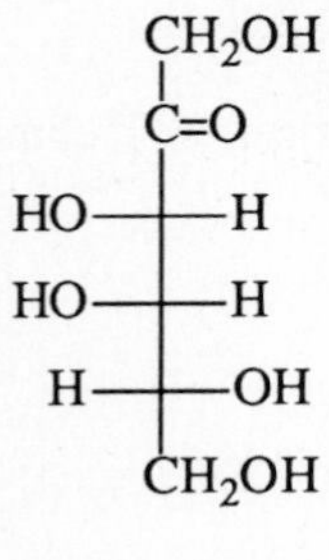

9.   (a) Using the structure of β-D-fructofuranose on text page 1209, we have:

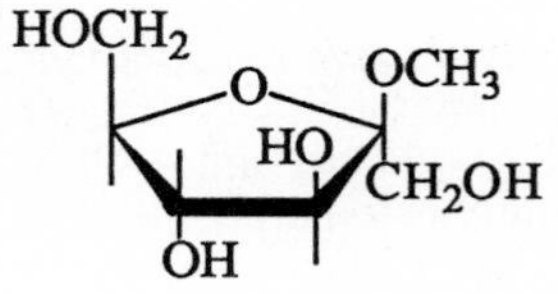

(b) This compound is a β-glycoside derived from *p*-nitrophenol and D-galactose. Hence, the compound is called *p*-nitrophenyl β-D-galactopyranoside.

(c) This compound will be hydrolyzed in aqueous acid to give *p*-nitrophenol and D-galactose.

10.   (a) The structure of adriamycinone:

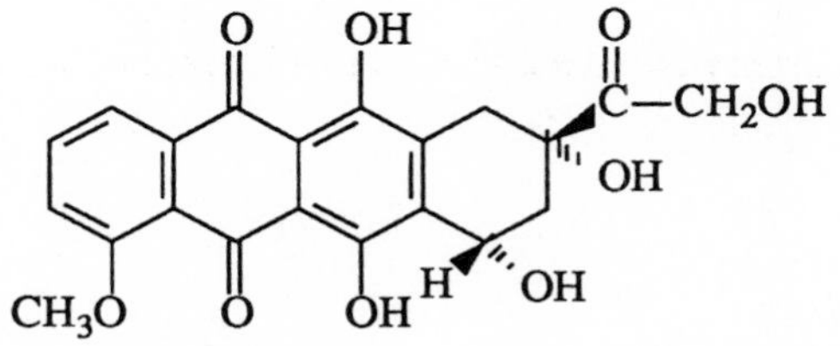

(b) Since the hydrolysis of glycosides gives an alcohol or phenol and a sugar, it follows that the glycosidic bond to a phenol is a bond between carbon-1 of a sugar and the phenolic oxygen:

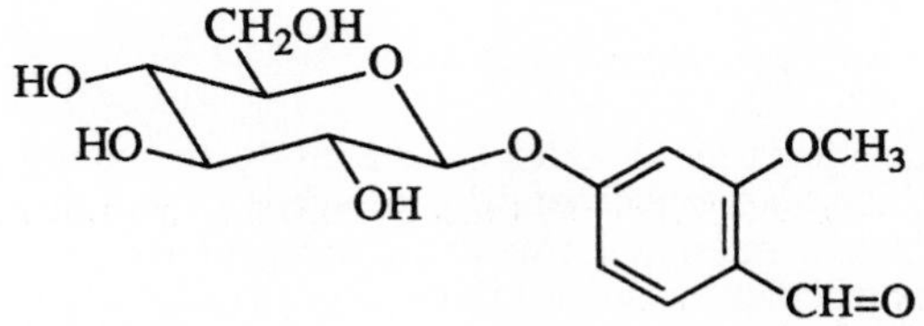

11.   The hydrolysis of an acetal involves an α-alkoxy carbocation, which is resonance-stabilized (see Eq. 19.47b, text page 789). Hydrolysis of ordinary ethers involves less stable carbocation intermediates. As is often the case (Hammond's postulate), reactions that involve more stable intermediates are faster.

12.   We can prepare the 1-*O*-ethyl derivative and then use the Williamson synthesis to introduce the remaining ether groups:

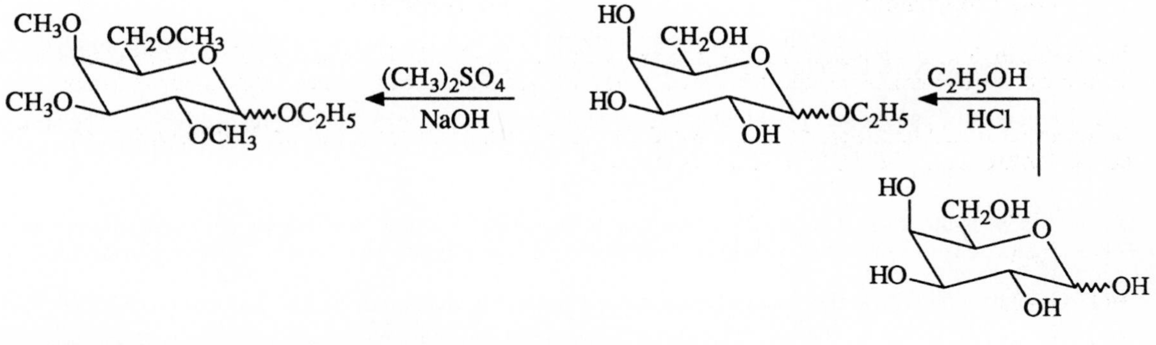

13.   The solution follows the problem in the text; the aldose is L-gulose.

14.   (a)   (1) This is a *meso*-compound, and is therefore neither D nor L.
            (2) This derivative has an unambiguous D configuration.
            (3) This compound has an unambiguous L configuration.

(4) This sugar can be viewed as either D-gularic acid, the oxidation product of D-gulose, or L-glucaric acid, the oxidation product of L-glucose.

(b) The way to solve this problem is to draw two aldoses that would be oxidized to the given dicarboxylic acid. The way to do this is simply to replace one —CO₂H group with a —CH=O group and the other —CO₂H group with a —CH₂OH group. For the second aldose, reverse the positions of the —CO₂H and —CH₂OH groups. Then look at the stereochemical relationship of the two aldoses. Applying this to part (i):

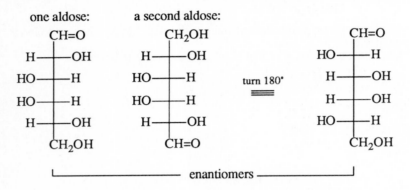

(i) Compound (1), as shown above, can be obtained by the oxidation of enantiomeric aldoses.
(ii) Compound (4) can be obtained by the oxidation of diastereomeric aldoses with opposite (D and L) configurations.
(iii) Compound (3) can be obtained by the oxidation of diastereomeric aldoses with the same (L) configuration.
(iv) Compound (2) can be obtained by the oxidation of a single aldose (mannose).

15. As Eq. 27.30a shows, periodate oxidation of a methyl pyranoside in the D-series gives a product containing carbons 1, 2, 5, and 6 of the sugar. In this product, only the carbons corresponding to carbons 1 and 5 in the sugar are asymmetric, and the groups corresponding to carbons 2 and 6 in the sugar are the same for every aldohexose. Since the configuration of carbon-5 determines whether the sugar has the D or the L configuration, and the configuration of carbon-1 determines whether the sugar is α or β, it follows that the fragment obtained from oxidation of a β-D-pyranoside will be the diastereomer of the fragment obtained from oxidation of an α-D-pyranoside. Diastereomers have different properties. Hence, these fragments can be used to determine whether the original pyranoside was α or β. This works not only for the methyl galactopyranosides, but for *any* pyranoside.

16. Either D-lyxose or D-xylose would give D-tartaric acid after the Wohl degradation followed by oxidation. Of the two, only D-xylose would be oxidized to an optically inactive (that is, *meso*) dicarboxylic acid. (The structures of these sugars are given on text page 1200.)

17. The aldopentose is ribose, and the aldohexose is allose. The data do not distinguish between D and L enantiomers. (See text page 1200 for the structures of these sugars.)

18. The aldopentose A is lyxose. The aldohexoses B and C are galactose and talose, respectively. (The structures of these sugars are found on text page 1200.) As in the previous problem, the data do not distinguish between D and L enantiomers.

19. D-(–)-Threose is the sugar that would be oxidized to an optically active dicarboxylic acid with dilute HNO₃. D-(–)-Erythrose is the sugar that would be oxidized to an optically inactive (*meso*) dicarboxylic acid.

20. D-(+)-Glucose would have the structure that is *enantiomeric* to the one in Table 27.1, text page 1200.

21. (a)

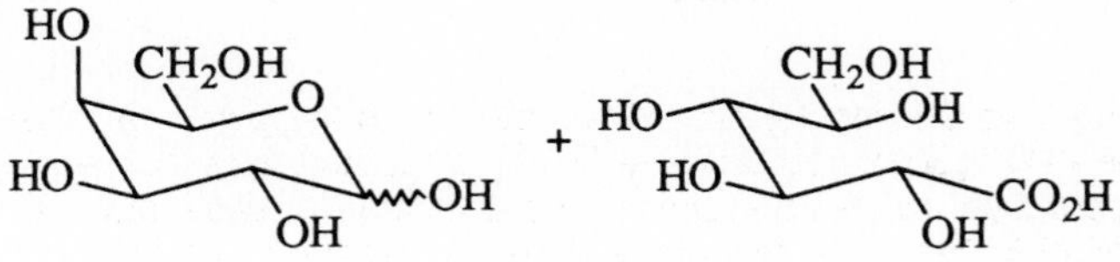

D-galactose   +   D-gluconic acid

(b)

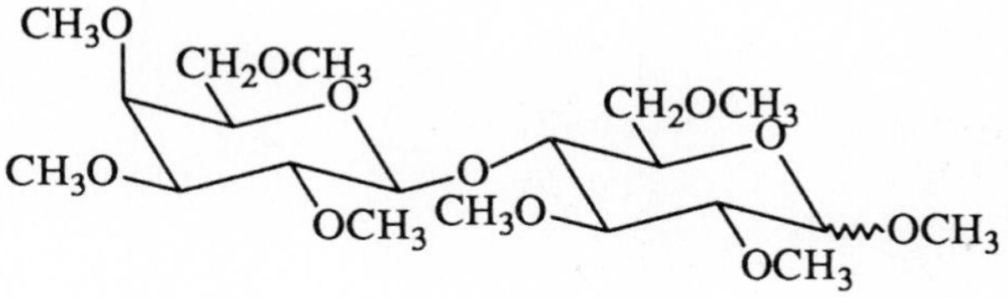

(c)

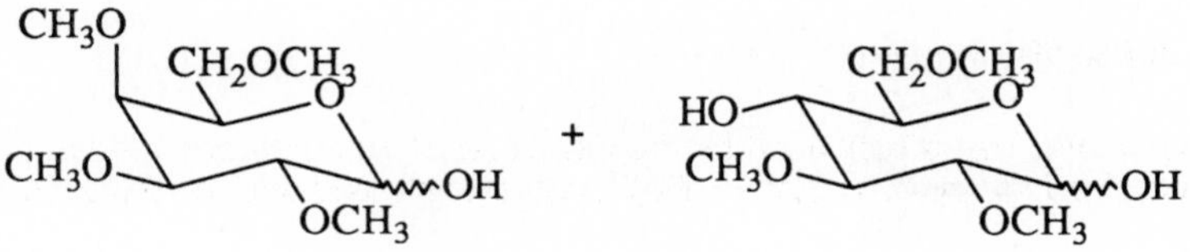

22. Cellobiose is hydrolyzed by aqueous HCl into two equivalents of glucose.

23. The products would be a small amount of 2,3,4,6-tetra-*O*-methyl-D-glucopyranose (*A*, from the residue at the nonreducing end of the polymer) and mostly 2,3,6-tri-*O*-methyl-D-glucopyranose (*B*):

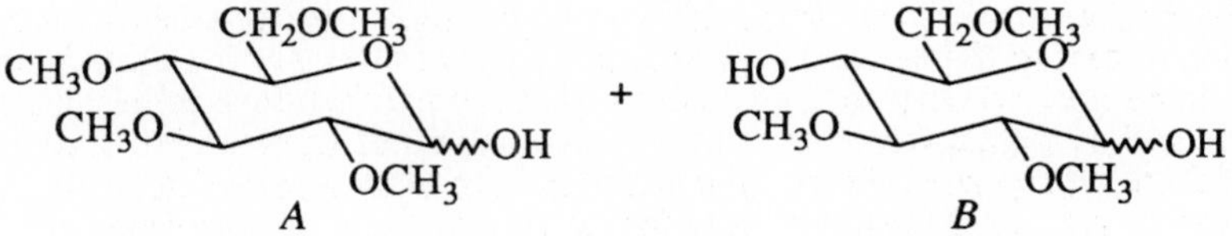

24. (a)   (b)

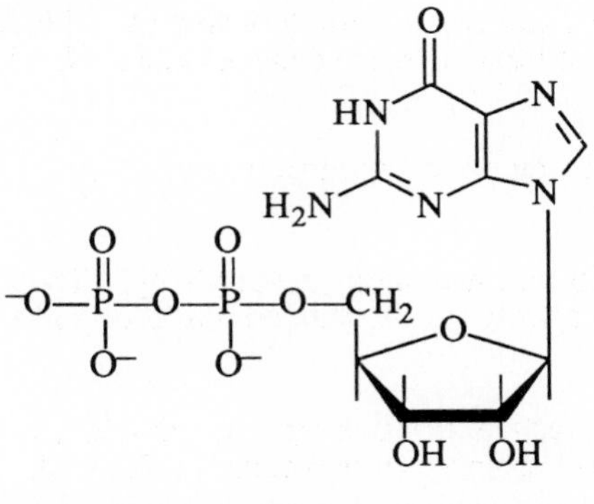

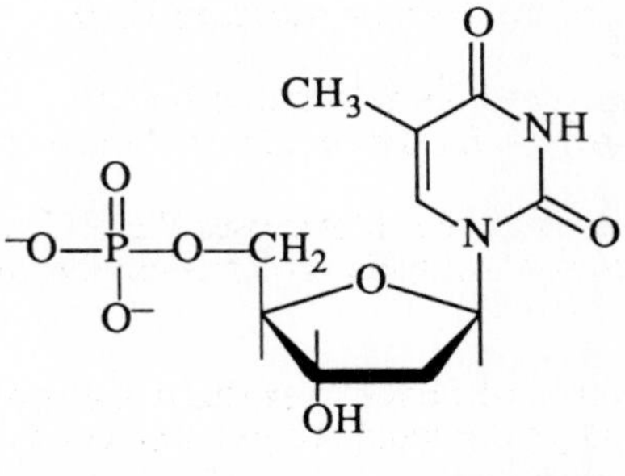

25. We would *not* expect Chargaff's rules to apply to the individual DNA strands because the rules govern the complementarity *between* strands.

26.

Solutions to Additional Problems

27. (a)

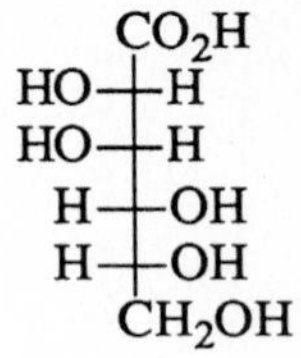

$$
\begin{array}{c}
CO_2H \\
HO \!-\!\!\!-\! H \\
HO \!-\!\!\!-\! H \\
H \!-\!\!\!-\! OH \\
H \!-\!\!\!-\! OH \\
CH_2OH
\end{array}
$$

(b) no reaction except mutarotation

(c)

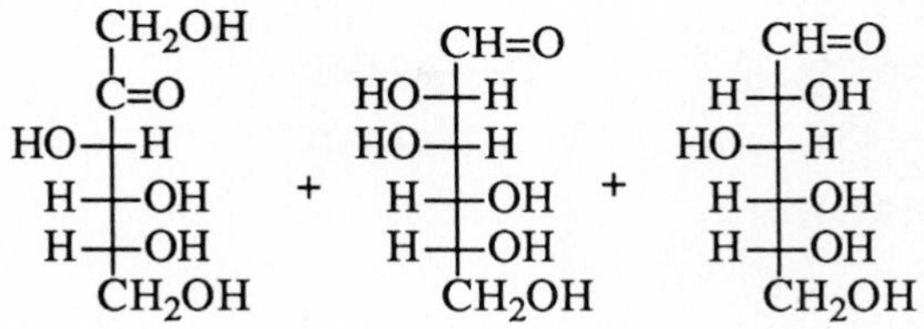

$$
\begin{array}{c}
CH_2OH \\
C\!=\!O \\
HO\!-\!\!\!-\!H \\
H\!-\!\!\!-\!OH \\
H\!-\!\!\!-\!OH \\
CH_2OH
\end{array}
\;+\;
\begin{array}{c}
CH\!=\!O \\
HO\!-\!\!\!-\!H \\
HO\!-\!\!\!-\!H \\
H\!-\!\!\!-\!OH \\
H\!-\!\!\!-\!OH \\
CH_2OH
\end{array}
\;+\;
\begin{array}{c}
CH\!=\!O \\
H\!-\!\!\!-\!OH \\
HO\!-\!\!\!-\!H \\
H\!-\!\!\!-\!OH \\
H\!-\!\!\!-\!OH \\
CH_2OH
\end{array}
$$

(d) Same as (a)

(e)

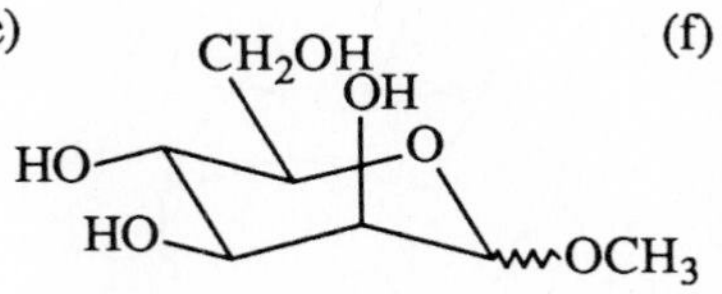

(f)

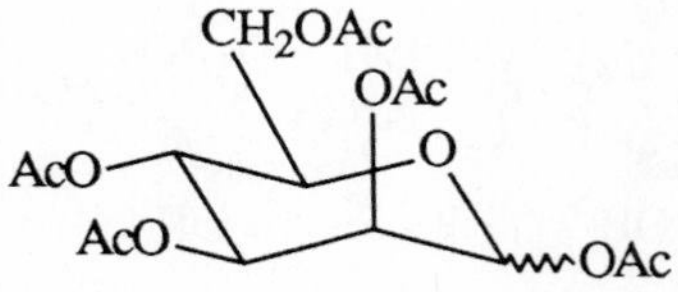

(g)

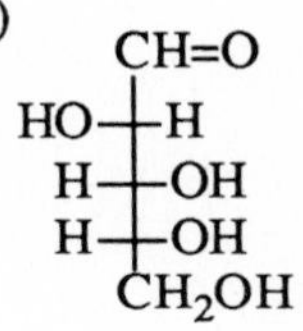

$$
\begin{array}{c}
CH\!=\!O \\
HO\!-\!\!\!-\!H \\
H\!-\!\!\!-\!OH \\
H\!-\!\!\!-\!OH \\
CH_2OH
\end{array}
$$

(h)

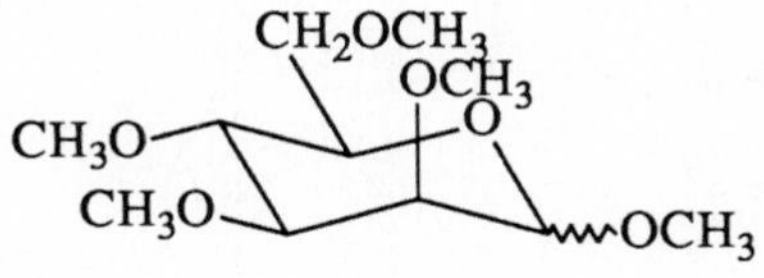

28. (a)

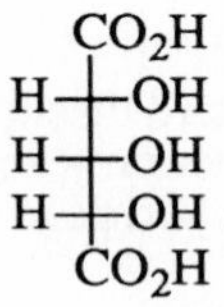

$$
\begin{array}{c}
CO_2H \\
H\!-\!\!\!-\!OH \\
H\!-\!\!\!-\!OH \\
H\!-\!\!\!-\!OH \\
CO_2H
\end{array}
$$

(b)

$$
\begin{array}{c}
CN \\
HO\!-\!\!\!-\!H \\
H\!-\!\!\!-\!OH \\
H\!-\!\!\!-\!OH \\
H\!-\!\!\!-\!OH \\
CH_2OH
\end{array}
\;+\;
\begin{array}{c}
CN \\
H\!-\!\!\!-\!OH \\
H\!-\!\!\!-\!OH \\
H\!-\!\!\!-\!OH \\
H\!-\!\!\!-\!OH \\
CH_2OH
\end{array}
$$

(c)

$$
\begin{array}{c}
CH\!=\!O \\
HO\!-\!\!\!-\!H \\
H\!-\!\!\!-\!OH \\
H\!-\!\!\!-\!OH \\
H\!-\!\!\!-\!OH \\
CH_2OH
\end{array}
\;+\;
\begin{array}{c}
CH\!=\!O \\
H\!-\!\!\!-\!OH \\
H\!-\!\!\!-\!OH \\
H\!-\!\!\!-\!OH \\
H\!-\!\!\!-\!OH \\
CH_2OH
\end{array}
$$

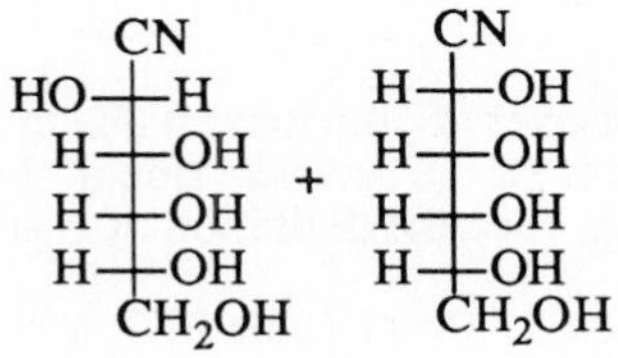

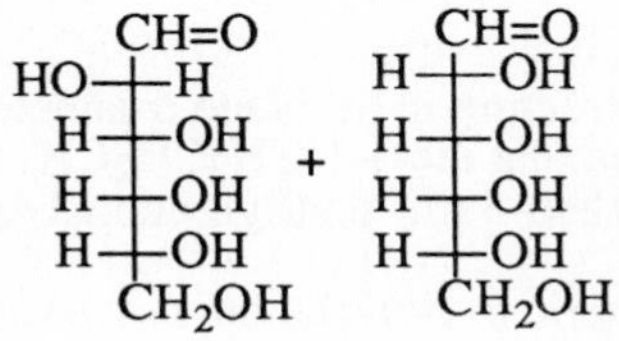

(d)

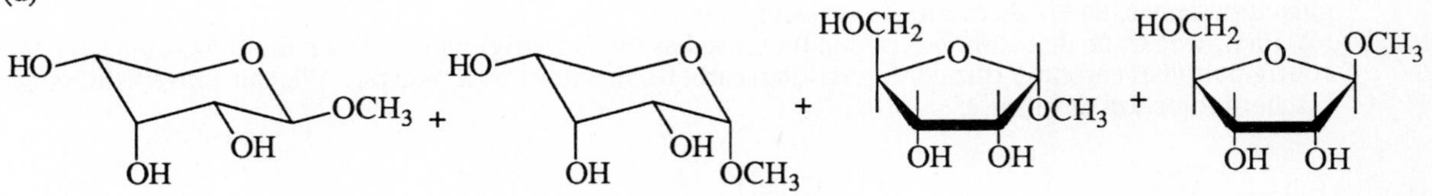

(e)

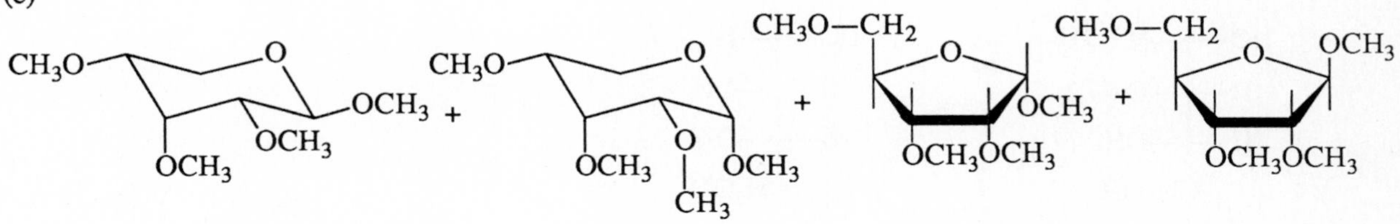

(f)

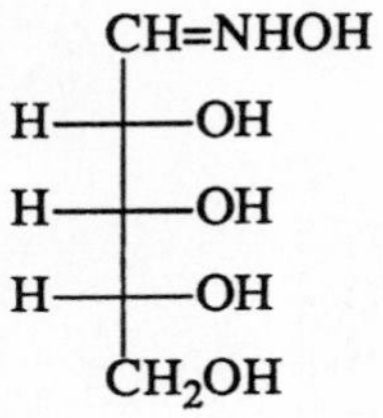

CH=NHOH

H———OH

H———OH

H———OH

CH₂OH

(g)

CH=O

H———OH

H———OH

CH₂OH

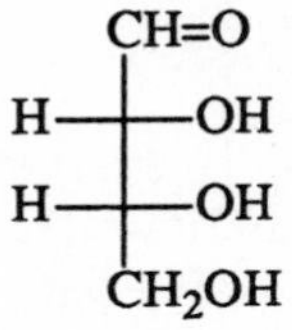

29. (a)

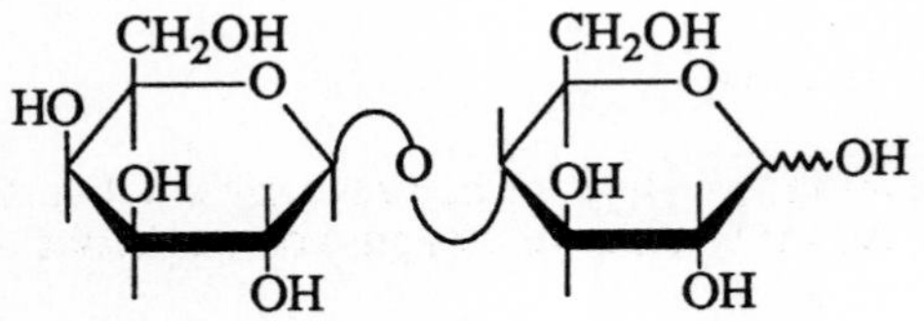

(b)

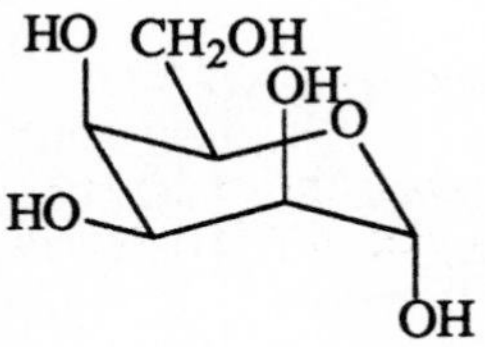

(c)

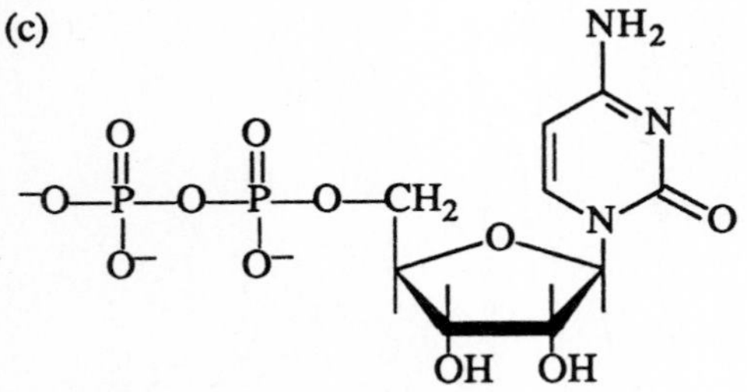

(d)

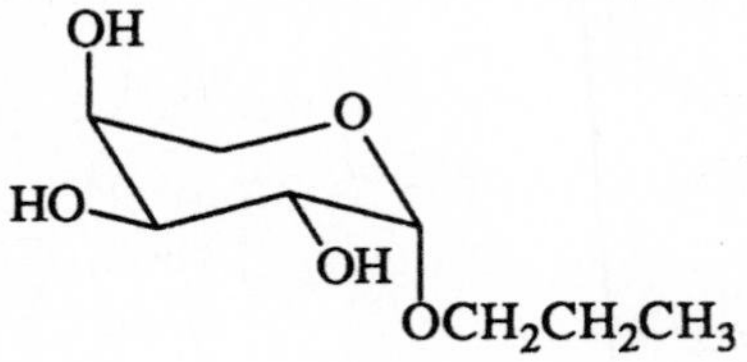

It may seem that the structure in (d) is the α-anomer; however, if you convert this to a standard Fischer projection, you will see that the —OCH₂CH₂CH₃ group is on the *opposite* side of the Fischer projection from the —OH group at carbon-4 (the configurational carbon). (See the definition of α and β on text page 1204.)

30. (a) This sugar is epimeric to β-D-glucopyranose at carbon-3. From Table 27.1, text page 1200, we see that this sugar must therefore be a form of allose. It is β-D-allopyranose.
(b) Turning the structure over 180° shows that this sugar is the nonsuperimposable mirror image of β-D-galactopyranose, and is therefore β-L-galactopyranose.
(c) First, we notice that carbon-5 of this furanose has the *R* configuration. Since the D-hexoses have the *R* configuration at carbon-5 (the configurational carbon), this must be a D-sugar. We can convert this sugar to a Fischer projection as follows:

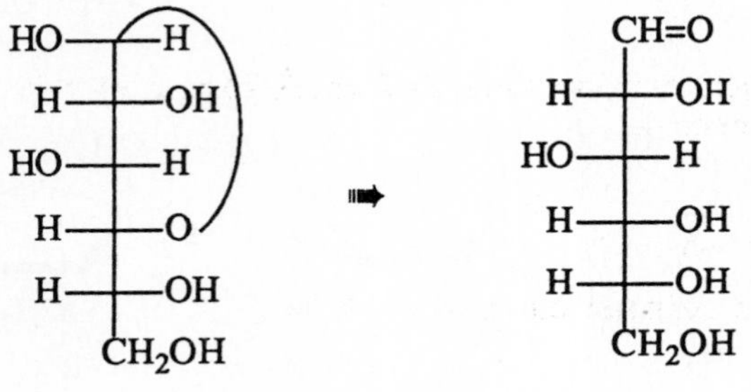

It's none other than D-glucose! Hence, this compound is β-D-glucofuranose.

31. (a) The 2-ketohexoses are as follows:

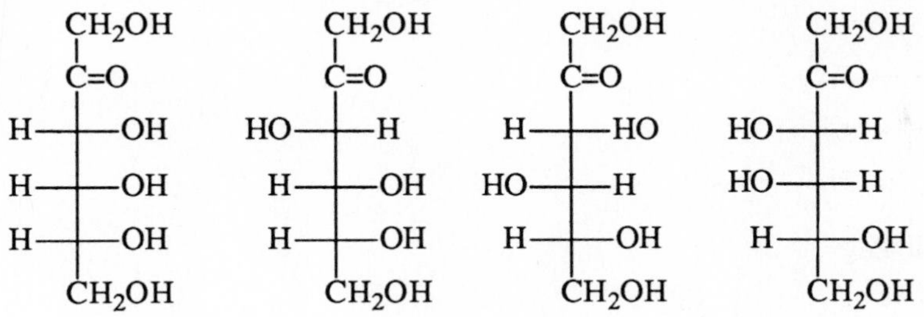

     psicose   fructose   sorbose   tagatose

These are the D-ketohexoses; each has an L-enantiomer. (Notice that there are half as many 2-ketohexoses as there are aldohexoses; why?) The problem did not ask for the names, but we thought you might like to know them anyway.

(b) The following 3-ketopentose is achiral because it is *meso*:

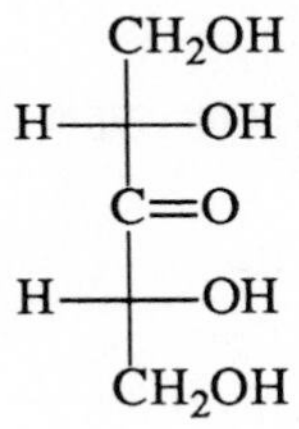

(c) The structure of α-D-galactofuranose is derived from the Fischer projection as follows:

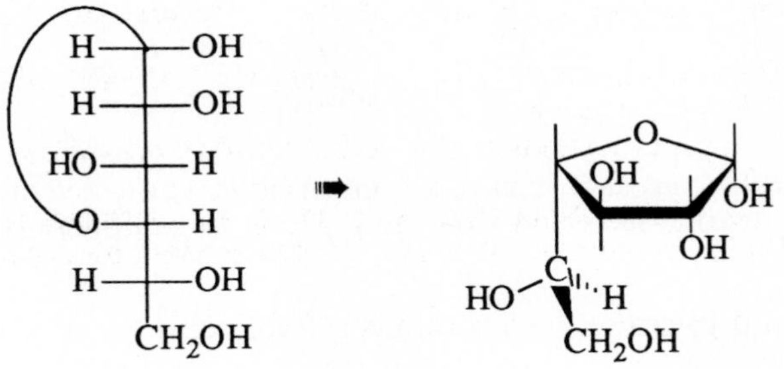

Notice that this structure is identical to the structure of β-D-glucofuranose in Problem 30(c) except for the configurations of the anomeric carbon (carbon-1) and carbon-4.

32. (a) Epimers, anomers, and diastereomers.
     (b) Epimers, diastereomers.

➤ Anomers are a type of epimer, and epimers are a type of diastereomer.

     (c) Enantiomers.
     (d) Structural isomers.
     (e) Structural isomers.
     (f) Structural isomers.

33. The following are forms of L-sorbose:

     (a), (b), (e), (g), (i), (l).

34. (a) Raffinose is a nonreducing sugar because it does not have a free hemiacetal linkage and thus does not exist in equilibrium with an aldehyde form.

(b) The glycosidic linkages:

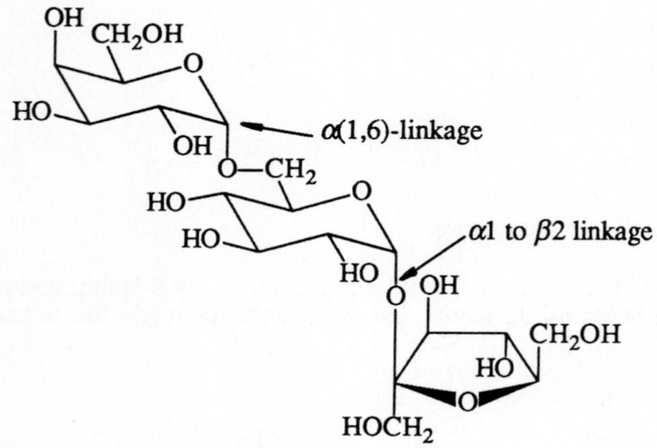

➤ The type of linkage to the furanose residue can be determined methodically by placing the sugar in a standard Haworth projection and then using this to draw the standard Fischer projection:

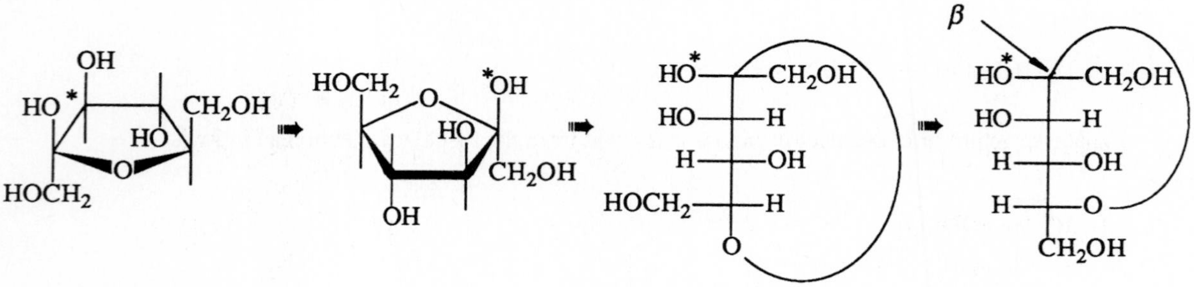

(The oxygen with the asterisk is the one involved in the glycosidic linkage.) A much easier way to determine the linkage is to notice that it is the same as that in sucrose, shown on text page 1231. In fact, raffinose is galactosyl-sucrose.

(c) Hydrolysis of raffinose yields equal amounts of D-galactose, D-glucose, and D-fructose.

(d) The products of methylation followed by hydrolysis are:

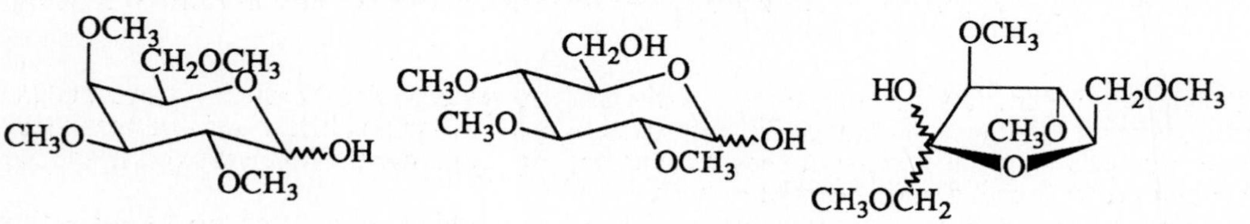

35. This solution is very similar to that of Problem 49, Chapter 7, on page 125 of this manual. Drawing the stereoisomers systematically gives the following structures, in which some of the internal mirror planes are shown as dashed lines:

meso

meso

meso

meso

meso

meso

d,l-pair

meso

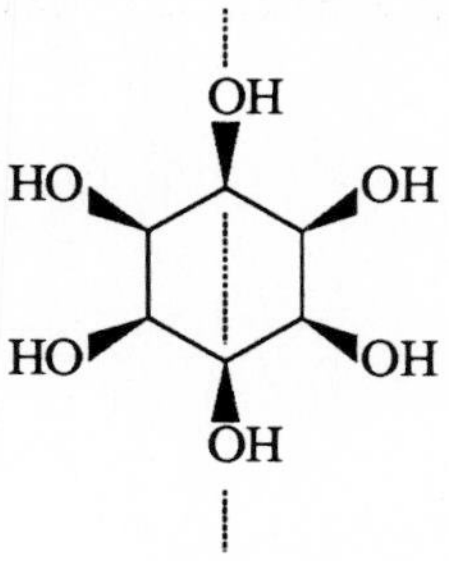

36. (a) The structure indicates that crystalline lactose is the α-anomer. When it is dissolved in water, lactose, like other reducing sugars, undergoes mutarotation; that is, it equilibrates with its β-anomer. (Notice that this discussion refers to the *hemiacetal* group at the reducing end of the molecule, and not to the glycosidic linkage between the two sugar residues.)
(b) The change that occurs in heating in acid is due to the conversion of lactose into a mixture of galactose and glucose.

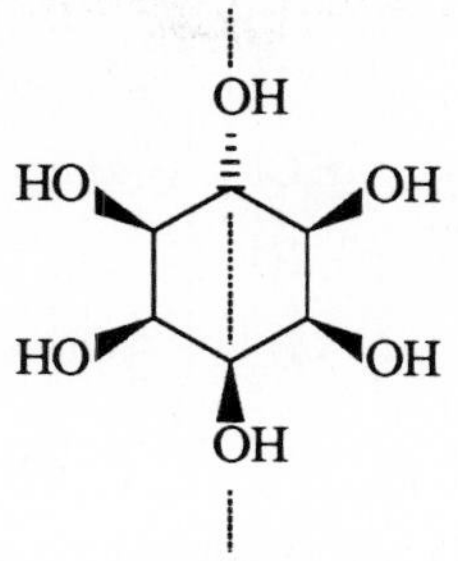

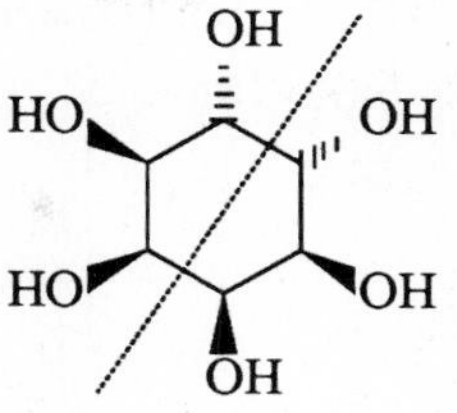

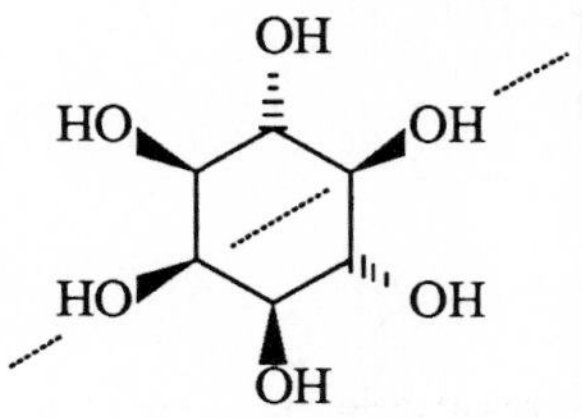

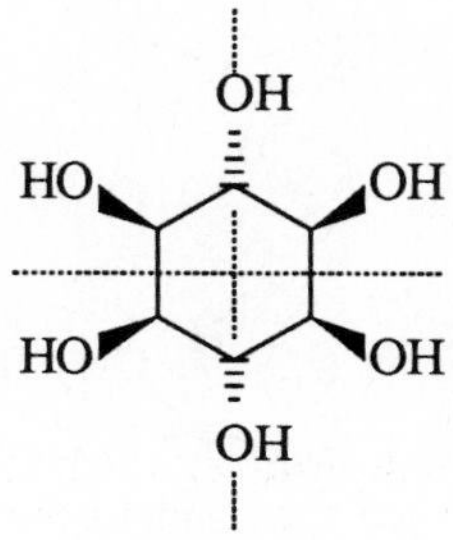

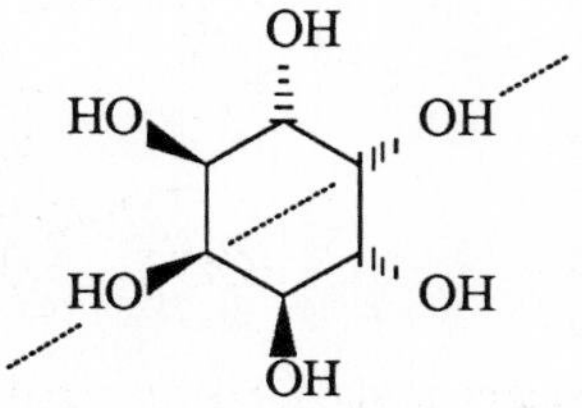

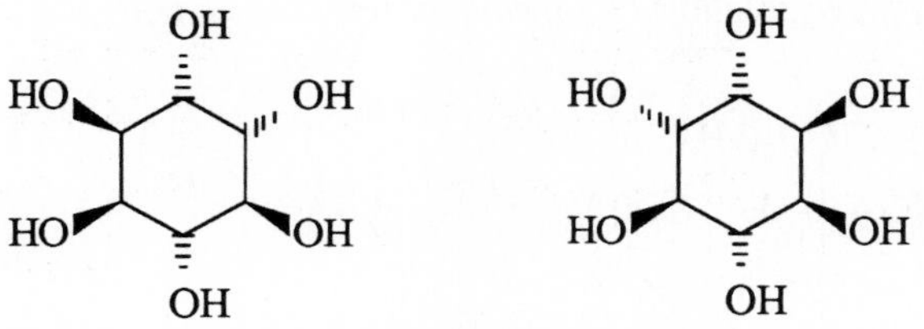

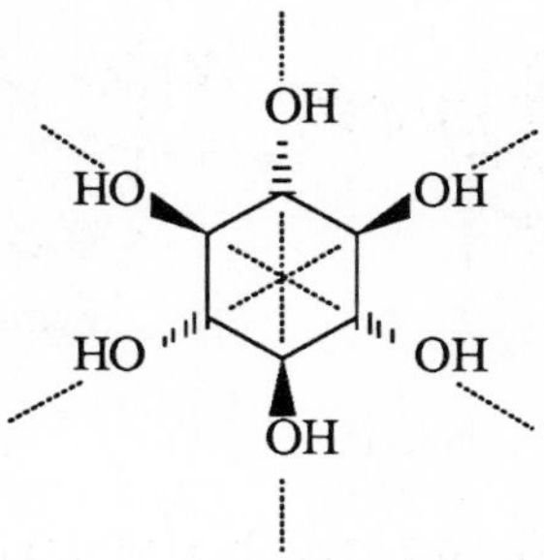

37. (a) The Tollens' test is generally positive only for aldehydes. However, Tollens' reagent is basic, and the basic conditions bring about an equilibration between fructose and the aldoses glucose and mannose (Sec. 27.4). These aldoses are oxidized by the Tollens' reagent, and the equilibrium between the ketose and the aldoses continues to shift until all the sugars have reacted.
(b) The epimerization requires an acidic α-hydrogen. Since D-glucitol has no carbonyl groups, it has no acidic α-hydrogen and therefore cannot epimerize.
(c) Amino sugars, like aldoses and ketoses, undergo base-catalyzed equilibration. In the case of a 2-deoxy-2-amino sugar, the "ketose" form is an imine. Imines, however, hydrolyze to carbonyl compounds and ammonia in aqueous base:

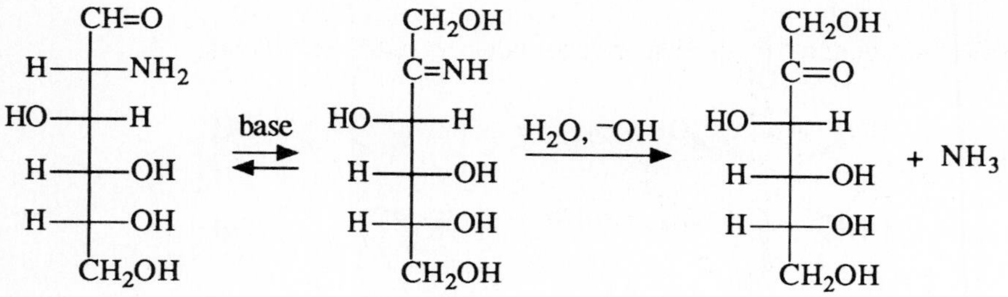

(d) The cleavage of cellulose followed by hydrolysis proceeds as follows:

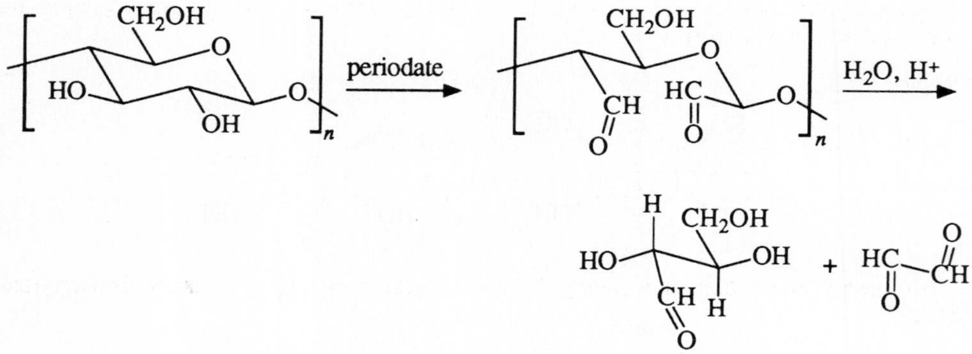

D-erythrose

(e) Reduction of the ketone carbonyl group of D-fructose establishes a newly asymmetric carbon, which can assume either the *R* or *S* configuration:

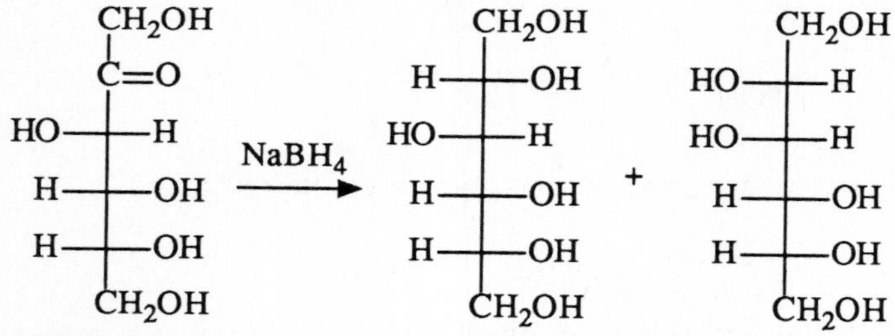

D-fructose   D-glucitol   D-mannitol

Reduction of the aldehyde group of glucose, in contrast, does not give a newly asymmetric center. Only D-glucitol is formed in the reduction of D-glucose.

(f) The sugars that liberate formaldehyde are the ones that have the following groups:

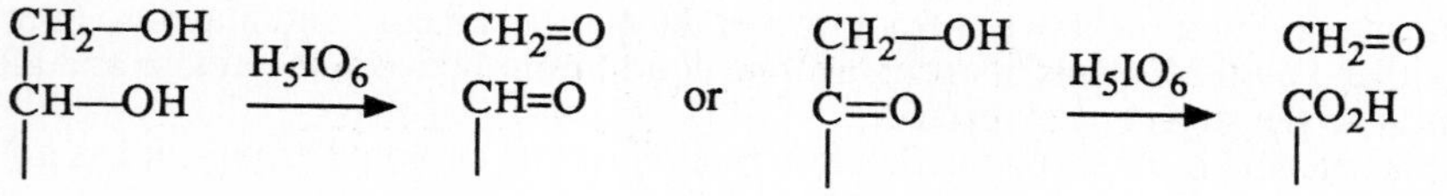

38. If the sugar is a furanoside, its structure and reaction with periodate would be as follows:

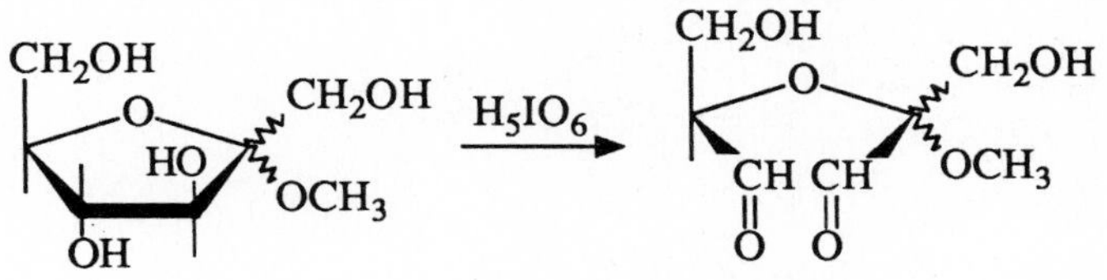

In fact, the reaction with periodate might not occur, because the —OH groups in the glycol unit are *trans* with a sizeable dihedral angle between them. (Recall from Sec. 10.6D that periodate cleavage of glycols does not occur when the cyclic periodate-ester intermediate is too strained.) If the sugar is a pyranoside, its structure and reaction with periodate would be as follows:

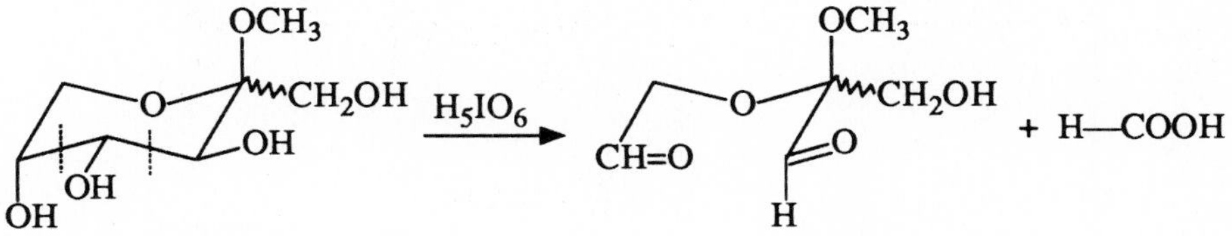

The two products of periodate oxidation are clearly different. Furthermore, only oxidation of the pyranoside liberates formic acid.

39. (a) *Hydrolysis* of a glycoside yields a sugar whose pyranose form has an —OH group at the anomeric carbon. By analogy, *methanolysis* yields a methyl acetal, which in this case is a methyl pyranoside. Since ring opening to the aldehyde form does not occur, the ring size cannot change.

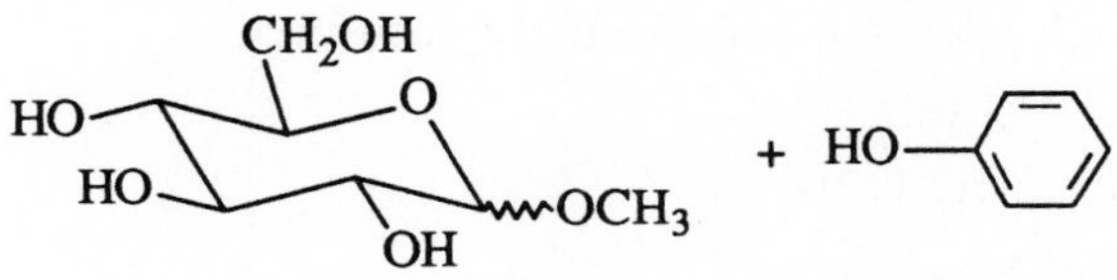

(b) The OsO_4 reaction gives a *cis*-glycol; reaction of acetone with the glycol gives an acetal:

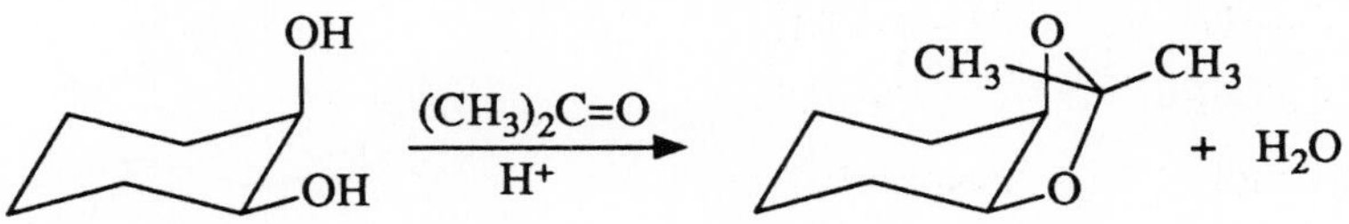

(c) The same *cis*-glycol as in part (b) would be formed; but it would be cleaved into a dialdehyde by periodate, and the dialdehyde would be reduced to 1,6-hexanediol:

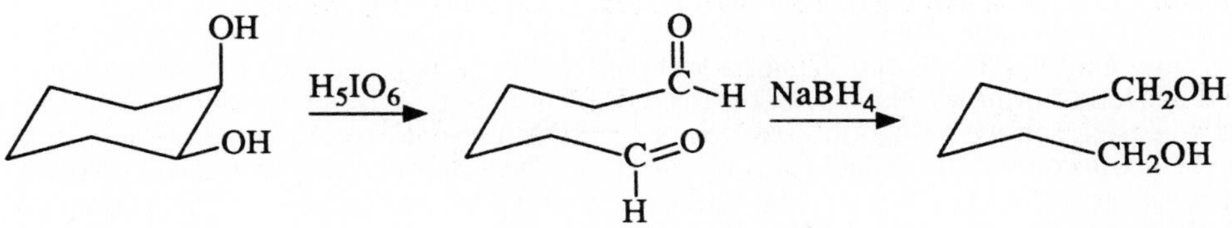

(d) A cyclic mixed acetal is formed analogous to a methyl pyranoside in sugar chemistry:

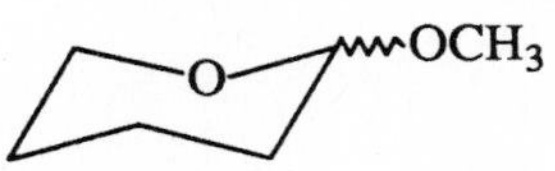

(e) Lactose is converted by *hydrolysis* into two sugars; it is converted by *ethanolysis* into two ethyl pyranosides, ethyl D-galactopyranoside and ethyl D-glucopyranoside:

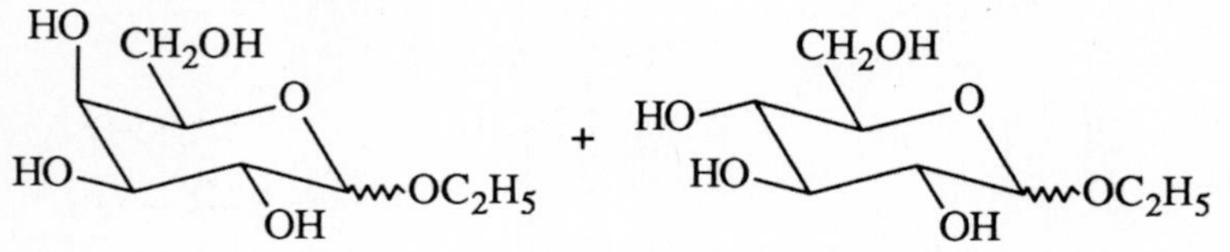

(f) The free —OH groups of sucrose are methylated to give sucrose octamethyl ether:

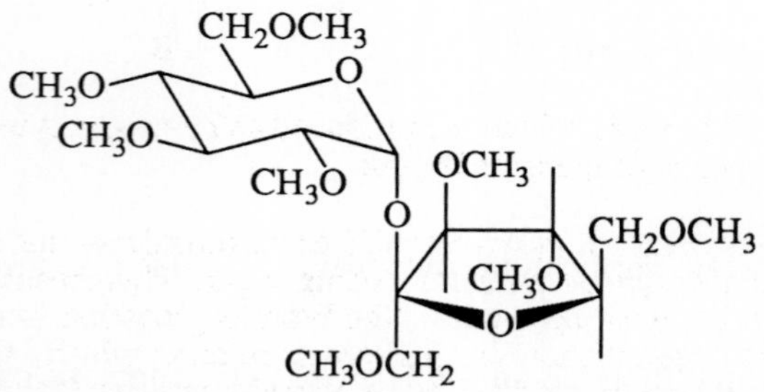

(g) Acid-catalyzed loss of methanol is followed by cyclization to give the methyl pyranoside:

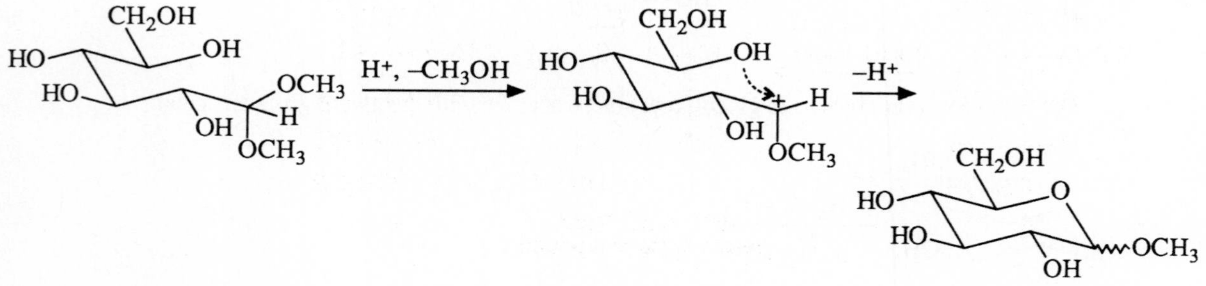

40. Compounds (a) and (b) are isotopically labeled analogs of glucose. Compound (a) is prepared by the Kiliani–Fischer synthesis shown in Eqs. 27.33 and 27.34 on text page 1222, except that radioactive sodium cyanide ($Na^{14}CN$) is used instead of ordinary NaCN. Compound (b) is prepared in the same way, except that ordinary (unlabeled) NaCN is used, and the reduction is carried out with tritium-enriched hydrogen ($^3H_2$). In both syntheses, labeled D-mannose will be isolated as a by-product. The synthesis of compound (c) requires removal of an *unlabeled* carbon from D-arabinose, replacing it with a labeled carbon, and then completion of an ordinary Kiliani–Fischer synthesis to give labeled mannose:

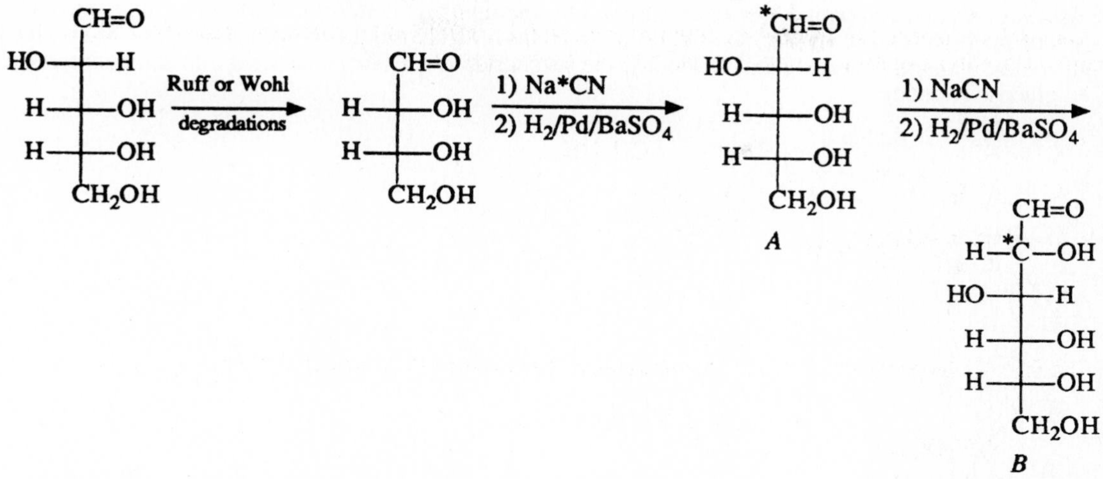

[Fischer projection reaction scheme: a hexose with CH=O at top, HO—H, H—OH, H—OH, CH$_2$OH undergoes **Ruff or Wohl degradations** to give a pentose (CH=O, H—OH, H—OH, CH$_2$OH). This is treated with 1) Na*CN 2) H$_2$/Pd/BaSO$_4$ to give *CH=O, HO—H, H—OH, H—OH, CH$_2$OH (**A**). **A** is treated with 1) NaCN 2) H$_2$/Pd/BaSO$_4$ to give CH=O, H—*C—OH, HO—H, H—OH, H—OH, CH$_2$OH (**B**).]

Derivatives *A* and *B* must be separated from their carbon-2 epimers, which are produced as by-products in the synthesis. These by-products could be "recycled" by base-catalyzed epimerization.

41. The results of the oxidation of *A* tell us that compound *A* is not a methyl pyranoside or furanoside — that is, that the methyl ether is not at carbon-1. The Wohl degradation yields another reducing sugar. This means that the methyl ether cannot be at carbon-2. The reason is that if it were at carbon-2, the Wohl degradation would stop after step (d) (Eq. 27.37, text page 1223). (α-Cyano ethers do not form aldehydes in base; why?). Only if the ether is at carbon-3 can one of the Kiliani–Fischer products be oxidized to an optically inactive (that is, *meso*) compound:

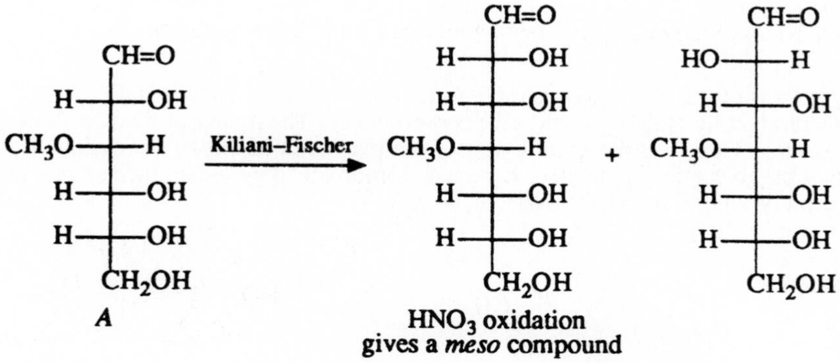

[Fischer projection: **A** = CH=O, H—OH, CH$_3$O—H, H—OH, H—OH, CH$_2$OH undergoes **Kiliani–Fischer** to give two products: CH=O, H—OH, H—OH, CH$_3$O—H, H—OH, H—OH, CH$_2$OH **+** CH=O, HO—H, H—OH, CH$_3$O—H, H—OH, H—OH, CH$_2$OH. The first is labeled: **HNO$_3$ oxidation gives a *meso* compound**.]

Hence, compound *A* is 3-*O*-methyl-D-glucose.

42. Compound *X* has one degree of unsaturation, and reduction gives alcohols that are epimeric at carbon-3. Hence, *X* is a 3-ketopentose. The following structure for *X* fits the data:

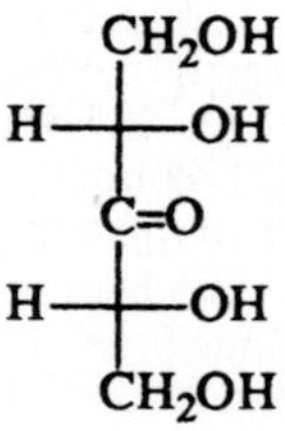

[Fischer projection: CH$_2$OH, H—OH, C=O, H—OH, CH$_2$OH.]

Periodate oxidation of this compound would indeed yield two equivalents of formaldehyde. [See also the solution to Problem 31(b).]

43. The data suggest that compound *A* is a hexasaccharide containing *no* hemiacetal linkages. Since the only product of methylation and hydrolysis is 2,3,6-tri-*O*-methyl-D-glucose, the oxygen at carbon-4 is involved in the glycosidic linkage of each sugar. Evidently, the saccharide is a *cyclic* hexasaccharide containing six α-1,4-linked glucose residues:

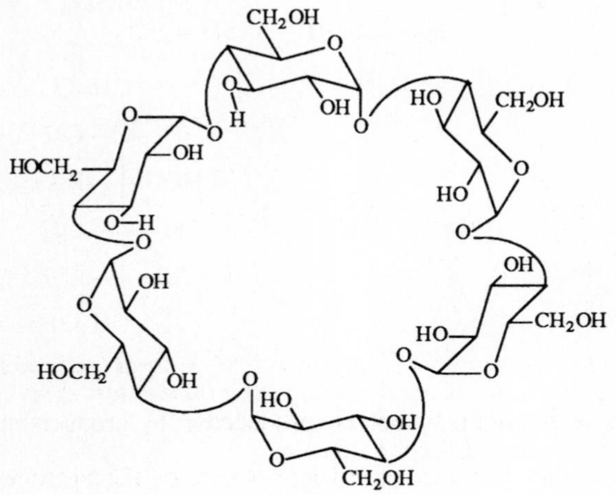

44. We would expect the following product from treatment of methyl α-D-rhamnopyranoside with periodic acid:

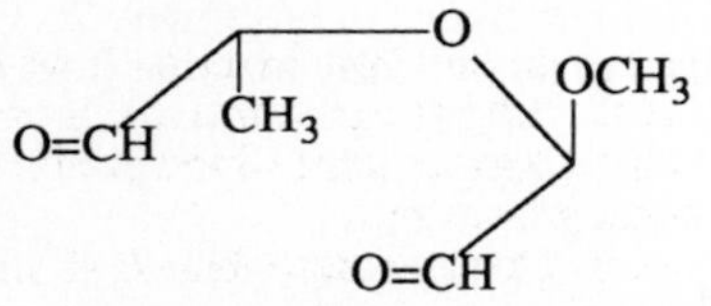

The formula of *X*, $C_6H_{10}O_4$, is short of the formula of actual product *A* by the elements of H_2O. Nevertheless, reduction of this product by $NaBH_4$ would give compound *C*. The methylation data show that compound *A* has two —OH groups. Compound *A* results, first, from hydration of one of the carbonyl groups of *X*; an —OH group of the hydrate then attacks the other carbonyl, forming a "double hemiacetal" *A*. The structure of *A* and its methylation product *B* are as follows:

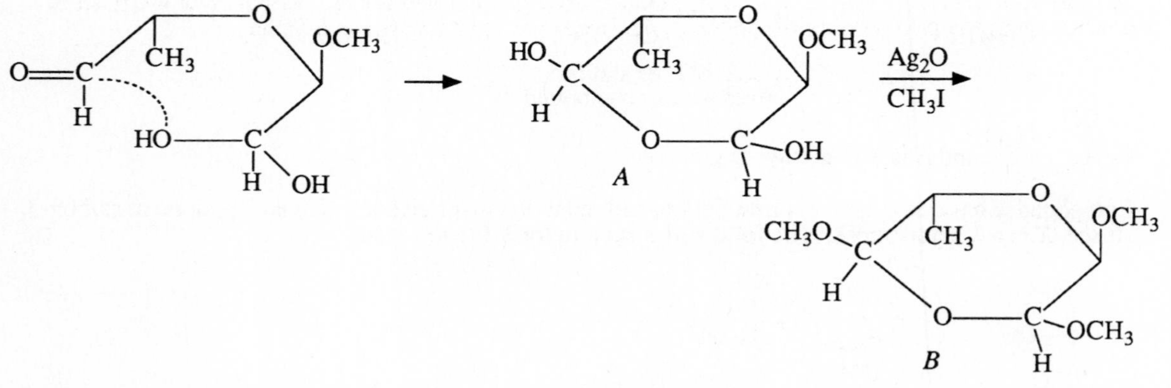

(The stereochemistry at the two hemiacetal carbons is probably mixed.) Because compound *A* is a hemiacetal, it shows no carbonyl absorption. However, it is in equilibrium with a small amount of the dialdehyde, which is reduced by $NaBH_4$ to give compound *C*. The reduction pulls the equilibrium between *A* and *X* toward *X* until all of this compound has been reduced.

45. (a) The reactions of the residue of RNA at the 3'-end are as follows:

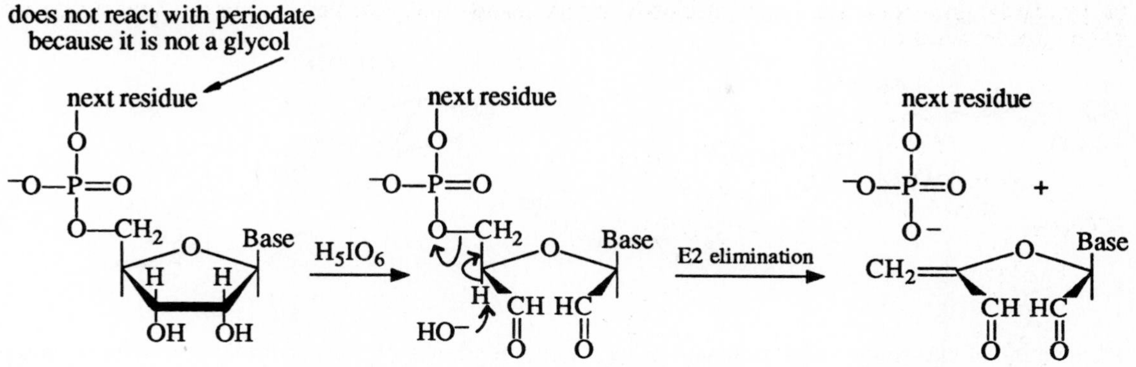

The periodate reaction forms a dialdehyde. In this dialdehyde, the α-hydrogen on the 4'-carbon is acidic and can be removed by base. The phosphate group at the 5'-carbon is a good leaving group and is lost in an elimination reaction; this reaction removes the residue at the 3'-end of the RNA molecule.

(b) Formation of a carbonyl group at the 3'-carbon is required for the elimination; otherwise, the hydrogen at the 4'-carbon is not acidic enough to be removed by base under conditions that do not affect the rest of the RNA molecule. In DNA, there is no —OH group at the 2'-carbon, and thus there is no glycol to react with periodate. Hence, DNA does not undergo this cleavage reaction.

46. (a) In Figure 27.8, we see that there are three hydrogen bonds in a G–C pair, but only two in an A–T pair. The hydrogen bonds hold the strands of the double helix together. Since the melting temperature is a measure of the forces holding the strands of the double helix together, the higher melting temperature of the polyG–polyC double helix is accounted for by the greater number of hydrogen bonds per residue.
(b) From part (a), we conclude that G–C rich DNA should have a higher melting temperature than A–T rich DNA. Hence, the human adenovirus I DNA contains the greater ratio of G + C.

47. The hydrolysis by almond emulsin establishes that an intact sucrose unit is connected to a galactose residue by an α-galactosyl glycosidic bond. The question, then, is which oxygen of the sucrose residue is involved in the glycosidic linkage to the galactose. Methylation followed by hydrolysis provides the answer. (It may be helpful to refer to the structure of sucrose on text page 1231.) If the fructose residue of sucrose were *not* connected to the galactose, it would have four —OH groups available for methylation: the —OH groups at carbons 1, 3, 4, and 6. Since the —OH group at carbon-6 is not methylated, this must be the point of attachment of the galactose residue. Hence, the structure of planteose is as follows:

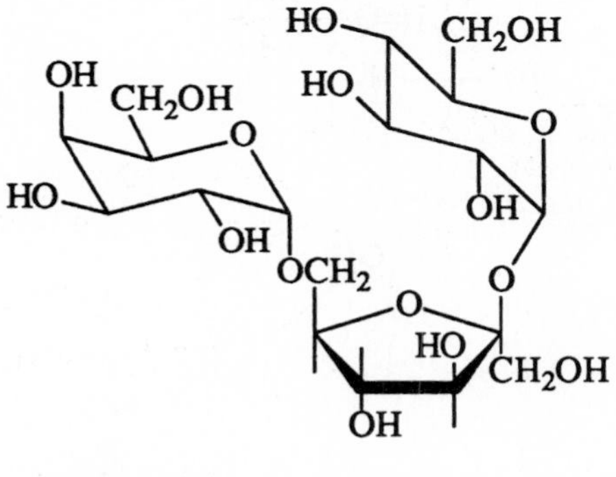

The linkage between the galactose and fructose residues is an α(1,6) linkage.

48. Maltose contains two glucose residues connected by an α-glycosidic bond. There must be a free hemiacetal group at carbon-1 of one of the glucose units. The 2,3,4,6-tetra-*O*-methyl-D-glucose must arise from the glucose residue at the nonreducing end. The question is which —OH group in the glucose residue at the reducing end is involved in the glycosidic linkage; the other product of methylation–hydrolysis provides

evidence on this point. Since the —OH groups at carbons 4 and 5 are not methylated in this product, one of these —OH groups is involved in pyranoside or furanoside ring formation, and the other is involved in the glycosidic linkage. Two structures satisfy these requirements:

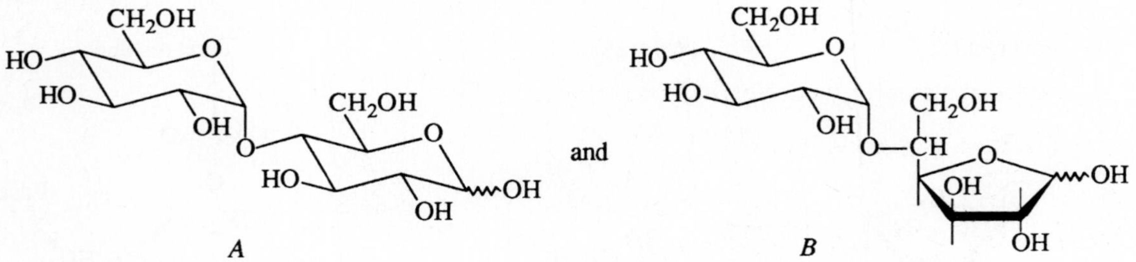

A and *B*

Methylation of maltobionic acid occurs under basic conditions; under these conditions any lactones present would be saponified. Hence, the additional —OH group that is methylated under these conditions must be the one *within* the glycoside ring at the reducing end of maltose. Oxidation and saponification liberate this —OH group and thus make it available for methylation. Since the —OH group at carbon-5 is methylated, it must have been within the sugar ring. Since the —OH at carbon-4 is *not* methylated, the oxygen at carbon-4 must be involved in the glycosidic bond. Hence, structure *A* is the correct one for maltose.

49. To illustrate, we apply the Weerman degradation to D-glucose. Compound *A* is the aldonolactone, and *B* is the amide formed by aminolysis. Hofmann rearrangement of the amide affords a carbinolamine, which breaks down under the aqueous conditions to an aldehyde — the aldose with one fewer carbon:

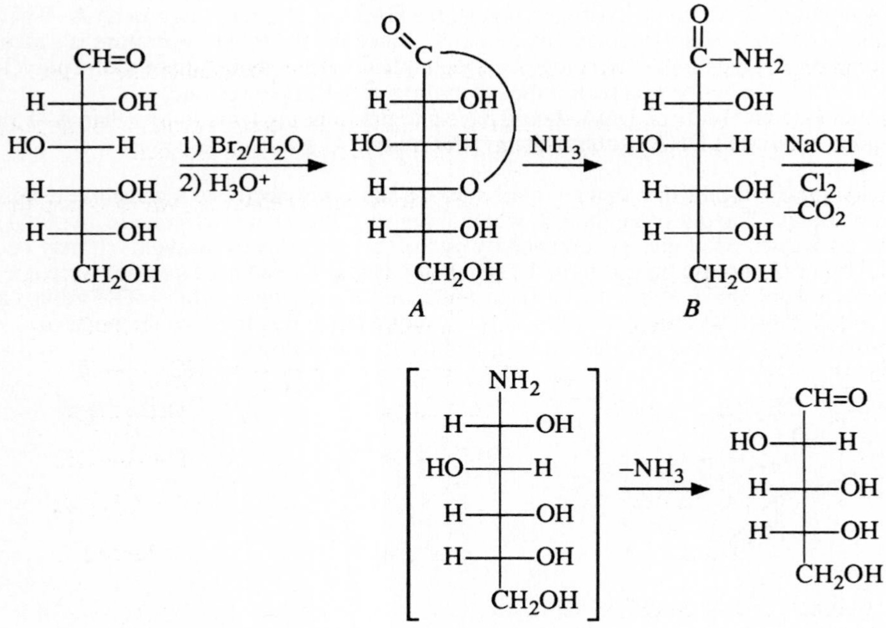

50. (a) (1) From the residue at the nonreducing end:

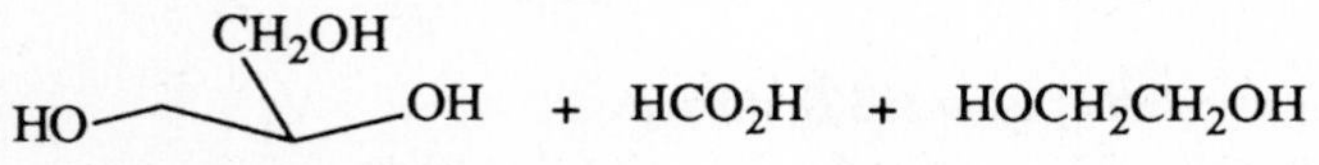

glycerol

(2) From the residue at the reducing end:

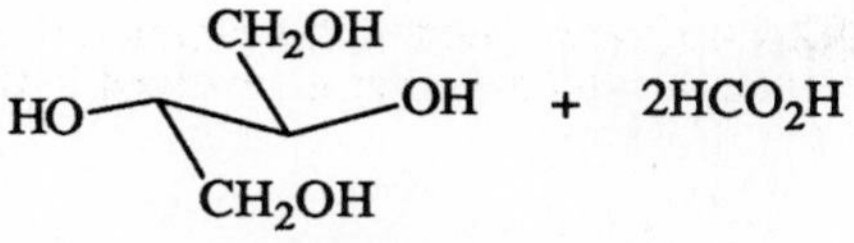

$$CH_2OH$$

HO—⟨ ⟩—OH   +   2HCO_2H

$$CH_2OH$$

erythritol

(The methanol comes from reduction of formaldehyde.)

(3) From the internal residues:

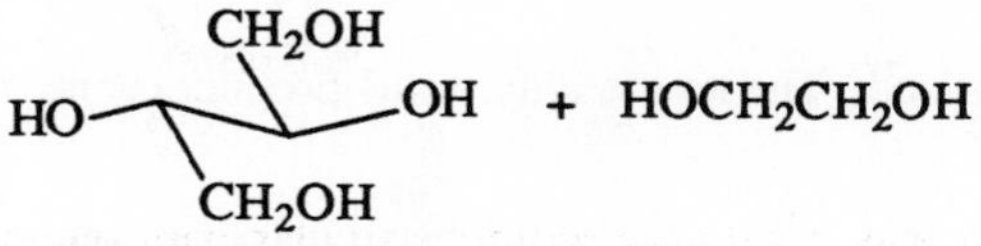

$$CH_2OH$$

HO—⟨ ⟩—OH   +   HOCH_2CH_2OH

$$CH_2OH$$

erythritol

(b) The data combined with the analysis above indicate that the saccharide is twelve residues in length.

51. The ribonucleotide sequence is translated from the 5'-end according to the genetic code in Table 27.3:

A-U-G-A-A-A-C-A-A-G-A-U-U-U-U-U-A-A|U-G-G-G-G-G
Met——Lys——Gln——Asp——Phe——STOP

The STOP signal (UAA) prevents the peptide from being translated beyond the phenylalanine residue.

➤ This illustrates how a mutation could cause an organism to be deficient in a certain protein. If the UAA code were generated by a mutation, synthesis of the corresponding protein would be blocked.

52. D-Glucose forms an imine with aniline, and the imine is in equilibrium with its enamine, which is also the enol of the product:

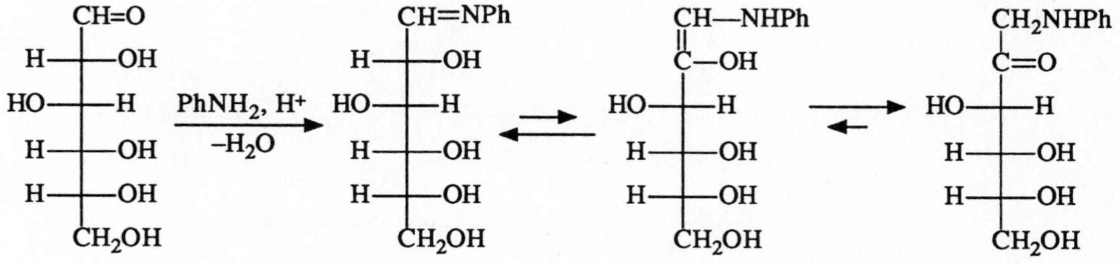

CH=O		CH=NPh		CH—NHPh		CH_2NHPh
H——OH		H——OH		C—OH		C=O
HO——H	PhNH_2, H^+	HO——H		HO——H		HO——H
H——OH	–H_2O	H——OH		H——OH		H——OH
H——OH		H——OH		H——OH		H——OH
CH_2OH		CH_2OH		CH_2OH		CH_2OH
		imine		enamine		ketone

Imine and enamine formation is discussed in Sec. 19.11.

53.

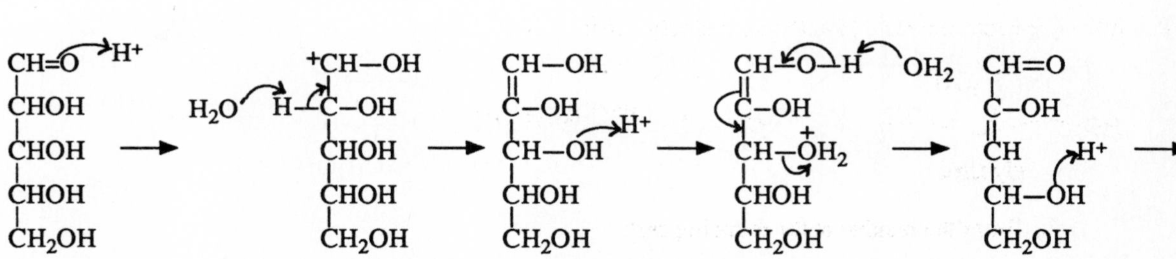

CH=O →H^+		+CH—OH		CH—OH		CH—O—H OH_2	CH=O
CHOH	H_2O	H—C—OH		C—OH		C—OH	C—OH
CHOH	→	CHOH	→	CH—OH	→H^+	CH—OH_2	CH
CHOH		CHOH		CHOH		CHOH	CH—OH
CH_2OH		CH_2OH		CH_2OH		CH_2OH	CH_2OH →H^+ →

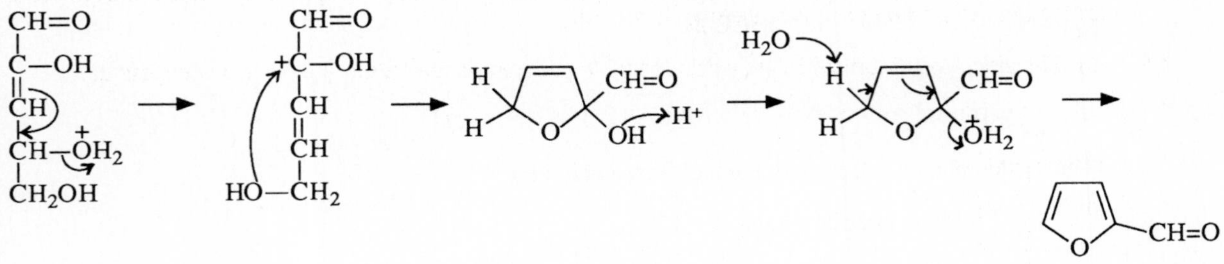

Each carbocation formed in this sequence is resonance-stabilized. The aromaticity of the product is one of the reasons this reaction goes to completion.

54. (a) The proton on the —OH group at carbon-3 is the most acidic. Its acidity is similar to that of a carboxylic acid because its conjugate-base anion, like that of an acid, is delocalized into a carbonyl group:

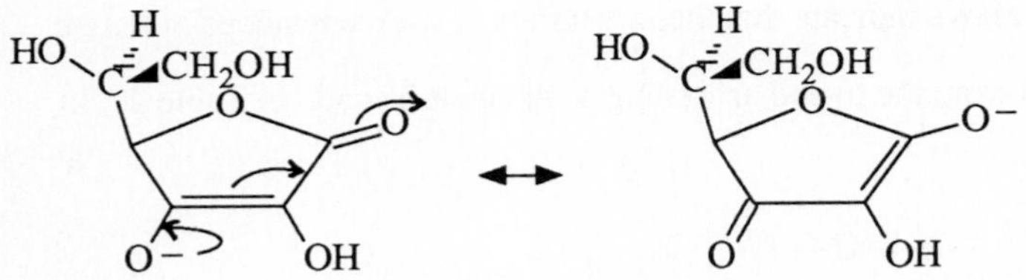

conjugate-base anion of ascorbic acid

(b) The reaction sequence with the missing structures added is as follows, beginning with compound A. We can tell that the —OH group at carbon-2 of L-sorbitol is the group that is oxidized because carbon-2 becomes the acetal carbon in the structure given after addition of compound C; this carbon is therefore at the ketone level of oxidation.

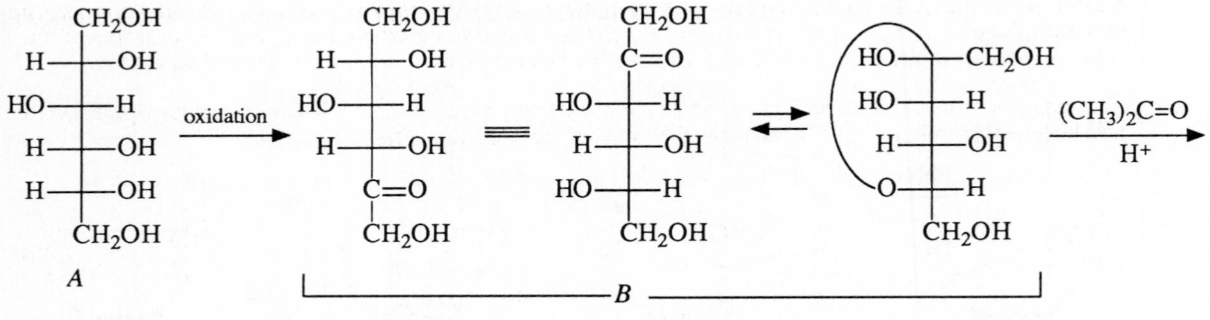

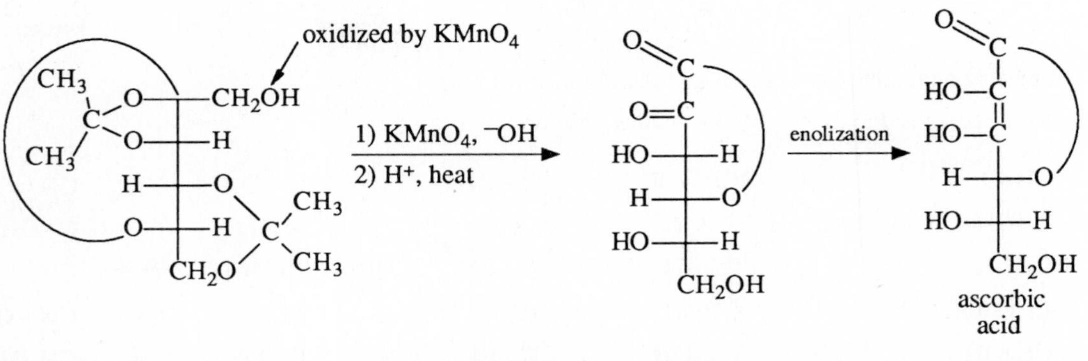

$KMnO_4$ oxidizes the —CH$_2$OH group; the other —OH groups are protected as acetals that are stable under the basic conditions of permanganate oxidation. Hydrolysis of the oxidation product in acid removes the acetal protecting groups and promotes lactone formation.

55. (a) The aldaric acid formed in the oxidation of D-galactose is *not* chiral; it is a *meso* compound:

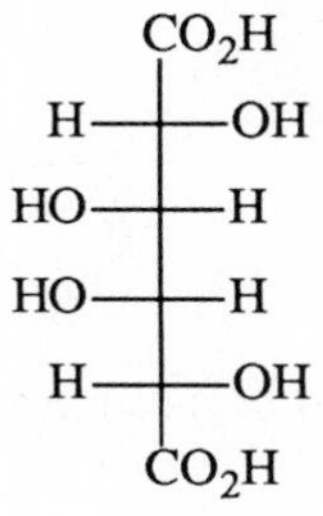

(b) There are two possible γ-lactones that could be formed from this acid; both are chiral:

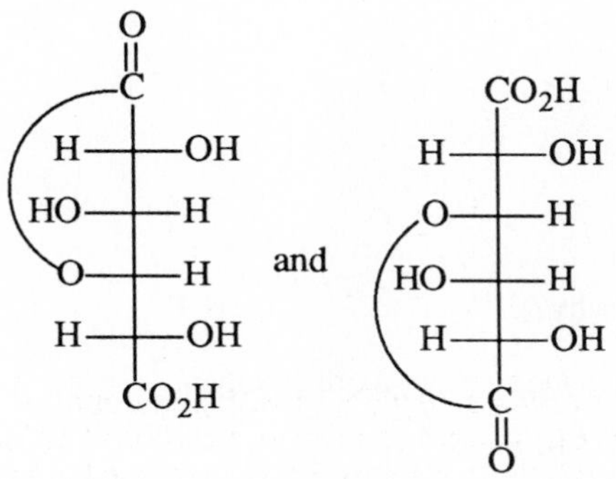

(c) The two γ-lactones in part (b) are enantiomers. (You can demonstrate this point by rotating either structure 180° in the plane of the paper.) Although both lactones are chiral, they are formed from an achiral starting material (the dicarboxylic acid) and therefore *must be formed in equal amounts*. Hence, a sample of the aldaric acid — whether in the dicarboxylic acid form or the lactone form — will not show optical activity.

56. The reaction of RNA involves ionization of the 2'-hydroxy group and its reaction as a nucleophile on the neighboring phosphate. Loss of the leaving group splits the internucleotide bond:

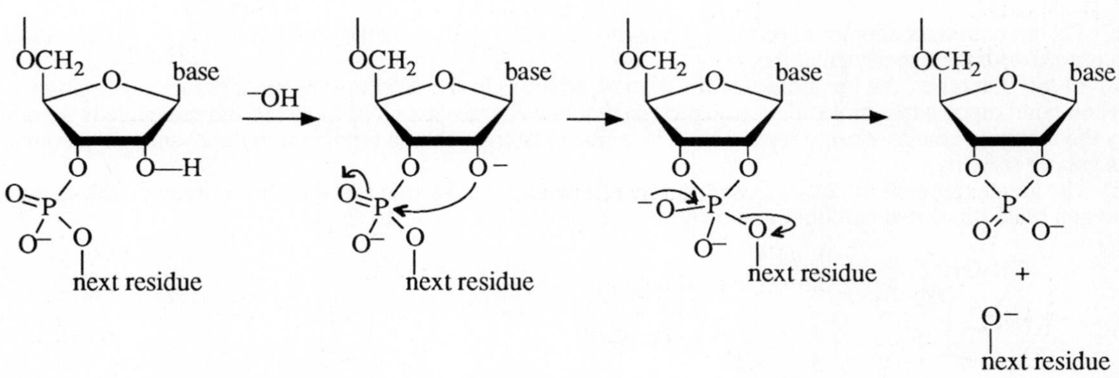

The cyclic phosphate is attacked by ⁻OH to give a mixture of 2'- and 3'-phosphates:

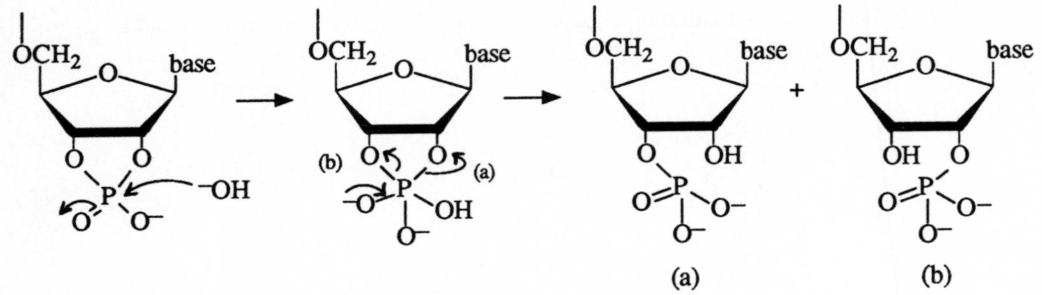

(a)   (b)

Because DNA lacks the nucleophilic 2'-hydroxy group, it does not undergo this reaction.

57. (a) The anhydro form of the sugar exists in the following conformation:

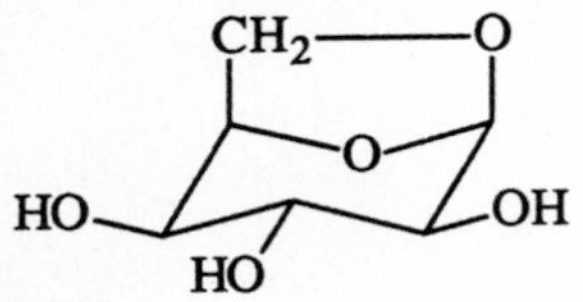

Chair-to-chair interconversion of this compound is not possible (why?).

(b) The 1,6-anhydro form of D-glucose is less stable because it has many more axial groups:

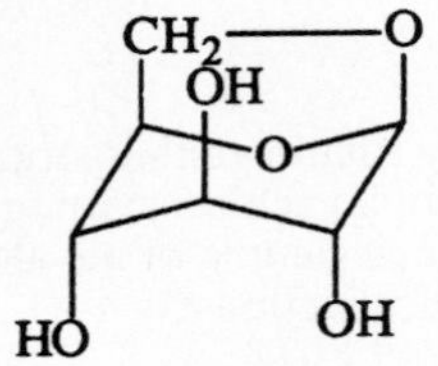

Glucose prefers instead the chair form in which most of the —OH groups are equatorial. Hence, glucose contains considerably less anhydro form than idose.

58. (a) The predominant anomer expected from conformational analysis is the equatorial one; this expectation is not in accord with the experimental facts.
(b) In the β-anomer, the bond dipoles are aligned, whereas in the α-form they are more nearly opposed. When bond dipoles in a molecule are aligned so that like charges are close together, the molecule is destabilized by the resulting charge–charge repulsion. The reduced charge–charge repulsion in the α-anomer accounts for its greater stability.
(c) The greater amount of α-D-mannopyranose can be attributed to the fact that in this anomer, the carbon–oxygen bond dipoles at carbon-1 and carbon-2 are opposed:

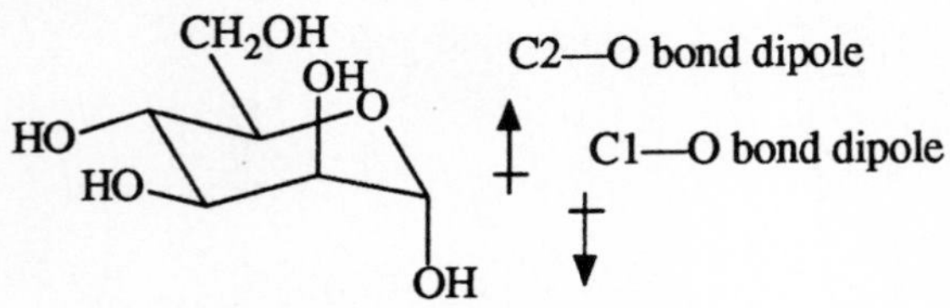

C2—O bond dipole

C1—O bond dipole

This opposition reduces the unfavorable interactions between these dipoles. Hence, the α-form is more stable than the β-anomer, in which these bond dipoles are more nearly aligned.